Molecular Cloning

A LABORATORY MANUAL

THIRD EDITION

Associate Authors

Nina Irwin
HARVARD MEDICAL SCHOOL AND CHILDREN'S HOSPITAL, BOSTON

Kaaren A. Janssen
COLD SPRING HARBOR LABORATORY

Managing Editor: Jan Argentine
Science Editor: Nina Irwin
Senior Developmental Editor: Kaaren A. Janssen
Developmental Editors: Siân Curtis and Michael Zierler
Project Coordinators: Maryliz Dickerson and Inez Sialiano
Permissions Editor: Nora McInerny
Production Editor: Dorothy Brown
Desktop Editor: Susan Schaefer
Prepress Technician: Danny deBruin
Interior Book Design: Ed Atkeson (Berg Design) and Denise Weiss
Cover Design: Ed Atkeson (Berg Design)
Original and Redrawn Illustrations: Mark D. Curtis

Molecular Cloning
A LABORATORY MANUAL

THIRD EDITION

www.MolecularCloning.com

Joseph Sambrook
PETER MACCALLUM CANCER INSTITUTE AND THE UNIVERSITY OF MELBOURNE, AUSTRALIA

David W. Russell
UNIVERSITY OF TEXAS SOUTHWESTERN MEDICAL CENTER, DALLAS

COLD SPRING HARBOR LABORATORY PRESS
Cold Spring Harbor, New York

Molecular Cloning
A LABORATORY MANUAL

THIRD EDITION

Front cover (paperback): The gene encoding green fluorescent protein was cloned from *Aequorea victoria*, a jellyfish found in abundance in Puget Sound, Washington State. This picture of a 50-mm medusa was taken on color film by flash photography and shows light reflected from various morphological features of the animal. The small bright roundish blobs in the photograph are symbiotic amphipods living on or in the medusa. The bright ragged area in the center is the jellyfish's mouth.

Bioluminescence from *Aequorea* is emitted only from the margins of the medusae and cannot be seen in this image. Bioluminescence of *Aequorea*, as in most species of jellyfish, does not look like a soft overall glow, but occurs only at the rim of the bell and, given the right viewing conditions, would appear as a string of nearly microscopic fusiform green lights. The primary luminescence produced by *Aequorea* is actually bluish in color and is emitted by the protein aequorin. In a living jellyfish, light is emitted via the coupled green fluorescent protein, which causes the luminescence to appear green to the observer.

The figure and legend were kindly provided by Claudia Mills of the University of Washington, Friday Harbor. For further information, please see Mills, C.E. 1999–2000. Bioluminescence of *Aequorea*, a hydromedusa. Electronic Internet document available at http://faculty. washington.edu/cemills/Aequorea.html. Published by the author, web page established June 1999, last updated 23 August 2000.

Back cover (paperback): A portion of a human cDNA array hybridized with a red fluor-tagged experimental sample and a green fluor-tagged reference sample. Please see Appendix 10 for details. (Image provided by Vivek Mittal and Michael Wigler, Cold Spring Harbor Laboratory.)

Library of Congress Cataloging-in-Publication Data

Sambrook, Joseph.
    Molecular cloning : a laboratory manual / Joseph Sambrook, David W.
Russell.-- 3rd ed.
        p. ; cm.
    Includes bibliographical references and index.
    ISBN 0-87969-576-5 (cloth) -- ISBN 0-87969-577-3 (pbk)
    1. Molecular cloning--Laboratory manuals.
    [DNLM: 1. Cloning, Molecular--Laboratory Manuals. QH 440.5 S187m
2001] I. Russell, David W. (David William), 1954-   . II. Title.
    QH442.2 .S26 2001
    572.8--dc21

                                                    00-064380

10 9 8 7 6 5 4 3 2 1

Contents

Volume 1

Chapter 1

Plasmids and Their Usefulness in Molecular Cloning   1.1

INTRODUCTION

PROTOCOLS

Chapter 2

Bacteriophage λ and Its Vectors

2.1

INTRODUCTION

PROTOCOLS

Chapter 3
Working with Bacteriophage M13 Vectors   3.1

Chapter 4
Working with High-capacity Vectors   4.1

Chapter 5
Gel Electrophoresis of DNA and Pulsed-field Agarose Gel Electrophoresis   5.1

Chapter 6

Preparation and Analysis of Eukaryotic Genomic DNA   6.1

Chapter 7

Extraction, Purification, and Analysis of mRNA from Eukaryotic Cells   7.1

INFORMATION PANELS

Volume 2

Chapter 8

In Vitro Amplification of DNA by the Polymerase Chain Reaction

8.1

INTRODUCTION
PROTOCOLS

Chapter 9

Preparation of Radiolabeled DNA and RNA Probes   9.1

Chapter 10
Working with Synthetic Oligonucleotide Probes   10.1

Chapter 11
Preparation of cDNA Libraries and Gene Identification   11.1

Chapter 12

DNA Sequencing   12.1

INFORMATION PANELS

Chapter 13

Mutagenesis   13.1

INTRODUCTION
PROTOCOLS

Chapter 14

Screening Expression Libraries   14.1

INTRODUCTION

PROTOCOLS

Volume 3

Chapter 15
Expression of Cloned Genes in *Escherichia coli* {15.1}

Chapter 16
Introducing Cloned Genes into Cultured Mammalian Cells {16.1}

Chapter 17
Analysis of Gene Expression in Cultured Mammalian Cells   17.1

Chapter 18

Protein Interaction Technologies   18.1

INFORMATION PANELS

Appendices

Preface

THE FIRST EDITION OF THIS MANUAL was written some 20 years ago, when basic methods in molecular cloning were far from robust and were established in only a few laboratories. The appearance of that book did much to change the picture. The manual's didactic character gave readers confidence to use techniques that still seemed magical during the late 1970s and early 1980s. The second edition, published just 7 years after the first, was smoother in style and far richer in reliable content. By then, individual methods had become more durable and portable, but it was still difficult to string them successfully together into multistep procedures. This new edition, almost certainly the last to appear in book form, reflects a mature discipline working at full power and with high reliability. During the 1990s, many of the drearier, more repetitive techniques of molecular biology have been automated; demanding, multistep procedures have been converted into kits; high-quality genomic and cDNA libraries are now available from the shelves of commercial manufacturers; and all manipulations involving nucleic acids have benefited greatly from improvements in the quality of reagents and enzymes. As a consequence of these and other advances, competent laboratory workers can now easily avoid experimental problems that beset even the best investigators just a few years ago. This is not to say that everything works perfectly all of the time or that no further improvement is possible. However, difficulties now can largely be avoided by careful planning and application of existing knowledge rather than by experimental trial and error.

A major goal of all three editions of *Molecular Cloning* has been to provide researchers with up-to-date protocols that work reproducibly. Users of the previous editions will recognize many of the organizational features in the experimental sections of this book. Nevertheless, the revision of the text has been extensive and detailed. Ancient protocols have been modernized, while new protocols have been added to reflect the continuing penetration of molecular cloning into almost all areas of biomedical research. Of equal importance has been our desire to explain how and why particular methods work, and with reasoned arguments for choosing between alternative procedures. This edition therefore contains not only annotations at crucial points in the protocols, but also an abundance of material in the form of Information Panels, which are placed at the end of the chapters as well as in Appendix 9. We hope that these 115 panels spread throughout the three volumes of the book will provide clear insights into the reasons why methods are carried out in a certain manner and how techniques have progressively evolved. Finally, we have provided extensive references to the scientific literature so that curious readers can trace methods and ideas to their roots. Few will read this book from beginning to end. But we hope that the community of cloners will find in these pages much to stimulate the mind and to facilitate the work of their hands.

As might be imagined of a book that has been long in the making, scores of individuals have provided material. We particularly thank Erica Golemis and her colleagues for Chapter 18 on

"Protein Interaction Techniques," a large and rapidly changing field that neither of us felt comfortable covering. The people listed on the facing page have all made valuable contributions — some verbal, some written, and some corrective — that we gratefully acknowledge. Other colleagues have provided, sometimes unwittingly, critical insights into problems of both style and substance. In addition, the chocolate-loving editorial and production staff at Cold Spring Harbor Laboratory Press have spent thousands of hours meticulously checking references, facts, and grammar and producing, we think, a book of harmonious and elegant design. Without the enduring efforts, diligence, and cheerful dedication of Maryliz Dickerson, Inez Sialiano, Joan Ebert, Mary Cozza, Dorothy Brown, Susan Schaefer, Danny deBruin, Nora McInerny, and Denise Weiss, this book, if it existed at all, would be an embarrassment. The manual could not have been completed without the patient understanding and speedy responses of the librarians at Cold Spring Harbor Laboratory, The University of Texas Southwestern Medical Center at Dallas, and the Peter MacCallum Cancer Institute, Melbourne.

We owe deep debts to our Associate Authors, Kaaren Janssen and Nina Irwin, who have given us unstinting support, expert work, clarifying ideas, and dedicated and unflagging optimism. Siân Curtis and Michael Zierler ironed out scientific problems in the protocols, and Siân also assembled the appendices. Mark Curtis converted rough drafts drawn on scraps of paper into elegant and intelligent illustrations. All of these people came up with many good suggestions. Foolishly, perhaps, we did not accept them all, so any remaining errors of fact or interpretation are ours alone.

Personal debts can never be adequately acknowledged. Jan Argentine, our Managing Editor, has given us support in more ways than we can list here. She has given ungrudgingly of her time and has brought common sense, order, civility, and timeliness to a process that sometimes threatened to fall out of control. No writers could have received greater help and friendship. We owe special thanks to Daphne Davis, who cheerfully provided answers to many questions concerning experimental details. We have also benefited from the encouragement and sustaining enthusiasm of many others — in particular, John Inglis and Jim Watson at Cold Spring Harbor, Nancy Ford, who worked with us during the early stages of this project, and Rose Williams in Melbourne. Kate Simpson, a person of rare charm and intelligence, worked on the manual for a few months but did not live long enough to see the project completed. We hope that some of her lively grace shines through these pages. Finally, we owe an unquantifiable debt to our families, who have seen these three volumes built sentence by sentence and whose encouragement has never flagged.

Joe Sambrook
David Russell

Acknowledgments

THE AUTHORS WISH TO THANK the following colleagues for their valuable assistance:

Stefan Andersson
Jane Armes
Rhonda Bassel-Duby
Jim Bense
David Berman
David Bowtell
Michael Briggs
Kristi Cala
Ellson Chen
W.J. Chen
Deanna M. Church
Jeffrey Cormier
Elisabeth Cuddihy
Judy Cuddihy
Jennifer Cuthbert
Julian Davies
Daphne Davis
Ellen deBruin
Peter Espenshade
Mark Evans
Rohan Farrell
Steve Finkbeiner
Richard Flavell
Elena Ford
Sue Forrest
Katheleen Gardiner
Mary-Jane Gething
Joe Goldstein

Brad Graves
Carol Greider
Horace Grey
Doug Hanahan
M.B. Henderson
Margaret Henderson
Nouria Hernandez
Helen Hobbs
Tim Hoey
Peter Hudson
Thomas Hughes
Tommy Hyatt
Diane Jelinek
Leigh Johnson
Pegram Johnson
Elsy Jones
Song Ke
Alison Kibel
Christine Kim-Garcia
Carolyn Koo
Larry Kricka
Monty Krieger
Michael Krien
Jacob Kupersztoch
Charles Landrum
Mark Lehrman
Michael Lovett
Ros Low

Stephanie MacCallum
Ray MacDonald
Ed Madison
Mala Mahendroo
Makoto Makishima
David Mangelsdorf
Mala Mazzullo
William McAllister
Dennis McKearin
Steve McKnight
Tzu-Ching Meng
William Merrick
Lois Miller
Claudia Mills
Laura Mintz
Vivek Mittal
David Mount
Warwick Murphy
Noreen Murray
Nick Muzyczka
Karl Normington
Rosemary Paxton
Bobbi Peters
Andreja Pirkmaier
Mila Pollock
Elizabeth Powers
Rob Rawson
Pranitha Reddy

Linda Rodgers
Elliot Ross
John Sanford
David Schatz
Brian Seed
Penny Shockett
Michael Smith
David Smoller
David Spector
Steve Sprang
Wanda Stolen
Bill Studier
Thomas Südhof
Galvin Swift
Bob Tjian
Nick Tonks
Richard Treisman
Deon Venter
Xiadong Wang
Barry Wanner
Jim Wells
Barbara Wold
David Woodcock
Chuck York
Dorothy Yuan
Aina Zailitis
Zhiguo Zhang
Mark Zoller

The *Molecular Cloning* Web Site:
Access to the On-line Laboratory Manual

THIS PRINT EDITION OF *MOLECULAR CLONING* is associated with a Web Site (www.MolecularCloning.com) that is evolving into an on-line laboratory manual.

When the site is launched, registered purchasers of the book will be able to:

- *Print Protocols:* Print the step-by-step instructions needed for each procedure, in an easy-to-read format for convenient use at the bench.

- *Search Protocols:* Search by title or by keyword to ensure comprehensive access to all relevant information.

- *Receive Announcements about Updates and Additions:* Receive e-mail alerts about peer-reviewed, new, and updated information that extends the scope of the manual and enhances the value of the existing protocols.

- *Share Experience:* Communicate with other protocol users through a moderated bulletin board.

- *Access Other On-line Resources:* Link with Medline and other databases of value to working scientists.

Other valuable functions and content will be added after the site is launched.

To register at www.MolecularCloning.com:

1. Open the home page of the site.

2. Follow the registration procedure that begins on that page.

3. When prompted, enter the unique access code that is printed on the inside front cover of Volume 1 of *Molecular Cloning: A Laboratory Manual.*

4. When prompted, enter your e-mail address as your user name and a password of your choice.

5. Complete the registration procedure as requested.

The public pages of the site contain answers to FAQs about the registration procedure and a demonstration of the functions available to registered users. For additional assistance with registration, and for all other inquiries about the *Molecular Cloning* Web Site, please e-mail molecular.cloning@cshl.org or call 1-800-843-4388 (in the continental U.S. and Canada) or 516-349-1930 (all other locations) between 8:00 A.M. and 5:00 P.M. Eastern U.S. time.

Quotation Credits

For out of olde feldes, as men seyth,
Cometh al this newe corn from yer to yere,
And out of olde bokes, in good feyth,
Cometh al this newe science that men lere.
GEOFFREY CHAUCER

Excerpt from "The Parliament of Fowls" by Geoffrey Chaucer in *The Riverside Chaucer* 3/e (ed. Benson L.D, Pratt R.A., and Robinson F.N.]), copyright ©1987 Houghton Mifflin Company, used by permission of the publisher.

p. 1.62, Excerpt from *The Trouble with Being Born* by E.M. Cioran is copyright ©1973 by Editions Gallimard; English-language copyright ©1976 by Seaver Books.

p. 1.153, Excerpt from "Personal Recollections of Lysozyme and Fleming" in *Lysozyme* (ed. Osserman E.F., Canfield R.E. and Beychok S.), pp. xiii–xviii, copyright ©1974 by *Academic Press*, reprinted by permission of the publisher.

p. 6.2, "Cell DNA" from *New Selected Poems* by Les Murray (1998 Duffy and Snellgrove, P.O. Box 177, Potts Point NSW 1335, Australia) is reproduced with permission of the author and the publisher.

p. 8.2, Excerpt from Kleppe et al. (*J. Mol. Biol.* 56: 341 [1971]) is reprinted, with permission, from Academic Press Ltd., London, UK.

p. 8.3, Excerpt from Mullis K.B. (*Sci. Am. 262: 56* [1990]) is reprinted by permission of Kary B. Mullis, copyright ©1990. All rights reserved.

p. 8.106, Excerpt from *George Bernard Shaw: Man of the Century*, p. 839, by Archibald Henderson (1956 Appleton-Century-Crofts, New York).

p. 9.2, Excerpt from *The Crazy Ape; Written by a Biologist for the Young* by Albert Szent-Györgyi (1970 Philosophical Library, New York.)

p. 10.10, Excerpt from Introduction, 1974, to the French edition of *Crash* by J.G. Ballard (1973 Columbia).

p. 11.36, Excerpt from *The Black Cloud* ©1957, 1958, renewed 1985, 1986 by Fred Hoyle (by permission of HarperCollins Publishers Inc.).

p. 12.2, Excerpt from *What Mad Pursuit: A Personal View of Scientific Discovery* ©1988 by Francis Crick (Basic Books; by permission of Perseus Books Group).

p. 12.93, Excerpt from "The Marburg Sisters" in *SHIP FEVER*: A Collection of Short Stories by Andrea Barrett (1996 W.W. Norton & Co., Inc., New York), used by permission of the publisher.

p. 13.10, Excerpt from *The Lost Worlds of 2001* by Arthur C. Clarke, used by permission of Scovil Chicak Galen Literary Agency.

p. 14.3, Excerpt from *The Language of Genes* by Steve Jones (1995 Doubleday [US]; HarperCollins [UK]), used by permission of the author and the publisher.

p. 15.13, Excerpt from *History of Western Philosophy*, p. 512, by Bertrand Russell (1979 Allen and Unwin, London).

p. 16.6, Excerpt from "The Behavior of the Hawkweeds" in *SHIP FEVER*: A Collection of Short Stories by Andrea Barrett (1996 W.W. Norton & Co., Inc., New York), used by permission of the publisher.

p. 17.3, From *La Science et l'hypothèse* by Henri Poincaré (1902 Flammarion, 26 rue Racine 75006 Paris France).

p. 18.5, From *Pensees* (1660) by Blaise Pascal.

Before index: Excerpt from "Little Gidding" in FOUR QUARTETS, copyright 1942 by T.S. Eliot and renewed 1970 by Esme Valerie Eliot, reprinted by permission of Harcourt, Inc.

End of index: "When I Look at the Flight of the Leaves," from THE SELECTED POEMS OF MARINA TSVETAEVA by Marina Tsvetaeva, translated by Elaine Feinstein, copyright ©1971, 1981 by Elaine Feinstein. Used by permission of Dutton, a division of Penguin Putnam Inc.

Last page: Excerpt from "East Coker" in FOUR QUARTETS, copyright ©1940 by T.S. Eliot and renewed 1968 by Esme Valerie Eliot, reprinted by permission of Harcourt, Inc.

Chapter 1

Plasmids and Their Usefulness in Molecular Cloning

INTRODUCTION

PROTOCOLS

P LASMIDS ARE EXTRACHROMOSOMAL MOLECULES OF DNA that vary in size from 1 kb to more than 200 kb. Most of them are double-stranded, covalently closed, circular molecules that can be isolated from bacterial cells in a superhelical form. Plasmids:

- are found in a wide variety of bacterial species; most plasmids have a narrow host range and can be maintained only in a limited set of closely related species.

- are extrachromosomal elements that behave as accessory genetic units that replicate and are inherited independently of the bacterial chromosome.

- have evolved a variety of mechanisms to maintain a stable copy number of the plasmid in their bacterial hosts and to partition plasmid molecules accurately to daughter cells.

- are dependent, to a greater or lesser extent, on the enzymes and proteins encoded by their host for their replication and transcription.

• frequently contain genes coding for enzymes that are advantageous to the bacterial host. These genes specify a remarkably diverse set of traits, many of which are of great medical and commercial significance. Among the phenotypes conferred by plasmids are resistance to and production of antibiotics, degradation of complex organic compounds, and production of colicins, enterotoxins, and restriction and modification enzymes.

> The word "plasmid," introduced by Joshua Lederberg in 1952, was defined as an extrachromosomal genetic element. It was supplanted for a while by "episome," a term proposed by Jacob and Wollman (1958) to describe an accessory genetic element that is transmissable from cell to cell and may be propagated either in the cytoplasm or, after insertion, as part of the bacterial chromosome. However, operational difficulties soon arose in deciding whether some extrachromosomal elements were plasmids, because they were never seen to insert into the host chromosome, or episomes that inserted at very low frequency. Hayes (1969) therefore suggested that the term episome "should be thanked for its services and sent into honourable retirement." This has not happened: Both words are now in common use, and the distinction between them has become blurred. However, most of the vectors discussed in this chapter are plasmids as defined by Lederberg and not episomes as defined by Jacob and Wollman. So, for readers who desire firm guidance in this matter, we say that "plasmid" is more correct than "episome" most of the time, but there are of course always exceptions.

THE REPLICONS OF PLASMIDS DEFINE THEIR COPY NUMBER

A replicon is a genetic unit consisting of an origin of DNA replication and its associated control elements. In plasmids, the origin of replication is a defined segment of DNA several hundred base pairs in length: Its set of associated *cis*-acting controlling elements contains sites for diffusible plasmid- and host-encoded factors involved in initiation of DNA synthesis. A plasmid replicon can therefore be defined as the smallest piece of plasmid DNA that is able to replicate autonomously and maintain normal copy number.

> The term "replicon" was first used at the 1963 Cold Spring Harbor Symposium (Jacob et al. 1964) in a theoretical paper explaining how circular, extrachromosomal DNA molecules in bacteria might replicate. Since then, many of the predictions of the original prokaryotic model have been validated by biochemical and genetic experiments, and the definition of replicon has expanded to include chromosomal and extrachromosomal replication units in both prokaryotes and eukaryotes.

More than 30 different replicons have been identified in plasmids. However, almost all plasmids used routinely in molecular cloning carry a replicon derived from pMB1, a plasmid originally isolated from a clinical specimen (Hershfield et al. 1974). Plasmids carrying the primeval pMB1 replicon (or its close relative, the colicin E1 [colE1] replicon [Balbas et al. 1986]) maintain between 15 and 20 copies in each bacterial cell. However, over the years, the pMB1/colE1 replicon has been extensively modified to increase the copy number, and hence the yield, of plasmid DNA. High-copy-number plasmid vectors are available in huge variety, are the workhorses of molecular cloning, and are used for almost all routine manipulation of small segments of recombinant DNAs (<15 kb in size). By contrast, low-copy-number vectors, which carry replicons from sources other than pMB1/colE1 (Table 1-1), are required for special purposes. These include (1) cloning of DNA sequences that are unstable and genes that are lethal when propagated in high-copy-number plasmids and (2) constructing bacterial artificial chromosomes (BACs), which are vectors used to propagate large (~100 kb) segments of foreign DNA as plasmids in *Escherichia coli* (please see Chapter 2).

TABLE 1-1 Replicons Carried by Plasmid Vectors

PLASMID	REPLICON	COPY NUMBER	REFERENCES
pBR322	pMB1	15–20	Bolivar et al. (1977b)
pUC	modified form of pMB1	500–700	Vieira and Messing (1982, 1987); Messing (1983); Lin-Chao et al. (1992)
pMOB45	pKN402	15–118	Bittner and Vapnek (1981)
pACYC	p15A	18–22	Chang and Cohen (1978)
pSC101	pSC101	~5	Stoker et al. (1982)
colE1	colE1	15–20	Kahn et al. (1979)

REPLICATION OF PLASMIDS

Stringent and Relaxed Replication

The copy number of a plasmid is defined as the average number of plasmids per bacterial cell or per chromosome under normal growth conditions. Controlled by the plasmid replicon, the copy number can increase or decrease within a narrow range in response to changes in the growth conditions of the bacterial culture. At steady state, the population of plasmid doubles at exactly the same rate as the population of host cells, and the copy number remains constant.

Plasmids, whatever their replicon, maintain harmony between their rate of replication and that of the host by rationing the supply of a molecule that affects the frequency of initiation of plasmid DNA synthesis. In plasmids carrying the pMB1/colE1 replicon, this positive regulatory molecule is an RNA, known as RNAII, which is used to prime initiation of leading-strand DNA synthesis. However, the regulatory molecule of other replicons (e.g., pSC101) is a *cis*-acting protein (RepA) that acts positively on the origin of replication and negatively regulates the transcription of its own gene (Linder et al. 1985; for reviews, please see Nordström 1990; Nordström and Wagner 1994; Helinski et al. 1996). In all cases, the synthesis and activity of positive regulatory RNA and protein molecules are modulated by ancillary *trans*-acting products whose concentration is responsive to plasmid copy number or to alterations in the physiology of the host bacterium.

Plasmids whose positive regulatory molecule is an RNA molecule generally have high copy numbers and do not require any plasmid-encoded proteins for replication. Instead, they rely entirely on long-lived enzymes and proteins supplied by the host, including chaperones, DNA polymerases I and III, DNA-dependent RNA polymerase, ribonuclease H (RNase H), DNA gyrase, and topoisomerase I (for review, please see Helinski et al. 1996). These plasmids, which are said to replicate in a "relaxed" fashion, continue to duplicate when protein synthesis is inhibited by amino acid starvation (Bazaral and Helinski 1968) or by addition of an antibiotic such as chloramphenicol (Clewell and Helinski 1969) (please see the information panel on **CHLORAMPHENICOL**). Because protein synthesis is required for initiation of each round of host DNA synthesis but not for plasmid replication, the content of plasmid DNA in cells exposed to chloramphenicol increases relative to the amount of chromosomal DNA (Clewell 1972). Over the course of several hours of amplification, thousands of copies of a relaxed plasmid may accumulate in the cell; at the end of the process, plasmid DNA may account for 50% or more of the total cellular DNA. By contrast, plasmids such as pSC101 require ongoing synthesis of the RepA protein for replication, and their copy number cannot be amplified, nor their yield increased, by inhibiting cellular protein synthesis. Such plasmids are said to replicate under "stringent" control.

Initiation of DNA Synthesis at colE1 Origins Is Primed by RNAII

Initiation occurs within a 600-nucleotide region that contains all of the *cis*-acting elements required for replication. Synthesis of leading-strand DNA is primed by RNAII (Figure 1-1) (for review, please see Eguchi et al. 1991).

Synthesis of the precursor to RNAII is initiated at a promoter 550 bp upstream of the origin, proceeds through the origin, and terminates at one of a number of closely spaced sites locat-

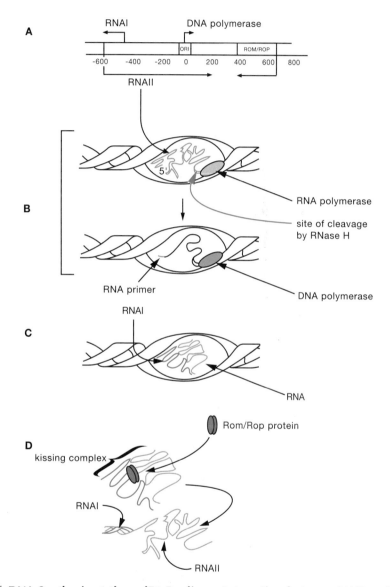

FIGURE 1-1 DNA Synthesis at the colE1 Replicon: Interaction between RNAI and RNAII

(*A*) Genetic map of the colE1 replicon with transcription patterns of this region. (*B*) RNAII serves as the primer for DNA synthesis at the colE1 replicon. During synthesis of RNAII, the 5´ region of the nascent molecule folds into a specific conformation that allows the growing 3´end to form a persistent DNA-RNA hybrid with the DNA template at the origin of replication. The 3´region of RNAII is processed by RNase H to generate a primer that is used for synthesis of the leading strand by DNA polymerase I. (*C*) The "kissing complex" between RNAI and RNAII is stabilized by binding of dimeric Rom/Rop protein. (*D*) Blow up of the "kissing complex" between RNAI and RNAII. The stable complex between RNAI and RNAII prevents DNA synthesis by suppressing the formation of the stable hybrid between RNAII and DNA.

ed ~150 nucleotides downstream. The 5′ end of the ~750-nucleotide primary transcript folds into a complex secondary structure that brings a G-rich loop in RNAII into alignment with a C-rich stretch of plasmid DNA located 20 nucleotides upstream of the origin on the template strand. The RNAII transcript is then processed into mature primer by RNase H, which cleaves the RNA within a sequence of five A residues at the origin. The resulting 555-nucleotide mature RNAII is used as a primer by DNA polymerase I to initiate synthesis of the leading strand (for reviews and references, please see Kües and Stahl 1989; Cesareni et al. 1991; Helinski et al. 1996). Extension of the stable DNA-RNA hybrid exposes sites on the complementary strand of DNA at which discontinuous synthesis of the lagging strand is initiated. Because lagging-strand synthesis is blocked ~20 nucleotides upstream of the origin by the unhybridized segments of RNAII, replication progresses unidirectionally in Cairns or θ structures in plasmids carrying pMB1/colE1 replicons.

RNAI Is a Negative Regulator of Replication

The colE1 replicon is unable to influence the activity of the host enzymes required for plasmid replication and, therefore, is unable to alter the speed or course of events that occur after DNA synthesis has been initiated. Consequently, control of copy number must be exerted at or before initiation of DNA replication. Synthesis of plasmid DNA depends on the formation of a persistent DNA-RNAII hybrid at the origin of replication. Under normal circumstances, initiation is controlled by altering the equilibrium between correctly folded RNAII, which can form the persistent hybrid, and inappropriately folded structures of RNAII, which cannot.

Sway over this equilibrium lies chiefly in the hands of RNAI, a small transcript of 108 bases encoded by the antisense strand of the RNAII gene. RNAI folds into a cloverleaf structure that binds to the nascent RNAII precursor and thereby prevents its folding into the secondary structure required for formation of the persistent hybrid (Lacatena and Cesareni 1981).

The mechanism by which RNAI and RNAII interact has been described in great detail by Tomizawa and his colleagues (e.g., please see Tomizawa 1990a). The picture that emerges is one of dynamic interactions between RNAI and short-lived folding intermediates of RNAII. The folding of RNAII is particularly vulnerable to interference by RNAI when the nascent RNAII transcript is between 80 and 360 nucleotides in length. The initial contacts occur between stem-loops in the two RNA molecules and lead to formation of a segment of double-stranded RNA that involves the 5′ sequences of RNAII and the entire length of RNAI. RNAI therefore controls plasmid copy number by acting as a negative regulator of initiation of plasmid DNA synthesis.

> The copy number of the pUC family of plasmids is much higher than that of other plasmids carrying a pMB1 or colE1 replicon. This is because pUC plasmids carry a point mutation that alters the secondary structure of the positive regulatory molecule (RNAII) in a temperature-dependent fashion. At 37°C or 42°C, RNAII appears to fold into a conformation that is resistant to inhibition by RNAI. Initiation of DNA synthesis is enhanced, resulting in abnormally high copy number. When the bacterial culture is grown at 30°C, the copy number of pUC plasmids is restored to normal (Lin-Chao et al. 1992).

The simplest hypothesis to explain the maintenance of plasmid copy number is that the steady-state concentration of cytoplasmic RNAI is determined by gene dosage (Tomizawa 1987; Chiang and Bremer 1991). Thus, if the copy number of the plasmid increases above normal, the concentration of RNAI will rise and plasmid DNA replication will be inhibited. However, this coupling between plasmid copy number and fluctuations in inhibitor concentration can work only if the half-life of RNAI is short (Pritchard 1984) and if the rate of degradation of RNAI is proportional to the rate of growth of the culture. These two conditions both appear to be fulfilled under normal conditions of cell growth, where the half-life of RNAI is 1–2 minutes. Kinetic calculations show that this period is sufficiently short for the molecule to act as a real-time sensor of plasmid copy number (Brendel and Perelson 1993).

Degradation of RNAI proceeds in two stages. First, the five 5′-terminal nucleotides are removed by endonucleolytic cleavage by RNase E. The truncated molecule can still bind to RNAII but is now susceptible to degradation by a ribonuclease whose activity is responsive to growth rate (Lin-Chao and Cohen 1991). This regulation provides a mechanism to maintain a constant number of plasmids even when the growth rate of cells is fitful.

The Rom/Rop Protein Empowers the Negative Regulatory Activity of RNAI

The efficiency of binding of RNAI to RNAII is improved by a plasmid-encoded protein known as Rom (RNAI modulator) or Rop (repressor of primer). By improving the efficiency of hybrid formation between RNAI and RNAII, Rom enhances the negative regulatory action of RNAI. Accordingly, deletion of the *rom/rop* gene increases the copy number of colE1 plasmids by at least two orders of magnitude (Twigg and Sherratt 1980). For example, deletion of the *rom/rop* genes raises the copy number of the old war horse pBR322 from 15–20 copies to more than 500 copies per bacterial cell, whereas insertion of a segment of foreign DNA into the *rom/rop* gene causes lethal runaway plasmid DNA replication (Giza and Huang 1989).

> Rom is a homodimer of a 63-amino-acid polypeptide encoded by a gene lying 400 nucleotides downstream from the colE1 origin of replication (Twigg and Sherratt 1980; Tomizawa and Som 1984). Each subunit of the dimer consists of two α helices connected by a sharp bend; therefore, the dimer is a tight bundle of four α helices exhibiting twofold symmetry (Banner et al. 1987). Rom binds to RNAI and RNAII with similar affinities (Helmer-Citterich et al. 1988) and drives unstable intermediates formed between the two complementary RNAs into a more stable structure (Lacatena et al. 1984; Tomizawa and Som 1984; Tomizawa 1990b). Most probably, each of the two subunits of Rom recognizes sequence and structural elements in both RNAI and RNAII. Rom binds to a stem on the interacting RNAs, stabilizing the "kissing" complex (Tomizawa 1985) and initiating formation of a perfect RNAI-RNAII hybrid (Eguchi and Tomizawa 1990).

INCOMPATIBILITY OF PLASMIDS

When two plasmids share elements of the same replication machinery, they compete with each other during both replication and the subsequent step of partitioning into daughter cells. Such plasmids are unable to coexist without selection in bacterial cultures. This phenomenon is known as incompatibility (for reviews, please see Davison 1984; Novick 1987).

> Plasmids carrying the same replicon belong to the same incompatibility group and are unable to be maintained within the same bacterium. Plasmids carrying replicons whose components are not interchangeable belong to different incompatibility groups and can be maintained in the same bacterium. Examples of plasmids that are compatible with colE1-type plasmids are p15A, R6K, and F.

Plasmids carrying the same replicon are selected at random from the intracellular pool for replication. However, this does not guarantee that the copy numbers of two plasmids will remain constant in a bacterial population. Larger plasmids, for example, require more time to replicate than do smaller plasmids and are at a selective disadvantage in every cell of the bacterial population. Plasmids of similar size may also be incompatible because of imbalances in the efficiency of initiation resulting from stochastic processes within individual bacterial cells. Such turns of

TABLE 1-2 Control Elements That Regulate Replication

INCOMPATIBILITY GROUPS	NEGATIVE CONTROL ELEMENT	COMMENT
colE1, pMB1	RNAI	controls processing of pre-RNAII into primer
IncFII, pT181	RNA	controls synthesis of RepA protein
P1, F, R6K, pSC101, p15A	iterons	sequesters RepA protein

chance can lead rapidly to drastic differences in the copy number of the two plasmids. In some cells, one plasmid might dominate, whereas in other cells, its incompatible partner might prosper. Over the course of a few generations of bacterial growth in the absence of selection, the minority plasmid may be completely eliminated from some cells of the population. Descendants of the original cell may contain one plasmid or the other, but very rarely both.

The regions of plasmid DNA that confer incompatibility can be identified by introducing segments of the DNA into an unrelated multicopy replicon and determining the ability of a test plasmid to coexist with the hybrid. For example, the incompatibility locus of the stringent, low-copy-number plasmid pSC101 maps to a series of directly repeated ~20-bp sequences known as iterons, located at the origin of replication. The iterons, in conjunction with the nearby *cis*-acting *par* locus, appear to "handcuff" plasmid DNA molecules by sequestering the plasmid-encoded RepA protein so that it can no longer facilitate binding of host-encoded proteins to the origin (for review, please see Nordström 1990). By contrast, in the case of colE1 described above, incompatibility is defined by the inhibitory activity of RNAI (for review, please see Novick 1987). Any two plasmids that are isogenic for RNAI and use it for regulation are incompatible, whether or not they share any other functions (Tomizawa and Itoh 1981).

As discussed earlier, most vectors in current use carry a replicon derived from the plasmid pMB1. These vectors are incompatible with all other plasmids carrying the colE1 replicon but are fully compatible with iteron-binding replicons such as those in pSC101 and its derivatives. Table 1-2 lists several well-known plasmids and negative control elements involved in regulating their replication.

PLASMID VECTORS

Selectable Markers

Plasmid vectors contain genetic markers that confer strong growth advantages upon plasmid-bearing bacteria under selective conditions. In molecular cloning, these markers are used:

- *To select clones of plasmid-bearing bacteria:* In the laboratory, plasmid DNA can be introduced into bacteria by the artificial process of transformation. However, even under the best conditions, transformation is generally inefficient, and plasmids become stably established in only a small minority of the bacterial population. Selectable markers carried by the plasmid allow these rare transformants to be selected with ease. These plasmid-encoded markers provide specific resistance to (i.e., the ability to grow in the presence of) antibiotics such as the kanamycins, ampicillin and carbenicillin, and the tetracyclines. The properties and modes of action of these antibiotics are discussed in information panels at the end of this chapter.

- *To indemnify transformed bacteria against the risks imposed by their burden of plasmid DNA or plasmid-encoded proteins:* Plasmids present at low copy numbers (<20 copies/cell) do not appear to unduly handicap their host cells. However, much evidence shows that high-copy-number plasmids and large quantities of recombinant proteins can severely hamper the growth, and even the survival, of transformed cells (Murray and Kelley 1979; Beck and Bremer 1980). To prevent the emergence of bacteria from which the plasmid has been eliminated, it is important to sustain selective pressure by including the appropriate antibiotic in the culture medium at all times.

1973–1978

In the early 1970s, selectable markers, typically *kan*[r] or *amp*[r] or *tet*[r], were introduced into plasmids carrying the pMB1 (or colE1) replicon (please see the information panels on KANAMYCINS, TETRACYCLINE, and AMPICILLIN AND CARBENICILLIN). The first plasmids used as cloning vectors — pSC101 (Cohen et al. 1973), colE1 (Hershfield et al. 1974), and pCR1 (Covey et al. 1976) — were limited in their versatility: Either they replicated poorly or they carried unsuitable selectable markers, and none of them contained more than two restriction sites that could be used for cloning. The first plasmid to combine all of the then-available desirable features was pBR313 (Bolivar et al. 1977a,b; please see the information panel on pBR322). It replicated in a relaxed fashion, contained two selectable markers (*tet*[r] and *amp*[r]), and carried a number of useful restriction sites. However, pBR313 was unnecessarily large; more than half of its DNA was not essential for its role as a vector. The first phase of plasmid vector development ended with the construction of pBR322 (Bolivar et al. 1977b), a plasmid of 4.36 kb from which most of these unnecessary sequences had been eliminated. pBR322 was the most widely used cloning vehicle of its day, and many of the plasmid vectors in current use are its distant descendants (for review, please see Balbas et al. 1986).

1978–1983

This period saw the evolution of clunky plasmids such as pBR322 into vectors that were smaller in size, higher in copy number, and able to accept fragments of foreign DNA generated by cleavage with a wider range of restriction enzymes. There is no strict upper limit to the size of DNA fragments that can be cloned in plasmids. However, there are advantages in reducing the size of plasmid vectors to a minimum. Plasmid copy number, stability, and transforming efficiency all increase as the size of their DNA is reduced. Smaller plasmids can accommodate larger segments of foreign DNA before their efficiency begins to deteriorate. In addition, because smaller colE1 plasmids replicate to higher copy numbers, the yield of foreign DNA is increased and hybridization signals are fortified when transformed colonies containing cloned foreign DNA sequences are screened with radiolabeled probes.

In the late 1970s and early 1980s, the problems of unwieldiness and inefficiency were addressed when streamlined derivatives of pBR322 were constructed. These plasmids lacked ancillary sequences involved in the control of copy number and mobilization. Unfortunately, the first-generation high-copy-number plasmids, of which pXf3 (Hanahan 1983) and pAT53 (Twigg and Sherratt 1980) were the best known, suffered from a major defect: Foreign DNA sequences could be inserted only at a limited number of restriction sites located within the "natural" sequences used to construct the plasmid. Within a year or two, these plasmids had been replaced by a revolutionary series of vectors (pUC vectors), in which the number of restriction enzyme cleavage sites was expanded and their distribution within the vector was rationalized (Messing

1983; Norrander et al. 1983; Yanisch-Perron et al. 1985; Vieira and Messing 1987). The pUC vectors were the first plasmids to contain a closely arranged series of synthetic cloning sites, termed polylinkers, multiple cloning sites, or polycloning sites, that consist of banks of sequences recognized by restriction enzymes. In most cases, these restriction sites are unique; i.e., they are not found elsewhere in the plasmid vector. For example, the polycloning site from the vector pUC19 consists of a tandem array of unique cleavage sites for 13 restriction enzymes: *Hin*dIII, *Sph*I, *Pst*I, *Sal*I, *Acc*I, *Hin*cII, *Xba*I, *Bam*HI, *Sma*I, *Xma*I, *Kpn*I, *Sac*I, and *Eco*RI.

Such arrays of recognition sequences provide a vast variety of targets that can be used singly or in combination to clone DNA fragments generated by cleavage with a large number of restriction enzymes. Furthermore, fragments inserted at one restriction site can often be excised by cleavage of the recombinant plasmid with restriction enzymes that cleave at flanking sites. Insertion of a segment of DNA into a polycloning site is therefore equivalent to adding synthetic linkers to its termini. The availability of these flanking sites greatly simplifies the task of mapping the segment of foreign DNA.

A potential disadvantage of drawing together all cloning sites into one location in a plasmid is the inability to use inactivation of a selectable marker to screen for recombinants. This method had been used extensively with first-generation plasmids, such as pBR322, that carry two or more different selectable markers, e.g., *tet*^r^ and *amp*^r^, each containing a "natural" restriction site. Insertion of foreign DNA sequences into one of these sites inactivated one of the two markers. Bacteria containing recombinant plasmids could therefore be distinguished from those carrying the empty parental vector by virtue of their ability to grow in only one of the two sets of selective conditions (please see the information panel on AMPICILLIN AND CARBENICILLIN).

Insertional inactivation is not possible with pUC vectors, which carry only one antibiotic resistance gene (typically *amp*^r^) and an aggregated set of cloning sites. However, recombinant plasmids can be readily distinguished from parental pUC plasmids by screening the color of bacterial colonies. pUC vectors and many of their derivatives carry a short segment of *E. coli* DNA that contains the regulatory sequences of the *lacZ* gene and the coding information for the amino-terminal 146 amino acids of β-galactosidase. Embedded in the coding information, just downstream from the initiating ATG, is a multiple cloning site. The small amino-terminal fragment of β-galactosidase expressed by pUC vectors in transformed bacteria has no endogenous β-galactosidase activity. However, the amino-terminal fragment, known as the α-fragment, can complement certain mutants of β-galactosidase, which are themselves inactive, producing an enzyme that has abundant catalytic activity. α-complementation occurs when pUC plasmids are introduced into strains of *E. coli* that express an inactive carboxy-terminal fragment (the ω-fragment) of β-galactosidase.

When a segment of foreign DNA is cloned into the multiple cloning site of pUC vectors, the sequence encoding the α-fragment is disrupted, and α-complemention is either greatly suppressed or abolished altogether. Bacterial colonies containing recombinant plasmids are therefore *amp*^r^ and contain little or no β-galactosidase activity. By contrast, bacterial colonies containing empty plasmids are *amp*^r^ and are able to hydrolyze nonfermentable, chromogenic substrates such as 5-bromo-4-chloro-3-indole-β-D-galactoside (X-gal) (Horwitz et al. 1964; Davies and Jacob 1968; please see the information panels on X-GAL and on α-COMPLEMENTATION). The two types of colonies can therefore be distinguished by a simple, nondestructive histochemical test (Miller 1972). When X-gal is included in the agar medium, colonies carrying parental nonrecombinant plasmids become deep blue, whereas those containing recombinant plasmids either remain an ordinary creamy white or become tinted in pale egg-shell blue (for more details, please see the information panel on α-COMPLEMENTATION).

1983–Present

The latest phase of construction of plasmid vectors has involved the incorporation of ancillary sequences that are used for a variety of purposes, including generation of single-stranded DNA templates for DNA sequencing, transcription of foreign DNA sequences in vitro, direct selection of recombinant clones, and expression of large amounts of foreign proteins. These specialized functions are discussed briefly here and in more detail in later chapters.

Plasmid Vectors Carrying Origins of Replication Derived from Single-stranded Bacteriophages

Many plasmid vectors in current use carry the origin of DNA replication from the genome of a single-stranded filamentous bacteriophage such as M13 or f1 (please see Chapter 3). Such vectors, which are sometimes called phagemids, combine the best features of plasmid and single-stranded bacteriophage vectors and have the advantage of two separate modes of replication: as a conventional double-stranded DNA plasmid and as a template to produce single-stranded copies of one of the phagemid strands. A phagemid can therefore be used in the same way as an orthodox plasmid vector, or it can be used to produce filamentous bacteriophage particles that contain single-stranded copies of cloned segments of DNA. Since their introduction in the early 1980s, phagemids have eliminated much of the need to subclone segments of foreign DNA from plasmids into conventional single-stranded bacteriophage vectors.

Production of single-stranded DNA is induced when bacteria carrying a phagemid are infected with a helper bacteriophage that carries the genes required to (1) generate single-stranded DNA from a double-stranded template and (2) package the single-stranded DNA into filamentous virus particles. The defective filamentous virions secreted from a small-scale culture of infected bacteria contain sufficient single-stranded DNA for sequencing (please see Chapter 12; for preparation of radiolabeled single-stranded probes, please see Chapter 9 or for site-directed mutagenesis, please see Chapter 13).

In most cases, pairs of plasmid vectors are available that differ in the orientation of the bacteriophage origin of replication. The orientation of the origin determines which of the two DNA strands will be encapsidated into bacteriophage particles. By convention, a plus sign (+) indicates that the origin in the plasmid and that in the bacteriophage particle are in the same orientation. For more details on the design and use of phagemids, please see Chapter 3.

Plasmid Vectors Carrying Bacteriophage Promoters

Many plasmid vectors carry promoters derived from bacteriophages T3, T7, and/or SP6 adjacent to the multiple cloning site (MCS). Foreign DNAs inserted at restriction sites within the MCS can therefore be transcribed in vitro when the linearized recombinant plasmid DNA is incubated with the appropriate DNA-dependent RNA polymerase and ribonucleotide precursors (please see Chapter 9). These promoters are so specific that RNA polymerase from SP6, for example, will not synthesize RNA from any other bacteriophage promoter located elsewhere in the plasmid.

Many commercial vectors (e.g., vectors of the pGEM series or the Bluescript series) carry two bacteriophage promoters in opposite orientations, located on each side of the multiple cloning site (Short et al. 1988). This organization allows RNA to be synthesized in vitro from either end and either strand of the foreign DNA, depending on the type of RNA polymerase used in the transcription reaction. The RNAs generated in this way can be used as hybridization probes or can be translated in cell-free protein-synthesizing systems. In addition, vectors carrying the T7 promoter can be used to express cloned DNA sequences in bacteria expressing T7 RNA polymerase (please see Chapter 9, Protocol 8) (Tabor and Richardson 1985).

Positive Selection Vectors

Identifying plasmids with DNA inserts can be frustrating and time-consuming. However, a variety of cloning vectors have been developed that allow growth only of bacterial colonies carrying recombinant plasmids (for reviews, please see Burns and Beacham 1984; Hengen 1997). Bacteria containing the empty parental plasmid are unable to form colonies under selective conditions. Typically, the plasmids used in these systems express a gene product that is lethal for certain bacterial hosts; cloning a segment of foreign DNA into the plasmid inactivates the gene and relieves the toxicity. For example, Bochner et al. (1980), Maloy and Nunn (1981), and Craine (1982) describe conditions under which transformed bacteria carrying plasmid vectors coding for *tet* [r] will die, whereas recombinant plasmids carrying a segment of foreign DNA within the *tet* [r] gene will grow. Other conditionally lethal genes used in various positive selection vectors include those encoding the bacteriophage λ repressor (Nilsson et al. 1983; Mongolsuk et al. 1994), *Eco*RI methylase (Cheng and Modrich 1983), *Eco*RI endonuclease (Kuhn et al. 1986), galactokinase (Ahmed 1984), colicin E3 (Vernet et al. 1985), transcription factor GATA-1(Trudel et al. 1996), the lysis protein of φX174 (Henrich and Plapp 1986), the *ccdB* gene of *E. coli* (Bernard 1995, 1996), and barnase (Yazynin et al. 1996). Ingenious as these positive selection systems may be, few of them have found wide use. In many cases, the number of potential cloning sites is limited, the efficiency of the selection may be variable, special host cells may be required, and the plasmids may be devoid of desirable features (e.g., bacteriophage promoters and bacteriophage M13 origin of DNA replication). In consequence, most investigators prefer to reduce the background of empty plasmids by other means, for example, by optimizing the ratio of vector DNA to insert in the ligation reaction, dephosphorylating the vector, or using directional cloning. Colonies containing the desired recombinant are then identified by hybridization in situ to radiolabeled probes, restriction analysis of small-scale preparations of plasmids, and/or polymerase chain reaction (PCR) amplification of inserts.

Low-copy-number Plasmid Vectors

By contrast to conventional high-copy-number plasmid vectors, which carry souped-up versions of the colE1 replicon, low-copy-number plasmid vectors are built around replicons such as R1 that keep plasmid DNA synthesis under a very tight rein.

The first generation of low-copy vectors — rather bulky and fairly rough-hewn by today's standards — was designed to solve problems of toxicity that arose when particular types of foreign genes and DNA sequences were cloned in plasmid vectors. Many genes coding for membrane and DNA-binding proteins fall into this class, as do certain promoters and regulatory sequences (e.g., please see Fiil et al. 1979; Hansen and von Meyenberg 1979; Little 1979; Murray and Kelley 1979; Beck and Bremer 1980; Spratt et al. 1980; Claverie-Martin et al. 1989). Sometimes, these DNA sequences and gene products are so toxic to the host bacteria that it is simply impossible to isolate transformed strains using high-copy-number vectors. If transformants are obtained, their growth rate is often frustratingly slow, and the cloned foreign DNA sequences are often unstable. To solve these problems, multipurpose low-copy-number vectors have been developed that carry tightly regulated prokaryotic promoters with a low level of basal expression, for example, the pET series of vectors, and prokaryotic transcription terminators to prevent spurious transcription of foreign DNA sequences from upstream plasmid promoters. These low-copy-number vectors now come equipped with multiple cloning sites, origins of replication of single-stranded bacteriophages, T3 and T7 promoters, and other useful modular conveniences of proven worth. Most modern low-copy-number vectors also carry *par* loci that promote accurate partitioning of plasmid molecules into daughter cells during cell division. Problems of plasmid instability may also be solved by using an *E. coli* strain that suppresses replication of colE1 plasmids. Most strains of *E. coli* used as hosts for colE1 plasmids carry a wild-type version of a gene known as *pcnB*, which codes for poly(A) polymerase. Wild-type *pcnB* promotes the decay of RNAI, the negative regulator of copy number of colE1 plasmids, by adding adenylate residues to the 3′ terminus of RNAI. In its polyadenylated form, RNAI is highly unstable and is therefore unable to prevent formation of RNAII, the primer for plasmid DNA synthesis. In strains of *E. coli* bearing a mutant *pcnB* allele, RNAI remains unadenylated and its half-life is extended. Processing of RNAII is suppressed and the copy number of colE1 plasmids is thereby reduced by a factor of ~10. Many recombinant colE1 plasmids that are unstable in conventional *E. coli* hosts can be grown successfully in *pcnB* mutant strains (He et al. 1993; Ellis et al. 1995; Podkovryov and Larson 1995; Pierson and Barcak 1999).

Runaway-replication Plasmid Vectors

Runaway vectors replicate in a normal fashion at temperatures up to 34°C. However, their copy number increases as the temperature of the culture is raised until, at 39°C, plasmid replication becomes uncontrolled. Vectors based on the low-copy-number IncFII plasmid R1 have been converted to runaway-replication vectors by artificially increasing the rate of synthesis of *repA* mRNA, for example, by placing the *repA* gene under the control of the bacteriophage λ p_R or p_L promoter. The activity of this promoter is in turn controlled by the temperature-sensitive λ repressor *cI*857 (for review, please see Nordström and Uhlin 1992). Because runaway amplification occurs in the presence of protein synthesis, the expressed product of a foreign DNA cloned in a runaway plasmid may eventually constitute 50% of the protein in a bacterial cell in which plasmid replication has gone amok (e.g., please see Remaut et al. 1983).

Runaway plasmid replication and associated production of plasmid-encoded proteins place the cell under severe metabolic strain that is reflected in a decreased growth rate and, sometimes, cell death (Uhlin and Nordström 1978; Uhlin et al. 1979; Remaut et al. 1983). For this reason, it is important to ascertain the time of induction required to obtain maximal yields of the intact target protein.

Plasmid Expression Vectors

A large number of plasmid vectors have been constructed that contain powerful promoters capable of generating large amounts of mRNA in vivo from cloned foreign genes. Nowadays, the activity of many of these promoters can be stringently regulated so that there is (1) minimal basal expression of the target gene under repressed conditions and (2) fast and dramatic induction of expression of the cloned gene in response to simple changes in the conditions of culture. For native proteins to be produced in large quantities, the vector must contain an efficient Shine-Dalgarno sequence upstream of the initiating ATG codon. The distance between the Shine-Dalgarno sequence and the ATG codon is crucial (Shine and Dalgarno 1975) if maximal expression of the foreign protein is to be achieved.

In many cases, plasmid expression vectors are designed to express foreign proteins that are not linked to any prokaryotic sequences; more commonly, however, expression vectors generate fusion proteins that are encoded partly by the vector and partly by an open reading frame in the cloned segment of foreign DNA. The foreign protein is therefore synthesized as a fused polypeptide containing a tract of amino acids that are not normally part of the native protein. In the early days of cloning, the tract of foreign amino acids was often large enough to produce dramatic changes in the physical and biological properties of the protein under study. Solubility and stability could be altered for better or worse, and there was a good chance that the biological properties of the protein would be compromised, at least to some extent.

During the last few years, the sequences contributed by the vector have shrunk dramatically in size. In most cases, they are less than a dozen residues in length and generally do not affect the function of the protein under study. Frequently, these "tags" are antigenic determinants (epitopes) that are recognized by specific antibodies. Epitope-tagged proteins can be purified with an existing epitope-specific antibody (for reviews, please see Kolodziej and Young 1991; Keesey 1996). The same antibody can be used to detect the epitope tag in a variety of expressed proteins.

The virtues and limitations of expressing proteins in these three forms — as native proteins, as fusion proteins, and as epitope-tagged proteins — are discussed in more detail in Chapter 18.

Finding Plasmid Vectors Appropriate for Specific Tasks

When looking for common or garden-variety plasmids that can be used for a wide range of general purposes, the first port of call should be the catalogs of commercial suppliers. Often, these companies will have something with a suitable combination of markers, modules, cloning sites, and epitopes that can be used without extensive engineering. These off-the-shelf vectors have been tested under a wide variety of conditions in many laboratories. It does not take a rocket scientist to make them work well.

Unfortunately, there is no easy and certain way to search the literature for descriptions of plasmid vectors with unusual properties that are suited to particular purposes. Obviously, the ability to carry out Boolean searches of databases such as Medline, Entrez, and PubMed with the logic operators AND, OR, and NOT is a great advantage. For example, trawling most Medline-based databases with the string (p15A or IncFII)[TW] AND T7[TW] AND low-copy-number should generate a list of references to papers whose title includes "low-copy-number" and whose text contains the words "T7" and either "p15A" or "IncFII." In addition, papers describing specialized or novel plasmid vectors are still published regularly in archival journals such as *Gene* and *BioTechnology*. Once one or two promising papers have been identified — either from the scientific literature or by Boolean searching — they can be used as starting points for an expanded search of databases for additional papers on the same or closely related topics. The PubMed system, which can be accessed via the Internet, is very good at assembling clusters of papers on topics related to a particular keyword. The address of PubMed is http://www.ncbi.nlm.nih.gov/PubMed/.

One never knows whether a vector unearthed from the literature will work as advertised and if it is actually the best currently available. The authors of the paper are usually able to offer sensible advice in this regard. However, beware if they start talking about making improvements to the published vector. This is a sure sign that the original vector did not work as well as advertised; the chances are that the improved version will not be much better. If possible, find out the names of other investigators who have used the vector and who may have found ways to identify and solve the problems.

Choosing an Appropriate Strain of *E. coli*

Most investigators want to use strains of *E. coli* that are easy to transform with plasmid DNA (e.g., DH1 or MM294; for a full list of useful strains, please see Appendix 3). The vast majority of colE1-type plasmids introduced into these strains replicate to high copy number and can be isolated in high yield. However, a significant minority of recombinant plasmids transform strains of *E. coli* such as DH1 and MM294 with low efficiency, generate transformed colonies that are smaller than usual, and produce low yields of plasmid DNA. Most of these "difficult" plasmids can be shown to encode a protein that is toxic to *E. coli* or to contain inverted or repeated DNA sequences.

The problem of toxic proteins can be alleviated by switching to an amplifiable low-copy-number vector or to a high-copy-number vector containing prokaryotic transcription termination signals that suppress readthrough transcription of foreign DNA sequences. Another possibility, however, is to use strains of *E. coli* that suppress the copy number of colE1-based plasmids. Several commercially available strains of *E. coli* (e.g., ABLE C and ABLE K strains from Stratagene) reduce the copy number of colE1 plasmids (and hence the level of plasmid-encoded toxic proteins) by four- to tenfold. The yield of plasmid DNA from such strains, albeit reduced, is sufficient for most purposes in molecular cloning.

If there is reason to suspect that a plasmid may carry repeated DNA sequences that are substrates for the general recombination systems of *E. coli*, consider the possibility of switching to a recombination-deficient strain. For example, strains carrying a *recA* mutation have almost no recombination capacity (Weinstock 1987) and are the preferred hosts for many targeting vectors used in gene knock-out experiments in mice, such as vectors that contain two copies of a viral thymidine kinase gene. Wayward inserts can also be stabilized in strains carrying *recB* mutations, which inactivate exonuclease V and reduce general recombination to a few percent of normal. Finally, improved yields of certain plasmids have been reported in strains deficient in SOS repair or DNA repair that carry mutations in the *umuC* and *uvrC* genes (Doherty et al. 1993).

Inverted repeat sequences are often lethal to their carrier plasmid. Thus, recombinant plasmids containing perfect or near-perfect inverted repeats longer than ~300 bp fail to transform conventional host strains of *E. coli* or do so with very low efficiency. In many cases, the forced propagation of such clones provokes internal deletions or other rearrangements that remove the center of symmetry of the palindrome (e.g., please see Hagan and Warren 1983). Sequences containing head-to-head palindromes are lethal, perhaps because they inhibit DNA replication by interfering with the passage of replication forks or because they deleteriously affect the state of supercoiling of the plasmid, leaving it open to attack by nucleases (Collins and Hohn 1978; Lilley 1980; Collins 1981; Mizuuchi et al. 1982; Hagan and Warren 1983).

No strain of *E. coli* exists that is guaranteed to propagate all recombinant clones containing palindromic sequences. *E. coli* strains carrying mutations in *recBC* and *sbcBC* genes will support growth of plasmids containing certain palindromic sequences of a variety of sizes and sources. However, plasmids with a colE1 origin are unstable in *recBC, sbcBC* hosts because they form linear multimers (e.g., please see Cohen and Clark 1986), which apparently interfere with replication and partition of chromosomal DNA (Kusano et al. 1989). Multimer formation is dependent on a subset of proteins involved in the RecF recombination pathway function and does not occur in cells that are deficient in RecF, RecJ, RecA, RecO, or RecQ function.

Only a few strains deficient in *recBC* and *sbcBC* genes also contain mutations that eliminate all known restriction systems. These include PMC128, which is *mcrAΔ(mcrBC-hsd-mrr)recBC sbcBC* (Doherty et al. 1993), and SURE, and SRB (Stratagene), which carry similar mutations.

Finally, if plasmid vectors are used to propagate methylated DNA (e.g., mammalian genomic DNA or DNA synthesized in vitro using methylated analogs of deoxynucleoside triphosphates), then it is essential to use a strain that is deficient in the McrA, McrBC, and Mrr/Mcf restriction systems. The McrA and McrBC systems recognize and restrict certain DNA sequences containing methylated cytosine residues (Raleigh and Wilson 1986), whereas the Mrr/Mcf system recognizes and restricts certain DNA sequences containing methylated adenine DNA residues (Heitman and Model 1987), as well as additional DNA sequences that contain methylated cytosine residues.

Further information on restriction modification systems can be obtained from REBASE, the Restriction Enzyme Database at http://www.neb.com/rebase. For more details on the properties of useful *E. coli* strains, see Appendix 3.

EXTRACTION AND PURIFICATION OF PLASMID DNA

Many methods have been developed to purify plasmids from bacteria. These methods invariably involve three steps:

- growth of the bacterial culture
- harvesting and lysis of the bacteria
- purification of the plasmid DNA

Growth of the Bacterial Culture

Wherever possible, plasmids should be purified from bacterial cultures that have been inoculated with a single transformed colony picked from an agar plate. Usually, the colony is transferred to a small starter culture, which is grown to late log phase. Aliquots of this culture can be used to prepare small amounts of the plasmid DNA (minipreparation) for analysis and/or as the inoculum for a large-scale culture. The conditions of growth of the large-scale culture depend chiefly on the copy number of the plasmid and whether it replicates in a stringent or relaxed fashion (please see Table 1-3). At all times, the transformed bacteria should be grown in selective conditions, i.e., in the presence of the appropriate antibiotic.

Harvesting and Lysis of the Culture

Bacteria are recovered by centrifugation and lysed by any one of a large number of methods, including treatment with nonionic or ionic detergents, organic solvents, alkali, and heat. The choice among these methods is dictated by three factors: the size of the plasmid, the strain of *E. coli*, and the technique used subsequently to purify the plasmid DNA. Although it is impractical to give precise conditions for all possible combinations of plasmid and host, the following general guidelines can be used to choose a method that will give satisfactory results.

Large Plasmids (>15 kb in Size) Must Be Handled with Care

Plasmids >15 kb in size are susceptible to damage during both cell lysis and subsequent handling. Gentle lysis is best accomplished by suspending the bacteria in an isosmotic solution of sucrose and treating them with lysozyme and EDTA (ethylenediaminetetraacetic acid), which removes much of the cell wall. The resulting spheroplasts are lysed by adding an anionic detergent such as SDS. For methods for tender handling of large DNAs, please see the information panel on MINI-MIZING DAMAGE TO DNA MOLECULES in Chapter 2.

Smaller Plasmids (<15 kb in Size) Are More Durable

When handling smaller plasmids, more severe methods of lysis can be used, and no special care need be taken to minimize shearing forces. Typically, bacterial suspensions are exposed to deter-

TABLE 1-3 Plasmid Growth and Replication

REPLICON (EXAMPLE)	COPY NUMBER	STRINGENT OR RELAXED	COMMENTS
Modified pMB1 (pUC)	several hundred	relaxed	pUC plasmids contain a modified pMB1 replicon and replicate to a very high copy number. Further amplification of the copy number by addition of chloramphenicol to the growing bacterial culture is unnecessary; instead, the culture should be grown to late log phase with vigorous shaking.
colE1 (pBR322)	15–20	relaxed	The yield of pBR322 and other relaxed plasmids that maintain a low-moderate copy number in transformed cells can be dramatically increased by adding chloramphenicol (final concentration 170 μg/ml) to mid-log phase cultures and continuing incubation for a further 8 hours. Chloramphenicol inhibits host protein synthesis and, as a result, prevents replication of the host chromosome. However, replication of relaxed plasmids continues, and their copy number increases progressively for several hours.
pSC101 (pSC101)	~5	stringent	Stringently replicating, low-copy-number plasmids can be a challenge to grow. Obviously, adding chloramphenicol to the culture is not an option and the only available variable is the culture medium. For example, "Terrific Broth," which has been reported to increase the yield of difficult plasmids (Tartof and Hobbs 1987) might be a better option than standard Luria Broth (LB).

As discussed above, the copy numbers of the current generation of plasmids are now so high that selective amplification in the presence of chloramphenicol is no longer required to achieve high yields of plasmid DNA. However, some investigators continue to use chloramphenicol, not necessarily to increase the yield of plasmid DNA but to reduce the bulk of bacterial cells in large-scale preparations. Handling large quantities of viscous lysates of concentrated suspensions of bacteria is a frustrating and messy business that can be avoided if chloramphenicol is added to the culture at mid-log phase. Because some amplification of copy number — even of such feverishly replicating plasmids as pUC — occurs in the presence of chloramphenicol, equivalent yields of plasmid DNA are obtained from smaller numbers of cells that have been exposed to the drug as from larger number of cells that have not.

gent and lysed by boiling or treatment with alkali. This disrupts base pairing and causes the linear stretches of sheared or disrupted chromosomal DNA of the host to denature. However, the strands of closed circular plasmid DNA are unable to separate from each other because they are topologically intertwined. When conditions are returned to normal, the strands of plasmid DNA fall into perfect register and native superhelical molecules are re-formed.

Prolonged exposure to denaturing conditions causes closed circular DNA to enter an irreversibly denatured state (Vinograd and Lebowitz 1966). The resulting collapsed coil, which cannot be cleaved with restriction enzymes, migrates through agarose gels at about twice the rate of native superhelical closed circular DNA and stains poorly with intercalating dyes such as ethidium bromide. Varying amounts of this collapsed form of DNA can usually be seen in plasmids prepared by alkaline or thermal lysis of bacteria.

Some Strains of E. coli *Should Not Be Lysed by Heat*

Some strains of *E. coli*, particularly those derived from HB101, release relatively large amounts of carbohydrate when they are lysed by detergent and heat. This can be a nuisance when the plasmid DNA is subsequently purified by equilibrium centrifugation in cesium chloride (CsCl)-ethidium bromide gradients. The carbohydrate forms a dense fuzzy band close to the place in the gradient (ρ = 1.59) occupied by the superhelical plasmid DNA. It is therefore difficult to avoid contaminating the plasmid DNA with carbohydrate, which inhibits the activity of many restriction enzymes and polymerases. Boiling should therefore not be used when making large-scale preparations of plasmids from strains of *E. coli* such as HB101 and TG1.

The boiling method also is not recommended when making small-scale plasmid preparations from strains of *E. coli* that express endonuclease A (*endA*$^+$ strains), which include HB101. Because endonuclease A is not completely inactivated by the boiling procedure, the plasmid DNA is degraded during subsequent incubation in the presence of Mg^{2+} (e.g., during incubation with restriction enzymes). This problem can be avoided by including an extra step — extraction with phenol:chloroform — in the purification protocol.

Purification of the Plasmid DNA

All three methods of lysis yield preparations of plasmid DNA that are always contaminated with considerable quantities of RNA and variable amounts of *E. coli* chromosomal DNA. Crude preparations of plasmid DNA can be readily visualized in agarose gels and can be used as templates and substrates for most restriction enzymes and DNA polymerases. However, contaminants must be removed — or at least reduced to manageable levels — whenever purified plasmids are necessary or desirable, for example, when transfecting mammalian cells.

For the last 20 years, descriptions of "new" purification schemes have appeared in the scientific literature at an average rate of one a week. Notwithstanding the virtues claimed by their inventors, very few of these methods have found widespread acceptance. Many of them, in fact, are but minor variations or questionable embellishments of much older methods. By and large, these original older methods are entirely satisfactory and they continue to find widespread use.

Old or new, all schemes for purification of plasmids take advantage of the relatively small size and covalently closed structure of plasmid DNA. The most venerable method for separating closed circular plasmid DNA from contaminating fragments of bacterial DNA is buoyant density centrifugation in gradients of CsCl-ethidium bromide (Clewell and Helinski 1969). This technique is still regarded as the standard against which all others should be judged. Separation depends on differences in the amounts of ethidium bromide that can be bound to linear and closed circular DNA molecules. Ethidium bromide binds very tightly to DNA in concentrated salt solutions. The dye intercalates between the bases, causing the double helix to unwind and leading to an increase in length of double-stranded linear or relaxed circular DNA molecules (for review, please see Vinograd and Lebowitz 1966). Closed circular DNA molecules have no free ends and can unwind only by twisting. As more and more ethidium bromide molecules intercalate into the DNA, the density of superhelical twists becomes so great that the addition of further ethidium bromide is prevented. Linear molecules, which are not constrained, continue to bind ethidium bromide until saturation is reached (an average of one ethidium bromide molecule for every 2.5 bp; Cantor and Schimmel 1980). Binding of ethidium bromide causes a decrease in the buoyant density of both linear and closed circular DNAs. However, because linear DNAs bind more ethidium bromide, they have a lower buoyant density than closed circular DNAs in CsCl gradients containing saturating amounts of ethidium bromide (linear double-stranded DNAs, 1.54 g/cm^3; closed circular DNAs, 1.59 g/cm^3). Closed circular DNAs therefore come to equilibrium at a lower position than linear DNAs in CsCl gradients containing saturating amounts of ethidium bromide (for a more detailed discussion, please see the information panel on **ETHIDIUM BROMIDE**).

For many years, equilibrium centrifugation in CsCl-ethidium bromide gradients was the method of choice to prepare large amounts of plasmid DNA. However, this process is time-consuming (3–5 days) and requires expensive equipment and reagents. Today, equilibrium centrifugation is used chiefly for the purification of (1) very large plasmids that are vulnerable to nicking, (2) closed circular DNAs that are to be microinjected into mammalian cell, and (3) plasmids that are used for biophysical measurements. Nowadays, less expensive and faster methods are available to purify smaller plasmids (<15 kb) for use as substrates and templates in all enzymatic reactions and procedures commonly undertaken in molecular cloning. The great majority of these purification schemes rely on differential precipitation, ion-exchange chromatography, or gel filtration to separate plasmid DNA from cellular nucleic acids.

A variety of kits for plasmid purification are available from commercial vendors. These kits consist of disposable chromatography columns that are used for batch absorbtion and elution of plasmid DNA. Many different matrices are available, including glass, diatomaceous earth, and, most popular of all, anionic resins such as DEAE (diethylaminoethyl) or QAE (diethyl[2-hydroxypropyl]aminoethyl). It is certainly a convenience to have the necessary buffers, resins, and disposable columns ready for use. However, this convenience comes at a price and one must wonder whether it is worthwhile to use on a routine basis expensive kits that do not perform significantly better than standard reagents which can easily be prepared in bulk by any competent laboratory worker. Certainly, kits are unnecessary for minipreparations of plasmid DNA to be used for routine analysis. Of the hundreds of methods to purify plasmid DNA described in the literature, the alkaline lysis method (Birnboim and Doly 1979; Ish-Horowicz and Burke 1981) is by far the most popular because of its simplicity, relatively low cost, and reproducibility. Alkaline lysis has been used successfully for more than 20 years in hundreds of laboratories to generate millions of minipreparations. For larger-scale preparations, the method of choice is alkaline lysis followed by differential precipitation of plasmid DNA with polyethylene glycol (Lis 1980; R. Treisman, unpubl.), which yields DNAs that are clean enough for transfection of mammalian cells and all enzymatic reactions, including DNA sequencing. In those rare circumstances where ultrapure closed circular DNA is required (e.g., for microinjection into mammalian cells), there is a choice between using centrifugation to equilibrium in CsCl-ethidium bromide gradients or a commercial kit. If choosing to use a kit, follow the manufacturer's instructions precisely as their protocol has presumably been tested extensively and optimized.

CLONING IN PLASMID VECTORS

In principle, cloning in plasmid vectors is very straightforward. Closed circular plasmid DNA is cleaved with one or more restriction enzymes and ligated in vitro to foreign DNA bearing compatible termini. The products of the ligation reaction are then used to transform an appropriate strain of *E. coli*. The resulting transformed colonies are screened by hybridization, by PCR, or by digestion with restriction enzymes to identify those that carry the desired DNA sequences.

This sounds easy enough. However, planning and thought are required if cloning in plasmid vectors is to be as smooth in practice as in prospect. Before a pipette is lifted, decisions must be made about:

- the choice of a plasmid vector suitable for the task at hand

- the choice of restriction sites within vector

- the optimal conditions for the ligation reaction

- the strain of *E. coli* best suited to propagate a plasmid carrying the foreign DNA of interest

- the methods used to screen transformants and the techniques used to validate clones of interest

● whether special steps are required to decrease the background of transformed colonies that contain "empty" parental plasmid

● the controls that are necessary at each stage

After these matters have been settled, the next step is to make a detailed plan and a timetable so that fragments, plasmids, competent cells, and probes can be prepared in the correct order and in good time. In most cases, several different strategies can be used to create a particular recombinant in a plasmid vector. It is important to have a backup scheme in case the original plan proves to be unexpectedly difficult.

Cloning DNA Fragments with Protruding Ends

The easiest DNA fragments to clone are those with 5′ or 3′ protruding ends. These single-stranded termini, 1–6 bp in length, are most easily created by digesting the vector and the target DNA with restriction enzymes that cleave asymmetrically within the recognition sequence (please see Figure 1-2). When the ends protruding from the DNA fragment and the vector are compatible, they can anneal to form a linear hybrid molecule whose two parts are held together by pairing between the bases in the protruding termini. Formation of a circular recombinant plasmid capable of transforming *E. coli,* therefore, occurs in a two-step reaction (please see Figure 1-3):

● an *inter*molecular reaction between linear plasmid and incoming DNA, which generates a non-covalently bonded, linear hybrid

● an *intra*molecular reaction, in which the protruding termini of the linear hybrid are joined together, forming a noncovalently bonded, circular recombinant molecule

Annealing brings the 5′-phosphate and 3′-hydroxyl residues on vector and target DNAs into close alignment, which allows DNA ligase to catalyze the formation of phosphodiester bonds.

The circular monomeric plasmids can have the foreign DNA fragment inserted in either orientation (please see Figure 1-4). Monomeric circular recombinant plasmids are, however, only one of a large number of potential products formed in ligation reactions between DNA molecules with compatible protruding termini. Other, less desirable products include linear and circular homo- and heteropolymers of varying sizes, orientations, and compositions. Ligation reactions should be designed with care so as to maximize the yield of circular monomeric recombinants. This is not a simple task. The first, intermolecular stage of the reaction requires high concentra-

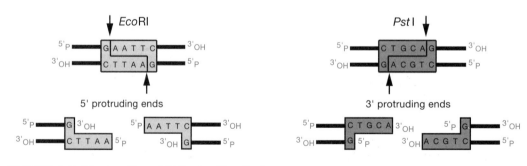

FIGURE 1-2 Cloning 5′ and 3′ Protruding Ends

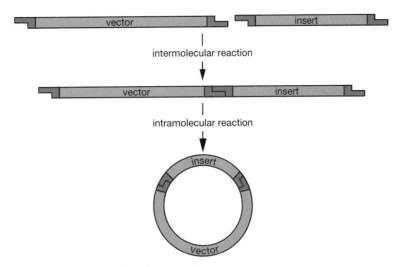

FIGURE 1-3 Inter- and Intramolecular Reactions

Vector sequences are represented by darker shading, and insert sequences by lighter shading.

tions of DNA, whereas the second intramolecular reaction works most efficiently when the concentration of DNA is low. However, as a general rule, acceptable yields of monomeric circular recombinants can usually be obtained from ligation reactions containing equimolar amounts of plasmid and target DNA, with the total DNA concentration <10 µg/ml (Bercovich et al. 1992). For a discussion of the reason why this should be so, please see Sambrook et al. (1989). If the molar ratio of plasmid vector to target DNA is incorrect, then the ligation reaction may generate an undesirably high proportion of empty plasmids (containing no insert at all) or plasmids carrying tandem inserts of foreign DNA. The number of inserts in each recombinant clone must always be validated by restriction endonuclease mapping or by some other means. The orientation of the foreign DNA insert must also be ascertained.

Directional Cloning

So far, we have been dealing with ligations in which all DNA termini are equivalent, as is the case when both plasmid and foreign DNAs are prepared by cleavage with a single restriction enzyme.

FIGURE 1-4 Cloning Bidirectional Insert DNA into a Single Site

Vector sequences are represented by darker shading, and insert sequences by lighter shading.

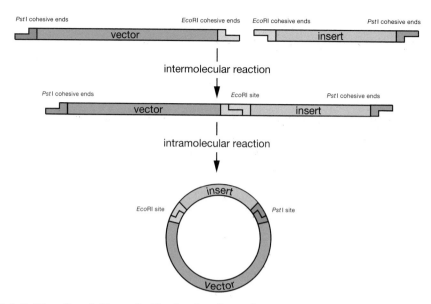

FIGURE 1-5 Directional (Forced) Cloning in Plasmid Vectors

Vector sequences are represented by darker shading, and insert sequences by lighter shading.

One way to increase the yield of circular monomeric recombinants is to use a cloning strategy in which the termini in the ligation reaction are not all equivalent; for example, when the foreign DNA fragment is produced by digestion with two restriction enzymes with different recognition sequences. In this case, the termini of the foreign DNA fragment will be noncomplementary and unable to ligate to each other. However, the foreign DNA will ligate eagerly to a plasmid vector that has been prepared by cleavage with the same two enzymes, generating a high yield of circular recombinants containing a single insert in a predefined orientation. This process is known as forced ligation or directional cloning (please see Figure 1-5).

Cloning Blunt-ended DNA Fragments

Fragments of foreign DNA carrying blunt-ended termini may be cloned into a linearized plasmid vector bearing blunt ends (please see Figure 1-6). Ligation of blunt-ended termini is a comparatively inefficient reaction. The following are optimal conditions for cloning blunt-ended DNA fragments (Sgaramella and Khorana 1972; Sgaramella and Ehrlich 1978):

- low concentrations (0.5 mM) of ATP

- the absence of polyamines such as spermidine

- very high concentrations of ligase (50 Weiss units/ml)

- high concentrations of blunt-ended termini

The last condition is the main key to success. At high concentrations, blunt-ended DNA molecules form fruitful, if temporary, liaisons that bring their 5′-phosphate and 3′-hydroxyl residues into close alignment. DNA ligase seizes upon these short-lived substrates and forges per-

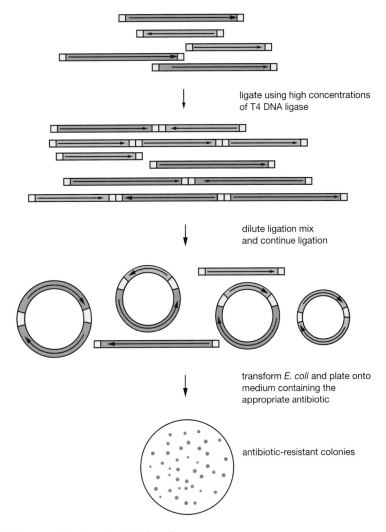

FIGURE 1-6 Cloning Blunt-ended Molecules

Antibiotic-resistant colonies arise due to the presence of vector reclosing, vector dimers, and vector-insert recombinants. These colonies are screened for those carrying vector-insert recombinants. Vector sequences are represented by darker shading, and insert sequences by lighter shading.

manent phosphodiester bonds between residues on different molecules. The resulting linear, covalently joined hybrids may be converted to circular recombinant plasmids capable of transforming *E. coli* by an intramolecular ligation reaction between the blunt termini. Ideally, the first reaction contains high concentrations of DNA, whereas the second works most efficiently when the concentration of DNA is low. Some investigators therefore carry out the first stage of the ligation reaction at high DNA concentrations. After incubating for 1 hour, the reaction is diluted 20-fold with ligase buffer, supplemented with fresh ligase, and incubated for a further 4 hours (Bercovich et al. 1992; Damak and Bullock 1993).

When DNA is in short supply, the problem of attaining adequate concentrations of blunt ends can be ameliorated by including in the reaction mixture substances that increase macro-molecular crowding (e.g., 5% polyethylene glycol 8000 [PEG 8000]) (Pheiffer and Zimmerman 1983; Zimmerman and Pheiffer 1983; Upcroft and Healey 1987) or substances that cause DNA molecules to condense into aggregates (e.g., 1.0 mM hexamminecobalt chloride) (Rusche and Howard-Flanders 1985). These crowding and condensing agents accelerate the rate of ligation of blunt-ended DNA by one to three orders of magnitude, promote intermolecular ligation, and suppress intramolecular ligation (please see the information panel on CONDENSING AND CROWDING REAGENTS).

Despite its power and usefulness, cloning in plasmid vectors is based on a remarkably small number of basic methods, which are easy to master. Protocols 17 and 19 describe fundamental techniques for joining plasmid vectors to DNA fragments with protruding ends and blunt ends. Protocols 18, 20, 21, and 22 describe various strategies for optimizing the recovery of the appropriate recombinant. These techniques, each one simple in itself, can be woven together to build recombinant plasmids of complex beauty and high sophistication.

PREPARATION AND TRANSFORMATION OF COMPETENT *E. COLI*

Nucleic acids do not enter bacteria under their own power, but require assistance traversing the outer and inner cell membranes and in reaching an intracellular site where they can be expressed and replicated. The methods that have been devised to achieve these goals fall into two classes: chemical and physical.

Chemical Methods

E. coli cells washed in cocktails of simple salt solutions achieve a state of competence during which DNA molecules may be admitted to the cell. Most of the chemical methods currently used for bacterial transformation are based on the observations of Mandel and Higa (1970), who showed that bacteria treated with ice-cold solutions of $CaCl_2$ and then briefly heated to 37°C or 42°C could be transfected with bacteriophage λ DNA. The same method was subsequently used to transform bacteria with plasmid DNA (Cohen et al. 1972) and *E. coli* chromosomal DNA (Oishi and Cosloy 1972).

This simple and robust procedure regularly generates between 10^5 and 10^6 transformed colonies of *E. coli* per μg of supercoiled plasmid DNA. This is more than enough for routine tasks such as propagating a plasmid or transferring a plasmid from one strain of *E. coli* to another. However, higher efficiencies of transformation are required when recovery of every possible clone is of paramount importance, for example, when constructing cDNA libraries or when only minute amounts of foreign DNA are available. Starting in the 1970s and continuing to this day, many variations on the basic technique have been described in the literature, all directed toward optimizing the efficiency of transformation of different bacterial strains by plasmids. The variations include using complex cocktails of divalent cations in different buffers, treating cells with reducing agents, adjusting the ingredients of the cocktail to the genetic constitution of particular strains of *E. coli*, harvesting cells at specific stages of the growth cycle, altering the temperature of growth of the culture before exposure to chemicals, optimizing the extent and temperature of heat shock, freezing and thawing cells, and exposing cells to organic solvents after washing in divalent cations. By all these treatments and more, it is now possible on a routine basis to achieve transformation frequencies ranging from 10^6 to 10^9 transformants/μg of superhelical plasmid DNA (for reviews, please see Hanahan 1987; Hanahan et al. 1995; Hanahan and Bloom 1996; Hengen 1996).

The improvements in transformation frequency are a tribute to the power of empirical experimentation. How these combinations of chemical agents and physical treatments induce a state of competence remains as obscure today as in Mandel and Higa's time, as does the mechanism by which plasmid DNA enters and establishes itself in competent *E. coli*. Nevertheless, the improvements made since the late 1970s have eliminated the efficiency of transformation as a potential limiting factor in molecular cloning.

There are two ways to obtain stocks of chemically induced competent *E. coli*. The first option is to purchase frozen competent bacteria from a commercial source. These products are very reliable and generally yield transformants at frequencies >10^8 colonies/μg of supercoiled plasmid DNA. However, they are many times more expensive than competent cells prepared in the laboratory. Commercially produced competent cells are nevertheless an excellent yardstick to measure the efficiency of locally generated stocks of competent cells — and they are a godsend to investigators who carry out transformations so infrequently that it is not economical for them to expend the effort required to produce their own competent cultures. In addition, several companies sell competent stocks of strains of *E. coli* that carry specific genetic markers and are used for particular purposes in molecular cloning. Examples of these include (1) SURE strains, which carry disabling mutations in DNA-repair pathways responsible for the high rate of rearrangement of certain eukaryotic genomic sequences, and (2) strains deficient in methylases such as Dam and Dcm. Plasmids propagated in these strains can be cleaved by restriction enzymes whose activity is normally blocked by methylation of overlapping Dam or Dcm sites. It is cost-effective and far less aggravating to purchase competent stocks of strains such as these, which are tricky to grow and difficult to transform.

For laboratories using standard strains of *E. coli*, it makes sense to prepare stocks of competent bacteria in-house. The procedure for high-efficiency transformation (Hanahan 1983), described in Protocol 23, works well with K-12 strains of *E. coli* such as DH1, DH5, and MM294 and yields competent cultures that can be either used immediately or stored in small aliquots at –70ºC until required. If prepared carefully, these competent bacteria can yield up to 10^9 transformed colonies/μg of supercoiled plasmid DNA. Similar efficiencies can be achieved with the method using "ultra-competent" bacteria (Inoue et al. 1990), described in Protocol 24, in which the bacterial culture is grown at room temperature. However, as discussed above, such high frequencies of transformation are required only rarely; for most routine cloning tasks, competent bacteria prepared by simpler procedures are more than adequate. As a general rule, the more sophisticated the method used to prepare competent cells, the more inconsistent the results. The final method in the series of transformation protocols (Protocol 25) (Cohen et al. 1972) is both robust and durable and yields competent cells that generate 10^6 to 10^7 transformed colonies/μg of supercoiled plasmid DNA.

Physical Methods

Exposure to an electrical charge destabilizes the membranes of *E. coli* and induces the formation of transient membrane pores through which DNA molecules can pass (Neumann and Rosenheck 1972; for reviews, please see Zimmerman 1982; Tsong 1991; Weaver 1993). This method, which is known as electroporation, was originally developed to introduce DNA into eukaryotic cells (Neumann et al. 1982) and was subsequently adapted for transformation of *E. coli* (Dower et al. 1988; Taketo 1988) and other bacteria by plasmids (Chassy and Flickinger 1987; Fiedler and Wirth 1988; Miller et al. 1988). It is the easiest, fastest, most efficient, and most reproducible method for transformation of bacterial cells with DNA.

- Transformation efficiencies in excess of 10^{10} transformants/μg of DNA have been achieved by optimizing various parameters, including the strength of the electrical field, the length of the electrical pulse, the concentration of DNA, and the composition of the electroporation buffer (Dower et al. 1988; Tung and Chow 1995).

- More than 80% of the cells in a culture can be transformed to ampicillin resistance by electroporation, and efficiencies approaching the theoretical maximum of one transformant per molecule of plasmid DNA have been reported (Smith et al. 1990).

- Plasmids ranging in size from 2.6 kb to 85 kb can be introduced with efficiencies ranging from 6×10^{10} transformants/μg of DNA to 1×10^7 transformants/μg DNA, respectively. This is 10–20 times higher than can be achieved with competent cells prepared by chemical methods. Transformation frequencies of this magnitude are especially useful when constructing large and highly complex cDNA libraries (please see Chapter 11).

- Electroporation works well with most commonly used laboratory strains of *E. coli* (Dower et al. 1988; Tung and Chow 1995).

Unlike chemical transformation, the number of transformants generated by electroporation is marker-dependent. For example, when pBR322, which carries genes conferring resistance to two antibiotics (ampicillin and tetracycline), is introduced into *E. coli* by electroporation, the number of tetracycline-resistant transformants is ~100-fold less than the number of ampicillin-resistant transformants (Steele et al. 1994). This effect is not seen when the plasmid is introduced into the bacteria by chemical transformation. A likely explanation is that damage or depolarization caused by the pulse of electrical current prevents or delays insertion into the inner cell membrane of the antiporter protein responsible for tetracycline resistance.

Of course, the ease and efficiency of electroporation come at a price. Electroporation is an expensive business, requiring costly electrical equipment and highly priced specially designed cuvettes. Nevertheless, for many investigators, electroporation, because of its reproducibility and lack of mumbo-jumbo, is the preferred option. For a method for the electroporation of bacterial cells, see Protocol 26. For more details, please see the information panel on ELECTROPORATION.

SCREENING FOR RECOMBINANT PLASMIDS

Only rarely is it possible to determine by looking whether a colony of transformed bacteria carries a recombinant plasmid or an empty vector. In a few exceptional cases, colonies containing a recombinant plasmid may be smaller than normal because the plasmid expresses a foreign protein that retards growth of the host cells. This situation can arise when foreign DNA sequences encoding regulatory or membrane proteins, for example, are cloned in plasmid expression vectors. However, foreign proteins are normally not expressed to significant levels in plasmid vectors commonly used for cloning.

Over the years, many methods have been devised to distinguish bacteria transformed by recombinant plasmids from those carrying empty wild-type plasmids. The most durable and general of these methods uses a nondestructive histochemical procedure to detect β-galactosidase activity in transformed bacteria. This procedure is commonly used as a test to distinguish colonies of bacterial cells that carry recombinant plasmids from those that do not. Alternatively, in situ hybridization methods may be used to identify with certainty bacterial colonies that have been transformed with recombinant plasmids which carry specific sequences of foreign DNA. Other generally useful methods are available to analyze the size of recombinant plasmids and to screen transformed colonies by PCR.

We have not included here any protocols dealing with the use of any of the "positive-selection systems" that allow bacteria transformed by recombinant plasmids to grow while suppressing the growth of bacteria transformed by nonrecombinant plasmids. These positive selection systems are rarely used, and, indeed, it is possible to spend an entire lifetime working with recombinant DNA without ever needing them. Investigators who have an appetite for esoterica of this type should read the discussion on page 1.12 of the introduction to this chapter and the papers cited therein.

Identifying Recombinant Plasmids by α-Complementation

Many plasmid vectors (e.g., the pUC series, Bluescript, pGem, and their derivatives) carry a short segment of *E. coli* DNA containing the regulatory sequences and the coding information for the first 146 amino acids of β-galactosidase. Embedded in the coding region is a polycloning site that maintains the reading frame and results in the harmless interpolation of a small number of amino acids into the amino-terminal fragment of β-galactosidase. Vectors of this type are used in host cells that express the carboxy-terminal portion of β-galactosidase. Although neither the host-encoded fragments nor the plasmid-encoded fragments of β-galactosidase are themselves active, they can associate to form an enzymatically active protein. This type of complementation, in which deletion mutants of the operator-proximal segment of the *lacZ* gene are complemented by β-galactosidase-negative mutants that have the operator-proximal region intact, is called α-complementation (Ullmann et al. 1967) (for more information, please see the information panel on α-COMPLEMENTATION). The lac^+ bacteria that result from α-complementation are easily recognized because they form blue colonies in the presence of the chromogenic substrate X-gal (Horwitz et al. 1964; Davies and Jacob 1968) (please see the information panel on X-GAL). However, insertion of a fragment of foreign DNA into the polycloning site of the plasmid almost invariably results in production of an amino-terminal fragment that is no longer capable of α-complementation. Bacteria carrying recombinant plasmids therefore form white colonies. The development of this simple color test has greatly simplified the identification of recombinants constructed in plasmid vectors. It is easy to screen many thousands of transformed colonies and to recognize from their white appearance those that carry putative recombinant plasmids. The structure of these recombinants can then be verified by restriction analysis of minipreparations of vector DNA or by other diagnostic criteria. For procedures for screening recombinants using α-complemetation, please see Protocol 27. Screening by α-complementation is highly dependable but not completely infallible:

- Insertion of foreign DNA does not always inactivate the complementing activity of the α-fragment of β-galactosidase. If the foreign DNA is small (<100 bp) and if the insertion neither disrupts the reading frame nor affects the structure of the α-fragment, α-complementation may not be seriously affected. Examples of this phenomenon have been documented, but they are very rare and of significance only to the investigator who encounters this problem.

- Not all white colonies carry recombinant plasmids. Mutation or loss of *lac* sequences may purge the plasmid of its ability to express the α-fragment. However, this is not a problem in practice because the frequency of *lac⁻* mutants in the plasmid population is usually far lower than the number of recombinants generated in a ligation reaction.

Identifying Recombinant Plasmids by Hybridization

In the mid-1960s, after Nygaard and Hall (1963) had shown that single-stranded DNA could be immobilized on nitrocellulose filters, Denhardt (1966) and Gillespie and Spiegelman (1965) demonstrated that nucleic acids fixed in this way could be detected with exquisite sensitivity by hybridization to radiolabeled probes. The method quickly became a mainstay of molecular biology and was used in an essentially unchanged form for an entire decade.

In the mid 1970s, radical extensions to the technique came from two different continents. In Scotland, Ed Southern (1975) showed that hybridization could be used to detect specific sequences in complex populations of DNA fragments. In this method, DNA fragments generated by digestion with restriction enzymes were separated by electrophoresis through agarose gels and then transferred onto nitrocellulose filters for hybridization with specific probes. In the same year, Grunstein and Hogness (1975) in California adapted the method to screen large numbers of bacterial colonies for plasmids that carry specific sequences of foreign DNA. Bacterial colonies growing on the surfaces of nitrocellulose filters were lysed in situ, and the released denatured single-stranded DNA was fixed to the filter and hybridized to radiolabeled nucleic acid probes, essentially as described by Denhardt (1966). Although minor modifications have been introduced over the years, the protocol originally described by Grunstein and Hogness has proven to be remarkably durable. It remains the most commonly used technique to identify individual bacterial colonies carrying cosmids or plasmids that contain DNA sequences of interest.

The last protocols in this chapter describe methods used to transfer bacterial colonies from plates to filters (Protocols 28, 29, and 30); to release, denature, and immobilize the bacterial and plasmid DNA (Protocol 31); and to hybridize the fixed DNA with radiolabeled probes and to recover from a master plate the colonies that hybridize specifically to the probe (Protocol 32). These techniques are designed to be used with probes that are on average longer than 100 nucleotides in length. For methods for screening bacterial colonies with shorter radiolabeled oligonucleotides, see Chapter 10. No matter whether the probes are long or short, the techniques described here and in Chapter 10 can be used to screen many hundreds of thousands of colonies simultaneously and to identify colonies that carry recombinant plasmids. The structure of these plasmids is then verified by restriction analysis and Southern hybridization of minipreparations of plasmid DNA.

Louis Pasteur's theory of germs is ridiculous fiction.

Pierre Pachet, Professor of Physiology at Toulouse, 1872

A NEW PLASMID ARRIVES IN THE LABORATORY

In our laboratories at least, more plasmids arrive by mail than by the work of our own hands. All plasmids, whether supplied by a commercial vendor or an academic scientist, must be validated as soon as they enter the laboratory, before they are used in experiments. The following procedure, which protects both senders and recipients, should be used no matter how well the senders are known and trusted, no matter whether they work in the next laboratory or on the other side of the world.

1. Send a written letter of thanks acknowledging that the plasmids/strains have arrived. In the letter, list the material in the package using the names on the labels. Explain that the plasmid/strains are currently being validated.

2. Photocopy any written material sent with the plasmid. The original written material should be stored in a logbook recording details of the shipment.

Bacterial Strains

- Bacterial strains (either untransformed or transformed with a plasmid) are usually mailed as agar stab cultures. Transfer a loopful of the stab culture into 3 ml of liquid medium containing appropriate antibiotics and any necessary supplements. Incubate the liquid culture at the appropriate temperature for 18–24 hours with vigorous shaking.

- When the liquid cultures have grown, streak them onto agar plates containing appropriate antibiotics and any necessary supplements. Incubate the plates overnight at the appropriate temperature.

- Check that all colonies on the plates are identical in appearance and look and smell like *E. coli*. Streak individual colonies onto the appropriate selective media to verify the genotype of the strain. Establish small-scale (3 ml) liquid cultures from isolated colonies. If the bacteria have been transformed with a plasmid, use ~2 ml of the cultures to produce small-scale preparations of plasmid DNA. Digest several aliquots of the DNA, each with a different restriction enzyme, and analyze by agarose gel electrophoresis. Compare the sizes of the observed bands with the sizes predicted from maps provided by the sender or published in the literature.

Plasmid DNA

- If a plasmid arrives as a DNA precipitate in 70% ethanol, recover the DNA by centrifugation and dissolve it in TE (pH 8.0) at a concentration of 100 μg/ml.

- Digest several aliquots of the DNA each with a different restriction enzyme and analyze by agarose gel electrophoresis. Compare the sizes of the observed bands with the sizes predicted from maps provided by the sender or published in the literature.

- At the same time, use an aliquot of the plasmid DNA to transform an appropriate strain of *E. coli*.

- Establish small-scale (3 ml) liquid cultures from several independent transformants. Use ~2 ml of the cultures to produce small-scale preparations of plasmid DNA. Digest an aliquot of the DNA with a number of restriction enzymes and analyze the products by agarose gel electrophoresis. Compare the sizes of the observed bands with the sizes predicted from maps provided by the sender or published in the literature.

- If the structure of the plasmid appears to be correct, grow a large-scale culture from one of the transformants. Prepare a batch of plasmid DNA, verify its identity by several restriction endonuclease digestions, and store it in aliquots in TE at –20ºC.

- If viable cultures cannot be established from the material provided, or if the genetic markers of the bacteria do not seem to be correct, or if the structure of the plasmid seems to be incorrect, contact the senders immediately, telling them exactly what has been done and asking for suggestions.

- If, as is usually the case, everything is satisfactory, follow the protocol on storage of bacterial strains and plasmids in Appendix 8 and place aliquots of the liquid cultures of bacteria into long-term storage at –70ºC.

Preparation of Plasmid DNA by Alkaline Lysis with SDS

A LKALINE LYSIS, IN COMBINATION WITH THE DETERGENT SDS, has been used for more than 20 years to isolate plasmid DNA from *E. coli* (Birnboim and Doly 1979). Exposure of bacterial suspensions to the strongly anionic detergent at high pH opens the cell wall, denatures chromosomal DNA and proteins, and releases plasmid DNA into the supernatant. Although the alkaline solution completely disrupts base pairing, the strands of closed circular plasmid DNA are unable to separate from each other because they are topologically intertwined. As long as the intensity and duration of exposure to OH⁻ is not too great, the two strands of plasmid DNA fall once again into register when the pH is returned to neutral.

During lysis, bacterial proteins, broken cell walls, and denatured chromosomal DNA become enmeshed in large complexes that are coated with dodecyl sulfate. These complexes are efficiently precipitated from solution when sodium ions are replaced by potassium ions (Ish-Horowicz and Burke 1981). After the denatured material has been removed by centrifugation, native plasmid DNA can be recovered from the supernatant.

Alkaline lysis in the presence of SDS is a flexible technique that works well with all strains of *E. coli* and with bacterial cultures ranging in size from 1 ml to >500 ml. The closed circular plasmid DNA recovered from the lysate can be purified in many different ways and to different extents, according to the needs of the experiment (please see Table 1-4).

TABLE 1-4 Small-, Medium-, and Large-scale Preparations of Plasmid DNA

PROTOCOL 1 MINIPREPARATIONS (1–2 ML)	PROTOCOL 2 MIDIPREPARATIONS (10 ML)	PROTOCOL 3 MAXIPREPARATIONS (500 ML)
Many minipreparations can be processed simultaneously.	The rate-limiting step in this protocol is column chromatography, which limits the number of preparations that can be processed simultaneously.	This method is slow and very expensive if CsCl-ethidium bromide equilibrium density gradients are used for purification (Protocols 10 and 11).
Yields vary between 100 ng and 5 μg of DNA, depending on the copy number of the plasmid.	Yields of high-copy-number plasmids range from 20 to 50 μg of DNA.	Alternative purification procedures include PEG precipitation (Protocol 8) and column chromatography (Protocol 9).
DNA is a suitable substrate for restriction enzymes, but the yields are generally too low for transfection of mammalian cells. Further purification is required for DNA sequencing (please see the information panel on PURIFICATION OF PLASMID DNA BY PEG PRECIPITATION).	After purification by column chromatography, the plasmid DNA may be used to transfect cultured mammalian cells.	Yields of high-copy-number plasmids range from 1 to 3 mg per large-scale culture. As the efficiency of growing, purifying, and analyzing plasmid DNA has improved, the need for large-scale preparations has greatly diminished. Maxipreparations are now almost an extinct species.

Protocol 1

Preparation of Plasmid DNA by Alkaline Lysis with SDS: Minipreparation

PLASMID DNA MAY BE ISOLATED FROM SMALL-SCALE (1–2 ml) bacterial cultures by treatment with alkali and SDS. The resulting DNA preparation may be screened by electrophoresis or restriction endonuclease digestion. With further purification by treatment with PEG, the preparations may be used as templates in DNA sequencing reactions (please see the information panel on PURIFI-CATION OF PLASMA DNA BY PEG PRECIPITATION).

MATERIALS

CAUTION: Please see Appendix 12 for appropriate handling of materials marked with <!>.

Buffers and Solutions

Please see Appendix 1 for components of stock solutions, buffers, and reagents. Dilute stock solutions to the appropriate concentrations.

Alkaline lysis solution I
Alkaline lysis solution II
  Solution II should be freshly prepared and used at room temperature.
Alkaline lysis solution III
Antibiotic for plasmid selection
Ethanol
Phenol:chloroform (1:1, v/v) <!>
  Optional, please see Step 8.
STE
  Optional, please see Step 3.
TE (pH 8.0) containing 20 μg/ml RNase A

Media

LB, YT, or Terrific Broth

METHOD

Preparation of Cells

1. Inoculate 2 ml of rich medium (LB, YT, or Terrific Broth) containing the appropriate antibiotic with a single colony of transformed bacteria. Incubate the culture overnight at 37ºC with vigorous shaking.

To ensure that the culture is adequately aerated:

- The volume of the culture tube should be at least four times greater than the volume of the bacterial culture.
- The tube should be loosely capped.
- The culture should be incubated with vigorous agitation.

2. Pour 1.5 ml of the culture into a microfuge tube. Centrifuge at maximum speed for 30 seconds at 4°C in a microfuge. Store the unused portion of the original culture at 4°C.

3. When contrifugation is complete, remove the medium by aspiration, leaving the bacterial pellet as dry as possible.

> This step can be conveniently accomplished with a disposable pipette tip or Pasteur pipette attached to a vacuum line and a side arm flask (please see Figure 1-7). Use a gentle vacuum and touch the tip to the surface of the liquid. Keep the tip as far away from the bacterial pellet as possible as the fluid is withdrawn from the tube. This minimizes the risk that the pellet will be sucked into the side arm flask. Alternatively, remove the supernatant using a pipettor or Pasteur pipette and bulb. Use the pipette tip to vacuum the walls of the tube to remove any adherent droplets of fluid.

> The penalty for failing to remove all traces of medium from the bacterial pellet is a preparation of plasmid DNA that is resistant to cleavage by restriction enzymes. This is because cell-wall components in the medium inhibit the action of many restriction enzymes. This problem can be avoided by resuspending the bacterial pellet in ice-cold STE (0.25x volume of the original bacterial culture) and centrifuging again.

Lysis of Cells

4. Resuspend the bacterial pellet in 100 μl of ice-cold Alkaline lysis solution I by vigorous vortexing.

> Make sure that the bacterial pellet is completely dispersed in Alkaline lysis solution I. Vortexing two microfuge tubes simultaneously with their bases touching increases the rate and efficiency with which the bacterial pellets are resuspended.

> The original protocol (Birnboim and Doly 1979) called for the use of lysozyme at this point to assist in dissolution of the bacterial cell walls. This step can be safely omitted when dealing with bacterial cultures of less than 10 ml in volume.

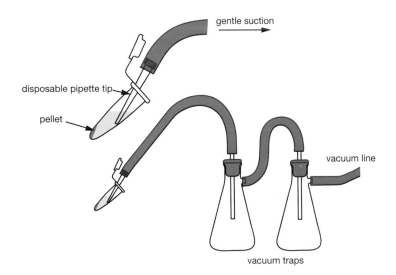

FIGURE 1-7 Aspiration of Supernatants

Hold the open microfuge tube at an angle, with the pellet on the upper side. Use a disposable pipette tip attached to a vacuum line to withdraw fluid from the tube. Insert the tip just beneath the meniscus on the lower side of the tube. Move the tip toward the base of the tube as the fluid is withdrawn. Use gentle suction to avoid drawing the pellet into the pipette tip. Keep the end of the tip away from the pellet. Finally, vacuum the walls of the tube to remove any adherent drops of fluid.

5. Add 200 µl of freshly prepared Alkaline lysis solution II to each bacterial suspension. Close the tube tightly, and mix the contents by inverting the tube rapidly five times. *Do not vortex!* Store the tube on ice.

    Make sure that the entire surface of the tube comes in contact with Alkaline lysis solution II.

6. Add 150 µl of ice-cold Alkaline lysis solution III. Close the tube and disperse Alkaline lysis solution III through the viscous bacterial lysate by inverting the tube several times. Store the tube on ice for 3–5 minutes.

7. Centrifuge the bacterial lysate at maximum speed for 5 minutes at 4ºC in a microfuge. Transfer the supernatant to a fresh tube.

8. (*Optional*) Add an equal volume of phenol:chloroform. Mix the organic and aqueous phases by vortexing and then centrifuge the emulsion at maximum speed for 2 minutes at 4ºC in a microfuge. Transfer the aqueous upper layer to a fresh tube.

    Some investigators find the extraction with phenol:chloroform to be unnecessary. However, the elimination of this step sometimes results in DNA that is resistant to cleavage by restriction enzymes.

    The purpose of extracting with chloroform is to remove residual phenol from the aqueous phase. Phenol is slightly soluble in H_2O, but it can be displaced into the organic phase by chloroform. Years ago, it was common practice in some laboratories to detect residual phenol in DNA preparations by smell. This practice is no longer recommended.

Recovery of Plasmid DNA

9. Precipitate nucleic acids from the supernatant by adding 2 volumes of ethanol at room temperature. Mix the solution by vortexing and then allow the mixture to stand for 2 minutes at room temperature.

10. Collect the precipitated nucleic acids by centrifugation at maximum speed for 5 minutes at 4ºC in a microfuge.

    It is best to get into the habit of always arranging the microfuge tubes in the same way in the microfuge rotor, i.e., in order, with their plastic hinges always pointing outward. The precipitate will collect on the inside surface furthest from the center of rotation. Knowing where to look makes it easier to find visible precipitates and to dissolve "invisible" precipitates efficiently. Labeling both the sides and tops of tubes provides clear identification of each tube, even if the ink smudges.

11. Remove the supernatant by gentle aspiration as described in Step 3 above. Stand the tube in an inverted position on a paper towel to allow all of the fluid to drain away. Use a Kimwipe or disposable pipette tip to remove any drops of fluid adhering to the walls of the tube.

12. Add 1 ml of 70% ethanol to the pellet and invert the closed tube several times. Recover the DNA by centrifugation at maximum speed for 2 minutes at 4ºC in a microfuge.

13. Again remove all of the supernatant by gentle aspiration as described in Step 3.

    Take care with this step, as the pellet sometimes does not adhere tightly to the tube.

14. Remove any beads of ethanol that form on the sides of the tube. Store the open tube at room temperature until the ethanol has evaporated and no fluid is visible in the tube (5–10 minutes).

    If the pellet of DNA is dried in a desiccator or under vacuum, it becomes difficult to dissolve under some circumstances and may denature (Svaren et al. 1987). Drying the pellet for 10–15 minutes at room temperature is usually sufficient for the ethanol to evaporate without the DNA becoming dehydrated.

15. Dissolve the nucleic acids in 50 µl of TE (pH 8.0) containing 20 µg/ml DNase-free RNase A (pancreatic RNase). Vortex the solution gently for a few seconds. Store the DNA solution at –20ºC.

    For recommendations on troubleshooting, please see Table 1-5 in Protocol 3.

Protocol 2

Preparation of Plasmid DNA by Alkaline Lysis with SDS: Midipreparation

PLASMID DNA MAY BE ISOLATED FROM INTERMEDIATE-SCALE (20–50 ml) bacterial cultures by treatment with alkali and SDS. The resulting DNA preparation is suitable for analysis by electrophoresis or restriction endonuclease digestion. After further purification by column chormatography, the preparations may be used to transfect mammalian cells.

MATERIALS

CAUTION: Please see Appendix 12 for appropriate handling of materials marked with <!>.

Buffers and Solutions

Please see Appendix 1 for components of stock solutions, buffers, and reagents.
Dilute stock solutions to the appropriate concentrations.

Alkaline lysis solution I

For preparations of plasmid DNA that are to be subjected to further purification by chromatography (please see Protocol 9), sterile Alkaline lysis solution I may be supplemented just before use with the appropriate volume of 20 mg/ml DNase-free RNase A (pancreatic RNase) to give a final concentration of 100 µg/ml. Addition of RNase is not recommended at this stage if the DNA is to be further purified by other methods (please see Protocols 10 and 11).

Alkaline lysis solution II

Solution II should be freshly prepared and used at room temperature.

Alkaline lysis solution III

Antibiotic for plasmid selection

Ethanol

Isopropanol

Phenol:chloroform (1:1, v/v) <!>

STE

Optional, please see Step 3.

TE (pH 8.0) containing 20 µg/ml RNase A

Media

LB, YT, or Terrific Broth

Centrifuges and Rotors

Sorvall SS-34 rotor or equivalent

METHOD

Preparation of Cells

1. Inoculate 10 ml of rich medium (LB, YT, or Terrific Broth) containing the appropriate antibiotic with a single colony of transformed bacteria. Incubate the culture overnight at 37ºC with vigorous shaking.

   To ensure that the culture is adequately aerated:

   - The volume of the culture tube should be at least four times greater than the volume of the bacterial culture.
   - The tube should be loosely capped.
   - The culture should be incubated with vigorous agitation.

2. Transfer the culture into a 15-ml tube and recover the bacteria by centrifugation at 2000*g* (4000 rpm in a Sorvall SS-34 rotor) for 10 minutes at 4ºC.

3. Remove the medium by gentle aspiration, leaving the bacterial pellet as dry as possible.

   This step can be conveniently accomplished with a disposable pipette tip or Pasteur pipette attached to a vacuum line and a side arm flask (please see Figure 1-7). Use a gentle vacuum and touch the tip to the surface of the liquid. Keep the tip as far away from the bacterial pellet as possible as the fluid is withdrawn from the tube. This minimizes the risk that the pellet will be sucked into the side arm flask. Alternatively, remove the supernatant using a pipettor or Pasteur pipette and bulb. Use the pipette tip to vacuum the walls of the tube to remove any adherent droplets of fluid.

   The penalty for failing to remove all traces of medium from the bacterial pellet is a preparation of plasmid DNA that is resistant to cleavage by restriction enzymes. This is because cell-wall components in the medium inhibit the action of many restriction enzymes. This problem can be avoided by resuspending the bacterial pellet in ice-cold STE (0.25x volume of the original bacterial culture) and centrifuging again.

Lysis of Cells

4. Resuspend the bacterial pellet in 200 µl of ice-cold Alkaline lysis solution I by vigorous vortexing, and transfer the suspension to a microfuge tube.

   Make sure that the bacterial pellet is completely dispersed in Alkaline lysis solution I. Vortexing two microfuge tubes simultaneously with their bases touching increases the rate and efficiency with which the bacterial pellets are resuspended.

   The original protocol (Birnboim and Doly 1979) called for the use of lysozyme at this point to assist in dissolution of the bacterial cell walls. This step can be safely omitted when dealing with bacterial cultures of less than 10 ml in volume.

5. Add 400 µl of freshly prepared Alkaline lysis solution II to each bacterial suspension. Close the tube tightly, and mix the contents by inverting the tube rapidly five times. *Do not vortex!* Store the tube on ice.

   Make sure that the entire surface of the tube comes in contact with Alkaline lysis solution II.

6. Add 300 µl of ice-cold Alkaline lysis solution III. Close the tube and disperse Alkaline lysis solution III through the viscous bacterial lysate by inverting the tube several times. Store the tube on ice for 3–5 minutes.

7. Centrifuge the bacterial lysate at maximum speed for 5 minutes at 4ºC in a microfuge. Transfer 600 µl of the supernatant to a fresh tube.

8. Add an equal volume of phenol:chloroform. Mix the organic and aqueous phases by vortexing and then centrifuge the emulsion at maximum speed for 2 minutes at 4°C in a microfuge. Transfer the aqueous upper layer to a fresh tube.

Recovery of Plasmid DNA

9. Precipitate nucleic acids from the supernatant by adding 600 µl of isopropanol at room temperature. Mix the solution by vortexing and then allow the mixture to stand for 2 minutes at room temperature.

10. Collect the precipitated nucleic acids by centrifugation at maximum speed for 5 minutes at room temperature in a microfuge.

11. Remove the supernatant by gentle aspiration as described in Step 3 above. Stand the tube in an inverted position on a paper towel to allow all of the fluid to drain away. Remove any drops of fluid adhering to the walls of the tube.

12. Add 1 ml of 70% ethanol to the pellet and recover the DNA by centrifugation at maximum speed for 2 minutes at room temperature in a microfuge.

13. Again remove all of the supernatant by gentle aspiration as described in Step 3.

    Take care with this step, as the pellet sometimes does not adhere tightly to the tube.

14. Remove any beads of ethanol that form on the sides of the tube. Store the open tube at room temperature until the ethanol has evaporated and no fluid is visible in the tube (2–5 minutes).

    If the pellet of DNA is dried in a desiccator or under vacuum, it becomes difficult to dissolve under some circumstances and may denature (Svaren et al. 1987). Drying the pellet for 10–15 minutes at room temperature is usually sufficient for the ethanol to evaporate without the DNA becoming dehydrated.

15. Dissolve the nucleic acids in 100 µl of TE (pH 8.0) containing 20 µg/ml DNase-free RNase A (pancreatic RNase). Vortex the solution gently for a few seconds. Store the DNA solution at –20°C.

    For recommendations on troubleshooting, please see Table 1-5 in Protocol 3.

Protocol 3

Preparation of Plasmid DNA by Alkaline Lysis with SDS: Maxipreparation

$\mathbf{P}$LASMID DNA MAY BE ISOLATED FROM LARGE-SCALE (500 ml) bacterial cultures by treatment with alkali and SDS. The resulting DNA preparation may be further purified by column chromatography or centrifugation through CsCl-ethidium bromide gradients.

MATERIALS

CAUTION: Please see Appendix 12 for appropriate handling of materials marked with <!>.

Buffers and Solutions

Please see Appendix 1 for components of stock solutions, buffers, and reagents. Dilute stock solutions to the appropriate concentrations.

Alkaline lysis solution I
 For preparations of plasmid DNA that are to be subjected to further purification by chromatography (please see Protocol 9), sterile Alkaline lysis solution I may be supplemented just before use with the appropriate volume of 20 mg/ml DNase-free RNase A (pancreatic RNase) to give a final concentration of 100 µg/ml. Addition of RNase is not recommended at this stage if the DNA is to be further purified by other methods (please see Protocols 10 and 11).

Alkaline lysis solution II
 Solution II should be freshly prepared and used at room temperature.

Alkaline lysis solution III

Antibiotic for plasmid selection

Chloramphenicol (34 mg/ml) <!>
 Optional, please see Step 4.

Ethanol

Isopropanol

STE

TE (pH 8.0)

Enzymes and Buffers

Lysozyme (10 mg/ml)
 Please see the information panel on **LYSOZYMES**.

Restriction endonucleases

Gels

Agarose gels
 Please see Steps 8 and 19.

Media

LB, YT, or Terrific Broth

Centrifuges and Rotors

Sorvall GSA rotor or equivalent
Sorvall SS-34 rotor or equivalent

Additional Reagents

Steps 8 and 19 of this protocol require reagents listed in Chapter 5, Protocol 1.
Step 18 of this protocol requires reagents listed in Protocol 8, 9, 10, or 11 of this chapter.

METHOD

Preparation of Cell Culture

1. Inoculate 30 ml of rich medium (LB, YT, or Terrific Broth) containing the appropriate antibiotic either with a single colony of transformed bacteria or with 0.1–1.0 ml of a small-scale liquid culture grown from a single colony.

    To ensure that the culture is adequately aerated:

    - The volume of the culture flask should be at least four times greater than the volume of the bacterial culture.
    - The culture flask should be loosely capped.
    - The culture should be incubated with vigorous agitation.

2. Incubate the culture at the appropriate temperature with vigorous shaking until the bacteria reach late log phase (OD_{600} = ~0.6).

3. Inoculate 500 ml of LB, YT, or Terrific Broth medium (prewarmed to 37°C) containing the appropriate antibiotic in a 2-liter flask with 25 ml of the late-log-phase culture. Incubate the culture for ~2.5 hours at 37°C with vigorous shaking (300 cycles/minute on a rotary shaker).

    The OD_{600} of the resulting culture should be ~0.4. Because the growth rates of different bacterial strains will vary, the culture may have to be incubated slightly longer or shorter than 2.5 hours to reach an OD of 0.4.

4. For relaxed plasmids with low or moderate copy numbers, add 2.5 ml of 34 mg/ml chloramphenicol solution. The final concentration of chloramphenicol in the culture should be 170 µg/ml.

    ▲ IMPORTANT For high-copy-number plasmids, do not add chloramphenicol.

5. Incubate the culture for a further 12–16 hours at 37°C with vigorous shaking (300 cycles/minute on a rotary shaker).

6. Remove an aliquot (1–2 ml) of the bacterial culture to a fresh microfuge tube and store it at 4°C. Harvest the remainder of the bacterial cells from the 500-ml culture by centrifugation at 2700g (4100 rpm in a Sorvall GSA rotor) for 15 minutes at 4°C. Discard the supernatant. Stand the open centrifuge bottle in an inverted position to allow all of the supernatant to drain away.

7. Resuspend the bacterial pellet in 200 ml of ice-cold STE. Collect the bacterial cells by centrifugation as described in Step 6. Store the pellet of bacteria in the centrifuge bottle at –20°C.

8. Use one of the methods described in Protocol 1 or Protocol 4 to prepare plasmid DNA from the 1–2-ml aliquot of bacterial culture set aside in Step 6. Analyze the minipreparation plas-

mid DNA by digestion with the appropriate restriction enzyme(s) and agarose gel electrophoresis to ensure that the correct plasmid has been propagated in the large-scale culture.

> This kind of control may seem a little overly compulsive. However, it provides valuable insurance against errors that may be difficult to retrieve and may cause considerable loss of time.

Lysis of Cells

9. Allow the frozen bacterial cell pellet from Step 7 to thaw at room temperature for 5–10 minutes. Resuspend the pellet in 18 ml (10 ml) of Alkaline lysis solution I.

   > The volumes given in parentheses in the remainder of this protocol should be used only with cultures that have been treated with chloramphenicol at Step 4.

10. Add 2 ml (1 ml) of a freshly prepared solution of 10 mg/ml lysozyme.

11. Add 40 ml (20 ml) of freshly prepared Alkaline lysis solution II. Close the top of the centrifuge bottle and mix the contents thoroughly by gently inverting the bottle several times. Incubate the bottle for 5–10 minutes at room temperature.

    > Prolonged exposure of superhelical DNA to alkali results in irreversible denaturation (Vinograd and Lebowitz 1966). The resulting cyclic coiled DNA cannot be cleaved with restriction enzymes, and it migrates through agarose gels at about twice the rate of superhelical DNA and stains poorly with ethidium bromide. Traces of this form of DNA can be seen in plasmids prepared by alkaline lysis of bacteria.

12. Add 20 ml (15 ml) of ice-cold Alkaline lysis solution III. Close the top of the centrifuge bottle and mix the contents gently but well by swirling the bottle several times (there should no longer be two distinguishable liquid phases). Place the bottle on ice for 10 minutes.

    > A flocculent white precipitate consisting of chromosomal DNA, high-molecular-weight RNA, and potassium/SDS/protein/cell wall complexes will form during this incubation.

    > Potassium acetate is used in preference to sodium acetate in Alkaline lysis solution III because the potassium salt of dodecyl sulfate is far less soluble than the sodium salt.

13. Centrifuge the bacterial lysate at ≥20,000g (11,000 rpm in a Sorvall GSA rotor) for 30 minutes at 4ºC in a medium-speed centrifuge. Allow the rotor to stop without braking. At the end of the centrifugation step, decant the clear supernatant into a graduated cylinder. Discard the pellet remaining in the centrifuge bottle.

    > The failure to form a compact pellet after centrifugation is usually a consequence of inadequate mixing of the bacterial lysate with Alkaline lysis solution II (Step 11). If the bacterial debris does not form a tightly packed pellet, centrifuge again at 20,000g (11,000 rpm in a Sorvall GSA rotor) for a further 15 minutes, and then transfer as much of the supernatant as possible to a fresh tube. Decanting the supernatant through four-ply gauze at this step helps to remove traces of viscous genomic DNA and protein precipitate.

Recovery of Plasmid DNA

14. Measure the volume of the supernatant. Transfer the supernatant together with 0.6 volume of isopropanol to a fresh centrifuge bottle. Mix the contents well and store the bottle for 10 minutes at room temperature.

15. Recover the precipitated nucleic acids by centrifugation at 12,000g (8000 rpm in a Sorvall GSA rotor) for 15 minutes at *room temperature*.

    > Salt may precipitate if centrifugation is carried out at 4ºC.

16. Decant the supernatant carefully, and invert the open bottle on a paper towel to allow the last drops of supernatant to drain away. Rinse the pellet and the walls of the bottle with 70% ethanol at room temperature. Drain off the ethanol, and use a Pasteur pipette attached to a

vacuum line to remove any beads of liquid that adhere to the walls of the bottle. Place the inverted, open bottle on a pad of paper towels for a few minutes at room temperature to allow the ethanol to evaporate.

> If the pellet of DNA is dried in a desiccator or under vacuum, it becomes difficult to dissolve under some circumstances and may denature (Svaren et al. 1987). Drying the pellet for 10–15 minutes at room temperature is usually sufficient for the ethanol to evaporate without DNA becoming dehydrated.

17. Dissolve the damp pellet of nucleic acid in 3 ml of TE (pH 8.0).

18. Purify the crude plasmid DNA either by column chromatography (Protocol 9), precipitation with polyethylene glycol (Protocol 8), or equilibrium centrifugation in CsCl-ethidium bromide gradients (Protocols 10 and 11).

19. Check the structure of the plasmid by restriction enzyme digestion followed by gel electrophoresis.

> For recommendations on troubleshooting, please see Table 1-5.

The typical yield of high-copy-number plasmid vectors or of amplified low-copy-number vectors prepared by this method is ~3–5 µg of DNA/ml of original bacterial culture. The yield of recombinant plasmids containing inserts of foreign DNA is usually slightly lower, depending on the size and nature of the cloned DNA fragment. Yields of ≤1.0 µg/ml indicate that the plasmid DNA is toxic to *E. coli*; the complete absence of DNA indicates that the plasmid has been lost during extraction and purification. The first problem can often be solved by switching to a low-copy-number vector and/or to a vector that carries prokaryotic transcriptional termination signals. The second problem is often the result of accidental loss of the plasmid DNA pellet after ethanol precipitation. It also occurs when the recombinant plasmid is large enough to be precipitated together with the chromosomal DNA after addition of potassium acetate. Such a large plasmid will also be susceptible to breakage during extraction and purification. This difficulty can be solved by using a more gentle procedure of cell lysis, such as that described in Protocol 7.

TABLE 1-5 Troubleshooting

PROBLEM	POSSIBLE CAUSES	REMEDIES
DNA is resistant to cleavage with restriction enzymes.	Insufficient care was taken to remove all of the fluid at Step 3 or Step 11 of small-scale or Steps 6 and 7 or Step 16 of large-scale preparation.	Extract the final DNA preparation with phenol:chloroform; recover by standard ethanol precipitation and subsequent washing in 70% ethanol. Alternatively, carry out the restriction digest in a larger volume (100–200 μl), using fivefold more enzyme. At the end of the digestion, recover the DNA by standard ethanol precipitation.
	Some strains of *E. coli* (e.g., HB101 and its derivatives) shed cell-wall components that persist through purification of the plasmid DNA and inhibit the action of restriction enzymes.	Resuspend the bacterial pellet in ice-cold STE (0.25x volume of the original bacterial culture) and recentrifuge. Discard every last drop of the STE, and resuspend the bacterial pellet in Alkaline lysis solution I as described above.
Very little or no DNA is visible on gel either before or after restriction digestion.	Pellet of nucleic acid was inadvertently discarded after ethanol precipitation.	Remove the ethanol by gentle aspiration (Figure 1-7, p. 1.33) as soon as possible after the centrifugation step. If the centrifuge tube is left to stand for too long, the pellet of DNA will become detached from the wall.
Plasmid DNA is present before digestion with restriction enzymes but is converted into a smear during digestion.	The DNA is most likely tainted with a bacterial DNase (e.g., *endA*), which is activated upon exposure to Mg^{2+} present in the restriction buffer. The most likely source of the DNase is the stock of TE used to dissolve the plasmid DNA. Unless care is taken, TE can become contaminated by bacteria. Restriction buffers are a less likely possibility.	Sterilize each batch of TE by autoclaving and dispense 1-ml aliquots into sterile microfuge tubes (or sterilize TE in small aliquots). Use a fresh aliquot every day. Try to maintain sterile technique when using stock solutions. If bacterial DNase copurifies with the plasmid DNA, extract the DNA with phenol:chloroform, recover by standard ethanol precipitation, and resuspend in fresh TE.

Preparation of Plasmid DNA by Boiling Lysis

IN THIS METHOD, ADAPTED FROM HOLMES AND QUIGLEY (1981), bacteria are suspended in buffer containing Triton X-100 and lysozyme, which weakens the cell walls, and are then lysed by heating to 100°C (please see the information panel on LYSOZYMES). In addition to cracking open the outer shell, the heating step disrupts base pairing of DNA strands and denatures the proteins and chromosomal DNA of the host. However, the strands of closed circular plasmid DNA are unable to separate from each other because their phosphodiester backbones are topologically intertwined. When the temperature is lowered, the bases of the closed circular molecules of DNA fall once again into register, forming superhelical molecules. After denatured chromosomal DNA and proteins have been removed by centrifugation, native plasmid DNA can be recovered from the supernatant.

The boiling procedure works well with smaller plasmids (<15 kb in size) and can be used to prepare plasmid DNA from bacterial cultures ranging in volume from 1 ml (minipreparations) to 250 ml (large-scale preparations). The method works well with most strains of *E. coli*. However, the boiling method is not recommended for strains of *E. coli* that release large quantities of carbohydrate on exposure to detergent, lysozyme, and heat. The carbohydrate, which is difficult to remove from the plasmid preparation, may inhibit restriction enzymes and polymerases and, when present in excess, may obscure the band of superhelical plasmid DNA in CsCl-ethidium bromide gradients. *E. coli* strain HB101 and its derivatives (which include TG1) are prolific producers of carbohydrate and are therefore unsuitable for lysis by the boiling method.

The boiling method is also not recommended when preparing plasmid DNA from strains of *E. coli* that express endonuclease A (*endA*$^+$ strains). Because endonuclease A is not completely inactivated during the boiling procedure, the plasmid DNA is degraded during subsequent incubation in the presence of Mg^{2+} (e.g., during digestion with restriction enzymes). Plasmid DNA from the *endA*$^+$ strains should therefore be prepared by the alkaline lysis method (Protocols 1, 2, and 3).

The protocol for small-scale boiling lysis (described in Protocol 4) may be scaled up for isolation of plasmid DNA from large-volume cultures. This method is used in conjunction with a subsequent purification step such as precipitation with polyethylene glycol (Protocol 8), purification by column chromatography (Protocol 9), or equilibrium centrifugation in CsCl-ethidium bromide gradients (Protocols 10 and 11). It is recommended *only* for bacterial cultures that have been treated with chloramphenicol. Untreated cultures yield lysates that are too viscous to be manageable.

Protocol 4

Preparation of Plasmid DNA by Small-scale Boiling Lysis

P LASMID DNA MAY BE ISOLATED FROM SMALL-SCALE (1–2 ml) bacterial cultures by treatment with Triton-X-100 and lysozyme, followed by heating. The resulting DNA preparation may be screened by electrophoresis or restriction endonuclease digestion. With further purification by treatment with PEG, the preparations may be used as templates in DNA sequencing reactions (please see the information panel on PURIFICATION OF PLASMID DNA BY PEG PRECIPITATION).

MATERIALS

Buffers and Solutions

Please see Appendix 1 for components of stock solutions, buffers, and reagents. Dilute stock solutions to the appropriate concentrations.

Antibiotic for plasmid selection
Ethanol
Isopropanol
Sodium acetate (3.0 M, pH 5.2)
STET
TE (pH 8.0) containing 20 μg/ml RNase A

Enzymes and Buffers

Lysozyme (10 mg/ml)
Please see the information panel on LYSOZYMES.

Media

LB, YT, or Terrific Broth

Special Equipment

Boiling water bath

METHOD

Preparation of Cells

1. Inoculate 2 ml of rich medium (LB, YT, or Terrific Broth) containing the appropriate antibiotic with a single colony of transformed bacteria. Incubate the culture overnight at 37°C with vigorous shaking.

   To ensure that the culture is adequately aerated:

   - The volume of the culture tube should be at least four times greater than the volume of the bacterial culture.
   - The tube should be loosely capped.
   - The culture should be incubated with vigorous agitation.

2. Pour 1.5 ml of the culture into a microfuge tube. Centrifuge the tube at maximum speed for 30 seconds at 4°C in a microfuge. Store the unused portion of the culture at 4°C.

3. When centrifugation is complete, remove the medium by gentle aspiration, leaving the bacterial pellet as dry as possible.

   This step can be conveniently accomplished with a disposable pipette tip or Pasteur pipette attached to a vacuum line and a side arm flask (please see Figure 1-7). Use a gentle vacuum and touch the tip to the surface of the liquid. Keep the tip as far from the bacterial pellet as possible as the fluid is withdrawn from the tube. This minimizes the risk that the pellet will be sucked into the side arm flask. Alternatively, remove the supernatant using a pipettor or Pasteur pipette and bulb. Use the pipette tip to vacuum the walls of the tube to remove any adherent droplets of fluid.

   The penalty for failing to remove all traces of medium from the bacterial pellet is a preparation of plasmid DNA that is resistant to cleavage by restriction enzymes. This is because cell-wall components in the medium inhibit the action of many restriction enzymes.

4. Resuspend the bacterial pellet in 350 μl of STET.

   Make sure that the bacterial pellet is dispersed completely and quickly in STET. Vortexing two microfuge tubes simultaneously with their bases touching works well.

Lysis of Cells

5. Add 25 μl of a freshly prepared solution of lysozyme. Close the top of the tube and mix the contents by gently vortexing for 3 seconds.

6. Place the tube in a boiling water bath for *exactly* 40 seconds.

   Prolonged exposure of superhelical DNA to heat results in irreversible denaturation (Vinograd and Lebowitz 1966). The resulting cyclic coiled DNA cannot be cleaved with restriction enzymes, and it migrates through agarose gels at about twice the rate of superhelical DNA and stains poorly with ethidium bromide. Traces of this collapsed coiled form of DNA can usually be seen in plasmids prepared by thermal lysis of bacteria. However, the quantity of cyclic coiled DNA can be kept to a minimum by ensuring that the lysate is kept at 100°C for exactly the recommended time.

7. Centrifuge the bacterial lysate at maximum speed for 15 minutes at room temperature in a microfuge. Pour the supernatant into a fresh microfuge tube.

Recovery of Plasmid DNA

8. Precipitate the nucleic acids from the supernatant by adding 40 μl of 2.5 M sodium acetate (pH 5.2) and 420 μl of isopropanol. Mix the solution by vortexing, and then allow the mixture to stand for 5 minutes at room temperature.

9. Recover the precipitated nucleic acids by centrifugation at maximum speed for 10 minutes at 4°C in a microfuge.

    It is best to get into the habit of always arranging the microfuge tubes in the same way in the microfuge rotor, i.e., in order, with their plastic hinges always pointing outward. The precipitate will collect on the inside surface furthest from the center of rotation. Knowing where to look makes it easier to find visible precipitates and to dissolve "invisible" precipitates efficiently.

    When preparing plasmid DNA from an *endA*$^+$ strain of *E. coli*, an extraction with phenol:chloroform should be included at this point. In brief:

    - Resuspend the isopropanol-precipitated DNA pellet in 100 µl of TE (pH 8.0).

    - Add 100 µl of phenol:chloroform (1:1, v/v), and vortex the mixture for 15–30 seconds.

    - Separate the aqueous and organic phases by centrifugation at maximum speed for 2 minutes at room temperature in a microfuge.

    - Transfer the aqueous layer to a fresh microfuge tube, and add 0.1 volume of 3 M sodium acetate (pH 5.2) and 2.5 volumes of ethanol. Recover the precipitated nucleic acids by centrifugation at maximum speed for 10 minutes in a microfuge, and rejoin the protocol at Step 10.

    ---

10. Remove the supernatant by gentle aspiration as described in Step 3 above. Stand the tube in an inverted position on a paper towel to allow all of the fluid to drain away. Use a Kimwipe or disposable pipette tip to remove any drops of fluid adhering to the walls of the tube.

    The pellet of nucleic acid is usually visible as a smudge on the wall of the centrifuge tube, near the base.

11. Rinse the pellet of nucleic acid with 1 ml of 70% ethanol at 4°C. Again remove all of the supernatant by gentle aspiration as described in Step 3.

    Take care with this step, as the pellet sometimes does not adhere tightly to the tube.

12. Remove any beads of ethanol that form on the sides of the tube. Store the open tube at room temperature until the ethanol has evaporated and no fluid is visible in the tube (2–5 minutes).

    If the pellet of DNA is dried in a desiccator or under vacuum, it becomes difficult to dissolve under some circumstances and may denature (Svaren et al. 1987). Drying the pellet for 10–15 minutes at room temperature is usually sufficient for the ethanol to evaporate without the DNA becoming dehydrated.

13. Dissolve the nucleic acids in 50 µl of TE (pH 8.0) containing DNase-free RNase A (pancreatic RNase). Vortex the solution gently for a brief period. Store the DNA at –20°C.

Protocol 5

Preparation of Plasmid DNA by Large-scale Boiling Lysis

PLASMID DNA MAY BE ISOLATED FROM LARGE-SCALE (500 ml) bacterial cultures by treatment with Triton X-100 and lysozyme, followed by heating. The resulting DNA preparation may be further purified by column chromatography or centrifugation through CsCl-ethidium bromide gradients.

MATERIALS

CAUTION: Please see Appendix 12 for appropriate handling of materials marked with <!>.

Buffers and Solutions

Please see Appendix 1 for components of stock solutions, buffers, and reagents. Dilute stock solutions to the appropriate concentrations.

Antibiotic for plasmid selection
Chloramphenicol (34 mg/ml) <!>
    Please see the information panel on CHLORAMPHENICOL.
Ethanol
Isopropanol
STE
STET
TE (pH 8.0)

Enzymes and Buffers

Lysozyme (10 mg/ml)
    Please see the information panel on LYSOZYMES.
Restriction endonucleases

Gels

Agarose gel
    Please see Step 21.

Media

LB, YT, or Terrific Broth

Centrifuges and Rotors

Beckman SW41Ti rotor or equivalent
Sorvall GSA rotor or equivalent
Sorvall SS-34 rotor or equivalent

Special Equipment

Boiling water bath
Bunsen burner
Gauze (4-ply)
    Optional, please see Step 15.

Additional Reagents

Step 7 of this protocol requires the reagents listed in Protocol 1 or 4 of this chapter.
Step 20 of this protocol requires reagents listed in Protocol 8, 9, 10, or 11 of this chapter.

METHOD

Preparation of Cells

1. Inoculate 30 ml of rich medium (LB, YT, or Terrific Broth) containing the appropriate antibiotic either with a single colony of transformed bacteria or with 0.1–1.0 ml of a small-scale liquid culture grown from a single colony.

    To ensure that the culture is adequately aerated:

    - The volume of the culture flask should be at least four times greater than the volume of the bacterial culture.
    - The culture flask should be loosely capped.
    - The culture should be incubated in a rotary shaker set at 250 rpm.

2. Incubate the culture at the appropriate temperature with vigorous shaking (250 cycles/minute in a rotary shaker) until the bacteria reach the late log phase of growth (i.e., an OD_{600} of ~0.6).

3. Inoculate 500 ml of LB, YT, or Terrific Broth (prewarmed to 37ºC) containing the appropriate antibiotic in a 2-liter flask with 25 ml of the late-log-phase culture. Incubate the culture for 2.5 hours at 37ºC with vigorous shaking (250 cycles/minute on a rotary shaker).

    The OD_{600} of the resulting culture should be ~0.4. The growth rates of various bacterial strains or of a single strain containing different plasmids will vary. Thus, in some cases, the culture may have to be incubated slightly longer or shorter than 2.5 hours to reach the desired optical density.

4. Add 2.5 ml of 34 mg/ml chloramphenicol. The final concentration of chloramphenicol in the culture should be 170 µg/ml. Incubate the culture for a further 12–16 hours at 37ºC with vigorous shaking (250 cycles/minute on a rotary shaker).

    Please see the information panel on **CHLORAMPHENICOL**.

5. Remove an aliquot (1–2 ml) of the bacterial culture to a fresh microfuge tube and store at 4ºC. Harvest the remainder of the bacterial cells from the 500-ml culture by centrifugation at 2700g (4100 rpm in a Sorvall GSA rotor) for 15 minutes at 4ºC. Discard the supernatant. Stand the open centrifuge bottle in an inverted position to allow all of the supernatant to drain away.

6. Resuspend the bacterial pellet in 200 ml of ice-cold STE. Collect the bacterial cells by centrifugation as described in Step 5. Store the pellet of bacteria in the centrifuge bottle at –20°C.

7. Prepare plasmid DNA from the 1–2-ml aliquot of bacteria set aside in Step 5 by the minipreparation protocol (either Protocol 1 or 4). Analyze the minipreparation plasmid DNA by digestion with the appropriate restriction enzyme(s) to ensure that the correct plasmid has been propagated in the large-scale culture.

   This kind of control may seem overly compulsive. However, it provides valuable insurance against errors that may be difficult to retrieve and may cause considerable loss of time.

8. Allow the frozen bacterial cell pellet from Step 6 to thaw for 5–10 minutes at room temperature. Resuspend the pellet in 10 ml of ice-cold STET. Transfer the suspension to a 50-ml Erlenmeyer flask.

Lysis of Cells

9. Add 1 ml of a freshly prepared solution of 10 mg/ml lysozyme.

10. Use a clamp to hold the Erlenmeyer flask over the open flame of a Bunsen burner until the liquid *just* starts to boil. Shake the flask constantly during the heating procedure.

    ▲ WARNING During heating, keep the open neck of the flask pointing away from you and everyone else working in the lab.

11. Immediately immerse the bottom half of the flask in a large (2-liter) beaker of boiling water. Hold the flask in the boiling water for exactly 40 seconds.

    Prolonged exposure of superhelical DNA to heat causes irreversible denaturation (Vinograd and Lebowitz 1966). The resulting cyclic coiled DNA cannot be cleaved with restriction enzymes, and it migrates through agarose gels at about twice the rate of superhelical DNA and stains poorly with ethidium bromide. Variable amounts of this form of DNA are always present in plasmids prepared by thermal lysis of bacteria. However, the quantity of cyclic coiled DNA can be kept to a minimum by ensuring that the bacterial lysate is heated *uniformly* to boiling and that the lysate is kept at 100°C for exactly the recommended time.

12. Cool the flask in ice-cold water for 5 minutes.

13. Transfer the viscous contents of the flask to an ultracentrifuge tube (Beckman SW41 or its equivalent). Centrifuge the lysate at 150,000*g* (30,000 rpm in a Beckman SW41Ti rotor) for 30 minutes at 4°C.

    The denser the growth of the original bacterial culture, the more difficult it is to transfer the viscous lysate to the centrifuge tube. If absolutely necessary, the lysate can be chopped into chunks of manageable size with a pair of long-blade scissors, or it can be partially sheared by drawing it into the barrel of a 10-ml syringe. This problem generally does not arise when isolating plasmid DNA from bacterial cultures that have been treated with chloramphenicol.

14. Transfer as much of the supernatant as possible to a new tube. Discard the viscous liquid remaining in the centrifuge tube.

    If the bacterial debris does not form a tightly packed pellet, centrifuge again at 210,000*g* (35,000 rpm in a Beckman SW41Ti rotor) for a further 20 minutes, and then transfer the supernatant as described above.

15. (*Optional*) If the supernatant contains visible strings of genomic chromatin or flocculent precipitate of proteins, filter it through 4-ply gauze before proceeding (Huang and Campbell 1993).

Recovery of Plasmid DNA

16. Measure the volume of the supernatant. Transfer the supernatant, together with 0.6 volume of isopropanol, to a fresh centrifuge tube(s). Store the tube(s) for 10 minutes at room temperature, after mixing the contents well.

17. Recover the precipitated nucleic acids by centrifugation at 12,000g (10,000 rpm in a Sorvall SS-34 rotor) for 15 minutes at *room temperature.*

    Salt may precipitate if centrifugation is carried out at 4ºC.

18. Decant the supernatant carefully, and invert the open tube(s) on a paper towel to allow the last drops of supernatant to drain away. Rinse the pellet and the walls of the tube(s) with 70% ethanol at room temperature. Drain off the ethanol, and use a Pasteur pipette attached to a vacuum line to remove any beads of liquid that adhere to the walls of the tube(s). Place the inverted, open tube(s) on a pad of paper towels for a few minutes at room temperature until no trace of ethanol is visible. At this stage, the pellet should still be damp.

19. Dissolve the pellet of nucleic acid in 3 ml of TE (pH 8.0).

20. Purify the crude plasmid DNA either by chromatography on commercial resins (please see Protocol 9), precipitation with polyethylene glycol (Protocol 8), or equilibrium centrifugation in CsCl-ethidium bromide gradients (Protocols 10 and 11).

21. Check the structure of the plasmid by restriction enzyme digestion followed by gel electrophoresis.

The typical yield of high-copy-number plasmid vectors or of amplified low-copy-number vectors prepared by this method is ~3–5 µg of DNA/ml of original bacterial culture. The yield of recombinant plasmids containing inserts of foreign DNA is usually slightly lower, depending on the size and nature of the cloned DNA fragment. Yields of ≤1.0 µg/ml indicate that the plasmid DNA is toxic to *E. coli*; the complete absence of DNA indicates that the plasmid has been lost during extraction and purification. The first problem can often be solved by switching to a low-copy-number vector and/or to a vector that carries prokaryotic transcriptional termination signals. The second problem is often the result of accidental loss of the plasmid DNA pellet after ethanol precipitation. It also occurs when the recombinant plasmid is large enough to be precipitated together with the chromosomal DNA after boiling. Such a large plasmid will also be susceptible to breakage during extraction and purification. This difficulty can solved by using a more gentle procedure of cell lysis, such as that described in Protocol 7.

Protocol 6

Preparation of Plasmid DNA: Toothpick Minipreparations

PLASMID DNA CAN BE PREPARED DIRECTLY FROM BACTERIAL COLONIES plucked from the surface of agar media with toothpicks. The closed circular DNA is too dirty to be used as a substrate for most restriction enzymes. However, the toothpick method can be used to identify bacterial colonies containing recombinant plasmids after transformation, to estimate the size of the plasmids in individual transformants by agarose gel electrophoresis, and to compare the copy number of different plasmids in the same host. The nature of the insert in putative recombinant plasmids can be confirmed by Southern hybridization (please see Chapter 6, Protocol 10) and by polymerase chain reaction (PCR) (please see Chapter 8, Protocol 12).

The simple procedure described below, a modification of the method of Barnes (1977), works best with large colonies (2–3 mm diameter) and yields enough DNA to load on a single lane of an agarose gel.

In addition to Wayne Barnes' "toothpick assay," the January 28, 1977 issue of *Science* printed an apocryphal warning to would-be gene splicers of the time. On page 378, Nicholas Wade, in his best sensational style, tells of three "near disasters" in molecular cloning in which, horror of horrors, an *E. coli* with a plasmid containing a cellulase gene, a hybrid adenovirus-SV40, and an *E. coli* with a plasmid containing the SV40 genome were, or almost were, constructed. Looking back, we observe that all of these "potentially grave hazards" were later constructed in the laboratory without incident, and each provided unique insight into biotechnology, virology, oncology, and molecular cloning. It seems entirely appropriate that Barnes' assay continues to be useful while Wade's imaginary monsters have been long since laid to rest.

MATERIALS

CAUTION: Please see Appendix 12 for appropriate handling of materials marked with <!>.

Buffers and Solutions

Please see Appendix 1 for components of stock solutions, buffers, and reagents.
Dilute stock solutions to the appropriate concentrations.

Antibiotic for plasmid selection
Bromophenol blue solution (0.4% w/v)
or
Cresol red solution (10 mM)
    Please see Step 10.
EDTA (0.5 M, pH 8.0)

Ethidium bromide (10 mg/ml) <!>
or
SYBR Gold <!>
KCl (4 M)
NSS solution
> 0.2 N NaOH
> 0.5% SDS
> 20% sucrose
>
> This solution should be made fresh for each use. Store the solution at room temperature until it is required. Discard any NSS solution that remains unused.

Gels

Agarose gel (0.7%, 5-mm thick), cast in Tris-borate buffer or in Tris-acetate buffer without ethidium bromide
> When only a small difference in size is anticipated among plasmids, the agarose gel should be cast and run in Tris-acetate electrophoresis buffer (TAE; please see Chapter 5, Protocol 1), because of its superior ability to resolve superhelical DNAs of different sizes. Otherwise, Tris-borate-EDTA (TBE) is the better choice because of its higher buffering capacity.

Agarose gel
> Please see Step 14.

Media

LB, YT, or SOB (rich broth for growing E. coli)
LB, YT, or SOB agar plates containing the appropriate antibiotic

Special Equipment

Thermal cycler
Water bath preset to 70°C
Wooden toothpicks

Additional Reagents

Step 12 of this protocol requires the reagents listed in Chapter 8, Protocol 1.
Step 14 of this protocol requires the reagents listed in Protocol 1 or 4 of this chapter.

METHOD

Preparation of Cells

1. Grow bacterial colonies, transformed with recombinant plasmid, on rich agar medium (LB, YT, or SOB) containing the appropriate antibiotic until they are ~2–3 mm in diameter (~18–24 hours at 37°C for most bacterial strains).

2. Use a sterile toothpick or disposable loop to transfer a small segment of a bacterial colony to a streak or patch on a master agar plate containing the appropriate antibiotic. Transfer the remainder of the colony to a numbered microfuge tube containing 50 μl of sterile 10 mM EDTA (pH 8.0).

   > In addition to the colonies under test, transfer a number of colonies containing the "empty," nonrecombinant plasmid vector. These samples are used as markers in gel electrophoresis (please see Step 11).

3. Repeat Step 2 until the desired number of colonies has been harvested.

4. When all of the colonies have been replicated and transferred, incubate the master plate for several hours at 37°C and then store it at 4°C until the results of the gel electrophoresis (Step

11 of this protocol) are available. Colonies containing plasmids of the desired size can then be recovered from the master plate.

5. While the master plate is incubating, process the bacterial suspensions as follows: To each microfuge tube in turn, add 50 µl of a freshly made solution of NSS. Close the top of the tubes and then mix their contents by vortexing for 30 seconds.

6. Transfer the tubes to a 70°C water bath. Incubate the tubes for 5 minutes and then allow them to cool to room temperature.

7. To each tube, add 1.5 µl of a solution of 4 M KCl. Vortex the tubes for 30 seconds.

8. Incubate the tubes for 5 minutes on ice.

9. Remove bacterial debris by centrifugation at maximum speed for 3 minutes at 4°C in a microfuge.

Analysis of Plasmids by Gel Electrophoresis

10. Transfer each of the supernatants in turn to fresh microfuge tubes. Add to each tube 0.5 µl of a solution containing 0.4% bromophenol blue if the samples are to be analyzed only by agarose gel electrophoresis *or* 2 µl of 10 mM cresol red if the samples are to be analyzed both by PCR and by agarose gel electrophoresis. Load 50 µl of the supernatant into a slot (5 mm in length × 2.5 mm in width) cast in a 0.7% agarose gel (5 mm thick).

    The agarose gel is poured and run in the absence of ethidium bromide because the rate of migration of superhelical DNA in the absence of ethidium bromide reflects its molecular weight more faithfully than its rate of migration in the presence of the intercalating dye. This simplifies the task of distinguishing among plasmids of different sizes.

11. After the bromophenol blue dye has migrated two-thirds to three-fourths the length of the gel, or the cresol red dye about one-half the length of the gel, stain the gel by soaking it for 30–45 minutes in a solution of ethidium bromide (0.5 µg/ml in H_2O) at room temperature. Examine and photograph the gel under UV illumination.

    More sensitive dyes such as SYBR Gold (Molecular Probes) can be used to stain the agarose gel after electrophoresis when working with low-copy-number plasmids (please see Chapter 5, Protocol 1). For more information, please see the discussion on SYBR dyes in Appendix 9.

    > Colonies that contain a recombinant plasmid will yield bands of DNA that migrate through the agarose gel more slowly than the empty vector DNA. It is important to use as controls plasmids of known size that have been prepared by the toothpick method. Plasmids prepared by other methods are not reliable as controls because they will be dissolved in buffers of different ionic strengths and constitutions. The rate of migration of superhelical DNAs can be markedly affected by the ionic strength of the solution loaded into the wells of the gel.
    >
    > The pattern of bands can be quite complicated, consisting of superhelical, open circular, and linear forms of plasmid DNAs, in addition, perhaps, to traces of bacterial chromosomal DNA.

12. If cresol red has been used at Step 10, analyze the supernatants by performing PCR as described in Chapter 8, Protocol 1, using the remainder of each sample as a template.

    Cresol red (Merck Index) is orange to amber in acidic solutions (pH 2–3), yellow in solutions of pH 7.2, and red in alkaline solutions. In contrast to bromophenol blue and xylene cyanol, cresol red does not inhibit the thermostable DNA polymerase from *Thermus aquaticus* (*Taq* polymerase) (Hoppe et al. 1992). Thus, DNA solutions containing cresol red are viable templates in most amplification reactions. The dye migrates between xylene cyanol and bromophenol blue during agarose gel electrophoresis, with a size of ~300 bp in a 2% agarose gel (Hoppe et al. 1992). Cresol red does not produce a shadow on photographs of agarose gels stained with ethidium bromide.

13. Prepare small-scale cultures of the putative recombinant clones by inoculating 2 ml of liquid medium (LB, YT, or SOB) containing the appropriate antibiotic with bacteria growing on the master plate.

    It is not necessary to wait for florid growth of bacteria on the master plate. Even a faint opaque film of bacteria is sufficient to locate the desired isolates and to inoculate liquid cultures.

14. Use the small-scale bacterial cultures to generate minipreparations (please see Protocol 1 or 4) of the putative recombinant plasmids. Analyze the plasmid DNAs by digestion with restriction enzymes and agarose gel electrophoresis to confirm that they have the desired size and structure.

Protocol 7

Preparation of Plasmid DNA by Lysis with SDS

THIS GENTLE METHOD (ADAPTED FROM GODSON AND VAPNEK 1973) has advantages over the alkaline lysis and boiling methods when dealing with large plasmids (>15 kb). However, the price of lenity in this case is low yield: A significant fraction of the plasmid DNA becomes enmeshed in the cell debris and is lost at an early stage of the protocol.

MATERIALS

CAUTION: Please see Appendix 12 for appropriate handling of materials marked with <!>.

Buffers and Solutions

Please see Appendix 1 for components of stock solutions, buffers, and reagents. Dilute stock solutions to the appropriate concentrations.

Antibiotic for plasmid selection
Chloramphenicol (34 mg/ml) <!>
 Optional, please see Step 4. Please see the information panel on CHLORAMPHENICOL.
Chloroform <!>
EDTA (0.5 M, pH 8.0)
Ethanol
NaCl (5 M)
Phenol:chloroform (1:1, v/v) <!>
SDS (10% w/v)
STE, ice cold
TE (pH 8.0)
Tris-sucrose

Enzymes and Buffers

Lysozyme (10 mg/ml)
 Please see the information panel on LYSOZYMES.
Restriction endonucleases

Gels

Agarose gels
 Please see Steps 8 and 22.

Media

LB, YT, or Terrific Broth

Centrifuges and Rotors

Beckman type-50 ultracentrifuge rotor or equivalent with Oak Ridge plastic centrifuge tubes (30-ml screw cap, Nalgene)
Sorvall GSA rotor or equivalent

Special Equipment

Sturdy glass rod

Additional Reagents

Step 8 of this protocol requires the reagents listed in Protocol 1 or 4 of this chapter.
Step 21 of this protocol requires the reagents listed in Protocol 9 or 10 of this chapter.

METHOD

Preparation of Cells

1. Inoculate 30 ml of rich medium (LB, YT, or Terrific Broth) containing the appropriate antibiotic with a single transformed bacterial colony or with 0.1–1.0 ml of a late-log-phase culture grown from a single transformed colony.

2. Incubate the culture with vigorous shaking until the bacteria enters the late log phase of growth (i.e., an OD_{600} of ~0.6).

    To ensure that the culture is adequately aerated:

    - The volume of the culture flask should be at least four times greater than the volume of the bacterial culture.
    - The flask should be loosely capped.
    - The culture should be incubated with vigorous agitation.

3. Inoculate 500 ml of LB, YT, or Terrific Broth (prewarmed to 37ºC) containing the appropriate antibiotic in a 2-liter flask with 25 ml of the late-log-phase culture. Incubate the culture for ~2.5 hours at 37ºC with vigorous shaking (250 cycles/minute on a rotary shaker).

    The OD_{600} of the resulting culture should be ~0.4. The growth rates of various bacterial strains or of a single strain containing different plasmids will vary. Thus, in some cases, the culture may have to be incubated slightly longer or shorter than 2.5 hours to reach the desired optical density.

4. For relaxed plasmids with low or moderate copy numbers, add 2.5 ml of 34 mg/ml chloramphenicol. The final concentration of chloramphenicol in the culture should be 170 µg/ml.

    ▲ IMPORTANT For high-copy-number plasmids, do not add chloramphenicol.

5. Incubate the culture for a further 12–16 hours at 37ºC with vigorous shaking (250 cycles/minute on a rotary shaker)

6. Remove an aliquot (1–2 ml) of the bacterial culture to a fresh microfuge tube and store it at 4ºC. Harvest the remainder of the bacterial cells from the 500-ml culture by centrifugation at 2700g (4100 rpm in a Sorvall GSA rotor) for 15 minutes at 4ºC. Discard the supernatant. Stand the open centrifuge bottle in an inverted position to allow all of the supernatant to drain away.

7. Resuspend the bacterial pellet in 200 ml of ice-cold STE. Collect the bacterial cells by centrifugation as described in Step 6. Store the pellet of bacteria in the centrifuge bottle at −20°C.

8. Use one of the methods described in Protocol 1 or 4 to prepare plasmid DNA from the 1–2-ml aliquot of bacterial culture set aside in Step 6. Analyze the minipreparation plasmid DNA by digestion with the appropriate restriction enzyme(s) and agarose gel electrophoresis to ensure that the correct plasmid has been propagated in the large-scale culture.

    > This kind of control may seem a little overly compulsive. However, it provides valuable insurance against errors that may be difficult to retrieve and may cause considerable loss of time.

Lysis of Cells

9. Allow the frozen bacterial cell pellet from Step 7 to thaw at room temperature for 5–10 minutes. Resuspend the pellet in 10 ml of ice-cold Tris-sucrose solution. Transfer the suspension to a 30-ml plastic screw-cap tube.

10. Add 2 ml of a freshly prepared lysozyme solution (10 mg/ml) followed by 8 ml of 0.25 M EDTA (pH 8.0).

11. Mix the suspension by gently inverting the tube several times. Store the tube on ice for 10 minutes.

    > The combination of lysozyme and EDTA breaks down the bacterial cell walls and punctures the outer membrane. The resulting spheroplasts, although leaky, are stabilized by the isosmotic sucrose solution.

12. Add 4 ml of 10% SDS. Immediately mix the contents of the tube with a glass rod so as to disperse the solution of SDS evenly throughout the bacterial suspension. Be as gentle as possible to minimize shearing of the liberated chromosomal DNA.

13. As soon as mixing is completed, add 6 ml of 5 M NaCl (final concentration = 1 M). Again, use a glass rod to mix the contents of the tube gently but thoroughly. Place the tube on ice for at least 1 hour.

Recovery of Plasmid DNA

14. Remove high-molecular-weight DNA and bacterial debris by centrifugation at 71,000*g* (30,000 rpm in a Beckman Type 50 rotor) for 30 minutes at 4°C. Carefully transfer the supernatant to a 50-ml disposable plastic centrifuge tube. Discard the pellet.

    > If the bacterial debris does not form a tightly packed pellet, centrifuge again at 96,000*g* (35,000 rpm in a Beckman Type 50 rotor) for a further 20 minutes, and transfer as much of the supernatant as possible to a fresh tube. Discard the viscous liquid remaining in the centrifuge tube.

15. Extract the supernatant once with phenol:chloroform and once with chloroform.

16. Transfer the aqueous phase to a 250-ml centrifuge bottle. Add 2 volumes (~60 ml) of ethanol at room temperature. Mix the solution well. Store the solution for 1–2 hours at room temperature.

17. Recover the nucleic acids by centrifugation at 5000*g* (5500 rpm in a Sorvall GSA rotor or 5100 rpm in a Sorvall HS4 swing-out rotor) for 20 minutes at 4°C.

    > Swing-out (horizontal) rotors are better than angle rotors for this step, since they concentrate the nucleic acids on the bottom of the bottle rather than smearing them on the walls.

18. Discard the supernatant. Wash the pellet and sides of the centrifuge tube with 70% ethanol at room temperature and then centrifuge as in Step 17.

19. Discard as much of the ethanol as possible, and then invert the centrifuge bottle on a pad of paper towels to allow the last of the ethanol to drain away. Use a vacuum aspirator to remove droplets of ethanol from the walls of the centrifuge bottle. Stand the bottle in an inverted position until no trace of ethanol is visible. At this stage, the pellet should still be damp.

20. Dissolve the damp pellet of nucleic acid in 3 ml of TE (pH 8.0).

21. Purify the crude plasmid DNA either by chromatography on commercial resins (please see Protocol 9) or isopycnic centrifugation in CsCl-ethidium bromide gradients (please see Protocols 10 and 11).

    Large plasmids (>15 kb) are vulnerable to nicking during the several precipitation steps that are used in purification of plasmid DNA by polyethylene glycol.

22. Check the structure of the plasmid by restriction enzyme digestion followed by gel electrophoresis.

Protocol 8

Purification of Plasmid DNA by Precipitation with Polyethylene Glycol

THIS METHOD WAS ORIGINALLY DEVISED BY RICHARD TREISMAN (ICRF, London, United Kingdom) following the work of Lis (1980), who pioneered the use of polyethylene glycol (PEG) to fractionate DNAs of different sizes. Treisman's method is widely used to purify plasmid DNA prepared by the alkaline lysis method (Protocol 3). Crude preparations of plasmid DNA are first treated with lithium chloride to precipitate large RNAs and with RNase to digest smaller contaminating RNAs. A solution of PEG in high salt is then used to precipitate the large plasmid DNA selectively, leaving short RNA and DNA fragments in the supernatant. The precipitated plasmid DNA is purified by extraction with phenol:chloroform and ethanol precipitation. A modification of the Treisman procedure is described here in which a solution of PEG and $MgCl_2$ is used to precipitate the plasmid DNA (Nicoletti and Condorelli 1993). For further information, please see the information panel on **POLYETHYLENE GLYCOL**.

Precipitation with PEG/$MgCl_2$ differs from purification of plasmid DNAs by column chromatography (Protocol 9) and equilibrium centrifugation in CsCl-ethidium bromide gradients (Protocol 10) in one major respect: It does not efficiently separate nicked circular molecules from the closed circular form of plasmid DNA. The latter two protocols are the methods of choice for the purification of very large plasmids (>15 kb) that are vulnerable to nicking and closed circular plasmids that are to be used for biophysical measurements. However, plasmid DNA purified by PEG/$MgCl_2$ precipitation is suitable for all enzymatic reactions commonly used in molecular cloning (including DNA sequencing) and can also be used to transfect mammalian cells with high efficiency.

LITHIUM CHLORIDE

LiCl is a strong dehydrating reagent that lowers the solubility of RNA (Hearst and Vinograd 1961a,b) and strips proteins from chromatin (Kondo et al. 1979). Contaminating high-molecular-weight RNA and proteins can therefore be precipitated from crude plasmid preparations by high concentrations of LiCl and removed by low-speed centrifugation (e.g., please see Kondo et al. 1991). The use of LiCl as a selective precipitator of high-molecular-weight RNA was first reported in 1963 by Bob Williamson and colleagues (Barlow et al. 1963).

MATERIALS

CAUTION: Please see Appendix 12 for appropriate handling of materials marked with <!>.

Buffers and Solutions

Please see Appendix 1 for components of stock solutions, buffers, and reagents. Dilute stock solutions to the appropriate concentrations.

Chloroform <!>
Ethanol
Isopropanol
LiCl (5 M)
    Please see the panel on **LITHIUM CHLORIDE**.
PEG-MgCl$_2$ solution <!>
Phenol:chloroform (1:1, v/v) <!>
Sodium acetate (3 M, pH 5.2)
TE (pH 8.0)
TE (pH 8.0) containing 20 µg/ml RNase A

Nucleic Acids and Oligonucleotides

Crude plasmid preparation
    Use material from either Step 17 of Protocol 3 or Step 19 of Protocol 5 of this chapter.

Centrifuges and Rotors

Sorvall SS-34 or equivalent

Special Equipment

Ice water bath

METHOD

1. Transfer 3 ml of the crude large-scale plasmid preparation to a 15-ml Corex tube and chill the solution to 0°C in an ice bath.

2. Add 3 ml of an ice-cold solution of 5 M LiCl to the crude plasmid preparation, mix well, and centrifuge the solution at 12,000g (10,000 rpm in a Sorvall SS-34 rotor) for 10 minutes at 4°C.

3. Transfer the supernatant to a fresh 30-ml Corex tube. Add an equal volume of isopropanol. Mix well. Recover the precipitated nucleic acids by centrifugation at 12,000g (10,000 rpm in a Sorvall SS-34 rotor) for 10 minutes at room temperature.

4. Decant the supernatant carefully, and invert the open tube to allow the last drops of supernatant to drain away. Rinse the pellet and the walls of the tube with 70% ethanol at room temperature. Carefully discard the bulk of the ethanol, and then use a vacuum aspirator to remove any beads of liquid that adhere to the walls of the tube. Place the inverted, open tube on a pad of paper towels for a few minutes until no trace of ethanol is visible. At this stage, the pellet should still be damp.

5. Dissolve the damp pellet of nucleic acid in 500 µl of TE (pH 8.0) containing RNase A. Transfer the solution to a microfuge tube and store it for 30 minutes at room temperature.

6. Extract the plasmid-RNase mixture once with phenol:chloroform and once with chloroform.

7. Recover the DNA by standard ethanol precipitation.

8. Dissolve the pellet of plasmid DNA in 1 ml of sterile H_2O, and then add 0.5 ml of PEG-$MgCl_2$ solution.

9. Store the solution for ≥ 10 minutes at room temperature, and then collect the precipitated plasmid DNA by centrifugation at maximum speed for 20 minutes at room temperature in a microfuge.

10. Remove traces of PEG by resuspending the pellet of nucleic acid in 0.5 ml of 70% ethanol. Collect the nucleic acid by centrifugation at maximum speed for 5 minutes in a microfuge.

11. Remove the ethanol by aspiration and repeat Step 10. Following the second rinse, store the open tube on the bench for 10–20 minutes to allow the ethanol to evaporate.

12. Dissolve the damp pellet in 500 μl of TE (pH 8.0). Measure the OD_{260} of a 1:100 dilution in TE (pH 8.0) of the solution, and calculate the concentration of the plasmid DNA assuming that 1 OD_{260} = 50 μg of plasmid DNA/ml.

     For information on absorbtion spectroscopy of DNA, please see Appendix 8.

13. Store the DNA in aliquots at –20°C.

Protocol 9

Purification of Plasmid DNA
by Chromatography

DURING THE 1990S, MANY CLONERS — ESPECIALLY THE YOUNG — became addicted to commercially available chromatography resins used to purify plasmid DNA to near homogeneity. Their dependence on these resins, most of which come in the form of a kit, is a remarkable phenomenon. After all, isolation and purification of plasmid DNAs by conventional techniques are hardly intellectual challenges, and there is no convincing evidence that old-fashioned plasmid preparations are inferior to those emerging from the backend of a kit. Why, then, have cloners turned to expensive kits, whose components are largely unknown to them, in preference to well-tried, published methods that use simple ingredients? A small part of the answer must lie in the incessant advertising by manufacturers, whose aim is to persuade the gullible that they will become better scientists by using kits to purify their plasmids. These kits also play on the fear of failure. No one wants to screw up a routine plasmid preparation — so much better to avoid embarrassment by buying a kit and blaming the manufacturer if something goes wrong.

On the positive side, kits have changed for the better the way cloning in plasmids is done. In the old days, when dirty minipreparations of plasmids were the norm, vectors were routinely purified by buoyant density centrifugation in CsCl-ethidium bromide gradients; when enzymes to manipulate DNA were less reliable than they now are, the ability to generate fragments of DNA with desired termini and to join them accurately to plasmid vectors was an uncertain business; when the preparation of highly competent populations of *E. coli* was a form of alchemy, it was an achievement to generate even a modest number of putative recombinants. All too frequently, there was little difference between the numbers of transformed colonies generated by the vector alone and those obtained from ligation reactions. Transformants containing putative recombinant plasmids were routinely screened either by hybridization or by laborious manual analysis of many individual minipreparations. It was not uncommon in those days to process and analyze

There is never too great a distinction made between those who have paid for the tiniest step forward and those, incomparably more numerous, who have received a convenient, indifferent knowledge, a knowledge without ordeals.

The Trouble with Being Born
by E.M. Cioran

upward of 100 minipreparations before finding a transformant containing the clone of interest. At Cold Spring Harbor Laboratory, the record, established in 1981, stood at 168 minipreparations completed by one person in the course of a single day. Today, however, with the widespread use of kits, this is not a particularly impressive number.

Effort on this scale is no longer required or expected. Cloning — even of "difficult" constructs in plasmid vectors — goes much faster and is much more efficient. The development of high-copy-number vectors has eliminated much of the need to grow and process large-scale cultures. And because of the advent of kits, the quality of the DNA in minipreparations is so high that routine purification of plasmids by buoyant density centrifugation is no longer necessary or desirable. We describe here a general method for purifying plasmid DNA using chromatographic methods. The way to carry out this protocol is to buy a kit and use it according to the manufacturer's directions. For a further explanation of how these kits work, please read on.

The chromatography resins supplied in kits come in two general types: those that yield plasmid DNA sufficiently pure for enzymatic manipulation (e.g., PCR, restriction, and ligation) and prokaryotic cell transformation but not necessarily eukaryotic cell transfection, and those that yield quite pure plasmid DNA suitable for all of these purposes. Both types of resins can be used to purify DNA from crude lysates of bacteria prepared by methods described in Protocols 1 through 5 and in Protocol 7.

The chemical structures of most of the commercial resins are largely proprietary, which means that wily chemist colleagues cannot cheaply synthesize a large batch of resin for laboratory use (but please see Carter and Milton 1993; Boyle and Lew 1995). In general, the resins fall into two classes: those that use hydrophobic interactions to purify the nucleic acids and those that rely on mixed ion-exchange/adsorption interactions for purification (Table 1-6). The most popular resins for the generation of plasmid DNA for eukaryotic cell transfection utilize ion-exchange/adsorption interaction chromatography. The development of this class of resins is an interesting story.

It has been known since the 1950s that DNA binds in a reversible manner to silica in the presence of chaotropic salts. The interaction between double-stranded DNA and the silicate matrix is thought to be due to the dehydration of the phosphodiester backbone by chaotropic salts, which allows the exposed phosphate residues to adsorb to the silica. Once adsorbed, the double-stranded DNA remains in either a native or partially denatured (single-stranded) state and cannot be eluted from the matrix by solvents (e.g., 50% ethanol) that displace other biopolymers such as RNA and carbohydrate. However, when the immobilized DNA is rehydrated by washing with aqueous buffers (typically TE or H_2O), it can be quantitatively recovered in the column effluent. This body of basic research was exploited in the 1980s by chemists such as Chuck York at Promega, and by others at different molecular biology reagent companies, to develop the resins now commercially available.

The adsorption of double-stranded DNA to silica is independent of base composition and topology. These features of the resin make it ideal for the purification of circular plasmid DNAs and long linear DNA fragments. However, the interaction is length-dependent, and DNAs that are less than 100–200 bp in length adsorb poorly to the resin. For this reason, currently available silica-based chromatography reagents are not used for purifying small DNA fragments.

The amount of resin required for purification of plasmids depends on the amount of bacterial lysate. Thus, different kits are purchased for purification of plasmid DNA from small (1–10 ml), medium (10–100 ml), or large cultures (>100 ml). The resins are supplied either in bulk, from which they may be placed in a column or syringe for use in DNA purification, or prepacked into columns for immediate use. The chemical composition of the binding, washing, and elution buffers for a particular resin is supplied by the manufacturer. A money-saving alternative is to

TABLE 1-6 Commercially Available Resins and Their Uses

RESIN	MANUFACTURER	CHEMISTRY	USE	NOTES
Qiagen	Qiagen	macroporous silica gel, anion-exchange (DEAE)	transfection of eukaryotic cells[a]	some batch-to-batch variation; pH-sensitive
QIAprep	Qiagen	silica gel	enzymic manipulation[b]	different columns available for purification of double- or single-stranded DNAs
Wizard	Promega	silica particle	additional ethanol precipitation required for transfection of eukaryotic cells[a]	inexpensive, reproducible
FlexiPrep	Pharmacia	anion exchange	enzymic manipulation[b]	transfection requires further purification
Glass-Max	Life Technologies	silica matrix	enzymic manipulation[b]	minipreps only
GeniePrep	Ambion	hydrophobic interactions, glass fiber	enzymic manipulation[b]	miniprep only; made in Texas
Perfect Prep	Eppendorf 5 Prime	silica matrix	transfection of eukaryotic cells[a]	very fast; miniprep only
ClearCut Miniprep Kit	Stratagene	silica resin, hydrophobic interaction	enzymic manipulation[b]	can be used for miniprep plasmid or DNA fragment purification
Concert, rapid and high purity systems	Life Technologies	silica gel	enzymatic manipulation[b] and transfection of eukaryotic cells[a]	mini- and maxipreps
NucleoBond AX	Nest Group, Inc.	macroporous silica gel anion exchange	transfection of eukaryotic cells[a]	five column sizes; resin good for large DNA purification, including cosmids and P1 DNAs

[a]Plasmid DNA prepared using this resin is suitable for transfection of eukaryotic cells by one or more of the methods described in Chapter 16, for restriction enzyme digestion, for bacterial transformation, and for use as a template in PCR and DNA sequencing reactions. For transformation of less robust cell lines, such as B or T cells, or where problems are encountered, the use of endotoxin-free DNA is recommended. Endotoxin-free DNA purification kits are commercially available (e.g., Wizard PureFection from Promega).

[b]Plasmid DNA prepared using this resin is suitable for restriction enzyme digestion, for bacterial transformation, or for use as a template in PCR and DNA sequencing reactions. Transfection of cultured mammalian cells with this plasmid DNA usually requires additional purification steps.

purchase a resin in bulk, followed by preparation of the column buffers. Vacuum manifolds for use with prepacked columns that allow the simultaneous preparation of minipreparation plasmid DNA from as many as 96 bacterial cultures are available from several companies.

Individual manufacturers supply detailed protocols for use with a particular resin. Because the binding and elution of plasmid DNA depend on the structure and derivatization of the resin, the manufacturers' instructions should be followed to the letter.

Table 1-6 summarizes some of the salient features of the commercial resins currently available for plasmid purification.

Protocol 10

Purification of Closed Circular DNA by Equilibrium Centrifugation in CsCl-Ethidium Bromide Gradients: Continuous Gradients

$\mathbf{S}$EPARATION OF PLASMID AND CHROMOSOMAL DNAs by buoyant density centrifugation gradients containing cesium chloride and ethidium bromide depends on differences between the amounts of ethidium bromide that can be bound to linear and closed circular DNA molecules (please see the information panel on **CESIUM CHLORIDE**).

For many years, equilibrium centrifugation in CsCl-ethidium bromide gradients was the method of choice to prepare large amounts of plasmid DNA. However, this process is expensive and time-consuming, and many alternative methods have been developed, including differential precipitation (Protocol 8) and column chromatography (Protocol 9). Nevertheless, traditionalists, of whom there are many, still believe that plasmids purified by banding in CsCl-ethidium bromide gradients are the purest and best DNAs for molecular biological experiments. Closed circular DNAs prepared by isopycnic centrifugation in CsCl-ethidium bromide gradients are contaminated by small fragments of DNA and RNA derived from the host bacteria. These small fragments take far longer to reach equilibrium in CsCl-ethidium bromide gradients than the larger plasmid DNAs. Hence, when molecules of closed circular DNA are at equilibrium, small fragments are still fairly evenly distributed throughout the gradient. This problem can be solved by abandoning CsCl-ethidium gradients and purifying plasmids by chromatography on commercial resins (Schleef and Heimann 1993), or it can be alleviated by subjecting closed circular plasmid DNA recovered from one CsCl-ethidium gradient to a second cycle of equilibrium centrifugation.

In another method, known as discontinuous CsCl gradient centrifugation (please see Protocol 11), three solutions containing different concentrations of CsCl are layered into the centrifuge tube. During subsequent centrifugation, the CsCl gradient forms more quickly, which allows the centrifugation time to be reduced to 6 hours. The resolution of closed circular plasmid DNAs from chromosomal and open circular plasmid DNAs is not quite as good in discontinuous CsCl gradients as in continuous gradients.

In the procedure for continuous gradients, described below, ethidium bromide and crude plasmid DNA are mixed with a CsCl solution of density ρ = ~1.55. When the mixture is centrifuged at high speed, the centrifugal force is sufficient to generate and maintain a gradient of cesium atoms. During formation of the gradient, DNAs of different buoyant densities migrate to positions in the tube at which the density of the surrounding CsCl solution equals that of the DNA itself. In earlier technology, long (24–48 hours) centrifuge times were required to bring the gradient to equilibrium. However, in modern vertical-tube rotors with their high g forces and small radii, self-forming gradients develop much more quickly than in older and slower fixed-angle rotors.

MATERIALS

CAUTION: Please see Appendix 12 for appropriate handling of materials marked with <!>.

Buffers and Solutions

Please see Appendix 1 for components of stock solutions, buffers, and reagents. Dilute stock solutions to the appropriate concentrations.

CsCl (solid)
CsCl rebanding solution
    Optional, please see Steps 4 and 8.
Ethanol
Ethidium bromide (10 mg/ml) <!>
Paraffin oil

Nucleic Acids and Oligonucleotides

Crude plasmid preparation
    Use material from either Step 17 of Protocol 3, Step 19 of Protocol 5, or Step 20 of Protocol 7 of this chapter.

Centrifuges and Rotors

Sorvall SS-34 rotor or equivalent
Ultracentrifuge rotor (vertical rotors are preferred) and tubes
    For example, Beckman VTi65; angle Ti50, Ti65, or Ti70 rotors or their Sorvall equivalents are acceptable if centrifuge time is not a limiting factor. Use a Quick-seal polyallomer tube or equivalent.

Special Equipment

Hypodermic needle (21 gauge)
Pasteur pipette or a disposable syringe fitted with a large-gauge needle
Refractometer (optional)
    Although not essential, a refractometer is extremely useful for estimating the density of CsCl solutions.
Syringe (5–10 cc) disposable, fitted with a sterile 18-gauge hypodermic needle

Additional Reagents

Step 8 of this protocol requires the reagents listed in Protocol 12 or 13 of this chapter.

METHOD

1. Measure the mass of the crude plasmid DNA preparation. Measurement is best done by transferring the solution into a fresh tube that has been tared on a top-loading balance. For every gram of plasmid DNA solution, add exactly 1.01 g of solid CsCl. Close the top of the tube to prevent evaporation and then warm the solution to 30ºC to facilitate the dissolution of the CsCl salt. Mix the solution gently until the salt is dissolved.

    As a rule of thumb, the crude plasmid preparation from no more than 50 ml of an overnight culture should be used per gradient. As vertical tubes for the Beckman VTi65.2 rotor can accommodate ~5 ml of CsCl-ethidium bromide solution, the crude plasmid preparation from 50-ml cultures should be reconstituted in ~3 ml of TE (pH 8.0).

2. Add 100 µl of 10 mg/ml ethidium bromide for each 5 g of original DNA solution.

    The final density of the solution should be ~1.55 g/ml (refractive index = 1.3860), and the concentration of ethidium bromide should be ~200 µg/ml. In the past, much larger amounts of ethidium bromide were used (Radloff et al. 1967). These were thought to be necessary to achieve saturating binding of the drug to closed circular DNA and linear DNAs. However, high concentrations of unbound ethidium bromide may obscure faint bands of DNA to such an extent that UV illumination is required for visualization. Recently, lower concentrations of ethidium bromide have been used successfully, allowing bands of DNA to be seen in visible light (e.g., please see Good and Nazar 1995). However, problems can arise if gradients containing lower concentrations of ethidium bromide are overloaded with nucleic acids. In this case, there may not be sufficient drug to achieve saturation binding to closed circular DNA and linear DNAs. Because most of the ethidium bromide in CsCl-ethidium bromide gradients binds not to DNA but to bacterial RNA present in the crude preparation of plasmid DNA, this problem can be solved by treating the preparation with DNase-free RNase before ultracentrifugation. This treatment is not usually necessary if the crude plasmid preparation from a 50-ml bacterial culture is reconstituted in ~3 ml of TE (pH 8.0) and used to prepare a single 5-ml CsCl-ethidium bromide gradient.

3. If Corex glass tubes are used, centrifuge the solution at 7700*g* (8000 rpm in a Sorvall SS-34 rotor) for 5 minutes at room temperature. If disposable polypropylene tubes are used, centrifuge at 1100*g* (3000 rpm in a Sorvall SS-34 rotor) for 10 minutes.

   The dark red scummy precipitate that floats to the top of the centrifuge tube consists of complexes formed between the ethidium bromide and bacterial proteins. The pellet at the bottom of the tube consists of larger chunks of bacterial debris, resulting from the lysis of the host bacteria by SDS and/or heat. These unappetizing delicacies are commonly encountered when the host bacteria are lysed by SDS or by the boiling procedure. Smaller amounts of debris are visible in alkaline lysates.

4. Use a Pasteur pipette or a disposable syringe fitted with a large-gauge needle to transfer the clear, red solution under the scum and above the pellet to a tube suitable for centrifugation in an ultracentrifuge rotor. Top off the partially filled centrifuge tubes with light paraffin oil or rebanding solution. Make sure that the weights of tubes opposite each other in the rotor are equal. Seal the tubes according to the manufacturer's instructions.

   Make a note of the DNA samples loaded into each numbered place in the rotor.

5. Centrifuge the density gradients at 20°C as appropriate for the rotor:

Beckman NVT 65 rotor	366,000*g* (62,000 rpm)	for 6 hours
Beckman VTi65 rotor	194,000*g* (45,000 rpm)	for 16 hours
Beckman Type 50Ti rotor	180,000*g* (45,000 rpm)	for 48 hours
Beckman Type 65Ti rotor	314,000*g* (60,000 rpm)	for 24 hours
Beckman Type 70.1Ti rotor	331,000*g* (60,000 rpm)	for 24 hours

6. At the end of the centrifuge run, gently remove the rotor from the centrifuge and place it on a flat surface. Carefully remove each tube and place it in a test tube rack covered with tin foil. In a dimly lit room (i.e., with the overhead fluorescent lights turned off), mount one tube in a clamp attached to a ring stand as shown in Figure 1-8.

   Two bands of DNA, located in the center of the gradient, should be visible in ordinary light (please see Figure 1-8). The upper band, which usually contains less material, consists of linear bacterial (chromosomal) DNA and nicked circular plasmid DNA; the lower band consists of closed circular plasmid DNA. The deep-red pellet on the bottom of the tube consists of ethidium bromide/RNA complexes. The material between the CsCl solution and the paraffin oil is protein.

   In cases where the yield of plasmid DNA is low, a hand-held, long-wavelength UV lamp can be used to visualize the DNA after centrifugation. The lamp is mounted with a clamp on the same ring stand used to support the centrifuge tube containing the separated DNAs. Shining UV light on the tube will cause the ethidium bromide-DNA complexes to fluoresce a bright orange, thereby facilitating their withdrawal with the needle/syringe. If a lamp is used, then the plasmid DNA should be retrieved as quickly as possible since excess exposure of the plasmid DNA to UV light will damage the DNA. In addition, wear a face shield to protect the eyes from damage by UV light. Whereas long-wavelength UV irradiation causes less damage to DNA than shorter wavelength, it is potent enough to still cause injury to the eyes.

7. Collect the band of closed circular DNA (please see Figure 1-8).

   a. Use a 21-gauge hypodermic needle to make a small hole in the top of the tube to allow air to enter when fluid is withdrawn (Figure 1-8A).

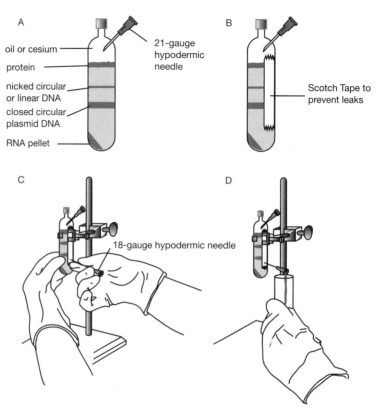

FIGURE 1-8 Collection of Superhelical Plasmid DNA from CsCl Gradients Containing Ethidium Bromide

Please see Step 7 for details.

b. Carefully wipe the outside of the tube with ethanol to remove any grease or oil, and then attach a piece of Scotch Tape or Time tape to the outside of the tube (Figure 1-8B)

> The tape will act as a seal to reduce leaks after needle puncture.

c. Attach a 5–10-cc disposable syringe to a sterile 18-gauge hypodermic needle and insert the needle (beveled side up) into the tube through the tape so that the open, beveled side of the needle is positioned just below the lower DNA band (closed circular plasmid DNA; Figure 1-8C).

d. Slowly withdraw the plasmid DNA, taking care not to disturb the upper viscous band of chromosomal DNA (Figure 1-8D)

> To avoid contamination with the chromosomal DNA, do not attempt to remove every visible trace of closed circular plasmid DNA from the gradient.

> Some investigators prefer to remove the upper DNA band before removing the lower closed circular plasmid DNA band. This can be tricky, as the viscous, high-molecular-weight chromosomal DNA in the upper band can enmesh the closed circular plasmid DNA and drag it from the tube.

8. Remove ethidium bromide from the DNA as described in one of the methods presented in Protocols 12 and 13.

> Some diehards reband their closed circular DNA in an effort to reduce contamination of the band of closed circular DNA with fragments of chromosomal DNA and RNA. To reband the plasmid DNA, slowly transfer the contents of the syringe to a fresh Quick-seal polyallomer centrifugation tube and fill the tube with CsCl rebanding solution. Seal the tube, repeat the centrifugation, and recover the closed circular plasmid DNA as described in Steps 5 through 7 above. Remove ethidium bromide from the DNA as described in Protocol 12 or 13.

Protocol 11

Purification of Closed Circular DNA by Equilibrium Centrifugation in CsCl-Ethidium Bromide Gradients: Discontinuous Gradients

FOR CENTRIFUGATION THROUGH DISCONTINUOUS OR PREFORMED CsCl gradients, solutions containing different concentrations of CsCl are layered into the centrifuge tube. The sample can be in the middle layer (three-step gradient) or the bottom layer (two-step gradient). During subsequent centrifugation, the DNA finds its isopycnic point during formation of the gradient, which allows the centrifugation time to be greatly reduced. For further information on cesium chloride, please see the information panel on CESIUM CHLORIDE.

Because discontinuous gradients do not come to true equilibrium, the resolution of closed circular plasmid DNAs from chromosomal DNA is not as high as in self-forming gradients (please see Protocol 10). In general, three-step gradients give better results in a shorter time than two-step gradients (Dorin and Bornecque 1995).

MATERIALS

CAUTION: Please see Appendix 12 for appropriate handling of materials marked with <!>.

Buffers and Solutions

Please see Appendix 1 for components of stock solutions, buffers, and reagents. Dilute stock solutions to the appropriate concentrations.

CsCl (solid)
CsCl layers for a three-step discontinuous gradient
   Prepare the layers for a three-step gradient as described in Table 1-7.
Ethidium bromide (10 mg/ml) <!>
TE (pH 8.0)

Nucleic Acids and Oligonucleotides

Crude plasmid preparation
   Use material from either Step 16 of Protocol 3, Step 18 of Protocol 5, or Step 19 of Protocol 7 of this chapter.
   As a rule of thumb, the crude plasmid DNA prepared from no more than 50 ml of an overnight culture should be used per gradient. The crude plasmid preparation from a 100-ml culture should be reconstituted in ~0.9 ml of TE (pH 8.0), which is enough to form the middle layer of two discontinuous gradients.

TABLE 1-7 Three-step Discontinuous Gradient Layers

LAYER	MOLARITY CsCL (w/w)	REFRACTIVE INDEX	PREPARATION[a]
Top layer	2.806 (35%)	1.3670	Dissolve 4.720 g of CsCl in 8 ml of TE (pH 8.0). Adjust the volume to exactly 10 ml. Then add 120 µl of 10 mg/ml ethidium bromide.
Middle layer	3.870 (44%)	1.3792	Dissolve 0.8 g of CsCl in exactly 1 ml of the crude DNA preparation. Then add 30 µl of 10 mg/ml ethidium bromide.
Bottom layer	6.180 (59%)	1.4052	Dissolve 10.4 g of CsCl in 7 ml of TE. Adjust the volume to exactly 10 ml. Then add 120 µl of 10 mg/ml ethidium bromide.

[a]Molecular biology grade CsCl is available in solid form from several commercial manufacturers.

Special Equipment

Hypodermic needle (21 gauge)

Refractometer (optional)
Although not essential, a refractometer is extremely useful for estimating the density of CsCl solutions.

Syringes (3 cc, 5 cc, and 5–10 cc) fitted with 18-gauge bone marrow (10 cm) needles

Tuberculin syringe (1 cc) fitted with an 18-gauge bone marrow (10 cm) needle

Centrifuges and Rotors

Ultracentrifuge rotor and tubes
Beckman Type 70.1Ti or Sorvall 65.13 with 5-ml or 10-ml polyallomer ultracentrifuge tubes (Beckman Quick-Seal or equivalent).

Additional Reagents

Step 6 of this protocol requires the reagents listed in Protocol 12 or 13 of this chapter.

METHOD

1. Use a 3-cc hypodermic syringe equipped with an 18-gauge bone marrow (10 cm) needle to transfer 1.5 ml of the top layer (35%) CsCl solution to a 5-ml polyallomer ultracentrifuge tube (Beckman Quick-Seal or equivalent).

2. Use a 1-cc tuberculin syringe equipped with an 18-gauge bone marrow (10 cm) needle to layer 0.5 ml of the middle layer (44%) CsCl solution, containing the plasmid DNA, into the bottom of the tube *under* the top layer solution.

3. Use a 5-cc hypodermic syringe equipped with an 18-gauge bone marrow (10 cm) needle to fill the tube by layering the bottom layer (59%) CsCl solution *under* the middle layer CsCl solution.

4. Centrifuge the sealed tubes at 330,000*g* (60,000 rpm in a Beckman Type 70.1Ti rotor) for 5 hours. Make sure that the weights of tubes opposite each other in the rotor are equal. Seal the tubes according to the manufacturer's instructions.

The use of a centrifuge and rotor capable of higher speeds can reduce the centrifugation time still further. For example, in a VTi90 rotor in a Beckman Xl-90, only 20 minutes of centrifugation is needed.

5. Collect the band of closed circular DNA (Figure 1-8, p. 1.68):

   a. Use a 21-gauge hypodermic needle to make a small hole in the top of the tube to allow air to enter when fluid is withdrawn.

   b. Carefully wipe the outside of the tube with ethanol to remove any grease or oil, and then attach a piece of Scotch Tape or Time tape to the outside of the tube.

      The tape will act as a seal to reduce leaks after needle puncture.

   c. Attach a 5–10-cc disposable syringe to a sterile 18-gauge hypodermic needle and insert the needle (beveled side up) into the tube through the tape so that the open, beveled side of the needle is positioned just below the lower DNA band (closed circular plasmid DNA).

   d. Slowly withdraw the plasmid DNA, taking care not to disturb the upper viscous band of chromosomal DNA.

      To avoid contamination with the chromosomal DNA, do not attempt to remove every visible trace of closed circular plasmid DNA from the gradient.

      Some investigators prefer to remove the upper DNA band before removing the lower closed circular plasmid DNA band. This can be tricky, as the viscous high-molecular-weight chromosomal DNA in the upper band can enmesh the closed circular plasmid DNA and drag it from the tube.

6. Remove ethidium bromide from the DNA as described in one of the methods presented in Protocol 12 or 13.

Protocol 12

Removal of Ethidium Bromide from DNA by Extraction with Organic Solvents

ETHIDIUM BROMIDE IS USUALLY REMOVED FROM DNA purified through a CsCl gradient by repeated extraction with organic solvents. The CsCl is subsequently removed by dialysis or by precipitation. Protocol 13 describes an alternative method for removal of CsCl by ion-exchange chromatography. The two methods are both highly effective in removing ethidium bromide from DNA purified by equilibrium centrifugation in CsCl-ethidium bromide gradients. For further information, please see the information panel on **ETHIDIUM BROMIDE**.

MATERIALS

CAUTION: Please see Appendix 12 for appropriate handling of materials marked with <!>.

Buffers and Solutions

Please see Appendix 1 for components of stock solutions, buffers, and reagents. Dilute stock solutions to the appropriate concentrations.

Ethanol
Isoamyl alcohol or n-butanol, saturated with H_2O <!>
   One or the other of these organic solvents is required to remove ethidium bromide from the DNA preparation after centrifugation.
Phenol <!>
   Optional, please see Step 13.
Phenol:chloroform (1:1 v/v) <!>
   Optional, please see Step 13.
TE (pH 8.0)

Nucleic Acids and Oligonucleotides

DNA sample, purified through CsCl gradient
   Use material from either Step 7 of Protocol 10 or Step 5 of Protocol 11 of this chapter.

Centrifuges and Rotors

Sorvall RT-6000 centrifuge with an HL-4 rotor and 50-ml buckets or equivalent
Sorvall SS-34 rotor or equivalent

Special Equipment

Dialysis tubing and clips
or
Equipment for spin dialysis through a microconcentrator (Amicon)
   Optional, please see Step 6. For preparation of dialysis tubing, please see Appendix 8.

METHOD

Extraction of DNA Solution to Remove Ethidium Bromide

1. To the solution of DNA in a glass or polypropylene tube, add an equal volume of either water-saturated *n*-butanol or isoamyl alcohol. Close the cap of the tube tightly.

2. Mix the organic and aqueous phases by vortexing.

3. Centrifuge the mixture at 450*g* (1500 rpm in a Sorvall RT-6000 centrifuge with an HL-4 rotor and 50-ml buckets) for 3 minutes at room temperature or stand the solution at room temperature until the organic and aqueous phases have separated.

4. Use a Pasteur pipette to transfer the upper (organic) phase, which is now a beautiful deep pink color, to an appropriate waste container.

5. Repeat the extraction (Steps 1–4) four to six times until all the pink color disappears from both the aqueous phase and organic phases.

Removal of CsCl from the DNA Solution

6. Remove the CsCl from the DNA solution by ethanol precipitation (please follow Steps 7 through 12), by spin dialysis through a microconcentrator (Amicon), or by dialysis overnight (16 hours) against 2 liters of TE (pH 8.0) (change buffer frequently). If one of the latter two methods is used, then proceed to Step 13.

7. To precipitate the DNA from the CsCl-DNA solution, measure the volume of the CsCl solution, add three volumes of H_2O, and mix the solution well.

    This addition dilutes the CsCl and prevents precipitation of the salt by ethanol.

8. Add 8 volumes of ethanol (1 volume is equal to that of the CsCl-DNA solution prior to dilution with H_2O in Step 7) to the DNA solution and mix well. Store the mixture for at least 15 minutes at 4ºC.

    Higher recoveries of DNA can be realized if the precipitation reaction is allowed to occur overnight at 4ºC.

    ▲ IMPORTANT CsCl precipitates if the ethanolic solution of DNA is stored at –20ºC.

9. Collect the precipitate of DNA by centrifugation at 20,000*g* (13,000 rpm in a Sorvall SS-34 rotor) for 15 minutes at 4ºC.

10. Decant the supernatant to a fresh centrifuge tube. Add an equal volume of absolute ethanol to the supernatant. Store the mixture for at least 15 minutes at 4ºC and then collect the precipitate of DNA by centrifugation at 20,000*g* (13,000 rpm in a Sorvall SS-34 rotor) for 15 minutes.

    Not all of the plasmid DNA is recovered in the first precipitation, hence the addition of a second batch of ethanol (Hildeman and Muller 1997).

11. Wash the two DNA precipitates with 70% ethanol. Remove as much of the 70% ethanol as possible and then allow any remaining fluid to evaporate at room temperature.

12. Dissolve the precipitated DNA in 2 ml of H_2O or TE (pH 8.0).

    For DNA sequencing, the DNA should be dissolved in H_2O. TE (pH 8.0) is a better option if the DNA is to be stored for a long period of time.

13. If the resuspended DNA contains significant quantities of ethidium bromide, as judged from its color or its emission of fluorescence when illuminated by UV light, extract the solution once with phenol and once with phenol:chloroform, and then again precipitate the DNA with ethanol.

14. Measure the OD_{260} of the final solution of DNA, and calculate the concentration of DNA. Store the DNA in aliquots at -20ºC.

Protocol 13

Removal of Ethidium Bromide from DNA by Ion-exchange Chromatography

Ethidium bromide may be removed from DNA purified through a CsCl gradient by ion-exchange chromatography. The CsCl is subsequently removed by precipitation with ethanol. For an alternative method for removal of CsCl by repeated extraction with organic solvents, please see Protocol 12.

MATERIALS

CAUTION: Please see Appendix 12 for appropriate handling of materials marked with <!>.

Buffers and Solutions

Please see Appendix 1 for components of stock solutions, buffers, and reagents. Dilute stock solutions to the appropriate concentrations.

Ethanol
HCl (1 N) <!>
NaCl (5 M)
Phenol <!>
   Optional, please see Step 9.
Phenol:chloroform (1:1, v/v) <!>
   Optional, please see Step 9.
TE (pH 8.0)
TEN buffer
TEN buffer containing 0.2% sodium azide <!>

Nucleic Acids and Oligonucleotides

DNA sample, purified through CsCl gradient
   Use material from either Step 7 of Protocol 10 or Step 5 of Protocol 11 of this chapter.

Centrifuges and Rotors

Sorvall SS-34 rotor or equivalent

Special Equipment

Dowex AG50W-X8 (100–200 dry mesh size)
   Dowex AG50W-X8, a cation exchange resin, is available from Bio-Rad.

Glass wool
Refractometer (optional)
   Although not essential, a refractometer is extremely useful for estimating the density of CsCl solutions.

METHOD

1. Before using, equilibrate the Dowex AG50 resin:

   a. Stir ~20 g of Dowex AG50 in ~100 ml of 1 M NaCl for 5 minutes. Allow the resin to settle, and remove the supernatant by aspiration.

   b. Add ~100 ml of 1 N HCl, and stir the slurry for a further 5 minutes. Again allow the resin to settle, and remove the supernatant by aspiration.

   c. Continue the process with two washes with H_2O (100 ml each), followed by one wash with 100 ml of TEN buffer.

   d. Store the equilibrated resin at 4°C in TEN buffer containing 0.2% sodium azide.

2. Construct a 1-ml column of Dowex AG50 in a Pasteur pipette as shown in Figure 1-9.

3. Remove the buffer above the resin, and rinse the column with 2 column volumes of TE (pH 8.0). Apply the solution of DNA containing ethidium bromide and CsCl directly to the resin.

4. Immediately begin collecting the effluent from the column. After all of the DNA solution has entered the column, wash the resin with 1.2 column volumes of TE (pH 8.0) and continue to collect the eluate into a 30-ml Corex tube.

5. After the column has run dry, dilute the eluate with 2.5 column volumes of H_2O.

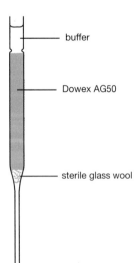

buffer

Dowex AG50

sterile glass wool

FIGURE 1-9 Removal of Ethidium Bromide from DNA by Chromatography through Dowex AG50

Please see Step 1 for details.

6. Precipitate the DNA by adding eight volumes of ethanol followed by incubation for 15 minutes at 4°C. Collect the DNA by centrifugation at 17,000g (12,000 rpm in a Sorvall SS-34 rotor) for 15 minutes at 4°C.

7. Decant the supernatant to a fresh centrifuge tube. Add an equal volume of absolute ethanol to the supernatant. Store the mixture for at least 15 minutes at 4°C and then collect the precipitate of DNA by centrifugation at 20,000g (13,000 rpm in a Sorvall SS-34 rotor) for 15 minutes.

   Not all of the plasmid DNA is recovered in the first precipitation, hence the addition of a second batch of ethanol (Hildeman and Muller 1997).

8. Wash the two DNA precipitates with 70% ethanol. Remove as much as possible of the 70% ethanol and then allow any remaining fluid to evaporate at room temperature.

9. Dissolve the precipitated DNA in 2 ml of H_2O or TE (pH 8.0).

   For DNA sequencing, the DNA should be dissolved in H_2O. TE (pH 8.0) is a better option if the DNA is to be stored for a long period of time.

10. If the resuspended DNA contains significant quantities of ethidium bromide, as judged from its color or its emission of fluorescence when illuminated by UV light, extract the solution once with phenol and once with phenol:chloroform, and then again precipitate the DNA with ethanol.

11. Measure the OD_{260} of the final solution of DNA, and calculate the concentration of DNA. Store the DNA in aliquots at –20°C.

Protocol 14

Removal of Small Fragments of Nucleic Acid from Preparations of Plasmid DNA by Centrifugation through NaCl

ROUTINE PREPARATIONS OF PLASMID DNA ARE CONTAMINATED to varying degrees by small fragments of RNA and DNA, derived either from the bacterial chromosome or from broken plasmid molecules. Although the weight of these contaminants is usually low, their number can be large and can contribute significantly to the total number of 5′ and 3′ termini in the preparation. For some purposes (e.g., digestion with BAL 31, labeling the 5′ termini of restriction enzyme fragments of plasmid DNA with bacteriophage T4 polynucleotide kinase, and adding tails to the 3′ termini with terminal transferase), it is essential to obtain DNA preparations that are free of low-molecular-weight contaminants. The absence of these components is also desirable when the DNA is to be used for sequencing and amplification by PCR. Plasmids purified by chromatography on commercial resins are usually contaminated to a lesser extent than plasmids prepared by the alkaline or boiling methods (e.g., please see Schleef and Heimann 1993).

Contamination by fragments of nucleic acids can be reduced to an acceptable level by centrifugation through 1 M sodium chloride. This method, designed to remove small fragments of RNA from plasmid preparations, was devised by Brian Seed when he was a student at Harvard University. For other methods to achieve these ends, please see Protocols 15 and 16.

MATERIALS

Buffers and Solutions

Please see Appendix 1 for components of stock solutions, buffers, and reagents. Dilute stock solutions to the appropriate concentrations.

Ethanol
NaCl (1 M) in TE (pH 8.0)
Sodium acetate (3 M, pH 5.2)
TE (pH 8.0)

Enzymes and Buffers

DNase-free Pancreatic RNase

Nucleic Acids and Oligonucleotides

DNA sample, purified through CsCl gradient
Use material from either Step 14 of Protocol 12 or Step 11 of Protocol 13 of this chapter.

Centrifuges and Rotors

Beckman SW50.1 rotor or equivalent with appropriate tubes
Sorvall SS-34 rotor or equivalent

METHOD

1. Measure the volume of the plasmid preparation. Add 0.1 volume of 3 M sodium acetate (pH 5.2) and 2 volumes of ethanol. Store the mixture for 30 minutes at 4°C.

2. Recover the precipitate of nucleic acids by centrifugation at >10,000g (>9100 rpm in a Sorvall SS-34 rotor) for 15 minutes at 4°C. Decant as much of the supernatant as possible, and then store the open tube on the bench for a few minutes to allow the ethanol to evaporate.

3. Dissolve the damp pellet in 0.5–1.0 ml of TE (pH 8.0).

   The concentration of the plasmid DNA should be ≥100 µg/ml.

4. Add DNase-free RNase to a final concentration fo 10 µg/ml. Incubate the mixture for 1 hour at room temperature.

5. Add 4 ml of 1 M NaCl in TE (pH 8.0) to a Beckman SW50.1 centrifuge tube (or its equivalent). Use an automatic pipette with a disposable tip to layer up to 1 ml of the plasmid preparation on top of the 1 M NaCl solution. If necessary, fill the tube with TE (pH 8.0).

6. Centrifuge the solution at 150,000g (40,000 rpm in a Beckman SW50.1 rotor) for 6 hours at 20°C. Carefully discard the supernatant.

   The plasmid DNA sediments to the bottom of the tube while the oligoribonucleotides and small fragments of DNA remain in the supernatant.

7. Dissolve the pellet of plasmid DNA in 0.5 ml of TE (pH 8.0). Add 50 µl of 3 M sodium acetate (pH 5.2), and transfer the DNA solution to a microfuge tube.

8. Precipitate the DNA by addition of 2 volumes of ethanol, and store the ethanolic solution for 10 minutes at 4°C. Recover the DNA by centrifugation at maximum speed for 15 minutes at 4°C in a microfuge. Decant as much of the supernatant as possible and then store the open tube on the bench for a few minutes to allow the ethanol to evaporate.

9. Dissolve the damp pellet of DNA in TE (pH 8.0).

Protocol 15

Removal of Small Fragments of Nucleic Acid from Preparations of Plasmid DNA by Chromatography through Sephacryl S-1000

CHROMATOGRAPHY THROUGH SEPHACRYL S-1000 is the method of choice to separate plasmid DNA from smaller species of nucleic acid (both DNA and RNA). This procedure for removal of small nucleic acids, originally obtained from F. DeNoto and H. Goodman at the Massachusetts General Hospital in Boston, is incorporated into a paper published by Gómez-Márquez et al. (1987). Because it is impossible to remove all traces of plasmid DNA from the column of Sephacryl S-1000, particularly in PCR, discard each column after use.

MATERIALS

CAUTION: Please see Appendix 12 for appropriate handling of materials marked with <!>.

Buffers and Solutions

Please see Appendix 1 for components of stock solutions, buffers, and reagents. Dilute stock solutions to the appropriate concentrations.

Bromophenol blue dye sucrose solution
Ethanol
Phenol <!>
Sephacryl equilibration buffer
Sodium acetate (3 M, pH 5.2)
TE (pH 8.0) containing 20 µg/ml RNase A

Gels

Agarose gel (0.7%) cast in TBE

Nucleic Acids and Oligonucleotides

DNA sample, purified through CsCl gradient
Use material from either Step 14 of Protocol 12 or Step 11 of Protocol 13 of this chapter.

Centrifuges and Rotors

Sorvall SS-34 rotor or equivalent

Special Equipment

Column (1 x 10 cm) for Sephacryl resin
Sephacryl S-1000 gel filtration resin (Pharmacia)

METHOD

1. Prepare a 1 x 10-cm column of Sephacryl S-1000, equilibrated in Sephacryl equilibration buffer.

   A column of this size can accommodate >2 mg of plasmid DNA in a volume of 0.5 ml.

2. Measure the volume of the plasmid preparation. Add 0.1 volume of 3 M sodium acetate (pH 5.2) and 2 volumes of ethanol. Store the mixture for 30 minutes at 4ºC.

3. Recover the precipitate of nucleic acids by centrifugation at >10,000*g* (>9100 rpm in a Sorvall SS-34 rotor) for 15 minutes at 4ºC. Drain off as much of the supernatant as possible, and then store the open tube on the bench for a few minutes to allow the ethanol to evaporate.

4. Dissolve the damp pellet of nucleic acids in a small volume (<400 μl) of TE (pH 8.0) containing RNase A at a final DNA concentration of at least 100 μg/ml.

5. Incubate the mixture for 1 hour at room temperature.

6. Extract the solution once with an equal volume of phenol equilibrated in TE (pH 8.0).

7. Recover the aqueous layer, and add 100 μl of bromophenol blue dye sucrose solution. Layer the blue aqueous phase on the column of Sephacryl S-1000.

8. Wash the DNA into the column, and apply a reservoir of Sephacryl equilibration buffer. Immediately begin collecting 0.5-ml fractions.

9. When 15 fractions have been collected, clamp off the bottom of the column. At this stage, the blue dye should have traveled about half the length of the column.

10. Analyze 10 μl of each fraction by electrophoresis through a 0.7% agarose gel or by ethidium bromide fluorescence (please see Appendix 9) to identify the fractions containing plasmid DNA.

11. Pool the fractions containing plasmid DNA, and recover the DNA by precipitation with 2 volumes of ethanol for 10 minutes at 4ºC and centrifugation at 10,000*g* (9200 rpm in a Sorvall SS-34 rotor) for 15 minutes at 4ºC.

12. Decant as much of the supernatant as possible, and then store the open tube on the bench for a few minutes to allow the ethanol to evaporate.

13. Dissolve the damp pellet in TE (pH 8.0).

Protocol 16

Removal of Small Fragments of Nucleic Acid from Preparations of Plasmid DNA by Precipitation with Lithium Chloride

IN THIS PROTOCOL, THE SEPARATION OF PLASMID DNA from smaller species of nucleic acid (both DNA and RNA) is based on the differential solubility of the two nucleic acids in solutions of lithium chloride (LiCl). LiCl is a strong dehydrating reagent that lowers the solubility of RNA (Hearst and Vinograd 1961a,b) and strips proteins from chromatin (Kondo et al. 1979). Contaminating high-molecular-weight RNA and proteins can therefore be precipitated from crude plasmid preparations by high concentrations of LiCl and removed by low-speed centrifugation (e.g., please see Kondo et al. 1991). The use of LiCl as a selective precipitator of high-molecular-weight RNA was first reported in 1963 by Bob Williamson and colleagues (Barlow et al. 1963).

MATERIALS

Buffers and Solutions

Please see Appendix 1 for components of stock solutions, buffers, and reagents. Dilute stock solutions to the appropriate concentrations.

Ethanol

Isopropanol

LiCl (4 M)

Sodium acetate (3 M, pH 5.2)

TE (pH 8.0)

TE (pH 8.0) containing 20 µg/ml RNase A

Nucleic Acids and Oligonucleotides

DNA sample, purified through CsCl gradient
Use material from either Step 14 of Protocol 12 or Step 11 of Protocol 13 of this chapter.

Centrifuges and Rotors

Sorvall SS-34 rotor or equivalent

METHOD

1. Measure the volume of the plasmid preparation. Add 0.1 volume of 3 M sodium acetate (pH 5.2) and 2 volumes of ethanol. Store the mixture for 30 minutes at 4°C.

2. Recover the precipitate of nucleic acids by centrifugation at >10,000*g* (>9100 rpm in a Sorvall SS-34 rotor) for 15 minutes at 4°C. Drain off as much of the supernatant as possible, and then store the open tube on the bench for a few minutes to allow the ethanol to evaporate.

3. Dissolve the damp pellet in 1 ml of TE (pH 8.0) containing RNase A at a concentration of ≥100 µg/ml.

4. Add 3 ml of 4 M LiCl solution. Incubate the mixture on ice for 30 minutes.

5. Separate the plasmid DNA from the precipitated nucleic acids by centrifugation at 12,000*g* (10,000 rpm in a Sorvall SS-34 rotor) for 15 minutes at 4°C.

6. Transfer the supernatant to a fresh centrifuge tube and add 6 ml of isopropanol. Allow the plasmid DNA to precipitate for 30 minutes at room temperature.

7. Recover the precipitated plasmid DNA by centrifugation at 12,000*g* (10,000 rpm in a Sorvall SS-34 rotor) for 15 minutes at 4°C.

8. Carefully remove the supernatant and add 5–10 ml of 70% ethanol to the tube. Vortex the tube briefly, and then recentrifuge at 12,000*g* for 10 minutes at 4°C.

9. Carefully remove the supernatant, and store the open tube on the bench top for a few minutes until the ethanol has evaporated.

10. Dissolve the damp pellet of DNA in TE (pH 8.0).

Protocol 17

Directional Cloning into Plasmid Vectors

Most plasmid vectors in common use contain multiple cloning sites that have recognition sequences for many different restriction enzymes. Given the large variety of multiple cloning sites currently available (as many as 46 unique sites are present in some polylinkers, e.g., pSE280 from Invitrogen; and still longer polylinkers have been assembled; Brosius 1992), it is almost always possible to find a vector carrying restriction sites that are compatible with the termini of a particular fragment of foreign DNA.

Directional cloning usually requires incompatible termini at the opposite ends of both vector and target DNAs. However, in certain circumstances, directional cloning can be achieved when both the target and plasmid DNAs carry identical termini at both ends. For example, the restriction enzymes *Bam*HI and *Bgl*II, which recognize different hexanucleotide sequences (GGATCC and AGATCT, respectively), generate restriction fragments with identical 3′ protruding termini. If a DNA fragment carrying *Bam*HI and *Bgl*II termini is ligated into a vector that has been cleaved with the same two enzymes, then the foreign DNA can be inserted in either orientation. However, if one of the two restriction enzymes is included in the ligation mixture, or if the enzyme is used to digest the ligated DNA before transformation, then only those ligation events in which the *Bam*HI end is joined to the *Bgl*II end and vice versa (which destroys the recognition sites of both enzymes) will give rise to recombinant products in *E. coli*. This strategy takes advantage of the observation that closed circular DNAs transform bacterial cells with a much higher frequency than linear DNAs. Variations on this theme can also be used to improve the efficiency of cloning blunt-ended DNAs (please see Protocol 19).

Occasionally, it is impossible find a suitable combination of vector, target DNA, and restriction enzymes that will allow directional cloning. There are several solutions to this problem:

- Synthetic linkers or adaptors can be ligated to the termini of the linearized plasmid and/or fragment of foreign DNA (for further details, please see Protocols 18 and 21 and the information panel on ADAPTORS).

- The fragment of foreign DNA can be amplified by PCR using oligonucleotide primers that add the desired restriction sites to one or both termini (please see Chapter 8).

- DNA fragments with recessed 3′ termini can be partially filled in controlled reactions using the Klenow fragment of *E. coli* DNA polymerase I (please see Figure 1-10). As discussed in Chapter 9, this procedure often generates complementary termini from restriction sites that are otherwise incompatible, thus facilitating ligation of the vector and foreign DNAs. Because partial filling eliminates the ability of termini on the same molecule to pair with one another, the fre-

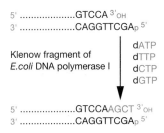

FIGURE 1-10 Filling of Recessed 3′ Termini by the Klenow Fragment of *E. coli* DNA Polymerase I

The Klenow fragment of *E. coli* DNA polymerase I catalyzes the template-directed addition of deoxynucleotide triphosphates to a recessed 3′-hydroxyl group. Synthesis occurs in a 5′→3′ direction until the recessed terminus is completely filled.

quencies of circularization and self-oligomerization during the ligation reaction are also reduced (Hung and Wensink 1984; Zabarovsky and Allikmets 1986). Keep in mind that micromolar concentrations of dATP can inhibit bacteriophage T4 DNA ligase. Thus, if dATP is used as a substrate in a partial end-filling reaction, the modified DNA product should be purified by spun-column chromatography or by two rounds of ethanol precipitation in the presence of ammonium acetate. This removes unincorporated dATP from the DNA preparation.

This protocol describes a standard procedure for cloning DNA fragments with protruding ends. Protocol 18 provides a method for attaching adaptors to a DNA fragment with protruding ends in order to introduce a particular restriction endonuclease recognition site. The slightly more difficult task of cloning blunt-end DNAs is presented in Protocol 19, whereas Protocol 20 describes methods for treating linearized plasmid DNA with alkaline phosphatases. For further details on ligation, please see the information panel on DNA LIGASES.

MATERIALS

CAUTION: Please see Appendix 12 for appropriate handling of materials marked with <!>.

Buffers and Solutions

Please see Appendix 1 for components of stock solutions, buffers, and reagents. Dilute stock solutions to the appropriate concentrations.

ATP (10 mM)
Ethanol
Phenol:chloroform (1:1, v/v) <!>
Sodium acetate (3 M, pH 5.2)
TE (pH 8.0)

Enzymes and Buffers

Bacteriophage T4 DNA ligase
Please see the information panel on DNA LIGASES.
Restriction endonucleases

Gels

Agarose gels
Optional, please see Steps 1, 2, and 4.
Polyacrylamide gel <!>
Optional, please see Step 2.

Nucleic Acids and Oligonucleotides

Vector DNA (plasmid)

Foreign or target DNA fragment

Adaptors may be added to the target DNA as described in Protocol 18 of this chapter.

Special Equipment

Equipment for spun-column chromatography

Water bath preset to 16°C

Additional Reagents

Step 7 of this protocol requires the reagents listed in Protocol 23, 24, 25, or 26 of this chapter.

METHOD

1. Digest the vector (10 μg) and foreign DNA with the two appropriate restriction enzymes.

    Closed circular plasmid vectors are prepared for directional cloning by digestion with two restriction enzymes that cleave at different sequences and generate different termini. Wherever possible, try to avoid using restriction enzymes that cleave within 12 bp of each other in the multiple cloning site. After one of these sites has been cleaved, the second site will be located too close to the end of the linear DNA to allow efficient cleavage by the second enzyme. An excellent tabulation of the efficiency with which different restriction enzymes cleave sites located near the ends of DNA molecules is presented in the Appendix of the New England Biolabs catalog (www.neb.com/neb/frame_tech.html).

    Read the manufacturer's instructions to determine if the two restriction enzymes work optimally in the same digestion buffer. If so, digestion of the vector DNA can be carried out simultaneously with both enzymes. If the two restriction enzymes require different buffers, it is best to carry out the digestions sequentially. In this case, the enzyme that prefers the lower concentration of salt should be used first. At the end of the reaction, analyze an aliquot of the DNA by gel electrophoresis to confirm that all of the plasmid DNA has been converted from circular to linear molecules. Then adjust the salt concentration appropriately and add the second enzyme.

2. Purify the digested foreign DNA by extraction with phenol:chloroform and standard ethanol precipitation.

    Depending on the experiment, it may be necessary or desirable to isolate the target fragment(s) of foreign DNA by neutral agarose or polyacrylamide gel electrophoresis as described in Chapter 5. This purification is generally done when there are many restriction fragments in the preparation of foreign DNA that can ligate to the vector. Rather than screening large numbers of transformants for the desired clone(s), many investigators prefer to enrich for the foreign sequences of interest before ligation, e.g., by agarose gel electrophoresis.

3. Purify the vector DNA by spun-column chromatography followed by standard ethanol precipitation.

    This procedure eliminates from the vector preparation the small fragment of DNA generated by digesting the plasmid at two closely spaced restriction sites within the multiple cloning site.

4. Reconstitute the precipitated DNAs separately in TE (pH 8.0) at a concentration of ~100 μg/ml. Calculate the concentration of the DNA (in pmole/ml), assuming that 1 bp has a mass of 660 daltons.

    Confirm the approximate concentration of the two DNAs by analyzing aliquots by agarose gel electophoresis.

5. Transfer appropriate amounts of the DNAs to sterile 0.5-ml microfuge tubes as follows:

Tube	DNA
A and D	vector (30 fmoles [~100 ng])
B	insert (foreign) (30 fmoles [~ 10 ng])
C and E	vector (30 fmoles) plus insert (foreign) (30 fmoles)
F	superhelical vector (3 fmoles [~10 ng])

The molar ratio of plasmid vector to insert DNA fragment should be ~1:1 in the ligation reaction. The final DNA concentration should be ~10 ng/μl.

a. To Tubes A, B, and C add:

10x Ligation buffer	1.0 μl
Bacteriophage T4 DNA ligase	0.1 Weiss unit
10 mM ATP	1.0 μl
H_2O	to 10 μl

b. To Tubes D and E, add:

10x Ligation buffer	1.0 μl
10 mM ATP	1.0 μl
H_2O	to 10 μl
no DNA ligase	

The DNA fragments can be added to the tubes together with the H_2O and then warmed to 45°C for 5 minutes to melt any cohesive termini that have reannealed during fragment preparation. Chill the DNA solution to 0°C before the remainder of the ligation reagents are added. To achieve the maximum efficiency of ligation, set up the reactions in as small a volume as possible (5–10 μl). Adding ATP as a component of the 10x ligation buffer leaves more volume for vector or foreign DNA in the reaction mixture. Some commercial ligase buffers contain ATP. When using such buffers, the addition of ATP is no longer required. For a definition of Weiss units, please see the information panel on **DNA LIGASES**.

6. Incubate the reaction mixtures overnight at 16°C or for 4 hours at 20°C.

7. Transform competent *E. coli* with dilutions of each of the ligation reactions as described in Protocol 23, 24, 25, or 26. As controls, include known amounts of a standard preparation of superhelical plasmid DNA to check the efficiency of transformation.

Tube	DNA	Ligase	Expected number of transformed colonies
A	vector	+	~0 (~10^4 fewer than Tube F)[1]
B	insert	+	0
C	vector and insert	+	~10-fold more than Tube A or D
D	vector	–	~0 (~10^4 fewer than Tube F)
E	vector and insert	–	some, but fewer than Tube C
F	superhelical vector	–	>2 x 10^5

[1]Transformants arising from ligation of vector DNA alone are due either to failure of one or both restriction endonucleases to digest the DNA to completion or to ligation of the vector to residual amounts of the small fragment of the multiple cloning site.

Protocol 18

Attaching Adaptors to Protruding Termini

PROTOCOL 17 IS EASILY MODIFIED TO ACCOMMODATE the addition of an adaptor to a DNA fragment with protruding ends. Adaptors may be purchased in both phosphorylated and unphosphorylated forms (i.e., with phosphate residues or hydroxyl groups at their 5′ termini; please see the information panel on ADAPTORS and Table 1-13. Because DNA ligase requires 5-phosphoryl termini, unphosphorylated adaptors must be modified before use by transferring the γ-phosphate from ATP to the 5′-hydroxyl group. This reaction is catalyzed by the bacteriophage-T4-encoded enzyme polynucleotide kinase. If phosphorylated adaptors are purchased, omit Step 1 (phosphorylation step) of the protocol, and begin with Step 2.

MATERIALS

CAUTION: Please see Appendix 12 for appropriate handling of materials marked with <!>.

Buffers and Solutions

Please see Appendix 1 for components of stock solutions, buffers, and reagents. Dilute stock solutions to the appropriate concentrations.

ATP (10 mM)
    Omit ATP from the ligation reaction in Step 2 if the ligation buffer contains ATP.
Ethanol
10x Linker kinase buffer
Phenol:chloroform (1:1, v/v) <!>
Sodium acetate (3 M, pH 5.2)
TE (pH 8.0)

Enzymes and Buffers

Bacteriophage T4 DNA ligase
    Please see the information panel on DNA LIGASES.
Polynucleotide kinase
Restriction endonucleases

Nucleic Acids and Oligonucleotides

Foreign or target DNA fragment
Synthetic oligonucleotide or adaptor dissolved in TE (pH 8.0) at a concentration of ~400 μg/ml.
    For a hexamer, this concentration is equivalent to a 50 μM solution.
    Adaptors are available from Stratagene. Please see the information panel on ADAPTORS.

Special Equipment

Equipment for spun-column chromatography (please see Appendix 8)
Water bath preset to 65°C

METHOD

1. To phosphorylate the adaptors, add to a sterile microfuge tube:

synthetic oligonucleotide or adaptor	0.5–2.0 µg, dissolved in TE (pH 8.0)
10x linker kinase buffer	1.0 µl
10 mM ATP	1.0 µl
H_2O	to 10 µl
bacteriophage T4 polynucleotide kinase	1.0 unit

   Incubate the reaction for 1 hour at 37°C.

   > There is no need to purify the phosphorylated adaptors: Aliquots of the reaction mixture can be transferred directly into ligation reactions.

2. To ligate the phophorylated adaptors to a DNA fragment with complementary protruding ends, set up a ligation reaction as follows:

DNA fragment	100–200 ng
phosphorylated adaptor	10–20-fold molar excess
10x ligation buffer	1.0 µl
bacteriophage T4 DNA ligase	0.1 Weiss unit
10 mM ATP	1.0 µl
H_2O	to 10 µl

   Incubate the ligation mixture for 6–16 hours at 4°C.

   > To achieve the maximum efficiency of ligation, set up the reactions in as small a volume as possible (5–10 µl). Adding ATP as a component of the 10x ligation buffer leaves more volume for vector or foreign DNA in the reaction mixture. Some commercial ligase buffers contain ATP. When using such buffers, the addition of ATP is not required.

3. Inactivate the DNA ligase by incubating the reaction mixture for 15 minutes at 65°C.

4. Dilute the ligation reaction with 10 µl of the appropriate 10x restriction enzyme buffer. Add sterile H_2O to a final volume of 100 µl followed by 50–100 units of restriction enzyme.

5. Incubate the reaction for 1–3 hours at 37°C.

   > The restriction enzyme catalyzes the removal of polymerized linkers from the ends of the DNA fragment and creates protruding termini. A huge amount of restriction enzyme is required to digest the large quantities of adaptors present in the reaction.

6. Extract the restriction digestion with phenol:chloroform and recover the DNA by standard ethanol precipitation.

7. Collect the precipitated DNA by centrifugation at maximum speed for 15 minutes at 4°C in a microfuge, and resuspend the DNA in 50 µl of TE (pH 8.0).

8. Pass the resuspended DNA through a spun column to remove excess adaptors and their cleavage products.

9. The modified DNA fragment can now be ligated to a plasmid vector with protruding ends that are complementary to those of the cleaved adaptor (please see Protocol 17).

Protocol 19

Blunt-ended Cloning into Plasmid Vectors

T O OBTAIN THE MAXIMUM NUMBER OF "CORRECT" LIGATION products in cloning blunt-end target fragments, the two components of DNA in the ligation reaction must be present at an appropriate ratio. If the molar ratio of plasmid vector to target DNA is too high, then the ligation reaction may generate an undesirable number of circular empty plasmids, both monomeric and polymeric; if too low, the ligation reaction may generate an excess of linear and circular homo- and heteropolymers of varying sizes, orientations, and compositions. For this reason, the orientation of the foreign DNA and the number of inserts in each recombinant clone must always be validated by restriction endonuclease mapping or some other means. As a general rule, acceptable yields of monomeric circular recombinants can be obtained from ligation reactions containing equimolar amounts of plasmid and target DNAs, with the total DNA concentration <100 µg/ml (Bercovich et al. 1992).

This protocol describes procedures for cloning blunt-ended DNA fragments into linearized plasmid vectors. Protocols 20 and 21 present further strategies to facilitate the recovery of the correct ligation products in blunt-ended cloning. Removal of 5′-phosphate residues from the vector (please see Protocol 20) will suppress recircularization of the linear plasmid. Note, however, that opinions vary as to whether dephosphorylation is advantageous; for further discussion of this issue, please refer to the introduction to Protocol 20. As a more effective approach, synthetic linkers encoding restriction endonuclease recognition sites may be ligated to blunt-ended DNA termini (please see Protocol 21) to provide cohesive ends for cloning by the method in Protocol 17. Protocols for filling recessed 3′ termini or for removing protruding 5′ or 3′ termini are described in Chapter 9, Protocol 10.

MATERIALS

CAUTION: Please see Appendix 12 for appropriate handling of materials marked with <!>.

Buffers and Solutions

Please see Appendix 1 for components of stock solutions, buffers, and reagents. Dilute stock solutions to the appropriate concentrations.

ATP (10 mM)
   Omit ATP from the ligation reaction in Step 2 if the ligation buffer contains ATP.
Ethanol
Phenol:chloroform (1:1, v/v) <!>
Polyethylene glycol (30% w/v PEG 8000 solution) <!>
Sodium acetate (3 M, pH 5.2)
TE (pH 8.0)

Enzymes and Buffers

Bacteriophage T4 DNA ligase
Please see the information panel on **DNA LIGASES**.
Restriction endonucleases

Gels

Agarose gels
Optional, please see Steps 2 and 3.
Polyacrylamide gels <!>
Optional, please see Step 2.

Nucleic Acids and Oligonucleotides

Foreign or target DNA (blunt-end fragment)
Vector (plasmid) DNA

Additional Reagents

Step 4 of this protocol requires the reagents listed in Protocol 20 of this chapter.
Step 7 of this protocol requires the reagents listed in Protocol 23, 24, 25, or 26 of this chapter.

METHOD

1. In separate reactions, digest 1–10 μg of the plasmid DNA and foreign DNA with the appropriate restriction enzyme(s) that generate blunt ends.

2. Purify the digested foreign DNA and vector DNA by extraction with phenol:chloroform and standard ethanol precipitation (please see Appendix 8).

   Depending on the experiment, it may be necessary or desirable to isolate the target fragment(s) of foreign DNA by neutral agarose or polyacrylamide gel electrophoresis as described in Chapter 5. This isolation is generally done when there are a large number of restriction fragments in the preparation of foreign DNA that can ligate to the vector. Rather than screening multiple transformants for the desired clone(s), many investigators prefer to enrich for the foreign sequences of interest before ligation.

3. Reconstitute the precipitated DNAs separately in TE (pH 8.0) at a concentration of ~100 μg/ml. Calculate the concentration of the DNAs (in pmole/ml) assuming that 1 bp has a mass of 660 daltons.

   Confirm the approximate concentration of the two DNAs by analyzing aliquots by agarose gel electophoresis.

4. Dephosphorylate the plasmid vector DNA as described in Protocol 20.

5. Transfer appropriate amounts of the DNAs to sterile 0.5-ml microfuge tubes as follows:

Tube	DNA
A and E	vector[1] (60 fmoles [~100 ng])
B	foreign[2] (60 fmoles [~10 ng])
C and F	vector[1] (60 fmoles) plus foreign (60 fmoles)[3]
D	linearized vector (contains 5′-terminal phosphates) (60 fmoles)
G	superhelical vector (6 fmoles [~10 ng])

   [1]Vector DNA is dephosphorylated as described in Protocol 20.
   [2]Linkers may be ligated to foreign target DNA.
   [3]The molar ratio of plasmid vector to insert DNA fragment should be ~1:1 in the ligation reaction. The total DNA concentration in the ligation reaction should be ~10 ng/μl.

a. To Tubes A, B, and C add:

10× Ligation buffer	1.0 µl
Bacteriophage T4 DNA ligase	0.5 Weiss unit
5 mM ATP	1.0 µl
H$_2$O	to 8.5 µl
30% PEG 8000	1–1.5 µl

b. To Tubes D, E, and F add:

10× Ligation buffer	1.0 µl
5 mM ATP	1.0 µl
H$_2$O	to 8.5 µl
30% PEG 8000	1–1.5 µl
no DNA ligase	

To achieve the maximum efficiency of ligation, set up the reactions in as small a volume as possible (5–10 µl). Adding ATP as a component of the 10× ligation buffer leaves more volume for vector or foreign DNA in the reaction mixture. Some commercial ligase buffers contain ATP. When using such buffers, the addition of ATP is not required.

The DNA fragments can be added to the tubes together with the H$_2$O and then warmed to 45ºC for 5 minutes to help dissociate any clumps of DNA that have formed during fragment preparation. Chill the DNA solution to 0ºC before the remainder of the ligation reagents are added. It is important (i) to warm the PEG stock (30%) solution to room temperature before adding to the ligation reaction and (ii) to add this ingredient last. DNA can precipitate at cold temperatures in the presence of PEG 8000.

6. Incubate the reaction mixtures overnight at 16ºC or for 4 hours at 20ºC.

7. Transform competent *E. coli* with dilutions of each of the ligation reactions, using one of the methods described in Protocols 23 through 26. As controls, include known amounts of a standard preparation of superhelical plasmid DNA to check the efficiency of transformation.

Tube	DNA	Ligase	Expected number of transformants
A	vector[1]	+	~0[3]
B	insert	+	0
C	vector[1] and insert	+	~5-fold more than Tube F
D	vector[1]	–	~0
E	vector[2]	–	~50-fold more than Tube D
F	vector[1] and insert	–	~50-fold more than Tube D
G	superhelical vector	–	2 × 10^5

[1]Dephosphorylated.
[2]Not dephosphorylated.
[3]Transformants arising from ligation of dephosphorylated vector DNA alone are due to failure to remove 5′ residues during treatment with alkaline phosphatase.

Protocol 20

Dephosphorylation of Plasmid DNA

Removal of terminal 5′-phosphate groups may be used to suppress self-ligation and circularization of plasmid DNA. During ligation in vitro, DNA ligase will catalyze the formation of a phosphodiester bond between adjacent nucleotides only if one nucleotide carries a 5′-phosphate residue and the other carries a 3′-hydroxyl terminus. Recircularization of plasmid DNA can therefore be minimized by removing the 5′-phosphate residues from both termini of the plasmid DNA with alkaline phosphatase (Seeburg et al. 1977; Ullrich et al. 1977). However, a foreign DNA segment with intact 5′-terminal phosphate residues can be ligated efficiently in vitro to the dephosphorylated plasmid DNA to generate an open circular molecule containing two nicks (please see Figure 1-11). Because these open circular DNA molecules transform *E. coli* more efficiently than dephosphorylated linear DNA, most of the transformants should, in theory, contain recombinant plasmids.

Despite its logical appeal, many investigators continue to have doubts about the value of dephosphorylation. There is no question that removal of the 5′-phosphate residues suppresses recircularization of linear plasmid DNA and therefore diminishes the background of transformed bacterial colonies that carry "empty" plasmids. All too frequently, however, there is a parallel decline in the number of colonies that carry the desired recombinant. In addition, some investigators believe that the presence of 5′-hydroxyl groups may lead to an increase in the frequency of rearranged or deleted clones. For these reasons, directional cloning is the preferred method of cloning in plasmids whenever the appropriate restriction sites are available. Dephosphorylation of the vector is now recommended only when:

- *The DNA insert to be cloned is only available in small amounts.* In this situation, the use of a tenfold molar excess of dephosphorylated vector over insert will ensure that all available insert is ligated to the vector.

- *When the transformants are to be screened by restriction enzyme digestion of minipreparations of plasmid DNA.* Because preparing plasmid DNA from more than a dozen or two small-scale cultures of bacteria is tedious, the use of a dephosphorylated vector will ensure a high frequency of the desired recombinants in a small sample of transformants.

- *When cloning blunt-ended fragments of DNA* (please see protocol 19).

- *If a vector that has been prepared by cleavage with two different enzymes generates a large number of transformed colonies.* This indicates *either* that one of the two enzymes used to prepare the vector failed to cleave the DNA to completion *or* that the small fragment of DNA released from the multiple cloning site has not been removed from the vector preparation but

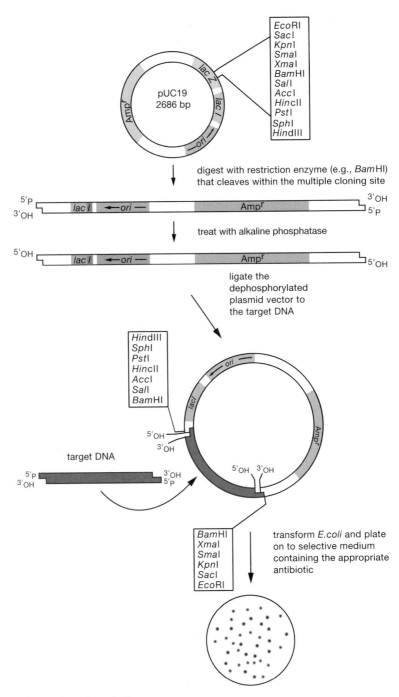

FIGURE 1-11 Dephosphorylation

The diagram shows the use of phosphatase to prevent recircularization of vector DNA.

instead is ligated into the vector. In both cases, dephosphorylation of the vector can be of use since removal of the 5′-terminal phosphate residues prevents reconstitution of closed circular plasmid DNAs.

Dephosphorylation is, however, *not* needed when cloning DNA fragments with complementary protruding ends provided recombinants are screened by α-complementation and/or identified by colony hybridization (Protocols 27 and 28). Because large numbers of colonies may be readily screened on a single plate, rare recombinants can easily be identified and recovered, even when the number of background colonies is high. This protocol presents a method to remove 5´-phosphate residues from protruding or blunt termini of linearized plasmids.

MATERIALS

CAUTION: Please see Appendix 12 for appropriate handling of materials marked <!>.

Buffers and Solutions

Please see Appendix 1 for components of stock solutions, buffers, and reagents. Dilute stock solutions to the appropriate concentrations.

EDTA (0.5 M, pH 8.0)
EGTA (0.5 M, pH 8.0)
  Optional, please see Step 6.
Ethanol
Phenol <!>
Phenol:chloroform (1:1, v/v) <!>
SDS (10% w/v)
Sodium acetate (3 M, pH 5.2 and pH 7.0)
TE (pH 8.0)
Tris-Cl (10 mM, pH 8.3)

Enzymes and Buffers

Calf intestinal alkaline phosphatase (CIP)
or
Shrimp alkaline phosphatase (SAP)
Proteinase K (10 mg/ml)
  Please see the discussion on Proteinase K in Appendix 4.
Restriction endonucleases

Gels

Agarose gel (0.7%) cast in TBE containing 0.5 µg/ml ethidium bromide <!>
  Please see Step 2.

Nucleic Acids and Oligonucleotides

Vector DNA (closed circular plasmid)

Special Equipment

Water bath preset to 56ºC or 65ºC
  Please see Step 6.

METHOD

1. Digest a reasonable quantity of closed circular plasmid DNA (10 µg) with a two- to threefold excess of the desired restriction enzyme for 1 hour.

2. Remove an aliquot (0.1 µg), and analyze the extent of digestion by electrophoresis through a 0.7% agarose gel containing ethidium bromide (please see Chapter 5, Protocol 1), using undigested plasmid DNA as a marker. If digestion is not complete, add more restriction enzyme and continue the incubation.

TABLE 1-8 Conditions for Dephosphorylation of 5´-phosphate Residues from DNA

TYPE OF TERMINUS	ENZYME/AMOUNT PER MOLE DNA ENDS	INCUBATION TEMPERATURE/TIME
5´-Protruding	0.01 unit CIP[a]	37°C/30 minutes
	0.1 unit SAP	37°C/60 minutes
3´-Protruding	0.1–0.5 unit CIP[b]	37°C/15 minutes *then* 55°C/45 minutes
	0.5 unit SAP	37°C/60 minutes
Blunt	0.1–0.5 unit CIP[b]	37°C/15 minutes *then* 55°C/45 minutes
	0.2 unit SAP	37°C/60 minutes

[a]After the initial 30-minute incubation, add a second aliquot of CIP enzyme and continue incubation for another 30 minutes at 37°C.

[b]Add a second aliquot of CIP just before beginning the incubation at 55°C.

3. When digestion is complete, extract the sample once with phenol:chloroform and recover the DNA by standard precipitation with ethanol. Store the ethanolic solution on ice for 15 minutes.

4. Recover the DNA by centrifugation at maximum speed for 10 minutes at 4°C in a microfuge, and dissolve the DNA in 110 µl of 10 mM Tris-Cl (pH 8.3).

   Reserve 20 µl of the DNA preparation for later use as a control (please see Protocol 19).

5. To the remaining 90 µl of the linearized plasmid DNA, add 10 µl of 10× CIP or 10× SAP buffer and the appropriate amount of calf intestinal phosphatase (CIP) or shrimp alkaline phosphatase (SAP) and incubate as described in Table 1-8.

6. Inactivate the phosphatase activity:

   To inactivate CIP at the end of the incubation period: Add SDS and EDTA (pH 8.0) to final concentrations of 0.5% and 5 mM, respectively. Mix well, and add proteinase K to a final concentration of 100 µg/ml. Incubate for 30 minutes at 55°C.

   Alternatively, CIP can be inactivated by heating to 65°C for 30 minutes (or 75°C for 10 minutes) in the presence of 5 mM EDTA or 10 mM EGTA (both at pH 8.0).

   or

   To inactivate SAP: Incubate the reaction mixture for 15 minutes at 65°C in the dephosphorylation buffer.

   At the end of the dephosphorylation reaction, it is crucial to remove or completely inactivate the alkaline phosphatase before setting up the ligation reactions. Although both CIP and SAP can be inactivated by heating as described above, we recommend that the dephosphorylation reaction be extracted with phenol/chloroform before using the dephosphorylated DNA in a ligation reaction.

7. Cool the reaction mixture to room temperature, and then extract it once with phenol and once with phenol:chloroform.

8. Recover the DNA by standard precipitation with ethanol. Mix the solution again and store it for 15 minutes at 0°C.

9. Recover the DNA by centrifugation at maximum speed for 10 minutes at 4°C in a microfuge. Wash the pellet with 70% ethanol at 4°C and centrifuge again.

10. Carefully remove the supernatant and leave the open tube on the bench to allow the ethanol to evaporate.

11. Dissolve the precipitated DNA in TE (pH 8.0) at a concentration of 100 µg/ml. Store the DNA in aliquots at −20°C.

Protocol 21

Addition of Synthetic Linkers to Blunt-ended DNA

Linkers are small self-complementary pieces of synthetic DNA, usually 8–16 nucleotides in length, that anneal to form blunt-ended, double-stranded molecules containing a recognition site for a restriction enzyme (please see Figure 1-12).

Linkers are used to equip blunt-ended termini of DNA with restriction sites as an aid to cloning (Scheller et al. 1977). A large variety of linkers available from commercial suppliers can

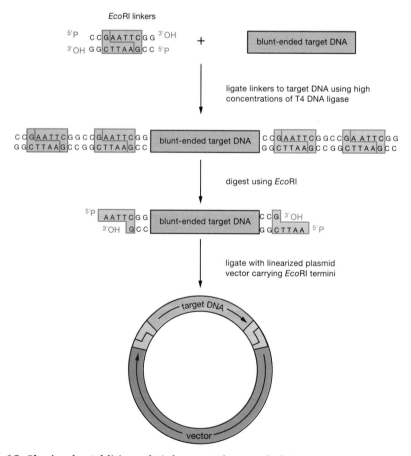

FIGURE 1-12 Cloning by Addition of Linkers to Blunt-ended Target DNA

TABLE 1-9 Linker Sequences

*Bam*HI	d(CGGGATCCCG)
*Bam*HI	d(CGCGGATCCGCG)
*Bgl*II	d(GAAGATCTTC)
*Eco*RI	d(GGAATTCC)
*Eco*RI	d(CGGAATTCCG)
*Eco*RI	d(CCGGAATTCCGG)
*Hind*III	d(CCAAGCTTGG)
*Hind*III	d(CCCAAGCTTGGG)
*Nco*I	d(CATGCCATGGCATG)
*Nde*I	d(CCATATGG)
*Nhe*I	d(CTAGCTAGCTAG)
*Not*I	d(AGCGGCCGCT)
*Pst*I	d(GCTGCAGC)
*Sac*I	d(CGAGCTCG)
*Sal*I	d(CGGTCGACCG)
*Sma*I	d(TCCCCCGGGGGA)
*Spe*I	d(CGGACTAGTCCG)
*Srf*I	d(AGCCCGGGCT)
*Xba*I	d(CTAGTCTAGACTAG)
*Xho*I	d(CCGCTCGAGCGG)

Modified with permission, ©1999 Stratagene.

be purchased in two forms that carry either a phosphate group or a hydroxyl group on the 5′ termini (please see Table 1-9). Only phosphorylated molecules are substrates for T4 DNA ligase, and nonphosphorylated linkers must therefore be treated with bacteriophage T4 polynucleotide kinase and ATP before they can be joined to DNA. In a typical experiment, phosphorylated linkers are ligated in 75–100-fold molar excess in the presence of a blunt-ended target molecule. This heavily skewed stoichiometry drives end-to-end ligation of linkers and polymerization of linkers to each end of the target DNA. The excess linkers are cleaved from the DNA fragment by the appropriate restriction enzyme, and their remnants are removed by gel filtration or gel electrophoresis. The purified DNA fragment, now a few nucleotides longer and equipped with conventional cohesive termini, may be ligated into a vector carrying compatible termini (please see Figure 1-12).

In many cases, particular linkers are chosen because they carry a restriction site that is known to be absent from the body of an individual target DNA. However, a different strategy is required when linkers are used to clone populations of DNA molecules whose sequences are unknown, e.g., a population of cDNAs. This can be achieved as follows:

- Use the cognate methylating enzyme to modify internal recognition sites in the cDNAs and thereby protect them against cleavage by the restriction enzymes used to trim the polymerized linkers from the termini of the cDNAs. For example, *Eco*RI linkers can be added to a DNA fragment that contains one or more internal recognition sites by treating the DNA with *Eco*RI methylase in the presence of *S*-adenosylmethionine (SAM, a methyl group donor) before linker addition. Methylation of the first adenosyl residue in the GAATTC recognition site prevents subsequent cleavage by the *Eco*RI restriction enzyme when polymerized linkers are removed from the ends of the modified DNA. For more details, please consult Appendix 4.

- Partially fill recessed 3′ termini of an *Xho*I cloning site on the vector and ligate to the cDNA carrying phosphorylated adaptors with 3-base protruding termini complementary to the partially filled *Xho*I site. Neither the vector nor the cDNA molecules can anneal to themselves, but they can join to one another. Because the *Xho*I site is regenerated, the cloned cDNA can be recovered by digestion with *Xho*I. This strategy greatly improves the efficiency of the ligation step in cDNA cloning and eliminates the need to methylate the cDNA or to digest it with restriction enzymes before insertion into the vector (Yang et al. 1986; Elledge et al. 1991). For more information, please see the information panel on **ADAPTORS**.

Finally, in some blunt-ended DNA ligations, it is possible to include a restriction enzyme in the ligation reaction or to restrict the ligated DNA before transformation, in order to increase the proportion of bacterial colonies carrying the desired recombinants. For example, *Sma*I and *Hinc*II are two restriction enzymes that cleave to yield blunt ends and whose recognition sites are included in most multiple cloning sites. In ligations where these two sites will not be regenerated when the target DNA is ligated to the vector, and in which the two enzymes do not cleave within the DNA fragment to be ligated, the *Sma*I or *Hinc*II enzyme can be included in the ligation reaction. Alternatively, and more efficiently, after ligation, the reaction can be diluted into a final volume of 100 μl of 1x restriction enzyme buffer and digested with 5–10 units of the appropriate enzyme for 1–3 hours. Either of these treatments prior to transformation will result in cleavage of self-ligated vector DNA, thereby enriching for recombinants whose *Sma*I or *Hinc*II sites have been eliminated by ligation of the insert. Because circular DNAs produce manyfold more transformants/μg than linear DNAs, most *E. coli* colonies arising after transformation will carry the desired recombinants. A similar strategy can be used when cloning blunt-ended DNA fragments generated by PCR. Stratagene markets a kit, pCR-ScriptSK(+), for this purpose.

MATERIALS

CAUTION: Please see Appendix 12 for appropriate handling of materials marked with <!>.

Buffers and Solutions

Please see Appendix 1 for components of stock solutions, buffers, and reagents. Dilute stock solutions to the appropriate concentrations.

Ammonium acetate (4 M, pH 4.8)

ATP (5 mM and 10 mM)
    Omit 5 mM from the ligation reaction in Step 2 if the ligation buffer contains ATP.

Ethanol

10x Linker kinase buffer
    600 mM Tris-Cl (pH 7.6)
    100 mM MgCl$_2$
    100 mM dithiothreitol
    2 mg/ml bovine serum albumin

Phenol:chloroform (1:1, v/v) <!>

Sodium acetate (3 M, pH 5.2)

TE (pH 8.0)

Enzymes and Buffers

Bacteriophage T4 DNA ligase
    Please see the information panel on **DNA LIGASES**.

Bacteriophage T4 polynucleotide kinase
Restriction endonucleases

Gels

Polyacrylamide gel (10%) <!> or agarose gel (0.7%) (optional)
These gels may be used to assess the results of ligation and digestion. Please see the note to Step 7.

Nucleic Acids and Oligonucleotides

Foreign or target DNA (blunt-end fragment)
Synthetic linkers dissolved in TE (pH 8.0) at a concentration of 400 μg/ml
For a dodecamer, this concentration is a equivalent to a 50 μM solution.

Radioactive Compounds

[γ-^{32}P]ATP <!> (1–10 μCi)
Optional for phosphorylation reaction. Please see the note to Step 2.

Special Equipment

Equipment for spun-column chromatography
Water bath preset to 65°C

METHOD

Phosphorylation of Linkers (If Necessary)

1. Assemble the following reaction mixture in a sterile 0.5-ml microfuge tube:

10x linker kinase buffer	1.0 μl
10 mM ATP	1.0 μl
synthetic linker dissolved in TE (pH 8.0)	2.0 μg[1]
H$_2$O	to 9 μl
bacteriophage T4 polynucleotide kinase	10 units

   [1]Approximately 250 pmoles of a dodecamer.

   Incubate the reaction for 1 hour at 37°C.

   > If necessary, methylation of internal restriction sites in the target DNA should be carried out at this stage, i.e., carried out before linker addition and according to the manufacturer's instructions.

Ligation of Phosphorylated Linkers to Blunt-ended DNA

2. Calculate the concentration of termini in the preparation of blunt-ended DNA and then assemble the following ligation mixture in the order given in a sterile 0.5-ml microfuge tube:

   50 μg of a 1 kb segment of double-stranded DNA = 78.7 nmoles or 157.4 nM of termini.

blunt-ended DNA	2 pmoles of termini
phosphorylated linkers	150–200 pmoles of termini
H$_2$O	to 7.5 μl
10x ligation buffer	1.0 μl
5 mM ATP (free acid)	1.0 μl
bacteriophage T4 DNA ligase	1.0 Weiss unit

   Incubate the reaction mixtures for 12–16 hours at 4°C.

   > To achieve the maximum efficiency of ligation, set up the reactions in as small a volume as possible (5–10 μl). Addition of ATP as a component of the 10x ligation buffer leaves more volume for

vector or foreign DNA in the reaction mixture. Some commercial ligase buffers contain ATP. When using such buffers, the addition of ATP is no longer required. For a definition of Weiss units, please see the information panel on **DNA LIGASES**.

3. Inactivate the bacteriophage T4 DNA ligase by heating the reaction mixture to 65°C for 15 minutes.

4. Cool the ligation mixture to room temperature and then add:

10x restriction enzyme buffer	10 µl
restriction enzyme	50 units
sterile H_2O	to a final volume of 100 µl

   Incubate the reaction for 1–3 hours at 37°C.

Recovery of Ligated DNA

5. Purify the restricted DNA by extraction with phenol:chloroform. Precipitate the DNA with 2 volumes of ethanol in the presence of 2 M ammonium acetate.

6. Collect the precipitated DNA by centrifugation at maximum speed for 15 minutes at 4°C in a microfuge, and dissolve the pellet in 50 µl of TE (pH 8.0).

7. Pass the resuspended DNA through a spun column to remove excess linkers (please see Appendix 8).

Usually, the ligation and restriction endonuclease reactions go well and there is no need to check the products before proceeding. If necessary, however, these steps can be checked as follows:

- During ligation, phosphorylated linkers assemble into polymers (e.g., dimers, trimers, and tetramers) that can be detected when 1.0 µl of the reaction mixture (Step 2) is analyzed by electrophoresis through a neutral 10% polyacrylamide gel. A ladder of multimers should be visible when the gel is stained by ethidium bromide or SYBR Gold.

- If radiolabeled linkers are used and if the ligation is successful, the radioactive linkers will form a series of radioactive bands that can be resolved by electrophoresis through a neutral 10% polyacrylamide gel. However, instead of staining, the radiolabeled linkers may be detected by autoradiography or phosphorimaging. When the linker is labeled to high specific activity, it is possible to verify that the radiolabeled linker has become attached to the target DNA because some of the radioactivity elutes with the target DNA during spun-column chromatography (Step 7). Alternatively, an aliquot of the reaction mixture can be analyzed by electrophoresis through an agarose gel. After ligation, a small fraction of the radiolabel should comigrate with the target fragment.

- To verify that the restriction enzyme has cleaved the polymerized linkers to completion, analyze 10 µl of the restriction digest by polyacrylamide gel electrophoresis. The linker ladder should now be reduced to monomers.

---

8. Recover the DNA by standard ethanol precipitation and dissolve the precipitate in 10–20 µl of TE (pH 8.0).

The modified DNA fragment can now be ligated as described in Protocol 17 into a plasmid (or bacteriophage) vector with protruding ends that are complementary to those introduced by the linker.

Protocol 22

Ligating Plasmid and Target DNAs in Low-melting-temperature Agarose

THE SLOWEST STEP IN CLONING IN PLASMIDS is the electrophoretic purification of the desired restriction fragment of foreign DNA and the appropriate segment of plasmid DNA. In the protocol given below (adapted from Struhl 1985), ligation of plasmid and foreign DNAs is carried out in the presence of low-melting-temperature agarose (please see Chapter 5). The method works for both blunt-end ligation and ligation of cohesive termini, but it requires a large amount of ligase and its efficiency is about one to two orders of magnitude lower than ligation with purified DNA (Protocols 17 and 19). For this reason, the method is not suitable for construction of libraries and is used chiefly for rapid subcloning of segments from large fragments of DNA in dephosphorylated vectors and for assembling recombinant constructs.

MATERIALS

CAUTION: Please see Appendix 12 for appropriate handling of materials marked with <!>.

Enzymes and Buffers

2x Bacteriophage T4 DNA ligase mixture

1 M Tris-Cl (pH 7.6)	1.0 µl
100 mM MgCl$_2$	2.0 µl
200 mM dithiothreitol	1.0 µl
10 mM ATP	1.0 µl
H$_2$O	4.5 µl
Bacteriophage T4 DNA ligase	1 Weiss unit

10 µl is required for each ligation.

Prepare fresh for each use in a microfuge tube chilled on ice. Store the reaction mixture in ice until needed. For definition of Weiss units, please see the information panel on **DNA LIGASES**.

Restriction endonucleases

Gels

Low-melting-temperature agarose gel
Please see Chapter 5.

Nucleic Acids and Oligonucleotides

Foreign DNA
Plasmid DNA (~100 µg/ml, dephosphorylated)
Approximately 100 ng of dephosphorylated DNA is required for each ligation.

Special Equipment

Heating block preset to 70°C
Ultraviolet lamp, hand-held, long wavelength (302 nm) <!>
Water bath preset to 16°C

METHOD

1. Use the appropriate restriction enzyme(s) to digest an amount of target DNA sufficient to yield ~250 ng of the desired fragment. Perform the digestion in a volume of 20 µl or less.

2. Separate the DNA fragments by electrophoresis through a low-melting/gelling-temperature agarose gel.

3. Examine the agarose gel under long-wavelength UV illumination. From the relative fluorescent intensities of the desired bands, estimate the amounts of DNA that they contain. Use a clean razor blade to cut out the desired bands in the smallest possible volume of agarose (usually 40–50 µl). Leave a small amount of each band in the gel to mark the positions of the DNA fragments and then photograph the dissected gel.

4. Place the excised and trimmed slices of gel in separate, labeled microfuge tubes.

   If necessary, the agarose slices may be stored for a few days at 4°C in closed tubes.

5. Melt the agarose by heating the tubes to 70°C for 15 minutes in a heating block. Estimate the volume of the melted agarose in the tube and calculate the volume that would contain ~200 ng of DNA.

   The aim is to harvest ~200 ng of foreign DNA in a volume of 10 µl or less. This takes practice. However, ligations work, albeit less efficiently, for bands containing as little as 10 ng of DNA that are only just visible in the gel.

6. In a sterile microfuge tube warmed to 37°C, combine the following:

dephosphorylated plasmid DNA	60 fmoles
foreign DNA fragment	120–240 fmoles (in a volume of 10 µl or less)

   Mix the contents of the tube quickly with a sterile disposable pipette tip before the agarose solidifies.

   The molar ratio of foreign DNA to plasmid vector in the ligation reaction should be no less than 2:1 and no more than 4:1.

7. In separate tubes, set up two additional ligations as controls, one containing only the dephosphorylated plasmid vector and the other containing only the fragment of foreign DNA.

8. Incubate the three tubes for 5–10 minutes at 37°C, and then add to each tube 10 µl of ice-cold 2x bacteriophage T4 DNA ligase mixture. Mix the contents of the tube quickly with a sterile disposable pipette tip before the agarose solidifies. Incubate the reactions for 12–16 hours at 16°C.

   The recombinants, products of the ligation reaction, can now be used directly for transformation (as described in Protocol 23, 24, or 25 or for electroporation as described in Protocol 26) into *E. coli*. Remelt the agarose in the ligation mixtures by heating the sealed microfuge tubes to 70°C for 10–15 minutes in a heating block before transformation or electroporation.

   Typically, 1–5 µl of each ligation reaction is used to transform chemically prepared competent bacterial cells. Only 0.1–1.0 µl of the ligation reaction is required for tranformation of bacterial cells by the more efficient method of electroporation. Addition of a greater volume of the ligation mixture will increase the solute concentration in the electroporation cell to the point where arcing becomes a distinct possibility.

Protocol 23

The Hanahan Method for Preparation and Transformation of Competent *E. coli*: High-efficiency Transformation

Wₕₑₙ Doug Hanahan was a graduate student at Cold Spring Harbor Laboratory and Harvard University in the late 1970s and early 1980s, he achieved transformation efficiencies that were unheard of previously, but then became standard. Hanahan drove a fast car, worked mostly at night and with some secrecy, never telling the ingredients of the transformation buffer that gave him such spectacular results. However, he freely and generously distributed the buffer to anyone whose experiment needed high efficiencies of transformation. A good many of the cDNA libraries generated on the East Coast in the early 1980s were established with Hanahan's transformation buffer, which was known as "Liquid Gold" because of its beautiful shimmering color.

Eventually, the formula for Liquid Gold was published, together with a detailed description of how to achieve high efficiencies of transformation (Hanahan 1983). If followed scrupulously, Hanahan's procedure can reproducibly generate competent cultures of *E. coli* that can be transformed at high frequencies (5×10^8 transformed colonies/µg of superhelical plasmid DNA). The key word here is scrupulously. Follow Hanahan's instructions *exactly* and all will be well. Take a short cut, use dirty glassware, impure water, or a stale chemical and disappointment will follow, which may explain why some investigators struggle to reproduce Hanahan's results.

Three factors appear to be crucial for obtaining consistently high frequencies of transformation of competent cells prepared by the Hanahan procedure:

- *The purity of the reagents used in the transformation buffers.* It is most important to prepare the competent cells using water and dimethylsulfoxide (DMSO) of the highest purity (Hanahan 1985). Some reagents, including components of bacterial media, decline with storage. Whenever possible, use freshly purchased reagents and growth media. If problems arise, individual reagents (e.g., DMSO, dithiothreitol [DTT], glycerol, and 2-[*N*-morpholino]ethanesulfonic acid [MES]) should be substituted one at a time in the transformation protocol to ascertain the quality of a given batch of reagent and its effect on the transformation frequency.

- *The state of growth of the cells.* For unknown reasons, the highest frequencies of transformation are obtained with cultures that have been grown directly from a master stock stored in freezing medium at –70ºC. Cultures that have been passaged continuously in the laboratory or that have been stored at 4ºC or at room temperature should not be used.

- *The cleanliness of the glassware and plasticware.* Because trace amounts of detergent or other chemicals greatly reduce the efficiency of bacterial transformation, it is best to set aside a batch of glassware that is used for no other purpose than to prepare competent bacteria. This glassware should be washed and rinsed by hand, filled with pure water (Milli-Q or equivalent), and sterilized by autoclaving. The water should be discarded just before the glassware is used. Keep in mind that many manufactured plastics and filters used for sterilization contain detergents that can severely reduce the transformation frequency.

Hanahan's procedure works well with strains of *E. coli* commonly used in molecular cloning, including DH1, DH5, MM294, JM108/9, DH5α, and many others. However, a few strains of *E. coli* (e.g., MC1061) are refractory to this method. For further details and the extension of the method to other species of bacteria, see Hanahan et al. (1991, 1995). Other methods for transformation are described in Protocol 24 (preparation of "ultra-competent" cells) and Protocol 25 (transformation using calcium chloride).

MATERIALS

CAUTION: Please see Appendix 12 for appropriate handling of materials marked with <!>.

Buffers and Solutions

Please see Appendix 1 for components of stock solutions, buffers, and reagents. Dilute stock solutions to the appropriate concentrations.

DMSO <!>
Oxidation products of DMSO, presumably dimethyl sulfone and dimethyl sulfide, are inhibitors of transformation (Hanahan 1985).

DnD (DMSO and DTT) solution
1.53 g of dithiothreitol
9 ml of DMSO
100 μl of 1 M potassium acetate (pH 7.5)
H_2O to 10 ml

Sterilize the DnD solution by filtration through a Millex SR membrane unit (Millipore), which is designed to withstand organic solvents. Dispense 160-μl aliquots of the DnD solution into sterile 0.5-ml microfuge tubes. Close the tubes tightly and store them at –20ºC.

For preparation of 1 M potassium acetate (pH 7.5), please see Appendix 1.

Transformation buffers (please see Step 1)
Standard transformation buffer (TFB) is used when preparing competent cells for immediate use. Frozen storage buffer (FSB) is used to prepare stocks of competent cells that are to be stored at –70ºC.

Media

SOB agar plates containing 20 mM MgSO₄ and the appropriate antibiotic
Standard SOB contains 10 mM $MgSO_4$.
SOB medium containing 20 mM MgSO₄
Standard SOB contains 10 mM $MgSO_4$.
SOC medium
Approximately 1 ml of this medium is needed for each transformation reaction.

Nucleic Acids and Oligonucleotides

Plasmid DNA (recombinant plasmid)
Construct using one of the methods described in Protocols 17 through 22 of this chapter.

Centrifuges and Rotors

Sorvall GSA rotor or equivalent

Special Equipment

> *Liquid nitrogen <!>*
> *Polypropylene tubes (50 ml), chilled in ice*
> *Polypropylene tubes (17 x 100 mm; Falcon 2059), chilled in ice*
> *Water bath preset to 42°C*

Vectors and Bacterial Strains

> E. coli *strain to be transformed (frozen stock)*
> The strain should be stored at –70°C in freezing medium (please see Appendices 1 and 8).

METHOD

▲ IMPORTANT All steps in this protocol should be carried out aseptically.

Preparation of Cells

1. Prepare transformation buffer.

    TFB is used when preparing competent cells for immediate use. FSB is used to prepare stocks of competent cells that are to be stored at –70°C. Organic contaminants in the H_2O used to prepare transformation buffers can reduce the efficiency of transformation of competent bacteria. H_2O obtained directly from a well-serviced Milli-Q filtration system (Millipore) usually gives good results. If problems should arise, treat the deionized H_2O with activated charcoal before use.

    ### To prepare standard transformation buffer

    a. Prepare 1 M MES by dissolving 19.52 g of MES in 80 ml of pure H_2O (Milli-Q, or equivalent). Adjust the pH of the solution to 6.3 with 5 M KOH, and add pure H_2O to bring the final volume to 100 ml. Sterilize the solution by filtration through a disposable prerinsed Nalgene filter (0.45-μm pore size). Divide into 10-ml aliquots and store at –20°C.

    b. Prepare TFB by dissolving all the solutes listed below in ~500 ml of H_2O and then add 10 ml of 1 M MES buffer (pH 6.3). Adjust the volume of the TFB to 1 liter with pure H_2O.

Reagent	Amount per liter	Final concentration
1 M MES (pH 6.3)	10 ml	10 mM
$MnCl_2 \cdot 4H_2O$	8.91 g	45 mM
$CaC_2 \cdot 2H_2O$	1.47 g	10 mM
KCl	7.46 g	100 mM
Hexamminecobalt chloride	0.80 g	3 mM
H_2O	to 1 liter	

    c. Sterilize the TFB by filtration through a disposable prerinsed Nalgene filter (0.45-μm pore size). Divide the solution into 40-ml aliquots in tissue-culture flasks (e.g., Corning, or equivalent) and store them at 4°C.

    ### To prepare frozen storage buffer

    a. Prepare 1 M potassium acetate by dissolving 9.82 g of potassium acetate in 90 ml of pure H_2O (Milli-Q, or equivalent). Adjust the pH of the solution to 7.5 with 2 M acetic acid, add pure H_2O to bring the final volume to 100 ml. Divide the solution into aliquots and store at –20°C.

b. Prepare FSB by dissolving all of the solutes listed below in ~500 ml of pure H_2O. After the components are dissolved, adjust the pH of the solution to 6.4 with 0.1 N HCl. Too high a pH cannot be adjusted by adding base; instead, discard the solution and and begin again. Adjust the volume of the final solution to 1 liter with pure H_2O.

Reagent	Amount per liter	Final concentration
1 M potassium acetate (pH 7.5)	10 ml	10.mM
$MnCl_2 \cdot 4H_2O$	8.91 g	45 mM
$CaCl_2 \cdot 2H_2O$	1.47 g	10 mM
KCl	7.46 g	10 mM
Hexamminecobalt chloride	0.80 g	100 mM
Glycerol	100 ml	10% (v/v)
H_2O	to 1 liter	

c. Sterilize the solution by filtration through a disposable prerinsed Nalgene filter (0.45-μm pore size). Dispense the solution into 40-ml aliquots and store the aliquots in tissue culture flasks (e.g., Corning, or equivalent) at 4ºC. During storage, the pH of the solution drifts down to a final value of 6.1–6.2 but then stabilizes.

2. Use an inoculating loop to streak *E. coli* of the desired strain directly from a frozen stock onto the surface of an SOB agar plate. Incubate the plate for 16 hours at 37ºC.

   It is not necessary to thaw the frozen stock of bacteria. Sufficient cells will stick to the loop when it is scratched across the surface of the frozen stock. A single tube of frozen stock can be used many times.

3. Transfer four or five well-isolated colonies into 1 ml of SOB containing 20 mM $MgSO_4$. Disperse the bacteria by vortexing at moderate speed, and then dilute the culture in 30–100 ml of SOB containing 20 mM $MgSO_4$ in a 1-liter flask.

   The colonies should be no more than 2–3 mm in diameter.

4. Grow the cells for 2.5–3.0 hours at 37ºC, monitoring the growth of the culture.

   For efficient transformation, it is essential that the number of *viable* cells not exceed 10^8 cells/ml, which for most strains of *E. coli* is equivalent to an OD_{600} of ~0.4. To ensure that the culture does not grow to a higher density, measure the OD_{600} of the culture every 15–20 minutes. Plot a graph of the data so that the time when the OD_{600} of the culture approaches 0.4 can be predicted with some accuracy. Begin to harvest the culture when the OD_{600} reaches 0.35.

   For reasons that are unclear, the highest efficiencies of transformation are obtained at two separate points in the growth curve of *E. coli*: in early- to mid-log phase (OD_{600} = 0.4) (Hanahan 1983) and in late-log phase (OD_{600} = 0.95) (Tang et al. 1994). The early peak is easier to work with because the high efficiency of transformation is sustained for a longer time. The later peak is much steeper and a 2–3-minute delay in collecting the cells can cost an order of magnitude in transformation efficiency.

   Because the relationship between the OD_{600} and the number of viable cells/ml varies somewhat from strain to strain, it is essential to calibrate the spectrophotometer by measuring the OD_{600} of a growing culture of the particular strain of *E. coli* at different times in its growth cycle and determining the number of viable cells at each of these times by plating dilutions of the culture on LB agar plates in the absence of antibiotics.

5. Transfer the cells to sterile, disposable, ice-cold 50-ml polypropylene tubes. Cool the cultures to 0ºC by storing the tubes on ice for 10 minutes.

6. Recover the cells by centrifugation at 2700*g* (4100 rpm in a Sorvall GSA rotor) for 10 minutes at 4ºC.

7. Decant the medium from the cell pellets. Stand the tubes in an inverted position for 1 minute to allow the last traces of medium to drain away.

8. Resuspend the pellets by swirling or gentle vortexing in ~20 ml (per 50-ml tube) of ice-cold TFB or FSB transformation buffer. Store the resuspended cells on ice for 10 minutes.

9. Recover the cells by centrifugation at 2700*g* (4100 rpm in a Sorvall GSA rotor) for 10 minutes at 4°C.

10. Decant the buffer from the cell pellets. Stand the tubes in an inverted position for 1 minute to allow the last traces of buffer to drain away.

11. Resuspend the pellets by swirling or gentle vortexing in 4 ml (per 50-ml tube) of ice-cold TFB or FSB. Proceed either with Step 12a if the competent cells are to be used immediately or with Step 12b if the competent cells are to be stored at –70°C and used at a later date.

Preparation of Competent Cells

12. Prepare competent cells for transformation.

   TO PREPARE FRESH COMPETENT CELLS

   a. Add 140 μl of DnD solution into the center of each cell suspension. Immediately mix by swirling gently, and then store the suspension on ice for 15 minutes.

   b. Add an additional 140 μl of DnD solution to each suspension. Mix by swirling gently, and then store the suspension on ice for a further 15 minutes.

   c. Dispense aliquots of the suspensions into chilled, sterile 17 x 100-mm polypropylene tubes. Store the tubes on ice.

   > For most cloning purposes, 50-μl aliquots of the competent-cell suspension will be more than adequate. However, when large numbers of transformed colonies are required (e.g., when constructing cDNA libraries), larger aliquots may be needed.
   >
   > Glass tubes should not be used as they lower the efficiency of transformation by ~10-fold.

   TO PREPARE FROZEN STOCKS OF COMPETENT CELLS

   a. Add 140 μl of DMSO per 4 ml of resuspended cells. Mix gently by swirling, and store the suspension on ice for 15 minutes.

   b. Add an additional 140 μl of DMSO to each suspension. Mix gently by swirling, and then return the suspensions to an ice bath.

   c. Working quickly, dispense aliquots of the suspensions into chilled, sterile microfuge tubes or tissue culture vials. Immediately snap-freeze the competent cells by immersing the tightly closed tubes in a bath of liquid nitrogen. Store the tubes at –70°C until needed.

   > For most cloning purposes, 50-μl aliquots of the competent-cell suspension will be more than adequate. However, when large numbers of transformed colonies are required (e.g., when constructing cDNA libraries), larger aliquots may be needed.

   d. When needed, remove a tube of competent cells from the –70°C freezer. Thaw the cells by holding the tube in the palm of the hand. Just as the cells thaw, transfer the tube to an ice bath. Store the cells on ice for 10 minutes.

   e. Use a chilled, sterile pipette tip to transfer the competent cells to chilled, sterile 17 x 100-mm polypropylene tubes. Store the cells on ice.

   > Glass tubes should not be used as they lower the efficiency of transformation by ~10-fold.

Transformation

Include all of the appropriate positive and negative controls (please see the panel on BACTERIAL TRANSFORMATION).

13. Add the transforming DNA (up to 25 ng per 50 µl of competent cells) in a volume not exceeding 5% of that of the competent cells. Swirl the tubes gently several times to mix their contents. Set up at least two control tubes for each transformation experiment, including a tube of competent bacteria that receives a known amount of a standard preparation of superhelical plasmid DNA and a tube of cells that receives no plasmid DNA at all. Store the tubes on ice for 30 minutes.

14. Transfer the tubes to a rack placed in a preheated 42°C circulating water bath. Store the tubes in the rack for exactly 90 seconds. Do not shake the tubes.

    Heat shock is a crucial step. It is very important that the cells be raised to exactly the right temperature at the correct rate. The incubation times and temperatures given here have been worked out using Falcon 2059 tubes. Other types of tubes will not necessarily yield equivalent results.

15. Rapidly transfer the tubes to an ice bath. Allow the cells to cool for 1–2 minutes.

16. Add 800 µl of SOC medium to each tube. Warm the cultures to 37°C in a water bath, and then transfer the tubes to a shaking incubator set at 37°C. Incubate the cultures for 45 minutes to allow the bacteria to recover and to express the antibiotic resistance marker encoded by the plasmid.

    To maximize the efficiency of transformation, gently agitate (<225 cycles/minute) the cells during the recovery period.

    If screening by α-complementation, proceed to Protocol 27 for plating.

17. Transfer the appropriate volume (up to 200 µl per 90-mm plate) of transformed competent cells onto agar SOB medium containing 20 mM $MgSO_4$ and the appropriate antibiotic.

    When selecting for resistance to tetracycline, the entire transformation mixture may be spread on a single plate (or plated in top agar). In this case, collect the bacteria by centrifuging for 20 seconds at room temperature in a microfuge, and then gently resuspend the cell pellet in 100 µl of SOC medium by tapping the sides of the tube.

    ▲ IMPORTANT Sterilize a bent glass rod by dipping it into ethanol and then in the flame of a Bunsen burner. When the rod has cooled to room temperature, spread the transformed cells gently over the surface of the agar plate.

    When selecting for resistance to ampicillin, transformed cells should be plated at low density (<10^4 colonies per 90-mm plate), and the plates should not be incubated for more than 20 hours at 37°C. The enzyme β-lactamase is secreted into the medium from ampicillin-resistant transformants and can rapidly inactivate the antibiotic in regions surrounding the colonies. Thus, plating cells at high density or incubating them for long periods of time results in the appearance of ampicillin-sensitive satellite colonies. This problem is ameliorated, but not completely eliminated, by using carbenicillin rather than ampicillin in selective media and increasing the concentration of antibiotic from 60 µg/ml to 100 µg/ml. The number of ampicillin-resistant colonies does not increase in linear proportion to the number of cells applied to the plate, perhaps because of growth-inhibiting substances released from the cells killed by the antibiotic.

18. Store the plates at room temperature until the liquid has been absorbed.

19. Invert the plates and incubate them at 37°C. Transformed colonies should appear in 12–16 hours.

    Transformed colonies may be screened for the presence of recombinant plasmids using one of the methods described in Protocols 27, 28, 31, and 32 of this chapter or Protocol 12 in Chapter 8.

BACTERIAL TRANSFORMATION

In every experiment, it is essential to include positive controls to measure the efficiency of transformation, and negative controls to eliminate the possibility of contamination and to identify the potential causes of failure.

Negative Controls

An aliquot of competent cells to which no DNA is added should be carried through the transformation experiment. The entire aliquot should be plated on a single agar plate containing the appropriate antibiotic used to select transformants. No bacterial colonies should grow on this plate or on a selective plate that received no bacteria at all. If any are detected, the following possibilities should be considered:

- *The competent cells are contaminated with an antibiotic-resistant strain of bacteria during the experiment.* Perhaps one of the solutions/reagents used in the transformation protocol is contaminated.

- *The selective plates are defective.* Perhaps the antibiotic was omitted altogether from the plates or was added to agar that was too hot.

- *The selective plates are contaminated with an antibiotic resistant strain of bacteria.* In this case, colonies usually appear both on the surface of the medium and in the agar.

Positive Controls

An aliquot of competent cells should be transformed with a known amount of a standard preparation of circular superhelical plasmid DNA. This control provides a measure of the efficiency of transformation and allows a standard for comparison with previous transformation experiments. We recommend preparing two large batches of diluted supercoiled plasmid DNA (1 ng/ml for the Hanahan and Inoue procedures; 500 ng/ml for the calcium chloride procedure). These preparations should be stored at –70°C in TE (pH 7.8) in very small aliquots. The appropriate standard preparation (2–5 µl) should be used to measure the efficiency of transformation of each new batch of competent cells and to check the efficiency of transformation in every experiment. Failure to obtain transformed colonies in a given experiment indicates problems with the competent bacteria or the transformation buffer.

When a ligation reaction is used as a source of transforming DNA, the transformation efficiency is reduced by at least two orders of magnitude compared with the supercoiled plasmid DNA control. The actual number of transformants obtained per µg of ligated DNA will depend on the amount of recombinant plasmid generated during the ligation reaction, and on the presence of inhibitors of transformation such as agarose and enzymes.

Protocol 24

The Inoue Method for Preparation and Transformation of Competent *E. Coli*: "Ultra-Competent" Cells

AT ITS BEST, THIS METHOD FOR PREPARING COMPETENT *E. coli* from Inoue et al. (1990) can challenge the efficiencies achieved by Hanahan (1983). However, under standard laboratory conditions, efficiencies of 1×10^8 to 3×10^8 transformed colonies/μg of plasmid DNA are more typical. The advantages of the procedure are that it is less finicky, more reproducible, and therefore more predictable than the original Hanahan method.

This protocol differs from other procedures in that the bacterial culture is grown at 18ºC rather than the conventional 37ºC. Otherwise, the protocol is unremarkable and follows a fairly standard course. Why growing the cells at low temperature should affect the efficiency of transformation is anybody's guess. Perhaps the composition or the physical characteristics of bacterial membranes synthesized at 18ºC are more favorable for uptake of DNA, or perhaps the phases of the growth cycle that favor efficient transformation are extended.

Incubating bacterial cultures at 18ºC is a challenge. Most laboratories do not have a shaking incubator that can accurately maintain a temperature of 18ºC summer and winter. One solution is to place an incubator in a 4ºC cold room and use the temperature control to heat the incubator to 18ºC. Alternatively, there is almost no loss of efficiency if the cultures are grown at 20–23ºC, which is the ambient temperature in many laboratories. Cultures incubated at these temperatures grow slowly with a doubling time of 2.5 to 4 hours. This can lead to frustration, especially late at night when it seems that the culture will never reach the desired OD_{600} of 0.6. The answer to this problem is to set up cultures in the evening and harvest the bacteria early the following morning. The procedure works well with many strains of *E. coli* in common use in molecular cloning, including XL1-Blue, DH1, JM103, JM108/9, DH5α, and HB101.

MATERIALS

CAUTION: Please see Appendix 12 for appropriate handling of materials marked with <!>.

Buffers and Solutions

Please see Appendix 1 for components of stock solutions, buffers, and reagents.
Dilute stock solutions to the appropriate concentrations.

DMSO <!>
  Oxidation products of DMSO, presumably dimethyl sulfone and dimethyl sulfide, are inhibitors of transformation (Hanahan 1985). To avoid problems, purchase DMSO of the highest quality.

Inoue transformation buffer (please see Step 1)
  Chilled to 0ºC before use.

Nucleic Acids and Oligonucleotides

Plasmid DNA (recombinant plasmid)
Construct using one of the methods described in Protocols 17 through 22 of this chapter.

Media

LB or SOB medium for initial growth of culture
SOB agar plates containing 20 mM MgSO₄ and the appropriate antibiotic
Standard SOB contains 10 mM MgSO₄.
SOB medium, for growth of culture to be transformed
Prepare three 1-liter flasks of 250 ml each and equilibrate the medium to 18–20°C before inoculation.
SOC medium
Approximately 1 ml of this medium is needed for each transformation reaction.

Centrifuges and Rotors

Sorvall GSA rotor or equivalent

Special Equipment

Liquid nitrogen <!>
Polypropylene tubes (17 x 100 mm; Falcon 2059), chilled in ice
Shaking Incubator (18°C)
Water bath preset to 42°C

METHOD

▲ IMPORTANT All steps in this protocol should be carried out aseptically.

Preparation of Cells

1. Prepare Inoue transformation buffer (chilled to 0°C before use).

   Organic contaminants in the H_2O used to prepare transformation buffers can reduce the efficiency of transformation of competent bacteria. H_2O obtained directly from a well-serviced Milli-Q filtration system (Millipore) usually gives good results. If problems should arise, treat the deionized H_2O with activated charcoal before use.

   a. Prepare 0.5 M PIPES (pH 6.7) (piperazine-1,2-bis[2-ethanesulfonic acid]) by dissolving 15.1 g of PIPES in 80 ml of pure H_2O (Milli-Q, or equivalent). Adjust the pH of the solution to 6.7 with 5 M KOH, and then add pure H_2O to bring the final volume to 100 ml. Sterilize the solution by filtration through a disposable prerinsed Nalgene filter (0.45-μm pore size). Divide into aliquots and store frozen at –20°C.

   b. Prepare Inoue transformation buffer by dissolving all of the solutes listed below in 800 ml of pure H_2O and then add 20 ml of 0.5 M PIPES (pH 6.7). Adjust the volume of the Inoue transformation buffer to 1 liter with pure H_2O.

Reagent	Amount per liter	Final concentration
$MnCl_2 \cdot 4H_2O$	10.88 g	55 mM
$CaCl_2 \cdot 2H_2O$	2.20 g	15 mM
KCl	18.65 g	250 mM
PIPES (0.5 M, pH 6.7)	20 ml	10 mM
H_2O	to 1 liter	

   c. Sterilize Inoue transformation buffer by filtration through a prerinsed 0.45-μm Nalgene filter. Divide into aliquots and store at –20°C.

2. Pick a single bacterial colony (2–3 mm in diameter) from a plate that has been incubated for 16–20 hours at 37ºC. Transfer the colony into 25 ml of LB broth or SOB medium in a 250-ml flask. Incubate the culture for 6–8 hours at 37ºC with vigorous shaking (250–300 rpm).

3. At about 6 o'clock in the evening, use this starter culture to inoculate three 1-liter flasks, each containing 250 ml of SOB. The first flask receives 10 ml of starter culture, the second receives 4 ml, and the third receives 2 ml. Incubate all three flasks overnight at 18–22ºC with moderate shaking.

4. The following morning, read the OD_{600} of all three cultures. Continue to monitor the OD every 45 minutes.

5. When the OD_{600} of one of the cultures reaches 0.55, transfer the culture vessel to an ice-water bath for 10 minutes. Discard the two other cultures.

   > The ambient temperature of most laboratories rises during the day and falls during the night. The number of degrees and the timing of the drop from peak to trough varies depending on the time of year, the number of people working in the laboratory at night, and so on. Because of this variability, it is difficult to predict the rate at which cultures will grow on any given night. Using three different inocula increases the chances that one of the cultures will be at the correct density after an overnight incubation.

6. Harvest the cells by centrifugation at 2500*g* (3900 rpm in a Sorvall GSA rotor) for 10 minutes at 4ºC.

7. Pour off the medium and store the open centrifuge bottle on a stack of paper towels for 2 minutes. Use a vacuum aspirator to remove any drops of remaining medium adhering to walls of the centrifuge bottle or trapped in its neck.

8. Resuspend the cells gently in 80 ml of ice-cold Inoue transformation buffer.

   > The cells are best suspended by swirling rather than pipetting or vortexing.

9. Harvest the cells by centrifugation at 2500*g* (3900 rpm in a Sorvall GSA rotor) for 10 minutes at 4ºC.

10. Pour off the medium and store the open centrifuge tube on a stack of paper towels for 2 minutes. Use a vacuum aspirator to remove any drops of remaining medium adhering to the walls of the centrifuge tube or trapped in its neck.

Freezing of Competent Cells

11. Resuspend the cells gently in 20 ml of ice-cold Inoue transformation buffer.

12. Add 1.5 ml of DMSO. Mix the bacterial suspension by swirling and then store it in ice for 10 minutes.

13. Working quickly, dispense aliquots of the suspensions into chilled, sterile microfuge tubes. Immediately snap-freeze the competent cells by immersing the tightly closed tubes in a bath of liquid nitrogen. Store the tubes at –70ºC until needed.

    > Freezing in liquid nitrogen enhances transformation efficiency by ~5-fold.
    >
    > For most cloning purposes, 50-μl aliquots of the competent-cell suspension will be more than adequate. However, when large numbers of transformed colonies are required (e.g., when constructing cDNA libraries), larger aliquots may be necessary.

14. When needed, remove a tube of competent cells from the –70ºC freezer. Thaw the cells by holding the tube in the palm of the hand. Just as the cells thaw, transfer the tube to an ice bath. Store the cells on ice for 10 minutes.

15. Use a chilled, sterile pipette tip to transfer the competent cells to chilled, sterile 17 × 100-mm polypropylene tubes. Store the cells on ice.

    Glass tubes should not be used since they lower the efficiency of transformation by ~10-fold

Transformation

Include all of the appropriate positive and negative controls (please see the panel on BACTERIAL TRANSFORMATION in Protocol 23).

16. Add the transforming DNA (up to 25 ng per 50 µl of competent cells) in a volume not exceeding 5% of that of the competent cells. Swirl the tubes gently several times to mix their contents. Set up at least two control tubes for each transformation experiment, including a tube of competent bacteria that receives a known amount of a standard preparation of super-helical plasmid DNA and a tube of cells that receives no plasmid DNA at all. Store the tubes on ice for 30 minutes.

17. Transfer the tubes to a rack placed in a preheated 42°C circulating water bath. Store the tubes in the rack for exactly 90 seconds. Do not shake the tubes.

    Heat shock is a crucial step. It is very important that the cells be raised to exactly the right temperature at the correct rate. The incubation times and temperatures given here have been worked out using Falcon 2059 tubes. Other types of tubes will not necessarily yield equivalent results.

18. Rapidly transfer the tubes to an ice bath. Allow the cells to cool for 1–2 minutes.

19. Add 800 µl of SOC medium to each tube. Warm the cultures to 37°C in a water bath, and then transfer the tubes to a shaking incubator set at 37°C. Incubate the cultures for 45 minutes to allow the bacteria to recover and to express the antibiotic resistance marker encoded by the plasmid.

    To maximize the efficiency of transformation, gently agitate (<225 cycles/minute) the cells during the recovery period.

    If screening by α-complementation, proceed to Protocol 27 for plating.

20. Transfer the appropriate volume (up to 200 µl per 90-mm plate) of transformed competent cells onto agar SOB medium containing 20 mM $MgSO_4$ and the appropriate antibiotic.

    When selecting for resistance to tetracycline, the entire transformation mixture may be spread on a single plate (or plated in top agar). In this case, collect the bacteria by centrifuging for 20 seconds at room temperature in a microfuge, and then gently resuspend the cell pellet in 100 µl of SOC medium by tapping the sides of the tube.

    ▲ IMPORTANT Sterilize a bent glass rod by dipping it into ethanol and then in the flame of a Bunsen burner. When the rod has cooled to room temperature, spread the transformed cells gently over the surface of the agar plate.

    When selecting for resistance to ampicillin, transformed cells should be plated at low density (<10^4 colonies per 90-mm plate), and the plates should not be incubated for more than 20 hours at 37°C. The enzyme β-lactamase is secreted into the medium from ampicillin-resistant transformants and can rapidly inactivate the antibiotic in regions surrounding the colonies. Thus, plating cells at high density or incubating them for long periods of time results in the appearance of ampicillin-sensitive satellite colonies. This problem is ameliorated, but not completely eliminated, by using carbenicillin rather than ampicillin in selective media and increasing the concentration of antibiotic from 60 µg/ml to 100 µg/ml. The number of ampicillin-resistant colonies does not increase in linear proportion to the number of cells applied to the plate, perhaps because of growth-inhibiting substances released from the cells killed by the antibiotic.

21. Store the plates at room temperature until the liquid has been absorbed.

22. Invert the plates and incubate them at 37°C. Transformed colonies should appear in 12–16 hours.

    Transformed colonies may be screened for the presence of recombinant plasmids using one of the methods described in Protocols 27, 28, 31, and 32 of this chapter or Protocol 12 in Chapter 8.

Protocol 25

Preparation and Transformation of Competent *E. coli* using Calcium Chloride

THE FOLLOWING SIMPLE AND RAPID VARIATION OF THE TECHNIQUE published by Cohen et al. (1972) is frequently used to prepare batches of competent bacteria that yield 5×10^6 to 2×10^7 transformed colonies/μg of supercoiled plasmid DNA. This efficiency of transformation is high enough to allow all routine cloning in plasmids to be performed with ease. Competent cells made by this procedure may be preserved at –70°C, although there may be some deterioration in the efficiency of transformation during prolonged storage.

MATERIALS

Buffers and Solutions

Please see Appendix 1 for components of stock solutions, buffers, and reagents. Dilute stock solutions to the appropriate concentrations.

$CaCl_2 \cdot 2H_2O$ (1 M)
When preparing competent cells, thaw a 10-ml aliquot of the stock solution and dilute it to 100 ml with 90 ml of pure H_2O. Sterilize the solution by filtration through a prerinsed Nalgene filter (0.45-μm pore size), and then chill it to 0°C.

or

Standard transformation buffer (TFB) (please see Protocol 23, Step 1)
For many strains of *E. coli*, standard TFB (Hanahan 1983) may be used instead of $CaCl_2$ with equivalent or better results.

$MgCl_2$–$CaCl_2$ solution, ice cold

Media

LB or SOB medium for initial growth of culture

SOB agar plates containing 20 mM $MgSO_4$ and the appropriate antibiotic
Standard SOB contains 10 mM $MgSO_4$.

SOC medium
Approximately 1 ml of this medium is required for each transformation reaction.

Nucleic Acids and Oligonucleotides

Plasmid DNA (recombinant plasmid)
Construct using one of the methods described in Protocols 17 through 22 of this chapter.

Centrifuges and Rotors

Sorvall GSA rotor or equivalent

Special Equipment

Polypropylene tube (50 ml), chilled in ice
Polypropylene tubes (17 x 100 mm; Falcon 2059), chilled in ice
Water bath preset to 42°C

METHOD

▲ IMPORTANT All steps in this procedure should be carried out aseptically.

Preparation of Cells

1. Pick a single bacterial colony (2–3 mm in diameter) from a plate that has been incubated for 16–20 hours at 37°C. Transfer the colony into 100 ml of LB broth or SOB medium in a 1-liter flask. Incubate the culture for 3 hours at 37°C with vigorous agitation, monitoring the growth of the culture. As a guideline, 1 OD_{600} of a culture of *E. coli* strain DH1 contains ~10^9 bacteria/ml.

   > For efficient transformation, it is essential that the number of *viable* cells not exceed 10^8 cells/ml, which for most strains of *E. coli* is equivalent to an OD_{600} of ~0.4. To ensure that the culture does not grow to a higher density, measure the OD_{600} of the culture every 15–20 minutes. Plot a graph of the data so that the time when the OD_{600} of the culture approaches 0.4 can be predicted with some accuracy. Begin to harvest the culture when the OD_{600} reaches 0.35.

   > Because the relationship between the OD_{600} and the number of viable cells/ml varies substantially from strain to strain, the spectrophotometer must be calibrated by measuring the OD_{600} of a growing culture of the particular strain of *E. coli* at different times in its growth cycle and determining the number of viable cells at each of these times by plating dilutions of the culture on LB agar plates in the absence of antibiotics.

2. Transfer the bacterial cells to sterile, disposable, ice-cold 50-ml polypropylene tubes. Cool the cultures to 0°C by storing the tubes on ice for 10 minutes.

3. Recover the cells by centrifugation at 2700*g* (4100 rpm in a Sorvall GSA rotor) for 10 minutes at 4°C.

4. Decant the medium from the cell pellets. Stand the tubes in an inverted position on a pad of paper towels for 1 minute to allow the last traces of media to drain away.

5. Resuspend each pellet by swirling or gentle vortexing in 30 ml of ice-cold $MgCl_2$–$CaCl_2$ solution (80 mM $MgCl_2$, 20 mM $CaCl_2$).

6. Recover the cells by centrifugation at 2700*g* (4100 rpm in a Sorvall GSA rotor) for 10 minutes at 4°C.

7. Decant the medium from the cell pellets. Stand the tubes in an inverted position on a pad of paper towels for 1 minute to allow the last traces of media to drain away.

8. Resuspend the pellet by swirling or gentle vortexing in 2 ml of ice-cold 0.1 M $CaCl_2$ (or TFB) for each 50 ml of original culture.

9. At this point, either use the cells directly for transformation as described in Steps 10 through 16 below or dispense into aliquots and freeze at –70°C (please see Protocol 23, Step 12).

For most strains of *E. coli* (except for MC1061), TFB may be used at this stage instead of $CaCl_2$ with equivalent or better results.

The cells may be stored at 4°C in $CaCl_2$ solution for 24–48 hours (Dagert and Ehrlich 1979). The efficiency of transformation increases four- to sixfold during the first 12–24 hours of storage and thereafter decreases to the original level.

Transformation

Include all of the appropriate positive and negative controls (please see the panel on BACTERIAL TRANSFORMATION in Protocol 23).

10. To transform the $CaCl_2$-treated cells directly, transfer 200 µl of each suspension of competent cells to a sterile, chilled 17 × 100-mm polypropylene tube using a chilled micropipette tip. Add DNA (no more than 50 ng in a volume of 10 µl or less) to each tube. Mix the contents of the tubes by swirling gently. Store the tubes on ice for 30 minutes.

11. Transfer the tubes to a rack placed in a preheated 42°C circulating water bath. Store the tubes in the rack for exactly 90 seconds. Do not shake the tubes.

    Heat shock is a crucial step. It is very important that the cells be raised to exactly the right temperature at the correct rate.

12. Rapidly transfer the tubes to an ice bath. Allow the cells to chill for 1–2 minutes.

13. Add 800 µl of SOC medium to each tube. Incubate the cultures for 45 minutes in a water bath set at 37°C to allow the bacteria to recover and to express the antibiotic resistance marker encoded by the plasmid.

    The cells may be gently agitated (50 cycles/minute or less in a rotary shaker) at 37°C during the recovery period.

    If screening by α-complementation, proceed to Protocol 27 for plating.

14. Transfer the appropriate volume (up to 200 µl per 90-mm plate) of transformed competent cells onto agar SOB medium containing 20 mM $MgSO_4$ and the appropriate antibiotic.

    When selecting for resistance to tetracycline, the entire transformation mixture may be spread on a single plate (or plated in top agar). In this case, collect the bacteria by centrifuging for 20 seconds at room temperature in a microfuge, and then gently resuspend the cell pellet in 100 µl of SOC medium by tapping the sides of the tube.

    ▲ IMPORTANT Sterilize a bent glass rod by dipping it into ethanol and then in the flame of a Bunsen burner. When the rod has cooled to room temperature, spread the transformed cells gently over the surface of the agar plate.

    When selecting for resistance to ampicillin, transformed cells should be plated at low density ($<10^4$ colonies per 90-mm plate), and the plates should not be incubated for more than 20 hours at 37°C. The enzyme β-lactamase is secreted into the medium from ampicillin-resistant transformants and can rapidly inactivate the antibiotic in regions surrounding the colonies. Thus, plating cells at high density or incubating them for long periods of time results in the appearance of ampicillin-sensitive satellite colonies. This problem is ameliorated, but not completely eliminated, by using carbenicillin rather than ampicillin in selective media and increasing the concentration of antibiotic from 60 µg/ml to 100 µg/ml. The number of ampicillin-resistant colonies does not increase in linear proportion to the number of cells applied to the plate, perhaps because of growth-inhibiting substances released from the cells killed by the antibiotic.

15. Store the plates at room temperature until the liquid has been absorbed.

16. Invert the plates and incubate at 37°C. Transformed colonies should appear in 12–16 hours.

    Transformed colonies may be screened for the presence of recombinant plasmids using one of the methods described in Protocols 27, 28, 31, and 32 of this chapter.

Protocol 26

Transformation of *E. coli* by Electroporation

Preparing electrocompetent bacteria is considerably easier than preparing cells for transformation by chemical methods. Bacteria are simply grown to mid-log phase, chilled, centrifuged, washed extensively with ice-cold buffer or H_2O to reduce the ionic strength of the cell suspension, and then suspended in an ice-cold buffer containing 10% glycerol. DNA may be introduced immediately into the bacteria by exposing them to a short high-voltage electrical discharge (Chassy and Flickinger 1987; Chassy et al. 1988; Dower et al. 1988; please see the information panel on ELECTROPORATION). Alternatively, the cell suspension may be snap-frozen and stored at –70ºC for up to 6 months before electroporation, without loss of transforming efficiency.

Because *E. coli* cells are small, they require very high field strengths (12.5–15 kV cm^{-1}) for electroporation compared to those used to introduce DNA into eukaryotic cells (Dower et al. 1988; Smith et al. 1990). Optimal efficiency is achieved using small volumes of a dense slurry of bacteria (~2 $\times$ 10^{10}/ml) contained in specially designed cuvettes fitted with closely spaced electrodes. Electroporation is temperature-dependent and is best carried out at 0–4ºC. The efficiency of transformation drops as much as 100-fold when electroporation is carried out at room temperature.

The highest *efficiency* of transformation (colonies/µg input plasmid DNA) is obtained when the concentration of input DNA is high (1–10 µg/ml) and when the length and intensity of the electrical pulse are such that only 30–50% of the cells survive the procedure. Under these conditions, as many as 80% of the surviving cells may be transformed. Higher *frequencies* of transformation (colonies/molecule input DNA) are obtained when the DNA concentration is low (~10 pg/ml). Most of the transformants then result from the introduction of a single plasmid molecule into an individual cell. High concentrations of DNA, on the other hand, favor the formation of cotransformants in which more than one plasmid molecule becomes established in transformed cells (Dower et al. 1988). This is highly undesirable in some circumstances, for example, when generating cDNA libraries in plasmid vectors.

The method outlined in this protocol works well with most strains of *E. coli* and with plasmids <15 kb in size. However, substantial variation in the efficiency of transformation between strains of *E. coli* has been reported (e.g., please see Elvin and Bingham 1991; Miller and Nickoloff 1995), and given what is known about the mechanism of uptake of DNA by electroporation, it would be reasonable to expect that very large plasmids would transform *E. coli* with reduced efficiency. As is the case with chemical transformation, linear plasmid DNAs introduced into *E. coli* by a pulsed electrical discharge transform very inefficiently — from 10- to 1000-fold less efficiently than the corresponding closed circular DNA — perhaps because the exposed termini of linear DNA are susceptible to attack by intracellular nucleases.

MATERIALS

CAUTION: Please see Appendix 12 for appropriate handling of materials marked with <!>.

Buffers and Solutions

Please see Appendix 1 for components of stock solutions, buffers, and reagents. Dilute stock solutions to the appropriate concentrations.

Glycerol (10% v/v) (molecular biology grade), ice cold
Pure H$_2$O
Milli-Q or equivalent, sterilized by filtration through prerinsed 0.45-μm filters. Store at 4°C.

Nucleic Acids and Oligonucleotides

Plasmid DNA (recombinant plasmid)
Construct using one of the methods described in Protocols 17 through 22 of this chapter.

Media

GYT medium, ice cold
    10% (v)v glycerol
    0.125% (w/v) yeast extract
    0.25% (w/v) tryptone
This recipe comes from Tung and Chow (1995).
LB medium, prewarmed to 37°C
SOB agar plates containing 20 mM MgSO$_4$ and the appropriate antibiotic
Standard SOB contains 10 mM MgSO$_4$.
SOC medium
Approximately 1 ml of this medium is needed for each transformation reaction.

Special Equipment

Electroporation device and cuvettes fitted with electrodes spaced 0.1–0.2 cm apart
The smaller the gap between the electrodes, the higher the strength of the electrical field generated by a given voltage. However, the risk of arcing increases as the distance between the electrodes decreases and as the applied voltage is raised. Conservative investigators will therefore choose cuvettes with a gap of 0.2 cm, whereas those who are willing to take risks with their experiments will opt for the smaller gap.
Ice water bath
Liquid nitrogen <!>

METHOD

▲ IMPORTANT All steps in this protocol should be carried out aseptically.

Preparation of Cells

1. Inoculate a single colony of *E. coli* from a fresh agar plate into a flask containing 50 ml of LB medium. Incubate the culture overnight at 37°C with vigorous aeration (250 rpm in a rotary shaker).

2. Inoculate two aliquots of 500 ml of prewarmed LB medium in separate 2-liter flasks with 25 ml of the overnight bacterial culture. Incubate the flasks at 37°C with agitation (300 cycles/minute in a rotary shaker). Measure the OD$_{600}$ of the growing bacterial cultures every 20 minutes.

Optimum results (>10^9 transformants/µg) are obtained with standard strains of *E. coli* (DH1, DH5α, JM103, JM109, HB101, and their derivatives) when the OD_{600} of the culture is 0.35–0.4. This density is usually achieved after ~2.5 hours of incubation.

For efficient transformation, it is essential that the number of *viable* cells not exceed 10^8 cells/ml, which for most strains of *E. coli* is equivalent to an OD_{600} of ~0.4. To ensure that the culture does not grow to a higher density, measure the OD_{600} of the culture every 15–20 minutes. Plot a graph of the data so that the time when the OD_{600} of the culture approaches 0.4 can be predicted with some accuracy. Begin to harvest the culture when the OD_{600} reaches 0.35.

3. When the OD_{600} of the cultures reaches 0.4, rapidly transfer the flasks to an ice-water bath for 15–30 minutes. Swirl the culture occasionally to ensure that cooling occurs evenly. In preparation for the next step, place the centrifuge bottles in an ice-water bath.

    For maximum efficiency of transformation, it is crucial that the temperature of the bacteria not rise above 4°C at any stage in the protocol.

4. Transfer the cultures to ice-cold centrifuge bottles. Harvest the cells by centrifugation at 1000g (2500 rpm in a Sorvall GSA rotor) for 15 minutes at 4°C. Decant the supernatant and resuspend the cell pellet in 500 ml of ice-cold pure H_2O.

5. Harvest the cells by centrifugation at 1000g (2500 rpm in a Sorvall GSA rotor) for 20 minutes at 4°C. Decant the supernatant and resuspend the cell pellet in 250 ml of ice-cold 10% glycerol.

6. Harvest the cells by centrifugation at 1000g (2500 rpm in a Sorvall GSA rotor) for 20 minutes at 4°C. Decant the supernatant and resuspend the pellet in 10 ml of ice-cold 10% glycerol.

    Take care when decanting because the bacterial pellets lose adherence in 10% glycerol.

7. Harvest cells by centrifugation at 1000g (2500 rpm in a Sorvall GSA rotor) for 20 minutes at 4°C. Carefully decant the supernatant and use a Pasteur pipette attached to a vacuum line to remove any remaining drops of buffer. Resuspend the pellet in 1 ml of ice-cold GYT medium.

    This is best done by gentle swirling rather than pipetting or vortexing.

8. Measure the OD_{600} of a 1:100 dilution of the cell suspension. Dilute the cell suspension to a concentration of 2 × 10^{10} to 3 × 10^{10} cells/ml (1.0 OD_{600} = ~2.5 × 10^8 cells/ml) with ice-cold GYT medium.

9. Transfer 40 µl of the suspension to an ice-cold electroporation cuvette (0.2-cm gap) and test whether arcing occurs when an electrical discharge is applied (please see Step 16 below). If so, wash the remainder of the cell suspension once more with ice-cold GYT medium to ensure that the conductivity of the bacterial suspension is sufficiently low (<5 mEq).

10. To use the electrocompetent cells immediately, proceed directly to Step 12. Otherwise, store the cells at –70°C until required. For storage, dispense 40-µl aliquots of the cell suspension into sterile, ice-cold 0.5-ml microfuge tubes, drop into a bath of liquid nitrogen, and transfer to a –70°C freezer.

11. To use frozen electrocompetent cells, remove an appropriate number of aliquots of cells from the –70°C freezer. Store the tubes at room temperature until the bacterial suspensions are thawed and then transfer the tubes to an ice bath.

Electroporation

12. Pipette 40 µl of the freshly made (or thawed) electrocompetent cells into ice-cold sterile 0.5-ml microfuge tubes. Place the cells on ice, together with an appropriate number of bacterial electroporation cuvettes.

13. Add 10 pg to 25 ng of the DNA to be electroporated in a volume of 1–2 μl to each microfuge tube and incubate the tube on ice for 30–60 seconds. Include all of the appropriate positive and negative controls (please see the panel on BACTERIAL TRANSFORMATION in Protocol 23).

    Ideally, the DNA to be electroporated should be resuspended at a concentration of 1–10 μg/ml in H₂O or TE (pH 8.0). Two options are available when a DNA ligation reaction is used directly for electroporation. Either the ligation reaction can be diluted 1/10 to 1/20 in H₂O or the DNA can be purified by spun-column chromatography or by extraction with phenol:chloroform followed by precipitation with ethanol in the presence of 2 M ammonium acetate. The precipitated DNA is then rinsed with 70% ethanol and resuspended in TE (pH 8.0) or H₂O at a concentration of 1–10 μg/ml.

    For the construction of libraries, where high efficiency is required and cotransformants are undesirable, total DNA concentrations of <10 ng/ml are recommended (Dower et al. 1988). For routine transformation of *E. coli* with a superhelical plasmid, 10–50 pg of DNA is adequate. When subcloning into a plasmid, up to 25 ng of DNA diluted from the ligation mixture can be used.

14. Set the electroporation apparatus to deliver an electrical pulse of 25 μF capacitance, 2.5 kV, and 200 ohm resistance.

15. Pipette the DNA/cell mixture into a cold electroporation cuvette. Tap the solution to ensure that the suspension of bacteria and DNA sits at the bottom of the cuvette. Dry condensation and moisture from the outside of the cuvette. Place the cuvette in the electroporation device.

16. Deliver a pulse of electricity to the cells at the settings indicated above. A time constant of 4–5 milliseconds with a field strength of 12.5 kV/cm should register on the machine.

    The presence of ions in the electroporation cuvette increases the conductivity of the solution and causes the electrical current to arc or skip through the solution of cells and DNA. Arcing is usually manifest by the generation of a popping sound in the cuvette during the electrical pulse. The uneven transfer of the charge through the cuvette drastically reduces the efficiency of transformation. Arcing increases at higher temperatures and occurs with solutions having an electrical conductance >5 mEq (e.g., 10 mM salt or 20 mM Mg²⁺ solutions). If arcing occurs in the presence of DNA but not in its absence, remove ions from the DNA preparation as described in Step 13.

17. As quickly as possible after the pulse, remove the electroporation cuvette and add 1 ml of SOC medium at room temperature.

    Some investigators believe that the addition of medium at room temperature provides a heat shock that increases the efficiency of transformation.

18. Transfer the cells to a 17 × 100-mm or 17 × 150-mm polypropylene tube and incubate the cultures with gentle rotation for 1 hour at 37°C.

    If screening by α-complementation, proceed to Protocol 27 for plating.

19. Plate different volumes (up to 200 μl per 90-mm plate) of the electroporated cells onto SOB agar medium containing 20 mM MgSO₄ and the appropriate antibiotic.

    When transforming with a superhelical plasmid, where transformants can be expected in abundance, a small volume of the bacterial culture can be streaked with a sterile loop onto an agar plate (or a segment of a plate) containing the appropriate antibiotics. However, if only small numbers of transformants are expected, it is best to spread 200-μl aliquots of the bacterial suspension on each of five plates. We do not recommend plating a concentrated suspension of the bacterial culture on a single plate since the large number of dead cells resulting from electroporation may inhibit the growth of rare transformants.

20. Store the plates at room temperature until the liquid has been absorbed.

21. Invert the plates and incubate them at 37°C. Transformed colonies should appear in 12–16 hours.

    Transformed colonies may be screened for the presence of recombinant plasmids using one of the methods described in Protocols 27, 28, 31, and 32 of this chapter.

Protocol 27

Screening Bacterial Colonies Using X-gal and IPTG: α-Complementation

THIS PROTOCOL PRESENTS METHODS FOR IDENTIFYING recombinant plasmids by α-complementation (for a detailed discussion of α-complementation, please see the introduction to this chapter). The chromogenic substrate X-gal (please see the information panel on X-GAL) is mixed with the bacterial culture, combined with molten top agar, and then spread on selection plates. If resources are limited, the required volume of X-gal can be spread on top of an agar plate (please see the panel on ALTERNATE PROTOCOL: DIRECT APPLICATION OF X-GAL AND IPTG TO AGAR PLATES at the end of this protocol). The efficiency of transformation is slightly higher when the bacteria are plated in top agar rather than on the surface of agar plates. Perhaps the transformed bacteria prefer the slightly anaerobic state within the soft agar or the isosmolarity provided by the agar medium. Include the following controls:

- A strain of *E. coli* synthesizing the ω-fragment of β-galactosidase. An ideal control is the parental untransformed strain from which the transformed colonies under test are derived. Colonies of the parental, untransformed strain should all be white.

- The same ω-producing strain transformed by the empty plasmid vector, which encodes the α-fragment of β-galactosidase. These colonies should all be blue.

Methods for performing α-complementation with bacteriophage λ and bacteriophage M13 vectors are described in Chapters 2 and 3, respectively.

MATERIALS

Buffers and Solutions

Please see Appendix 1 for components of stock solutions, buffers, and reagents. Dilute stock solutions to the appropriate concentrations.

IPTG solution (20% w/v)
X-gal solution <!> (2% w/v)
  Please see the information panel on X-GAL.

> IPTG (isopropyl-β-D-thiogalactoside) is a nonfermentable analog of lactose that inactivates the *lacZ* repressor (Barkley and Bourgeois 1978), and therefore induces transcription of the *lac* operon. Most strains of bacteria commonly used for α-complementation, however, do not synthesize significant quantities of *lac* repressor. Consequently, there is usually no need to induce synthesis of the host- and plasmid-encoded fragments of β-galactosidase for histochemical analysis of bacterial colonies. If the bacterial strain carries the I^Q allele of *lac* repressor and/or if the plasmid carries a *lacI* gene, IPTG should be used to induce synthesis of both fragments of the enzyme.

Media

LB or YT agar plates containing the appropriate antibiotic
LB or YT top agar

Special Equipment

Heating block preset to 45°C
Wooden toothpicks or Inoculating needles

Vectors and Bacterial Strains

E. coli *culture, transformed with recombinant plasmids*
Use bacteria transformed by one of the methods described in Protocols 23 through 26 of this chapter.

METHOD

1. Dispense aliquots of molten top agar into 17 × 100-mm tubes. Place the tubes in a 45°C heating block until they are needed.

   Use 3-ml aliquots for 90-mm plates and 7-ml aliquots for 150-ml plates.

2. Remove the first tube from the heating block. Working quickly, add 0.1 ml of bacterial suspension containing <3000 viable bacteria for a 90-mm plate and <10,000 for a 150-mm plate. Close the top of the tube and invert it several times to disperse the bacteria through the molten agar.

3. Open the tube and add the appropriate amounts of X-gal and IPTG (if required) as shown in Table 1-10. Close the top of the tube and gently invert it several times to mix the contents.

4. Quickly pour the molten top agar into the center of a hardened agar plate containing the appropriate antibiotic and distribute the solution by swirling.

5. Repeat Steps 2–4 until all of the samples have been plated.

6. Allow the soft agar to harden at room temperature, wipe any condensation from the lid of the plates, and then incubate the plates in an inverted position for 12–16 hours at 37°C.

TABLE 1-10 Components for Top Agar

SIZE OF PLATE	AMOUNT OF REAGENT		
	MOLTEN TOP AGAR	X-GAL	IPTG[a]
90 mm	3 ml	40 µl	7 µl
150 mm	7 ml	100 µl	20 µl

[a]May not be required; please see the entry on IPTG in the Materials list.

7. Remove the plates from the incubator and store them for several hours at 4ºC, to allow the blue color to develop.

8. Identify colonies carrying recombinant plasmids.

   - Colonies that carry wild-type plasmids contain active β-galactosidase. These colonies are pale blue in the center and dense blue at their periphery.

   - Colonies that carry recombinant plasmids do not contain active β-galactosidase. These colonies are creamy-white or eggshell blue, sometimes with a faint blue spot in the center.

   Viewing the plates against a canary yellow background can enhance the eye's ability to discriminate between blue and white colonies.

9. Select and culture colonies carrying recombinant plasmids.

   Blue or white colonies can develop in several different orientations in the soft agar, often resembling far off tilted galaxies. Regardless of the orientation, they are readily picked by stabbing into the thin layer of soft agar with a sterile inoculating needle or sterile toothpick and transferring the inoculum to a tube of medium containing the appropriate antibiotic.

ALTERNATIVE PROTOCOL: DIRECT APPLICATION OF X-GAL AND IPTG TO AGAR PLATES

An alternative to preparing top agar can be achieved by spreading a concentrated solution of X-gal on the surface of a premade agar plate, rather than incorporating the halogenated galactoside throughout the entire volume of the agar medium. Take care when spreading the X-gal solution. Colonies in the center of the plate may be a deeper blue due to variations in the concentration of X-gal across the plate.

Method

1. Pipette 40 μl of 2% X-gal solution and, if necessary, 7 μl of 20% IPTG solution onto the center of a premade 90-mm agar plate (e.g., LB or YT) containing the appropriate antibiotic. For a 15-cm diameter agar plate, transfer 100 μl of X-gal and, if necessary, 20 μl of IPTG to the center of the plate.

2. Use a sterile spreader (or a bent Pasteur pipette whose tip has been sealed in a flame) to spread the solutions over the entire surface of the plate. Incubate the plate at 37ºC until all of the fluid has disappeared.
   Because of the low volatility of dimethyl formamide, this procedure can take up to 3–4 hours if the plate is freshly made.

3. Inoculate the plate with the bacteria to be tested by streaking with a bacterial loop, by arranging clones with toothpicks, or by spreading up to 100 μl of a bacterial suspension (50,000 cells/ml) on the surface of a 90-mm agar plate or 200 μl on a 15-cm plate.

4. After the inoculum has been absorbed, incubate the plate in an inverted position for 12–19 hours at 37ºC.

5. Remove the plate from the incubator and store it at 4ºC for several hours, during which the blue color develops to its full extent.

6. Identify colonies carrying recombinant plasmids.

Protocol 28

Screening Bacterial Colonies by Hybridization: Small Numbers

THIS PROCEDURE IS USED TO SCREEN A SMALL NUMBER of transformed bacterial colonies (100–200) that are dispersed over several agar plates and are to be screened by hybridization to the same radiolabeled probe (Protocols 29 and 30 deal with the transfer of intermediate and large number of colonies, respectively). The colonies are consolidated (gridded) onto a master agar plate and onto a nitrocellulose or nylon filter laid on the surface of a second agar plate. After a period of growth, the colonies that have grown on the filter are lysed in situ and processed for hybridization, as described in Protocols 31 and 32. Meanwhile, the master plate is stored at 4°C until the results of the screening procedure become available.

Over the years, three types of solid supports have been used for in situ hybridization of lysed bacterial colonies: nitrocellulose filters, nylon filters, and Whatman 541 filter papers. Nylon filters are the most durable of the three and will withstand several rounds of hybridization and washing at elevated temperatures. They are therefore preferred when colonies are to be screened sequentially with a number of different probes. In side-by-side comparisons, nylon filters yield enhanced hybridization signals relative to nitrocellulose filters. However, when screening bacterial colonies, the hybridization signal is usually so strong that this difference between the two solid supports is not a significant factor. When they were first introduced, different treatments were required to fix efficiently DNA to nylon filters sold by different manufacturers. Although satisfactory results can be obtained by treating currently available nylon filters as if they were nitrocellulose, optimal performance still requires adherence to the manufacturers' instructions.

Whatman 541 filter paper, which has a high wet-strength, was first used to screen bacterial colonies by Gergen et al. (1979). It is now used chiefly to screen arrayed libraries that are stored as cultures of individual transformed colonies in separate wells of microtiter plates (Linbro Scientific). These ordered libraries are duplicated on the surface of agar medium (usually in square Petri dishes), and the resulting colonies are then transferred to Whatman 541 paper and lysed either by alkali or by a combination of alkali and heat (Maas 1983). Conditions for hybridization of the immobilized DNA are essentially identical to those established for nitrocellulose filters. Whatman 541 paper has some advantages over nitrocellulose filters: It is less expensive, more durable during hybridization, and less prone to distortion and cracking during drying. However, unless care is taken during the denaturation step (Maas 1983), the strength of the hybridization signal is significantly lower than that obtained from nitrocellulose filters. For routine screening of bacterial colonies, therefore, nitrocellulose or nylon filters remain the preferred choice as solid supports.

MATERIALS

CAUTION: Please see Appendix 12 for appropriate handling of materials marked with <!>.

Media

LB or SOB agar plates containing the appropriate antibiotic
LB or SOB agar plates containing chloramphenicol <!>
   Optional, please see Step 5. Chloramphenicol is supplemented at 170–200 µg/ml.

Special Equipment

Nitrocellulose (Millipore HAWP, or equivalent) or Nylon filters
   Filters need not be detergent-free or sterile.
Syringe (3 cc), Hypodermic needles (18 gauge), and Waterproof black drawing ink (India Ink)
   These materials are used to orient the filters on the master plates. For an alternative method, please see note to Step 6.
Wooden toothpicks or Inoculating loops

Additional Reagents

Step 8 of this protocol requires the reagents listed in Protocols 31 and 32 of this chapter.

Vectors and Bacterial Strains

E. coli strain, transformed with recombinant plasmids
   Use bacteria transformed by one of the methods described in Protocols 23 through 26 of this chapter.
E. coli strain, transformed with nonrecombinant plasmid (e.g., pUC, used as a negative control)

METHOD

1. Place a nitrocellulose or nylon filter on an agar plate (test plate) containing the selective antibiotic.

   Handle the filter with gloved hands as finger oils prevent wetting of the filter and prevent DNA transfer.

2. Draw a numbered grid on a piece of graph paper (1-cm-square grid). Number the base of each agar master plate and place the plate on the grid. Draw a mark on the side of the plate at the 6 o'clock position.

   This marking allows the master plate to be orientated with the grid.

3. Use sterile toothpicks or inoculating loops to transfer bacterial colonies one by one onto the filter on the test plate and then onto the master agar plate that contains the selective antibiotic but no filter. Make small streaks 2–3 mm in length (or dots) arranged according to the grid pattern under the dish. Streak each colony in an identical position on both plates.

   Up to 100 colonies can be streaked onto a single 90-mm plate.

4. Finally, streak a colony containing a nonrecombinant plasmid (e.g., pUC) onto the filter and the master plate.

   This negative control is necessary to show that the radiolabeled probe can discriminate between empty plasmids and recombinants. DNA fragments isolated from recombinant plasmids by restriction enzyme cleavage and agarose gel electrophoresis are often contaminated with plasmid DNA sequences, which can create problems when these fragments are used as hybridization probes for Grunstein-Hogness screening (Grunstein and Hogness 1975) of transformed bacterial colonies.

5. Invert the plates and incubate them at 37ºC until the bacterial streaks have grown to a width of 0.5–1.0 mm (typically 6–16 hours).

    At this stage, when the bacteria are still growing rapidly, the filter may be transferred to an agar plate containing chloramphenicol and incubated for a further 12 hours at 37ºC (Hanahan and Meselson 1980, 1983). This amplification step is necessary only when the copy number of the recombinant plasmid is expected to be low (e.g., if a large segment of foreign DNA has been inserted) or when highly degenerate oligonucleotides are used as probes. Under normal circumstances, cloned DNA sequences can be detected very easily by hybridization without prior amplification of the recombinant plasmid. Amplification can only be carried out with vectors that replicate in relaxed fashion (please see introduction to this chapter).

6. Mark the filter in three or more asymmetric locations by stabbing through it and into the agar of the test plate with an 18-gauge needle, attached to a syringe, dipped in waterproof black drawing ink (India Ink). Mark the master plate in approximately the same locations.

    With practice, it is possible to avoid the use of ink (which can be messy) by punching holes through the filter into the underlying agar with an empty 18-gauge needle. After hybridization, back lighting via a light box can be used to align the holes in the filter with the marks in the agar.

    Many investigators prefer to orient the filter by using sharp scissors to cut small notches at various points on its circumference. After the notched and numbered filter has been placed on the surface of the agar, the positions of the serrations are marked on the bottom of the plate. The shapes of the serrations and their positions define the orientation of the filter on the plate.

7. Seal the master plate with Parafilm and store it at 4ºC in an inverted position until the results of the hybridization reaction are available.

8. Lyse the bacteria adhering to the filter and bind the liberated DNA to the nitrocellulose or nylon filter using the procedures described in Protocol 31. Proceed with hybridization as described in Protocol 32.

Protocol 29

Screening Bacterial Colonies by Hybridization: Intermediate Numbers

BACTERIAL COLONIES GROWING ON AGAR PLATES can be transferred en masse to nitrocellulose filters. A sterile filter is placed directly onto the bacterial colonies. After a short period of time to allow transfer of bacterial cells to the filter, the filter is gently removed and prepared for hybridization. However, if the copy number of the recombinant plasmid is expected to be low (e.g., if a large segment of foreign DNA has been inserted) or when highly degenerate oligonucleotides are used as probes, the filter may be placed (colony side up) on the surface of a fresh agar plate containing the appropriate antibiotic. After incubation for a few hours, the filter with its cargo of enlarged colonies is prepared for hybridization. Meanwhile, the original (master) plate is incubated for a few hours to allow the bacterial colonies to regrow in their original positions.

These procedures work with bacterial colonies of any size, but small colonies give the clearest results as they produce sharp hybridization signals and do not smear during transfer from the agar plate to the filter. The method works best with 90-mm plates containing up to 2500 colonies. Larger filters are difficult to place perfectly on the surface of 150-mm plates without air bubbles. For further information on filters, please refer to the introduction to Protocol 28.

MATERIALS

CAUTION: Please see Appendix 12 for appropriate handling of materials marked with <!>.

Media

LB or SOB agar plates (90-mm) containing appropriate antibiotics
Plates that are 2–3 days old give the best results in this protocol because they absorb fluid from the bacterial inoculum more readily.

LB or SOB plates containing chloramphenicol <!>
Optional, please see Step 6. Chloramphenicol is used at 170–200 µg/ml.

Special Equipment

Nitrocellulose (Millipore HATF, or equivalent) or Nylon filters, sterile and detergent-free

Syringe (3 cc), Hypodermic needles (23 gauge), and Waterproof black drawing ink (India Ink)
These materials are used to orient the filters on the master plates. For an alternative method, please see note to Step 4.

Whatman 3MM circular filter papers
Prepare in advance a stack of Whatman 3MM papers (one for each nitrocellulose or nylon, plus a few spares) cut to a size slightly larger than the filters. These are commercially available as precut circles from several manufacturers.

Additional Reagents

Step 6 of this protocol requires the reagents listed in Protocols 31 and 32 of this chapter.

Vectors and Bacterial Strains

E. coli *strain, transformed with recombinant plasmids, as culture*

Use bacteria transformed by one of the methods described in Protocols 23 through 26 of this chapter.

METHOD

1. Plate out the transformed *E. coli* culture onto 90-mm LB or SOB agar plates, at dilutions calculated to generate up to 2500 transformed colonies. When the colonies reach an average size of 1.5 mm, transfer the plates from the incubator to a cold room.

2. Number the dry filters with a soft-lead pencil or a ball-point pen, wet them with water, and interleave them between dry Whatman 3MM filters. Wrap the stack of filters loosely in aluminum foil, and sterilize them by autoclaving (15 psi [1.05 kg/cm²] for 10 minutes on liquid cycle).

   Prepare enough filters to make one or two replicas from the starting agar plates. Although sterile filters are preferred for this procedure, nonsterile filters may be used if no more replicas are to be made from the master plate.

3. Place a dry, sterile detergent-free nitrocellulose filter, numbered side down, on the surface of the LB (or SOB) agar medium, in contact with the bacterial colonies (plated in Step 1), until it is completely wet.

   Take care to prevent air bubbles from becoming trapped between the filter and the agar. This is best done by bending the filter slightly so that contact is first made between the center of the filter and the agar medium. Be careful not to move the filter relative to the agar medium after contact has been made.

4. Once the filter is in place, key the filter to the underlying medium by stabbing in three or more asymmetric locations through the filter with a 23-gauge needle attached to a syringe, dipped in waterproof black drawing ink.

   A 23-gauge needle or smaller dipped in ink works best (dip once per plate, three holes per plate).

   With practice, it is possible to avoid the use of ink (which can be messy) by punching holes through the filter into the underlying agar with an empty 18-gauge needle. After hybridization, back lighting via a light box can be used to align the holes in the filter with the marks in the agar.

   Many investigators prefer to orient the filter by using sharp scissors to cut small notches at various points on its circumference. After the notched and numbered filter has been placed on the surface of the agar, the positions of the serrations are marked on the bottom of the plate. The shapes of the serrations and their positions define the orientation of the filter on the plate.

5. Grip the edge of the filter with blunt-ended forceps and, in a single smooth movement, peel the filter from the surface of the agar.

   Usually, the colonies are transferred in their entirety from the agar to the filter leaving behind small indentations in the surface of the medium. When the master plate is incubated at 37°C, the remaining bacteria grow to fill the indentations but do not expand further.

6. Proceed with one of the following options as appropriate:

   - Lyse the bacteria adhering to the filter and bind the liberated DNA to the nitrocellulose or nylon filter using the procedures described in Protocol 31. Proceed with hybridization as described in Protocol 32.

   - Lyse the bacteria and immobilize the DNA as described in the alternative protocol at the end of this protocol.

- Place the filter, colony side up, on the surface of a fresh LB (or SOB) agar plate containing the appropriate antibiotic. After incubation for a few hours, when the colonies have grown to a size of 2–3 mm, remove the filter and proceed with lysis and hybridization as described in Protocols 31 and 32.

  This option should be taken only when the transfer of the colonies to the filter is poor or uneven, which is not usually the case.

- Amplify the colonies on the filter by transferring the filter to an agar plate containing chloramphenicol (170–200 µg/ml) and incubating for 12 hours at 37°C. Proceed with lysis and hybridization (Protocols 31 and 32).

  This amplification step (Hanahan and Meselson 1980, 1983) is necessary only when the copy number of the recombinant plasmid is expected to be low (e.g., if a large segment of foreign DNA has been inserted) or when highly degenerate oligonucleotides are used as probes. Under normal circumstances, cloned DNA sequences can be detected very easily by hybridization without prior amplification of the recombinant plasmid. Amplification can only be carried out with vectors that replicate in relaxed fashion (please see introduction to this chapter).

- Use the filter to prepare a second replica:

  a. Place the filter colony side up on the surface of a fresh LB (or SOB) agar plate containing the appropriate antibiotic.

  b. Lay a dry nitrocellulose filter carefully on top of the first and key to it as described in Step 4 above.

  c. Incubate the "filter sandwich" for several hours at 37°C.

    The plasmids are amplified, if desired, by further incubation on an agar plate containing chloramphenicol.

  d. Proceed with lysis and hybridization (Protocols 31 and 32), keeping the filters as a sandwich during the lysis and neutralization steps, but peeling them apart before the final wash (Ish-Horowicz and Burke 1981).

7. Incubate the master plate for 5–7 hours at 37°C until the colonies have regrown (please see note to Step 5). Seal the plate with Parafilm, and store it at 4°C in an inverted position.

ALTERNATIVE PROTOCOL: RAPID LYSIS OF COLONIES AND BINDING OF DNA TO NYLON FILTERS

The following procedure, based on a protocol developed by Gary Struhl in 1983 while he was a post-doc in Tom Maniatis' laboratory, eliminates treatment of nylon filters with alkali and can save time when dealing with large numbers of filters. Note that nitrocellulose filters may only be used in this procedure if they have been autoclaved prior to colony transfer.

Method

1. After removing the filters from the top agarose (Step 5), place them, DNA side up, on paper towels for 5–10 minutes.

2. When their edges begin to curl, place the filters in stacks of ten interleaved with circular Whatman 3MM papers. Place a few 3MM papers on the top and bottom of the stack.

3. Place the stacks on a small platform (e.g., an inverted Pyrex dish) in an autoclave. Expose the filters to "streaming steam" for 3 minutes (i.e., 100°C; avoid super-heated steam).

4. Transfer the stack of filter papers and nitrocellulose filters to a vacuum oven. Bake for 2 hours at 80°C while drawing a vacuum continuously. Remove any 3MM paper that sticks to the nitrocellulose filters by soaking in 2x SSPE before prehybridizing.

Protocol 30

Screening Bacterial Colonies by Hybridization: Large Numbers

THIS METHOD IS USED TO PLATE AND SUBSEQUENTLY REPLICATE large numbers of colonies onto nitrocellulose or nylon filters. The procedure is derived from Hanahan and Meselson (1980, 1983) and is chiefly used when plating out bacteria transformed by a plasmid cDNA library. The bacteria are plated directly from a transformation mixture or an amplified aliquot of the cDNA library onto detergent-free nitrocellulose filters, and replica filters are prepared by filter-to-filter contact. Using this technique, as many as 2×10^4 colonies per 150-mm plate or 10^4 colonies per 90-mm plate can be replicated and subsequently screened by hybridization. For further information on filters, please refer to the introduction to Protocol 28.

MATERIALS

CAUTION: Please see Appendix 12 for appropriate handling of materials marked with <!>.

Media

LB or SOB agar plates containing appropriate antibiotics
   Plates that are 2–3 days old give the best results in this protocol because they absorb fluid from the bacterial inoculum more readily.

LB or SOB agar plates containing appropriate antibiotics and 25% (v/v) glycerol

LB or SOB plates containing chloramphenicol <!>
   Optional, please see Step 12. Chloramphenicol is supplemented at 170–200 µg/ml.

Special Equipment

Blunt-ended forceps (e.g., Millipore forceps)
Hypodermic needles (18 gauge)
Nitrocellulose (Millipore HATF, or equivalent) or Nylon filters, sterile and detergent-free
Syringe barrel (3 cc)
Whatman 3MM circular filter papers
   Prepare a stack of Whatman 3MM papers in advance (one for each nitrocellulose or nylon filter, plus a few spares) cut to a size slightly larger than the filters. These are commercially available as precut circles from several manufacturers. Wrap the stack of Whatman 3MM papers in aluminum foil and sterilize them by autoclaving for 10 minutes at 15 psi (1.05 kg/cm^2) on liquid cycle.

Additional Reagents

Step 14 of this protocol requires the reagents listed in Protocols 31 and 32 of this chapter.

Vectors and Bacterial Strains

E. coli *strain, transformed with recombinant plasmids, as culture*

Use bacteria transformed by one of the methods described in Protocols 23 through 26 of this chapter.

or

Amplified aliquot of cDNA library, grown as culture

Please see Chapter 11, Protocol 1.

METHOD

Plating Out the Transformation Mix

1. Number the dry filters with a soft-lead pencil or a ball-point pen, wet them with water, and interleave them between dry Whatman 3MM filters. Wrap the stack of filters loosely in aluminum foil, and sterilize them by autoclaving (15 psi [1.05 kg/cm^2] for 10 minutes on liquid cycle).

    Prepare enough filters to make one or two replicas from the starting agar plates. Although sterile filters are preferred for this procedure, nonsterile filters may be used if no more replicas are to be made from the master plate.

2. Use sterile, blunt-ended forceps to lay a sterile filter, numbered side down, on a 2–3-day-old LB (or SOB) agar plate containing the appropriate antibiotic. When the filter is thoroughly wet, peel it from the plate and replace it, numbered side up, on the surface of the agar.

3. Apply the bacteria, in a small volume of liquid, to the center of the filter on the surface of the agar plate. Use a sterile glass spreader to disperse the fluid evenly, leaving a border 2–3 mm wide around the circumference of the filter free of bacteria.

    A large filter (137-mm diameter) will accommodate up to 0.5 ml of liquid containing 2×10^4 viable bacteria. A small filter (82-mm diameter) will accommodate up to 0.2 ml of liquid containing a ~10^4 bacteria.

4. Incubate the plate (noninverted) with the lid ajar for a few minutes in a laminar flow hood to allow the inoculum to evaporate. Then close the lid, invert the plate, and incubate at 37ºC until small colonies (0.1–0.2-mm diameter) appear (~8–10 hours).

5. If desired, replica filters may be prepared at this stage (proceed with Step 6). Otherwise, prepare the bacterial colonies for storage at –20ºC:

    a. Transfer the filter colony side up to a labeled LB (or SOB) agar plate containing the appropriate antibiotic and 25% glycerol.

    b. Incubate the plate for 2 hours at 37ºC.

        When working with a cDNA library, it is best to freeze the master plate. Freezing decreases the possibility of contamination with molds and fungi and preserves the master plate for many months. Alternatively, the master filters can be stored for up to 2 weeks at 4ºC on LB or SOB plates containing antibiotic and no glycerol.

    c. Seal the plate well with Parafilm, and store it in an inverted position in a sealed plastic bag at –20ºC.

        Replicas can be made after thawing the master plate at room temperature (still in the inverted position).

Making the Replica Filters

6. Lay the master nitrocellulose or nylon filter colony side up on a sterile Whatman 3MM paper.

7. Number a damp, sterile nitrocellulose or nylon filter, and lay it on the master filter. Take care to prevent air bubbles from becoming trapped between the two filters.

   This is best done by bending the second filter slightly so that contact is first made between the centers of the filters. Be careful not to move the filters relative to one another once contact has been made. Try to arrange the filters so that they do not overlap exactly; this makes it easier to separate the two filters later on.

8. Cover the filter sandwich with a second 3MM circle and place the bottom of a Petri dish on top of the 3MM paper. Press down firmly on the Petri dish with the palm of the hand to facilitate transfer of bacteria from the master filter to the replica.

9. Dismantle the Petri dish bottom and top 3MM paper, and orient the two filters by making a series of holes with an 18-gauge needle attached to a syringe.

   Make sure the needle punctures both filters!

10. Peel the filters apart. Lay the replica on a fresh LB (or SOB) agar plate containing the appropriate antibiotic.

    A second replica can be made from the master filter at this point by repeating Steps 6 through 9. Key the second replica to the existing holes in the master filter.

11. Place the second replica filter (if made) and the master filter on a fresh LB (or SOB) agar plate containing the appropriate antibiotic and incubate all plates at 37ºC until colonies appear (4–6 hours).

12. At this stage, when the bacteria are still growing rapidly, the filter may be transferred to an agar plate containing chloramphenicol (170–200 μg/ml) and incubated for 12 hours at 37ºC.

13. Move the master nitrocellulose filter to a fresh LB (or SOB) agar plate containing the appropriate antibiotic and 25% glycerol. Then freeze it as described in Step 5.

14. Lyse the bacteria adhering to the replica filters and bind the liberated DNA to the nitrocellulose or nylon filter using the procedures described in Protocol 31. Proceed with hybridization as described in Protocol 32.

Protocol 31

Lysing Colonies and Binding of DNA to Filters

THIS PROTOCOL DESCRIBES THE LIBERATION OF DNA from bacterial colonies transformed with recombinant plasmids, and the subsequent fixing of the nucleic acid to the nitrocellulose or nylon filters in situ. The method is based on the original procedure of Grunstein and Hogness (1975). The hybridization of radiolabeled probes to nucleic acids immobilized on filters is presented in Protocol 32.

Both baking and cross-linking serve to fix the bacterial DNA to the nylon or nitrocellulose filters. The choice between the two methods depends on the equipment at hand and the way in which the filters will be used. If the filters are to be hybridized with several different probes and stripped between probing reactions, then it is better to cross-link the DNA to the filters with UV light. For single hybridization reactions, we have not been able to discern a difference between the two fixation methods regarding the efficiencies with which DNA is fixed to the filter, the amount of nonspecific background hybridization, or the intensity or crispness of the autoradiographic signal from a positive colony. Cross-linking is faster than baking, requiring 20–30 seconds per filter, compared to a 1–2-hour bake. However, cross-linking is usually carried out in a machine that is adjusted to deliver a set amount of energy to each filter. These UV light cross-linkers are expensive and generally have a life of ~1 year in an active laboratory. Vacuum baking ovens cost about the same amount but last 10 years or more in very active departments.

MATERIALS

CAUTION: Please see Appendix 12 for appropriate handling of materials marked with <!>.

Buffers and Solutions

Please see Appendix 1 for components of stock solutions, buffers, and reagents. Dilute stock solutions to the appropriate concentrations.

Denaturing solution
Neutralizing solution
SDS (10% w/v)
   Optional, please see Steps 1 and 3.
2x SSPE

Special Equipment

Glass or plastic trays for processing filters
   Cafeteria trays are ideal for this purpose, as they can accommodate batches of up to 25 filters of 9–10-cm diameter.

> *Microwave oven, Vacuum baking oven, preset to 80°C, or UV light<!> cross-linking device*
>   Please see Source book for a list of manufacturers of cross-linking devices.
> *Whatman 3MM paper*

Vectors and Bacterial Strains

> *Filters carrying colonies of* E. coli *transformants*
>   Use transformants prepared by one of the methods described in Protocols 28 through 30 of this chapter.

METHOD

1. Cut four pieces of Whatman 3MM paper (or an equivalent) to an appropriate size and shape and fit them neatly onto the bottoms of four glass or plastic trays. Saturate each of the pieces of 3MM paper with one of the following solutions:
     10% SDS (optional)
     denaturing solution
     neutralizing solution
     2x SSPE

2. Pour off any excess liquid and roll a 10-ml pipette along the sheet to smooth out any air bubbles that occur between the 3MM paper and the bottom of the container.

   > If the 3MM paper is too wet, the bacterial colonies swell and diffuse during lysis. The hybridization signals then become blurred and attenuated, and it is very difficult to identify individual colonies that give rise to the signal.

3. Use blunt-ended forceps to peel the nitrocellulose or nylon filters from their plates and place them colony side up on the SDS-impregnated 3MM paper for 3 minutes.

   > This treatment limits the diffusion of the plasmid DNA during subsequent denaturation and neutralization and results in a sharper hybridization signal.

4. After the first filter has been exposed to the SDS solution for 3 minutes, transfer it to the second sheet of 3MM paper saturated with denaturing solution. Transfer the remainder of the filters in the same order in which they were removed from their agar plates. Expose each filter to the denaturing solution for 5 minutes.

   > When transferring filters from one tray to another, use the edge of the first tray as a scraper to remove as much fluid as possible from the underside of the filter. Alternatively, remove excess liquid by transferring the filter briefly to a dry paper towel. Try to avoid getting fluid on the side of the filter carrying the bacterial colonies.

5. Transfer the filters to the third sheet of 3MM paper, which has been saturated with neutralizing solution. Leave the filters for 5 minutes.

   > *Optional:* Repeat this step once.

6. Transfer the filters to the last sheet of 3MM paper, which has been saturated with 2x SSPE. Leave the filters for 5 minutes.

   > We prefer to fill a tray or tub (such as that used in washing filters after hybridization) with a volume of 2x SSPE and then to float the filters from Step 5 on the surface of this solution for several minutes. Thereafter, the container is agitated to sink the filter below the surface of the solution and left until the last filter to be worked up is similarly treated. This step accomplishes two goals: rinsing the filter of neutralization solution and inundating the filter with EDTA to chelate divalent cations such as Mg^{2+} and thereby to inhibit the action of any residual nucleases that degrade DNA.

7. Dry the filters using one of the methods below.

   If the DNA is to be fixed to the filters by baking: Lay the filters, colony side up, on a sheet of dry 3MM paper and allow them to dry at room temperature for at least 30 minutes.

   If the DNA is to be fixed to the filters by cross-linking with UV light: Lay the filters on a sheet of 2x SSPE-impregnated 3MM paper or on dry paper, depending on the manufacturer's recommendation.

8. Fix the DNA to the filters using one of the methods below.

   For baking: Sandwich the filters between two sheets of dry 3MM paper, and fix the DNA to the filters by baking for 1–2 hours at 80ºC in a vacuum oven.

   > Overbaking can cause the filters to become brittle. Nitrocellulose filters that have not been completely neutralized turn yellow or brown during baking and chip very easily. The background of nonspecific hybridization also increases dramatically in this situation.

   For cross-linking with UV light: Follow the manufacturer's instructions for fixing DNA to filters using a commercial device for this purpose.

9. Hybridize the DNA immobilized on the filters to a labeled probe as described in Protocol 32.

   > Any filters not used immediately in hybridization reactions should be interleaved between 3MM filters and stored covered in aluminum foil at room temperature.

Protocol 32

Hybridization of Bacterial DNA on Filters

THIS PROTOCOL PROVIDES PROCEDURES TO HYBRIDIZE DNA from transformed colonies immobilized onto filters with radiolabeled probes and to recover from a master plate the corresponding colonies that hybridize specifically to the probe. These techniques are designed to be used with probes that are on average longer than 100 nucleotides in length. Methods for screening bacterial colonies with shorter radiolabeled oligonucleotides are given in Chapter 10.

The purity of a radiolabeled DNA or RNA probe is important when screening plasmid-containing bacterial colonies. Cloned DNA fragments excised from plasmids are commonly used to prepare the hybridization probe. However, even a small amount of contamination by vector sequences will generate probes that hybridize to bacterial colonies transformed by any plasmid used in molecular cloning. This lack of specificity can also occur when using probes prepared from bacteriophages to screen plasmids (or vice versa), since many vectors contain fragments of the *lacZ* gene. To ensure that a DNA fragment that will be used to prepare a hybridization probe does not contain vector sequences, we recommend purifying the DNA through two gels (agarose or polyacrylamide) as described in Chapter 5, before carrying out the radiolabeling reaction.

The following protocol is designed for 30 circular nitrocellulose filters, 82 mm in diameter. Appropriate adjustments to the volumes should be made when carrying out hybridization reactions with different numbers or sizes of filters.

MATERIALS

CAUTION: Please see Appendix 12 for appropriate handling of materials marked with <!>.

Buffers and Solutions

Please see Appendix 1 for components of stock solutions, buffers, and reagents.
Dilute stock solutions to the appropriate concentrations.

Formamide <!>
Optional, please see the panel on **PREHYBRIDIZATION AND HYBRIDIZATION SOLUTIONS** following Step 5. Many batches of reagent-grade formamide are sufficiently pure to be used without further treatment. However, if any yellow color is present, the formamide should be deionized (please see Appendix 1).

Prehybridization/hybridization solution
Please see the panel on **PREHYBRIDIZATION AND HYBRIDIZATION SOLUTIONS** following Step 5.

1x BLOTTO <!>

1x BLOTTO (Bovine Lacto Transfer Technique Optimizer [Johnson et al. 1984]) is as effective a blocking agent as Denhardt's reagent, but much less expensive.

> BLOTTO should not be used in combination with high concentrations of SDS, which will cause the milk proteins to precipitate. If background hybridization is a problem, NP-40 may be added to the hybridization solution to a final concentration of 1%. BLOTTO should not be used as a blocking reagent when radiolabeled RNA is used as the hybridization probe, because of the possibility that the dried milk may contain significant amounts of RNase activity. In this situation, 5x Denhardt's solution (please see Appendix 1) should be substituted for BLOTTO.

Prewashing solution
6x SSC or 6x SSPE

Wash solution 1
2x SSC
0.1% (w/v) SDS

Wash solution 2
1x SSC
0.1% (w/v) SDS

Wash solution 3
0.1x SSC
0.1% (w/v) SDS

Media

LB, YT, or Terrific Broth containing the appropriate antibiotic

Nucleic Acids and Oligonucleotides

Filters with immobilized DNA from transformed colonies
Use filters prepared as described in Protocol 31.

Probes

^{32}P-labeled double-stranded DNA probe or Synthetic oligonucleotide probes
Prepare the probes as described in Chapter 9 (for double-stranded DNA probe) or Chapter 10 (for oligonucleotide probes). For a further discussion of probes for colony screening, please see the protocol introduction. Between 2×10^5 and 1×10^6 cpm of ^{32}P-labeled probe (specific activity ~5×10^7 cpm/µg) should be used per milliliter of prehybridization solution. When ^{32}P-labeled cDNA or RNA is used as a probe, poly(A) at a concentration of 1 µg/ml should be included in the prehybridization and hybridization solutions to prevent the probe from binding to T-rich sequences that are common in eukaryotic DNA.

Special Equipment

Boiling water bath
Glass baking dish (15 x 7.5 x 5 cm) or other hybridization chamber
Incubators preset to 42°C (if prehybridizing in formamide), 50°C, and 68°C

> **ALTERNATIVE HYBRIDIZATION CHAMBERS**
>
> Some investigators prefer to incubate filters in heat-sealable plastic bags (Sears Seal-A-Meal or equivalent) during the prehybridizaton and hybridization steps, rather than in crystallization dishes. The former method avoids problems with evaporation and, because the sealed bags can be submerged in a water bath, ensures that the temperatures during hybridization and washing are correct. The bags must be opened and resealed when changing buffers. To avoid radioactive contamination of the water bath, the resealed bag containing radioactivity should be sealed inside a second, noncontaminated bag.
>
> If only a small number of filters are subjected to hybridization, then a glass screw-top bottle that fits the rollers of a hybridization oven can be used in place of a crystallization dish or Seal-A-Meal bag. These bottles and ovens have the advantage that small volumes of hybridization solution can be used and the hybridization temperature can be accurately controlled. For further details, please see the panel on **HYBRIDIZATION CHAMBERS** in Chapter 6, Protocol 10.

Radioactive ink <!>

> Reusable alternatives to radioactive ink are chemiluminescent markers available from Stratagene (Glogos). The markers can be used multiple times and should be exposed to fluorescent light just prior to a new round of autoradiography.

Water-soluble glue stick

> For example, UHU Stic, distributed by FaberCastell.

Whatman 3MM paper or equivalent

Wooden toothpicks or Inoculating needle

Additional Reagents

Step 15 of this protocol requires the reagents listed in Protocol 1 or 4 of this chapter.

Step 15 may also require the reagents listed in Chapter 8, Protocol 12.

METHOD

Prewashing and Prehybridization of the Filters

1. Float the baked or cross-linked filters on the surface of a tray of 2× SSC until they have become thoroughly wetted from beneath. Submerge the filters for 5 minutes.

   > Because some batches of nitrocellulose filters swell and distort during hybridization and subsequent drying, it becomes difficult to align the orientation dots on the autoradiograph and filter or agar plate. This problem can be alleviated to some extent by autoclaving the dry filters between pieces of damp 3MM paper before use (10 psi [0.70 kg/cm^2] for 10 minutes on liquid cycle). Nylon filters do not suffer from this problem.

2. Transfer the filters to a glass baking dish containing at least 200 ml of prewashing solution. Stack the filters on top of one another in the solution. Cover the dish with Saran Wrap and transfer it to a rotating platform in an incubator. Incubate the filters for 30 minutes at 50°C.

   > This prewashing step removes bacterial colony debris and can substantially reduce background hybridization, especially when screening colonies at high density.

   > In this and all subsequent steps, the filters should be slowly agitated to prevent them from sticking to one another. Do not allow the filters to dry at any stage during the prewashing, prehybridization, or hybridization steps.

3. Gently scrape the bacterial debris from the surfaces of the filters using Kimwipes soaked in prewashing solution. This scraping ensures removal of colony debris and does not affect the intensity or sharpness of positive hybridization signals.

4. Transfer the filters to 150 ml of prehybridization solution in a glass baking dish. Incubate the filters with agitation for 1–2 hours or more at the appropriate temperature (i.e., 68°C when hybridization is to be carried out in aqueous solution; 42°C when hybridization is to be carried out in 50% formamide; please see panel below).

   > The filters should be completely covered by the prehybridization solution (please see the panel on ALTERNATIVE HYBRIDIZATION CHAMBERS). During prehybridization, sites on the nitrocellulose filter that nonspecifically bind single- or double-stranded DNA become blocked by proteins in the BLOTTO. Agitation ensures that the filters are continuously bathed in and evenly coated by the prehybridization fluid.

Denaturation of the Probe and Performance of Hybridization

5. Denature ^{32}P-labeled double-stranded DNA by heating to 100°C for 5 minutes. Chill the probe rapidly in ice water.

   > Alternatively, the probe may be denatured by adding 0.1 volume of 3 N NaOH. After 5 minutes at

> **PREHYBRIDIZATION AND HYBRIDIZATION SOLUTIONS**
>
> Whether or not to use a prehybridization solution containing formamide is largely a matter of personal preference. Both versions of these solutions give excellent results and neither has clear-cut advantages over the other. However, hybridization in 50% formamide at 42°C is less harsh on nitrocellulose filters than is hybridization at 68°C in aqueous solution. Offsetting this advantage is the two- to threefold slower rate of hybridization in solutions containing formamide. Nylon filters are impervious to the deleterious effects of aqueous hybridization at high temperatures.
>
> To maximize the rate of annealing of the probe with its target, hybridizations are usually carried out in solutions of high ionic strength (6x SSC or 6x SSPE) at a temperature that is 20–25°C below T_m (please see the information panel on MELTING TEMPERATURES in Chapter 10). Both solutions work equally well when hybridization is carried out in aqueous solvents. However, when formamide is included in the hybridization buffer, 6x SSPE is preferred because of its greater buffering power.

room temperature, transfer the probe to ice water and add 0.05 volume of 1 M Tris-Cl (pH 7.2) and 0.1 volume of 3 N HCl. Store the probe in ice water until it is needed.

Single-stranded probes need not be denatured.

6. Add the probe to the prehybridization solution covering the filters. Incubate at the appropriate temperature until 1–3 $C_o t_{1/2}$ is achieved. During the hybridization, keep the containers holding the filters tightly closed to prevent the loss of fluid by evaporation.

   Use between 2×10^5 and 1×10^6 cpm of ^{32}P-labeled probe (specific activity ~5 x 10^7 cpm/μg) per milliliter of prehybridization solution. Using more probe will cause the background of nonspecific hybridization to increase, whereas using less will reduce the rate of hybridization.

   If oligonucleotide probes are used, then please see Chapter 10, Protocol 8, for oligonucleotide hybridization and washing conditions.

   Hybridization mixtures containing radiolabeled single-stranded probes may be stored at 4°C for several days and reused without further treatment. In some cases, hybridization probes prepared from double-stranded DNA templates can be reused after freezing the solution, thawing, and boiling for 5 minutes in a chemical fume hood.

7. When the hybridization is complete, remove the hybridization solution and immediately immerse the filters in a large volume (300–500 ml) of Wash solution 1 at room temperature. Agitate the filters gently and turn them over at least once during washing. After 5 minutes, transfer the filters to a fresh batch of wash solution and continue to agitate them gently. Repeat the washing procedure twice more.

   At no stage during the washing procedure should the filters be allowed to dry.

8. Wash the filters twice for 0.5–1.5 hours in 300–500 ml of Wash solution 2 at 68°C.

   At this point, the background is usually low enough to put the filters on film. If the background is still high or if the experiment demands washing at high stringencies, immerse the filters for 60 minutes in 300–500 ml of Wash solution 3 at 68°C.

9. Dry the filters in the air at room temperature on 3MM paper. Streak the underside of the filters with a water-soluble glue stick and arrange the filters (numbered side up) on a clean, dry, flat sheet of 3MM paper. Press the filters firmly against the 3MM paper to ensure sticking.

10. Apply adhesive dot labels marked with either radioactive ink or chemiluminescent markers to several asymmetric locations on the 3MM paper. Cover the filters and labels with Saran Wrap. Use tape to secure the wrap to the back of the 3MM paper and stretch the wrap over the paper to remove wrinkles.

    These markers serve to align the autoradiograph with the filters.

Analysis of Hybridization Signal and Identification of Positive Colonies

11. Analyze the filters by phosphorimaging or exposing them to X-ray film (Kodak XAR-2, XAR-5, or their equivalents) for 12–16 hours at –70ºC with an intensifying screen.

    The optimum exposure must be empirically determined and will depend on the size of the colony, the copy number of the plasmid vector, the specific activity of the probe, and the type of filter used.

12. Develop the film and align it with the filters using the marks left by the radioactive ink. Use a nonradioactive fiber-tip pen in a nonblack color to mark the film with the positions of the asymmetrically located dots on the numbered filters.

13. Tape a piece of clear Mylar or other firm transparent sheet to the film. Mark on the clear sheet the positions of positive hybridization signals. Also mark (in a different color) the positions of the asymmetrically located dots. Remove the clear sheet from the film. Identify the positive colonies by aligning the dots on the clear sheet with those on the agar plate.

    Alternatively, place the film on a light box and align the agar plate containing the master colonies or filter with the stab marks in the agar/master filter. Identify positive colonies by aligning the hybridization signals with colonies on the master plate.

    When screening colonies at high density, it is sometimes easiest to remove the master filter from the agar plate and to place it directly on the autoradiograph. Line up the filter with the film via the needle/pen marks.

    Filters glued to 3MM paper are readily removed in preparation for stripping (please see Chapter 6, Protocol 10) by placing the 3MM paper with attached filters in a tub of 2× SSC. The water-soluble glue dissolves readily in this solution, releasing the filters for transfer to a stripping solution.

14. Use a sterile toothpick or inoculating needle to transfer each positive bacterial colony into 1–2 ml of rich medium (e.g., LB, YT, or Terrific Broth) containing the appropriate antibiotic.

    Often, the alignment of the filters with the plate does not permit identification of an individual hybridizing colony. In this case, several adjacent colonies should be pooled. The culture is grown for several hours, diluted, and replated on agar plates so as to obtain ~500 colonies per plate. These colonies are then screened a second time by hybridization. A single, well-isolated, positive colony should be picked from the secondary screen and used for further analysis.

15. After a period of growth, plasmid DNA can be isolated from the culture by one of the minipreparation methods described in Protocols 1 and 4 and can be further analyzed by restriction endonuclease digestion or by PCR (please see Chapter 8, Protocol 12).

CHLORAMPHENICOL

Chloramphenicol inhibits protein synthesis and blocks host DNA synthesis but has no effect on replication of relaxed plasmids. The copy number of relaxed plasmids therefore increases during incubation of the bacterial culture in the drug. Amplification is necessary to achieve high yields of relaxed plasmids, which normally replicate to only moderate numbers in their host bacteria. Plasmids of a later generation (e.g., pUC plasmids) carry a modified colE1 replicon and replicate to such high copy numbers that amplification is unnecessary. These high-copy-number plasmids can be purified in large yield from bacterial cultures that are allowed to grow to saturation in the absence of chloramphenicol. However, treatment with chloramphenicol still has some advantages even for these plasmids. Because it blocks bacterial replication, the bulk and viscosity of the bacterial lysate are reduced, which greatly simplifies purification of the plasmid. In general, the benefits of chloramphenicol treatment outweigh the small inconvenience involved in adding the drug to the growing bacterial culture.

Properties and Mode of Action of Chloramphenicol

- Chloramphenicol inhibits bacterial protein synthesis by decreasing the catalytic rate constant of peptidyl transferase, located on 70S ribosomes (Drainas et al. 1987).
- Chloramphenicol was first isolated from a soil actinomycete in 1947 (Ehrlich et al. 1947), and by 1950, it was available in a synthetic form that became widely used as a broad-spectrum antibiotic (please see Figure 1-13). However, its clinical use has since been curtailed because of drug-induced bone-marrow toxicity and because resistance to chloramphenicol develops readily in bacteria (for review, please see Shaw 1983).
- Because chloramphenicol inhibits bacterial protein synthesis, it prevents replication of the bacterial chromosome. However, replication of many "relaxed" plasmids, including virtually all vectors carrying the wild-type pMB1 (or colE1) replicon, continues in the presence of the drug until 2000 or 3000 copies have accumulated in the cell (Clewell 1972).
- Until the early 1980s, chloramphenicol was used routinely to obtain decent yields of plasmids containing the wild-type colE1 replicon from large-scale cultures. Most high-copy-number plasmid vectors constructed after 1982 carry mutations that prevent or destabilize the interactions between RNAI and RNAII and thereby release plasmid DNA from copy-number control. Because vectors containing these mutated versions of the colE1 origin are maintained at several hundred copies per cell, high yields of plasmid DNA can be obtained without inhibiting bacterial protein synthesis. Nevertheless, treating bacterial cultures with chloramphenicol still has some advantages: The copy number of the plasmids increases a further two- to threefold in the presence of the drug, and more significantly, the bulk and viscosity of the bacterial lysate are greatly reduced because host replication is inhibited. Many investigators find that adding chloramphenicol to the growing culture is far more convenient than dealing with a highly viscous lysate.
- For many years, it was thought that amplification of plasmids in the presence of chloramphenicol was effective only when the host bacteria were grown in minimal medium. However, a protocol that uses rich medium and chloramphenicol gives reproducibly high yields (≥1 mg of plasmid DNA per 500 ml of cul-

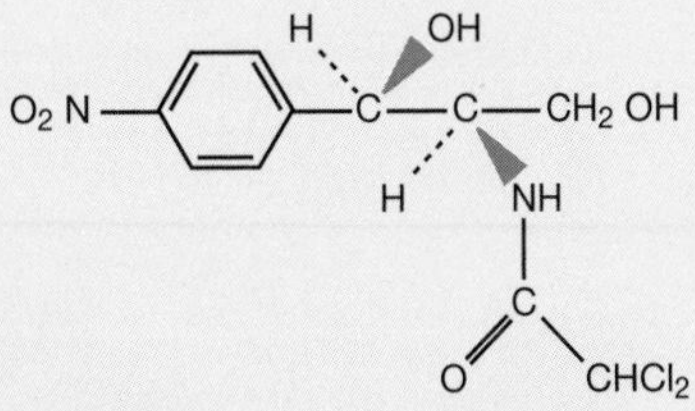

FIGURE 1-13 Structure of Chloramphenicol

Chemical bonds depicted by filled arrows appear above the plane of the figure; bonds represented by dashed lines appear below the plane of the figure.

ture) with strains of *E. coli* harboring low-copy-number plasmids carrying the pMB1 or colE1 replicon (e.g., please see Protocol 3).

- Improved yields of pBR322 and its derivatives have been obtained from bacterial cultures treated with low concentrations of chloramphenicol (10–20 μg/ml) that do not completely suppress host protein synthesis (Frenkel and Bremer 1986). The reason for this result is not understood, but it could be explained if the replication of plasmids carrying the colE1 origin required an unstable host factor that continues to be synthesized during partial inhibition of protein synthesis.

Mechanism of Resistance to Chloramphenicol

- Naturally occurring resistance to chloramphenicol in bacteria is due to the activity of the enzyme chloramphenicol acetyltransferase (encoded by the *cat* gene), which catalyzes the transfer of an acetyl group from acetyl coenzyme A (CoA) to the C3-hydroxyl group of the antibiotic. The product of the reaction, 3-acetoxychloramphenicol, neither binds to the pepidyl transferase center of 70S ribosomes nor inhibits peptidyl transferase.

- In field strains of Enterobacteriaceae and other Gram-negative bacteria, the *cat* gene is constitutively expressed and is usually carried on plasmids that confer multiple drug resistance.

- Several variants of the *cat* gene product have been described, all of which form trimers consisting of identical subunits of M_r ~25,000. The type I variant, which is encoded by a 1102-bp segment of transposon Tn9, is in wide use as a reporter gene. However, most kinetic and structural analyses have been carried out with the type III variant, which yields crystals suitable for X-ray analysis. The active site, which is located at the subunit interface, contains a histidine residue, which is postulated to act as a general base catalyst in the acetylation reaction (Leslie et al. 1988; Shaw et al. 1988). The two substrates (chloramphenicol and acetyl-CoA) approach the active site through tunnels located on opposite sides of the molecule.

KANAMYCINS

Properties and Mode of Action of Kanamycins

The kanamycins, which are members of the aminoglycoside family of antibiotics, were first isolated in 1957 at the Japanese National Institutes of Health from cultures of *Streptomyces kanamyceticus* (Umezawa et al. 1967), which synthesizes three forms of the antibiotic: kanamycins A, B, and C. Kanamycin A, the major component, has a broad spectrum of activity against many species of bacteria and for several years was an important antibiotic for the treatment of serious infections caused by Gram-negative bacilli. Its stereochemistry and absolute configuration were derived initially by chemical methods and nuclear magnetic resonance (NMR) and were later confirmed by X-ray crystallography (for review, please see Hooper 1982).

The aminoglycoside antibiotics are polycations that diffuse readily through porin channels in the outer membranes of Gram-negative bacteria. However, transport from the periplasmic space into the cytosol is driven by the negative membrane potential of the inner periplasmic membrane and is, therefore, an energy-dependent process. Once in the cytosol, these antibiotics interact with at least three ribosomal proteins and with specific bases within the decoding region of the smaller ribosomal RNA subunit, resulting in inhibition of protein synthesis and an increased frequency of induced translational errors (for reviews, please see Noller 1984; Cundliffe 1990).

In vitro, kanamycin and other aminoglycoside antibiotics that lack a guanido group (e.g., neomycin and gentamycin) also inhibit splicing of group I introns (von Ahsen et al. 1991, 1992; von Ahsen and Noller 1993). This observation supports the idea that the aminoglycoside antibiotics may recognize ancient structures in RNA that have been conserved through long stretches of evolutionary time (Davies 1990).

Mechanism of Resistance to Kanamycin

In structure, the kanamycins resemble gentamycin, neomycin, and geneticin (G418) (please see Figure 1-14), and they are inactivated by many of the same bacterial aminophosphotransferases (APHs) (for reviews, please see Davies and Smith 1978; Shaw et al. 1993). Of the seven major groups of APHs that have been distinguished on the basis of their substrate specificities, two have been used extensively as selectable markers for kanamycin resistance (Km^r): APH(3′)-I isolated from transposon Tn*903*, and APH(3′)-II isolated from Tn5. The APHs encoded by these genes inactivate kanamycin by transferring the γ-phosphate of ATP to the hydroxyl group in the 3′ position of the pseudosaccharide.

Both *aph(3′)-Ia* and *aph(3′)-IIa* have been used as selectable markers in prokaryotic vectors. However, it is not always easy to ascertain from the literature which gene has been used to construct particular vectors. This is unfortunate because the DNA sequences of *aph(3′)-Ia* and *aph(3′)-IIa* have diverged extensively (Shaw et al. 1993), such that the two genes have different restriction maps and will not cross-hybridize under normal conditions of stringency. Aph(3′)-II efficiently inactivates geneticin (G418) and is used as a dominant selectable marker in eukaryotic cells (e.g., please see Jimenez and Davies 1980; Colbère-Garapin et al. 1981; Southern and Berg 1982; Chen and Fukuhara 1988).

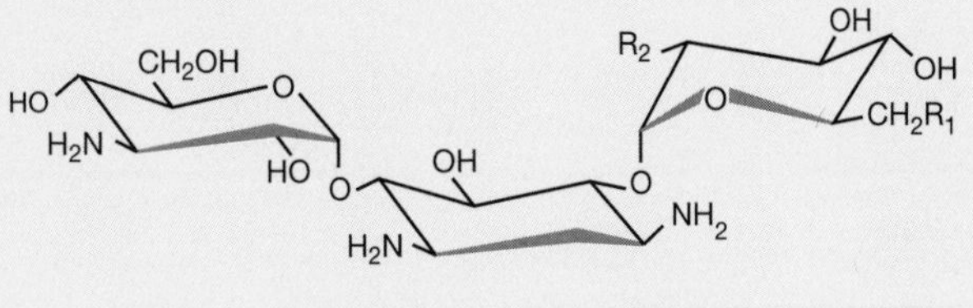

	R$_1$	R$_2$
Kanamycin A	NH$_2$	OH
Kanamycin B	NH$_2$	NH$_2$
Kanamycin C	OH	NH$_2$

FIGURE 1-14 Structures of Kanamycins

pBR322

- pBR322 and all of its derivatives replicate in a relaxed fashion. Their copy number can be increased from ~20 to >500 by inhibiting bacterial protein synthesis with an antibiotic such as chloramphenicol.

- pBR322 and some of its derivatives recombine to form multimers in *recA*⁺ hosts (Bedbrook et al. 1979). pBR322 does not carry a stability region (*cer*) that maintains the plasmid as monomers, which are more efficiently partitioned between daughter cells (Summers and Sherratt 1984). *cer* is a 280-bp sequence at which a host recombinase (*xerC*) acts in concert with ArgR and PepA proteins to reduce multimeric plasmid DNAs to a monomeric form (Colloms et al. 1990).

- pBR322 and its immediate derivatives lack a partition function and are readily lost from cells during sustained growth in minimal media in the absence of antibiotics. This problem was solved by the construction of plasmids that contain the *par* locus of pSC101 in a pBR322 backbone (Zurita et al. 1984). The *par* locus induces supercoiling of the origin of replication, which somehow allows each plasmid molecule in the intracellular pool to be treated as an individual unit of inheritance (Miller et al. 1990; Conley and Cohen 1995; Firshein and Kim 1997).

- pBR322, like almost all plasmid vectors commonly used in molecular cloning, is nonconjugative and is incapable of directing its conjugal transfer from one bacterium to another. This is because pBR322 lacks a region (*mob*) encoding proteins that bind to the plasmid DNA at the origin of transfer (*oriT*). Mob proteins introduce a single-strand nick at a site called *nic* located within a *cis*-acting region called *bom* (for reviews, please see Chan et al. 1984; Willetts and Wilkins 1984). pBR322 and some plasmid vectors of the same vintage can be mobilized if a conjugative plasmid that expresses Mob proteins is also present in the cell (Young and Poulis 1978). Mobilization of pBR322 then occurs from the *nic* site (nucleotide 2254 in the pBR sequence). Newer plasmid vectors lack the *nic/bom* site and cannot be mobilized (Twigg and Sherrat 1980; Covarrubias et al. 1981).

TETRACYCLINE

Properties and Mode of Action of Tetracycline

- All tetracyclines share an identical four-ring carbocyclic skeleton that supports a variety of groups (please see Figure 1-15).
- The first of the tetracyclines — chlortetracycline — was discovered in 1948 as a naturally occurring antibiotic synthesized by *Streptomyces aureofaciens* and active against a wide-range of Gram-positive and Gram-negative bacteria and protozoa. By 1980, ~1000 tetracycline derivatives had been isolated and/or synthesized, and the estimated global production was in excess of 500 metric tons (for review, please see Chopra et al. 1992).
- Tetracycline enters bacterial cells by passive diffusion across the outer membrane through porin channels, which are composed of the OmpF protein. Transport of the antibiotic across the cytoplasmic membrane and into the cytoplasm requires pH or electropotential gradients.
- Tetracycline inhibits bacterial growth by disrupting codon-anticodon interactions at the ribosome, which blocks protein synthesis (for reviews, please see Gale et al. 1981; Chopra 1985; Chopra et al. 1992). Specifically, the antibiotic binds to a single site on the 30S ribosomal subunit and thereby prevents attachment of aminoacyl-tRNA to the acceptor site.

Mechanism of Resistance of Tetracycline

- The chief mechanism by which *E. coli* becomes resistant to high concentrations of tetracycline involves antiporter proteins, known as Tet proteins, which are located in the bacterial inner membrane and, in exchange for a proton, expel intracellular tetracycline-metal complexes against a concentration gradient (for review, please see Chopra et al. 1992). Resistant cells are able to grow in the presence of tetracycline because they maintain a low intracellular concentration of the drug.
- The five known related tetracycline efflux genes, designated *tetA(A)* to *tetA(E)*, encode hydrophobic proteins of homologous sequence and similar structure.
- The *tetA(C)* gene of pBR322 and many other vectors encodes a 392-residue polypeptide composed of two domains each containing six transmembrane segments (for review and references, please see McNicholas et al. 1992). The TetA(C) protein assembles into a multimeric form in the inner membrane of *E. coli* (Hickman and Levy 1988).
- The expression of *tetA(C)* has several collateral effects on the cell (for references, please see Griffith et al. 1994). These effects include (1) reduced growth and viability, (2) increased supercoiling of plasmid DNA, (3) complementation of defects in potassium uptake, and (4) increased susceptibility to other antibacterial agents, including aminoglycoside antibiotics and lipophilic acids.

Inactivation of the *tetA(C)* gene therefore provides growth advantage to bacteria that are exposed to such agents. In the early days of molecular cloning, this effect was used to select for bacteria carrying recombinant plasmids in which the *tetA(C)* gene had been inactivated by insertion of a foreign DNA sequence (Bochner et al. 1980).

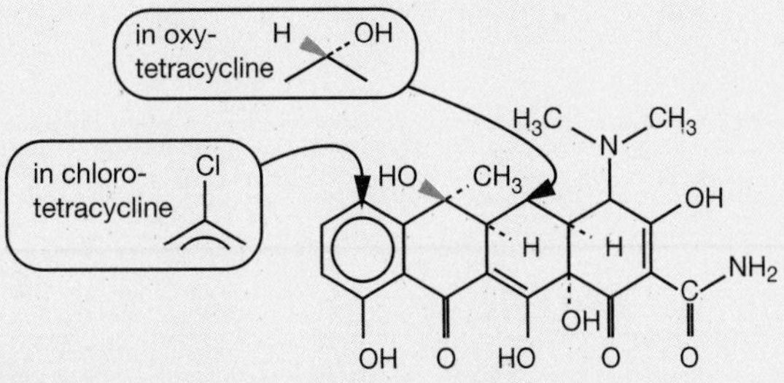

FIGURE 1-15 Structure and Synthesis of Tetracycline

The carbon atoms in the tetracycline skeleton carry substitute groups in various tetracycline derivatives. Chemical bonds (*filled arrows*) appear above the plane of the figure; bonds (*dashed lines*) appear below the plane of the figure.

AMPICILLIN AND CARBENICILLIN

Properties and Mode of Action of Ampicillin and Carbenicillin

- Ampicillin is an aminopenicillin; carbenicillin is a semi-synthetic carboxypenicillin (please see Figure 1-16).
- The antimicrobial activity of both compounds extends to Gram-negative organisms such as *Haemophilus influenzae* and *E. coli*. Carbenicillin was the first penicillin with significant activity against *Pseudomonas* species that are not susceptible to aminopenicillins, such as ampicillin.
- The rigidity of the cell walls of susceptible organisms is due in part to a thin layer of cross-linked peptidoglycan, just 1–2 molecules thick. The long glycan chains are composed entirely of amino sugars and are cross-linked by peptide chains containing D-amino acids. The penicillins inhibit the final stage of synthesis of cross-links, which occurs outside the cell and is catalyzed by a transpeptidase (for reviews, please see Neu 1985; Donowitz and Mandell 1988). Penicillins are most active against bacteria in the logarithmic phase of growth and have relatively little effect in the stationary phase, when synthesis of peptidoglycan is suppressed.
- In addition to their activity against transpeptidase, penicillins inhibit enzymes (called penicillin-binding proteins or PBPs) necessary for the rod-like structure of *E. coli* and for septum formation during division (Tomasz 1986).

Mechanism of Resistance to Ampicillin and Carbenicillin

- The periplasmic enzyme β-lactamase catalyzes hydrolysis of the cyclic amide bond of the β-lactam ring, with concomitant detoxification of ampicillin and carbenicillin (Abraham and Chain 1940; Bush and Sykes 1984).
- β-lactamases are present in small amounts in the periplasmic space of field strains of antibiotic-resistant, Gram-negative bacteria. They are coded either chromosomally or on plasmids. The most prevalent β-lactamase in Gram-negative bacteria — the TEM β-lactamase — is named after the initials of the Athenian girl from whom a strain of *E. coli* expressing the enzyme was first isolated in 1965 (Datta and Kontomichalou 1965). The TEM β-lactamase, which is widely used as a selectable marker in molecular cloning, is a 286-residue protein encoded by the *bla* gene (Sutcliffe 1978). The first 23 amino acids of the nascent lactamase protein function as a signal sequence cleaved during translocation of the protein into the periplasm.
- When β-lactamase is expressed from high-copy vectors, such as those used in molecular cloning, large amounts of the enzyme are secreted into the medium. Sufficient β-lactamase can be produced by a single transformed colony to hydrolyze the antibiotic in the surrounding medium and to create a protected zone in which antibiotic-sensitive colonies can grow. This leads to the appearance of nontransformed, satellite colonies. The problem is ameliorated, but not completely eliminated, by using carbenicillin rather than ampicillin in selective media, because carbenicillin is more resistant than ampicillin to hydrolysis by the β-lactamases of genera such as *Pseudomonas* and *Escherichia*.

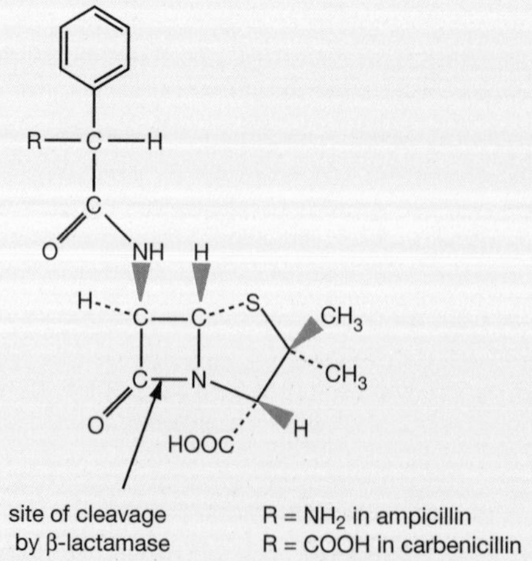

site of cleavage
by β-lactamase

R = NH₂ in ampicillin
R = COOH in carbenicillin

FIGURE 1-16 Cleavage of β-Lactam Antibiotics by β-Lactamase

Chemical bonds (*filled arrows*) appear above the plane of the figure; bonds (*dashed lines*) appear below the plane of the figure.

X-GAL

E. coli encodes a β-galactosidase that hydrolyzes the disaccharide lactose into the monosaccharides glucose and galactose. The activity of the enzyme can be assayed with a chromogenic substrate such as X-gal (5-bromo-4-chloro-3-indolyl-β-D-galactoside), which is converted by β-galactosidase into an insoluble dense blue compound (Horwitz et al. 1964; Davies and Jacob 1968).

This discovery came about when, in 1967, Julian Davies, working at the Pasteur Institute, was trying to develop nondestructive histochemical stains that would allow him to distinguish between Lac$^+$ and Lac$^-$ colonies. This goal required finding a specific chromogenic substrate that would be hydrolyzed by β-galactosidase to highly colored products that were both nondiffusible and nontoxic. Davies was pleased to find that phenyl-β-galactosides produced a satisfactory color reaction, but he was less gratified by their conversion to toxic nitrophenols that efficiently killed the very cells he was trying to identify. Understandably, Davies, who is voluble and Welsh, found this situation a little frustrating. He expressed his Cymric indignation to Mel Cohn, a visitor to the laboratory, who fortunately remembered reading a brief paper by Horwitz and his colleagues describing the use of dihalageno-indolyl compounds as histological stains for β-galactosidase (Horwitz et al. 1964). Davies' next problem was to persuade the people at the Pasteur to buy some X-gal. In those days, X-gal was not available commercially and custom synthesis cost $1000 per gram. After much discussion, X-gal was ordered, synthesized, and delivered. In addition to being sensitive and nontoxic, X-gal turned out to be an extremely beautiful histochemical reagent that has generated gorgeous pictures of β-galactosidase expression in flora and fauna of all types. When Jacques Monod first saw the brilliant blue color of induced bacterial colonies, he commented that this was proof that *E. coli* was the most intelligent organism in the world.

α-COMPLEMENTATION

α-Complementation occurs when two inactive fragments of *E. coli* β-galactosidase associate to form a functional enzyme. Deletion of the 5′ region of the *lacZ* gene encoding the initiating methionine residues causes translation to begin at a downstream methionine residue, generating a carboxy-terminal fragment of the enzyme (the ω- or α-acceptor fragment). An amino-terminal fragment (the α-donor fragment) is generated by deletion or chain-terminating mutations in the structural gene. Although neither the α-donor fragment nor the ω-acceptor fragment is enzymatically active, the two parts of the enzyme can associate to form an active β-galactosidase both in cells and in vitro (Ullmann et al. 1967). Many α donors of varying lengths are functional for complementation. The minimum requirement seems to be an α-peptide containing residues 3–41 (Langley et al. 1975; Zabin 1982; Weinstock et al. 1983; Henderson et al. 1986).

Analysis of the three-dimensional structure of *E. coli* β-galactosidase (Jacobson et al. 1994) provides a rational explanation for α-complementation. β-galactosidase is a tetramer composed of four identical monomers of 1023 amino acids, which are folded into five sequential domains. The amino-terminal segment of the monomer (the complementation region) directly participates in the interfacial association among monomers by forming contacts with domains 1, 2, and 3 of its own monomer. The complementation peptide also stabilizes an interfacial four-helix bundle composed of two helices from each of two monomers.

Many of the plasmid vectors carry a short segment of *E. coli* DNA containing the regulatory sequences and the coding information for the first 146 amino acids of the β-galactosidase gene. Embedded in the coding region is a polycloning site that maintains the reading frame and results in the harmless interpolation of a small number of amino acids into the amino-terminal fragment of β-galactosidase. Vectors of this type are used in host cells that express the carboxy-terminal portion of β-galactosidase. Although neither the host-encoded nor the plasmid-encoded fragments of β-galactosidase are themselves active, they can associate to form an enzymatically active protein. This type of complementation, in which deletion mutants of the operator-proximal segment of the *lacZ* gene are complemented by β-galactosidase-negative mutants that have the operator-proximal region intact, is called α-complementation (Ullmann et al. 1967). The *lac*[+] bacteria that result from α-complementation are easily recognized because they form blue colonies in the presence of the chromogenic X-gal (Horwitz et al. 1964; Davies and Jacob 1968; please see the information panel on X-GAL). However, insertion of a fragment of foreign DNA into the polycloning site of the plasmid almost invariably results in production of an amino-terminal fragment that is no longer capable of α-complementation. Bacteria carrying recombinant plasmids therefore form white colonies. The development of this simple color test has greatly simplified the identification of recombinants constructed in plasmid vectors. It is easy to screen many thousands of transformed colonies and to recognize from their white appearance those that carry putative recombinant plasmids. The structure of these recombinants can then be verified by restriction analysis of minipreparations of vector DNA or by other diagnostic criteria. For procedures for screening recombinants using α-complemetation, please see Protocol 27 and the panel on ALTERNATIVE PROTOCOL: ON DIRECT APPLICATION OF X-GAL AND IPTG TO AGAR PLATES.

Screening by α-complementation is highly dependable but not completely infallible:

- Insertion of foreign DNA does not always inactivate the complementing activity of the α-fragment of β-galactosidase. If the foreign DNA is small (<100 bp), and if the insertion neither disrupts the reading frame nor affects the structure of the α-fragment, α-complementation may not be seriously affected. Examples of this phenomenon have been documented but they are very rare and of significance only to the investigator who encounters this problem.
- Not all white colonies carry recombinant plasmids. Mutation or loss of *lac* sequences may purge the plasmid of its ability to express the α-fragment. However, this is not a problem in practice because the frequency of *lac*[−] mutants in the plasmid population is usually far lower than the number of recombinants generated in a ligation reaction.

In most bacterial strains used for α-complementation, the ω-fragment is encoded by the deletion mutant *lacZ*ΔM15, which lacks codons 11–41 of the β-galactosidase gene (Ullmann and Perrin 1970). This mutant gene is usually carried on an F′ plasmid.

Strains of bacteria commonly used for α-complementation do not synthesize significant quantities of *lac* repressor. Consequently, there is usually no need to induce synthesis of ω and α fragments for histochemical analysis of bacterial colonies. If necessary, synthesis of both fragments can be fully induced by IPTG, a nonfermentable lactose analog that inactivates the *lacZ* repressor (Barkley and Bourgeois 1978).

ETHIDIUM BROMIDE

Ethidium bromide (3,8-diamino-6-ethyl-5-phenylphenanthridium bromide) was synthesized in the 1950s in an effort to develop phenanthridine compounds as effective trypanocidal agents; the structure is shown in Figure 1-17. Ethidium emerged from the screening program with flying colors. It was 10–50-fold more effective against trypanosomes than the parent compound, was no more toxic to mice, and, unlike earlier phenanthridines, did not induce photosensitization in cattle (Watkins and Wolfe 1952). Ethidium bromide is still widely used for the treatment and prophylaxis of trypanomiasis in cattle in tropical and subtropical countries.

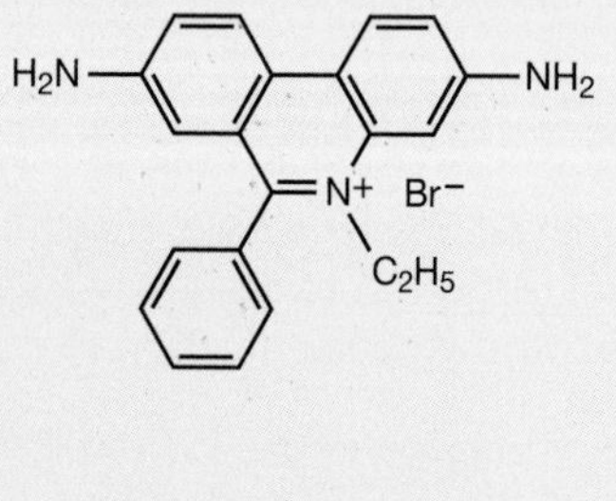

FIGURE 1-17 Structure of Ethidium Bromide

In addition to its veterinary uses, ethidium bromide has played an important part in the development of molecular cloning: Staining with a low concentration of ethidium bromide has been the standard method of detecting small quantities of DNA in agarose gels for more than 25 years (Sharp et al. 1973); and from 1966 to the mid-1980s, equilibrium CsCl-ethidium bromide centrifugation was the only reliable method available to purify closed circular DNAs (Bauer and Vinograd 1971). The usefulness of ethidium bromide for these tasks derives from its fluorescent properties in combination with its ability to intercalate between the base pairs of double-stranded DNA.

After insertion into the helix, the planar stacked tricyclic phenanthridine ring system of the drug lies perpendicular to the helical axis and makes van der Waals contacts with the base pairs above and below. At saturation in solutions of high ionic strength, approximately one ethidium molecule is intercalated per 2.5 bp, independent of the base composition of the DNA. The geometry of the base pairs and their positioning with respect to the helix are unchanged except for their displacement by 3.4 Å along the helix axis (Waring 1965). This causes a 27% increase in the length of double-stranded DNA (Freifelder 1971) saturated with ethidium bromide.

When isolated from host cells, closed circular DNA molecules display a right-handed superhelical structure that results from a deficiency of Watson-Crick turns. Intercalation of ethidium bromide requires local uncoiling of the helix at the point of insertion, which alters the average pitch of the helix and increases the average number of base pairs per turn until a critical value is reached when the circular DNA molecules are unstrained and free of all supercoils (Lerman 1961). As more drug is added, the additional uncoiling forces the circles to form left-handed supercoils (Crawford and Waring 1967; Bauer and Vinograd 1968). However, the binding affinity of the dye for closed circular DNA decreases progessively as the number of reversed supercoils increases. Because of this decrease in binding affinity, closed circular DNAs bind less drug at saturation than do nicked circles or linear molecules (Bauer and Vinograd 1968, 1970). Binding of ethidium bromide reduces the buoyancy of DNA in CsCl density gradients, and the magnitude of this decrease is a function of the average number of drug molecules bound per base pair. Because of the restricted binding of ethidium bromide to positively supercoiled DNAs, closed circular DNAs come to equilibrium at a denser position (~1.59 g/cc) in CsCl-ethidium bromide gradients than linear or nicked circular DNAs (1.55 g/cc).

The fixed position of the planar group of ethidium bromide and its close proximity to the bases cause the bound dye to display an increased fluorescent yield compared to the dye in free solution. Ultraviolet (UV) radiation at 254 nm is absorbed by the DNA and transmitted to the dye; radiation at 302 nm and 366 nm is absorbed by the dye itself. In both cases, a fraction of energy is re-emitted at 590 nm in the red-orange region of the visible spectrum (LePecq and Paoletti 1967). Most of the commercially available UV light sources emit UV light at 302 nm. The fluorescent yield of ethidium bromide-DNA complexes is considerably greater at this wavelength than at 366 nm but is slightly less than at shorter wavelength (254 nm). However, the amount of photobleaching and nicking of the DNA is much less at 302 nm than at 254 nm (Brunk and Simpson 1977).

The reaction between ethidium bromide and DNA is reversible (Waring 1965), but the dissociation of the complex is very slow and is measured in days rather than minutes or hours. For practical purposes, dissociation is achieved by passing the complex through a small column packed with a cation-exchange resin such as Dowex AG50W-X8 (Waring 1965; Radloff et al. 1967) or by extracting with organic solvents such as isopropanol (Cozzarelli et al. 1968) or *n*-butanol (Wang 1969). The former method has been shown to result in the removal of ethidium bromide to a binding ratio below that detectable by fluorescence, a molar ratio of dye to nucleic acid of 1:4000 (Radloff et al. 1967).

Ethidium bromide also binds with highly variable stoichiometry to RNA, heat-denatured or single-stranded DNA, and the cyclic-coil form of closed circular DNA. This is attributed to binding of the drug to helical regions formed by intrastrand interactions in these polynucleotides (Waring 1965, 1966; LePecq and Paoletti 1967).

CONDENSING AND CROWDING REAGENTS

Condensing reagents, like hexamminecobalt chloride and crowding reagents, such as polyethylene glycol, have two effects on ligation reactions:

- They accelerate the rate of ligation of blunt-ended DNA by one to three orders of magnitude. This increase allows ligation reactions to be performed at lower concentrations of enzyme and DNA.
- They alter the distribution of ligation products. Intramolecular ligation is suppressed, and the ligation products are created exclusively by intermolecular joining events. Thus, even at concentrations of DNA that favor circularization, all of the DNA products are linear multimers.

Different batches of PEG 8000 stimulate the ligation of blunt-ended DNAs to different extents. It is a good idea to test several batches of PEG 8000 to determine which one yields a maximum stimulation of ligation, and then to dedicate the chosen bottle for use in ligation reactions only. The maximum stimulation of ligation usually occurs between 3% and 5% PEG 8000 in the ligation reaction; however, this value can fluctuate between different batches and should be determined empirically. The PEG stock (13%) solution should be warmed to room temperature before being added to the ligation reaction, as DNA can precipitate at cold temperatures in the presence of PEG 8000. In addition, it is important that the PEG stock solution be added as the final ingredient to the ligation reaction. Stimulation of blunt-ended DNA ligation by PEG 8000 is highly dependent on the concentration of magnesium ions, which should be maintained in the 5–10 mM range in the ligation reaction.

In our hands, PEG gives more reproducible stimulation of blunt-end ligation than hexamminecobalt chloride.

PURIFICATION OF PLASMID DNA BY PEG PRECIPITATION

Minipreparations of plasmid DNA can be used as templates in dideoxysequencing reactions whose products can be analyzed on automated machines (please see Chapter 12). The length of the DNA sequence established in a run on one of these machines is determined largely by the purity of the plasmid DNA. The following steps can be added to the standard minipreparation of plasmid DNA by alkaline lysis with SDS to provide "sequencing-grade" plasmid DNA that reproducibly yields >600 bp of readable sequence on machines such as the Applied Biosystems Models 370A or 377.

1. To 50 μl of a minipreparation of plasmid DNA (prepared as described in Protocol 1), add 8.0 μl of 4 M NaCl and 40 μl of 13% (w/v) PEG 8000. Incubate the mixture on ice for 20–30 minutes.

2. Collect the DNA precipitate by centrifugation at maximum speed for 15 minutes at 4°C in a microfuge. Carefully remove the supernatant by gentle aspiration.

    The pellet of DNA is translucent and generally invisible at this stage.

3. Rinse the pellet with 500 μl of 70% ethanol.

    The precipitate changes to a milky-white color and becomes visible.

4. Carefully pour off the ethanol. Rinse the DNA pellet once more with 70% ethanol. Store the tube in an inverted position at room temperature until the last visible traces of ethanol have evaporated.

5. Dissolve the DNA in 20–30 μl of H_2O.

    1.5 ml of bacterial culture should yield 3–5 μg of purified plasmid DNA. Check the concentration and integrity of the preparation of plasmid DNA by agarose gel electrophoresis using known amounts of plasmid DNA of similar size as standards. Do not submit a plasmid DNA to a sequencing facility without first performing this agarose gel check.

LYSOZYMES

A drop from the nose of Fleming, who had a cold, fell onto an agar plate where large yellow colonies of a contaminant had grown, and lysozyme was discovered. He made this important discovery because when he saw that the colonies of the contaminant were fading, his mind went straight to the right cause of the phenomenon he was observing — that the drop from his nose contained a lytic substance. And, also immediately, he thought that this substance might be present in many secretions and tissues of the body. And he found that this was so — the substance was in tears, saliva, leucocytes, skin, fingernails, mother's milk — thus very widely distributed in amounts and also in plants.

Lady Amelia Fleming (Personal Recollections of Lysozyme and Fleming)

I have been trying to point out that in our lives chance may have an astonishing influence and, if I may offer advice to the young laboratory worker, it would be this — never to neglect an extraordinary appearance or happening. It may be — usually is, in fact — a false alarm that leads to nothing, but it may on the other hand be the clue provided by fate to lead you to some important advance.

Alexander Fleming (from his lecture at Harvard University)

- Lysozymes are a family of enzymes that catalyze the acid base hydrolysis of β-(1,4) linkages between *N*-acetylglucosamine and *N*-acetylmuramic acid residues in the proteoglycan of bacterial cell walls (Blake et al. 1967; Fursht 1985). They were discovered by Alexander Fleming, who identified an enzyme activity that rapidly lysed suspensions of bacteria (Fleming 1922). The products of digestion by vertebrate lysozymes of the cell walls of bacteria were identified in the late 1950s, which allowed the structure and composition of the substrate to be deduced (for review, please see Jollés 1960).
- Lysozymes are widely distributed in nature and are expressed wherever there is a need to lyse bacterial cells, for example, during release of bacteriophages from infected cells, on the surface of vertebrate mucosa, and in a great number of secretions of different animals, both vertebrate and invertebrate. No structural similarity exists between vertebrate and bacteriophage-encoded lysozymes such as bacteriophage λ endolysin and bacteriophage T4 endoacetylmuramidase.
- In molecular cloning, vertebrate lysozymes (e.g., egg-white lysozyme) are used at pH 8.0 in combination with EDTA and detergents to liberate cosmid and plasmid DNAs from their bacterial hosts (Godson and Vapnek 1973).

POLYETHYLENE GLYCOL

PEG is a straight chain polymer of a simple repeating unit $H(OCH_2 CH_2)_n OH$, and it is available in a range of molecular weights whose names reflect the number (n) of repeating units in each molecule. In PEG 400, for example, $n = 8$–9, whereas in PEG 4000, n ranges from 68 to 84.

PEG induces macromolecular crowding of solutes in aqueous solution (Zimmerman and Minton 1993) and has a range of uses in molecular cloning, including:

- Precipitation of DNA molecules according to their size. The concentration of PEG required for precipitation is in inverse proportion to the size of the DNA fragments (Lis and Schleif 1975a,b; Ogata and Gilbert 1977; Lis 1980). The precipitation of DNA by PEG is most efficient in the presence of 10 mM $MgCl_2$ at room temperature (Paithankar and Prasad 1991). Under these conditions, the efficiency of PEG precipitation approaches that obtainable with ethanol. Both long linear and circular forms of DNAs are efficiently precipitated; however, linear DNAs of less than 150 bp are not quantitatively precipitated by $PEG/MgCl_2$.
- Precipitation and purification of bacteriophage particles (Yamamoto et al. 1970).
- Increasing the efficiency of reassociation of complementary chains of nucleic acids during hybridization, blunt-end ligation of DNA molecules, and end-labeling of DNA with bacteriophage T4 polynucleotide kinase (Zimmerman and Minton 1993).
- Fusion of cultured cells with bacterial protoplasts (Schaffner 1980; Rassoulzadegan et al. 1982).

CESIUM CHLORIDE AND CESIUM CHLORIDE EQUILIBRIUM DENSITY GRADIENTS

Cesium, the 55th element, was discovered in 1855 by Wilhelm Bunsen, a German chemist better known for his burner.

Because cesium atoms are so heavy, concentrated solutions of CsCl form density gradients after only a few hours of high-speed centrifugation (Meselson et al. 1957). The buoyant density of a macromolecule is defined as the concentration of CsCl (in g/cm^3) at that exact point in the density gradient at which the macromolecule floats. The density of the initial solution of CsCl in the centrifuge tube is usually adjusted so that it corresponds to the density of the molecules or particles under investigation. For example, because the buoyant density of most double-stranded linear DNAs in CsCl is ~1.70 g/ml, gradients are usually formed from a CsCl solution whose initial density is also 1.70 g/ml.

Double-stranded DNAs

The density of double-stranded linear DNA in CsCl is a function of its base composition (Schildkraut et al. 1962).

$$\rho = (0.098)[G+C] + 1.660 \text{ g/cm}^3$$

where

ρ = buoyant density of DNA
[G+C] = mole fraction of G+C in double-stranded DNA

In solutions of Cs_2SO_4, the density of double-stranded DNA is insensitive to base composition.

Single-stranded DNAs

In CsCl solutions, the density of single-stranded DNA is ~0.015–0.020 g/cm^3 greater than that of double-stranded DNA of the same base composition.

RNA

The buoyant density of single-stranded RNA in CsCl is >1.8 gm/cm^3. This is approximately the density of a saturated solution of CsCl. RNA therefore forms a pellet on the bottom of CsCl density gradients. The difference in buoyant density of RNA and DNA forms the basis of an efficient method to prepare RNAs that are free of traces of DNA (Glišin et al. 1974).

Bacteriophage Particles

The buoyant density of protein in CsCl is ~1.3 g/cm^3, whereas the density of double-stranded DNA is ~1.70 g/cm^3. Virus particles have a density that reflects their ratio of nucleic acid to protein. For example, bacteriophage λ, which consists of almost equal parts of protein and double-stranded DNA has a density of ~1.48 g/cm^3. This is sufficiently different from other cellular components that equilibrium density centrifugation in CsCl has long been used as a standard method of purification of bacteriophage λ particles (Yamamoto et al. 1970).

Properties of CsCl Solutions

The concentration of CsCl corresponding to any desired density between 1.20 and 1.80 (30–60% w/w of CsCl at 25ºC) can be calculated from the following table.

The properties of aqueous solutions of CsCl are given in Table 1-11 on the following page.

TABLE 1-11 Properties of Solutions of Cesium Chloride

A % BY WEIGHT	D_{20}^{20}	Cs (G/LITER)	M (G-MOLE/LITER)	Cw (G/LITER)	Co-Cw (G/LITER)	$n-n_0$ (× 10⁴)	N	Δ °C	S (G-MOLE/LITER)
.00	1.0000	0	.000	998.2	0	0	1.3330	.00	.000
1.00	1.0076	10.1	.060	995.8	2.5	8	1.3338	.20	.057
2.00	1.0153	20.3	.120	993.3	5.0	15	1.3345	.40	.114
3.00	1.0232	30.6	.182	990.7	7.5	23	1.3353	.59	.172
4.00	1.0311	41.2	.245	988.2	10.1	31	1.3361	.80	.231
5.00	1.0392	51.9	.308	985.5	12.7	39	1.3369	1.00	.292
6.00	1.0475	62.7	.373	982.9	15.3	48	1.3378	1.21	.353
7.00	1.0558	73.8	.438	980.2	15.0	56	1.3386	1.42	.414
8.00	1.0643	85.0	.505	977.5	20.8	65	1.3395	1.63	.477
9.00	1.0730	96.4	.573	974.7	23.5	73	1.3403	1.85	.541
10.00	1.0818	108.0	.641	971.9	26.4	82	1.3412	2.07	.605
11.00	1.0907	119.8	.711	969.0	29.3	91	1.3421	2.29	.669
12.00	1.0997	131.7	.782	966.1	32.2	100	1.3430	2.52	.735
13.00	1.1089	143.9	.855	963.1	35.2	110	1.3439	2.75	.801
14.00	1.1183	156.3	.928	960.0	38.2	119	1.3449	2.99	.867
15.00	1.1278	168.9	1.003	956.9	41.3	128	1.3458	3.22	.934
16.00	1.1375	181.7	1.079	953.8	44.5	138	1.3468	3.46	1.002
17.00	1.1473	194.7	1.156	950.6	47.7	148	1.3478	3.71	1.070
18.00	1.1573	207.9	1.235	947.3	51.0	158	1.3488	3.96	1.139
19.00	1.1674	221.4	1.315	943.9	54.3	168	1.3498	4.21	1.215
20.00	1.1777	235.1	1.396	940.5	57.7	178	1.3508	4.47	1.286
22.00	1.1989	263.3	1.564	933.5	64.8	199	1.3529		
24.00	1.2207	292.4	1.737	926.1	72.1	220	1.3550		
26.00	1.2433	322.7	1.916	918.4	79.8	242	1.3572		
28.00	1.2666	354.0	2.103	910.4	87.9	265	1.3595		
30.00	1.2908	386.6	2.296	902.0	96.3	288	1.3618		
32.00	1.3158	420.3	2.496	893.1	105.1	312	1.3642		
34.00	1.3417	455.4,	2.705	883.9	114.3	337	1.3666		
36.00	1.3685	491.8	2.921	874.3	124.0	362	1.3692		
38.00	1.3963	529.6	3.146	864.2	134.1	388	1.3718		
40.00	1.4251	569.0	3.380	853.5	144.7	414	1.3744		
42.00	1.4550	610.0	3.623	842.4.	155.8	442	1.3772		
44.00	1.4861	652.7	3.877	830.8	167.5	470	1.3800		
46.00	1.5185	697.3	4.141	818.5	179.7	500	1.3829		
48.00	1.5522	743.7	4.417	805.7	192.5	530	1.3860		
50.00	1.5874	792.3	4.706	792.3	206.0	562	1.3891		
52.00	1.6241	843.0	5.007	778.2	220.0	595	1.3924		
54.00	1.6625	896.2	5.323	763.4	234.8	629	1.3959		
56.00	1.7029	951.9	5.654	747.9	250.3	665	1.3995		
58.00	1.7453	1010.5	6.001	731.7	266.5	703	1.4033		
60.00	1.7900	1072.1	6.367	714.7	283.5	744	1.4074		
62.00	1.8373	1137.1	6.754	696.9	301.3	787	1.4117		
64.00	1.8875	1205.9	7.162	678.3	319.9	833	1.4163		

Cesium chloride, CsCl; molecular weight = 168.37; relative specific refractivity = 0.465.

Reprinted, with permission, from CRC Handbook of Chemistry and Physics (1980–1981) (ed. R.C. Weast), 61st edition. Copyright CRC Press, Boca Raton, Florida.

DNA LIGASES

Ligases catalyze the formation of phosphodiester bonds between the directly adjacent 3′-hydroxyl and 5′-phosphoryl termini of nucleic acid molecules. The substrates may be DNA or RNA, and the cofactors that generate high-energy intermediates in the reaction may be ATP or NAD^+, depending on the type of ligase.

In vivo, DNA ligases are required for enzymatic completion of lagging-strand synthesis during replication of DNA, and they are also involved in genetic recombination and in DNA repair (Gottesman et al. 1973; Horiuchi et al. 1975; Waga et al. 1994; for review, please see Kornberg and Baker 1992; Shuman 1996; Lehman 1998). In vitro, DNA ligases are used chiefly to create novel combinations of nucleic acid molecules and to attach them to vectors before molecular cloning. More specialized uses of DNA ligases include the sealing of nicks in the second strand during synthesis of cDNA (Okayama and Berg 1982), the amplification of DNA segments that lie outside the boundaries of known DNA sequences (the inverse PCR) (Triglia et al. 1988), the detection of nicks in DNA by the release of AMP (Weiss et al. 1968b), and, more recently, the detection of point mutations in DNA by the ligase chain reaction (also known as the ligase amplification reaction) (Landegren et al. 1988; Wu and Wallace 1989; Barany 1991a,b).

DNA ligases used in molecular cloning are either of bacterial origin or bacteriophage-encoded. All eubacteria, whether thermophilic or mesophilic, contain a single ligase gene that encodes an NAD^+-dependent enzyme (Olivera and Lehman 1967; Takahashi et al. 1984). During the first step of a ligation reaction, the diphosphate linkage of NAD^+ is used as a phosphoanhydride and the adenyl group is transferred to the ε-amino group of a lysine residue (Zimmerman et al. 1967; Gumport and Lehman 1971). In the case of ligases encoded by the ATP-dependent ligases of eukaryotes and bacteriophages, the high-energy enzyme intermediate is formed more conventionally, by hydrolysis of the α,β pyrophosphate in ATP and transfer of the adenyl group to a lysine residue (Becker at al. 1967; Cozzarelli et al. 1967; Weiss and Richardson 1967; Weiss et al 1968a). From then on, however, the mechanism of the reaction catalyzed by the two types of enzymes is similar: The adenyl residue is transferred to the 5′-phosphate at the terminus of one DNA molecule, which is then open to nucleophilic attack by a hydroxyl group at the 3′ terminus of an immediately adjacent DNA molecule. This results in the formation of a phosphodiester bond, elimination of AMP, and covalent joining of the DNA strands (for reviews of the mechanism of the ligation reaction, please see Lehman 1974; Higgins and Cozzarelli 1979; Engler and Richardson 1982; Shuman 1996).

The amino acid sequences of *E. coli* ligase show little overall similarity to the sequences of bacteriophage-encoded DNA ligases, to eukaryotic ATP-dependent ligases, or to the ligases of thermophilic bacteria. However, in all ligases so far identified (including RNA ligases), the lysine residue that becomes adenylated during the reaction lies in the vicinity of a reasonably well-conserved hexapeptide motif (K*-Y-D-G-X-R in the case of T4 DNA Ligase) (Barker et al. 1985; Lauer et al. 1991; Kletzin 1992; Shuman 1996). In addition, the superfamily of ATP-dependent ligases shares five other linear sequence elements that are involved in contacts between the enzyme and ATP (Tomkinson et al. 1991; Shuman 1996).

The DNA ligases used in molecular cloning differ in their abilities to ligate noncanonical substrates, such as blunt-ended duplexes, DNA-RNA hybrids, or single-stranded DNAs. These and other properties are summarized in Table 1-12 on the following page.

Bacteriophage T4 DNA Ligase

- T4 DNA ligase, which is encoded by gene 30 of bacteriophage T4 (Wilson and Murray 1979), is a monomeric protein of 487 amino acids (calculated M_r = 55,230) (Weiss et al. 1968b; Armstrong et al. 1983).
- T4 DNA ligase, which is purified commercially from overproducing strains of *E. coli* (Tait et al. 1980), has a K_m of 6×10^{-7} M for cohesive termini (Sugino et al. 1977), 5×10^{-5} M for blunt ends, and 1.9×10^{-9} for nicks. The K_m of the enzyme for ATP is $\sim 5 \times 10^{-5}$ M (Weiss et al. 1968b).
- T4 RNA ligase has been reported to stimulate the activity of T4 DNA ligase (Sugino et al. 1977). However, agents such as polyethylene glycol (Pheiffer and Zimmerman 1983) and hexamminecobalt chloride (Rusche and Howard-Flanders 1985), which increase macromolecular crowding and increase the rate of ligation by three orders of magnitude, are less expensive (please see the information panel on CONDENSING AND CROWDING REAGENTS).

TABLE 1-12 DNA Ligases

LIGASE	SUBSTRATES[a]				COFACTORS AND ACTIVATORS	TEMPERATURE	SULFHYDRYL REAGENTS
	COHESIVE TERMINI	BLUNT ENDS	DNA-RNA HYBRIDS	RNA-RNA HYBRIDS			
E. coli ligase	yes	yes[b]	no	no	DPN$^+$ Mg^{2+} (1–3 mM)	10–15°C for cohesive termini 37°C for closing nicks[c]	not required[d]
T4 ligase	yes	yes[b]	yes[e]	yes[e]	ATP Mg^{2+} (10 mM)	4°C for cohesive termini[f] 15–25°C for blunt ends[h] 37°C for closing nicks[i]	dithiothreitol required[g]
Ligases of thermophilic bacteria	yes	no	no	no	DPN^{+j} Mg^{2+} (10 mM)	24–37°C for cohesive termini 65–72°C for closing nicks[k,l,m]	required[k,m]

[a]DNA ligases will not join pairs of DNAs whose termini carry the following groups at the point of ligation:
  5′-hydroxyl and 3′-hydroxyl
  5′-hydroxyl and 3′-phosphate
  5′-phosphate and 3′-dideoxynucleoside
  5′-triphosphate and 3′-hydroxyl

[b]*E. coli* DNA ligase was originally reported (Sugino et al. 1977) to be incompetent at joining of blunt-ended DNA molecules except in the presence of condensing agents such as PEG or Ficoll (Zimmerman and Pheiffer 1983) and with monovalent cations such as Na$^+$ (Hayashi et al. 1985a,b). More recently, however, Barringer et al. (1990) have shown that *E. coli* DNA ligase is capable of joining blunt-ended and some single-stranded nucleic acids with kinetics that are dependent on enzyme and substrate concentration. However, for routine ligation of blunt-ended DNAs, bacteriophage T4 ligase is the enzyme of choice. T4 DNA ligase will ligate blunt-ended molecules (Ehrlich et al. 1977; Sgaramella and Ehrlich 1978), but the rate of reaction is not linearly dependent on enzyme concentration and works efficiently only in high concentrations of DNA and enzyme. In addition, condensing agents such as PEG, Ficoll, and hexamminecobalt chloride accelerate the rate of blunt-end ligation by T4 DNA ligases by a factor of 1000 and permit ligation at lower enzyme, ATP, and DNA concentrations (Zimmerman and Pheiffer 1983; Rusche and Howard-Flanders 1985). Blunt-end ligation is inhibited by high concentrations of Na$^+$ (≥50 mM) and phosphate (≥25 mM) (Raae et al. 1975).

[c]Dugaiczyk et al. (1975).

[d]Weiss and Richardson (1967).

[e]T4 DNA ligase can join RNA molecules annealed to either complementary DNA or RNA templates, albeit with low efficiency (Kleppe et al. 1970).

[f]Ferretti and Sgaramella (1981).

[g]Weiss et al. (1968a,b).

[h]Sgaramella and Ehrlich (1978).

[i]Pohl et al. (1982).

[j]Almost all thermophilic ligases, like mesophilic eubacterial ligases, use DPN$^+$ as a cofactor. However, one thermostable ligase that requires ATP as a cofactor has been cloned and sequenced (Kletzin 1992). The properties of this enzyme have not been investigated in detail.

[k]Takahashi et al. (1984).

[l]Takahashi and Uchida (1986).

[m]Barany (1991a,b).

- As shown in Table 1-12, T4 DNA ligase can catalyze the ligation of cohesive termini (Hedgpeth et al. 1972; Mertz and Davis 1972), oligodeoxynucleotides, or oligoribonucleotides in RNA-DNA hybrids (Olivera and Lehman 1968; Kleppe et al. 1970; Fareed et al. 1971). In addition, the enzyme can efficiently promote the end-to-end joining of two duplex molecules with fully base-paired termini (Sgaramella et al. 1970; Ehrlich et al. 1977).

- T4 DNA ligase shows a strong (Wiaderkiewicz and Ruiz-Carillo 1987; Landegren et al. 1988; Wu and Wallace 1989), but not absolute, aversion (Goffin et al. 1987) to joining oligonucleotides that are hybridized to a complementary template and contain a mispaired base at either the 3′ or 5′ junction of the two strands. This ability to discriminate between perfectly and imperfectly paired termini allowed the development of oligonucleotide ligation and amplification systems to detect mutations in genes of medical interest.

- High concentrations (>100 mM) of monovalent cations such as Na$^+$ and K$^+$ inhibit the activity of T4 DNA ligase, the extent of the inhibition varying with the terminal sequences of the substrate DNAs (Hayashi et al. 1985a). However, in the presence of crowding agents such as 10% PEG, monovalent cations have a paradoxical effect and stimulate the activity of the enzyme.

E. coli DNA Ligase

- *E. coli* DNA ligase is encoded by the *lig* gene that lies at 52 minutes on the *E. coli* genetic map (Gottesman et al. 1973; Bachmann 1990).
- The *lig* gene (Gottesman 1976) and *lop11 lig*[+] (Cameron et al. 1975), a regulatory mutant overproducing the enzyme, have been cloned into bacteriophage λ vectors, thus facilitating large-scale purification of the enzyme (Panasenko et al. 1977, 1978). The nucleotide sequence of the *lig* gene (Ishino et al. 1986) shows that *E. coli* DNA ligase consists of 671 amino acids with a molecular weight of 73,690.
- For several years, it was believed that *E. coli* DNA ligase would not ligate blunt-ended double-stranded DNA. However, following cloning and expression of the ligase gene, highly active preparations of the enzyme became available that were able to catalyze blunt-end ligation with moderate efficiency (Barringer et al. 1990). Blunt-end ligation is stimulated about tenfold when the reaction mixture contains 10–15% PEG and high concentrations of K^+ (Hayashi et al. 1985b). Nevertheless, *E. coli* DNA ligase is not widely used in molecular cloning procedures, since T4 DNA ligase is capable of efficiently joining blunt-ended DNAs in the absence of crowding agents.
- Unlike T4 DNA ligase, *E. coli* DNA ligase will not efficiently join RNA to DNA and is therefore unable to join adjacent RNA and DNA segments that arise during replacement synthesis of second-strand cDNA (Okayama and Berg 1982). The bacterial enzyme can therefore be used to generate long strands of cDNA that are uninterrupted by segments of RNA.

Thermostable DNA Ligases

- The genes encoding thermostable ligases from several thermophilic bacteria have been cloned, sequenced, and expressed to high levels in *E. coli* (e.g., please see Takahashi et al. 1984; Barany and Gelfand 1991; Lauer et al. 1991; Jónsson et al. 1994). Several of these enzymes are available from commercial sources.
- Like the *E. coli* enzyme, almost all thermostable ligases use NAD^+ as a cofactor and work preferentially at nicks in double-stranded DNA. In addition, thermostable ligases, like their mesophilic homolog, can catalyze blunt-end ligation in the presence of crowding agents, even at elevated temperatures (Takahashi and Uchida 1986).
- Because thermostable ligases retain activity after multiple rounds of thermal cycling, they are used extensively in the ligase amplification reaction to detect mutations in mammalian DNAs.

Units of Ligase Activity

The standardization of ligase activity in units that are meaningful to both biochemists and molecular cloners has proven to be an elusive goal. For the last 20 years, at least three different units have been used to measure ligase activity:

- A *Weiss unit* (Weiss et al. 1968b) is defined as the amount of ligase that catalyzes the exchange of 1 nmole of ^{32}P from inorganic pyrophosphate to ATP in 20 minutes at 37ºC.
- The *Modrich-Lehman* unit (Modrich and Lehman 1971), now rarely used, is based on the conversion of radiolabeled d(A-T)$_n$ copolymer with 3´-hydroxyl and 5´-phosphoryl termini to a form resistant to digestion with exonuclease III. One Modrich-Lehman unit is defined as the amount of enzyme required to convert 100 nmoles of d(A-T)$_n$ to an exonuclease-III-resistant form in 30 minutes under standard assay conditions.
- *Arbitrary units*, defined by commercial suppliers, are based on the ability of ligase to ligate cohesive ends of DNA. These units are often more subjective than quantitative and provide little guidance to an investigator who values precision. In the absence of meaningful information, most investigators setting up ligation reactions must resort to guesswork, which inevitably means that more ligase will be used than is necessary. This, of course, is exactly what the commercial companies seek. As a rough guide, 1 Weiss unit is approximately equivalent to 60 cohesive end units (as defined by New England Biolabs). Thus, in 30 minutes at 16ºC, 0.015 Weiss units of T4 DNA ligase should ligate 50% of fragments derived by digestion of 5 μg of bacteriophage λ DNA with *Hin*dIII.

ADAPTORS

Adaptors are used to replace one type of protruding terminus with another. They are short double-stranded synthetic oligonucleotides that carry an internal restriction endonuclease recognition site and single-stranded tails at one or both ends (please see Table 1-13). This protruding sequence can be ligated to DNA fragments containing a complementary single-stranded terminus. After ligation, the DNA can be cleaved with the appropriate restriction enzyme to create a new protruding terminus.

Adaptors are available in two basic designs and a variety of specificities. Some adaptors consist of a partial duplex formed between two oligonucleotides of different lengths; for example, the *Eco*RI-*Not*I adaptor from Stratgene has the following structure:

5′ AATTCGCGGCCGC 3′
3′ GCGCCGGCGp 5′

During ligation, the protruding 5′ end of the adaptor becomes joined to the complementary terminus of the target DNA, restoring an *Eco*RI site (GAATTC). In addition, the ligation of the phosphorylated blunt ends allows the adaptors to form dimers that contain internal *Not*I recognition sites (GCGGCCGC). Higher-order polymer formation cannot occur because the protruding 5′ terminus is not phosphorylated.

By contrast, another class of adaptors is supplied as an unphosphorylated single oligonucleotide whose sequence is partially self-complementary. After duplex formation, the *Eco*RI-*Pst*I adaptor from U.S. Specialty Biochemicals has the following structure:

5′ AATTCCTGCAGG 3′
3′ GGACGTCCTTAA 5′

During ligation, one strand of the adaptor becomes joined to the complementary terminus of the target DNA, restoring an *Eco*RI site. No further ligation is possible unless the adaptor has been phosphorylated in the investigator's laboratory, in which case the adaptors can form tandem arrays. Phosphorylation is recommended because tandem arrays of adaptors are cleaved more efficiently than single adaptors by the second restriction enzyme, in this case, *Pst*I (site: CTGCAG).

Adaptors also offer an excellent way to ligate cDNA to vectors during the construction of cDNA libraries. The recessed 3′ termini of an *Xho*I cloning site on the vector are partially filled, and phosphorylated adaptors with 3-base protruding termini complementary to the partially filled *Xho*I site are attached to the cDNA. Neither the vector nor the cDNA molecules can anneal to themselves, but they can join to one another. Because the *Xho*I site is regenerated, the cloned cDNA can be recovered by digestion with *Xho*I. This strategy greatly improves the efficiency of the ligation step in cDNA cloning and eliminates the need to methylate the cDNA or to digest it with restriction enzymes before insertion into the vector (Yang et al. 1986; Elledge et al. 1991).

Alternatively, PCR can be used to add a desired restriction site or sites at the 5′ and 3′ ends of a fragment of amplified DNA by simply incorporating the recognition sequence at the 5′ ends of the oligonucleotide primers. In many cases, the target DNA can be cloned into one restriction site in a polylinker and then excised by digestion with another restriction enzyme or combination of enzymes. For routine subcloning, this is often the method of choice because the target DNA can be inserted into a polylinker that contains several useful flanking restriction sites. However, a polylinker is not always available that carries the desired restriction site in an appropriate location. This problem can be solved by using an adaptor with the appropriate length of "spacer" between the protruding terminus and the internal restriction site. Adaptors therefore simplify the task of creating genes that efficiently express fusion proteins because they allow the target DNA, free of potentially deleterious flanking sequences, to be inserted in-frame into the desired expression vector.

TABLE 1-13 Adaptor Sequences

*Eco*RI-*Not*I	5´ AATTCGCGGCCGC 3´
	3´ GCGCCGGCG 5´
*Bam*HI-*Sma*I	5´ GATCCCCCGGG 3´
	3´ GGGGCCC 5´
*Eco*RI-*Sma*I	5´ AATTCCCCGGG 3´
	3´ GGGGCCC 5´
*Sal*I-*Sma*I	5´ TCGACCCCGGG 3´
	3´ GGGGCCC 5´
*Hind*III-*Sma*I	5´ AGCTTCCCGGG 3´
	3´ AGGGCCC 5´
*Bam*HI-*Pst*I	5´ GATCCCTGCAG 3´
	3´ GGACGTC 5´
*Eco*RI-*Eco*RI	5´ AATTCGAATTC 3´
	3´ GCTTAAG 5´
*Eco*RI-*Xho*I	5´ AATTCGGCTCGAG 3´
	3´ GCCGAGCTC 5´
*Xho*III-*Eco*RI	5´ AGCTTGAATTC 3´
	3´ ACTTAAG 5´
*Xho*I-*Eco*RI	5´ TCGAGGAATTC 3´
	3´ CCTTAAG 5´
*Bam*HI-*Eco*RI	5´ GATCCGAATTC 3´
	3´ GCTTAAG 5´
*Sal*I-*Not*I	5´ TCGACGCGGCCGC 3´
	3´ GCGCCGGCG 5´
*Hind*III-*Not*I	5´ AGCTTGCGGCCGC 3´
	3´ ACGCCGGCG 5´
*Xho*I-*Not*I	5´ TCGAGGCGGCCGC 3´
	3´ CCGCCGGCG 5´
*Sal*I-*Xho*I	5´ TCGACCTCGAG 3´
	3´ GGAGCTC 5´

Modified with permission, © 1999 Stratagene.

ELECTROPORATION

The application of a sharp pulse of electricity is thought to cause dimpling of membranes followed by formation of transient hydrophobic pores whose diameter fluctuates from a minimum of 2 nm to a maximum of several nm. Some of the larger hydrophobic pores are converted to hydrophilic pores because the energy needed to create and maintain a hydrophilic pore is reduced as the transmembrane voltage is increased (Weaver 1993). Reclosing of pores seems to be a stochastic process that can be delayed by keeping the cells at low temperature. While the pores remain open, DNA molecules can easily pass from the medium into the cytoplasm (please see Figure 1-18).

The transmembrane voltage required for formation of large hydrophobic pores varies in direct proportion to the diameter of the target cell. Most manufacturers of electroporation machines provide literature describing the approximate voltages required for transfection of specific cell types in their particular apparatus. Three important parameters of the pulse affect the efficiency of electroporation:

- *Length* of pulse is determined mainly by the value of the capacitor and the conductivity of the medium. Most commercial electroporation machines use capacitative discharge to produce controlled pulses.
- *Field strength* varies in direct proportion to the applied voltage and in inverse proportion to the distance between the electrodes. Most manufacturers provide cuvettes of various sizes to suit the task at hand and recommend that the cuvettes be used only once. However, many investigators, in an effort to reduce costs, wash and re-use the cuvettes several times. The wisdom of this practice is a topic of ongoing debate (e.g., please see Hengen 1995).
- *Shape* is determined by the design of the electroporation device. The wave form produced by most commercial machines is simply the exponential decay pattern of a discharging capacitor (Dower et al. 1988).

For most commonly used strains of *E. coli*, maximum rates of transformation are achieved after a single electrical pulse with a field strength of 12.5–15 kV cm^{-1} and a length of 4.5–5.5 milliseconds. Under these conditions, ~50% of the cells survive.

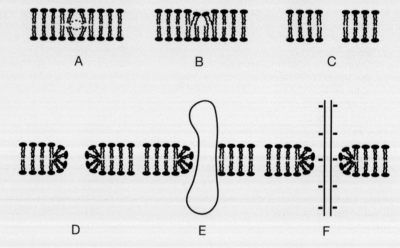

A   B   C

D   E   F

FIGURE 1-18 Changes in the Membrane during Electroporation

Drawings of hypothetical structures for transient and metastable membrane conformations believed to be relevant to electroporation. (*A*) Fredd volume fluctuation; (*B*) aqueous protrusion or "dimple"; (*C,D*) hydrophobic pores usually regarded as the "primary pores" through which ions and molecules pass; (*E*) composite pore with "foot in the door" charged macromolecule inserted into a hydrophilic pore. The transient aqueous pore model assumes that transitions from A→B→C or D occur with increasing frequency as U is increased. Type F may form by entry of a tethered macromolecule, while the transmembrane voltage is significantly elevated, and then persist after U has decayed to a small value through pore conduction. It is emphasized that these hypothetical structures have not been directly observed and that support for them derives from the interpretation of a variety of experiments involving electrical, optical, mechanical, and molecular transport behavior. (Reprinted, with permission, from Weaver 1993 [copyright Wiley-Liss, Inc.].)

REFERENCES

Abraham E.P. and Chain E. 1940. An enzyme from bacteria able to destroy penicillin. *Nature* **146:** 837.

Ahmed A. 1984. Plasmid vectors for positive galactose-resistance selection of cloned DNA in *Escherichia coli. Gene* **28:** 37–43.

Armstrong J., Brown R.S., and Tsugita A. 1983. Primary structure and genetic organization of phage T4 DNA ligase. *Nucleic Acids Res.* **11:** 7145–7156.

Bachmann B.J. 1990. Linkage map of *Escherichia coli* K-12, edition 8 (erratum *Microbiol. Rev.* [1991] **55:** 191). *Microbiol. Rev.* **54:** 130–197.

Balbas P., Soberón X., Merino E., Zurita M., Lomeli H., Valle F., Flores N., and Bolivar F. 1986. Plasmid vector pBR322 and its special purpose derivatives—A review. *Gene* **50:** 3–40.

Banner D.W., Kokkindis M., and Tsernoglou D. 1987. Structure of the ColE1 Rop protein at 1.7Å resolution. *J. Mol. Biol.* **196:** 657–675.

Barany F. 1991a. Genetic disease detection and DNA amplification using cloned thermostable ligase. *Proc. Natl. Acad. Sci.* **88:** 189–193.

———. 1991b. The ligase chain reaction in a PCR world (erratum *PCR Methods Appl.* [1991] **1:** 149). *PCR Methods Appl.* **1:** 5–16.

Barany F. and Gelfand D.H. 1991. Cloning, overexpression and nucleotide sequence of a thermostable DNA ligase-encoding gene. *Gene* **109:** 1–11.

Barker D.G., White J.H., and Johnston L.H. 1985. The nucleotide sequence of the DNA ligase gene (CDC9) from *Saccharomyces cerevisiae*: A gene which is cell-cycle regulated and induced in response to DNA damage. *Nucleic Acids Res.* **13:** 8323–8337.

Barkley M.D. and Bourgeois S. 1978. Repressor recognition of operator and effectors. In *The operon* (ed. J.H. Miller and W.S. Reznikoff), pp. 177–220. Cold Spring Harbor Laboratory, Cold Spring Harbor, New York.

Barlow J.J., Mathias A.P., Williamson R., and Gammack D.B. 1963. A simple method for quantitative isolation of undegraded high molecular weight ribonucleic acid. *Biochem. Biophys. Res. Commun.* **13:** 61–66.

Barnes W.M. 1977. Plasmid detection and sizing in single colony lysates. *Science* **195:** 393–394.

Barringer K.J., Orgel L., Wahl G., and Gingeras T.R. 1990. Blunt-end and single-strand ligations by *Escherichia coli* ligase: Influence on an in vitro amplification scheme. *Gene* **89:** 117–122.

Bauer W. and Vinograd J. 1968. The interaction of closed circular DNA with intercalative dyes. I. The superhelix density of SV-40 DNA in the presence and absence of dye. *J. Mol. Biol.* **33:** 141–171.

———. 1970. Interaction of closed circular DNA with intercalative dyes. II. The free energy of superhelix formation in SV-40 DNA. *J. Mol. Biol.* **47:** 419–435.

———. 1971. The use of intercalative dyes in the study of closed circular DNA. *Progr. Mol. Subcell. Biol.* **2:** 181–215.

Bazaral M. and Helinski D.R. 1968. Circular DNA forms of colicinogenic factors E1, E2 and E3 from *Escherichia coli. J. Mol. Biol.* **36:** 185–194.

Beck E. and Bremer E. 1980. Nucleotide sequence of the gene *omp*A coding the outer membrane protein II of *Escherichia coli* K-12. *Nucleic Acids Res.* **8:** 3011–3027.

Becker A., Lyn G., Gefter M., and Hurwitz J. 1967. The enzymatic repair of DNA. II. Characterization of phage-induced sealase. *Proc. Natl. Acad. Sci.* **58:** 1996–2003.

Bedbrook J.R., Lehrach H., and Ausubel F.M. 1979. Directive segregation in the basis of ColE1 plasmid incompatibility. *Nature* **281:** 447–452.

Bercovich J.A., Grinstein S., and Zorzopulos J. 1992. Effect of DNA concentration of recombinant plasmid recovery after blunt-end ligation. *BioTechniques* **12:** 190–193.

Bernard P. 1995. New *ccdB* positive-selection cloning vectors with kanamycin of chloramphenicol selectable markers. *Gene* **162:** 159–160.

———. 1996. Positive selection of recombinant DNA by *CcdB. BioTechniques* **21:** 320–323.

Birnboim H.C. and Doly J. 1979. A rapid alkaline procedure for screening recombinant plasmid DNA. *Nucleic Acids Res.* **7:** 1513–1523.

Bittner M. and Vapnek D. 1981. Versatile cloning vectors derived from the runaway-replication plasmid pKN402. *Gene* **15:** 319–329.

Blake C.C.F., Johnson L.N., Mair G.A., North A.C.T., Phillips D.C., and Sarma V.R. 1967. Crystallographic studies of the activity of hen egg-white lysozyme. *Proc. R. Soc. Lond. B Biol. Sci.* **167:** 378–388.

Bochner B., Huang H., Schiever G., and Ames B. 1980. Positive selection for loss of tetracycline resistance. *J. Bacteriol.* **143:** 926–933.

Bolivar F., Rodriguez R.L., Betlach M.C., and Boyer H.W. 1977a. Construction and characterization of new cloning vehicles. I. Ampicillin-resistant derivatives of plasmid pMB9. *Gene* **2:** 75–93.

Bolivar F., Rodriguez R.L., Green P.J., Betlach M.C., Heyneker H.L., Boyer H.W., Crosa J.H., and Falkow S. 1977b. Construction and characterization of new cloning vehicles. II. A multipurpose cloning system. *Gene* **2:** 95–113.

Boyle J.S. and Lew A.M. 1995. An inexpensive alternative to glass-milk for DNA purification. *Trends Genet.* **11:** 8.

Brendel V. and Perelson A.S. 1993. Quantitative model of ColE1 plasmid number copy control. *J. Mol. Biol.* **229:** 860–872.

Brosius J. 1992. Compilation of superlinker vectors. *Methods Enzymol.* **216:** 469–483.

Brunk C.F. and Simpson L. 1977. Comparison of various ultraviolet sources for fluorescent detection of ethidium bromide-DNA complexes in polyacrylamide gels. *Anal. Biochem.* **82:** 455–462.

Burns D.M. and Beacham I.R. 1984. Positive selection vectors: A small plasmid vector useful for the direct selection of *Sau*3A-generated overlapping DNA fragments. *Gene* **27:** 323–325.

Bush K. and Sykes R.B. 1984. Interaction of β-lactam antibiotics with β-lactamases as a cause for resistance. In *Antimicrobial drug resistance* (ed. L.E. Bryan), pp. 1–31. Academic Press, New York.

Cameron J.R., Panasenko S.M., Lehman I.R., and Davis R.W. 1975. In vitro construction of bacteriophage lambda carrying segments of the *Escherichia coli* chromosome: Selection of hybrids containing the gene for DNA ligase. *Proc. Natl. Acad. Sci.* **72:** 3416–3420.

Cantor C.R. and Schimmel P.R. 1980. *Biophysical chemistry.* Part III. *The behavior of biological macromolecules,* p. 1251. W.H. Freeman, San Francisco, California.

Carter M.J. and Milton I.D. 1993. An inexpensive and simple

method for DNA purification on silica particles. *Nucleic Acids Res.* **21:** 1044.

Cesareni G., Helmer-Citterich M., and Castagnoli L. 1991. Control of ColE1 plasmid replication by antisense RNA. *Trends Genet.* **7:** 230–235.

Chan P.T., Ohmori H., Tomizawa J.-I., and Lebowitz J. 1984. Nucleotide sequence and gene organization of ColE1 DNA. *J. Biol. Chem.* **260:** 8925–8935.

Chang A.C.Y. and Cohen S.N. 1978. Construction and characterization of amplifiable multicopy DNA cloning vehicles derived from the p15A cryptic miniplasmid. *J. Bacteriol.* **134:** 1141–1156.

Chassy B.M. and Flickinger J.L. 1987. Transformation of *Lactobacillus casei* by electroporation. *FEMS Microbiol. Lett.* **44:** 173–177.

Chassy B.M., Mercenier A., and Flickinger J. 1988. Transformation of bacteria by electroporation. *Trends Biotechnol.* **6:** 303–309.

Chen X.J. and Fukuhara H. 1988. A gene fusion system using the aminoglycoside 3′-phosphotransferase gene of the kanamycin-resistance transposon Tn903: Use in the yeast *Kluyveromyces lactis* and *Saccharomyces cerevisiae*. *Gene* **69:** 181–192.

Cheng S. and Modrich P. 1983. Positive selection cloning vehicle useful for overproduction of hybrid proteins. *J. Bacteriol.* **154:** 1005–1008.

Chiang C.-S. and Bremer H. 1991. Maintenance of pBR322-derived plasmids without functional RNAI. *Plasmid* **26:** 186–200.

Chopra I. 1985. Mode of action of the tetracyclines and the nature of bacterial resistance to them. In *The tetracyclines* (ed. J.J. Hlavka and J.H. Boothe), pp. 317–392. Springer-Verlag, Berlin, Germany.

Chopra I., Hawkey P.M., and Hinton M. 1992. Tetracyclines, molecular and clinical aspects. *J. Antimicrob. Chemother.* **29:** 245–277.

Claverie-Martin F., Diaz-Torres M.R., Yacey S.D., and Kushner S.R. 1989. Cloning of the altered mRNA stability (*ams*) gene of *Escherichia coli* K-12. *J. Bacteriol.* **171:** 5479–5486.

Clewell D.B. 1972. Nature of ColE1 plasmid replication in *Escherichia coli* in the presence of chloramphenicol. *J. Bacteriol.* **110:** 667–676.

Clewell D.B. and Helinski D.R. 1969 Supercoiled circular DNA-protein complex in *Escherichia coli:* Purification and induced conversion to an open circular form. *Proc. Natl. Acad. Sci.* **62:** 1159–1166.

Cohen A. and Clark A.J. 1986. Synthesis of linear plasmid multimers in *Escherichia coli* K-12. *J. Bacteriol.* **167:** 327–335.

Cohen S.N., Chang A.C.Y., and Hsu L. 1972. Nonchromosomal antibiotic resistance in bacteria: Genetic transformation of *Escherichia coli* by R-factor DNA. *Proc. Natl. Acad. Sci.* **69:** 2110–2114.

Cohen S.N., Chang A.C.Y., Boyer H.W., and Helling R.B. 1973. Construction of biologically functional bacterial plasmids *in vitro*. *Proc. Natl. Acad. Sci.* **73:** 3240–3244.

Colbère-Garapin F., Horodniceanu F., Kourilsky P., and Garapin A.C. 1981. A new dominant hybrid selective marker for higher eukaryotic cells. *J. Mol. Biol.* **150:** 1–14.

Collins J. 1981. Instability of palindromic DNA in *Escherichia coli*. *Cold Spring Harbor Symp. Quant. Biol.* **45:** 409–416.

Collins J. and Hohn B. 1978. Cosmids: A type of plasmid gene-cloning vector that is packageable *in vitro* in bacteriophage lambda heads. *Proc. Natl. Acad. Sci.* **75:** 4242–4246.

Colloms S.D., Sykora P., Szatmari G., and Sherratt D.J. 1990. Recombination at ColE1 *cer* requires the *Escherichia coli*

XerC gene product, a member of the lambda integrase family of site specific recombinases. *J. Bacteriol.* **172:** 6973–6980.

Conley D.L. and Cohen S.N. 1995. Effects of the pSC101 partition (*par*) locus on *in vivo* DNA supercoiling near the plasmid replication origin. *Nucleic Acids Res.* **23:** 701–707.

Covarrubias L., Cervantes L., Covarrubias A., Soberón X., Vichido I., Blanco A., Kupersztoch-Portnoy Y.M., and Bolivar F. 1981. Construction and characterization of new cloning vehicles. V. Mobilization and coding properties of pBR322 and several deletion derivatives, including pBR327 and pBR328. *Gene* **13:** 25–35.

Covey C., Richardson D., and Carbon J. 1976. A method for the deletion of restriction sites in bacterial plasmid deoxyribonucleic acid. *Mol. Gen. Genet.* **145:** 155–158.

Cozzarelli N.R., Kelly R.B., and Kornberg A. 1968. A minute circular DNA from *Escherichia coli* 15. *Proc. Natl. Acad. Sci.* **60:** 992–999.

Cozzarelli N.R., Melechen N.E., Jovin T.M., and Kornberg A. 1967. Polynucleotide cellulose as a substrate for a polynucleotide ligase induced by phage T4. *Biochem. Biophys. Res. Commun.* **28:** 578–586.

Craine B.L. 1982. Novel selection for tetracycline- or chloramphenicol-sensitive *Escherichia coli*. *J. Bacteriol.* **151:** 487–490.

Crawford L.V. and Waring M.J. 1967. Supercoiling of polyoma virus DNA measured by its interaction with ethidium bromide. *J. Mol. Biol.* **25:** 23–30.

Cundliffe E. 1990. Recognition sites for antibiotics within rRNA. In *The ribosome: Structure, function, and evolution* (ed. W.E. Hill et al.), pp. 479–490. American Society for Microbiology, Washington, D.C.

Dagert M. and Ehrlich S.D. 1979. Prolonged incubation in calcium chloride improves the competence of *Escherichia coli* cells. *Gene* **6:** 23–28.

Damak S. and Bullock D.W. 1993. A simple two-step method for efficient blunt-end ligation of DNA fragments. *BioTechniques* **15:** 448–452.

Datta N. and Kontomichalou P. 1965. Penicillinase synthesis controlled by infectious R factors in *Enterbacteriaceae*. *Nature* **208:** 239–241.

Davies J. 1990. What are antibiotics? Archaic functions for modern activities. *Mol. Microbiol.* **4:** 1227–1232.

Davies J. and Jacob F. 1968. Genetic mapping of the regulator and operator genes of the lac operon. *J. Mol. Biol.* **36:** 413–417.

Davies J. and Smith D.I. 1978. Plasmid-determined resistance to antimicrobial agents. *Annu. Rev. Microbiol.* **32:** 469–518.

Davison J. 1984. Mechanism of control of DNA replication and incompatibility in ColE1-type plasmids—A review. *Gene* **28:** 1–15.

Denhardt D.T. 1966. A membrane-filter technique for the detection of complementary DNA. *Biochem. Biophys. Res. Commun.* **23:** 641–646.

Doherty J.P., Lindeman R., Trent R.J., Graham M.W., and Woodcock D.M. 1993. *Escherichia coli* host strains SURE and SRB fail to preserve a palindrome cloned in λ phage: Improved alternate host strains. *Gene* **124:** 29–35.

Donowitz G.R. and Mandell G.L. 1988. β-lactam antibiotics. *N. Engl. J. Med.* **318:** 419–426 and 490–500.

Dorin M. and Bornecque C.A. 1995. Fast separations of plasmid DNA using discontinuous gradients in the preparative ultracentrifuge. *BioTechniques* **18:** 90–91.

Dower W.J., Miller J.F., and Ragsdale C.W. 1988. High efficiency transformation of *E. coli* by high voltage electroporation. *Nucleic Acids Res.* **16:** 6127–6145.

Drainas D., Kalpaxis D.L., and Coutsogeorgopoulos C. 1987. Inhibition of ribosomal peptidyltransferase by chloramphenicol. Kinetic studies. *Eur. J. Biochem.* **164:** 53–58.

Dugaiczyk A., Boyer H.W., and Goodman H.M. 1975. Ligation of *Eco*RI endonuclease-generated DNA fragments into linear and circular structures. *J. Mol. Biol.* **96:** 171–184.

Eguchi Y. and Tomizawa J. 1990. Complex formed by complementary RNA stem-loops and its stabilization by a protein: Function of ColE1 Rom protein. *Cell* **60:** 199–209.

Eguchi Y., Itoh T., and Tomizawa J. 1991. Antisense RNA. *Annu. Rev. Biochem.* **60:** 631–652.

Ehrlich S.D., Sgaramella V., and Lederberg J. 1977. T4 ligase joins flush-ended DNA duplexes generated by restriction endonucleases. In *Nucleic acid-protein recognition* (ed. H.J. Vogel), pp. 261–268. Academic Press, New York.

Ehrlich J., Bartz Q.R., Smith R.M., Joslyn D.A., and Burkholder P.R. 1947. Chloromycetin, a new antibiotic from a soil actinomycete. *Science* **106:** 417.

Elledge S.J., Mulligan J.T., Ramer S.W., Spottswood M., and Davis R.W. 1991. λYES: A multifunctional cDNA expression vector for the isolation of genes by complementation of yeast and *Escherichia coli* mutations. *Proc. Natl. Acad. Sci.* **88:** 1731–1735.

Ellis J., Carlin A., Steffes C., Wu J., Liu J., and Rosen B.P. 1995. Topological analysis of the lysine-specific permease of *Escherichia coli*. *Microbiology* **141:** 1927–1935.

Elvin S. and Bingham A.H.A. 1991. Electroporation-induced transformation of *Escherichia coli*: Evaluation of a square waveform pulse. *Lett. Appl. Microbiol.* **12:** 39–42.

Engler M.J. and Richardson C.C. 1982. DNA ligases. In *The enzymes* (ed. P.D. Boyer), vol. 15, pp. 3–29. Academic Press, New York.

Fareed G.C., Wilt E.M., and Richardson C.C. 1971. Enzymatic breakage and joining of deoxyribonucleic acid. 8. Hybrids of ribo- and deoxyribonucleotide homopolymers as substrates for polynucleotide ligase of bacteriophage T4. *J. Biol. Chem.* **246:** 925–932.

Ferretti L. and Sgaramella V. 1981. Temperature dependence of the joining by T4 DNA ligase of termini produced by type II restriction endonucleases. *Nucleic Acids Res.* **9:** 85–93.

Fiedler S. and Wirth R. 1988. Transformation of bacteria with plasmid DNA by electroporation. *Anal. Biochem.* **170:** 38–44.

Fiil N.P., Bendiak D., Collins J., and Friesen J.D. 1979. Expression of *Escherichia coli* ribosomal protein and RNA polymerase genes cloned on plasmids. *Mol. Gen. Genet.* **173:** 39–50.

Firshein W. and Kim P. 1997. Plasmid replication and partition in *Escherichia coli*: Is the cell membrane the key? *Mol. Microbiol.* **23:** 1–10.

Fleming A. 1922. On a remarkable bacteriolytic element found in tissues and secretions. *Proc. R. Soc. Lond. B Biol. Sci.* **93:** 306–317.

Frenkel L. and Bremer H. 1986. Increased amplification of plasmids pBR322 and pBR327 by low concentrations of chloramphenicol. *DNA* **5:** 539–544.

Freifelder D. 1971. Electron microscopic study of the ethidium bromide-DNA complex. *J. Mol. Biol.* **60:** 401–403.

Fursht A. 1985. *Enzyme structure and mechanism*, 2nd edition. W.H. Freeman, New York.

Gale E.F., Cundliffe E., Reynolds P.E., Richmond M.H., and Waring M.J. 1981. Antibiotic inhibitors of ribosome function. In *The molecular basis of antibiotic action*, 2nd edition, pp. 402–408. John Wiley, Chichester, United Kingdom.

Gergen J.P., Stern R.H., and Wensink P.C. 1979. Filter replicas and permanent collections of recombinant DNA plasmids. *Nucleic Acids Res.* **7:** 2115–2136.

Gillespie D. and Spiegelman S. 1965. A quantitative assay for DNA-RNA hybrids with DNA immobilized on a membrane. *J. Mol. Biol.* **12:** 829–842.

Giza P.E. and Huang R.C. 1989. A self-inducing runaway-replication plasmid expression system utilizing the Rop protein. *Gene* **78:** 73–84.

Glišin V., Crkvenjakov R., and Byus C. 1974. Ribonucleic acid isolated by cesium chloride centrifugation. *Biochemistry* **13:** 2633–2637.

Godson G.N. and Vapnek D. 1973. A simple method of preparing large amounts of φX174 RFI supercoiled DNA. *Biochim. Biophys. Acta* **299:** 516–520.

Goffin C., Bailly V., and Verly W.G. 1987. Nicks 3′ or 5′ to AP sites or to mispaired bases, and one-nucleotide gaps can be sealed by T4 DNA ligase. *Nucleic Acids Res.* **15:** 8755–8771.

Gómez-Márquez J., Friere M., and Segade F. 1987. A simple procedure for the large-scale purification of plasmid DNA. *Gene* **54:** 255–259.

Good L. and Nazar R.N. 1995. Visualization of CsCl/EtdBr plasmid preparations under visible light. *BioTechniques* **18:** 556–557.

Gottesman M.M. 1976. Isolation and characterization of a lambda specialized transducing phage for the *Escherichia coli* DNA ligase gene. *Virology* **72:** 33–44.

Gottesman M.M., Hicks M.L., and Gellert M. 1973. Genetics and function of DNA ligase in *Escherichia coli*. *J. Mol. Biol.* **77:** 531–547.

Griffith J.K., Cuellar D.H., Fordyce C.A., Hutchings K.G., and Mondragon A.A. 1994. Structure and function of the class C tetracycline/H⁺ antiporter: Three independent groups of phenotypes are conferred by TetAχ. *Mol. Membr. Biol.* **11:** 271–277.

Grunstein M. and Hogness D.S. 1975. Colony hybridization: A method for the isolation of cloned DNAs that contain a specific gene. *Proc. Natl. Acad. Sci.* **72:** 3961–3965.

Gumport R.I. and Lehman I.R. 1971. Structure of the DNA ligase-adenylate intermediate: Lysine (epsilon-amino)-linked adenosine monophosphoramidate. *Proc. Natl. Acad. Sci.* **68:** 2559–2563.

Hagan C.E. and Warren G.J. 1983. Viability of palindromic DNA is restored by deletions occurring at low but variable frequency in plasmids of *E. coli*. *Gene* **24:** 317–326.

Hanahan D. 1983. Studies on transformation of *Escherichia coli* with plasmids. *J. Mol. Biol.* **166:** 557–580.

———. 1985. Techniques for transformation of *E. coli*. In *DNA cloning: A practical approach* (ed. D.M. Glover), vol. 1, pp. 109–135. IRL Press, Oxford, United Kingdom.

———. 1987. Mechanisms of DNA transformation. In *Escherichia coli and* Salmonella typhimurium: *Cellular and molecular biology* (ed. F.C. Neidhardt et al.), vol. 2, pp. 1177–1183. American Society for Microbiology, Washington, D.C.

Hanahan D. and Bloom F.R. 1996. Mechanisms of DNA transformation. In *Escherichia coli and* Salmonella: *Cellular and molecular biology*, 2nd edition (ed. F.C. Neidhardt et al.), vol. 2, pp. 2449–2459. American Society for Microbiology, Washington, D.C.

Hanahan D. and Meselson M. 1980. Plasmid screening at high colony density. *Gene* **10:** 63–67.

———. 1983. Plasmid screening at high colony density. *Methods Enzymol.* **100:** 333–342.

Hanahan D., Jessee J., and Bloom F.R. 1991. Plasmid transformation of *E. coli* and other bacteria. *Methods Enzymol.* **204:** 63–113.

———. 1995. Techniques for transformation of *E. coli*. In *DNA cloning: A practical approach*, 2nd edition. *Core techniques* (ed. D.M. Glover and B.D. Hames), vol. 1, pp. 1–36. IRL Press, Oxford, United Kingdom.

Hansen F.G. and von Meyenberg K. 1979. Characterization of the *dnaA*, *gyrB* and other genes in the *dnaA* region of the *Escherichia coli* chromosome on specialized transducing phages λ*tna Mol. Gen. Genet.* **175:** 135–144.

Hayashi K., Nakazawa M., Ishizaki Y., and Obayashi A. 1985a. Influence of monovalent cations on the activity of T4 DNA ligase in the presence of polyethylene glycol. *Nucleic Acids Res.* **13:** 3261–3271.

Hayashi K., Nakazawa M., Ishizaki Y., Hiraoka N., and Obayashi A. 1985b. Stimulation of intermolecular ligation with *E. coli* DNA ligase by high concentrations of monovalent cations in polyethylene glycol solutions. *Nucleic Acids Res.* **13:** 7979–7992.

Hayes W. 1969. Introduction: What are episomes and plasmids? In *Bacterial episomes and plasmids* (ed. G.E.W. Wolstenholme and M. O'Connor), pp. 4–8. Little, Brown and Co., Boston, Massachusetts.

He L., Soderbom F., Wagner E.G., Binnie U., Binns N., and Masters M. 1993. PcnB is required for the rapid degradation of RNAI, the antisense RNA that controls the copy number of ColE1-related plasmids. *Mol. Microbiol.* **9:** 1131–1142.

Hearst J.E. and Vinograd J. 1961a. The net hydration of deoxyribonucleic acid. *Proc. Natl. Acad. Sci.* **47:** 825–830.

———. 1961b. The net hydration of T-4 bacteriophage deoxyribonucleic acid and the effect of hydration on buoyant behavior in a density gradient at equilibrium in the ultracentrifuge. *Proc. Natl. Acad. Sci.* **47:** 1005–1014.

Hedgpeth J., Goodman H.M., and Boyer H.W. 1972. DNA nucleotide sequence restricted by the RI endonuclease. *Proc. Natl. Acad. Sci.* **69:** 3448–3452.

Heitman J. and Model P. 1987. Site-specific methylases induce the SOS repair response in *Escherichia coli*. *J. Bacteriol.* **169:** 3243–3250.

Helinski D.R., Toukdarian A.E., and Novick R.P. 1996. Replication control and other stable maintenance mechanisms of plasmids. In Escherichia coli *and* Salmonella: *Cellular and molecular biology,* 2nd edition (ed. F.C. Neidhardt et al.), vol. 2, pp. 2295–2323. American Society for Microbiology, Washington, D.C.

Helmer-Citterich M., Anceschi M.M., Banner D.W., and Cesareni G. 1988. Control of ColE1 replication: Low affinity specific binding of Rop (Rom) to RNAI and RNAII. *EMBO J.* **7:** 557–566.

Henderson D.R., Friedman S.B., Harris J.D., Manning W.B., and Zoccoli M.A. 1986. CEDIA, a new homogeneous immunoassay system. *Clin. Chem.* **32:** 1637–1641.

Hengen P. 1995. Electrotransformation of *Escherichia coli* with plasmid DNA. *Trends Biochem. Sci.* **20:** 248–249.

———. 1996. Methods and reagents. Preparing ultra-competent *Escherichia coli*. *Trends Biochem. Sci.* **21:** 75–76.

———. 1997. Methods and reagents. Reducing background colonies with positive selection vectors. *Trends Biochem. Sci.* **22:** 105–106.

Henrich B. and Plapp R. 1986. Use of the lysis gene of bacteriophage ϕX174 for the construction of a positive selection vector. *Gene* **42:** 345–349.

Hershfield V., Boyer H.W., Yanofsky C., Lovett M.A., and Helinski D.R. 1974. Plasmid ColE1 as a molecular vehicle for cloning

and amplification of DNA. *Proc. Natl. Acad. Sci.* **71:** 3455–3459.

Hickman R.K. and Levy S.B. 1988. Evidence that TET protein functions as a multimer in the inner membrane of *Escherichia coli*. *J. Bacteriol.* **170:** 1715–1720.

Higgins N.P. and Cozzarelli N.R. 1979. DNA-joining enzymes: A review. *Methods Enzymol.* **68:** 50–71.

Hildeman D.A. and Muller D. 1997. Increased yield of plasmid DNA during removal of CsCl by ethanol precipitation. *BioTechniques* **22:** 878–879.

Holmes D.S. and Quigley M. 1981. A rapid boiling method for the preparation of bacterial plasmids. *Anal. Biochem* **114:** 193–197.

Hooper I.R. 1982. The naturally occurring aminoglycoside antibiotics. In *Aminoglycoside antibiotics* (ed. H. Umezawa and I.R. Hooper), pp. 1–35. Springer-Verlag, Berlin, Germany.

Hoppe B.L., Conti-Tronconi B.M., and Horton R.M. 1992. Gel-loading dyes compatible with PCR. *BioTechniques* **12:** 679–680.

Horiuchi T., Sato T., and Nagata T. 1975. DNA degradation in an amber mutant of *Escherichia coli* K12 affecting DNA ligase and viability. *J. Mol. Biol.* **95:** 271–287.

Horwitz J.P., Chua J., Curby R.J., Tomson A.J., DaRooge M.A., Fisher B.E., Mauricio J., and Klundt I. 1964. Substrates for cytochemical demonstration of enzyme activity. I. Some substituted 3-indolyl-β-D-glycopyranosides. *J. Med. Chem.* **7:** 574–575.

Huang A. and Campbell J. 1993. A simple improvement to the Triton lysis procedure for plasmid isolation. *BioTechniques* **14:** 730.

Hung M.-C. and Wensink P.C. 1984. Different restriction enzyme-generated sticky DNA ends can be joined in vitro. *Nucleic Acids Res.* **12:** 1863–1874.

Inoue H., Nojima H., and Okayama H. 1990. High efficiency transformation of *Escherichia coli* with plasmids. *Gene* **96:** 23–28.

Ish-Horowicz D. and Burke J.F. 1981. Rapid and efficient cosmid cloning. *Nucleic Acids Res.* **9:** 2989–2998.

Ishino Y., Shinagawa H., Makino K., Tsunasawa S., Sakiyama F., and Nakata A. 1986. Nucleotide sequence of the *lig* gene and primary structure of DNA ligase of *Escherichia coli*. *Mol. Gen. Genet.* **204:** 1–7.

Jacob F. and Wollman E.L. 1958. Les episomes, elements genetiques ajoutes. *C.R. Acad. Sci.* **247:** 154–156.

Jacob F., Brenner S., and Cuzin F. 1964. On the regulation of DNA replication in bacteria. *Cold Spring Harbor Symp. Quant. Biol.* **28:** 329–348.

Jacobson R.H., Zhang X.-J., DuBose R.F., and Matthews B.W. 1994. Three dimensional structure of β-galactosidase from *E. coli*. *Nature* **369:** 761–766.

Jimenez A. and Davies J. 1980. Expression of a transposable antibiotic resistance element in *Saccharomyces*. *Nature* **287:** 869–871.

Johnson D.A., Gautsch J.W., Sportsman J.R., and Elder J.H. 1984. Improved technique utilizing nonfat dry milk for analysis of proteins and nucleic acids transferred to nitrocellulose. *Gene Anal. Tech.* **1:** 3–8.

Jollés P. 1960. Lysozyme. In *The enzymes,* 2nd edition (ed. P.D. Boyer et al.), vol. 4, pp. 431–445. Academic Press, New York.

Jónsson Z.O., Thorbjarnardóttir S.H., Eggertsson G., and Palsdottir A. 1994. Sequence of the DNA ligase-encoding gene from *Thermus scotoductus* and conserved motifs in DNA ligases. *Gene* **151:** 177–180.

Kahn M., Kolter R., Thomas C., Figurski D., Meyer R., Remaut E., and Helinski D.R. 1979. Plasmid cloning vehicles derived from plasmids ColE1, F, R6K, and RK2. *Methods Enzymol.* **68:** 268–280.

Keesey J. 1996. *Epitope tagging: Basic laboratory methods* (catalog no. 1674773). Boehringer Mannheim, Indianapolis, Indiana.

Kleppe K., Van de Sande J.H., and Khorana H.G. 1970. Polynucleotide ligase-catalyzed joining of deoxyribo-oligonucleotides on ribopolynucleotide templates and of ribo-oligonucleotides on deoxyribopolynucleotide templates. *Proc. Natl. Acad. Sci.* **67:** 68–73.

Kletzin A. 1992. Molecular characterisation of a DNA ligase gene of the extremely thermophilic archaeon *Desulfurolobus ambivalens* shows close phylogenetic relationship to eukaryotic ligases. *Nucleic Acids Res.* **20:** 5389–5396.

Kolodziej P.A. and Young R.A. 1991. Epitope tagging and protein surveillance. *Methods Enzymol.* **194:** 508–519.

Kondo T., Mukai M., and Kondo Y. 1991. Rapid isolation of plasmid DNA and LiCl-ethidium bromide treatment and gel filtration. *Anal. Biochem.* **198:** 30–35.

Kondo T., Nakajima Y., and Kawakami M. 1979. Effect of salts and chromatin concentrations on the buoyant density of chromatin in metrizamide gradient. *Biochim. Biophys. Acta* **561:** 526–534.

Kornberg A. and Baker T.A. 1992. *DNA replication*, 2nd edition. W.H. Freeman, New York.

Kües U. and Stahl U. 1989. Replication of plasmids in gram-negative bacteria. *Microbiol. Rev.* **53:** 491–516.

Kuhn I., Stephenson F.H., Boyer H.W., and Greene P.J. 1986. Positive selection vectors utilizing lethality of the *Eco*RI endonuclease. *Gene* **42:** 253–263.

Kusano K., Nakayama K., and Nakyama H. 1989. Plasmid-mediated lethality and plasmid multimer formation in an *Escherichia coli recBC sbcBC* mutant. Involvement of recF recombination pathway genes. *J. Mol. Biol.* **209:** 623–634.

Lacatena R.M. and Cesareni G. 1981. Base pairing of RNAI with its complementary sequence in the primer precursor inhibits ColE1 replication. *Nature* **294:** 623–626.

Lacatena R.M., Banner D.W., Castognoli L., and Cesarini G. 1984. Control of pMB1 replication: Purified Rop protein and RNAI affect primer production *in vitro*. *Cell* **37:** 1009–1014.

Landegren U., Kaiser R., Sanders J., and Hood L. 1988. A ligase-mediated gene detection technique. *Science* **241:** 1077–1080.

Langley K.E., Villarejo M.R., Fowler A.V., Zamenhof P.J., and Zabin I. 1975. Molecular basis of β-galactosidase α-complementation. *Proc. Natl. Acad. Sci.* **72:** 1254–1257.

Lauer G., Rudd E.A., McKay D.L., Ally A., Ally D., and Backman K.C. 1991. Cloning, nucleotide sequence, and engineered expression of *Thermus thermophilus* DNA ligase, a homolog of *Escherichia coli* DNA ligase. *J. Bacteriol.* **173:** 5047–5053.

Lederberg J. 1952. Cell genetics and hereditary symbiosis. *Physiol. Rev.* **32:** 403–430.

Lehman I.R. 1974. DNA ligase: Structure, mechanism, and function. *Science* **186:** 790–797.

———. 1998. Recollections of a DNA enzymologist. *Protein Sci.* **7:** 1061–1066.

LePecq J.B. and Paoletti C. 1967. A fluorescent complex between ethidium bromide and nucleic acids. Physical-chemical characterization. *J. Mol. Biol.* **27:** 87–106.

Lerman L.S. 1961. Structural considerations in interaction of DNA and acridines. *J. Mol. Biol.* **3:** 18–30.

Leslie A.G., Moody P.C., and Shaw W.V. 1988. Structure of chloramphenicol acetyltransferase at 1.75Å resolution. *Proc. Natl. Acad. Sci.* **85:** 4133–4137.

Lilley D.M. 1980. The inverted repeat as a recognizable structural feature in supercoiled DNA molecules. *Proc. Natl. Acad. Sci.* **77:** 6468–6472.

Lin-Chao S. and Cohen S.N. 1991. The rate of processing and degradation of antisense RNAI regulates the replication of ColE1-type plasmids in vivo. *Cell* **65:** 1233–1242.

Lin-Chao S., Chen W.-T., and Wong T.-T. 1992. High copy number of the pUC plasmid results from a Rom/Rop-suppressible point mutation in RNAII. *Mol. Microbiol.* **6:** 3385–3393.

Linder P., Churchward G., Xia G.X., Yu Y.Y., and Caro L. 1985. An essential replication gene, repA, of plasmid pSC101 is autoregulated. *J. Mol. Biol.* **181:** 383–393.

Lis J.T. 1980. Fractionation of DNA fragments by polyethylene glycol induced precipitation. *Methods Enzymol.* **65:** 347–353.

Lis J.T. and Schleif R. 1975a. Size fractionation of double-stranded DNA by precipitation with polyethylene glycol. *Nucleic Acids Res.* **2:** 383–389.

———. 1975b. The regulatory region of the L-arabinose operon: Its isolation on a 1000 base-pair fragment from DNA heteroduplexes. *J. Mol. Biol.* **95:** 409–416.

Little J.W. 1979. Construction and characterization of a plasmid coding for a fragment of the *Escherichia coli recA* protein. *Mol. Gen. Genet.* **177:** 13–22.

Maas R. 1983. An improved colony hybridization method with significantly increased sensitivity for detection of single genes. *Plasmid* **10:** 296–298.

Maloy S.R. and Nunn W.D. 1981. Selection for loss of tetracycline resistance by *Escherichia coli*. *J. Bacteriol.* **145:** 1110–1111.

Mandel M. and Higa A. 1970. Calcium-dependent bacteriophage DNA infection. *J. Mol. Biol.* **53:** 159–162.

McNicholas P., Chopra I., and Rothstein D.M. 1992. Genetic analysis of the *tetA*(C) gene on plasmid pBR322. *J. Bacteriol.* **174:** 7926–7933.

Mertz J.E. and Davis R.W. 1972. Cleavage of DNA by R 1 restriction endonuclease generates cohesive ends. *Proc. Natl. Acad. Sci.* **69:** 3370–3374.

Meselson M., Stahl F.W., and Vinograd J. 1957. Equilibrium sedimentation of macromolecules in density gradients. *Proc. Natl. Acad. Sci.* **43:** 581–588.

Messing J. 1983. New M13 vectors for cloning. *Methods Enzymol.* **101:** 20–78.

Miller C.A., Beaucage S.L., and Cohen S.N. 1990. Role of DNA superhelicity in partitioning of the pSC 101 plasmid. *Cell* **62:** 127–133.

Miller E.M. and Nickoloff J.A. 1995. *Escherichia coli* electrotransformation. *Methods Mol. Biol.* **47:** 105–113.

Miller J.F., Dower W.J., and Tompkins L.S. 1988. High-voltage electroporation of bacteria: Genetic transformation of *Campylobacter jejuni* with plasmid DNA. *Proc. Natl. Acad. Sci.* **85:** 856–860.

Miller J.H. 1972. *Experiments in molecular genetics.* Cold Spring Harbor Laboratory, Cold Spring Harbor, New York.

Mizuuchi K., Mizuuchi M., and Gellert M.J. 1982. Cruciform structures in palindromic DNA are favored by DNA supercoiling. *J. Mol. Biol.* **156:** 229–243.

Modrich P. and Lehman I.R. 1971. Enzymatic characterization of a mutant of *Escherichia coli* with an altered DNA ligase. *Proc. Natl. Acad. Sci.* **68:** 1002–1005.

Mongolsuk S., Rabibhadana S., Vattanaviboon P., and Loprasert S. 1994. Generalized and mobilizable positive-selection cloning vectors. *Gene* **143:** 145–146.

Murray N.E. and Kelley W.S. 1979. Characterization of the λ*polA* transducing phages: Effective expression of the *E. coli polA* gene. *Mol. Gen. Genet.* **175:** 77–87.

Neu H.C. 1985. Penicillins. In *Principles and practice of infectious diseases*, 2nd edition (ed. G.L. Mandell et al.), pp. 166–180. Wiley, New York.

Neumann E. and Rosenheck K. 1972. Permeability changes induced by electric impulses in vesicular membranes. *J. Membr. Biol.* **10:** 279–290.

Neumann E., Schaefer-Ridder M., Wang Y., and Hofschneider P.H. 1982. Gene transfer into mouse lyoma cells by electroporation in high electric fields. *EMBO J.* **1:** 841–845.

Nicoletti V.G. and Condorelli D.F. 1993. Optimized PEG method for rapid plasmid DNA purification: High yield from "midiprep." *BioTechniques* **14:** 532–534, 536.

Nilsson B., Uhlen M., Josephson S., Gattenbeck S., and Philipson L. 1983. An improved positive selection vector constructed by oligonucleotide-mediated mutagenesis. *Nucleic Acids Res.* **11:** 8019–8030.

Noller H.F. 1984. Structure of ribosomal RNA. *Annu. Rev. Biochem.* **53:** 119–162.

Nordström K. 1990. Control of plasmid replication—How do DNA iterons set the replication frequency? *Cell* **63:** 1121–1124.

Nordström K. and Uhlin B.E. 1992. Runaway-replication plasmids as tools to produce large quantities of proteins from cloned genes in bacteria. *Bio/Technology* **10:** 661–666.

Nordström K. and Wagner E.G. 1994. Kinetic aspects of control of plasmid replication by antisense RNA. *Trends Biochem. Sci.* **19:** 294–300.

Norrander J., Kempe T., and Messing J. 1983. Construction of improved M13 vectors using oligodeoxynucleotide-directed mutagenesis. *Gene* **26:** 101–106.

Novick R.P. 1987. Plasmid incompatibility. *Microbiol. Rev.* **51:** 381–395.

Nygaard A.P. and Hall B.D. 1963. A method for the detection of RNA-DNA complexes. *Biochem. Biophys. Res. Commun.* **120:** 98–104.

Ogata R. and Gilbert W. 1977. Contacts between the lac repressor and the thymines in the lac operator. *Proc. Natl. Acad. Sci.* **74:** 4973–4976.

Oishi M. and Cosloy S.D. 1972. The genetic and biochemical basis of the transformability of *Escherichia coli* K12. *Biochem. Biophys. Res. Commun.* **49:** 1568–1572.

Okayama H. and Berg P. 1982. High-efficiency cloning of full-length cDNA. *Mol. Cell. Biol.* **2:** 161–170.

Olivera B.M. and Lehman I.R. 1967. Diphosphopyridine nucleotide: A cofactor for the polynucleotide-joining enzyme from *Escherichia coli*. *Proc. Natl. Acad. Sci.* **57:** 1700–1704.

———. 1968. Enzymic joining of polynucleotides. 3. The polydeoxyadenylate-polydeoxythymidylate homopolymer pair. *J. Mol. Biol.* **36:** 261–274.

Paithankar K.R. and Prasad K.S.N. 1991. Precipitation of DNA by polyethylene glycol and ethanol. *Nucleic Acids Res.* **19:** 1346.

Panasenko S.M., Alazard R.J., and Lehman I.R. 1978. A simple, three-step procedure for the large scale purification of DNA ligase from a hybrid lambda lysogen constructed in vitro. *J. Biol. Chem.* **253:** 4590–4592.

Panasenko S.M., Cameron J.R., Davis R.W., and Lehman I.R. 1977. Five hundredfold overproduction of DNA ligase after induction of a hybrid lambda lysogen constructed in vitro. *Science* **196:** 188–189.

Pheiffer B.H. and Zimmerman S.B. 1983. Polymer-stimulated ligation: Enhanced blunt- or cohesive-end ligation of DNA or deoxyribooligonucleotides by T4 DNA ligase in polymer

solutions. *Nucleic Acids Res.* **11:** 7853–7871.

Pierson V.L. and Barcak G.J. 1999. Development of *E. coli* host strains tolerating unstable DNA sequences on ColE1 vectors. *Focus* (Life Technologies) **21:** 18–19.

Podkovyrov S.M. and Larson T.J. 1995. A new vector-host system for construction of lacZ transcriptional fusions where only low-level gene expression is desirable. *Gene* **156:** 151–152.

Pohl F.M., Thomae R., and Karst A. 1982. Temperature dependence of the activity of DNA-modifying enzymes: Endonucleases and DNA ligase. *Eur. J. Biochem.* **123:** 141–152.

Pritchard R.H. 1984. Control of DNA replication in bacteria. In *The microbial cell cycle* (ed. P. Nurse and E. Streiblová), pp. 19–27. CRC Press, Boca Raton, Florida.

Raae A.J., Kleppe R.K., and Kleppe K. 1975. Kinetics and effect of salts and polyamines on T4 polynucleotide ligase. *Eur. J. Biochem.* **60:** 437–443.

Radloff R., Bauer W., and Vinograd J. 1967. A dye-buoyant density method for the detection and isolation of closed circular duplex DNA: The closed circular DNA in HeLa cells. *Proc. Natl. Acad. Sci.* **57:** 1514–1521.

Raleigh E.A. and Wilson G. 1986. *Escherichia coli* K-12 restricts DNA containing 5-methylcytosine. *Proc. Natl. Acad. Sci.* **83:** 9070–9074.

Rassoulzadegan M., Binetruy B., and Cuzin F. 1982. High frequency of gene transfer after fusion between bacteria and eukaryotic cells. *Nature* **295:** 257–259.

Remaut E., Tsao H., and Fiers W. 1983. Improved plasmid vectors with a thermoinducible expression and temperature-regulated runaway replication. *Gene* **22:** 103–113.

Rusche J.R. and Howard-Flanders P. 1985. Hexamine cobalt chloride promotes intermolecular ligation of blunt end DNA fragments by T4 DNA ligase. *Nucleic Acids Res.* **13:** 1997– 2008.

Sambrook J., Fritsch E.F., and Maniatis T. 1989. *Molecular cloning: A laboratory manual*, 2nd edition. Cold Spring Harbor Laboratory Press, Cold Spring Harbor, New York.

Schaffner W. 1980. Direct transfer of cloned genes from bacteria to mammalian cells. *Proc. Natl. Acad. Sci.* **77:** 2163–2167.

Scheller R.H., Dickerson R.E., Boyer H.W., Riggs A.D., and Itakura K. 1977. Chemical synthesis of restriction enzyme recognition sites useful for cloning. *Science* **196:** 177–180.

Schildkraut C., Marmur J., and Doty P. 1962. Determination of base composition of deoxyribonucleic acid from its buoyant density in CsCl. *J. Mol. Biol.* **4:** 430–443.

Schleef M. and Heimann P. 1993. Cesium chloride or column preparation? An electron microscopical view of plasmid preparations. *BioTechniques* **14:** 544.

Seeburg P., Shine J., Martial J.A., Baxter J.D., and Goodman H.M. 1977. Nucleotide sequence and amplification in bacteria of structural gene for rat growth hormone. *Nature* **270:** 486–494.

Sgaramella V. and Ehrlich S.D. 1978. Use of the T4 polynucleotide ligase in the joining of flush-ended DNA segments generated by restriction endonucleases. *Eur. J. Biochem.* **86:** 531–537.

Sgaramella V. and Khorana H.G. 1972. CXII. Total synthesis of the structural gene for an alanine transfer RNA from yeast. Enzymic joining of the chemically synthesized polydeoxynucleotides to form the DNA duplex representing nucleotide sequence 1 to 20. *J. Mol. Biol.* **72:** 427–444.

Sgaramella V., Van de Sande J.H., and Khorana H.G. 1970. Studies on polynucleotides, C. A novel joining reaction catalyzed by the T4-polynucleotide ligase. *Proc. Natl. Acad. Sci.* **67:** 1468– 1475.

Sharp P.A., Sugden B., and Sambrook J. 1973. Detection of two restriction endonuclease activities in *Haemophilus influenzae* using analytical agarose-ethidium bromide electrophoresis. *Biochemistry* **12**: 3055–3063.

Shaw K.J., Rather P.N., Hare R.S., and Miller G.H. 1993. Molecular genetics of aminoglycoside resistance genes and familial relationships of the aminoglycoside-modifying enzymes. *Microbiol. Rev.* **57**: 138–163.

Shaw W.V. 1983. Chloramphenicol acetyltransferase: Enzymology and molecular biology. *CRC Crit. Rev. Biochem.* **14**: 1–46.

Shaw W.V., Day P., Lewendon A., and Murray I.A. 1988. Tinkering with antibiotic resistance: Chloramphenicol acetyltransferase and its substrates. *Biochem. Soc. Trans.* **16**: 939–942.

Shine J. and Dalgarno L. 1975. Determination of cistron specificity in bacterial ribosomes. *Nature* **254**: 34–38.

Short J.M., Fernandez J.M., Sorge J.A., and Huse W.D. 1988. λZAP: A bacteriophage λ expression vector with in vivo excision properties. *Nucleic Acids Res.* **16**: 7583–7600.

Shuman S. 1996. Closing the gap on DNA ligase. *Structure* **4**: 653–656.

Smith M., Jessee J., Landers T., and Jordan J. 1990. High efficiency bacterial electroporation 1 x 10^{10} E. coli transformants per microgram. *Focus* (Life Technologies) **12**: 38–40.

Southern E.M. 1975. Detection of specific sequences among DNA fragments separated by gel electrophoresis. *J. Mol. Biol.* **98**: 503–517.

Southern P.J. and Berg P. 1982. Transformation of mammalian cells to antibiotic resistance with a bacterial gene under control of the SV40 early region promoter. *J. Mol. Appl. Genet.* **1**: 327–341.

Spratt B.G., Boyd A., and Stoker N. 1980. Defective and plaque-forming lambda transducing bacteriophage carrying penicillin-binding protein-cell shape genes: Genetic and physical mapping and identification of gene products from the *lipdacA-rodA-pbpA-leuS* region of the *Escherichia coli* chromosome. *J. Bacteriol.* **143**: 569–581.

Steele C., Zhang S., and Shillitoe E.J. 1994. Effect of different antibiotics on efficiency of transformation of bacteria by electroporation. *BioTechniques* **17**: 360–365.

Stoker N.G., Fairweather N.F., and Spratt B.G. 1982. Versatile low-copy-number plasmid vectors for cloning in *Escherichia coli*. *Gene* **18**: 335–341.

Struhl K. 1985. A rapid method for creating recombinant DNA molecules. *BioTechniques* **3**: 452–453.

Sugino A., Goodman H.M., Heyneker H.L., Shine J., Boyer H.W., and Cozzarelli N.R. 1977. Interaction of bacteriophage T4 RNA and DNA ligases in joining of duplex DNA at base-paired ends. *J. Biol. Chem.* **252**: 3987–3994.

Summers D.K. and Sherratt D.J. 1984. Multimerization of high copy number plasmids causes instability: ColE1 encodes a determinant for plasmid monomerization and stability. *Cell* **36**: 1097–1103.

Sutcliffe J.G. 1978. Nucleotide sequence of the ampicillin resistance gene of *Escherichia coli* plasmid pBR322. *Proc. Natl. Acad. Sci.* **75**: 3737–3741.

Svaren J., Inagami S., Lovegren E., and Chalkley R. 1987. DNA denatures upon drying after ethanol precipitation. *Nucleic Acids Res.* **15**: 8739–8754.

Tabor S. and Richardson C.C. 1985. A bacteriophage T7 RNA polymerase/promoter system for controlled exclusive expression of specific genes. *Proc. Natl. Acad. Sci.* **82**: 1074–1078.

Tait R.C., Rodriguez R.L., and West R.W.J. 1980. The rapid purification of T4 DNA ligase from a lambda T4 lig lysogen. *J. Biol. Chem.* **255**: 813–815.

Takahashi M. and Uchida T. 1986. Thermophilic HB8 DNA ligase: Effects of polyethylene glycols and polyamines on blunt-end ligation of DNA. *J. Biochem.* **100**: 123–131.

Takahashi M., Yamaguchi E., and Uchida T. 1984. Thermophilic DNA ligase. Purification and properties of the enzyme from *Thermus thermophilus* HB8. *J. Biol. Chem.* **259**: 10041–10047.

Taketo A. 1988. Sensitivity of *Escherichia coli* to viral nucleic acid. 17. DNA transfection of *Escherichia coli* by electroporation. *Biochim. Biophys. Acta* **949**: 318–324.

Tang X., Nakata Y., Li H.O., Zhang M., Gao H., Fujita A., Sakatsume O., Ohta T., and Yokoyama K. 1994. The optimization of preparations of competent cells for transformation of E. coli. *Nucleic Acids Res.* **22**: 2857–2858.

Tartof K.D. and Hobbs C.A. 1987. Improved media for growing plasmid and cosmid clones. *Focus* (Life Technologies) **9**: 12.

Tomasz A. 1986. Penicillin-binding proteins and the antibacterial effectiveness of β-lactam antibiotics. *Rev. Infect. Dis.* (suppl. 3) **8**: S260–S278.

Tomizawa J. 1985. Control of ColE1 replication: Initial interaction of RNAI and the primer transcript is reversible. *Cell* **40**: 527–535.

———. 1987. Regulation of ColE1 replication by antisense RNA. In *Molecular biology of RNA: New perspectives* (ed. M. Inoue and B. Dudock), pp. 249–259. Academic Press, New York.

———. 1990a. Control of ColE1 plasmid replication. Intermediates in the binding of RNAI and RNAII. *J. Mol. Biol.* **212**: 683–694.

———. 1990b. Control of ColE1 plasmid replication. Interaction of Rom protein with an unstable complex formed by RNAI and RNAII. *J. Mol. Biol.* **212**: 695–708.

Tomizawa J. and Itoh T. 1981. Plasmid ColE1 incompatibility determined by interaction of RNA I with primer transcript. *Proc. Natl. Acad. Sci.* **78**: 6096–6100.

Tomizawa J. and Som T. 1984. Control of ColE1 plasmid replication: Enhancement of the binding of RNAI to the primer transcript by the Rom protein. *Cell* **38**: 871–878.

Tomkinson A.E., Totty N.F., Ginsburg M., and Lindahl T. 1991. Location of the active site for enzyme-adenylate formation in DNA ligases. *Proc. Natl. Acad. Sci.* **88**: 400-404.

Triglia T., Peterson M.G., and Kemp D.J. 1988. A procedure for in vitro amplification of DNA segments that lie outside the boundaries of known sequences. *Nucleic Acids Res.* **16**: 8186.

Trudel P., Provost S., Massie B., Chartrand P., and Wall L. 1996. pGATA: A positive selection vector based on the toxicity of the transcription factor GATA-1 to bacteria. *BioTechniques* **20**: 684–693.

Tsong T.Y. 1991. Electroporation of cell membranes. *Biophys. J.* **60**: 297–306.

Tung W.L. and Chow K.C. 1995. A modified medium for efficient electrotransformation of E. coli. *Trends Genet.* **11**: 128–129.

Twigg A.J. and Sherratt D. 1980. Trans-complementable copy-number mutants of plasmid ColE1. *Nature* **283**: 216–218.

Uhlin B.E. and Nordström K. 1978. A runaway-replication mutant of plasmid R1drd-19: Temperature-dependent loss of copy number control. *Mol. Gen. Genet.* **165**: 167–179.

Uhlin B.E., Molin S., Gustaffson P., and Nordström K. 1979. Plasmids with temperature-dependent copy numbers for amplification of cloned genes and their products. *Gene* **6**: 91–106.

Ullmann A. and Perrin D. 1970. Complementation in β-galactosidase. In *The lactose operon* (ed. J.R. Beckwith and D. Zipser), pp. 143–172. Cold Spring Harbor Laboratory, Cold Spring Harbor, New York.

Ullmann A., Jacob F., and Monod J. 1967. Characterization by in vitro complementation of a peptide corresponding to an operator-proximal segment of the beta-galactosidase structural gene of *Escherichia coli*. *J. Mol. Biol.* **24:** 339–343.

Ullrich A., Shine J., Chirgwin J., Pictet R., Tischer E., Rutter W.J., and Goodman H.M. 1977. Rat insulin genes: Construction of plasmids containing the coding sequences. *Science* **196:** 1313–1319.

Umezawa H., Okanishi M., Utahara R., Maeda K., and Kondo S. 1967. Isolation and structure of kanamycin inactivated by a cell free system of kanamycin-resistant *E. coli*. *J. Antibiot.* **20:** 136–141.

Upcroft P. and Healey A. 1987. Rapid and efficient method for cloning of blunt-ended DNA fragments. *Gene* **51:** 69–75.

Vernet T., Lau P.C., Narang S.A., and Visentin L.P. 1985. A direct selection vector derived from pColE3-CA38 and adapted for foreign gene expression. *Gene* **34:** 87–93.

Vieira J. and Messing J. 1982. The pUC plasmids, an M13-mp7-derived system for insertion mutagenesis and sequencing with synthetic universal primers. *Gene* **19:** 259–268.

———. 1987. Production of single-stranded plasmid DNA. *Methods Enzymol.* **153:** 3–11.

Vinograd J. and Lebowitz J. 1966. Physical and topological properties of circular DNA. *J. Gen. Physiol.* **49:** 103–125.

von Ahsen U. and Noller H.F. 1993. Footprinting the sites of interaction of antibiotics with catalytic group I intron RNA. *Science* **260:** 1500–1503.

von Ahsen U., Davies J., and Schroeder R. 1991. Antibiotic inhibition of group I ribozyme function. *Nature* **353:** 368–370.

———. 1992. Non-competitive inhibition of group I intron RNA self-splicing by aminoglycoside antibiotics. *J. Mol. Biol.* **226:** 935–941.

Wade N. 1977. Dicing with nature: Three narrow escapes. *Science* **195:** 378.

Waga S., Bauer G., and Stillman B. 1994. Reconstitution of complete SV40 DNA replication with purified replication factors. *J. Biol. Chem.* **269:** 10923–10934.

Wang J.C. 1969. Variation of the average rotation angle of the DNA helix and the superhelical turns of covalently closed cyclic λ DNA. *J. Mol. Biol.* **43:** 25–39.

Waring M.J. 1965. Complex formation between ethidium bromide and nucleic acids. *J. Mol. Biol.* **13:** 269–282.

———. 1966. Structural requirements for the binding of ethidium bromide to nucleic acids. *Biochim. Biophys. Acta* **114:** 234–244.

Watkins T.I. and Wolfe G. 1952. Effect of changing the quaternizing group on the trypanocidal activity of dimidum bromide. *Nature* **169:** 506.

Weaver J.C. 1993. Electroporation: A general phenomenon for manipulating cells and tissues. *J. Cell. Biochem.* **51:** 426–435.

Weinstock G.M. 1987. General recombination in *Escherichia coli*. In Escherichia coli *and* Salmonella typhimurium: *Cellular and molecular biology* (ed. F.C. Neidhardt et al.), vol. 2, pp. 1034–1043. American Society for Microbiology, Washington, D.C.

Weinstock G.M., Berman M.L., and Silhavy T.J. 1983. Chimeric genetics with β-galactosidase. In *Expression of cloned genes in prokaryotic and eukaryotic cells: Gene amplification and analysis* (ed. T.S. Papas et al.), vol. 3, pp. 27–64. Elsevier, New York.

Weiss B. and Richardson C.C. 1967. Enzymatic breakage and joining of deoxyribonucleic acid. III. An enzyme-adenylate intermediate in the polynucleotide ligase reaction. *J. Biol.*

Chem. **242:** 4270–4272.

Weiss B., Thompson A., and Richardson C.C. 1968a. Ezymatic breakage and joining of deoxyribonucleic acid. VII. Properties of the enzyme-adenylate intermediate in the polynucleotide ligase reaction. *J. Biol. Chem.* **243:** 4556–4563.

Weiss B., Jacquemin-Sablon A., Live T.R., Fareed G.C., and Richardson C.C. 1968b. Enzymatic breakage and joining of deoxyribonucleic acid. VI. Further purification and properties of polynucleotide ligase from *Escherichia coli* infected with bacteriophage T4. *J. Biol. Chem.* **243:** 4543–4555.

Wiaderkiewicz R. and Ruiz-Carrillo A. 1987. Mismatch and blunt to protruding-end joining by DNA ligases. *Nucleic Acids Res.* **15:** 7831–7848.

Willetts N. and Wilkins B. 1984. Processing of plasmid DNA during bacterial conjugation. *Microbiol. Rev.* **48:** 24–41.

Wilson G.G. and Murray N.E. 1979. Molecular cloning of the DNA ligase gene from bacteriophage T4. I. Characterisation of the recombinants. *J. Mol. Biol.* **132:** 471–491.

Wu D.Y. and Wallace R.B. 1989. The ligation amplification reaction (LAR)—Amplification of specific DNA sequences using sequential rounds of template-dependent ligation. *Genomics* **4:** 560–569.

Yamamoto K.R., Alberts B.M., Benzinger R., Lawhorne L., and Treiber G. 1970. Rapid bacteriophage sedimentation in the presence of polyethylene glycol and its application to large-scale virus purification. *Virology* **40:** 734–744.

Yang Y.C., Ciarletta A.B., Temple P.A., Chung M.P., Kovacic S., Witek-Giannotti J.S., Leary A.C., Kriz R., Donahue R.E., Wong G.G., Clark S., et al. 1986. Human IL-3 (multi-CSF): Identification by expression cloning of a novel hematopoietic growth factor related to murine IL-3. *Cell* **47:** 3–10.

Yanisch-Perron C., Vieira J., and Messing J. 1985. Improved M13 phage cloning vectors and host strains: Nucleotide sequences of the M13mp18 and pUC19 vectors. *Gene* **33:** 103–119.

Yazynin S.A., Deyev S.M., Jucovic M., and Hartley R.W. 1996. A plasmid vector with positive selection and directional cloning based on a conditionally lethal gene. *Gene* **169:** 131–132.

Young I.G. and Poulis M.I. 1978. Conjugal transfer of cloning vectors derived from ColE1. *Gene* **4:** 175–179.

Zabarovsky E.R. and Allikmets R.L. 1986. An improved technique for the efficient construction of gene libraries by partial filling-in of cohesive ends. *Gene* **42:** 119–123.

Zabin I. 1982. Beta-galactosidase alpha-complementation. A model of protein-protein interaction. *Mol. Cell. Biochem.* **49:** 87–96.

Zimmerman S.B. and Minton A.P. 1993. Macromolecular crowding: Biochemical, biophysical and physiological consequences. *Annu. Rev. Biophys. Biomol. Struct.* **22:** 27–65.

Zimmerman S.B. and Pheiffer B.H. 1983. Macromolecular crowding allows blunt-end ligation by DNA ligases from rat liver or *Escherichia coli*. *Proc. Natl. Acad. Sci.* **80:** 5852–5856.

Zimmerman S.B., Little J.W., Oshinsky C.K., and Gellert M. 1967. Enzymatic joining of DNA strands: A novel reaction of diphosphopyridine nucleotide. *Proc. Natl. Acad. Sci.* **57:** 1841–1848.

Zimmerman U. 1982. Electric field-mediated fusion and related electrical phenomena. *Biochim. Biophys. Acta* **694:** 227–277.

Zurita M., Bolivar F., and Soberón X. 1984. Construction and characterization of new cloning vehicles. VII. Construction of a plasmid pBR327*par*, a completely sequenced, stable derivative of pBR327 containing the *par* locus of pSC101. *Gene* **28:** 119–122.

Chapter 2

Bacteriophage λ and Its Vectors

INFORMATION PANELS

SINCE BACTERIOPHAGE λ WAS FIRST USED AS A CLONING VEHICLE in the early 1970s (Murray and Murray 1974; Rambach and Tiollais 1974; Thomas et al. 1974), more than 400 different vectors have been described. Some of these vectors are the direct descendants of field strains of lambdoid bacteriophages; others are far more esoteric (please see the information panel on BACTERIOPHAGES: HISTORICAL PERSPECTIVE). This introduction contains information on the genetics and molecular biology of the virus that is required for the investigator to choose wisely among these vectors and to use them effectively.

The word that comes to mind when thinking about λ is elegance. The genetic circuitry of the virus is etched into DNA with great delicacy and the utmost economy. The experiments to trace the filigree of connecting regulatory loops within this circuitry match the virus itself in both beauty and subtlety. The distillation of these findings into a harmonious and general theory of gene control is an intellectual achievement that equals any other in biology in this century. And, as an early phage worker has written, "at each (of these) steps, the situation was aesthetically so pleasant that everybody felt happy with the picture." (Thomas 1993)

A direct bequest of the store of detailed knowledge and physiology of bacteriophage λ accumulated during the past 40 years has been the development of versatile and sophisticated vectors for the cloning, propagation, and expression of eukaryotic genes.

The genome of wild-type bacteriophage λ is a double-stranded DNA molecule, 48,502 bp in length. Figure 2-1 shows a sketch of the structure of bacteriophage λ. The sequences of the DNAs of two strains of λ are known in their entirety (Sanger et al. 1982; Daniels et al. 1983a,b); partial sequences of many other strains and vectors are scattered throughout various databases. The DNA is carried in bacteriophage particles as a linear double-stranded molecule with single-stranded termini 12 nucleotides in length (cohesive termini or *cos*). Soon after entering a host bacterium, the cohesive termini associate by base pairing to form a circular molecule with two

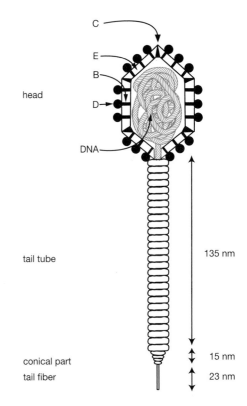

C

E

B

head

D

DNA

tail tube

135 nm

conical part   15 nm

tail fiber   23 nm

FIGURE 2-1 Structure of Bacteriophage λ

The schematic drawing depicts the components of the bacteriophage λ particle. Arrows indicate the locations within the particle of the proteins encoded by genes *C*, *E*, *B*, and *D*.

staggered nicks 12 nucleotides apart (Wu and Taylor 1971; Yarmolinski 1971; Weigel et al. 1973; Nichols and Donelson 1978). These nicks are rapidly sealed by the host's DNA ligase and gyrase to generate a closed circular DNA molecule that serves as the template for transcription during the early, uncommitted phase of infection.

During lytic growth, the circular DNA directs the synthesis of ~30 proteins required for its replication, the assembly of bacteriophage particles, and cell lysis. The lytic cycle takes 40–45 minutes and generates ~100 infectious virus particles per infected bacterium.

In its lysogenic state, bacteriophage λ DNA is integrated into the bacterial genome, is replicated as part of the bacterial chromosome, and is thus transmitted to progeny bacteria like a chromosomal gene. During establishment of lysogeny, only a small number of λ genes are expressed, including the *cI* gene, which inhibits expression of lytic functions and positively regulates transcription of its own gene, and *int*, which is required for integration of the phage DNA into the bacterial chromosome.

During maintenance of lysogeny, much of the integrated bacteriophage genome is quiescent, with only three genes being transcribed: *rexA, rexB*, and *cI. rexA* and *rexB* prevent superinfection of λ lysogens by certain other bacteriophages, whereas, as mentioned previously, the CI protein blocks transcription of genes required for lytic infection.

GENOMIC ORGANIZATION

The genome of bacteriophage λ carries a complement of at least 30 genes. The order of many of these genes was originally established by assaying the ability of bacteriophages carrying substitutions and/or deletions to rescue mutations (Kaiser 1955) and by measuring the frequency of genetic recombination between mutants of various types. The recombination frequency between distant genetic markers is ~15%, whereas the smallest reported recombination frequency (between mutations separated by just 4 bp) is 0.05% (McDermit et al. 1976; Rosenberg et al. 1978).

Although the order of genes ascertained by these methods was essentially correct, estimates of genetic distances between mutations did not always correspond to the physical distances because of local variation in recombination rates. Measurements of the distances between markers, genes, and mutations became precise only when bacteriophage λ DNA was sequenced (please see Figure 2-2). The genes of bacteriophage λ are organized into functionally related clusters.

- The left-hand region includes genes *Nu1* through *J* whose products are used to package the viral DNA into bacteriophage heads and to assemble infectious virions from filled heads and preformed tails.

- The central region (*J* through *gam*) codes for functions involved in gene regulation, establishment and maintenance of lysogeny, and genetic recombination. Many genes of the central region are not essential for lytic growth and can be sacrificed during construction of bacteriophage λ vectors to make room for segments of foreign DNA.

- The right-hand region (*gam* through *Rz*) contains essential genes used in replication of bacteriophage λ and lysis of infected bacteria.

THE UNCOMMITTED PHASE OF INFECTION

Adsorption

Bacteriophage λ adsorbs to the trimeric maltoporin receptor, an outer membrane protein consisting of three identical 421-residue monomers, each folded into an 18-strand β-barrel (Thirion and Hofnung 1972; Schwartz 1975; Neuhaus 1982). Adsorption involves interaction between maltoporin receptors and the carboxy-terminal residues of the 1133-residue viral J protein (Werts et al. 1994), which is located at the tip of the tail fiber (Schirmer et al. 1995). All three monomers are involved in binding and adsorption of phage (Marchal and Hofnung 1983). About half of the binding sites are exposed on long peptide loops projecting into the periplasm, whereas the rest are buried at locations where the loops pack together into the β-barrel.

As its name suggests, the maltoporin receptor is normally used to facilitate diffusion of maltose and maltodextrins into the cell (Szmelcman and Hofnung 1975; Ferenci and Boos 1980). Synthesis of these receptors, which are encoded by the bacterial *lamB* gene, is repressed by glucose and induced by maltose (Schwartz 1967). The outer membrane of a fully induced bacterial cell contains ~5×10^4 maltoporin receptors.

Infection by bacteriophage λ initially involves formation of reversible phage-receptor complexes that progress to irreversible complexes (Lieb 1953a) when contacts are established between components of the tail fiber and a membrane-bound mannose phosphotransferase encoded by the bacterial gene *ptsM* (Postma 1987). The reversible attachment of the bacteriophage is facilitated by magnesium ions and occurs rapidly (within a few minutes) both at room temperature and at 37ºC (Lieb 1953a). The linear viral DNA is then injected into the bacterium, right end first, through the bacteriophage's tail tube (Chattoraj and Inman 1974; Saigo and Uchida 1974; Thomas 1974). However, injection of the viral DNA and the subsequent events in the lytic cycle do not occur efficiently at room temperature (MacKay and Bode 1976). Plaques of bacteriophage λ will, therefore, not form unless bacterial lawns are incubated at temperatures higher than ~28ºC.

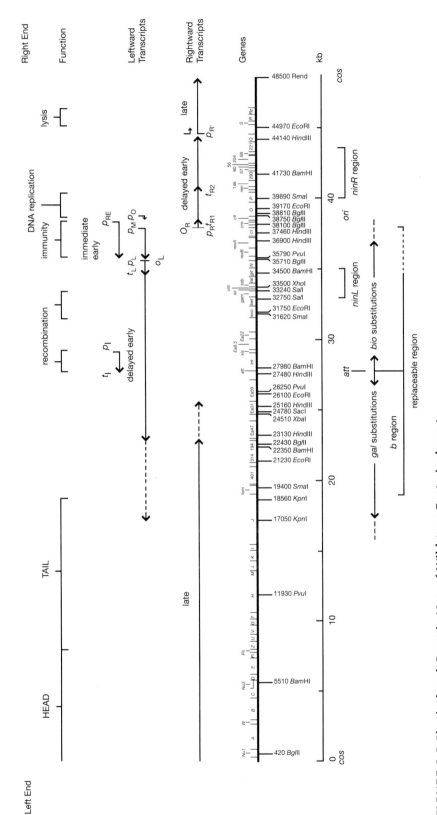

FIGURE 2-2 Physical and Genetic Map of Wild-type Bacteriophage λ

The general locations of genes that encode various lytic and lysogenic functions are indicated at the top of the figure by brackets. The genetic map below the brackets shows the specific bacteriophage λ genes (for a description of the function of each of these genes, please see Hendrix et al. 1983). The locations of restriction endonuclease cleavage sites are indicated below the genetic map. Distances from the left end are given in base pairs. Leftward and rightward transcripts are shown above the genetic map. Promoters are indicated by *p*; a subscript denotes the point of origin. (p_I) *int* promoter; (p_E) establishment promoter for cI; (p_M) maintenance promoter for cI; (p_L) major leftward promoter; (p_R) major rightward promoter; (p_O) *oop* promoter; ($p_{R'}$) late promoter; (*short rightward arrow*) transcription products; (*long rightward arrow*) readthrough; (t_L, t_{R1}, t_{R2}) locations of *p*-mediated termination sites. Regions where substitutions and deletion mutations are located are shown below the genetic map (Hendrix et al. 1983). (Modified, with permission, from Daniels et al. 1983a.)

Immediate Early Transcription

After the linear viral DNA has been converted to a superhelical, covalently closed circle, early transcription is initiated at two divergent promoters, p_L and p_R, which are located to the left and right, respectively, of the *cI* (repressor) gene. The resulting "immediate early" RNAs terminate at the ends of the *N* and *cro* genes, at sites t_L and t_{R1}, respectively, although ~40% of the rightward transcripts continue through genes *O* and *P* (which encode proteins involved in DNA replication) and terminate at t_{R2}. Transcription from p_L and p_R is carried out by *E. coli* RNA polymerase, whereas termination of RNA synthesis at t_L, t_{R1}, and t_{R2} is mediated by the *E. coli*-encoded protein ρ (for review, please see Friedman 1988; Das 1993; Oppenheim et al. 1993). The 12S leftward transcript codes for the N protein (pN), an antiterminator whose action is essential for the next phase of lytic infection.

Delayed Early Transcription

The delayed early genes of bacteriophage λ flank the immediate early genes *N* and *cro*. Their transcription is dependent on the product of the immediate early gene *N*, which allows the host RNA polymerase to read through the transcriptional terminators t_L and t_{RI} into the flanking delayed early genes, *cII* and *cIII*. Because pN is unstable ($t_{1/2}$ = 1–2 minutes) in *lon*$^+$ bacteria (Gottesman et al. 1981), expression of *cII* and *cIII* requires continued synthesis of the 12S immediate early RNA (please see Figure 2-3). Transcription of *N* from p_L is negatively controlled by the bacteriophage-encoded repressors CI and Cro and positively controlled by the *E. coli*-encoded RNase III (Oppenheim et al. 1993). In addition, pN may negatively autoregulate its own translation.

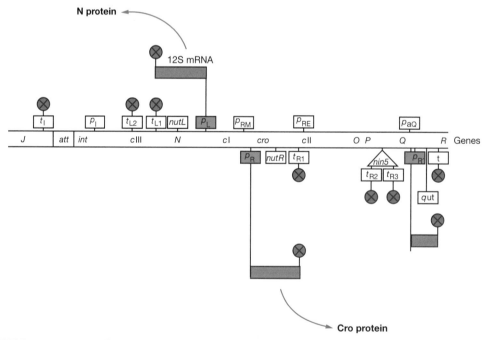

FIGURE 2-3 Bacteriophage λ Immediate Early Transcription

RNA polymerase binds to three promoters p_R, $p_R{'}$, and p_L and transcribes the DNA until it encounters a *ρ*-dependent termination site (⊗). The major gene product of leftward transcription is the N protein. The major gene product of rightward transcription is the Cro protein. No protein is synthesized from the small transcript initiated from the $p_R{'}$ promoter. (*Shaded boxes*) The products of transcription.

The specific binding sites for pN, called *nutL* and *nutR* (for *N-u*tilization), are embedded in the leftward and rightward immediate early RNAs. Each *nut* site contains a unique hairpin structure called *boxB* to which dimers of pN bind soon after *nut* is transcribed. Full activity of pN, however, requires a set of accessory antitermination factors encoded by the host bacterium: NusA, NusB, NusG, and the ribosomal protein S10 (for reviews, please see Das 1993; Roberts 1993). The pN-*boxB* complex interacts with these factors and the RNA polymerase, allowing the enzyme to elongate nascent RNA chains at an increased rate and to skip through sites of transcriptional pausing.

pN is thus an RNA-binding protein that acts as an operon-specific antiterminator by recognizing a signal in immediate early RNAs and binding to the transcription complex. This binding allows RNA synthesis to proceed through several ρ-dependent and ρ-independent terminators. The N protein is therefore a positive regulatory element whose activity is necessary for the lytic growth of bacteriophages carrying t_{R2}. However, mutants of bacteriophage λ that carry a deletion of t_{R2} can grow (albeit poorly). Such bacteriophages are known as *nin* (*N-in*dependent) mutants (Court and Sato 1969). The *nin5* mutation (please see Figures 2-2 and 2-3), which is carried in many bacteriophage λ vectors, is a deletion of 2800 bp between genes *P* and *Q* that removes t_{R2} and some genes relevant to recombination between plasmids and bacteriophage DNA.

Infection Reaches an Important Crossroad

The outcome of infection — lysogeny or vegetative growth — remains unresolved until the end of the delayed early phase. By this stage, the bacteriophage proteins required for the next steps in both pathways are present in the infected cells, which are therefore poised to follow either course as circumstances dictate. In wild-type *E. coli*, the decision between lysogeny and the lytic cycle is influenced by the multiplicity of infection and by the nutritional state of the cell. The higher the multiplicity (Boyd 1951; Lieb 1953b) and the worse the nutritional state of cell (Kourilsky 1973; Herskowitz and Hagen 1980), the higher the frequency of lysogenization. The biochemical mediator of lysogeny may be 3′-5′ cAMP, whose intracellular concentration alters in response to changes in nutritional conditions (Hong et al. 1971; Grodzicker et al. 1972). When bacteria are grown in rich medium, the intracellular concentrations of cAMP are low, and the lytic pathway is favored. In mutant cells that lack cAMP, the lytic pathway is heavily favored. Because none of the known bacteriophage promoters are responsive to cAMP, it seems likely that the decision between lysogeny and lytic infection is influenced in part by a bacterial gene or genes that are regulated by cAMP.

A key element in the decision between lysis and lysogeny is the bacteriophage-encoded CII protein (please see the panel on CII PROTEIN), the activator of transcription of λ genes that (1)

CII PROTEIN

- The CII protein is synthesized as a 97-amino-acid polypeptide. After removal of the amino-terminal methionine and the subterminal valine, the polypeptide associates into an active tetrameric form.

- It is a DNA-binding protein that interacts specifically and with reasonable affinity (3×10^{-7} M) with a 20–25-bp region of three leftward promoters: p_{RE}, p_I, and p_{aQ}. The consensus sequence for binding is TTGCN$_6$TTGC.

- CII and RNA polymerase interact with the three leftward promoters in a cooperative manner, such that full activation of transcription occurs when the concentration of cII is tenfold less (3×10^{-8} M) than that required for maximal binding of cII alone.

- The CII protein is unstable (half-life = 2 minutes) but is partially stabilized by the bacteriophage CIII protein. In addition, its natural rate of degradation is diminished or enhanced by several bacterial gene products. Mutations in the *E. coli lon* and *cya* genes increase the rate of degradation of CII and, therefore, favor the lytic response, whereas mutations in the *hflA* and *hflB* loci extend the half-life of the protein and facilitate the lysogenic response (Hoyt et al. 1982; Banuett et al. 1986; for reviews, please see Friedman et al. 1984; Ho and Rosenberg 1988).

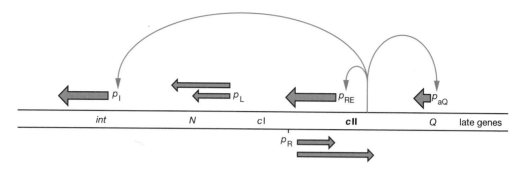

FIGURE 2-4 The Bacteriophage λ CII Protein Is a Transcriptional Activator

The product of the *cII* gene transcribed from the p_R promoter is a transcriptional activator that stimulates leftward transcription (*thick arrows*) from p_I, p_{RE}, and p_{aQ}. The promoter p_{RE} controls expression of the CI (repressor) protein, whereas p_I controls expression of *int* (encoding integrase). The promoter p_{aQ} directs the synthesis of an antisense RNA that is believed to reduce expression of the Q (antiterminator) gene product. The products of early transcription initiated from the promoters p_L and p_R are represented by thin arrows. (Modified, with permission, from Ho and Rosenberg 1988.)

represses lytic functions and (2) catalyzes integration of the viral DNA into the host chromosome (Echols 1980; Herskowitz and Hagen 1980; Wulff and Rosenberg 1983). A high intracellular concentration of CII favors lysogeny, whereas a low concentration tips the balance in favor of lysis. The CII protein coordinately regulates transcription from three separate leftward promoters: p_{RE}, p_I, and p_{aQ} (please see Figure 2-4). Thus, when a sufficient concentration of CII is present in the infected cell, transcription of *int* and *cI* genes is activated. The integrase (Int) protein, synthesized from p_I, catalyzes a breaking and joining event that leads to insertion of the viral DNA into the host chromosome. The product of the *cI* gene — λ repressor — binds to three 17-bp operators in each of the early promoters p_R and p_L, thereby denying access of RNA polymerase to the promoters and hence blocking transcription of phage early genes *N*, *cro*, *O*, *P*, and *Q*, whose products are essential for onward progression of the lytic cycle (please see the panel on **CI PROTEIN**). This stranglehold can be broken by another transcriptional repressor — Cro — which competes with CI protein for occupation of the operator O_R (please see Figure 2-5). The outcome of this compe-

---

CI PROTEIN

Bacteriophage λ CI protein (236 amino acids; $M_r = 26,228$) is an inactive monomer at very low concentrations ($<10^{-9}$ M), but at physiological concentrations, it forms functional homodimers. Although commonly called λ repressor because of its negative regulatory functions at o_L and o_R, CI protein is also a positive regulator of gene transcription and can activate transcription of its own gene.

- The DNA-binding domain of CI protein lies within the amino-terminal region of the molecule (Sauer et al. 1979) and contains five stretches of α-helix, of which two (helices 2 and 3) form a helix-loop-helix motif and are involved in sequence-specific binding to the major groove of DNA (Pabo and Lewis 1982; Beamer and Pabo 1992; for more details, please see review by Hochschild 1994). The CI protein binds symmetrically to DNA, so that each amino-terminal domain contacts a similar set of bases.

- The carboxy-terminal domain of the CI protein contains the major sites for dimerization and oligomerization (Pabo et al. 1979).

- o_L and o_R both contain three binding sites for CI protein. In each case, site 1 (i.e., o_{L1} and o_{R1}) has a ~10-fold greater affinity than the other sites for CI protein. The repressor, therefore, always binds first to o_{L1} and o_{R1} and then binds to the other sites in the operator in a cooperative manner (Johnson et al. 1979). Cooperativity is mediated by the carboxy-terminal domains of repressor dimers.

- When incubated at high pH in vitro, CI protein undergoes an autocatalytic cleavage at a Gly-Ala peptide bond located between the two domains. In vivo, autocatalytic cleavage occurs in the presence of bacterial RecA protein, which acts as a coprotease (Little 1984; for review, please see Little 1993).

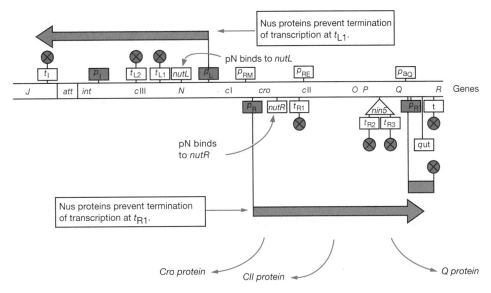

FIGURE 2-5 Bacteriophage λ Delayed Early Transcription

N protein turns on genes to the left of *N*, including *cIII* and genes involved in recombination and, in addition, genes to the right of *cro*, including *cII* and the DNA replication genes *O* and *P* and the positive regulator of late transcription, *Q*. During the delayed early phase of transcription, the fate of the infected cell remains undecided, and infection can progress either to lysogeny or to a cycle of vegetative growth. By the end of the delayed early phase, an irrevocable decision has been taken to proceed down one pathway or the other. (*Shaded boxes*) The products of transcription; (⊗) transcription termination sites.

THE DISCOVERY OF BACTERIOPHAGE λ

Bacteriophage λ first appeared in the laboratory in 1951, when Esther Lederberg found that certain mutants of *Escherichia coli* K-12, which survived following treatment with intensive ultraviolet (UV) irradiation, grew normally in pure culture but died of a bacteriophage infection after conjugation to other bacterial strains. The parental wild-type K-12 strain, like most others in use at that time, was naturally lysogenic for bacteriophage λ. Exposure to UV irradiation cured the surviving bacteria of prophage, generating bacterial strains that were no longer immune to external infection by the bacteriophage. Strains "cured" in this way fell victim to lysis by bacteriophage λ (1) when incubated with lysogenic strains, which spontaneously produce infectious phage particles at a low rate, or (2) when during conjugation, the DNA of a lysogenic strain was transferred to a nonlysogenic recipient. In both cases, the incoming bacteriophage genome entered a repressor-free cell and established a cycle of lytic growth, generating a batch of progeny particles that could lytically infect the remaining nonlysogenic cells in the culture.

Lysogeny was not a new phenomenon, having already been studied over the course of 40 or more years by an illustrious cadre of phage workers including Macfarlane Burnet, Eugène and Elizabeth Wollmann, Jules Bordet, and Felix D'Herelle (for a review of early work on lysogeny, please see Brock 1990). However, none of their experiments provided a satisfying explanation of the constant production of small amounts of infectious bacteriophages by pure cultures of bacteria and the episodic and unpredictable occurrence of massive lysis. "Worthless" was Max Delbrück's succinct description of a half century of honest effort.

All this changed as a result of André Lwoff's elegant experiments showing first that exposure to small amounts of UV irradiation reproducibly caused an entire culture of lysogenic *Bacillus megaterium* to liberate bacteriophage particles in a synchronous fashion (Lwoff and Gutmann 1950), and second that every cell of the culture carried a prophage (for review, please see Lwoff 1953). The discovery of induction was of great importance because it made possible both genetic and biochemical studies of the production of temperate bacteriophages. Lwoff's papers caused tremendous excitement in the phage world and were sufficient to persuade sceptics that the phenomenon of lysogeny was both real and accessible. Writing 15 years later in prose that was still passionate, Lwoff (1966) describes the discovery of induction as the highlight of his scientific life. By contrast, Esther Lederberg's paper — far more laconic and pallid — gives no sign that she had discovered the bacteriophage that was to become the defining crucible for molecular studies of prokaryotic gene control.

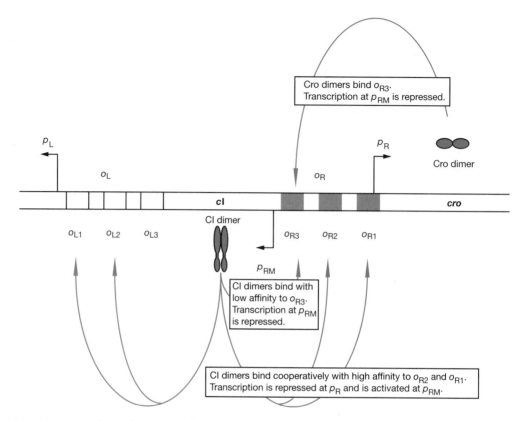

FIGURE 2-6 **Wiring Diagram of the Switch between Lytic Infection and Lysogeny**

Dimers of the CI repressor bind most tightly to o_{R1} and least tightly to o_{R3}. Cro has the opposite relative affinities. Transcription at promoter p_R is repressed when p_{R1} is occupied by CI; transcription at p_{RM} is repressed when o_{R3} is occupied by CI. Thus, CI establishes lysogeny by throttling expression of genes transcribed from p_R and, once the lysogenic state is achieved, controls its own concentration by inhibiting transcription at p_{RM}. Because binding of CI to adjacent sites is cooperative, the proximity of o_{R2} ensures a sharp concentration dependence of binding to o_{R1}. Binding of CI to o_{R2} also activates transcription from p_{RM}. On induction, CI protein is inactivated by cleavage and transcription from p_R resumes. The first product of transcription is the mRNA for Cro. Binding of Cro to o_{R3} prevents further synthesis of CI protein. Repression of transcription is relieved at p_L and established at p_{RM}. The switch to lytic infection is then permanent (Ptashne 1986). (Modified, with permission, from Harrison 1992.)

tition determines whether the cell will become lysogenic or will advance to the late stages of lytic infection. The three binding sites of O_R are arranged within and between two divergent promoters for the genes encoding the two repressors. Cro and the CI protein bind to these sites with different preferences (order of binding, cooperativity, and affinity) (Johnson et al. 1979). Thus, the CI protein binds to sites o_{R1} and o_{R2} strongly and cooperatively, whereas Cro binds to o_{R3} strongly and to o_{R1} weakly (Cro does not bind cooperatively). Each protein turns off the gene encoding its competitor as well as the appropriate downstream genes that are required for lytic growth or lysogeny. The two repressors therefore not only compete for the same sites, but also have mutually antagonistic physiological effects (for reviews, please see Gussin et al. 1983; Ptashne 1992).

In addition to its repressive effects on rightward transcription, the CI protein stimulates leftward transcription of its own gene by a factor of ~10. This effect is mediated by binding of a repressor dimer at o_{R2}; a repressor dimer bound at o_{R1} interacts cooperatively with repressor bound at o_{R2} to stabilize binding to the DNA (please see Figure 2-6) (Meyer et al. 1980). The bound repressor is able to make direct contact with RNA polymerase at the leftward promoter,

p_{RM} (Guarente et al. 1982: Hochschild et al. 1983) and thereby to stimulate the transition from the closed to the open transcription complex (Hawley and McClure 1983; Fong et al. 1993). Transcription from p_{RM} may also be stimulated by CI-mediated exclusion of RNA polymerase from binding to p_R (Hershberger et al. 1993).

In summary, during establishment of lysogeny, repressor synthesis is directed by the promoter p_{RE} under positive regulation by the CII and CIII proteins. However, because repressor prevents transcription from p_R and p_L, it blocks further expression of *cII* and *cIII*, respectively. Thus, these genes are inactive in lysogens (Bode and Kaiser 1965). Furthermore, since CII and CIII are unstable, CI protein must eventually suppress, albeit indirectly, transcription from p_{RE}. Transcription of *cI* from a second promoter p_{RM} is therefore required for the maintenance of lysogeny (please see Lysogeny [p. 2.15] and Figure 2-6).

LATE LYTIC INFECTION

DNA Replication

Two genes, *O* and *P*, are weakly transcribed from p_R immediately after infection and more strongly later as a consequence of pN-mediated antitermination. The products of these genes, together with some of the host replication proteins and stress proteins, are required for replication of bacteriophage DNA (for reviews, please see Furth and Wickner 1983; Kornberg and Baker 1992). During the early phase of infection, bacteriophage λ DNA replicates bidirectionally as a Cairns or θ (circle to circle) form, using a single origin (*ori*) that is activated by proteins pO and pP. In a wild-type *E. coli* infected with wild-type bacteriophage λ, ~50 monomeric, circular bacteriophage genomes are synthesized before replication shifts to a rolling circle mode. Linear DNA molecules are then generated that consist of tandem polymers of the bacteriophage genome arranged head to tail. These long concatemeric molecules are cut and packaged into proheads of progeny particles (please see Figure 2-7 and DNA Packaging [p. 2.14]).

It is not known what triggers the mid-stream shift from θ to rolling circle replication. However, the conversion from one mode to another is inhibited by the heterotrimeric exonuclease V, which is encoded by the bacterial *recB*, *recC*, and *recD* genes (Telander-Muskavitch and Linn 1981). Nevertheless, the production of concatenated DNA is not affected in *recBCD*$^+$ cells as long as the infecting bacteriophage carries a functional *gam* gene. The product of this gene binds to exonuclease V and inactivates its exonucleolytic activity (Unger and Clark 1972; Kuzminov et al. 1994). In the absence of Gam protein, the potent, multifunctional RecBCD nuclease degrades the concatenated linear bacteriophage DNA produced by rolling circle replication. Gam protein is not needed for production of linear concatenates of viral DNA if the RecBCD nuclease is defective or absent (Greenstein and Skalka 1975). Most bacteriophage λ vectors lack the *gam* gene but can nevertheless multiply to a passable extent in *recBCD*$^+$ cells if they are able to generate concatemeric forms of the genome that are suitable substrates for packaging of progeny particles. Such concatemers can be formed by recombination between monomeric circular DNA molecules that are produced by θ-type replication.

Recombination Systems in Cells Infected with Bacteriophage λ

Both bacteriophage λ and *E. coli* encode recombination systems (*red* and *recA*, respectively) that can produce dimeric and multimeric circles from the replicating θ form. Most bacteriophage λ vectors that are *gam*$^-$ are also *red*$^-$ and must therefore be propagated on *recA*$^+$ strains of bacteria in order to promote the efficient production of circular multimers. During packaging, these circular forms, like the head-to-tail tandem polymers produced by rolling circle replication, are cleaved at the *cosL* and *cosR* sites by the terminase function of the bacteriophage-encoded A protein. However, the presence of an active bacterial recombination system can sometimes lead to instability in sequences cloned in bacteriophage λ vectors, particularly in genomic sequences that contain repetitive elements. There are three ways to avoid this problem:

- Several vectors have been designed that carry the *gam* gene on one of the arms of the bacteriophage genome. Examples of such vectors are Charon 32–35 and 40 (Loenen and Blattner 1983; Dunn and Blattner 1987).

- Gam protein can be supplied in *trans* from a plasmid (Crouse 1985). In this system, the expression of *gam* is controlled by the product of the *Q* gene of the incoming bacteriophage. Inactivation of exonuclease V can therefore occur only after infection.

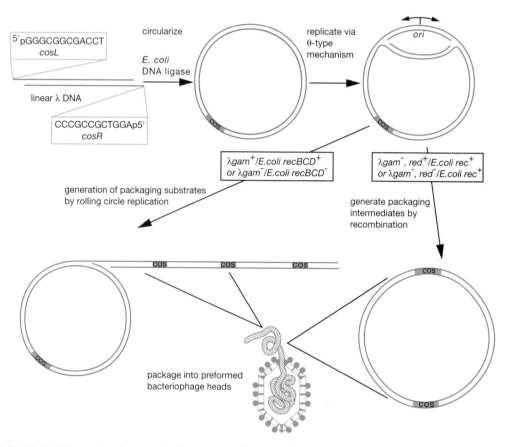

FIGURE 2-7 Bacteriophage λ Replication and Recombination

During lytic infection, bacteriophage λ DNA, which is injected into the cell as a linear molecule, is rapidly converted to a closed circular form by ligation of the cohesive ends (*cos*). During the early phase of infection, DNA replication proceeds bidirectionally (θ-type replication) and generates ~50 monomeric copies of the circular viral DNA per cell. In the presence of the *gam* gene product in host cells that are *recBCD*$^+$, or in the absence of the *gam* gene product in host cells that are *recBCD*$^-$, replication converts to a rolling circle mode. The events of replication generate linear concatemers of viral DNA, which are substrates for packaging of the viral DNA into the preformed heads of bacteriophage particles. In *recBCD*$^+$ cells that are infected with a *gam*$^-$ phage, rolling circle replication cannot be established. Under such circumstances, progeny particles cannot be produced unless a suitable system is available to catalyze recombination between circular monomers of viral DNA, generating multimeric circles that are acceptable substrates for packaging into preformed bacteriophage heads.

- A number of mutant strains of *E. coli* are available that are recombination-proficient but deficient in exonuclease V. These include strains that are defective in *recB* or *recC*, as well as strains carrying the mutations *sbcA* or *sbcB*, both of which suppress mutations in *recBC*.

Because synthesis of catenated bacteriophage DNA is impeded by exonuclease V, red^- gam^- bacteriophages produce small plaques when plated on wild-type *E. coli*. However, recombination-deficient bacteriophage mutants carrying an octameric χ DNA sequence known as χ (chi) produce plaques that are close to normal in size (Lam et al. 1974: Henderson and Weil 1975; please see the panel on CHI χ SITE). The presence of (1) the χ sequence in the bacteriophage genome and (2) an active recombination RecBCD system provided by the host leads to an increase in the efficiency of recombination events that generate closed circular dimers and multimers from θ forms. red^- gam^- bacteriophages package these multimers efficiently, and red^- gam^- χ^+ bacteriophages grow to a reasonable yield in wild-type *E. coli*.

CHI (χ) SITE

χ is an 8-bp-long sequence of double-stranded genomic DNA (5′ GCTGGTGG 3′) that, in *E. coli*, causes increased recombination over a region of several kilobases located asymmetrically around the χ sequence. The stimulatory effect of χ sequences on recombination is due to the formation of a nick about five nucleotides 3′ of the χ site by the *E. coli* RecBCD protein, a heterotrimeric enzyme encoded by the *recB, recC, recD* genes (Taylor et al. 1985; for review, please see Taylor 1988). The nick only occurs when the enzyme passes through the χ sequence in one direction (from right to left, as written above), unwinding the DNA as it goes (Faulds et al. 1979; Yagil et al. 1980; Smith et al. 1981). The combination of unwinding and nicking generates a single-stranded "tail" with a χ sequence near its 3′ end. This tail is believed to be a potent substrate for RecA protein, which catalyzes the formation of recombinant molecules between the single-stranded tail and homologous double-stranded DNA (for review, please see Smith 1990).

Of the several major pathways of recombination in *E. coli*, only RecBCD is stimulated by χ sites. χ sites are therefore inactive in *recB*, *recC*, and *recBC* double mutants. Normally, the RecBCD protein expresses a powerful exonuclease V activity (Telander-Muskavitch and Linn 1981) that is used, e.g., to destroy foreign DNA that has been cleaved by restriction enzymes (Simmon and Lederberg 1972; Oliver and Goldberg 1977). However, χ sites protect linear DNA from degradation both in vivo and in vitro, perhaps by inactivating the exonuclease V activity of the RecBCD nuclease (Kuzminov et al. 1994). With the help of the RecA protein, the frayed end of DNA invades a homologous sequence to form a branched structure that can be converted into a replication fork and resolved by recombination.

χ sequences were first discovered in bacteriophage λ as mutations creating recombinational hot spots for RecBCD-promoted recombination (Lam et al. 1974; Henderson and Weil 1975; Stahl et al. 1975); there are no χ sites in wild-type λ DNA. However, χ sequences have been created by single-base changes at several widely spaced sites in the bacteriophage λ genome. The *E. coli* genome contains a total of ~10^3 χ sites, ~1 per 4–5 kb (Faulds et al. 1979; Blaisdell et al. 1993; Burland et al. 1993; for reviews, please see Smith 1983; Murray 1991). Of these sites in the *E. coli* chromosome, 90% are oriented such that they will protect against degradation of DNA proceeding toward the origin of replication (Burland et al. 1993; Médigue et al. 1993). χ sites, therefore, serve as bulwarks, which are strategically deployed to protect crucial sites in DNA against the ravages of the RecBCD protein.

Because recombination is essential for efficient replication and packaging of bacteriophage λ genomes, the presence or absence of χ sites and the state of the host recombination machinery are important factors to consider when selecting a host cell for a particular bacteriophage λ vector. The requirement for a χ site in red^- gam^- bacteriophages can be eliminated by using as hosts bacterial strains that carry *recD* mutations. These strains, which are superproficient in recombination but defective in exonuclease V production (Amundsen et al. 1986), generate concatemers of bacteriophage λ DNA by both recombination and rolling circle replication. The recombination system in $recD^-$ mutants is so active that a χ sequence is no longer required in red^- gam^- bacteriophages. Because some bacteriophage λ vectors are red^- gam^- and do not carry a χ site, recombinants would normally be expected to display a small-plaque phenotype on wild-type *E. coli*. However, eukaryotic DNAs contain sequences that can mimic χ sites. Thus, some recombinant bacteriophages will carry insertions of foreign DNA that contain χ sequences and others will not. The recombinants that contain the χ sequences will grow to higher titer, form larger plaques, and become overrepresented during amplification of libraries. This problem can be overcome by avoiding vectors (such as Charon 28 and 30) which give rise to gam^- recombinants that do not contain a χ site. These vectors should only be used for construction of libraries if the recombinants are propagated on $recBC^-$ or $recD^-$ hosts.

Late Transcription

As discussed earlier, the mRNA synthesized from p_R encodes a repressor, Cro, that competes with CI protein for binding to three sites in each of two operator regions, o_L and o_R (Johnson et al. 1978, 1979; for reviews, please see Gussin et al. 1983; Ptashne 1992). Binding of Cro to o_{R3} prevents further synthesis of CI protein and makes the commitment to the lytic pathway irreversible. By this stage, sufficient amounts of another positive control protein, encoded by gene Q, have been synthesized to ensure efficient transcription of late viral genes (Dove 1966; Joyner et al. 1966). These genes encode proteins that will be assembled into bacteriophage heads and tails. In addition, pQ regulates genes required for cell lysis. Like pN, pQ is an antiterminator that modifies RNA polymerase so that the enzyme no longer recognizes downstream terminators. Unlike pN, which binds to a unique hairpin in nascent RNA, pQ binds to a specific DNA sequence, *qut*, that overlaps with $p_{R'}$. From this site and while the enzyme is stalled at the transcriptional pause site, pQ transforms RNA polymerase into an antiterminating state. This modification, whose nature is unknown, may lower the K_m of the enzyme for nucleoside triphosphates (NTPs) (Yarnell and Roberts 1992).

Functions expressed late in bacteriophage development are controlled primarily through termination and antitermination of transcription (Roberts 1975). $p_{R'}$ — the sole promoter used for transcription of the entire late region — is active at early times during infection. However, in the absence of pQ, the transcription complex pauses for several minutes at base pair 16/17 of the transcript and then terminates at a strong terminator, $t_{R'}$, located at base pair 194 (Grayhack et al. 1985; for reviews, please see Friedman 1988; Das 1993). Under the influence of pQ and in the presence of the host factor NusA, transcripts initiated at $p_{R'}$ are rapidly extended through both the pause site at base pair 16 and the terminator at $t_{R'}$. Transcription then proceeds around the circular genome through the late genes and terminates within the *b* region (please see Figure 2-6).

DNA Packaging and Assembly of Bacteriophage Particles

In the late stages of lytic infection, duplex concatemeric DNA is packaged into a DNA-free prohead according to the scheme outlined in Figures 2-7 and 2-8 (for reviews, please see Black 1988; Casjens and Hendrix 1988). An early precursor in the pathway leading to head assembly is a scaffolded prehead. Further maturation, which involves removal of the scaffolding protein and proteolytic processing of other components, depends on a protein (the product of *groE* gene) supplied by the host. The resulting structures are called preheads. Packaging the bacteriophage genome into preheads requires two phage-encoded proteins, Nu1 and A, which bind to the concatenated linear DNA near left *cos* sites (please see the panel on λ TERMINASE). Two adjacent *cos* sites of the concatenated linear DNA are brought close together at the entrance to the head, where they are cleaved in a staggered fashion by the terminase function of the A protein to generate the 12-nucleotide cohesive termini. The cleaved DNA-protein complex then becomes attached to a defined area on the prehead (Frackman et al. 1984). In the presence of protein FI, the DNA, left-hand end first, is pumped into the prehead by an ATP-dependent process (Emmons 1974; Kaiser et al. 1975; Hsaio and Black 1977; Hendrix 1978; for review, please see Black 1988). During filling, the prehead increases in size by ~11–45% (Hohn 1983). Finally, the D, or "decoration," protein attaches to the outside of the filled capsid, locking the head in place around the DNA (Sternberg and Weisberg 1977). The head is also stabilized by the addition of one final protein, the product of gene *FII*, which forms at least a portion of the site to which the tails bind (Casjens et al. 1972; Tsui and Hendrix 1980).

λ TERMINASE

λ terminase is a packaging enzyme that fashions concatemers of viral DNA into unit-length genomes with protruding 5′ termini, 12 bp in length (for reviews, please see Feiss and Becker 1983; Feiss 1986; Becker and Murialdo 1990). The site of action of terminase is called the cohesive end site or *cos* (Emmons 1974; Feiss and Campbell 1974). Unit-length λ chromosomes are therefore normally generated by cleavage of linear concatemers at two *cos* sites spaced one genome length apart.

Terminase is a hetero-oligomer of polypeptides encoded by the two leftmost genes on the bacteriophage λ genome: the *Nu1* gene (which encodes a 181-amino-acid polypeptide) and the *A* gene (which encodes a 641-amino-acid polypeptide) (for review, please see Feiss and Becker 1983). Both subunits can hydrolyze ATP (Parris et al. 1988), and mutants of either gene display the same phenotype, i.e., the accumulation of concatemers and empty proheads (Murialdo and Siminovitch 1972).

The DNA sequence that is recognized and cleaved by terminase consists of two subsites, the *cosN* (*cos* nicking) site, previously called *cos*, and the adjacent *cosB* (*cos* binding) site. Under normal conditions, cleavage at *cosN* is carried out by the larger subunit of terminase (gpA) and is accompanied by hydrolysis of ATP (Gold and Becker 1983), which acts both as an allosteric effector of terminase and to melt the *cos* ends after cleavage (Higgins et al. 1988; Cue and Feiss 1993). Following nicking at *cosN*, terminase remains tightly bound to the left end of the λ chromosome in a complex called complex I (Becker et al. 1977; Sippy and Feiss 1992; Cue and Feiss 1993). Complex I then binds to the portal protein (encoded by the bacteriophage λ *B* gene), which serves as the site of DNA entry into the prohead (Yeo and Feiss 1995). Terminase remains bound to the portal protein as DNA is reeled from the cleaved concatemer into the prohead. Packaging ceases when terminase introduces staggered nicks at the next *cos* site, by which time the prohead contains a complete linear bacteriophage λ genome ~50 kb in length. The filled heads then associate with preformed tail units, which have been assembled by a separate pathway.

The noncontractile tail shaft of bacteriophage λ consists of ~32 rings of V protein, each containing six polypeptide subunits (for review, please see Casjens and Hendrix 1988). These subunits form a hollow tube 9 nm in diameter through which the DNA is injected on infection. Very little is known about the structure of the proximal end of the tail except that small numbers of the gene *U* and possibly gene *Z* proteins are located there. It is not understood how the preformed tail and filled heads are assembled into bacteriophage particles. The distal tip of the tail contains at least six different polypeptides, including two or three molecules of the gene *J* protein that is involved in attachment to the *lamB* receptor during adsorbtion (please see the section entitled Adsorption, p. 2.4).

Lysis

Lysis of the host bacterium by bacteriophage λ requires proteins encoded by the first three genes in the late transcript: *S*, *R*, and *Rz* (for review, please see Young 1992). The functions of these three genes and the properties of the proteins they encode are summarized in Table 2-1. Many of the bacteriophage λ strains used in the laboratory carry an amber mutation *Sam7* in the *S* gene. This mutation prevents or delays lysis, allowing the assembly of progeny particles to continue for an extended period of time. The accumulated intracellular particles can be liberated artificially by lysing the infected cell with chloroform.

LYSOGENY

Only a fraction of wild-type cells infected with bacteriophage λ undergo a lytic cycle of infection. Instead, in a large proportion of the infected population, the lytic cycle is aborted, and the surviving cells thereafter carry a copy of the viral DNA integrated into their genome.

TABLE 2-1 Lysis Genes of Bacteriophage λ

GENE	SIZE AND PROPERTIES OF PROTEIN	FUNCTION OF WILD-TYPE PROTEIN	PHENOTYPE OF MUTANTS
S	an 8.5-kD (107-residue) inner membrane protein, S is lethal when expressed at physiological levels	homo-oligomers of S form holes in the inner membrane, which allow R protein to enter the periplasmic space	most mutants display delayed lysis, which leads to an intra-cellular accumulation of assembled bacteriophage particles; addition of chloro-form to an induced S lysogen results in instantaneous lysis of the culture
R	a soluble 17.5-kD trans-glycosylase	attacks glycosidic bonds in the peptidoglycan cell wall, gener-ating a 1,6-disaccharide product	lysis is abolished but the infected cells die at the usual time of lysis
Rz	a membrane protein of ~19 kD	possibly an endopeptidase that cleaves oligopeptide cross-links in the peptidoglycan cell wall	lysis in liquid culture is unaffected unless 5–10 mM divalent cations are present, in which case, spheroplasts form at the normal time for lysis

For references, please see review by Young (1992).

Integration

Two proteins — the bacteriophage-encoded integrase (Int, Gingery and Echols 1967; Zissler 1967) and host-encoded integration host factor (IHF, Miller and Friedman 1977; Nash et al. 1977; Nash and Robertson 1981) — are required for the integration of bacteriophage DNA into the host chromosome (please see the panel on INT AND ATT). The unique regions of bacterial and viral DNAs involved in the recombination event are called *attB* and *attP* sites, respectively (for reviews, please see Weisberg and Landy 1983; Landy 1989; Nash 1990; Friedman 1992; Campbell 1993).

INT AND ATT

Int recombinase (356 amino acids) is a type I topoisomerase that cuts and rejoins DNA strands one at a time (Kikuchi and Nash 1979a,b; Hoess et al. 1980; Craig and Nash 1983). Its preferred substrate, at least in vitro, is closed circular DNA containing negative superhelical turns (Mizuuchi et al. 1978; Richet et al. 1986). Int gen-erates a Holliday structure by catalyzing a two-strand exchange at a precise nucleotide by way of a transient DNA-protein bond on a tyrosine residue. Branch migration then occurs across a 7-bp segment of the core, and the Holliday structure is resolved by exchange between the two other strands.

Proper positioning of integrase is facilitated by IHF, which bends the DNA duplex into structures compat-ible with the required DNA-protein interactions (for reviews, please see Nash 1990; Kim and Landy 1992). IHF is a heterodimer of two small polypeptides, IHFα and IHFβ, encoded by *himA* and *himD* (*hip*), respectively (Miller et al. 1979).

attP spans ~240 bp of bacteriophage DNA centered on a 15-bp core that is identical between bacterio-phage and host chromosomes and includes the crossover point (Weisberg and Landy 1983). *attB* is 21 bp long and is composed chiefly of the core region. During integration, *attP* recombines with *attB* to form a prophage flanked by recombinant *attL* and *attR* sites. The inserted prophage is therefore bracketed by a 15-bp repeat in direct orientation. During excision, these flanking repeats serve as substrates for recombination, regenerating the *attB* and *attP* sites.

Transcription of Prophage Genes

Almost all viral transcription is repressed in the integrated state; the *rexA*, *rexB*, and *cI* genes, however, continue to be expressed. The *cI* gene product not only blocks transcription of early genes from the p_R and p_L promoters, but also positively regulates its own synthesis. Low concentrations of the repressor cause the activity of the maintenance promoter, p_{RM} to increase; high concentrations inhibit initiation of transcription at p_{RM} (for review, please see Ptashne 1992). All of these effects are mediated by the binding of repressor to two operator regions (o_L and o_R) (please see Figure 2-6) (Johnson et al. 1979). Bacteriophages with mutations in gene *cI*, *cII*, or *cIII* are unable to establish repression efficiently; they therefore form clear plaques.

Wild-type prophages can be induced by cleavage of the CI repressor following exposure to agents that damage DNA (for review, please see Roberts and Devoret 1983). Cleavage occurs between an alanine and a glycine residue in the hinge region linking the DNA-binding amino-terminal domain and the carboxy-terminal dimerization domain. Little (1984) has shown that cleavage of the CI protein occurs autocatalytically at pH 10 in an intramolecular reaction that displays first-order kinetics and is independent of protein concentration. In vivo, cleavage of the Ala-Gly

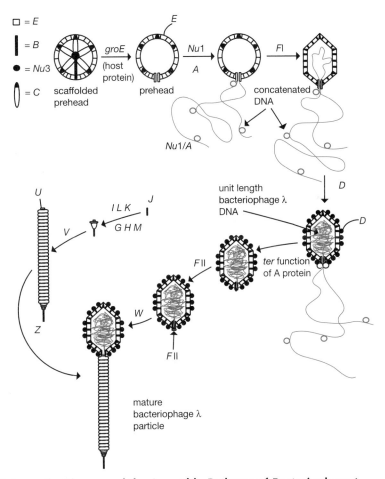

FIGURE 2-8 Schematic Diagram of the Assembly Pathway of Bacteriophage λ

The gene products involved in each step are indicated (for details, please see the accompanying text and Hohn [1979]). The letters signify the bacteriophage genes encoding various structural proteins used in the construction of bacteriophage particles.

bond and the consequent inactivation of CI protein requires the host RecA protein. Mutant CI proteins (encoded by *cI ind⁻* mutants) are resistant to RecA-mediated cleavage and cannot undergo autodigestion in vitro. This and many other lines of evidence indicate that the function of RecA protein is to stimulate self-cleavage of the CI protein (for reviews, please see Little 1991, 1993).

Bacteriophages carrying a temperature-sensitive mutation in the *cI* gene are able to establish and maintain the lysogenic state as long as the cells are propagated at low temperature (30°C). At this temperature, the repressor retains its ability to inhibit transcription from p_L and p_R. However, lytic growth can be induced by heating the bacterial culture for 10–15 minutes to 45°C, which partially inactivates the *cIts*857 repressor (Sussman and Jacob 1962). Although the repressor can renature when the culture is cooled to 37°C (Mandal and Lieb 1976), its concentration is too low to allow reestablishment of lysogeny. Instead, transcription resumes from p_L and p_R when ~80% of the CI protein has been inactivated. At this stage, only ~40 monomers of repressor remain in the cell, too small a number to sustain cooperative binding to o_{R1} and o_{R2}. In addition, because CI protein stimulates transcription of its own gene, synthesis of new repressor molecules decreases as the concentration of CI falls. The first protein synthesized when transcription resumes from p_R is Cro, which binds to o_{R3}, blocking any further synthesis of repressor, and thereby committing the viral genome to a cycle of vegetative growth. The integration and excision proteins, Int and Xis, act together to cause the *att* sites to recombine, resulting in excision of the prophage DNA from the host chromosome. The lytic cycle then follows its usual course.

CONSTRUCTION OF BACTERIOPHAGE λ VECTORS

At first glance, the adaptation of bacteriophage λ, with its large and complex genome, for use as a vector would seem to be a bleak prospect. The DNA of wild-type strains contains multiple sites for many of the most useful restriction enzymes, and these sites are often located in regions of the genome essential for lytic growth of the virus. Moreover, because bacteriophage λ particles will not accommodate molecules of DNA that are much longer than the viral genome, it might seem that the virus would be useful as a vector for only small pieces of foreign DNA.

These problems, however, are not as formidable as they might at first appear. First, the central third of the viral genome is not essential for lytic growth. By the late 1960s, much work had been carried out on specialized transducing bacteriophages, which are formed when excision of λ prophages from the bacterial chromosome occurs by illegitimate recombination, rather than the normal homologous exchange between *att* sites. Part of the central region of the viral genome becomes replaced by the segment of the bacterial chromosome flanking the integrated prophage. Specialized transducing particles derived from lysogens carrying the λ prophage at its normal integration site in the bacterial chromosome can carry the host's neighboring *gal* or *bio* genes. Lysogens carrying prophages at ectopic integration sites produce transducing particles carrying other parts of the *E. coli* chromosome. Genetic studies of these specialized transducing bacteriophages had shown that the region of the bacteriophage λ genome lying between the *J* and *N* genes could be replaced by *E. coli* DNA (for reviews, please see Campbell 1962; Franklin 1971). The analysis of the structure and function of these transducing particles became a prelude to the exploration of bacteriophage λ as a vector.

During the early 1970s, methods were perfected for manipulating sites of cleavage by restriction enzymes in the bacteriophage λ genome. The first of these methods, based on the knowledge of the genetics of restriction and modification of DNA by *E. coli*, allowed selection in vivo of derivatives of bacteriophage λ from which all sites for *Eco*RI had been eliminated from the essential portion of the viral genome. By growing the virus alternatively in strains of *E. coli* that either possessed or lacked a plasmid coding for *Eco*RI, mutants of bacteriophage λ were isolated that contained only one or two targets for *Eco*RI located in the nonessential region of the genome (Murray and Murray 1974; Rambach and Tiollais 1974; Thomas et al. 1974). Because this kind of selection in vivo was possible only when the bacteriophage could be grown in hosts that synthesized the restriction enzyme of interest, it was necessary to develop alternative methods to obtain vectors suitable for use with other restriction enzymes. For example:

- Recombinants between bacteriophage λ and other lambdoid bacteriophages (e.g., φ80) were constructed that either contained or lacked particular restriction sites.

- The development of procedures for packaging purified bacteriophage λ DNA into infectious particles permitted vectors with the desired combination of restriction sites to be generated by in vitro manipulation. Bacteriophage λ DNA was digested with a restriction enzyme, and the surviving molecules were packaged into particles in vitro and propagated in *E. coli* (Klein and Murray 1979). After several successive cycles of digestion, packaging, and growth, bacteriophage genomes were obtained that had lost restriction sites by mutation while retaining infectivity.

- More recently, synthetic oligonucleotides have been used to construct specifically designed DNA fragments that are then inserted into the bacteriophage genome. Using this method, restriction sites were placed at desired locations with precision and high efficiency (Frischauf et al. 1983; Karn et al. 1984).

Together, these methods have led to the development of a large number of vectors that can accept and propagate fragments of foreign DNA generated by a variety of different restriction enzymes (for reviews, please see Murray 1983, 1991).

Insertion Vectors

Vectors that have a single target site for insertion of foreign DNA are known as insertion vectors. The genome of these bacteriophages is ~20% shorter than that of DNA of wild-type bacteriophage λ because many of the genes that are not required for lytic growth have been removed. Insertion of an appropriate segment of foreign DNA into the cloning site restores the genome to something like its full length and facilitates packaging into infectious particles in vitro (Murray et al. 1977; Sternberg et al. 1977; Williams and Blattner 1980). The maximum size of DNA that can be accommodated in an insertion vector varies from 5 kb to 11 kb, depending on the design of the particular vector.

Replacement Vectors

Bacteriophages that have a pair of cloning sites flanking a segment of nonessential DNA are known as replacement vectors. Digestion of linear vector DNA with the appropriate restriction enzymes generates two arms — left and right — that together carry all of the genes required for lytic infection. Removal of the central, nonessential "stuffer" fragment reduces the genome of the vector to a size that cannot be efficiently packaged into bacteriophage particles. Viable bacteriophages can only be formed by ligating a segment of foreign DNA between the purified left and right arms (Thomas et al. 1974). The largest segment of DNA that can be cloned in a replacement vector varies from 8 kb to 24 kb, depending on the vector. Cloning of longer DNA fragments requires deletion of essential bacteriophage genes, whose products must then be supplied in *trans*.

There is no single bacteriophage λ vector suitable for cloning all DNA fragments. Therefore, a careful choice must be made among the available vectors for the one best suited to the particular task at hand. Five obvious considerations influence this choice:

- the restriction enzyme(s) to be employed

- the size of the fragment of foreign DNA to be inserted

- whether the vector is to be used to express cloned DNA sequences in *E. coli*

- whether the foreign DNA is to be rescued from the bacteriophage vector in the form of a plasmid or phagemid

- whether the foreign DNA carried in the vector is to be assembled into a large overlapping contig of cloned DNAs

The development of vectors containing multiple cloning sites and the availability of a variety of restriction enzymes that cleave DNA to produce compatible cohesive termini have greatly simplified the mechanics of cloning into bacteriophage λ vectors. However, the size of the insert remains an important factor to be considered when choosing a vector. Only ~60% of the viral genome (the left arm, ~20 kb in length, including the head and tail genes *A–J*, and the right arm, 8–10 kb in length, from p_R through the *cosR* site) is necessary for lytic growth of the bacteriophage; the central one third of the genome can be replaced by foreign DNA. However, the viability of bacteriophages decreases dramatically when the lengths of their genomes are greater than 105% or less than 78% of that of wild-type bacteriophage λ. The combination of vector and foreign DNA must result in a recombinant bacteriophage that falls within acceptable size limits.

In the late 1970s and early 1980s, when cloning in bacteriophage vectors was still an adventure, difficulty was sometimes experienced in constructing very large libraries of recombinants. When the amount of starting DNA was limiting, the libraries often contained a high proportion of "empty" clones. To alleviate this problem, genetic markers were incorporated into the vectors to allow rapid selection or screening for recombinants and elimination of empty clones consisting only of vector sequences. Because of steady improvements in library construction, particularly in efficiency of packaging of bacteriophage λ particles and in the preparation of large quantities of DNA for cloning, these genetic markers are no longer used on a routine basis. However, they are still of some value when the starting material for cloning is in short supply, e.g., when genomic DNA is recovered from flow-sorted chromosomes or from microdissected tissue or when cDNA is prepared from mRNA extracted from a few hundred cells. Table 2-2 lists some of the genetic markers that have been used to select or screen for recombinants.

In addition to the markers listed in Table 2-2, certain vectors have been designed to take advantage of the fact that growth of wild-type bacteriophage λ is restricted in lysogens carrying prophage P2. This phenotype is called Spi[+] (sensitive to P2 interference). However, strains of bacteriophage λ lacking two genes involved in recombination (*red* and *gam*) grow in P2 lysogens and display the Spi[−] phenotype (Zissler et al. 1971) as long as they carry a χ site and the host strain is *rec*[+]. Several replacement vectors, such as λ2001, λDASH, and the EMBL series, carry the *red* and/or *gam* genes in the stuffer fragment. Replacement of the stuffer fragment with a piece of foreign DNA results in recombinant bacteriophages that are Spi[−] and thus able to grow in P2 lysogens of *E. coli* (Karn et al. 1980, 1984).

Because recombinant bacteriophages outgrow the parental vector in P2 lysogens, it would seem to be unnecessary to take steps to minimize the number of nonrecombinants formed when constructing genomic DNA libraries, e.g., by purifying the left and right arms of the vector from the stuffer fragment. In practice, however, removal of the stuffer fragment has been found to improve the efficiency with which fragments of foreign DNA can be cloned and propagated in

TABLE 2-2 Genetic Markers Used to Select or Screen for Bacteriophage λ Recombinants

GENETIC MARKER	VECTOR	PHENOTYPE		EXAMPLES OF VECTORS	REFERENCES
		RECOMBINANT			
Selectable Markers					
cI	Bacteriophages carrying a wild-type copy of the *cI* gene form plaques with very low efficiency on *hfl⁻* strains of *E. coli*.	Recombinants form plaques efficiently on *hfl⁻* strains of *E. coli* (e.g., NM514, Murray 1983)		λNM641 λNM1149 λNM1150 λgt10	Murray et al. (1977); Scalenghe et al. (1981); Scherer et al. (1981); Huynh et al. (1985); Murray (1983, 1991)
	Insertion vectors of this class are hybrids between λ and lambdoid phage 434 that contain a cloning site in the immunity region of 434. Such vectors form plaques with very low efficiency on strains of *E. coli* that carry an *hfl* marker. In the absence of the Hfl protease, the product of the bacteriophage λ *cII* gene accumulates to much higher levels than usual. *cII* is a positive regulator of the *cI* gene, so that the net effect of the *hfl⁻* mutation is to increase the amount of the CI repressor in the infected cell. Lytic growth of bacteriophage λ is curtailed, and the bacteriophage genome enters the lysogenic state with very high efficiency. Insertion of foreign DNA into the 434 immunity region inactivates the repressor and generates recombinants that are able to form plaques on *hfl⁻* strains. This property is extremely useful when constructing recombinant DNA libraries in λgt10. A single passage of such libraries in *hfl⁻* strains eliminates a high proportion of the nonrecombinant bacteriophages from the population and reduces significantly the labor of screening the library by hybridization. This class of vectors is known as immunity vectors.				
Bacteriophage *T5A3* gene	Replacement vectors of this class contain a stuffer fragment that carries two copies of the bacteriophage *T5A3* gene. Vectors will not form plaques on *E. coli* strains carrying plasmid ColIb.	Recombinants form plaques on *E. coli* strains carrying plasmid ColIb			Davison et al. (1979)
Spi	For details, please see text.				
Screening Markers					
lacZ	Forms blue plaques on strains of *lacZ⁻ E. coli* plated on media containing X-gal.	White plaques		λgt11 λgt22–23 λZAP	Blattner et al. (1977); Pourcel and Tiollais (1977); Pourcel et al. (1979); Huynh et al. (1985)
int	Forms red plaques on strains of *E. coli* growing on tetrazolium galactose plates and carrying a defective prophage in the *gal* operon. Infection by an *int⁺xis⁺* vector results in excision of the prophage restoring a functional *gal* operon.	White plaques			Enquist and Weisberg (1976); Klein and Murray (1979)

vectors of this type (Frischauf et al. 1983). The multiple restriction sites contained in the poly-cloning sites of the EMBL series of vectors (and in analogous vectors, λ2001 [Karn et al. 1984] and λDASH [Sorge 1988]) permit the stuffer fragment to be easily rendered unclonable by digestion with two different restriction enzymes.

The improved efficiency of cloning in vectors equipped with the Spi system comes at a price. As mentioned earlier, recombinants constructed in these vectors lack the *red* and *gam* genes, which can have disadvantages under certain circumstances. In bacteria infected by *gam⁻* bacteriophage, the only DNA molecules available for packaging are relatively rare, exonuclease-resistant, closed circular dimers generated by θ-form replication and subsequent recombination (catalyzed by the products of the bacteriophage λ *red* gene or the host *recA* gene). However, the presence of an active bacterial recombination system occasionally leads to rearrangements (in particular to deletion) of segments of foreign DNA that carry repeated sequences (e.g., please see Lauer et al. 1980). To avoid this problem, several vectors have been designed that carry the *gam* gene on one of the arms of the bacteriophage λ DNA. Examples of such vectors are Charon 32–35 and 40 (Loenen and Blattner 1983; Dunn and Blattner 1987). Since each of these vectors is *red⁻*, infected *recA* cells are phenotypically RecA⁻, RecBC⁻, and Red⁻. The use of such vectors has in some instances overcome the problems of cloning segments of foreign DNA containing recombinogenic sequences.

The final genetic factor to consider in choosing a vector is the presence of a χ site. As discussed earlier, the growth of *red⁻gam⁻* bacteriophages on wild-type *E. coli* is limited by the availability of concatenated DNA molecules that can be efficiently packaged into phage particles. However, the presence of a χ site increases the efficiency of the recombination process that gives rise to packaging substrates. As a result, the plaques formed by *red⁻gam⁻* χ bacteriophages are almost as large as those formed by *red⁺gam⁺* bacteriophages. Because most bacteriophage replacement λ vectors are *red⁻gam⁻* when the stuffer fragments are removed, recombinants would normally be expected to display the small-plaque phenotype. However, eukaryotic DNAs contain sequences that can mimic χ sites. Thus, some recombinant bacteriophages will carry insertions of foreign DNA that contain χ sequences and others will not. The recombinants that contain χ sequences will grow to higher titer, form larger plaques, and become overrepresented during amplification of libraries. This problem can be overcome by avoiding vectors (such as Charon 28 and 30) that give rise to *gam⁻* recombinants that do not contain a χ site. These vectors should only be used for construction of libraries if the recombinant bacteriophages are propagated on *recBC⁻* or *recD⁻* hosts. For construction of genomic DNA libraries, we recommend vectors such as λ2001, λDASH, λFIX, and the EMBL series, which contain χ sites in the arms, or Charon 32–35 and 40, which generate *red⁻gam⁺* recombinants. All of these vectors give rise to recombinant plaques of relatively uniform size.

Expression Vectors

Beginning in the mid 1980s and continuing to the present day, several bacteriophage expression vectors have been developed that permit not only the propagation of foreign sequences, but also their expression in bacterial cells, their transcription in vitro into RNA, and, in some cases, their automatic recovery as autonomously replicating phagemids. The prototype λ expression vector is λgt11 (Young and Davis 1983a; Huynh et al. 1985), which carries a portion of the *E. coli* β-galactosidase gene, including the upstream elements that are essential for its expression. The carboxy-terminal coding region of this gene contains a single *Eco*RI site into which foreign DNA can be inserted. λgt18–23 are derivatives of λgt11 that can accept larger inserts and that allow the use of up to four additional restriction enzymes (Han and Rutter 1987, 1988). In appropriate lytic or lysogenic hosts, the chimeric gene can be induced, resulting in the synthesis of a fusion protein consisting of the amino-terminal portion of the β-galactosidase gene fused to sequences encoded by the downstream open reading frame. cDNA libraries constructed in λgt11 and λgt18–23 may be screened immunologically for expression of specific antigens in *E. coli*. This approach has been remarkably successful and has led to the isolation of many genes encoding proteins for which no probes other than specific antisera were available.

Bacteriophage λ vectors such as λgt11 and λgt18–23 carry the *cIts*857 mutation in addition to an amber mutation in the *S* (lysis) gene, *Sam7*. At 42°C, where the *cIts*857 repressor is only partially functional (Lieb 1979), these vectors form plaques on strains of *E. coli* (such as Y1090*hsdR*) that carry the amber suppressor *supF*. At temperatures where the repressor is active (32°C), these bacteriophage strains can form lysogens. In the original description of λgt11 (Young and Davis 1983b), cDNA libraries constructed in λgt11 were screened as bacterial lysogens. The colonies were induced by heating and screened immunologically for production of foreign proteins encoded by the cloned cDNAs. Propagation and screening of expression libraries as lysogens appeared to offer two potential advantages: λgt11 genomes inherited as part of the host-cell chromosome would perhaps be more stable genetically than genomes propagated by lytic infection, and the repression of synthesis of potentially toxic fusion proteins might be more complete in cells containing only one integrated copy of the recombinant genome than in lytically infected cells that rapidly accumulate hundreds of copies. Despite these apparent advantages, libraries constructed in λgt11 are no longer propagated as lysogens nor screened after induction because some recombinants are unable to form stable lysogens (Huynh et al. 1985). Furthermore, when plaques, rather than colonies of induced lysogens, are screened with immunological or nucleic acid probes, the signal-to-noise ratio is much higher.

Perhaps the most versatile vector currently available is ZAP Express (Stratagene). cDNAs up to 12 kb in length can be cloned unidirectionally into this vector, automatically excised by superinfection with a filamentous helper bacteriophage, and recircularized to form a plasmid that will drive expression of the cloned cDNA in both bacteria (via the *lac* promoter) and mammalian cells (via the cytomegalovirus immediate early promoter). ZAP Express contains selectable markers for both prokaryotic and eukaryotic cells and carries a portmanteau of controlling elements derived from at least eight different organisms (SV40, cytomegalovirus, *E. coli*, bacteriophages f1, T3, and T7, various plasmids, and bacteriophage λ itself), as well as a medley of synthetic cloning sites and linkers. Although this synthetic genome may lack the elegance of wild-type λ, it is surely a testimony to the ingenuity and dexterity of its constructors and to the continuing tolerance of the bacteriophage to the works of Man.

CLONING IN BACTERIOPHAGE λ VECTORS

Bacteriophage λ has many uses as a cloning vehicle, ranging from subcloning of genomic DNA sequences initially cloned in vectors with larger capacity (e.g., bacterial artificial chromosomes or P1 bacteriophages) to construction of complex cDNA or genomic DNA libraries. Cloning in bacteriophage λ involves several steps that are summarized in the flow chart presented in Figure 2-9.

The protocols in this chapter describe methods to prepare and test bacteriophage λ vectors for cloning and to construct genomic DNA libraries in these vectors. Detailed procedures for the preparation of cDNA libraries are given in Chapter 11.

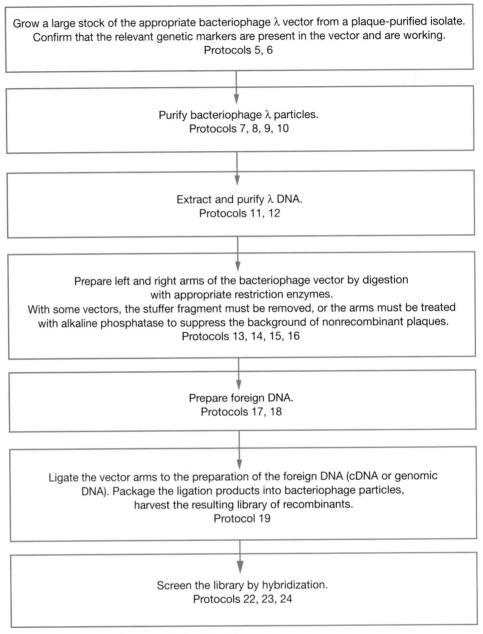

FIGURE 2-9 Flowchart of Protocols in This Chapter

Protocol 1

Plating Bacteriophage λ

A PLAQUE DERIVES FROM INFECTION OF A SINGLE BACTERIUM by a single bacteriophage particle. The progeny virus particles synthesized by this first infectious center adsorb to and infect neighboring bacteria, which in turn release another generation of daughter virus particles. If bacteria are growing in a semisolid medium (e.g., containing agarose or agar), the diffusion of the progeny virus particles is limited. Under these circumstances, the result of successive rounds of infection is a spreading zone of bacterial lysis that, after several hours of incubation, becomes visible to the naked eye as a relatively clear, circular area in an otherwise turbid background of bacterial growth. Because each plaque contains the progeny of a single virus particle, the bacteriophages derived from a single plaque are essentially genetically identical to one another. A method for generating macroplaques of bacteriophage λ is given at the end of this protocol. Bacteriophage λ vectors that carry the *E. coli lacZ* gene may be analyzed as described in the panel on ADDITIONAL PROTOCOL: PLAQUE ASSAY OF BACTERIOPHAGES THAT EXPRESS β-GALACTOSIDASE at the end of this protocol.

MATERIALS

CAUTION: Please see Appendix 12 for appropriate handling of materials marked with <!>.

Buffers and Solutions

Please see Appendix 1 for components of stock solutions, buffers, and reagents. Dilute stock solutions to the appropriate concentrations.

MgSO$_4$ (10 mM)
SM and SM plus gelatin

Media

LB or NZCYM (50-ml aliquots in 250-ml conical flasks)

The choice between these two media is largely a matter of personal preference. NZCYM, the richer of the two media, was introduced in the 1970s by the Wisconsin phage workers (Blattner et al. 1977) to grow the enfeebled strains of *E. coli* mandated by cloning regulations in force at that time. The medium has long outlived the regulations and remains in wide use today.

LB or NZCYM agar plates

Freshly poured plates are too wet for use in plaque assays. To prevent running and smearing of plaques, store the plates for 2 days at room temperature before use. They can then be transferred to plastic sleeves and stored at 4ºC. Plates stored at 4ºC should be placed at room temperature for 1–2 hours before use in Step 10 below. Warming the plates in this way reduces problems of condensation and allows the top agar subsequently to spread across the entire surface of the plate before it sets. For further information, please see note to Step 12.

> **ADDITION OF MALTOSE FOR GROWTH OF** λ
>
> Some investigators add maltose to media used to grow and plate bacteriophage λ. The presence of 0.2% maltose leads to a substantial induction of the maltose operon including the *lamB* gene, which encodes the cell surface receptor to which bacteriophage λ binds (Schwartz 1967). This induction should theoretically increase the efficiency of infection and hence the yield of bacteriophage. The use of maltose is a double-edged sword, however, since florid growth of some strains of *E. coli* in such rich medium may lead to cell lysis and the accumulation of cellular debris laden with the LamB protein. Binding of bacteriophage particles to this debris leads to futile release of the viral DNA and an unproductive infection. In our hands, there is little difference in bacteriophage yield from cultures grown in the presence or absence of maltose.

LB or NZCYM top agar or agarose (0.7%)

Melt the top agarose just before use by heating it in a microwave oven for a short period of time. Store aliquots of the melted solution in a 47ºC heating block or water bath to prevent the agarose from solidifying until needed in Step 10 below.

Agarose is preferred to agar in this protocol in order to minimize contamination with inhibitors that can interfere with subsequent enzymatic analysis of bacteriophage DNA.

This solution is also known as soft agar/agarose.

Centrifuges and Rotors

Sorvall SS-34 or equivalent

Special Equipment

Filter paper circles (to fit Petri dish)
Optional, please see note to Step 12.
Heating block or water bath preset to 47ºC

Vectors and Bacterial Strains

Bacteriophage λ stocks
E. coli strain

Be sure to use strains of *E. coli* that have been appropriately designed to support the growth of the vector. For a complete listing of relevant *E. coli* genetic markers found in strains used to propagate bacteriophage λ, please see Table 2-3. Before using a particular λ vector, consult the literature and/or heed the recommendations provided by commercial suppliers regarding the choice of a suitable strain of *E. coli*.

METHOD

Preparation of Plating Bacteria

1. Inoculate NZCYM or LB medium (50 ml in a 250-ml conical flask) with a single bacterial colony of the appropriate *E. coli* strain. Grow the culture overnight at 37ºC with moderate agitation.

   Some protocols recommend growing the culture at 30ºC instead of 37ºC. Growth at the lower temperature increases the chance that the cells will not have reached saturation during the overnight growth period, hence reducing the amount of cell debris in the medium. As noted earlier, bacteriophages added to saturated cultures can adsorb to the LamB protein present on cellular debris, thereby reducing the titer of the bacteriophage inoculum.

2. Centrifuge the cells at 4000*g* (5800 rpm in a Sorvall SS-34 rotor) for 10 minutes at room temperature.

3. Discard the supernatant, and resuspend the cell pellet in 20 ml of 10 mM $MgSO_4$. Measure the OD_{600} of a 1/100 dilution of the resuspended cells and dilute the cells to a final concentration of 2.0 OD_{600} with 10 mM $MgSO_4$.

    To improve the viability of the plating bacteria during storage, incubate the cell suspension in a 100-ml sterile flask for 1 hour at 37ºC with moderate agitation.

    For many strains of *E. coli*, 1.0 OD_{600}/ml is approximately equal to 1.0×10^9 bacterial cells/ml. However, the relationship between the OD_{600} and the number of viable cells/ml varies from strain to strain and is affected by the conditions of growth. It is advisable to carry out a calibration experiment to measure the OD_{600} of a culture of the particular strain of *E. coli* at different stages in its growth cycle and to count the number of viable cells at each of these times by plating dilutions of the culture on LB agar plates.

4. Store the suspension of plating bacteria at 4ºC.

    Suspensions of robust strains of *E. coli* may be used for up to 2–3 weeks. However, severely enfeebled strains of *E. coli* (e.g., *recA*⁻ strains) lose viability quickly when stored under conditions of starvation at 4ºC. Use fresh cultures of such strains for plating bacteriophage λ.

5. Melt top agar or agarose by heating it in a microwave oven for a short period of time. Store aliquots of the melted agar or agarose (3 ml for 100-mm plates, 7 ml for 200-mm plates) on a heating block or in a water bath at 47ºC to keep the solution molten.

Infection of Plating Bacteria

6. Prepare tenfold serial dilutions of the bacteriophage stocks (in SM plus gelatin). Mix each dilution by *gentle* vortexing or by tapping on the side of the tube.

    The gelatin helps to stabilize the bacteriophage particles.

    Excessive vortexing damages the tails of bacteriophage λ particles.

7. Dispense 0.1 ml of plating bacteria from Step 4 into a series of sterile tubes (13 or 17 × 100 mm).

8. Add 0.1 ml of each dilution of bacteriophage stock to a tube of plating bacteria. Mix the bacteria and bacteriophages by shaking or gently vortexing.

9. Incubate the mixture for 20 minutes at 37ºC to allow the bacteriophage particles to adsorb to the bacteria. Remove the tubes from the water bath and allow them to cool to room temperature.

    Always include a control tube that contains SM but no bacteriophage λ.

    Adsorption of bacteriophage λ to its receptor is fairly slow, hence the requirement for 20 minutes incubation.

10. Add an aliquot of molten agar or agarose to the first tube. Mix the contents of the tube by gentle tapping or vortexing for five seconds and, *without delay*, pour the entire contents of the tube onto the center of a labeled agar plate. Try to avoid creating air bubbles. Swirl the plate gently to ensure an even distribution of bacteria and top agarose. Repeat the procedure until the contents of all the tubes have been transferred to separate labeled plates.

11. Replace the lids on the plates. Allow the top agar/agarose to harden by standing the plates for 5 minutes at room temperature. Invert the closed plates and incubate them at 37ºC.

    With some *E. coli* strains and bacteriophage vectors, better plaques are formed when the plates are incubated at temperatures other than 37ºC. For example, when using the Stratagene *E. coli* strains SRBρ and SRB(P2)ρ as hosts, an incubation temperature of 39ºC is recommended. In addition, λgt10 vectors produce better plaques on *E. coli hfl*⁻ strains when incubated at 39ºC (for details, please see the introduction to Chapter 11).

TABLE 2-3 E. coli Strains Used to Propagate Bacteriophage λ Vectors

PHENOTYPE	RELEVANT GENOTYPE	STRAIN	USES	REFERENCES
Sup⁻	sup^0	R594	Nonpermissive for vectors carrying amber mutations	Campbell (1965); Borck et al. (1976)
r_k^-	supE hsdR	MM294, Q358, C600, BNN93, K802	Permissive for vectors carrying amber mutations Will modify but not restrict DNA at EcoRI sites	Appleyard (1954); Wood (1966); Meselson and Yuan (1968); Karn et al. (1980); Young and Davis (1983a)
r_k^-	supE supF hsdR	LE392, ED8654	Permissive for vectors carrying amber mutations Will modify but not restrict DNA at EcoRI sites	Borck et al. (1976); Murray et al. (1977)
r_k^-	supF hsdR	NM538	Permissive for vectors carrying amber mutations Will modify but not restrict DNA at EcoRI sites	Frischauf et al. (1983)
r_k^- Rec⁻	supE supF hsdR recA	NM531	Permissive for vectors carrying amber mutations Will modify but not restrict DNA at EcoRI sites recA⁻ strain	Arber et al. (1983)
r_k^- RecE⁻	hsdR recBC sbcA	NM519	Will modify but not restrict DNA at EcoRI sites Used for growth of Spi⁻ bacteriophages	Arber et al. (1983)
r_k^- RecD⁺	supE supF hsdR recC	TAP90	Used for production of high-titer lysates for growth of Spi⁻ bacteriophage Will modify but not restrict DNA at EcoRI sites	Patterson and Dean (1987)
r_k^- McrB⁻	hsdR mcrB Δlac	MBM7014.5, MC1061	Used for constructing libraries in bacteriophage λORF8 Will modify but not restrict DNA at EcoRI sites	Raleigh and Wilson (1986); Meissner et al. (1987)
r_k^- RecD⁻ Mcr⁻	supE hsdR mcrB mcrA recD	KW251	Permissive for vectors carrying amber mutations Used for propagation of high-titer lysates Will modify but not restrict DNA at EcoRI sites Permits propagation of cytosine methylated DNA	
r_k^- Lac⁻ Lon⁻	hsdR supF Δlac Δlon pMC9	Y1090hsdR	Permissive for growth of λgt11 and λgt18–23 Contains high levels of lac repressor Is deficient in the lon protease Will modify but not restrict DNA at EcoRI sites	Young and Davis (1983b); Jendrisak et al. (1987)
r_k^- Hfl⁻	supE hsdR hflA	BNN102 (C600hflA)	Will modify but not restrict DNA at EcoRI sites Nonpermissive for λgt10 Permissive for recombinants that have foreign DNA inserted in the cI gene	Young and Davis (1983a)
r_k^- Mcr RecA⁻ lacIqΔM15	supE Δ(mcrCB⁻ hsd SMR⁻ mcr recA lac F′ proAB⁺ lacIq ZΔM15 Tn10)	XL1-Blue MRF′	Permissive for vectors carrying amber mutations Will modify but not restrict DNA at EcoRI sites Permits α-complementation of β-galactosidase in a recA⁻ strain	Jerpseth et al. (1992)

Marker	Strain	Genotype	Comments	Reference
r_k^- lacZΔM15	BB4	supE supF hsdR F' proAB⁺ lacI^q lacZΔM15	Permissive for vectors carrying amber mutations Will modify but not restrict DNA at EcoRI sites Permits α-complementation of β-galactosidase	Bullock et al. (1987)
r_k^- lacZΔM15 Rec⁻	XL1-Blue	supE supF hsdR lac⁻ F' proAB⁺ lacI^q lacZΔM15	Will modify but not restrict DNA at EcoRI sites Permits α-complementation of β-galactosidase	Bullock et al. (1987)
r_k^- lacF^qΔM15	NM522	supE Δ(lac proAB) Δ(mcrB⁻ hsdSM)5 F' proAB lacI^q ZΔM15	Permissive for vectors carrying amber mutations Permits α-complementation of β-galactosidase Permits α-complementation of β-galactosidase recA⁻ strain	Gough and Murray (1983)
Lac⁻	CSH18	supE Δ(lac-pro) F' proAB⁺ lacI^q lacZ⁻	Permissive for vectors carrying amber mutations Used to screen recombinants made in vectors carrying a lacZ gene	Miller (1972); Williams and Blattner (1979)
$r_B^- m_B^-$-Rec⁻	HB101	hsdS recA	Nonpermissive for vectors carrying amber mutations Will not modify or restrict DNA at EcoRI sites recA⁻ strain	Boyer and Roulland-Dussoix (1969); Bolivar and Backman (1979)
$r_B^- m_B^-$	DP50supF	supE supF hsdS	Permissive for vectors carrying amber mutations Will not modify or restrict DNA at EcoRI sites	Leder et al. (1977); B. Bachmann (pers. comm.)
$r_B^- m_B^-$-Rec⁻	ED8767	supE supF hsdS recA	Permissive for vectors carrying amber mutations Will not modify or restrict DNA at EcoRI sites recA⁻ strain	Murray et al. (1977)
r_k^- (P2)	Q359	supE hsdR (P2)	Used for selection of Spi⁻ bacteriophage Will modify but not restrict DNA at EcoRI sites Permissive for vectors carrying amber mutations	Karn et al. (1980)
r_k^- (P2)	NM539	supF hsdR (P2cox)	Used for selection of Spi⁻ bacteriophage Will modify but not restrict DNA at EcoRI sites Permissive for vectors carrying amber mutations	Frischauf et al. (1983)
λEam	BHB2688	(N205 recA [λimm434 cIts b2 red Eam Sam/λ])	Used to prepare packaging extracts	Hohn and Murray (1977); Hohn (1979)
λDam	BHB2690	(N205 recA [λimm434 cIts b2 red Dam Sam/λ])	Used to prepare packaging extracts	Hohn and Murray (1977); Hohn (1979)
λcos2	SMR10	E. coli C (λcos2 ΔB xis red gam am210 cIts857 nin Sam/λ)	Used to prepare packaging extracts	Rosenberg (1985)

12. **Continue incubating the plates overnight, then count or select (pick) individual plaques.**

> Plaques begin to appear after ~7 hours of incubation and should be counted or picked after 12–16 hours. By this time, the plaques formed on robust strains of *E. coli* should be 2–3 mm in diameter.
>
> If the plates are too dry, the plaques will grow more slowly and will not reach their full size. Freshly poured plates have different problems. During incubation at 37ºC, droplets of moisture sweat onto the surface of the top agar and cause the developing plaques to streak and run into one another. This smearing can be avoided by storing the plates for 2 days at room temperature before use or by drying the plates with the lids ajar for 2 hours in a laminar-flow hood or (less desirable) a 37ºC incubator. In an emergency, when there is no time to dry the plates, remove any droplets of water from the lids of the plates after the top agar has set and insert a piece of (sterile) circular filter paper into each lid. During incubation of the inverted plates at 37ºC, the filter paper absorbs much of the humidity and keeps streaking to a minimum.
>
> With experience, the size of plaques can be adjusted to suit the task at hand. For example, when screening libraries by hybridization, it is often desirable to restrict the size of the plaques so that the maximum number of bacteriophages can be screened per plate. In this case, use well-aged plates and use slightly more bacteria than usual for each lawn. Under other conditions, e.g., when using enfeebled *red⁻ gam⁻* strains of bacteriophage λ, it may be necessary to reduce the bacterial inoculum and/or to use a lower (0.6%) concentration of top agar/agarose to obtain plaques of an acceptable size. Bacteriophage λ plaques do not increase in size after the bacterial lawn is fully grown and the cells have reached stationary phase.

ADDITIONAL PROTOCOL: PLAQUE-ASSAY OF BACTERIOPHAGES THAT EXPRESS β-GALACTOSIDASE

Many bacteriophage λ vectors contain a copy of the *E. coli lacZ* gene, which encodes β-galactosidase. When these vectors are plated in media containing X-gal (5-bromo-4-chloro-3-indolyl-β-D-galactopyranoside), a chromogenic substrate for β-galactosidase, a bright ring of blue dye is formed around the plaques. With time, the entire plaque assumes a blue tinge. When segments of foreign DNA are cloned into these vectors, the *lacZ* gene, and hence the chromogenic reaction, is disrupted and the plaques are no longer etched in blue. During construction of cDNA and genomic libraries in bacteriophage λ vectors, the relative number of blue and white plaques indicates the proportion of empty vectors (blue plaques) and potential recombinants (colorless plaques).

Additional Materials

CAUTION: Please see Appendix 12 for appropriate handling of materials marked with <!>.

LB or NZCYM top agar or agarose, containing X-gal <!>
  For 3 ml of top agar, use 40 µl of 2% X-gal. Add X-gal to cooled (47ºC) top agar just before use.
E. coli *plating bacteria*
  Use any strain of *E. coli* that will support lytic growth of the particular strain of bacteriophage λ (please see Table 2-3), as long as it is not an overproducer of β-galactosidase. The presence of a single copy of the *lacZ* gene in the bacterial chromosome does not interfere with the assay. Please see the information panel on α-COMPLEMENTATION (Chapter 1). Prepare the bacteria as described in Protocol 1.

Method

1. Dilute the bacteriophage stock in SM plus gelatin.

2. Infect 0.1-ml aliquots of plating bacteria with 10 µl of the appropriate dilutions of bacteriophage. Incubate the infected cultures for 20 minutes at 37ºC.

3. Add 3 ml of molten top agar (at 47ºC) containing X-gal to the first tube. Mix the contents of the tube by tapping or gentle vortexing. Pour the contents of the tube onto an agar plate.

4. Repeat Step 3 with the remaining dilutions of the bacteriophage stock.

5. When the top agar has set, invert the plates and incubate for 15–18 hours at 37ºC.

6. Remove the plates from the 37ºC incubator, place at room temperature for a further 2 hours, and then record the color of the plaques.

   > During incubation at room temperature, the intensity of the blue color is enhanced. For accurate comparison, the intensity of color in the plaques should be matched to color standards that can be obtained from Stratagene.

ADDITIONAL PROTOCOL: MACROPLAQUES

Macroplaques are areas of lysed bacteria (~0.5 cm in diameter) that are formed when bacteriophages from a single conventional plaque are dabbed onto a bacterial culture growing in top agar. A macroplaque typically contains ~20 times more infectious particles than a conventional plaque. Macroplaque stocks may be used to infect small-scale bacterial cultures (minipreparations) and to prepare plate lysates of bacteriophage λ.

Method

1. Add 0.1 ml of plating bacteria to 3 ml of molten top agar at 47°C. Mix the contents of the tube by tapping or gentle vortexing and then pour the contents of the tube onto an LB agar plate that has been equilibrated to room temperature. Store the plate at room temperature to allow the top agar to harden.

2. Use a sterile wooden toothpick to transfer bacteriophage from a single well-isolated plaque to the surface of the top agar. Inoculate an area ~0.3 cm in diameter by touching the toothpick lightly to the surface several times.

3. Incubate the plate for 6–8 hours at 37°C.

4. Harvest the macroplaques with the large end of a sterile borosilicate Pasteur pipette.

Each macroplaque yields several agar plugs that can be stored either together or separately in 400–500 μl of SM. The plugs can be stored in this form for several weeks at 4°C without significant loss of bacteriophage viability.

Protocol 2

Picking Bacteriophage λ Plaques

G ENETICALLY HOMOGENEOUS STOCKS OF BACTERIOPHAGE λ are generated by "picking" a well-isolated plaque and placing the agar/agarose containing the zone of lysis in storage solution. The resulting stock solution can be used to prepare plate lysates or liquid cultures of the bacteriophage or can be stored for later analysis. The following protocol describes a general method for picking and storing plaques.

MATERIALS

CAUTION: Please see Appendix 12 for appropriate handling of materials marked with <!>.

Buffers and Solutions

Please see Appendix 1 for components of stock solutions, buffers, and reagents.
Dilute stock solutions to the appropriate concentrations.

Chloroform <!>
SM

Special Equipment

Borosilicate Pasteur pipette (equipped with a rubber bulb) or a Micropipette
Microfuge tubes or Polypropylene test tubes (13 x 100 mm)

Vectors and Bacterial Strains

Bacteriophage λ, grown as well-isolated plaques on bacterial lawn (please see Protocol 1)

METHOD

1. Place 1 ml of SM in a sterile microfuge tube or polypropylene test tube. Add 1 drop (~50 µl) of chloroform.

    Polypropylene tubes are used because they are resistant to chloroform.

2. Use a borosilicate Pasteur pipette equipped with a rubber bulb, or a micropipette, to stab through the chosen plaque of bacteriophage λ into the hard agar beneath. Apply mild suction so that the plaque, together with the underlying agar, is drawn into the pipette.

    > Because bacteriophages can diffuse considerable distances through the layer of top agar, choose well-separated plaques. For the same reason, it is best, wherever possible, to pick plaques shortly after the bacterial lawn has grown up and the bacteriophage plaques have first appeared. Picking plaques early in their development also reduces the unwelcome possibility of obtaining a bacteriophage stock that contains significant numbers of undesirable mutants.

    > Alternatively, plaques may be picked by touching a sterile 8-cm wooden stick (also called an applicator or orange stick) or a sterile toothpick to the surface of the top agar/agarose in the center of the chosen plaque. Immediately place the stick in SM/chloroform in a 13 × 100-mm tube and mix the contents of the tube by vortexing to dislodge fragments of agar/agarose containing the bacteriophages.

    > Some investigators prefer to use the wide end of sterile borosilicate Pasteur pipettes (without cotton plugs). The agar plug stays in the pipette and can be expelled into a sterile polypropylene tube by a flick of the practiced wrist. Bacteriophages can be stored in these plugs for several weeks at 4ºC without significant loss of viability, as long as the plugs do not become dehydrated.

3. Wash out the fragments of agar from the borosilicate Pasteur pipette into the tube containing SM/chloroform (prepared in Step 1). Let the capped tube stand for 1–2 hours at room temperature to allow the bacteriophage particles to diffuse from the agar. To assist the elution of the virus, rock the tube gently on a rocking platform. Store the bacteriophage suspension at 4ºC.

    > An average bacteriophage plaque yields ~10^6 infectious bacteriophage particles, which can be stored indefinitely at 4ºC in SM/chloroform without loss of viability (please see the panel on **LONG-TERM STORAGE OF BACTERIOPHAGE λ STOCKS** in Protocol 3). The virus recovered from a plaque can be used as described in Protocols 3 and 4 to prepare larger stocks of bacteriophages by the plate lysis or the liquid culture methods. For screening recombinant plaques, please see the panel on **ANALYZING RECOMBINANTS USING PCR**.

ANALYZING RECOMBINANTS USING PCR

When screening cDNA libraries constructed in a bacteriophage λ vector such as λgt10 or λgt11, it is often useful to establish the length of a cDNA harbored in a hybridization-positive bacteriophage before growing up a small-scale preparation of the virus. With bacteriophage λ vectors whose entire DNA sequence is known, or for those in which at least the DNA sequence immediately adjacent to the cloning site is known, polymerase chain reaction (PCR) can be carried out directly on the plaque lysate to determine the size of the cDNA insert. Two oligonucleotide primers complementary to the vector DNA flanking the cloning site are used in PCR, together with an aliquot of the bacteriophage eluate in SM/chloroform. A complete protocol for direct PCR analysis of bacteriophage λ eluates is described in Chapter 8, Protocol 12.

Protocol 3

Preparing Stocks of Bacteriophage λ by Plate Lysis and Elution

Two methods are commonly used to prepare stocks from single plaques of bacteriophage λ: plate lysates (described in Protocol 3), in which the bacteriophages are propagated in bacteria grown in top agar or agarose, and small-scale liquid cultures (Protocol 4), in which the bacteriophages are propagated in bacteria growing in liquid medium. Although both methods yield useful bacteriophage stocks, the first has the advantage of allowing the investigator to determine whether or not the bacteriophages have grown successfully merely by looking at the degree of confluence of lysis. In addition, the titer of plate stocks is usually higher than that of stocks prepared from liquid cultures. A disadvantage of the first method, however, is that bacteriophage DNA isolated from plate stocks may be contaminated with sulfated polysaccharides and glycans that leach from the top agar/agarose. More often than not, these polysaccharides are innocuous and cause no trouble. Sometimes, however, they inhibit enzymes used to analyze or manipulate bacteriophage λ DNA. This protocol describes a reliable method for preparing plate lysates and recovering bacteriophage by elution from the top agar with SM. Alternatively, the bacteriophage may be recovered from "soft" (low concentration) top agarose by scraping the top agarose into SM (please see the panel on **ADDITIONAL PROTOCOL: PREPARING STOCKS OF BACTERIOPHAGE λ BY PLATE LYSIS AND SCRAPING** at the end of this protocol).

MATERIALS

CAUTION: Please see Appendix 12 for appropriate handling of materials marked with <!>.

Buffers and Solutions

Please see Appendix 1 for components of stock solutions, buffers, and reagents.
Dilute stock solutions to the appropriate concentrations.

Chloroform <!>
SM

Media

LB or NZCYM agar plates
Freshly poured plates (10-cm or 15-cm diameter) that have been equilibrated to room temperature give the best results in these methods. The older the plates, the lower the titer of the resulting plate stock.

Adequate yields of most strains of bacteriophage λ can be obtained by using LB or NZCYM bottom agar as described above. However, if problems arise, improved yields can often be obtained from LB bottom agar that has been supplemented with:

0.3% (w/v) glucose
0.075 mM $CaCl_2$
0.004 mM $FeCl_3$
2 mM $MgSO_4$

Glucose represses the *lamB* gene and thus reduces the amount of bacteriophage that is lost by adsorption to bacterial debris (please see the panel on **ADDITION OF MALTOSE FOR GROWTH OF** λ in Protocol 1). Calcium ions also reduce loss by readsorption, whereas ferric ions may stimulate respiration and suppress the lysogenic pathway of bacteriophage development (Arber et al. 1983).

LB or NZCYM top agarose (0.7%)

Agarose is preferred to agar in this protocol in order to minimize contamination with inhibitors that can interfere with subsequent enzymatic analysis of bacteriophage DNA.

Centrifuges and Rotors

Sorvall SS-34 or equivalent

Special Equipment

Heating block or water bath preset to 47ºC
Screw or snap-cap polypropylene tubes (13 x 100 mm or larger)

Additional Reagents

Step 9 of this protocol requires the reagents listed in Protocol 1 of this chapter.

Vectors and Bacterial Strains

Bacteriophage λ stock

Prepared as described in Protocol 2. Alternatively, the source of bacteriophage may be a macroplaque (please see the panel on **ADDITIONAL PROTOCOL: MACROPLAQUES** in Protocol 1).

E. coli *plating bacteria*

Prepared as described in Protocol 1 of this chapter.

METHOD

1. Prepare infected cultures for plating:

   For a 10-cm diameter Petri dish: Mix 10^5 pfu of bacteriophage (usually ~1/10 of a resuspended individual plaque or 1/100 of a macroplaque with 0.1 ml of plating bacteria).

   For a 15-cm Petri dish: Mix 2×10^5 pfu with 0.2 ml of plating cells.

   Always set up at least one control tube containing uninfected cells. Incubate the infected and control cultures for 20 minutes at 37ºC to allow the virus to attach to the cells.

   > When preparing stocks of isolated bacteriophage λ that grow poorly, increase the inoculum to 10^6 pfu per 0.1 ml of plating bacteria.

2. Add 3 ml of molten top agarose (47ºC) (10-cm plate) or 7.0 ml of molten top agarose (47ºC) (15-cm plate) to the first tube of infected cells. Mix the contents of the tube by gentle tapping or vortexing for a few seconds, and, *without delay*, pour the entire contents of the tube onto the center of a labeled agar plate. Try to avoid creating air bubbles. Swirl the plate gently to

ensure an even distribution of bacteria and top agarose. Repeat this step until the contents of each of the tubes have been transferred onto separate plates.

3. Incubate the plates *without inversion* for ~12–16 hours at 37ºC.

    Plates are not inverted during incubation to encourage sweating of fluid onto the surface of the dish, which allows the bacteriophages to spread more easily.

    At the time of harvesting, the plaques should touch one another, and the only visible bacterial growth should be a gauzy webbing that marks the junction between adjacent plaques. The plate containing uninfected cells should develop into a smooth lawn of confluent bacterial growth.

4. Remove the plates from the incubator and add SM (5 ml to each 10-cm plate or 10 ml to each 15-cm plate). Store the plates for several hours at 4ºC on a shaking platform.

5. Using a separate Pasteur pipette for each plate, transfer as much of the SM as possible into sterile screw- or snap-cap polypropylene tubes.

6. Add 1 ml of fresh SM to each plate, swirl the fluid gently, and store the plates for 15 minutes in a tilted position to allow all of the fluid to drain into one area. Again remove the SM and combine it with the first harvest. Discard the plate.

7. Add 0.1 ml of chloroform to each of the tubes containing SM, vortex the tubes briefly, and then remove the bacterial debris by centrifugation at 4000*g* (5800 rpm in a Sorvall SS-34 rotor) for 10 minutes at 4ºC.

8. Transfer the supernatants to fresh polypropylene tubes, and add 1 drop of chloroform to each tube. Store the resulting bacteriophage plate stocks at 4ºC.

9. Measure the concentration of infectious virus particles in each stock by plaque assay as described in Protocol 1.

    The titer of plate stocks should be ~10^9 to 10^{10} pfu/ml and should remain stable as long as the stock is stored properly (please see the panel on **LONG-TERM STORAGE OF BACTERIOPHAGE** λ **STOCKS**).

LONG-TERM STORAGE OF BACTERIOPHAGE λ STOCKS

Stocks of most strains of bacteriophage λ are stable for several years when stored at 4ºC in SM containing a small amount of chloroform (0.3% v/v). However, many investigators have found that some bacteriophage λ recombinants lose viability when stored in this way for a few months. This problem can usually be avoided by using freshly distilled chloroform or chloroform that has been extracted with anhydrous sodium bicarbonate to remove products of photolysis. However, we also recommend that the titer of master stocks be checked every 2–3 months and that master stocks of all important bacteriophage λ strains whose genotypes have been verified be stored at –70ºC. Before storage, add dimethylsulfoxide (DMSO) to the bacteriophage stock to a final concentration of 7% (v/v). Gently invert the tube several times to ensure that the DMSO and the virus stock are thoroughly mixed. Plunge the sealed tube into liquid nitrogen. When the liquid has frozen, transfer the tube to a –70ºC freezer for long-term storage. To recover the bacteriophages:

1. Add 0.1 ml of plating bacteria to 3 ml of molten top agar at 47ºC. Mix the contents of the tube by tapping or gentle vortexing and then pour the contents of the tube onto an LB agar plate that has been equilibrated to room temperature. Store the plate for 10 minutes at room temperature to allow the top agar to harden.

2. Scrape the surface of the frozen bacteriophage stock with a sterile 18-gauge needle. Gently streak the needle over the hardened surface of the top agar. Incubate the infected plate for 12–16 hours at the appropriate temperature to obtain bacteriophage plaques.

3. Pick a well-isolated plaque and generate a high-titer stock by one of the methods described in Protocol 3 or 4.

ALTERNATIVE PROTOCOL: PREPARING STOCKS OF BACTERIOPHAGE λ BY PLATE LYSIS AND SCRAPING

An alternative method for preparing plate lysates involves recovering the bacteriophages from the plate by scraping the soft agarose into SM. This approach suffers from the drawback of contamination with sulfated polysaccharides and glycans that may inhibit the activities of some enzymes used for further manipulations of recovered DNA.

Recovery of bacteriophage from plate stocks by elution is described in Protocol 3; preparation of bacteriophage stocks from small liquid cultures is presented in Protocol 4.

Additional Materials

LB or NZCYM top agarose

Prepare as a 0.5% (w/v) solution instead of the 0.7% solution. The use of the lower concentration of top agarose facilitates removal of the layer of top agarose. Agarose is preferred to agar in this protocol in order to minimize contamination with inhibitors that can interfere with subsequent enzymatic analysis of bacteriophage DNA.

Adequate yields of most strains of bacteriophage λ can be obtained by using LB or NZCYM bottom agar as described above. However, if problems arise, improved yields can often be obtained from LB bottom agar that has been supplemented with:

0.3% (w/v) glucose
0.075 mM $CaCl_2$
0.004 mM $FeCl_3$
2 mM $MgSO_4$

Glucose represses the *lamB* gene and thus reduces the amount of bacteriophage that is lost by adsorption to bacterial debris (please see the panel on **ADDITION OF MALTOSE FOR GROWTH OF** λ in Protocol 1). Calcium ions also reduce loss by readsorption, whereas ferric ions may stimulate respiration and suppress the lysogenic pathway of bacteriophage development (Arber et al. 1983).

Method

1. Prepare infected cultures for plating:

   For a 10-cm diameter Petri dish: Mix 10^5 pfu of bacteriophage (usually ~1/10 of a resuspended individual plaque or 1/100 of a macroplaque with 0.1 ml of plating bacteria).

   For a 15-cm Petri dish: Mix 2×10^5 pfu with 0.2 ml of plating cells.

   Always set up at least one control tube containing uninfected cells. Incubate the infected and control cultures for 20 minutes at 37°C to allow the virus to attach to the cells.

   > When preparing stocks of isolated bacteriophage λ that grow poorly, increase inoculum to 10^6 pfu/0.1 ml of plating bacteria.

2. Add 3 ml of molten top agarose (47°C) (10-cm plate) or 7.0 ml of molten top agarose (47°C) (15-cm plate) to the first tube of infected cells. Mix the contents of the tube by gentle tapping or vortexing for five seconds and, *without delay*, pour the entire contents of the tube onto the center of a labeled agar plate. Try to avoid creating air bubbles. Swirl the plate gently to ensure an even distribution of bacteria and top agarose. Repeat this step until the contents of all the tubes have been transferred onto separate plates.

3. Incubate the plates *without inversion* for 8 hours at 37°C.

   > Plates are not inverted during incubation to prevent the top agar/agarose from slipping and to encourage sweating of fluid onto the surface of the dish, which allows the bacteriophages to spread more easily.

   > At the time of harvesting, the plaques should touch one another, and the only visible bacterial growth should be a gauzy webbing that marks the junction between adjacent plaques. The plate containing uninfected cells should develop into a smooth lawn of confluent bacterial growth.

4. When confluent lysis has occurred, add 5 ml of SM to the plate and gently scrape the soft top agarose into a sterile centrifuge tube, using a sterile bent glass rod.

5. Add an additional 2 ml of SM to the plate to rinse off any remaining top agarose, and combine it with the top agarose in the centrifuge tube (from Step 4).

6. Add 0.1 ml of chloroform to the agarose suspension and mix the suspension by slow rotation or gentle shaking for 15 minutes at 37°C.

7. Centrifuge the suspension at 4000*g* (5800 rpm in a Sorvall SS-34 rotor) for 10 minutes at 4°C. Recover the supernatant, add 1 drop of chloroform, and store the virus stock as described in the panel on **LONG-TERM STORAGE OF BACTERIOPHAGE λ STOCKS**).

   > The titer of plate stocks should be ~10^9 to 10^{10} pfu/ml and should remain stable as long as the stock is stored properly.

Protocol 4

Preparing Stocks of Bacteriophage λ by Small-scale Liquid Culture

IGH-TITER STOCKS OF BACTERIOPHAGE λ MAY BE PREPARED from small-scale liquid cultures. The method presented here was originally described by Leder et al. (1977). In general, the yields of bacteriophage λ are lower and more variable than those obtained by plate lysis. A larger initial inoculum of bacteriophage is also required. However, stocks of bacteriophage λ grown in liquid culture are cleaner and free of sulfated polysaccharides that may contaminate plate lysates (please see Protocol 3).

MATERIALS

CAUTION: Please see Appendix 12 for appropriate handling of materials marked with <!>.

Buffers and Solutions

Please see Appendix 1 for components of stock solutions, buffers, and reagents. Dilute stock solutions to the appropriate concentrations.

Chloroform <!>
SM

Media

LB or NZCYM medium prewarmed to 37°C

Centrifuges and Rotors

Sorvall SS-34 or equivalent

Special Equipment

Incubator preset to 30°C
Polypropylene culture tube (17 x 100 mm)

Vectors and Bacterial Strains

Bacteriophage λ stock
Prepared as described in Protocol 2 of this chapter.

METHOD

1. Inoculate a single colony of an appropriate *E. coli* strain into 5 ml of NZCYM or LB medium in a sterile polypropylene culture tube. Incubate the culture overnight with vigorous shaking at 30ºC.

   Growth at lower temperature increases the chance that the cells will not have reached saturation during the overnight growth period, hence preventing the accumulation of large amounts of cell debris in the medium. Bacteriophages added to saturated cultures can adsorb to the LamB protein present on cellular debris, thereby reducing the titer of the bacteriophage inoculum.

   Alternatively, grow a small overnight culture at 37ºC, dilute into 5 ml of NZCYM or LB medium in a sterile polypropylene tube, and incubate the culture for 2–3 hours at 37ºC.

2. Transfer 0.1 ml of the fresh overnight bacterial culture (prepared in Step 1) to a sterile 17 x 100-mm polypropylene culture tube with a loose-fitting cap. Infect the culture with ~10^6 pfu of bacteriophage λ in 50–100 µl of SM.

   Although most strains of bacteriophage grow well in liquid culture and routinely yield lysates containing 5 x 10^8 pfu/ml, there are some strains that replicate poorly. This problem can often be solved by increasing the ratio of bacteriophage to bacteria in the infection or by growing the infected culture at 39ºC, the optimum temperature for growth of certain strains of bacteriophage. In addition, some investigators prefer to carry out the adsorption step at 0ºC in the presence of 5 mM $CaCl_2$ (Patterson and Dean 1987). This procedure allows a more uniform infection and synchronous growth of the bacteriophage.

3. Incubate the infected culture for 20 minutes at 37ºC to allow the bacteriophage particles to adsorb to the bacteria.

4. Add 4 ml of NZCYM or LB medium, prewarmed to 37ºC, and incubate the culture with vigorous agitation until lysis occurs (usually 8–12 hours at 37ºC).

   Agitation is best accomplished by positioning the culture tube in a shaker incubator (300 cycles/minute). To ensure adequate aeration, the cap of the culture tube *should not* be tightly closed.

   The onset of lysis is marked by a distinct decrease in turbidity of the culture caused by the destruction of the bacterial cells. If the culture is held up to the light, the Schlieren patterns and silky appearance of a dense, unlysed bacterial culture should not be visible. Cellular debris, appearing as whitish strings in the medium, may be visible upon lysis.

   If lysis does not occur or is incomplete after 12 hours of incubation, add an equal volume of prewarmed NZCYM or LB medium to the culture and continue incubation for a further 2–3 hours at 37ºC with vigorous agitation.

5. After lysis has occurred, add 2 drops (~100 µl) of chloroform and continue incubation for 15 minutes at 37ºC.

6. Centrifuge the culture at 4000*g* (5800 rpm in a Sorvall SS-34 rotor) for 10 minutes at 4ºC.

7. Recover the supernatant, add 1 drop (~50 µl) of chloroform, and store the virus stock as described in the panel on **LONG-TERM STORAGE OF BACTERIOPHAGE λ STOCKS** in Protocol 3.

Protocol 5

Large-scale Growth of Bacteriophage λ: Infection at Low Multiplicity

LARGE QUANTITIES OF BACTERIOPHAGE λ MAY BE PREPARED by infection of a bacterial culture at low multiplicity (described in this protocol) or by infection at high multiplicity (presented in the panel on ALTERNATIVE PROTOCOL: LARGE-SCALE GROWTH OF BACTERIOPHAGE λ: INFECTION AT HIGH MULTIPLICITY at the end of this protocol). After infection at low multiplicity, the culture is transferred immediately to a large volume of medium. Because only a small fraction of the initial bacterial population is infected, the uninfected cells in the culture continue to divide for several hours. However, successive rounds of growth and reinfection lead to the production of increasing quantities of bacteriophage. Eventually, all of the bacteria become infected and complete lysis of the culture occurs. Care is required with this method because small changes in the ratio of cells to bacteriophage particles in the initial infection greatly affect the final yield of bacteriophage particles. Furthermore, the optimum ratio varies for different strains of bacteriophage λ and bacteria. With a little effort, however, the method can be adapted for use with most combinations of virus and host cells. This approach is particularly well-suited to slow-growing strains of bacteriophage λ (e.g., those harboring large genomic DNA inserts).

This protocol is a modification of a method first described by Blattner et al. (1977) and is but one of many variants in common use.

MATERIALS

CAUTION: Please see Appendix 12 for appropriate handling of materials marked with <!>.

Buffers and Solutions

Please see Appendix 1 for components of stock solutions, buffers, and reagents. Dilute stock solutions to the appropriate concentrations.

Chloroform <!>
SM

Media

NZCYM

For a starter culture, prepare 100 ml of NZCYM in a 500-ml conical flask. For subsequent large-scale culture, prepare 4 x 500-ml aliquots of NZCYM in 2-liter flasks, prewarmed to 37°C. Four additional 500-ml aliquots may be needed for Step 9.

Centrifuges and Rotors

Sorvall SS-34 or equivalent

Additional Reagents

Step 11 of this protocol requires the reagents listed in Protocol 6 of this chapter.

Vectors and Bacterial Strains

High-titer stock of bacteriophage λ
Prepared as described in Protocol 3 or 4 of this chapter. The titer should be 10^9 to 10^{10} pfu/ml.

METHOD

1. Inoculate 100 ml of NZCYM in a 500-ml conical flask with a single colony of an appropriate bacterial host. Incubate the culture overnight at 37ºC with vigorous agitation.

2. Measure the OD_{600} of the culture. Calculate the cell concentration assuming that 1 OD_{600} = 1 x 10^9 cells/ml.

3. Withdraw four aliquots, each containing 10^{10} cells. Centrifuge each aliquot at 4000g (5800 rpm in a Sorvall SS-34 rotor) for 10 minutes at room temperature. Discard the supernatants.

4. Resuspend each bacterial pellet in 3 ml of SM.

5. Add the appropriate number of infectious bacteriophage particles and swirl the culture to ensure that the inoculum is dispersed rapidly throughout the culture.

   The number of bacteriophage particles used is crucial. For strains of bacteriophage λ that grow well (e.g., EMBL3 and 4 and λgt10), add 5 x 10^7 pfu to each suspension of 10^{10} cells; for bacteriophages that grow relatively poorly (e.g., the Charon series), it is better to increase the starting inoculum to 5 x 10^8 pfu. However, there are no hard and fast rules, and the conscientious investigator will undoubtedly want to experiment to find the multiplicity that gives the best results.

6. Incubate the infected cultures for 20 minutes at 37ºC with intermittent swirling.

7. Add each infected aliquot to 500 ml of NZCYM, prewarmed to 37ºC in 2-liter flasks. Incubate the cultures at 37ºC with vigorous shaking (300 cycles/minute in a rotary shaker).

8. Begin to monitor the cultures for lysis after 8 hours. Concomitant growth of bacteria and bacteriophages should occur, resulting in lysis of the culture after 8–12 hours. If lysis is observed, proceed to Step 10.

   A fully lysed culture contains a considerable amount of bacterial debris, which can vary in appearance from a fine, splintery precipitate to much larger, stringy clumps. If the cultures are held up to the light, the Schlieren patterns and silky appearance of a dense, unlysed bacterial culture should not be visible.

9. If lysis is not apparent after 12 hours, check a small sample of the cultures for evidence of bacteriophage growth.

   a. Transfer two aliquots (1 ml each) of the infected culture into glass tubes.

   b. Add 1 or 2 drops of chloroform (~50–100 µl) to one of the tubes, and incubate both tubes for 5–10 minutes at 37ºC with intermittent shaking.

c. Compare the appearance of the two cultures by holding the tubes up to a light. If infection is near completion but the cells have not yet lysed, the chloroform will cause the cells to burst and the turbid culture will clear to the point where it is translucent. In this case, proceed to Step 10.

> If lysis does not occur or is incomplete, the preparation can sometimes be rescued by adding to each of the cultures an additional 500 ml of NZCYM, preheated to 37ºC. Continue to incubate the cultures for a further 2–3 hours at 37ºC with vigorous shaking (300 cycles/minute in a rotary shaker).

10. Add 10 ml of chloroform to each flask, and continue the incubation for a further 10 minutes at 37ºC with shaking.

11. Cool the cultures to room temperature and proceed to precipitate the bacteriophage particles as described in Protocol 6.

> Further purification of bacteriophage particles may be achieved by using one of the methods presented in Protocols 8 through 10 of this chapter.

ALTERNATIVE PROTOCOL: LARGE-SCALE GROWTH OF BACTERIOPHAGE λ: INFECTION AT HIGH MULTIPLICITY

Large quantities of bacteriophage λ may be prepared by infection of a bacterial culture at high multiplicity as described in this protocol; alternative preparation of large quantities of bacteriophage by infection at low multiplicity is presented in Protocol 5. During infection at high multiplicity, most of the bacteria in the culture are infected at the beginning of the procedure. Therefore, growth of bacteriophages is completed in a short time (usually 3–4 hours) and is marked by complete lysis of the bacterial culture. This method is commonly used to prepare large stocks of rapidly growing strains of bacteriophage λ, for example, λgt10 recombinants containing cDNA inserts.

Additional Materials

NZCYM

> For the starter culture used in Step 1, prepare 5 ml of NZCYM in a 15-ml culture tube. For subsequent large-scale culture, prepare 4 x 500-ml aliquots of NZCYM in 2-liter flasks, prewarmed to 37ºC.

Step 5 of this protocol requires the reagents listed in Protocol 6 of this chapter.

Method

1. Inoculate 5 ml of NZCYM in a 15-ml culture tube with a single colony of an appropriate bacterial host. Incubate the culture overnight at 37ºC with vigorous agitation.

2. Inoculate 500 ml of NZCYM, prewarmed to 37ºC in each of four 2-liter flasks, with 1 ml of the overnight culture per flask. Incubate the cultures at 37ºC, with vigorous shaking, until the OD_{600} of the cultures reaches 0.5 (3–4 hours).

3. Add 10^{10} pfu of bacteriophage λ in SM to each flask, and continue incubating the cultures at 37ºC with vigorous shaking until lysis occurs (usually 3–5 hours).

   > To maximize the yield of particular strains of bacteriophage λ, it may be necessary to adjust the multiplicity of infection or the length of incubation.

4. Add 10 ml of chloroform to each flask, and continue the incubation for a further 10 minutes at 37ºC with shaking.

5. Cool the cultures to room temperature and precipitate the bacteriophage particles, as described in Protocol 6.

   > Further purification of bacteriophage particles may be achieved by using one of the methods presented in Protocols 8 through 10 of this chapter.

Protocol 6

Precipitation of Bacteriophage λ Particles from Large-scale Lysates

BACTERIOPHAGE λ, PREPARED FROM LARGE-SCALE CULTURES as described in Protocol 5, may be recovered from the lysate by precipitation with polyethylene glycol (PEG) in the presence of high salt. Residual cellular debris and PEG are subsequently extracted by treatment with chloroform, and the bacteriophage particles may be subjected to further purification as described in Protocols 8 through 10. Before further purification, we recommend analysis of the yield of the bacteriophage preparation (please see Protocol 7).

MATERIALS

CAUTION: Please see Appendix 12 for appropriate handling of materials marked with <!>.

Buffers and Solutions

Please see Appendix 1 for components of stock solutions, buffers, and reagents. Dilute stock solutions to the appropriate concentrations.

Chloroform <!>
NaCl (solid)
Polyethylene glycol (PEG 8000) <!>
  Use ~50 g for each 500 ml of culture.
SM

Enzymes and Buffers

Pancreatic DNase I (1 mg/ml)
Pancreatic RNase (1 mg/ml) in TE (pH 7.6)

Centrifuges and Rotors

Sorvall GSA rotor or equivalent

Special Equipment

Graduated cylinder (2 liters)

Vectors and Bacterial Strains

E. coli *culture, infected with bacteriophage* λ *and lysed*
  Prepared as described in Protocol 5 of this chapter.

METHOD

Precipitation of Bacteriophage Particles with PEG

1. Cool the lysed cultures containing bacteriophage λ to room temperature. Add pancreatic DNase I and RNase, each to a final concentration of 1 µg/ml. Incubate the lysed cultures for 30 minutes at room temperature.

   > Crude commercial preparations of both DNase I and RNase are more than adequate to digest the nucleic acids liberated from lysed bacteria in this step of the protocol. Without digestion, a significant number of bacteriophage particles become entrapped in the slime of host nucleic acids.

2. To each 500-ml culture, add 29.2 g of solid NaCl (final concentration, 1 M). Swirl the cultures until the salt has dissolved. Store the cultures for 1 hour on ice.

   > The addition of NaCl promotes dissociation of bacteriophage particles from bacterial debris and is required for efficient precipitation of bacteriophage particles by PEG. Some investigators prefer to add the PEG (Step 4) at the same time as the NaCl (Step 2). The centrifugation step (3) may then be omitted. However, be warned that the simultaneous addition of PEG and NaCl works efficiently only if the bacteriophage grows well and the titer of bacteriophage in the original lysed culture is $>2 \times 10^{10}$ pfu/ml.

3. Remove debris by centrifugation at 11,000g (8300 rpm in a Sorvall GSA rotor) for 10 minutes at 4ºC. Combine the supernatants from the four cultures into a clean 2-liter graduated cylinder.

4. Measure the volume of the pooled supernatants and then transfer the preparation to a clean 2-liter flask. Add solid PEG 8000 to a final concentration of 10% w/v (i.e., 50 g per 500 ml of supernatant). Dissolve the PEG by slow stirring on a magnetic stirrer at room temperature.

5. Transfer the solution to polypropylene centrifuge bottles, cool the bacteriophage/PEG solution in ice water, and store the centrifuge bottles for at least 1 hour on ice to allow the bacteriophage particles to precipitate.

6. Recover the precipitated bacteriophage particles by centrifugation at 11,000g (8300 rpm in a Sorvall GSA rotor) for 10 minutes at 4ºC. Discard the supernatants, and stand the inverted centrifuge bottles in a tilted position for 5 minutes to allow the remaining fluid to drain away from the pellet. Remove any residual fluid with a pipette.

Extraction of Bacterial Debris with Chloroform

7. Use a wide-bore pipette equipped with a rubber bulb to resuspend the bacteriophage pellet gently in SM (8 ml for each 500 ml of supernatant from Step 3). Place the centrifuge bottles on their sides at room temperature for 1 hour so that the SM covers and soaks the pellets.

   > Wash the walls of the centrifuge bottle gently but thoroughly, as the precipitate of bacteriophages sticks to them, especially if the bottle is old and pitted. The tails can be sheared from bacteriophage λ particles by violent pipetting.

8. Extract the PEG and cell debris from the bacteriophage suspension by adding an equal volume of chloroform. Vortex the mixture gently for 30 seconds. Separate the organic and aqueous phases by centrifugation at 3000g (4300 rpm in a Sorvall GSA rotor) for 15 minutes at 4ºC. Recover the aqueous phase, which contains the bacteriophage particles.

   > To determine yield, analyze the bacteriophage suspension by gel electrophoresis (Protocol 7); it may be subjected to further purification by centrifugation using one of the methods described in Protocols 8 through 10 of this chapter.

Protocol 7

Assaying the DNA Content of Bacteriophage λ Stocks and Lysates by Gel Electrophoresis

THIS PROTOCOL DESCRIBES A RAPID TECHNIQUE TO ESTIMATE the DNA content of bacteriophage λ stocks. The method can be used to (1) find out whether the yield of bacteriophage particles in stocks and lysates is sufficient to justify pressing ahead with full-scale purification and (2) monitor the purification process and to locate troublesome steps.

MATERIALS

CAUTION: Please see Appendix 12 for appropriate handling of materials marked with <!>.

Buffers and Solutions

Please see Appendix 1 for components of stock solutions, buffers, and reagents. Dilute stock solutions to the appropriate concentrations.

2.5x SDS-EDTA dye mix

Enzymes and Buffers

DNase I dilution buffer
Pancreatic DNase I (1 mg/ml)

Gels

Agarose gel (0.7%) cast in 0.5x TBE, containing 0.5 µg/ml ethidium bromide <!>

Nucleic Acids and Oligonucleotides

Bacteriophage λ DNA (control DNA)
Please see Step 5.

Special Equipment

Water bath preset to 65°C

Vectors and Bacterial Strains

Bacteriophage λ lysates or stocks
Prepared by using one of the methods described in Protocols 3 and 4 (for small-scale lysates) or Protocol 5 (for large-scale lysates) of this chapter.

METHOD

1. Make a working solution of pancreatic DNase I (1 µg/ml) as follows: Dilute 1 µl of the stock solution of DNase I with 1 ml of ice-cold DNase I dilution buffer.

2. Mix the solution by gently inverting the closed tube several times. Take care to avoid bubbles and foam. Store the solution in ice until needed. Discard the working solution after use.

   > Crude plate lysates usually yield a clean band of bacteriophage λ DNA. However, lysates of liquid cultures almost always contain an abundance of fragments of bacterial DNA that may obscure the band of bacteriophage DNA in the agarose gel. This problem can be avoided by treating aliquots of the crude lysates with pancreatic DNase I (Step 3) before releasing the bacteriophage λ DNA from the bacteriophage particles with SDS and EDTA (Step 4).

3. Transfer 10 µl of crude bacteriophage lysate or stock to a microfuge tube. Add 1 µl of the working solution of pancreatic DNase and incubate the mixture for 30 minutes at 37ºC.

4. Add 4 µl of 2.5x SDS-EDTA dye mixture and incubate the closed tube for 5 minutes at 65ºC.

   > This procedure cracks the bacteriophage coats, releases the viral DNA, and, at the same time, inactivates DNase.

5. Load the sample onto an 0.7% agarose gel containing 0.5 µg/ml ethidium bromide.

   > As controls, use samples containing 5, 25, and 100 ng of bacteriophage λ DNA.

6. Perform electrophoresis at <5 V/cm until the bromophenol blue has migrated 3–4 cm.

   > The bands of DNA will be smeared if the voltage is too high.

7. Examine the gel under UV illumination. Use the intensity of fluorescence of the DNA standards as a guide to estimate the amount of bacteriophage λ DNA in the test sample.

   > A high-titer lysate (10 µl) should contain between 10 ng and 50 ng of bacteriophage DNA.

Protocol 8

Purification of Bacteriophage λ Particles by Isopycnic Centrifugation through CsCl Gradients

SEVERAL VENERABLE METHODS ARE AVAILABLE TO PURIFY BACTERIOPHAGE λ particles from bacterial lysates. The choice among these methods is dictated by the size of the lysate and degree of purity required for the task at hand. Various options for purification are presented in this protocol, and in the panel on ALTERNATIVE PROTOCOL: PURIFICATION OF BACTERIOPHAGE λ PARTICLES BY ISOPYCNIC CENTRIFUGATION THROUGH CsCl EQUILIBRIUM GRADIENTS, as well as in Protocols 9 and 10.

Isopycnic centrifugation through CsCl gradients is used to prepare infectious bacteriophage λ particles of the highest purity that are essentially free of contaminating bacterial nucleic acids (please see the panels on CsCl STEP GRADIENTS and CsCl EQUILIBRIUM GRADIENTS in this protocol). DNA prepared from these particles is ideal for use as templates for DNA sequencing, for subcloning into plasmid vectors, and for generating probes that can be used for in situ hybridization. A secondary advantage is that the stocks are highly concentrated ($>10^{11}$ pfu/ml) and maintain their infectivity for many years when stored at 4ºC. The procedure given here is a modification of the classic method described by Yamamoto et al. (1970) and is suitable for large-scale (>1 liter) liquid cultures. Protocol 9 is a faster version that is more appropriate for smaller cultures.

In Protocols 9 and 10, bacteriophage λ particles are centrifuged at high speed and deposited at the bottom of the centrifuge tube. Although the resulting preparations are not as pure as those generated by isopynic centrifugation, they yield intact DNA suitable for routine subcloning or for preparation of bacteriophage λ arms.

MATERIALS

Buffers and Solutions

Please see Appendix 1 for components of stock solutions, buffers, and reagents. Dilute stock solutions to the appropriate concentrations.

CsCl (solid)

CsCl solutions

Use a high quality (molecular biology grade) of solid CsCl to prepare three solutions of different densities by adding solid CsCl to SM, as indicated below. Store the solutions at room temperature.

CsCl Solutions Prepared in SM (100 ml) for Step Gradients

Density ρ (g/ml)	CsCl (g)	SM (ml)	Refractive Index η
1.45	60	85	1.3768
1.50	67	82	1.3815
1.70	95	75	1.3990

Ethanol

Centrifuges and Rotors

Beckman SW41 or SW28 rotor or equivalent

Beckman Ti50 or SW50.1 rotor or equivalent, with clear centrifuge tubes (e.g., Beckman Ultra-Clear tubes)

Special Equipment

Hypodermic needle (21 gauge)

Vectors and Bacterial Strains

Suspension of bacteriophage λ particles
Prepared as described in Protocol 6 of this chapter.

METHOD

1. Measure the volume of the bacteriophage suspension, and add 0.5 g of solid CsCl per ml of bacteriophage suspension. Place the suspension on a rocking platform until the CsCl is completely dissolved.

2. Pour enough CsCl step gradients to fractionate the bacteriophage suspension. Each gradient can accommodate ~16 ml of bacteriophage suspension. The number of step gradients required equals the final aqueous volume (Step 1) divided by 0.4 x tube volume (please see note below). Use clear plastic centrifuge tubes (e.g., Beckman Ultra-Clear tubes) that fit the Beckman SW41 or SW28 rotor (or equivalent).

   The step gradients may be made either by carefully layering three CsCl solutions of decreasing density on top of one another or by layering solutions of increasing density under one another.

   Some types of centrifuge tubes (e.g., Ultra-Clear) are hydrophobic, which causes the CsCl solutions to run down the tubes as droplets rather than in a continuous stream. When using tubes of this type, it is better to form a density gradient by underlaying rather than overlaying the solution.

3. Make a mark with a permanent felt-tipped marker pen on the outside of the tube opposite the position of the interface between the $\rho = 1.50$ g/ml layer and the $\rho = 1.45$ g/ml layer (Figure 2-10).

   The CsCl step gradients should occupy ~60% of the volume of the ultracentrifuge tube. For example, in a Beckman SW28 tube (or equivalent), which hold 38 ml, the step gradients consist of 7.6 ml of each of the three CsCl solutions. Balance tubes should be poured with the same CsCl density solutions.

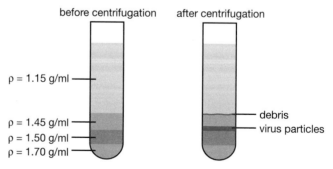

FIGURE 2-10 CsCl Gradients for Purifying Bacteriophage λ

After centrifugation, the bacteriophage particles form a visible band at the interface between the 1.45 g/ml and 1.50 g/ml CsCl layers.

4. Carefully layer the bacteriophage suspension over the step gradients. Centrifuge the gradients at 87,000*g* (22,000 rpm in a Beckman SW28 rotor) for 2 hours at 4°C.

CsCl STEP GRADIENTS

The CsCl step gradients separate the bacteriophage particles from most of the cellular proteins, including viral proteins that are used to package the bacteriophage DNA and that are synthesized in infected cells in large excess. Cellular and viral proteins have a density of ~1.3 g/ml. Wild-type bacteriophage λ has a density of ~1.5 g/ml, and the particles therefore become concentrated in a visible band at the interface between the 1.45-g/ml layer and the 1.50-g/ml layer. Some recombinant viruses have a higher density because they carry inserts of foreign DNA whose GC content is high or because the amount of DNA in the recombinant particles is larger than the genome of the parental vector. Usually, the bluish band of bacteriophage particles is thick (1–2 mm) and very easy to see. If the yield of bacteriophage particles is low, place the gradient against a black background and shine a light from above to locate the band of particles.

If the yields of purified bacteriophage are consistently low, the number of infectious bacteriophage particles should be measured in samples taken at various stages during the purification to determine where losses are occurring. Alternatively, monitor the amount of viral DNA present at different stages by gel electrophoresis. This rapid and inexpensive method helps to locate problem areas and, with practice, can be used routinely to determine whether the yield of bacteriophage particles is sufficient to justify pressing ahead with full-scale purification. The gel assay is described in Protocol 7.

Failure to include adequate concentrations of Mg^{2+} in solutions used during the purification of bacteriophage λ can drastically lower virus yields. The virus particles are exceedingly sensitive to EDTA and other chelators, and it is essential that Mg^{2+} (10–30 mM) be present at all stages of the purification to prevent disintegration of the particles.

---

5. Collect the bacteriophage particles by puncturing the side of the tube as follows.

   a. Carefully wipe the outside of the tube with ethanol to remove any grease or oil, and then attach a piece of Scotch Tape to the outside of the tube, level with the band of bacteriophage particles.

      The tape acts as a seal to prevent leakage around the needle.

   b. Use a 21-gauge hypodermic needle (no syringe-barrel required) to puncture the tube through the tape and collect the band of bacteriophage particles (Figure 2-11).

      Keep fingers away from the path of the needle in case the needle penetrates through the tube. Take care not to contaminate the bacteriophage particles with material from other bands that are visible in the gradient. These bands contain various types of bacterial debris and unassembled bacteriophage components.

6. Place the suspension of bacteriophage particles in an ultracentrifuge tube that fits a Beckman Ti50 or SW50.1 rotor (or equivalent) and fill the tube with CsCl solution (ρ = 1.5 g/ml in SM). Centrifuge at 150,000*g* (41,000 rpm in a Beckman Ti50 rotor) for 24 hours at 4°C or at 160,000*g* (36,000 rpm in a Beckman SW50.1 rotor) for 24 hours at 4°C.

CsCl EQUILIBRIUM GRADIENTS

The second CsCl centrifugation (Step 6) is an equilibrium gradient that separates the bacteriophage from contaminating RNA and DNA. Nucleic acids will not come to full equilibrium during an overnight centrifugation in CsCl and thus remain distributed throughout the tube. The resolution of this second centrifugation is higher than that obtained in the step gradient because the virus particles reach equilibrium in a very shallow density gradient (i.e., the density difference between the top and bottom of the gradient is quite small). As a consequence, the second centrifugation can often resolve two populations of bacteriophages that differ in the amount of DNA harbored in the viral genome. In a classic paper in human molecular genetics, Lauer et al. (1980) exploited this resolving power to show that bacteriophage clones harboring the hemoglobin α gene often rearrange upon propagation in *E. coli* to produce exactly the same deletion mutations found in certain subjects with α-thalassemia.

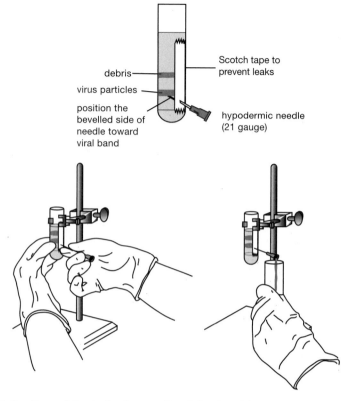

debris

virus particles

position the
bevelled side of
needle toward
viral band

Scotch tape to
prevent leaks

hypodermic needle
(21 gauge)

FIGURE 2-11 Collection of Bacteriophage λ Particles by Side Puncture

7. Collect the band of bacteriophage particles as described in Step 5. Store the bacteriophage suspension at 4°C in the CsCl solution in a tightly capped tube.

    Bacteriophage λ DNA may now be extracted from the suspension as described in Protocol 11.

8. (*Optional*) If necessary, the bacteriophage particles can be further purified and concentrated by a second round of equilibrium centrifugation in CsCl. Transfer the bacteriophage suspension to one or more ultracentrifuge tubes that fit a Beckman SW50.1 rotor (or equivalent). Fill the tubes with a solution of CsCl in SM (ρ = 1.5) and centrifuge the tubes at 160,000g (36,000 rpm in a Beckman SW50.1 rotor)) for 24 hours at 4°C. When centrifugation is complete, collect the bacteriophage particles as described in Steps 3 and 4 of the following alternative protocol.

ALTERNATIVE PROTOCOL: PURIFICATION OF BACTERIOPHAGE λ PARTICLES BY ISOPYCNIC CENTRIFUGATION THROUGH CSCL EQUILIBRIUM GRADIENTS

When dealing with small-scale preparations of bacteriophage λ (infected cultures of 1 liter or less), the CsCl step gradient (Protocol 8) can be omitted and replaced by a single round of equilibrium centrifugation. The resulting preparation of bacteriophage particles is essentially free of contaminating bacterial nucleic acids.

Additional Materials

CsCl (solid)

SM containing CsCl

Use a high quality (molecular biology grade) of solid CsCl to prepare a solution of 0.75 g/ml by adding solid CsCl to SM. Store the solution at room temperature.

Method

1. Measure the volume of the bacteriophage suspension and add 0.75 g of solid CsCl per ml of bacteriophage suspension. Mix the suspension gently to dissolve the CsCl.

2. Transfer the bacteriophage suspension to an ultracentrifuge tube that fits a Beckman Ti50 or SW50.1 rotor (or equivalent). Fill the tube with SM containing 0.75 g/ml CsCl and centrifuge it at 150,000*g* (41,000 rpm in a Beckman Ti50 rotor) for 24 hours at 4°C or at 160,000*g* (36,000 rpm in a Beckman SW50.1 rotor) for 24 hours at 4°C.

3. Collect the bacteriophage particles by puncturing the side of the tube as follows.

    a. Carefully wipe the outside of the tube with ethanol to remove any grease or oil, and then attach a piece of Scotch Tape to the outside of the tube, level with the band of bacteriophage particles.

    The tape acts as a seal to prevent leakage around the needle.

    b. Use a 21-gauge hypodermic needle (syringe-barrel optional) to puncture the tube through the tape and collect the band of bacteriophage particles (please see Figure 2-11).

    Keep fingers away from the path of the needle in case the needle penetrates through the tube. Take care not to contaminate the bacteriophage particles with material from other bands that are visible in the gradient. These bands contain various types of bacterial debris and unassembled bacteriophage components.

4. Store the bacteriophage suspension at 4°C in the CsCl solution in a tightly capped tube.

    Bacteriophage λ DNA may now be extracted from the suspension as described in Protocol 11.

Protocol 9

Purification of Bacteriophage λ Particles by Centrifugation through a Glycerol Step Gradient

THIS MODIFICATION OF THE YAMAMOTO PURIFICATION PROCEDURE (described in Protocol 8) involves the use of a glycerol step gradient in place of the two CsCl centrifugation runs (Vande Woude et al. 1979). Although the use of glycerol gradients to purify bacteriophage λ is a quicker procedure, it does not yield bacteriophage of high purity and should not be used to prepare storage stocks.

    This protocol is suitable for preparing bacteriophage particles that will yield DNA to be used for subcloning, for making bacteriophage stocks, or for preparing bacteriophage λ arms.

MATERIALS

Buffers and Solutions

Please see Appendix 1 for components of stock solutions, buffers, and reagents. Dilute stock solutions to the appropriate concentrations.

EDTA (0.5 M, pH 8.0)
Glycerol (5% and 40% v/v) in SM
SM

Enzymes and Buffers

Pancreatic DNase I (1 mg/ml)
Pancreatic RNase in TE (1 mg/ml, pH 7.6)

Centrifuges and Rotors

Beckman SW41 or SW28 rotor or equivalent, with clear centrifuge tubes (e.g., Beckman Ultra-Clear tubes)

Vectors and Bacterial Strains

Suspension of bacteriophage λ particles
Prepared as described in Protocol 6 of this chapter.

METHOD

1. Prepare a glycerol step gradient in a Beckman SW41 polycarbonate tube (or its equivalent; one tube is needed for each 5 ml of bacteriophage suspension):

   a. Pipette 3 ml of a solution consisting of 40% glycerol in SM into the bottom of the tube.

   b. Carefully layer 4 ml of a solution consisting of 5% glycerol in SM on top of the 40% glycerol solution.

   c. Carefully layer the bacteriophage suspension on top of the 5% glycerol layer. Fill the tube with SM.

2. Centrifuge the step gradient at 151,000*g* (35,000 rpm in a Beckman SW41 or SW28 rotor) for 60 minutes at 4°C.

3. Discard the supernatant, and resuspend the bacteriophage pellet in 1 ml of SM per liter of original culture.

4. Add pancreatic DNase I and RNase to final concentrations of 5 μg/ml and 1 μg/ml, respectively. Incubate the reaction mixture for 30 minutes at 37°C.

5. Add EDTA from a 0.5 M stock solution (pH 8.0) to a final concentration of 20 mM.

   Bacteriophage λ DNA may now be extracted from the suspension as described in Protocol 11.

Protocol 10

Purification of Bacteriophage λ Particles by Pelleting/Centrifugation

I F THE PURPOSE OF PURIFYING BACTERIOPHAGE PARTICLES is to obtain segments of foreign DNA for subsequent subcloning or to prepare bacteriophage λ arms, then the CsCl step gradient and equilibrium gradient (Protocol 8) can be replaced with a centrifugation step that deposits the bacteriophage particles on the bottom of the centrifuge tube. Preparations obtained in this manner are not as clean as those obtained by equilibrium gradient centrifugation or centrifugation through glycerol (Protocol 9), but they suffice for DNA extraction.

MATERIALS

Buffers and Solutions

Please see Appendix 1 for components of stock solutions, buffers, and reagents. Dilute stock solutions to the appropriate concentrations.

SM

Centrifuges and Rotors

Beckman SW28 rotor or equivalent

Vectors and Bacterial Strains

Suspension of bacteriophage λ particles
Prepared as described in Protocol 6 of this chapter.

METHOD

1. Transfer the bacteriophage suspension into a tube for use in a Beckman SW28 rotor (or equivalent).

2. Collect the bacteriophage particles by centrifugation at 110,000g (25,000 rpm in a Beckman SW28 rotor) for 2 hours at 4ºC.

3. Carefully pour off and discard the supernatant.

   A glassy pellet of bacteriophage particles should be visible on the bottom of the tube.

4. Add 1–2 ml of SM to the pellet, and store it overnight at 4°C, preferably on a slowly rocking platform.

5. The following morning, pipette the solution gently up and down to ensure that all of the bacteriophage particles have been resuspended.

   Bacteriophage λ DNA may now be extracted from the suspension as described in Protocol 11.

Protocol 11

Extraction of Bacteriophage λ DNA from Large-scale Cultures Using Proteinase K and SDS

Dna is best isolated from large-scale preparations of bacteriophage λ by digesting the viral coat proteins with a powerful protease such as proteinase K, followed by extraction with phenol:chloroform. This procedure also may be adapted for use with smaller (50–100 ml) preparations, as noted in the protocol. Protocol 12 describes an alternative, more rapid method to isolate viral DNA from bacteriophage particles purified by isopycnic centrifugation through CsCl gradients.

When purifying bacteriophage λ DNA, keep in mind that vector and recombinant genomes range between 43 kb and 53 kb in length and are thus susceptible to shearing. Take care to avoid creating shearing forces capable of breaking the DNA during extraction (please see the information panel on MINIMIZING DAMAGE TO LARGE DNA MOLECULES).

MATERIALS

CAUTION: Please see Appendix 12 for appropriate handling of materials marked with <!>.

Buffers and Solutions

Please see Appendix 1 for components of stock solutions, buffers, and reagents. Dilute stock solutions to the appropriate concentrations.

Chloroform <!>
Dialysis buffer
> *10 mM NaCl*
> *50 mM Tris-Cl (pH 8.0)*
> *10 mM MgCl$_2$*
> Two containers of dialysis buffer are required, each containing 1000 times the volume of the bacteriophage solution. Store at room temperature until needed.

EDTA (0.5 M, pH 8.0)
Ethanol
Phenol <!>
Phenol:chloroform (1:1, v/v) <!>
SDS (10% w/v)
Sodium acetate (3 M, pH 7.0)
TE (pH 7.6 and pH 8.0)

Enzymes and Buffers

Proteinase K
  Please see the entry on Proteinase K in Appendix 4.
Restriction endonucleases

Gels

Agarose gel (0.7%) cast in 0.5× TBE, containing 0.5 µg/ml ethidium bromide <!>

Centrifuges and Rotors

Sorvall SS-34 rotor or equivalent

Special Equipment

Borosilicate Pasteur pipette (sealed) or Shepherd's crook
Dialysis tubing, boiled
  For preparation of dialysis tubing for use with DNA, please see Appendix 8.
Water bath preset to 56°C

Vectors and Bacterial Strains

Bacteriophage λ particles in CsCl suspension
  Purify as described in Protocol 8, 9, or 10 of this chapter.

METHOD

Dialysis of Bacteriophage Suspension

1. Transfer the prepared bacteriophage suspension to a section of dialysis tubing sealed at one end with a knot or a plastic closure. Close the other end of the dialysis tube. Place the sealed tube in a flask containing a 1000-fold volume excess of dialysis buffer and a magnetic stir bar. Dialyze the bacteriophage suspension for 1 hour at room temperature with slow stirring.

   The purpose of this step is to reduce the concentration of CsCl in the preparation. Beautiful Schlieren patterns caused by the rapid escape of cesium ions from the dialysis tube will appear when the dialysis sac is dunked into the buffer.

2. Transfer the dialysis tube to a fresh flask of buffer and dialyze the bacteriophage suspension for an additional hour.

3. Transfer the bacteriophage suspension into a polypropylene centrifuge tube.

   The tube should not be more than one-third full.

4. To the dialyzed bacteriophage suspension, add 0.5 M EDTA (pH 8.0) to a final concentration of 20 mM.

Extraction of Bacteriophage Particles

5. To the suspension, add proteinase K to a final concentration of 50 µg/ml.

6. Add SDS to a final concentration of 0.5%, and mix the solution by gently inverting the tube several times.

    The solution will change rapidly in appearance from a bluish suspension of bacteriophage particles to a clear solution containing viral DNA and the products of proteolysis of the viral coat proteins.

7. Incubate the digestion mixture for 1 hour at 56°C and then cool the mixture to room temperature.

8. Add an equal volume of equilibrated phenol to the digestion mixture, and mix the organic and aqueous phases by gently inverting the tube several times until a complete emulsion has formed.

9. Separate the phases by centrifugation at 3000*g* (5000 rpm in a Sorvall SS-34 rotor) for 5 minutes at room temperature. Use a wide-bore pipette to transfer the aqueous phase to a clean tube (please see the information panel on MINIMIZING DAMAGE TO LARGE DNA MOLECULES).

10. Extract the aqueous phase once with a 1:1 mixture of equilibrated phenol and chloroform.

11. Recover the aqueous phase as described above (Step 9), and repeat the extraction with an equal volume of chloroform. For large-scale preparations, proceed to Step 12.

FOR SMALLER-SCALE QUANTITIES (BACTERIOPHAGE FROM 50- TO 100-ML CULTURES)

a. Recover the bacteriophage DNA by standard ethanol precipitation.

b. Store the solution for 30 minutes at room temperature.

    The bacteriophage λ DNA can usually be seen as a threadlike precipitate after addition of ethanol, which can be plucked from the solution on the outside of a sealed tip of a borosilicate Pasteur pipette or Shepherd's crook.

c. Redissolve the DNA in an appropriate volume of TE (pH 7.6), and proceed to Step 14.

Removal of CsCl

12. Transfer the aqueous phase to a dialysis sac.

13. Dialyze the preparation of bacteriophage DNA overnight at 4°C against three changes of a 1000-fold volume of TE (pH 8.0).

14. Measure the absorbance of the solution at 260 nm and calculate the concentration of the DNA.

    1 OD_{260} = 50 μg/ml of double-stranded DNA. A single particle of bacteriophage contains ~5 x 10^{-11} μg of DNA. The yield of bacteriophage DNA usually ranges from 500 μg to several mg per liter, depending on the titer of the bacteriophage in the lysed culture.

15. Check the integrity of the DNA by analyzing aliquots (0.5 μg) that are undigested or have been cleaved by appropriate restriction enzyme(s). Analyze the DNAs by electrophoresis through a 0.7% agarose gel, using markers of an appropriate size.

16. Store the stock of bacteriophage DNA at 4°C.

Protocol 12

Extraction of Bacteriophage λ DNA from Large-scale Cultures Using Formamide

FㅇRMAMIDE MAY BE USED INSTEAD OF SDS/PROTEINASE K (please see Protocol 11) to remove the bacteriophage coats from purified particles. Although not as effective, this method is somewhat quicker to perform than the preceding method. Please see the information panel on MINIMIZING DAMAGE TO LARGE DNA MOLECULES.

MATERIALS

CAUTION: Please see Appendix 12 for appropriate handling of materials marked with <!>.

Buffers and Solutions

Please see Appendix 1 for components of stock solutions, buffers, and reagents. Dilute stock solutions to the appropriate concentrations.

EDTA (0.5 M, pH 8.0)
Ethanol
Formamide, deionized <!>
NaCl (5 M)
TE (pH 8.0)
Tris-Cl (2 M, pH 8.5)

Enzymes and Buffers

Restriction endonucleases

Gels

Agarose gel (0.7%) cast in 0.5x TBE, containing 0.5 µg/ml ethidium bromide <!>

Special Equipment

Borosilicate Pasteur pipette (sealed) or Shepherd's crook

Vectors and Bacterial Strains

Bacteriophage λ particles
Purify as described in Protocol 9 or 10 of this chapter.

METHOD

1. If necessary, remove CsCl from the preparation of bacteriophage particles as described in Steps 1–4 of Protocol 11.

2. Measure the volume of the preparation of bacteriophage particles.

3. Add 0.1 volume of 2 M Tris (pH 8.5), 0.05 volume of 0.5 M EDTA (pH 8.0), and 1 volume of deionized formamide. Incubate the solution for 30 minutes at 37°C.

   During incubation, the milky suspension of bacteriophage particles clears to a transparent solution.

4. Precipitate the bacteriophage λ DNA by adding 1 volume (equal to the final volume in Step 3) of H_2O and 6 volumes (each equal to the final volume in Step 3) of ethanol.

5. Hook the precipitate of bacteriophage λ DNA onto the end of a sealed borosilicate Pasteur pipette or Shepherd's crook and transfer it to microfuge tube containing 70% ethanol.

6. Collect the DNA pellet by brief centrifugation (10 seconds) in a microfuge.

   Avoid lengthy centrifugation as this compacts the DNA, making it difficult to dissolve.

7. Discard the supernatant and store the open tube on the bench for a few minutes to allow the ethanol to evaporate. Redissolve the damp pellet of DNA in 300 μl of TE by tapping on the side of the tube. Try to avoid vortexing.

   This process can be lengthy. If the DNA proves difficult to dissolve, incubate the tube for 15 minutes at 50°C.

8. Reprecipitate the DNA by adding 6 μl of 5 M NaCl and 750 μl of ethanol. Collect the precipitated DNA and redissolve it as described in Steps 6 and 7.

9. Check the integrity of the DNA by analyzing aliquots (0.5 μg) that are undigested or have been cleaved by appropriate restriction enzyme(s). Analyze the DNAs by electrophoresis through a 0.7% agarose gel using markers of an appropriate size.

10. Store the stock of bacteriophage DNA at 4°C.

Protocol 13

Preparation of Bacteriophage λ DNA Cleaved with a Single Restriction Enzyme for Use as a Cloning Vector

IN SOME CASES, BACTERIOPHAGE λ DNA CAN BE PREPARED for cloning by simple digestion with restriction enzymes. This option is viable only when using vectors that allow genetic selection of recombinant bacteriophages carrying sequences of foreign DNA (e.g., the EMBL series, λ2001, λDASH, λZAP, and λgt10). In such cases, it is not necessary to take steps to minimize the formation of nonrecombinant bacteriophages. However, when genetic selection of recombinant bacteriophages is not possible or is inefficient, biochemical and physical methods are used to reduce the number of "empty" vectors in the recombinant population. These methods include physical separation of the stuffer fragment from the vector arms, treatment of the digested vector DNA with alkaline phosphatase to reduce the possibility of regenerating empty vector genomes by ligation of left and right arms, and digestion of vectors with combinations of restriction enzymes that will destroy the ability of the stuffer fragment to reinsert into the arms.

This protocol describes the preparation and characterization of bacteriophage λ vector DNA that is cleaved with a single restriction enzyme. Subsequent protocols describe the preparation of DNA cleaved with two restriction enzymes (Protocol 14) and treatment of vector DNA with alkaline phosphatase (Protocol 15).

MATERIALS

CAUTION: Please see Appendix 12 for appropriate handling of materials marked with <!>.

Buffers and Solutions

Please see Appendix 1 for components of stock solutions, buffers, and reagents. Dilute stock solutions to the appropriate concentrations.

ATP (10 mM)
   Omit ATP from Step 7 if the ligation buffer contains ATP.
Chloroform <!>
EDTA (0.5 M, pH 8.0)
Ethanol
Phenol:chloroform (1:1, v/v) <!>

Sodium acetate (3 M, pH 7.0)

It is important to use a solution of sodium acetate solution that has been equilibrated to pH 7.0 rather than the more common pH 5.3. EDTA, which is used to remove divalent cations from the restriction buffer after digestion, precipitates from solution at pH 5.3 when present at concentrations in excess of 5–10 mM.

Sucrose gel-loading buffer

Please see Table 5-4 in Chapter 5, Protocol 1.

TE (pH 7.6 and pH 8.0)

Enzymes and Buffers

Bacteriophage T4 DNA ligase
Restriction endonucleases with appropriate buffers

Gels

Agarose gel (0.7%) cast in 0.5x TBE, containing 0.5 μg/ml ethidium bromide <!>

Nucleic Acids and Oligonucleotides

Bacteriophage λ DNA

Prepared as described in Protocol 11 or 12 of this chapter.

Special Equipment

Water bath preset to 68°C

Additional Reagents

Step 7 (part e) of this protocol requires the reagents listed in Protocol 1 of this chapter.

Vectors and Bacterial Strains

Bacteriophage λ packaging mixtures

Packaging mixtures may be purchased in a kit form from any of several commercial manufacturers (e.g., Stratagene, Promega, and Life Technologies). Please see the information panel on **IN VITRO PACKAGING**.

METHOD

1. Mix 25–50 μg of bacteriophage λ DNA with TE (pH 8.0) to give a final volume of 170 μl.

2. Add 20 μl of the appropriate 10x restriction enzyme buffer. Remove two aliquots, each containing 0.2 μg of undigested bacteriophage λ DNA. Store the aliquots of undigested DNA on ice.

   These aliquots of undigested DNA will be used as controls during the agarose gel electrophoresis (Steps 4 and 7).

3. Add a threefold excess (75–150 units) of the appropriate restriction enzyme and incubate the digestion mixture for 1 hour at the temperature recommended by the manufacturer.

4. Cool the reaction to 0ºC on ice. Remove another aliquot (0.2 μg). Incubate this aliquot and one of the two aliquots of undigested DNA (Step 2 above) for 10 minutes at 68ºC to disrupt the cohesive termini of the bacteriophage DNA. Add a small amount (10 μl) of sucrose gel-loading buffer and immediately load the samples onto an 0.7% agarose gel.

   > If the restriction enzyme digestion is complete, then no DNA will migrate at the position of the undigested control bands. Instead, two or more (depending on the number of cleavage sites in the vector) smaller DNA fragments will be seen. Carefully examine the number and yield of these smaller fragments to ensure that no partial digestion products are present.

   > This step is not as easy as it sounds. The left and right arms of bacteriophage λ DNA carry complementary termini 12 bases in length that can reanneal with one another. The resulting hydrogen-bonded DNA species can be easily confused with uncleaved bacteriophage λ DNA. For this reason, it is important to load and run the gel immediately after the DNA samples have been removed from the 68ºC water bath.

   > If digestion is incomplete, warm the reaction to the appropriate temperature, add more restriction enzyme (50–100 units), and continue the incubation at the optimal temperature recommended by the manufacturer.

5. When digestion is complete, add 0.5 M EDTA (pH 8.0) to a final concentration of 5 mM, and extract the digestion mixture once with phenol:chloroform and once with chloroform.

6. Recover the DNA from the aqueous phase by ethanol precipitation in the presence of 0.3 M sodium acetate (pH 7.0). Collect the precipitate by centrifuging at maximum speed for 2 minutes at 4ºC in a microfuge. Wash the pellet in 70% ethanol and redissolve the DNA in 100 μl of TE (pH 7.6). Determine the concentration by measuring absorbance at 260 nm.

7. Remove an aliquot of DNA (0.5 μg), and test for its ability to be ligated as follows:

   a. Adjust the volume of the DNA solution to 17 μl with H₂O.

   b. Add 2 μl of 10x ligation buffer and, if necessary, 1 μl of 10 mM ATP.

      > Some commercial ligase buffers contain ATP. When using such buffers, the addition of ATP is no longer required.

   c. Remove 5 μl of the mixture prepared in Step b and store on ice.

   d. Add 0.2–0.5 Weiss unit of bacteriophage T4 DNA ligase to the remainder of the mixture (Step b), and incubate the reaction for 2 hours at 16ºC.

   e. Use a commercially available bacteriophage λ packaging reaction (please see the information panel on **IN VITRO PACKAGING**) to package 0.1 μg of the ligated and unligated samples and 0.1 μg of the undigested vector DNA from Step 2. Determine the titer (pfu/ml) of each packaged reaction as described in Protocol 1.

      > The background of plaques obtained after cleavage of bacteriophage λ vectors at a single restriction site is sometimes unacceptably high because of the accumulation of mutants in the original population that are resistant to cleavage with the restriction enzyme. This problem can be reduced if the bacteriophage λ vector is plaque-purified frequently.

      > The packaging efficiency of the digested vector should increase by nearly three orders of magnitude after ligation. The packaging efficiency of the ligated sample should be ~10% of that of undigested vector DNA.

Protocol 14

Preparation of Bacteriophage λ DNA Cleaved with Two Restriction Enzymes for Use as a Cloning Vector

Rᴇᴘʟᴀᴄᴇᴍᴇɴᴛ ᴠᴇᴄᴛᴏʀs, sᴜᴄʜ ᴀs λ2001, λDASH, ᴛʜᴇ EMBL series, and Charon 34, 35, and 40, contain a series of restriction sites, arranged in opposite orientations, at each end of the central stuffer fragment (Frischauf et al. 1983). In EMBL3A, for example, the order of restriction sites in the left polycloning site is *Sal*I-*Bam*HI-*Eco*RI and the order in the right polycloning site is *Eco*RI-

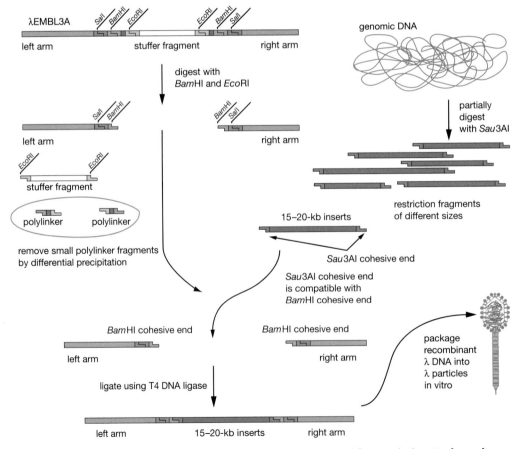

FIGURE 2-12 **Cleaving a Bacteriophage λ Replacement Vector with Restriction Endonucleases**

Please see text for details.

*Bam*HI-*Sal*I. Digestion of such a vector with both *Bam*HI and *Eco*RI yields left and right arms that carry *Bam*HI termini, a stuffer fragment carrying *Eco*RI termini, and short segments of the polycloning sites carrying *Eco*RI and *Bam*HI termini (please see Figure 2-12). These segments can easily be removed by differential precipitation with isopropanol or by spun column centrifugation (please see Appendix 8).

The arms can be efficiently ligated to target DNAs that carry termini compatible with *Bam*HI but are unable to ligate to *Eco*RI termini of the stuffer fragment. By suppressing ligation to the stuffer fragment in this way, the proportion of nonrecombinant bacteriophages in cDNA and genomic libraries can be decreased by two orders of magnitude. When this "biochemical selection" is used in combination with a genetic selection (e.g., Spi), the proportion of nonre-combinant bacteriophages can be reduced by a further 100-fold. Hence, with many replacement vectors, there is no need to remove the stuffer fragment or to purify the left and right arms by gel electrophoresis or sucrose density centrifugation.

MATERIALS

CAUTION: Please see Appendix 12 for appropriate handling of materials marked with <!>.

Buffers and Solutions

Please see Appendix 1 for components of stock solutions, buffers, and reagents. Dilute stock solutions to the appropriate concentrations.

ATP (10 mM)
Omit ATP from Step 10 if the ligation buffer contains ATP.

Chloroform <!>

Ethanol

Phenol:chloroform (1:1, v/v) <!>

Sodium acetate (3 M, pH 5.2)

Sucrose gel-loading buffer
Please see Table 5-4 in Chapter 5, Protocol 1.

TE (pH 7.6 and pH 8.0)

Enzymes and Buffers

Bacteriophage T4 DNA ligase

Restriction endonucleases

Gels

Agarose gel (0.7%) cast in 0.5x TBE, containing 0.5 μg/ml ethidium bromide <!>

Nucleic Acids and Oligonucleotides

Bacteriophage λ (replacement vector) DNA
Prepared as described in Protocol 11 or 12 of this chapter.

Special Equipment

Water bath preset to 68°C

Additional Reagents

Step 10 (part e) of this protocol requires the reagents listed in Protocol 1 of this chapter.

Vectors and Bacterial Strains

Bacteriophage λ packaging mixtures
Packaging mixtures may be purchased in kit form from any of several commercial manufacturers (e.g., Stratagene, Promega, Epicenter Technologies, and Life Technologies). Please see the information panel on **IN VITRO PACKAGING**.

METHOD

1. Mix 25–50 µg of bacteriophage λ DNA purified from a replacement vector with TE (pH 8.0) to give a final volume of 170 µl.

2. Add 20 µl of one of the two appropriate 10x restriction enzyme buffers. Remove two aliquots, each containing 0.2 µg of undigested bacteriophage λ DNA. Store the aliquots of undigested DNA on ice.

   These aliquots of undigested DNA will be used as controls during the agarose gel electrophoresis in Step 4 and in the test ligation in Step 10.

3. Add a fourfold excess (100–200 units) of one of the two appropriate restriction enzymes and incubate the digestion mixture for 4 hours at the temperature recommended by the manufacturer.

4. Cool the reaction to 0°C on ice. Remove two aliquots (0.2 µg). Incubate one of these aliquots (save the other for analysis in Step 10 below) and one of the two aliquots of undigested DNA (Step 2 above) for 10 minutes at 68°C to disrupt the cohesive termini of the bacteriophage DNA. Add a small amount (~10 µl) of sucrose gel-loading buffer and and *immediately* electrophorese the samples through an 0.7% agarose gel.

   If the restriction enzyme digestion is complete, no DNA will migrate at the position of the undigested control bands. Instead, three or more (depending on the number of cleavage sites in the vector) smaller DNA fragments will be seen. The number and yield of these smaller fragments should be examined carefully to ensure that no partial digestion products are present.

5. Purify the DNA by extracting twice with phenol:chloroform and once with chloroform.

6. Recover the DNA by standard ethanol precipitation.

The quality of the library and the efficiency of cloning target DNAs depends on the effectiveness of digestion with restriction enzymes in Steps 3 and 7. It is therefore worth investing some effort to make sure that digestion has been complete. The efficiency of digestion can be monitored in several ways. The best of these involves setting up a series of test reactions (Step 10 below) to compare the efficiency of packaging digested and undigested vector DNAs, before and after ligation. If the number of nonrecombinant bacteriophages is unacceptably high (>10^4 pfu/µg of cleaved vector DNA), then the digestion and analysis should be repeated.

Alternatively, the biochemical methods outlined below can be used to measure the efficiency of digestion. However, these surrogate assays are less satisfactory because they do not directly measure the ability of the DNA preparation to perform as a vector.

- A small fraction of the product of the first digestion can be end-labeled (please see Chapter 9, Protocol 10 or 11); the radiolabel can then be used to monitor digestion by the second restriction enzyme. If this method is used, it is important to ligate the cohesive termini of the vector DNA before digestion with the first restriction enzyme (please see Protocol 15). This ligation prevents incorporation of significant amounts of radiolabel into the cohesive termini. After end-labeling, add a small quantity of the radioactive DNA (0.01–0.1 µg) to the bulk of the vector preparation. Digestion with the second restriction enzyme should result in quantitative movement of the label from the large stuffer fragment and arms into the small polycloning site; this movement can be readily monitored by gel electrophoresis and autoradiography or phosphorimaging.
- PCRs can be set up using sets of primers that lie to the left and right of the target restriction sites (please see Chapter 8, Protocol 1). Cleavage of the restriction sites will eliminate (or greatly reduce) the PCR products. To obtain an estimate of the efficiency of cleavage, it is usually necessary to compare the amount of amplified products generated in a series of PCRs containing different quantities of undigested vector DNA and digested vector DNA.

7. Redissolve the DNA in TE (pH 8.0) at a concentration of 250 µg/ml. Add the appropriate 10x restriction buffer and digest the DNA with the second restriction enzyme. Use a fourfold excess of enzyme and incubate the reaction for 4 hours.

8. Purify the DNA by extracting twice with phenol:chloroform and once with chloroform. Recover the DNA by standard ethanol precipitation.

   Short fragments carrying the polycloning sites can be removed by isopropanol precipitation by spin column chromatography (Appendix 8).

9. Redissolve the DNA in TE (pH 7.6) at a concentration of 300–500 µg/ml. Store an aliquot (0.2 µg) at –20ºC.

10. To determine the effectiveness of the digestion procedure, set up trial ligation reactions using 0.2 µg of the vector digested with only the first enzyme (the aliquot set aside at Step 4 above) and 0.2 µg of the final preparation (Step 9). Package equivalent amounts of DNA (0.1 µg) from each ligation mixture and titrate the infectivity of the resulting bacteriophage particles.

    a. Adjust the volumes of the two DNA solutions to 17 µl with H_2O.

    b. Add to each sample 2 µl of 10x ligation buffer and, if necessary, 1 µl of 10 mM ATP.

       Omit ATP if using a commercial ligase buffer that contains ATP.

    c. Remove 10-µl aliquots of each of the mixtures prepared in Step b and store the aliquots on ice.

    d. Add 0.2–0.5 Weiss units of bacteriophage T4 DNA ligase to the remainder of the mixtures (Step b) and incubate the reactions for 2 hours at 16ºC.

    e. Use a commercial bacteriophage λ packaging reaction (please see the infomation panel on **IN VITRO PACKAGING**) to package 0.1 µg of the ligated and unligated samples and 0.1 µg of the undigested vector DNA from Step 2. Determine the titer (pfu/ml) of each packaged reaction as described in Protocol 1.

       The background of plaques obtained after cleavage of bacteriophage λ vectors at a restriction site is sometimes unacceptably high because of the accumulation of mutants in the original population that cannot be cleaved with the restriction enzyme. This problem can be reduced if the bacteriophage λ vector is plaque-purified frequently.

       The packaging efficiency of the vector digested with only one enzyme should increase by nearly three orders of magnitude after ligation. The packaging efficiency of the ligated sample should be ~10% of that of undigested vector DNA.

       The efficiency of packaging of the doubly digested vector should be two to three orders of magnitude *less* than that of the vector DNA digested with only one restriction enzyme.

Protocol 15

Alkaline Phosphatase Treatment of Bacteriophage λ Vector DNA

Removal of the 5′-phosphate groups from the internal termini of bacteriophage λ arms can effectively prevent self-ligation and reduce the background of nonrecombinant bacteriophages. This method is used to suppress the background of nonrecombinants when using insertion vectors that contain a single site for cloning (e.g., λgt10, λgt11, and λORF8) or when using an insertion vector with a polycloning site (e.g., λgt18–23 and λZAP) and cutting with a single enzyme.

The procedure also is effective when ligation to a stuffer fragment cannot be suppressed by physical procedures (please see this protocol and Protocols 13 and 14). It is very important that the cohesive (*cos*) termini of the vector be reannealed and ligated together *before* treatment with alkaline phosphatase. Unless the *cos* termini are protected in this way, the ability of the vector arms to form concatemers with target DNAs will be greatly reduced or eliminated, with disastrous effects on the efficiency of packaging.

MATERIALS

CAUTION: Please see Appendix 12 for appropriate handling of materials marked with <!>.

Buffers and Solutions

Please see Appendix 1 for components of stock solutions, buffers, and reagents.
Dilute stock solutions to the appropriate concentrations.

λ Annealing buffer
> 100 mM Tris-Cl (pH 7.6)
> 10 mM MgCl$_2$

ATP (10 mM)
> Omit ATP from Step 2 if the ligation buffer contains ATP.

Chloroform <!>

EDTA (0.5 M, pH 8.0)

Ethanol

Phenol:chloroform (1:1, v/v) <!>

SDS (10% w/v)

Sodium acetate (3 M, pH 5.2 and pH 7.0)
> It is important to use a sodium acetate solution equilibrated to pH 7.0 at Step 8 in this protocol, rather than the more common pH 5.3 solution. EDTA, which is used to inactivate the restriction enzyme after digestion, precipitates from solution at pH 5.3 when present at concentrations in excess of 5–10 mM.

TE (pH 7.6 and pH 8.0)

Tris-Cl (10 mM, pH 8.3)

Enzymes and Buffers

Bacteriophage T4 DNA ligase

Calf intestinal alkaline phosphatase

> Calf intestinal alkaline phosphatase (CIP) may be purchased as an aqueous solution; ~0.01 unit of CIP will remove the terminal phosphates from 1 pmole of 5′ termini of bacteriophage λ DNA (1 pmole of 5′ termini of a 40-kb linear DNA is 16 μg).
>
> Alkaline phosphatase enzymes from bacterial or crustacean sources can be substituted for CIP. For a discussion on the relative merits of these enzymes, please see Chapter 9, Protocol 13.

10x Dephosphorylation buffer

> 100 mM Tris-Cl (pH 8.3)
> 10 mM $ZnCl_2$
> 10 mM $MgCl_2$

Proteinase K

> Please see the entry on Proteinase K in Appendix 4.

Restriction endonucleases

Nucleic Acids and Oligonucleotides

Bacteriophage λ DNA

> Prepared as described in Protocol 11 or 12 of this chapter.

Special Equipment

Dog toe-nail clippers or Wide-bore pipette tips

Water baths preset to 16ºC, 42ºC, 56ºC, and 68ºC

Additional Reagents

Step 13 of this protocol requires the reagents listed in Protocols 1 and 14 of this chapter.

Vectors and Bacterial Strains

Bacteriophage λ packaging mixtures

> Packaging mixtures may be purchased in kit form from any of several commercial manufacturers (e.g., Stratagene, Promega, and Life Technologies). For ligation conditions, please see the information panel on **IN VITRO PACKAGING**.

METHOD

1. Dissolve 50–60 μg of DNA of the appropriate bacteriophage λ vector in a final volume of 150 μl of λ annealing buffer. Incubate the DNA for 1 hour at 42ºC to allow the ends of the viral DNA containing the *cos* sites to anneal.

2. Add 20 μl of 10x ligase buffer, 20 μl of 10 mM ATP (if necessary), and 0.2–0.5 Weiss unit of bacteriophage T4 DNA ligase/μg of DNA. Incubate the reaction for 1–2 hours at 16ºC.

   > Omit ATP if using a commercial ligase buffer that contains ATP.

3. Extract the ligation reaction with phenol:chloroform.

   > During ligation, the λ DNA will form closed circles and long concatemers and become sensitive to shearing (please see the information panel on **MINIMIZING DAMAGE TO LARGE DNA MOLECULES**). Handle the ligated DNA carefully! Do not vortex. Carry out the phenol:chloroform extraction by gently inverting the tube to elicit emulsion formation.

4. Separate the organic and aqueous phases by centrifugation for 1 minute at room temperature in a microfuge. Remove the aqueous phase containing the viral DNA to a new tube using an automatic pipetting device equipped with a disposable tip that has been snipped with dog toe-nail clippers to increase the diameter of the hole.

5. Recover the DNA by standard ethanol precipitation. Rinse the pellet with 1 ml of 70% ethanol and recentrifuge for 2 minutes. Remove the 70% ethanol supernatant and store the open tube on the bench to allow the ethanol to evaporate. Redissolve the damp pellet of DNA in 150 μl of TE (pH 8.0).

   Check that the ligation of *cos* termini has succeeded by heating an aliquot (0.2 μg) of the ligated DNA for 5 minutes at 68ºC in TE. Chill the DNA in ice water and then electrophorese the DNA immediately through a 0.6% agarose gel. As controls, use (i) bacteriophage λ DNA that has been heated but not ligated and (ii) bacteriophage λ DNA that has been ligated but not heated.

   Ligation should convert the bacteriophage λ DNA to closed circular and concatenated forms that show no change in migration after heating. The unligated, heated control DNA should migrate as a linear molecule, ~50 kb in length.

6. Digest the ligated DNA with one or more restriction enzymes as described in Protocol 13 or 14.

7. Repeat Steps 3 and 4 (above).

8. Add 0.1 volume of 3 M sodium acetate (pH 7.0) and 2 volumes of ethanol. Recover the precipitate of DNA by centrifugation for 10 minutes at 4ºC in a microfuge. Rinse the pellet with 1 ml of 70% ethanol and recentrifuge for 2 minutes. Remove the 70% ethanol supernatant and store the open tube on the bench to allow the ethanol to evaporate.

9. Dissolve the digested and ethanol-precipitated DNA at a concentration of 100 μg/ml in 10 mM Tris-Cl (pH 8.3), and store an aliquot (0.2 μg) on ice. Treat the remainder of the DNA with an excess of CIP for 1 hour at 37ºC as follows:

   a. Add 0.1 volume of 10x dephosphorylation buffer and 0.01 unit of CIP for every 10 μg of bacteriophage λ DNA.

   b. Mix, and incubate the reaction for 30 minutes at 37ºC. Add a second aliquot of CIP and continue incubation for an additional 30 minutes.

      Blunt and recessed 5′ termini are poor substrates for CIP. To improve the efficiency of dephosphorylation of termini of this type, carry out the second half of the incubation at 55ºC. At this temperature, the ends of double-stranded DNA molecules tend to breathe and fray, thereby allowing the enzyme to access recessed 5′-phosphate groups.

10. Add SDS and EDTA (pH 8.0) to final concentrations of 0.5% and 5 mM, respectively. Mix the solution by gentle vortexing and add proteinase K to a final concentration of 100 μg/ml. Incubate the mixture for 30 minutes at 56ºC.

    Proteinase K is used to digest CIP, which must be completely removed if the subsequent ligation reactions are to work efficiently. Alternatively, CIP (or shrimp alkaline phosphatase, please see Chapter 9, Protocol 13) can be inactivated by heating the reaction (at the end of Step 9) to 65ºC for 1 hour in the presence of 5 mM EDTA and then extracting the reaction mixture once with phenol:chloroform.

11. Cool the reaction mixture to room temperature, and purify the bacteriophage λ DNA by extracting once with phenol:chloroform and once with chloroform. Recover the DNA by ethanol precipitation in the presence of 0.3 M sodium acetate (pH 7.0).

12. Dissolve the DNA in TE (pH 7.6) at a concentration of 300–500 μg/ml. Store the dephosphorylated DNA at –20ºC in aliquots of 1–5 μg.

13. Measure the efficiency of dephosphorylation by ligating a portion (0.2 μg) of the digested vector before and after treatment with CIP (for ligation conditions, please see Protocol 13). Package the DNA into bacteriophage particles (for packaging conditions, please see Protocol 14), and titrate the infectivity.

    Phosphatase treatment should reduce ligation and the efficiency of packaging of the arms by two to three orders of magnitude.

Protocol 16

Purification of Bacteriophage λ Arms: Centrifugation through Sucrose Density Gradients

Unlike insertion vectors, the genomes of replacement vectors contain a central stuffer segment that must be removed to accommodate segments of foreign DNA. This process is generally referred to as "preparation of λ arms" and involves restriction endonuclease digestion of λ DNA to separate the two arms from the stuffer fragment, followed by purification of the arms. Two methods are commonly used to purify arms: sucrose density gradient centrifugation (described here) and centrifugation through NaCl density gradients. Although the latter procedure is quicker, the arms are sometimes contaminated by small amounts of stuffer fragment, perhaps because the resolving power of sodium chloride gradients is limited. Ethidium bromide, at a concentration of 2 µg/ml, can be included in sucrose or NaCl density gradients. The positions of the different species of DNA within the gradient can then be determined visually. With practice, it is possible to pool those fractions that contain the annealed arms without prior analysis by agarose gel electrophoresis. In some cases, for example, if the restriction endonuclease digested ends of the vector are to be treated with phosphatase, it is desirable to ligate the cohesive termini of vector DNA before digesting with restriction endonucleases. The accompanying panel on LIGATION FIRST (see Method) describes the series of steps required to perform the preliminary ligation.

Bacteriophage λ arms can also can be purified by preparative electrophoresis through 0.5% agarose gels. In general, however, the yield of DNA obtained by gel electrophoresis is lower than that obtained by density gradient centrifugation.

Purified arms of the most popular vectors (e.g., EMBL3 and EMBL4, λgt10, λgt11, λFixII, λDASH, and λZAP) are available from commercial sources. These are invaluable if something goes wrong or when cloning in bacteriophage λ for the first time. It may also be less expensive to use commercial arms rather than domestically produced reagents for the occasional small-scale cloning project, for example, subcloning from individual bacterial or yeast artificial chromosomes. However, if the arms are to be used regularly or for the construction of libraries, it is more economical to prepare them by density gradient centrifugation.

This method for purification of bacteriophage λ arms through sucrose density gradients is derived from Maniatis et al. (1978), and it can be used to prepare the arms of any bacteriophage λ vector.

MATERIALS

CAUTION: Please see Appendix 12 for appropriate handling of materials marked with <!>.

Buffers and Solutions

Please see Appendix 1 for components of stock solutions, buffers, and reagents. Dilute stock solutions to the appropriate concentrations.

EDTA (0.5 M, pH 8.0)
Ethanol
$MgCl_2$ (1 M)
NaCl (1 M)
n-butanol <!>
Sodium acetate (3 M, pH 5.2)
Sucrose gel-loading buffer
    Please see Table 5-4 in Chapter 5, Protocol 1.
TE (pH 7.6 and pH 8.0)

Gels

Agarose gel (0.5% and 0.7%) cast in 0.5x TBE, containing 0.5 µg/ml ethidium bromide <!>
    Please see Step 3.

Agarose gel (0.5%, 75 mm thick), cast in 0.5x TBE, containing 0.5 µg/ml ethidium bromide
    Please see Step 7.

Nucleic Acids and Oligonucleotides

Bacteriophage λ DNA
    Prepared as described in Protocol 11 or 12 of this chapter.

Centrifuges and Rotors

Beckman SW28 rotor or equivalent, with clear centrifuge tubes, 25 x 89 mm
    (e.g., Beckman SW28 tubes or equivalent)

Special Equipment

Dialysis tubing, boiled
    For preparation of dialysis tubing for use with DNA, please see Appendix 8.
Hypodermic needle (21 gauge)
Large-bore tips
Sucrose gradients
    Prepare two sucrose solutions, one containing 10% (w/v) sucrose and another containing 40% (w/v) sucrose in a buffer of 1 M NaCl, 20 mM Tris-Cl (pH 8.0), and 5 mM EDTA (pH 8.0). Sterilize the two solutions by filtration through 0.22-µm nitrocellulose filters. The gradients are prepared as described in Step 1.

    Alternatively, linear sucrose gradients can be formed by diffusion (Brakke 1958). Many investigators prefer to use this method when large numbers of gradients are required. Four sterile sucrose solutions are required (10%, 20%, 30%, and 40% [w/v] sucrose) in 1 M NaCl, 20 mM Tris-Cl (pH 8.0), and 5 mM EDTA (pH 8.0). To form a 38-ml gradient in a Beckman SW28 centrifuge tube (or equivalent), 9.5 ml of each of the four sucrose solutions is successively layered on top of each other. Most investigators prefer to place the 40% sucrose solution in the bottom of the tube and then to overlay carefully with the three remaining solutions in order of decreasing density: 30%, 20%, and finally 10% sucrose. However, the gradients can also be formed by placing the least dense sucrose solution (10%) in the bottom of the tube and underlaying with progressively more dense sucrose solutions. Allow the step gradients to stand undisturbed for 2.5–3.0 hours at room temperature. Place each gradient in a bath of ice water to cool for 15 minutes before centrifugation.
Water baths preset to 42°C and 68°C

Additional Reagents

Step 2 of this protocol requires the reagents listed in Protocol 13 or 14 of this chapter.

METHOD

> **LIGATION FIRST**
>
> This method serves as an optional preliminary sequence of steps that may be performed before Step 2 (restriction endonuclease digestion) of the protocol for purifying bacteriophage λ arms. In this "Ligation First" method, the cohesive termini of the vector DNA are ligated together before digesting with restriction enzyme(s). The resulting concatemers are then cleaved by the appropriate restriction enzymes into left and right arms (which remain joined together) and the stuffer fragment. Ligation, followed by restriction endonuclease digestion, ensures that a majority of the purified vector has intact *cos* sites. These, in turn, increase the efficiency of packaging in the subsequent cloning steps.
>
> 1. Incubate the undigested bacteriophage λ DNA for 1 hour at 42°C in 150 μl of 0.1 M Tris-Cl (pH 7.6), 10 mM MgCl$_2$ to allow the cohesive termini to anneal.
>
> 2. Add 20 μl of 10x ligation buffer (please see Protocol 13), 20 μl of 10 mM ATP (if necessary), and 0.2–0.5 Weiss unit of bacteriophage T4 DNA ligase/μg of DNA. Incubate the reaction mixture for 1–2 hours at 16°C.
>
> 3. Extract the ligated DNA once with phenol:chloroform.
>
>   During ligation, the bacteriophage λ DNA forms closed circles and long concatemers and will be more sensitive to shearing. Handle the ligated DNA carefully! Do not vortex. Carry out the phenol:chloroform extraction by gently inverting the tube to emulsify the two phases.
>
> 4. Centrifuge the emulsion for 1 minute at room temperature to separate the organic and aqueous phases. Transfer the aqueous phase containing the viral DNA to a new tube using an automatic pipetting device equipped with a large-bore tip.
>
> 5. Recover the DNA by standard ethanol precipitation.
>
> 6. Proceed with Step 2 of this protocol to digest the concatenated DNA with the appropriate restriction enzymes and fractionate the cleaved DNA by centrifugation through a sucrose gradient.

Preparation of Sucrose Gradients

1. Prepare one or more 38-ml (10–40% w/v) sucrose gradients in clear ultracentrifuge tubes. Store the gradients for 1–2 hours at 4°C in a quiet place until they are needed (Step 4).

   Continuous sucrose density gradients are best made in a gradient-making device such as those supplied by Bio-Rad or Techware. Each gradient should take 10–20 minutes to pour at room temperature using a gradient maker. Each gradient can accommodate 60–75 μg of digested bacteriophage λ DNA.

2. Digest and analyze ~60 μg of the bacteriophage λ vector DNA as described in Protocol 13 or 14. After standard ethanol precipitation, dissolve the DNA in TE (pH 7.6) at a concentration of 150 μg/ml. Set aside an aliquot (0.2 μg) for use as an electrophoretic control (Step 7).

   It is sometimes possible to digest the vector DNA with a restriction enzyme that cleaves within the stuffer fragment but not the arms. The aims of this strategy are both to reduce the size of the stuffer fragment(s) and thereby improve the separation of the stuffer from the arms and to produce termini that are incompatible with those of the arms. To determine whether this strategy can be used, consult a description of the vector.

   If the vector arms have been ligated first (please see the panel on **LIGATION FIRST**), proceed to Step 4.

3. Add MgCl$_2$ (1 M) to a final concentration of 10 mM, and incubate the solution of bacteriophage DNA for 1 hour at 42°C to allow the cohesive termini of bacteriophage λ DNA to anneal. Analyze an aliquot (0.2 μg) by electrophoresis through an 0.7% agarose gel to determine whether annealing has occurred.

   Use as markers 0.2 μg of intact bacteriophage λ DNA (Protocol 11 or 12), and an aliquot (0.2 μg) of the annealed DNA that has been heated to 68°C for 10 minutes to melt the cohesive termini.

4. Load onto each gradient no more than 75 μg of annealed, digested bacteriophage λ DNA in a volume of 500 μl or less.

    More DNA can cause the gradient to be overloaded and lead to poor separation of the stuffer fragments from the arms.

5. Centrifuge the gradients at 120,000*g* (26,000 rpm in a Beckman SW28 rotor) for 24 hours at 15ºC.

6. Collect 0.5-ml fractions through a 21-gauge needle inserted through the bottom of the centrifuge tube.

7. Take two 15-μl aliquots from every third fraction and dilute each with 35 μl of H$_2$O. Add 8 μl of sucrose gel-loading buffer, heat one aliquot from each fraction to 68ºC for 5 minutes, and leave the second aliquot untreated. Analyze all of the samples by electrophoresis through a thick 0.5% agarose gel. Use as markers intact bacteriophage λ DNA and the aliquot of digested DNA set aside in Step 2.

    Adjust the sucrose and salt concentrations of the markers to match those of the samples; otherwise, their electrophoretic mobilities will not be comparable.

    The annealed arms migrate through the 0.5% agarose gel at a rate that is usually indistinguishable from that of intact bacteriophage λ DNA. Do not run the analytical gels at high voltage or in electrophoresis buffers of high electrical resistance: Overheating melts the cohesive termini of bacteriophage λ DNA during electrophoresis.

8. After photographing the gel, locate and pool the fractions that contain the annealed arms (Figure 2-13).

    Be careful not to include fractions that are visibly contaminated with undigested bacteriophage λ DNA or fractions that contain significant quantities of unannealed left or right arms or stuffer fragment(s).

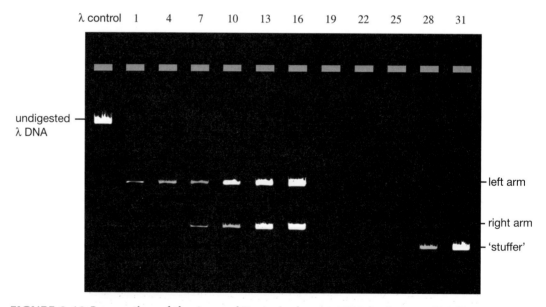

FIGURE 2-13 Preparation of the Arms of Bacteriophage λ DNA by Sucrose Gradient Centrifugation

In the experiment depicted here, the DNA of bacteriophage λ vector Charon 28 was digested with *Bam*HI, and centrifuged through a 10–40% linear sucrose gradient, which was then fractionated as described in the protocol. Aliquots from every third fraction were heated to 68°C for 5 minutes and then prepared for electrophoresis and analyzed on a 0.5% agarose gel. The positions of the left arm (23.5 kb), right arm (9 kb), "stuffer" fragments (6.5 kb), and undigested λ DNA are indicated. Fractions 1–16 containing the arms were pooled.

9. Dialyze the pooled fractions against a 1000-fold excess of TE (pH 8.0) for 12–16 hours at 4°C, with at least one change of buffer.

   Be sure to allow for a two- to threefold increase in volume during dialysis.

   Alternatively, if the volume of the pooled sample is small, the DNA can be precipitated with ethanol without prior dialysis by diluting the sample with TE (pH 7.6) so that the concentration of sucrose is reduced to ~10%. In this case, if ethidium bromide was included in the density gradients, extract the purified arms twice with isoamyl alcohol to remove residual dye from the DNA.

10. Extract the dialyzed sample several times with *n*-butanol to reduce its volume to less than 3 ml.

11. Recover the dialyzed DNA by standard ethanol precipitation.

12. Dissolve the DNA in TE (pH 7.6) at a concentration of 300–500 µg/ml.

13. Measure the concentration of the DNA spectrophotometrically (1 OD_{260} = ~50 µg/ml), and analyze an aliquot by electrophoresis through a 0.5% agarose gel to assess its purity. Store the DNA at –20°C in aliquots of 1–5 µg.

Protocol 17

Partial Digestion of Eukaryotic DNA for Use in Genomic Libraries: Pilot Reactions

Hᴵɢʜ-ᴹᴼᴸᴱᴄᵁᴸᴬᴿ-ᵂᴱᴵɢʜᵀ Dɴᴬ ᴄᴬɴ ʙᴱ ꜰᴿᴬɢᴹᴱɴᵀᴱᴅ in a quasi-random fashion, irrespective of its base composition and sequence, by hydrodynamic shearing (please see Table 12-1 in Chapter 12, Protocol 1). However, DNA prepared in this way requires extensive enzymatic manipulations (repair of termini, methylation, ligation to linkers, digestion of linkers) to protect internal restriction sites and to generate cohesive termini compatible with those of the vectors used to generate genomic DNA libraries (Maniatis et al. 1978). On the other hand, partial digestion with restriction enzymes that recognize frequently occurring tetranucleotide sequences within eukaryotic DNA yields a population of fragments that is close enough to random for many purposes and yet can be used without further manipulation to generate genomic libraries.

The following are four methods commonly used for partial digestion of high-molecular-weight DNA in solution:

- varying the concentration of the enzyme

- varying the length of the incubation

- limiting the concentration of Mg^{2+} (Albertsen et al. 1990)

- protecting a subset of restriction sites with the cognate methylase (Hoheisel et al. 1989)

The first of these methods is the simplest to set up and, in our hands, the most reproducible. The conditions for partial digestion are established empirically in pilot experiments presented in this protocol, whose intent is to maximize the yield of fragments of a size appropriate for insertion into a vector. The aim of these small-scale reactions is to determine the amount of enzyme required to reduce the modal size of the DNA to 20–25 kb (when bacteriophage λ is used as a vector) or ~45 kb (for construction of libraries in cosmids). The optimum amount of enzyme necessary will vary for each batch of enzyme and preparation of DNA. On the basis of the results obtained from the pilot experiments, large-scale preparative reactions are set up, each containing slightly different concentrations of restriction enzyme (Protocol 18).

To construct a genomic library, the average length of the starting genomic DNA should be at least eight times the capacity of the vector. This size range ensures that the majority of DNA molecules created by partial digestion with restriction enzyme(s) are derived from internal segments of the high-molecular-weight DNA and therefore carry termini that are compatible with those of the vector arms. Methods to isolate genomic DNA of the required size are presented in Chapter 6, Protocols 1 and 2. The size of the genomic DNA before digestion should be checked by pulsed-field electrophoresis or by conventional electrophoresis through a 0.7% agarose gel, using as markers oligomers of bacteriophage λ DNA. These can be either obtained commercially or generated in the laboratory.

Before using a preparation of genomic DNA, it is a good idea to set up a mock enzyme digestion that includes genomic DNA and 1x restriction enzyme buffer, but no enzyme. Incubate the solution for 1–2 hours at the optimum digestion temperature for the particular enzyme and then examine the DNA by electrophoresis through a 0.5% agarose gel or by pulsed-field gel electrophoresis. Compare the mock-digested DNA to a sample of DNA that has been incubated in TE for the same period of time and to a sample not subjected to incubation. There should be no difference in the size of the DNA present in the three samples. If degradation has occurred in the sample incubated in restriction enzyme buffer, then the starting DNA is probably contaminated with a nonspecific DNase that is activated by the presence of the Mg^{2+} ions in the buffer. This type of contaminant can be removed by gentle extraction with phenol:chloroform and dialysis against several changes of TE (pH 7.6).

MATERIALS

CAUTION: Please see Appendix 12 for appropriate handling of materials marked with <!>.

Buffers and Solutions

Please see Appendix 1 for components of stock solutions, buffers, and reagents. Dilute stock solutions to the appropriate concentrations.

Sucrose gel-loading buffer
Please see Table 5-4 in Chapter 5, Protocol 1.
Tris-Cl (10 mM, pH 8.0)

Enzymes and Buffers

Restriction endonucleases
The best results are obtained if the same batch of 10x buffer is used in both the pilot reactions and the large-scale reaction.

Gels

Agarose gel (0.6%) cast in 0.5x TBE, containing 0.5 μg/ml ethidium bromide <!>
or
Agarose gel for pulsed-field gel electrophoresis
Please see Step 8. For information on pulsed-field gel electrophoresis, please see Chapter 5.

Nucleic Acids and Oligonucleotides

Genomic DNA, high molecular weight
Oligomers of bacteriophage λ DNA and plasmids
Use as DNA size standards during gel electrophoresis. Please see Appendix 6.

Special Equipment

Capillary tube, sealed
Dialysis tubing, boiled
For preparation of dialysis tubing for use with DNA, please see Appendix 8.
Water bath preset to 70°C
Wide-bore pipette tips

METHOD

1. Set up pilot reactions using the same batch of genomic DNA that will be used to prepare fragments for cloning.

   a. Dilute 30 μg of high-molecular-weight eukaryotic DNA to 900 μl with 10 mM Tris-Cl (pH 8.0) and add 100 μl of the appropriate 10x restriction enzyme buffer.

   b. Use a sealed glass capillary to mix the solution gently. This mixing ensures that the high-molecular-weight DNA is distributed evenly throughout the restriction enzyme buffer.

   c. After mixing, store the diluted DNA for 1 hour at room temperature to allow any residual clumps of DNA to disperse (please also see the note to Step 8, below).

   > If the concentration of the high-molecular-weight DNA is low, it is best to increase the volume of the pilot reactions and concentrate the DNA after digestion by standard ethanol precipitation. This approach minimizes the possibility of shearing the high-molecular-weight DNA, which can occur if it is concentrated before digestion. Each pilot reaction should contain at least 1 μg of DNA to allow the heterogeneous products of digestion to be detected by staining with ethidium bromide.

2. Label a series of microfuge tubes 1 through 10. Use a wide-bore glass capillary or disposable plastic pipette tip to transfer 60 μl of the DNA solution to a microfuge tube (Tube 1). Transfer 30 μl of the DNA solution to each of nine additional labeled microfuge tubes. Incubate the tubes on ice.

3. Add 2 units of the appropriate restriction enzyme to Tube 1.

   > Use a sealed glass capillary to mix the restriction enzyme with the DNA. Do not allow the temperature of the reaction to rise above 4ºC.

4. Use a fresh pipette tip to transfer 30 μl of the reaction from Tube 1 to the next tube in the series. Mix as before, and continue transferring the reaction to successive tubes. Do not add anything to the tenth tube (the no enzyme control), but discard 30 μl from the ninth tube.

5. Incubate the reactions for 1 hour at 37ºC.

6. Inactivate the restriction enzyme by heating the reactions to 70ºC for 15 minutes.

   > For some enzymes, it is necessary to heat the reaction to 80ºC for 20 minutes. Check the product documentation in the manufacturer's catalog or Web site.

7. Cool the reactions to room temperature and add the appropriate amount of sucrose gel-loading buffer.

   > Use a sealed glass capillary to mix the solutions gently.

8. Use wide-bore plastic pipette tip or a disposable wide-bore glass capillary to transfer the solutions to the wells of a 0.6% agarose gel or, even better, to the lanes of an agarose gel for pulsed-field electrophoresis (please see Chapter 5). Perform electrophoresis.

   > When separating the partial digestion products by agarose gel electrophoresis, it is essential to run the gel under conditions of maximum resolution. Use the same batch of buffer to cast the gel and to fill the gel tank prior to electrophoresis. The gel should be run slowly (<1 V/cm) at 4ºC to prevent smearing of the fragments of DNA. Occasionally, problems arise during loading of the gel because the DNA solution will not sink to the bottom of the well. This floating occurs when very high-molecular-weight DNA is present in the preparation. To minimize the problem, make sure that the DNA is homogeneously dispersed and load the samples very slowly into the wells of the gel. After loading, allow the gel to stand for a few minutes so that the DNA can diffuse evenly throughout the wells.

9. Compare the size of the digested eukaryotic DNA with that of DNA standards composed of oligomers of bacteriophage λ DNA and plasmids. Identify the partial digestion conditions that result in a majority of the genomic DNA migrating in the desired size range.

   Before partial digestion of genomic DNA with the desired restriction enzyme, there should be no low-molecular-weight DNA detectable in the preparation. With increasing time of digestion or increasing amounts of restriction enzyme, the modal size of DNA should decrease monotonically, i.e., there should be no residual material at the top of the gel and no sign of a resistant fraction of DNA. Optimal conditions of digestion should yield a population of DNA molecules that migrates as a fairly compact band of the desired size. If the DNA smears into the lower part of the gel, do not proceed further. It is likely that the DNA has been asynchronously digested by the restriction enzyme, with some molecules in the starting population being cleaved more frequently than others. This phenomenon can occur if the restriction buffer and enzyme are not distributed homogeneously throughout the DNA solution at the start of the reaction. Clumps of DNA are relatively inaccessible to restriction enzymes and can be digested only from the outside. Unless the DNA is evenly dispersed, the rate of digestion cannot be predicted or controlled. One solution to this problem is to dialyze the DNA to be used for the pilot and large-scale digests for several hours against a 20-fold excess of the appropriate 1x restriction enzyme buffer. Alternatively, allow the DNA to stand for several hours at 4ºC after dilution and addition of 10x restriction enzyme buffer. Gently stir the DNA solution from time to time using a sealed glass capillary tube.

Protocol 18

Partial Digestion of Eukaryotic DNA for Use in Genomic Libraries: Preparative Reactions

H IGH-MOLECULAR-WEIGHT DNA CAN BE FRAGMENTED by partial digestion with restriction enzymes. (In particular circumstances, it may be desirable to perform a complete digestion of the DNA; for further discussion, please see the panel on CLONING SPECIFIC FRAGMENTS OF GENOMIC DNA.) The appropriate conditions for partial digestion are established in pilot experiments (please see Protocol 17). The results of the pilot experiments determine the conditions for three large-scale reactions for preparing genomic DNA for cloning, presented here. The reactions utilize the results generated in Protocol 17 as a starting point and make small adjustments in the ratio of enzyme to DNA substrate around the empirically determined optimum. Bracketing the conditions that are predicted to work well offers some insurance against problems that can arise during scale-up of pilot experiments. Nevertheless, it is important to ensure that the conditions for the large-scale digestion are as identical as possible to those used in the pilot experiment in Protocol 17. After preparative digestion, the products of the large-scale partial digestion are fractionated by sucrose gradient centrifugation, and the fragments of the desired size are recovered.

CLONING SPECIFIC FRAGMENTS OF GENOMIC DNA

In some cases, the size of the target DNA fragment in a genomic DNA sample is known. For example, a restriction fragment of a known size may be required to fill a gap in a cloned region, for constructing a knock-out vector, or for isolating a grossly rearranged allele of a target gene. In these situations, enriching the population of genomic DNA for fragments in the desired size range decreases the amount of screening of recombinants and increases the chance of isolating the desired clone. The protocol for partial purification is identical to that described above except that the genomic DNA is subject to complete digestion with the restriction enzyme instead of a partial digestion. Before sucrose gradient fractionation, the digested DNA can be subjected to Southern blotting (if an appropriate probe is available) to ensure that the digest is complete. In addition, if a probe is available, a Southern blot of the agarose gel used to analyze fractions isolated from the sucrose gradient (Step 5) can identify those containing the highest concentration of the target fragment. Thereafter, the pooled fractions can be dialyzed and the DNA recovered by standard ethanol precipitation before ligation into an appropriate vector.

MATERIALS

CAUTION: Please see Appendix 12 for appropriate handling of materials marked with <!>.

Buffers and Solutions

Please see Appendix 1 for components of stock solutions, buffers, and reagents. Dilute stock solutions to the appropriate concentrations.

Ammonium acetate (10 M)

Ethanol

n-butanol <!>

Phenol:chloroform (1:1, v/v) <!>

Sodium acetate (3 M, PH 5.2)

Sucrose gel-loading buffer
Please see Table 5-4 in Chapter 5, Protocol 1.

TE (pH 8.0)

Tris-Cl (10 mM, pH 8.0)

Enzymes and Buffers

Restriction endonucleases
The best results are obtained if the same batch of 10x buffer is used in both the pilot reactions and the large-scale reaction.

Gels

Agarose gel
Please see Step 2.

Agarose gel (0.6%) cast in 0.5× TBE, containing 0.5 µg/ml ethidium bromide <!>
Please see Step 7.

Agarose gel for pulsed-field gel electrophoresis
Please see Step 12. For information on pulsed-field gel electrophoresis, please see Chapter 5.

Nucleic Acids and Oligonucleotides

Genomic DNA, high molecular weight

Oligomers of bacteriophage λ DNA and plasmids
Use as DNA size standards during gel electrophoresis. Please see Appendix 6.

Centrifuges and Rotors

Beckman SW28 rotor or equivalent

Special Equipment

Dialysis tubing, boiled
For preparation of dialysis tubing for use with DNA, please see Appendix 8.

Gradient fractionating device (optional)
Please see Step 4. These devices are rather hard to come by, but they generally can be borrowed from aged biochemists. If all else fails, the gradients can be fractionated by puncturing the bottom of the centrifuge tube with a 21-gauge hypodermic needle (no syringe barrel required).

Sucrose gradients
Prepare two sucrose solutions, one containing 10% (w/v) sucrose and another containing 40% (w/v) sucrose in a buffer of 1 M NaCl, 20 mM Tris-Cl (pH 8.0), and 5 mM EDTA (pH 8.0). Sterilize the two solutions by filtration through 0.22-µm nitrocellulose filters. The gradients are prepared as described in Step 1.

Alternatively, linear sucrose gradients can be formed by diffusion (Brakke 1958). Many investigators prefer to use this method when large numbers of gradients are required. Four sterile sucrose solutions are required (10%, 20%, 30%, and 40% [w/v] sucrose) in 1 M NaCl, 20 mM Tris-Cl (pH 8.0), and 5 mM EDTA (pH 8.0). To form a 38-ml gradient in a Beckman SW28 centrifuge tube (or equivalent), 9.5 ml of each of the four sucrose solutions is successively layered on top of each other. Most investigators prefer to place the 40% sucrose solution in the bottom of the tube and then to overlay carefully with the three remaining solutions in order of decreasing density: 30%, 20%, and finally 10% sucrose. However, the gradients can also be formed by placing the least dense sucrose solution (10%) in the bottom of the tube and underlaying with progressively more dense sucrose solutions. Allow the step gradients to stand undisturbed for 2.5–3.0 hours at room temperature. Place each gradient in a bath of ice water to cool for 15 minutes before centrifugation.

Water bath preset to 68°C

METHOD

Preparation of the Gradient

1. Prepare one or more 38-ml (10–40% w/v) sucrose gradients in clear ultracentrifuge tubes. Store the gradients for 1–2 hours at 4°C in a quiet place until they are needed (Step 5).

   Continuous sucrose density gradients are best made in a gradient-making device such as those supplied by Bio-Rad or Techware. Each gradient should take 10–20 minutes to pour at room temperature using a gradient maker. Each gradient can accommodate 60–75 µg of digested bacteriophage λ DNA.

2. Set up a series of digestions, each containing 100 µg of high-molecular-weight DNA.

   a. Use three different concentrations of restriction enzyme that straddle the optimal concentration determined in the pilot experiments (Protocol 17).

   b. Incubate the reactions for the appropriate time with the restriction enzyme.

   c. Analyze an aliquot of the partially digested DNA by gel electrophoresis to ensure that the digestion has worked according to prediction. Until the results are available, store the remainder of the sample at 0°C.

3. Gently extract the digested DNA twice with phenol:chloroform.

4. Recover the DNA by standard precipitation with ethanol and dissolve it in 200 µl of TE (pH 8.0).

Size Fractionation of DNA through the Gradient

5. Heat the DNA sample (100 µg) for 10 minutes at 68°C, cool to 20°C, and gently layer the sample on the top of the gradient. Centrifuge the gradients at 83,000g (25,000 rpm in a Beckman SW28 rotor) for 22 hours at 20°C.

   Centrifugation is carried out at room temperature rather than 4°C to suppress intra- and intermolecular annealing of cohesive termini.

6. Use a 21-gauge needle or a gradient fractionation device to puncture the bottom of the tube and collect 350-µl fractions.

7. Mix 10 µl of every other fraction with 10 µl of H_2O and 5 µl of sucrose gel-loading buffer. Analyze the size of the DNA in each fraction by electrophoresis through a 0.6% agarose gel, using oligomers of plasmid DNA or other high-molecular-weight standards as markers. Adjust the sucrose and salt concentrations of the markers to correspond to those of the samples.

8. Following electrophoresis, pool the gradient fractions containing DNA fragments of the desired size (e.g., 35–45 kb for construction of libraries in cosmids and 20–25 kb for construction of libraries in bacteriophage λ vectors).

9. Dialyze the pooled fractions against 2 liters of TE (pH 8.0) for 12–16 hours at 4°C, with a change of buffer after 4–6 hours.

   Leave space in the dialysis sac for the sample to expand two- to threefold in volume.

   Alternatively, if the volume of the pooled sample is sufficiently small, the DNA can be precipitated with ethanol without prior dialysis after first diluting the sample with TE (pH 8.0) so that the concentration of sucrose is reduced to 10% or less.

10. Extract the dialyzed DNA several times with an equal volume of *n*-butanol until the volume is reduced to ~1 ml.

11. Precipitate the DNA with ethanol at room temperature in the presence of 2 M ammonium acetate (from a 10 M stock solution).

12. Recover the DNA by centrifugation and dissolve the DNA in TE (pH 8.0) at a concentration of 300–500 µg/ml. Analyze an aliquot of the DNA (0.5 µg) by electrophoresis through a conventional 0.6% agarose gel or by pulsed-field electrophoresis to check that the size distribution of the digestion products is correct. Store the DNA at 4°C.

13. To establish genomic DNA libraries, ligate the fractionated DNA to the arms of bacteriophage λ vectors as described in Protocol 19. For the preparation of cosmid libraries, please see Chapter 4, Protocol 1.

Protocol 19

Ligation of Bacteriophage λ Arms to Fragments of Foreign Genomic DNA

Two important parameters must be considered when ligating bacteriophage λ arms to segments of foreign DNA: the molar ratio of arms to potential inserts and the concentration of each DNA species in the reaction mixture. Optimum values for both of these parameters can be estimated from theoretical considerations (Dugaiczyk et al. 1975). By necessity, however, such calculations assume that all the DNA molecules in the ligation reaction are perfect. As this nirvana is rarely attained, it is advisable to carry out pilot reactions to check the efficiency of each new preparation of arms and potential inserts.

Typically, trial ligations contain ~0.5–1.0 μg of bacteriophage λ arms and different amounts of foreign DNA. The molar ratio of arms to potential inserts in the test ligations should range from 1:4 to 8:1 (please see Table 2-4) and the volume of the ligation mixture should be as small as possible (10 μl or less). The amounts of inserts recommended in Table 2-4 have been calculated on the assumption that the ligation reactions contain 1 μg of bacteriophage λ arms, 40 kb in size. In the ligation reactions containing the lowest recommended amount of foreign DNA, the bacteriophage λ arms will be present in eightfold molar excess; in mixtures containing the greatest amount of potential insert, the insert will be present in fourfold molar excess. It is essential to also include two controls containing (1) bacteriophage λ arms but no insert and (2) insert but no bacteriophage λ arms. Once assembled, the ligation reactions are usually incubated for 4–16 hours at 16ºC.

The success of the ligation reactions can be estimated by electrophoretic analysis of small aliquots, using a 0.5% agarose gel. If the ligation reactions have been successful, then almost all of the DNA should be at least as large as intact bacteriophage λ DNA. However, it is difficult to know whether a large DNA species on an agarose gel is composed of the desired vector-insert combinations or other undesirable combinations (e.g., [vector]$_n$, [insert]$_n$). A better method of judging the success of the ligation is to package a proportion of the ligation products (10–25%) into bacteriophage particles in vitro. The ligation reaction containing the optimum ratio of arms to inserts should yield at least 10^6 to 10^7 recombinants/μg of bacteriophage λ. After the ratio of arms to insert that gives the largest number of recombinant bacteriophage has been established, additional ligation and packaging reactions may be set up to generate a library of cloned fragments. This primary library can then be plated and screened by hybridization directly for recombinant bacteriophages of interest, or the library can be amplified, divided into aliquots, and stored.

TABLE 2-4 Amounts of Insert DNA Used in Trial Ligations Containing 1 μg of Bacteriophage λ Arms

SIZE OF POTENTIAL INSERT DNA (kb)	AMOUNT OF INSERT DNA (ng)
2–4	6–200
4–8	12–400
8–12	24–600
12–16	36–800
16–20	48–1000
20–24	60–1200

MATERIALS

CAUTION: Please see Appendix 12 for appropriate handling of materials marked with <!>.

Buffers and Solutions

Please see Appendix 1 for components of stock solutions, buffers, and reagents. Dilute stock solutions to the appropriate concentrations.

ATP (10 mM)
Omit ATP from Step 1 if the ligation buffer contains ATP.

SM and SM plus gelatin

Enzymes and Buffers

Bacteriophage T4 DNA ligase

Gels

Agarose gel (0.7%) cast in 0.5× TBE, containing 0.5 μg/ml ethidium bromide <!>
Please see Step 6.

Nucleic Acids and Oligonucleotides

Genomic DNA, of an appropriate size for the vector
Prepared as described in Protocol 18 of this chapter. In addition, please see the panel in the introduction to Protocol 18.

Media

LB or NZCYM agar plates

LB or NZCYM top agarose
For details on using top agarose, please see Protocol 1 of this chapter. Agarose is preferred to agar in this protocol in order to minimize contamination with inhibitors that can interfere with subsequent enzymatic analysis of bacteriophage.

Special Equipment

Heating block or water bath preset to 47°C (for top agarose)
Water bath preset to 16°C

Additional Reagents

Step 4 of this protocol requires the reagents listed in Protocol 1 of this chapter.

Vectors and Bacterial Strains

Bacteriophage λ packaging mixtures
These may be purchased in kit form from any of several commercial manufacturers (e.g., Epicentre Technology, Life Technologies, Promega, and Stratagene).
For a discussion of in vitro packaging extracts, please see the information panel on IN VITRO PACKAGING.

Bacteriophage λ DNA arms
　Prepared by one of the methods described in Protocols 11 through 15 of this chapter.

E. coli *plating bacteria*
　Prepared as described in Protocol 1 of this chapter.

METHOD

1. Use Table 2-4 as a guide to set up a series of ligation reactions that contain the following:

bacteriophage λ arms	0.5–1.0 µg
partially digested genomic DNA	6–1200 ng
10x ligation buffer	0.5–1.0 µl
10 mM ATP (if necessary)	0.5–1.0 µl
bacteriophage T4 DNA ligase	0.5–1.0 µl
H_2O	to 5 or 10 µl

   Set up two control reactions in which the vector and insert DNAs are each ligated in the absence of the other. Incubate the ligation reactions for 4–16 hours at 16°C.

   To achieve the maximum efficiency of ligation, set up the reactions in as small a volume as possible (5–10 µl). The addition of ATP as a component of the 10x ligation buffer leaves more volume for vector or foreign DNA in the reaction mixture.

   Omit ATP if using a commercial ligase buffer that contains ATP.

2. Package an aliquot (10–25%) of each of the ligation reactions into bacteriophage particles, following the instructions provided by the manufacturer of the packaging extract.

   Most manufacturers provide a control preparation of bacteriophage λ DNA that can be used as a standard to measure the efficiency of packaging.

3. Make a series of tenfold dilutions (10^{-1} to 10^{-5}) of the packaging reactions, using as a diluent SM plus gelatin or an equivalent buffer recommended by the manufacturer of the packaging extract.

4. Assay the number of plaque-forming units in 1 µl and 10 µl of each dilution as described in Protocol 1.

5. From the ligation reaction yielding the largest number of infectious bacteriophage particles, pick 6–12 plaques and prepare a small amount of recombinant DNA from each as described in Protocol 23.

6. Check the size of the inserts of genomic DNA by digestion with the appropriate restriction enzymes, followed by electrophoresis through a 0.7% agarose gel, using appropriate size markers.

7. If the bacteriophages are recombinants and contain inserts of the desired size, establish a genomic DNA library by setting up multiple ligation and packaging reactions. The ratio of insert to vector DNA in these reactions should be that which generated the greatest number of recombinant plaques in the trial reactions.

8. Estimate the total number of recombinant plaques generated in the large-scale ligation and packaging reactions. Calculate the depth to which a library of this size would cover the target genome.

   To provide fivefold coverage of a mammalian genome (3×10^9 bp), a bacteriophage λ library containing inserts whose average size is 20 kb would contain 2×10^6 independent recombinants.

Protocol 20

Amplification of Genomic Libraries

THE LIBRARY OF RECOMBINANT BACTERIOPHAGES MAY BE AMPLIFIED by growing plate stocks directly from the packaging mixture as described in this protocol. However, whenever possible, the amplification step should be omitted and the primary library screened directly for DNA sequences of interest. Amplification invariably decreases the complexity (the number of independent clones) present in the library, in part because slower-growing recombinant bacteriophages are disadvantaged during successive rounds of bacteriophage growth. Variation in the growth of individual bacteriophages can arise, for example, from the presence of sequences in the segment of foreign DNA that cannot be efficiently replicated or that are toxic for essential host or viral functions or from recombination events that decrease the size of the bacteriophage genome below that required for efficient packaging of the DNA. The greater the amplification of the library, the more distorted the population of recombinant bacteriophages becomes.

Direct screening of an unamplified library increases the chance of identifying and recovering recombinants of interest that grow slowly or produce lower yields of virus. Of course, the recombinant bacteriophage particles packaged from the ligation reactions are a finite resource. However, as long as the supply of foreign DNA is not limiting, it is preferable to set up additional ligation/packaging reactions, to forego amplification, and to screen bacteriophages directly from packaging reactions. If the source of foreign DNA is in short supply, amplification may be unavoidable, but should be kept to a minimum. For an alternative amplification method, please see the panel on **IN SITU AMPLIFICATION** in Protocol 21).

MATERIALS

CAUTION: Please see Appendix 12 for appropriate handling of materials marked with <!>.

Buffers and Solutions

Please see Appendix 1 for components of stock solutions, buffers, and reagents.
Dilute stock solutions to the appropriate concentrations.

Chloroform <!>
SM

Media

LB or NZCYM agar plates (150 mm)

LB or NZCYM top agarose

For details on using top agarose, please see Protocol 1 of this chapter. Agarose is preferred to agar in this protocol in order to minimize contamination with inhibitors that can interfere with subsequent enzymatic analysis of bacteriophage.

Centrifuges and Rotors

Sorvall SS-34 rotor or equivalent

Special Equipment

Water bath or heating block preset to 47ºC (for top agarose)

Vectors and Bacterial Strains

Bacteriophage λ library

Prepared as described in Protocol 19 of this chapter.

E. coli *plating bacteria*

Prepared as described in Protocol 1 of this chapter.

METHOD

1. To amplify a bacteriophage λ library, mix aliquots of the packaging mixture containing 10,000–20,000 recombinant bacteriophages in a volume of 50 µl or less with 0.2 ml of plating bacteria in a 13 x 100-mm tube. Incubate the infected culture for 20 minutes at 37ºC.

2. Add 6.5 ml of melted top agar/agarose (47ºC) to the first aliquot of infected bacteria. Mix the contents of the tube by tapping or by gentle vortexing, and spread the infected bacteria onto the surface of a freshly poured 150-mm plate of bottom agar. Repeat the procedure with the remaining infected cultures.

   Alternatively, as many as 450,000 bacteriophages may be mixed with 1.4 ml of bacteria and plated in 75 ml of top agar/agarose on 500 ml of bottom agar in a 23 x 33-cm glass baking dish. For a discussion of the pros and cons of using baking dishes, please see the note under the LB agar plates entry in the materials list in Protocol 21.

3. Incubate the plates for a maximum of 8–10 hours at 37ºC.

   Do not allow the plaques to grow so large that they touch one another. The short period of growth minimizes the chance for infection of bacteria with two different recombinants, thereby reducing the possibility of recombination between repetitive sequences carried by different recombinants with consequent "scrambling" of the library; and it decreases the opportunity for changes in the bacteriophage population that may occur because of variations in the rate of growth of different recombinants.

4. Overlay the plates with 12 ml of SM (or 150 ml of SM if baking dishes are used). Store the plates overnight at 4ºC on a level surface.

   The amplified recombinant bacteriophage will elute from the top agar into SM.

5. Harvest the SM from all of the plates into a single, sterile polypropylene centrifuge tube or bottle. Wash each plate with an additional 4 ml of SM, and combine the washings with the primary harvest. Add 0.2 ml of chloroform to the resulting amplified bacteriophage stock. Store the stock for 15 minutes at room temperature with occasional gentle shaking to allow time for the chloroform to lyse all of the infected cells.

6. Remove cell and agarose debris by centrifugation at 4000g (5800 rpm in a Sorvall SS-34 rotor) for 5 minutes at 4ºC.

7. Transfer the supernatant to a sterile glass tube or bottle. Divide the amplified bacteriophage library into aliquots and store them at 4ºC. Measure the titer of the library by plaque assay.

   The titer of the amplified library should be stable for several months. Nevertheless, to decrease the chance of mishaps, several aliquots of the library should be placed in long-term storage as described in the panel on **LONG-TERM STORAGE OF BACTERIOPHAGE λ STOCKS** in Protocol 3.

Protocol 21

Transfer of Bacteriophage DNA from Plaques to Filters

A METHOD TO IDENTIFY AND ISOLATE SPECIFIC RECOMBINANTS from libraries of bacteriophage λ was developed early in the history of molecular cloning by Benton and Davis (1977). The procedure, which remains in common use, involves mass screening of plaques by hybridization in situ with ^{32}P-labeled probes. With practice, it is possible to identify a single recombinant that carries the desired target sequence on a plate containing 15,000 or more plaques. For a method for amplification of bacteriophage particles on filters, please see the panel on IN SITU AMPLIFICATION at the end of this protocol. This protocol describes how plaques are transferred en masse from Petri dishes to nitrocellulose or nylon filters. The sequence of events is presented in Figure 2-14.

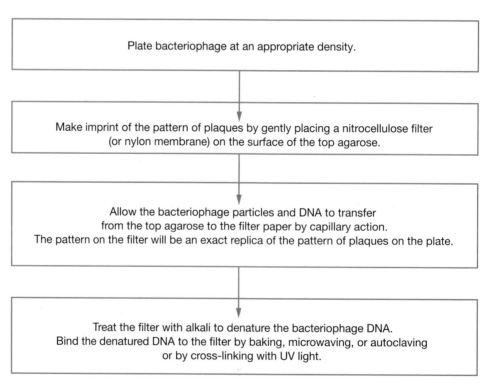

FIGURE 2-14 Flowchart: Sequence of Transfer Steps

MATERIALS

Buffers and Solutions

Please see Appendix 1 for components of stock solutions, buffers, and reagents. Dilute stock solutions to the appropriate concentrations.

Denaturing solution

Depending on the number of filters to be processed, 1 liter or more may be required.

Neutralizing solution

Depending on the number of filters to be processed, 1 liter or more may be required.

SM plus gelatin

2× SSPE

Depending on the number of filters to be processed, 1 liter or more may be required.

Media

LB or NZCYM agar plates

If the plates are not well-dried, the layer of top agarose will peel off the agar base when the filter is removed. Usually, 2-day-old plates that have been dried for several additional hours at 37ºC with the lids slightly open work well. In humid weather, however, incubation for 1 day or more at 41ºC may be necessary.

In the 1970s and 1980s, when screening large numbers of plaques, it was fashionable to use large Pyrex dishes instead of standard Petri dishes. This vogue was driven more by energetic investigators of the time than by common sense. For most laboratories, Pyrex dishes are an impractical option. They are heavy, breakable, have large footprints, require some sort of temporary covering during incubation, and need nitrocellulose or nylon sheets that have been specially cut to fit. Today, most laboratories use either the standard 100-mm plates or oversize (150-mm) plates, The choice between them is often determined by the size of the investigators hands.

LB or NZCYM top agarose

For details on using top agarose, please see Protocol 1 of this chapter. Agarose is preferred to agar in this protocol in order to minimize contamination with inhibitors that can interfere with subsequent enzymatic analysis of bacteriophage. In addition, top agarose is preferred because top agar often peels from the plate when the nitrocellulose or nylon filters are removed.

Melt the top agarose just before use by heating it in a microwave oven for a short period of time. Store the 3- or 7-ml aliquots of melted solution in a 47ºC heating block or water bath to prevent the agarose from solidifying until needed in Step 3 below.

Special Equipment

Cross-linking device (e.g., Stratalinker, Stratagene; GS Gene Linker, Bio-Rad), Microwave oven, or Vacuum oven preset to 80ºC

Hypodermic needle and syringe (21 gauge)

Nitrocellulose or Nylon filters

Detergent-free nitrocellulose (Millipore HATF or equivalent) or nylon filters are required. To reduce the possibility of contaminating the master plates, it is best to sterilize the filters before use as described in Step 1.

If the filters will be hybridized sequentially to a number of different probes, it is better to use nylon rather than nitrocellulose filters. Nylon filters are more pliable than nitrocellulose filters and are more resistant to repeated exposure to extremes of temperature. Nylon filters are also preferred when hybridization is to be carried out in solvents containing formamide or tetramethylammonium chloride (please see Chapter 6). However, different brands of nylon filters vary in their ability to bind DNA, in the ease with which they can be stripped of radiolabeled probes, and in the degree to which they distort during repeated rounds of stripping and rehybridization (Khandjian 1987). It would therefore be sensible to check the properties of nylon filters obtained from different manufacturers before attempting large-scale screening of bacteriophage λ libraries. Follow the manufacturer's recommendations closely, as they presumably have been shown to lead to optimal results. In our hands, however, the lysis and hybridization procedures described in Protocol 22 work well with most commercial brands of nitrocellulose or nylon filters.

Water baths preset to 47°C and 65°C
Waterproof black drawing ink (India Ink)
Whatman 3MM paper
Whatman 3MM filter papers (85-mm diameter)

Vectors and Bacterial Strains

Bacteriophage λ library
    Prepared as described in Protocol 19 of this chapter or purchase from a commercial source.
E. coli plating bacteria
    Prepared as described in Protocol 1 of this chapter.

METHOD

Preparation of Filters and Transfer of Plaques

1. Prepare the filters for transfer:

    a. Number the dry filters with a soft-lead pencil or a ball-point pen.

        Prepare enough filters to make one or two (duplicate) replicas from the starting agar plate. In the latter case, number two sets of filters 1A, 1B, 2A, 2B, etc.

    b. Soak the filters in water for 2 minutes.

    c. Arrange the filters in a stack with each filter separated from its neighbor by an 85-mm-diameter Whatman 3MM filter paper.

    d. Wrap the stack of filters in aluminum foil, and sterilize them by autoclaving for 15 minutes at 15 psi (1.05 kg/cm^2) on liquid cycle.

2. Make a dilution (in SM plus gelatin) of the packaging mixture, bacteriophage stock, or library. Mix aliquots of the diluted bacteriophage stock with the appropriate amount of freshly prepared plating bacteria (please see Table 2-5). Incubate the infected bacterial cultures for 20 minutes at 37°C.

    The diluted stock (100 μl) should contain ~15,000 infectious bacteriophages when using 100-mm plates or 50,000 infectious particles when using 150-mm plates.

    When screening bacteriophage libraries, it is best to infect the cells as a single pool. For example, when using ten 150-mm plates, 1 ml of diluted bacteriophage stock containing 500,000 pfu would be added to 3 ml of freshly prepared plating bacteria. After 20 minutes at 37°C, equal volumes of the infected culture are then distributed into 17 x 100-mm tubes for plating. This procedure ensures that each plate contains approximately the same number of plaques.

TABLE 2-5 Number of Plaques in Culture Dishes of Various Sizes

Size of Petri dish	90 mm	150 mm
Total area of dish	63.9 cm^2	176.7 cm^2
Volume of bottom agar	30 ml	80 ml
Volume of plating bacteria	0.1 ml	0.3 ml
Volume of top agarose	2.5 ml	6.5–7.5 ml
Maximum number of plaques/dish	15,000	50,000

To find a bacteriophage that carries a particular genomic sequence, it may be necessary to screen one million or more recombinants in a genomic DNA library. Table 2-5 shows the maximum number of plaques that can be efficiently screened in culture dishes of different sizes. If the bacteriophages are plated at too high a density, the plaques will be crowded and hence unable to expand to their full size. As a result, the hybridization signal will be attenuated. In addition, when the bacteriophage plaques form a confluent mass, the top agarose tends to peel from the plate during removal of the nitrocellulose or nylon filter. Although this is not a total disaster, it certainly makes the task of identifying and isolating desired recombinants far more difficult. It is therefore important to measure the titer of the library before plating to ensure that the number, size, and spacing of plaques are correct.

3. Add to each aliquot of infected cells 3 ml or 6.5 ml of molten (47°C) top agarose. Pour the contents of each tube onto separate, numbered 90-mm or 150-mm agar plates.

    Avoid bubbles since these will displace the filter and can generate background during the hybridization step.

4. Close the plates, allow the top agarose to harden, and incubate at 37°C in an inverted position until plaques appear and are just beginning to make contact with one another (10–12 hours).

    To minimize plate-to-plate variation, it is crucial that each plate be heated to the same extent when placed in the incubator. If possible, arrange the plates in a single layer rather than in stacks. If constrictions on incubator space force stacking, stagger the plates on top of each other to enhance exposure to the air in the incubator. During incubation, keep a close eye on the plates to monitor plaque formation and size. However, resist the temptation to open the inside incubator door too many times since this will alter the temperature of the incubator and retard plaque formation. The density and size of plaques are ideal when a wispy filigree of bacterial growth is visible between adjacent plaques, whose diameter should not exceed 1.0 mm. The yield of viruses is often low from plates that show confluent lysis with no visible remnants of the bacterial lawn, simply because of a shortage of bacteria for infection. The intensity of the hybridization signal is therefore reduced and is frequently below the limit of detection.

5. Chill the plates for at least 1 hour at 4°C to allow the top agarose to harden.

6. Remove the plates from the cold room or refrigerator. Make imprints of the plaques on each plate using the first set of labeled filters. Place a dry, labeled circular nitrocellulose or nylon filter neatly onto the surface of the top agarose so that it comes into direct contact with the plaques.

    Handle the filter with gloved hands; finger oils prevent wetting of the filter and affect transfer of DNA. Grasp the filter by its edges and allow the center of the slightly bent filter to make contact with the center of the top agar. Once contact has been made, slowly release the filter and allow it to flatten onto the surface of the top agarose. Do not attempt to adjust the position of the filter since this will inevitably lead to tearing of the top agarose. Be careful not to trap air bubbles, which will displace the filter and may generate background during hybridization.

7. Mark the filter in three or more asymmetric, peripheral locations by stabbing through it and into the agar beneath with a 21-gauge needle attached to a syringe containing waterproof black drawing ink.

    Make sure that the keying marks are asymmetrically placed and that both the filter and the plate are marked. There must be enough ink on the plate to be easily visible when a second filter is in place. Large blotches of ink, however, are undesirable. Ink often becomes contaminated with bacteriophages and bacteria if it has been used many times. This problem can be minimized by heating the ink in a microwave oven to inactivate contaminating viruses and microorganisms.

8. After 1–2 minutes, use blunt-ended forceps (e.g., Millipore forceps) to peel the filters from each plate in turn.

    This step is best done by pulling slowly upward on one edge of the filter and peeling the entire filter from the underlying agarose in a single smooth motion. At this stage, some investigators prefer to dry the filters for 15 minutes on paper towels or sheets of Whatman 3MM paper. However, in our hands, this step is unnecessary.

    At this point, the transferred bacteriophage may be amplified; please see the panel on **IN SITU AMPLIFICATION** at the end of this protocol.

Denaturation of the Bacteriophage DNA on the Filter

9. Transfer each filter, plaque side up, to a sheet of Whatman 3MM paper (or equivalent) impregnated with denaturing solution in a plastic cafeteria tray or Pyrex dish for 1–5 minutes.

   Make sure that excess denaturing solution does not rinse over the sides of the nitrocellulose or nylon filters. When transferring the filters, use the edge of cafeteria tray or dish to remove as much fluid as possible from the underside of the filters.

   Some investigators prefer to carry out the denaturation and neutralization (Steps 9 and 10) by immersing the filters in each solution. However, this results in weaker signals when the filters are probed by hybridization.

   For an alternative method for processing filters (replacing Steps 9–13), please see the panel on **ALTERNATIVE PROTOCOL: RAPID TRANSFER OF PLAQUES TO FILTERS.**

10. Transfer the filters, plaque side up, to a sheet of Whatman 3MM paper impregnated with neutralizing solution for five minutes.

    If nitrocellulose filters are used, repeat the neutralizing step using a fresh impregnated sheet of 3MM paper.

Fixation of Bacteriophage DNA to the Filters

11. Prepare the filters for fixing.

    To fix the DNA to the filters by microwaving or baking: If using a microwave oven, proceed directly to Step 13. If baking in a vacuum oven, transfer the filters, plaque side up, to a sheet of dry 3MM paper or a stack of paper towels. Allow filters to dry for at least 30 minutes at room temperature.

    To fix the DNA to nylon filters by cross-linking with UV light: Place the filters on a sheet of Whatman 3MM paper impregnated with 2x SSPE, and move the tray of 2x SSPE containing the filters to the vicinity of the UV light cross-linker.

12. After the first set of filters has been processed, use the second set of filters to take another imprint of the plaques, if required. Make sure that both sets of filters are keyed to the plate at the same positions.

    Generally, the second set of filters is left in contact with the plaques for 3 minutes, or until the filter is completely wet. As many as seven replicas have been prepared from a single plate (Benton and Davis 1977), but the strength of the hybridization signal decreases significantly after the third replica.

13. Fix the DNA from the plaques to the filter.

    To fix by treatment in a microwave oven: Place the damp filters on a sheet of dry Whatman 3MM paper and irradiate them for 2–3 minutes at full power in a microwave oven.

    To fix by baking: Arrange the dried filters (Step 10) in a stack with adjacent filters separated by a sheet of dry Whatman 3MM paper. Bake the stack of filters for 1–2 hours at 80ºC in a vacuum oven.

    Check the oven after 30 minutes and wipe away any condensation from the door. The filters must be baked under vacuum rather than stewed.

    Baking for more than 2 hours can cause nitrocellulose filters to become brittle. Baking at temperatures higher than 80ºC can cause nitrocellulose filters to explode.

    Nitrocellulose filters that have not been completely neutralized turn yellow or brown during baking and chip very easily. The background of nonspecific hybridization increases dramatically.

To fix by cross-linking with UV light: Carry out the procedure using a commercial device for this purpose and follow the manufacturer's instructions.

▲ IMPORTANT Do not allow the filters to dry out prior to cross-linking.

14. After baking or cross-linking, loosely wrap the dry filters in aluminum foil and store them at room temperature. Alternatively, if hybridization is to be carried out within a day or so, wash the filters for 30 minutes at 65°C in 0.1x SSC or SSPE, 0.5% SDS and store them wet in sealed plastic bags.

The filters may now be used for hybridization as described in Protocol 22.

IN SITU AMPLIFICATION

Woo et al. (1978) and Woo (1979) have described a modification of the Benton and Davis (1977) screening method that involves amplification of the bacteriophages on the nitrocellulose filter prior to hybridization. Because more bacteriophage DNA becomes attached to the nitrocellulose filter, the autoradiographic signals from positive clones are enhanced approximately fivefold. Amplification therefore leads to an improvement in the ratio of signal to noise and also allows the length of the autoradiographic exposure to be reduced. Amplification is particularly valuable when oligonucleotides of high degeneracy are used as probes (please see Chapter 10), when only a small amount of a valuable probe is available, or when screening under conditions of reduced stringency. A detailed protocol for in situ amplification is outlined on pages 2.112–2.113 of the Second Edition of *Molecular Cloning*.

ALTERNATIVE PROTOCOL: RAPID TRANSFER OF PLAQUES TO FILTERS

The following procedure, based on a protocol developed by Gary Struhl in 1983 while he was a postdoctoral fellow in Tom Maniatis' laboratory, eliminates treatment of filters with alkali, can save time when dealing with large numbers of filters, and may be used as an alternative to Steps 9 through 13. Nitrocellulose filters must be sterilized to prevent shrinkage (please see Step 1 above); however, nylon filters are, in our hands, superior and are therefore recommended.

Method

1. After removing the filters from the top agarose (Step 8), place them, DNA side up, on paper towels for 5–10 minutes.

2. When their edges begin to curl, place the filters in stacks of ten interleaved with circular Whatman 3MM papers. Place a few 3MM papers on the top and bottom of the stack.

3. Place the stacks on a small platform (e.g., an inverted Pyrex dish) in an autoclave. Expose the filters to "streaming steam" for 3 minutes (i.e., 100°C — avoid super-heated steam).

4. Transfer the stack of filter papers and nitrocellulose filters to a vacuum oven.

5. Bake for 2 hours at 80°C while drawing a vacuum continuously. Remove any 3MM paper that sticks to the nitrocellulose filters by soaking in 2x SSPE before prehybridizing.

6. Proceed to Step 14 of the protocol.

Protocol 22

Hybridization of Bacteriophage DNA on Filters

Filters carrying immobilized DNA from plaques are screened by hybridization in situ with ^{32}P-labeled probes. The technique is extremely robust, highly specific, and very sensitive and allows the identification of a single recombinant among several thousand plaques. The plaque identified as hybridization-positive is then purified by subsequent rounds of screening. The overall sequence of events is presented in Figure 2-15. For further details on the hybridization of DNA immobilized on filters, please see Chapter 6, Protocol 10.

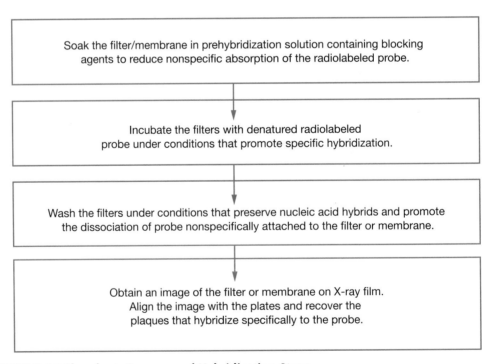

FIGURE 2-15 Flowchart: Sequence of Hybridization Steps

MATERIALS

CAUTION: Please see Appendix 12 for appropriate handling of materials marked with <!>.

Buffers and Solutions

Please see Appendix 1 for components of stock solutions, buffers, and reagents. Dilute stock solutions to the appropriate concentrations.

Chloroform <!>

Prehybridization solution <!>

Please see the panel on **PREHYBRIDIZATION AND HYBRIDIZATION SOLUTIONS** in Chapter 1, Protocol 32.

SM

2x SSPE

Depending on the number of filters to be processed, 1 liter or more may be required.

Wash solution 1

2x SSC

0.1% (w/v) SDS

Wash solution 2

1x SSC

0.1% (w/v) SDS

Wash solution 3

0.1x SSC

0.1% (w/v) SDS

Nucleic Acids and Oligonucleotides

Filters immobilized with bacteriophage DNA

Prepared as described in Protocol 21 of this chapter.

Radiolabeled probe <!>

Prepared as described in Chapter 9 or 10.

Special Equipment

Boiling water bath (for denaturing double-stranded probes)

Glass (Pyrex) baking dish or other hybridization chamber

ALTERNATIVE HYBRIDIZATION CHAMBERS

Some investigators prefer to incubate filters in heat-sealable plastic bags (Sears Seal-A-Meal or equivalent) (e.g., please see Chapter 6, Protocol 10) during the prehybridizaton and hybridization steps, rather than in crystallization dishes. The former method avoids problems with evaporation and, because the sealed bags can be submerged in a water bath, ensures that the temperatures during hybridization and washing are correct. The bags must be opened and resealed when changing buffers. To avoid radioactive contamination of the water bath, the resealed bag containing radioactivity should be sealed inside a second, noncontaminated bag.

   If only a small number of filters are subjected to hybridization, then use a glass screw-top bottle that fits the rollers of a hybridization oven in place of a crystallization dish or Seal-A-Meal bag. These bottles and ovens have the advantage that small volumes of hybridization solution can be used and the hybridization temperature can be accurately controlled.

Glue stick, water-soluble (e.g., UHU Stic distributed by FaberCastell)

Incubation chamber preset at the appropriate hybridization temperature

Please see Step 2.

Radioactive ink <!>

Radioactive ink is made by mixing a small amount of ^{32}P with waterproof black drawing ink. We find it convenient to make the ink in three grades: very hot (>2000 cps on a hand-held minimonitor), hot (>500 cps on a hand-held minimonitor), and cool (>50 cps on a hand-held minimonitor). Use a fiber-tip pen to apply ink of the desired hotness to the adhesive labels. Attach radioactive-warning tape to the pen, and store it in an appropriate place.

Reusable alternatives to radioactive ink are chemiluminescent markers available from Stratagene (Glogos). The markers can be used multiple times and should be exposed to fluorescent light just prior to a new round of autoradiography.

Whatman 3MM paper

METHOD

1. If the filters are dry, float the baked or cross-linked filters on the surface of 2x SSPE until they have become thoroughly wetted from beneath. Submerge the filters for 5 minutes.

   Make sure that no air bubbles are trapped under the filters. The filters should change from white to a bluish color as the aqueous solvent penetrates the pores of the filter. Make sure that there are no white spots or patches remaining on the filters before proceeding to Step 2.

2. Transfer the filters to a Pyrex dish or other hybridization chamber containing prehybridization solution. Use 3 ml of prehybridization solution per 82-mm filter or 5 ml per 132-mm filter. Incubate the filters with gentle agitation on a rocking platform for 1–2 hours or more at the appropriate temperature (i.e., 68°C when hybridization is to be carried out in aqueous solution; 42°C when hybridization is to be carried out in 50% formamide).

   Whatever type of container is used, the important point is that the filters are completely covered by the prehybridization solution. During prehybridization, sites on the nitrocellulose filter that nonspecifically bind single- or double-stranded DNA become bound by proteins in the blocking solution. Agitation ensures that the filters are continuously bathed in and evenly coated by the prehybridization fluid.

   Whether or not to use a prehybridization solution containing formamide is largely a matter of personal preference. Both versions of the recommended solutions give excellent results and neither has clear-cut advantages over the other. However, hybridization in 50% formamide at 42°C is less harsh on nitrocellulose filters than is hybridization at 68°C in aqueous solution. Offsetting this advantage is the two- to threefold slower rate of hybridization in solutions containing formamide. Nylon filters are impervious to the deleterious effects of aqueous hybridization at high temperatures.

3. Denature ^{32}P-labeled double-stranded probes by heating for 5 minutes at 100°C. Chill the probe rapidly in ice water. Single-stranded probes need not be denatured.

   Alternatively, the probe may be denatured by adding 0.1 volume of 3 N NaOH. After 5 minutes at room temperature, transfer the probe to ice water and add 0.1 volume of 1 M Tris-Cl (pH 7.2) and 0.1 volume of 2.5 N HCl. After denaturation, store the probes in ice water until needed. At low temperature, the rate of reassociation of DNA is extremely slow and essentially the probe remains in a single-stranded form.

   Between 2×10^5 and 1×10^6 cpm of ^{32}P-labeled probe (specific activity 5×10^7 cpm/μg) should be used per milliliter of hybridization solution. Using more probe causes the background of nonspecific hybridization to increase; using less reduces the rate of hybridization.

   If radiolabeled oligonucleotides are used as probes in this step, please see Chapter 6, Protocol 10, or Chapter 10, Protocol 8 for hybridization and washing conditions.

PURITY OF PROBES

It is essential that probes used to screen bacteriophage λ libraries contain no sequences that will hybridize to DNA sequences in the vector. Several bacteriophage λ vectors, such as λgt11, λORF8, lambda ZAP, and some of the λ Charon bacteriophages, contain the *E. coli lacZ* gene, either for immunochemical screening or as part of a plasmid integrated into the bacteriophage genome to assist with rescue of cloned sequences, or as part of the central stuffer fragment. Because DNA probes are often prepared from fragments of plasmids that contain all or part of the *lacZ* gene, even a small amount of contamination will cause the probe to hybridize indiscriminately to bacteriophage plaques. To ensure that a DNA fragment does not contain sequences that are complementary to the vector, we recommend (i) purifying the DNA successively through two gels (agarose or polyacrylamide) as described in Chapter 5, before carrying out the radiolabeling reaction, or (ii) preparing the probe by PCR amplification and purification (please see Chapter 8, Protocol 1).

---

4. Add the denatured probe to the prehybridization solution covering the filters. Incubate the filters for 12–16 hours at the appropriate temperature (please see Chapter 6, Protocol 10).

   During hybridization, keep the containers holding the filters tightly closed to prevent the loss of fluid by evaporation.

   To maximize the rate of annealing of the probe with its target, hybridizations are usually carried out in solutions of high ionic strength (6x SSC or 6x SSPE) at a temperature that is 20–25°C below the melting temperature (please see Chapter 1, Protocols 28–30 or Chapter 6, Protocol 10). Both SSPE and SSC work equally well when hybridization is carried out in aqueous solvents. However, when formamide is included in the hybridization buffer, 6x SSPE is preferred because of its greater buffering capacity. For a general discussion of the factors that affect the rate and specificity of hybridization of radioactive probes to nucleic acids immobilized on solid supports, please see Chapter 6, Protocol 10.

5. When the hybridization is completed, *quickly* remove filters from the hybridization solution and *immediately* immerse them in a large volume (300–500 ml) of Wash solution 1 at room temperature. Agitate the filters gently, turning them over at least once during washing. After 5 minutes, transfer the filters to a fresh batch of wash solution and continue to agitate them gently. Repeat the washing procedure twice more.

   At no stage during the washing procedure should the filters be allowed to dry or to stick together.

   Only a small fraction of the probe forms specific hybrids with the target sequences immobilized on the filters. Therefore, hybridization solutions may be recovered, stored, and reused for a second round of hybridization. However, the intensity of the signal obtained from recycled hybridization solution may be reduced for a variety of reasons: the reduced specific activity of the probe due to radioactive decay, degradation of the probe during incubation, and renaturation of double-stranded probe during the first hybridization step.

6. Wash the filters twice for 1–1.5 hours in 300–500 ml of Wash solution 2 at 68°C.

   With experience, it is possible to use a hand-held monitor to test whether washing is complete. If the background is still too high or if the experiment demands washing at high stringencies, immerse the filters for 60 minutes in 300–500 ml of Wash solution 3 at 68°C.

7. Dry the filters in the air at room temperature on sheets of Whatman 3MM paper or stacks of paper towels. Streak the underside of the filters with a water-soluble glue stick and arrange the filters (numbered side up) on a clean, dry, flat sheet of 3MM paper. Firmly press the filters against the 3MM paper to ensure that they do not move. Apply adhesive labels marked with radioactive ink or chemiluminescent markers to several asymmetric locations on the 3MM paper. These markers serve to align the autoradiograph with the filters. Cover the filters and labels with Saran Wrap/Cling Film. Use tape to secure the wrap to the back of the 3MM paper and stretch the wrap over the paper to remove wrinkles.

8. Expose the filters to X-ray film (Kodak XAR-2, XAR-5, or their equivalent) for 12–16 hours at –70°C with an intensifying screen.

9. Develop the film and align it with the filters using the marks left by the radioactive ink or fluorescent marker. Use a nonradioactive red fiber-tip pen to mark the film with the positions of the asymmetrically located dots on the numbered filters.

10. Identify the positive plaques by aligning the orientation marks with those on the agar plate.

    When duplicate sets of filters are hybridized to the same probe, there is less chance of confusing a background smudge with a positive plaque. Pick only those plaques that yield convincing hybridization signals on both sets of filters for further analysis. When screening a genomic library for a single-copy gene, expect to find no more than one positive clone per 10^5 plaques screened. When screening cDNA libraries, the number of positives depends on the abundance of the mRNA of interest.

    Filters glued to 3MM paper are readily removed in preparation for stripping (please see Chapter 6, Protocol 10) by placing the 3MM paper with attached membranes in a tub of 2x SSC. The water-soluble glue dissolves in this solution, releasing the filters for transfer to a stripping solution and a round of hybridization to another probe, if desired.

11. Pick each positive plaque as described in Protocol 2 and store in 1 ml of SM containing a drop (50 µl) of chloroform.

    If the alignment of the filters with the plate does not permit identification of an individual hybridizing plaque, an agar plug containing several plaques in the area of interest should be cored using the large end of a sterile Pasteur pipette. Use a fresh pipette to core each hybridization-positive area.

12. To purify a hybridization-positive plaque, plate an aliquot (usually 50 µl of a 10^{-2} dilution) of the bacteriophages that are recovered from the cored agar plug and proceed with subsequent rounds of screening by hybridization.

    Ideally, in a second round plating, there should be ~300 plaques on a 100-mm plate. These plaques are then screened a second time by hybridization. Pick a single, well-isolated positive plaque from the secondary screen and subject it to additional rounds of screening until the stock is genetically pure and every plaque hybridizes to the probe of interest. Use a plaque derived from the final round of screening to make a stock as described in Protocol 3 or 4.

Protocol 23

Rapid Analysis of Bacteriophage λ Isolates: Purification of λ DNA from Plate Lysates

ANALYSIS OF PROMISING GENOMIC OR CDNA CLONES often begins by digesting minipreparations of bacteriophage λ DNA with restriction enzymes and analyzing the products of digestion by agarose gel electrophoresis. The two methods presented here and in Protocol 24 are for the rapid preparation of small amounts of bacteriophage λ DNA that are suitable for use as substrates for restriction enzymes, as templates for RNA synthesis with DNA-dependent RNA polymerases encoded by bacteriophages SP6, T3, and T7, and as templates in the PCR.

This protocol (Xu 1986) is designed for use with bacteriophages prepared from plate lysates, whereas Protocol 24 is more suitable for bacteriophages grown in liquid cultures (Leder et al. 1977). Several other approaches are summarized in the panel on ALTERNATIVE PURIFICATION METHODS at the end of this protocol.

The clones also may be analyzed simply and directly as described in the panel on ANALYSIS OF CLONES USING PCR at the end of this protocol. In later chapters, we discuss additional methods that can be used to analyze inserts cloned in bacteriophage λ recombinants.

- Vectors such as λZAP and λZipLox have been designed to allow inserts to be recovered and analyzed as plasmids (for details, please see the introduction to Chapter 11). This method works best with small inserts (≤8 kb) and is chiefly of benefit when recovering cloned cDNA from bacteriophage λ recombinants.

- Small inserts also can be recovered by using specially designed thermostable DNA polymerases to catalyze long-range PCR (for details, please see Chapter 8, Protocol 13).

This method is derived from that described by Xu (1986) and was provided by Diane Jelinek and Daphne Davis (University of Texas Southwestern Medical Center, Dallas).

MATERIALS

CAUTION: Please see Appendix 12 for appropriate handling of materials marked with <!>.

Buffers and Solutions

Please see Appendix 1 for components of stock solutions, buffers, and reagents. Dilute stock solutions to the appropriate concentrations.

Chloroform <!>
Ethanol
High-salt buffer
> 20 mM Tris-Cl (pH 7.4)
> 1.0 M NaCl
> 1 mM EDTA (pH 8.0)

Isopropanol
Low-salt buffer
> 20 mM Tris-Cl (pH 7.4)
> 0.2 M NaCl
> 1 mM EDTA (pH 8.0)

Phenol:chloroform (1:1, v/v) <!>
SM
TE (pH 8.0)
TM

Media

LB or NZCYM agarose plates

Freshly poured plates (150-mm diameter) that have been equilibrated to room temperature give the best results in this method. Agarose is preferred to agar in order to minimize contaminants that can interfere with enzymatic analysis of DNA prepared from plate lysates of bacteriophage λ DNA.

LB or NZCYM top agarose

For details on using top agarose, please see Protocol 1 of this chapter. Agarose is preferred to agar in this protocol in order to minimize contamination with inhibitors that can interfere with subsequent enzymatic analysis of bacteriophage.

Centrifuges and Rotors

Sorvall SS-34 rotor or equivalent

Special Equipment

Borosilicate Pasteur pipette
Elutip-d columns (Schleicher & Schuell)
Water bath or heating block preset to 47°C
Whatman DE52

DE52 is a preparation of DEAE-cellulose, an anion-exchange resin, that is used in this protocol to remove host DNA and RNA from plate or liquid lysates. A preswollen version of DE52 is available from Whatman and works exceedingly well in this protocol. For each 150-mm plate lysate to be purified, 10 ml of a 2:1 slurry of DE52 in LB medium is required.

Vectors and Bacterial Strains

Bacteriophage λ, recombinant, grown as single well-isolated plaques on a lawn of bacteria
Prepared as described in Protocol 1 of this chapter.

E. coli plating bacteria
Prepared as described in Protocol 1 of this chapter.

METHOD

Preparation of Lysates

1. Use a borosilicate Pasteur pipette to pick 8–10 well-isolated bacteriophage plaques from a plate derived from a genetically pure, plaque-purified bacteriophage stock. Place the plaques in 1 ml of SM and 50 μl of chloroform. Store the suspension for 4–6 hours at 4°C to allow the bacteriophage particles to diffuse from the top agarose.

2. In a small, sterile culture tube, mix 50–100 μl of the bacteriophage suspension (~10^5 pfu) with 150 μl of plating bacteria. Incubate the infected culture for 20 minutes at 37°C. Add 7.0 ml of molten (47°C) top agarose (0.7%), and spread the bacterial suspension on the surface of a freshly poured 150-mm plate containing NZCYM agarose.

3. Incubate the inverted plate at 37°C until the plaques cover almost the entire surface of the plate (7–9 hours).

    Do not incubate the plates for too long, otherwise confluent lysis will occur, which reduces the yield of bacteriophage DNA.

4. Add 7 ml of TM directly onto the surface of the top agarose. Allow the bacteriophage particles to elute during 4 hours of incubation at 4°C with constant, gentle shaking.

5. Transfer the bacteriophage λ eluate to a centrifuge tube, and remove the bacterial debris by centrifugation at 4000g (58,000 rpm in a Sorvall SS-34 rotor) for 10 minutes at 4°C. A small aliquot of cleared lysate can be set aside at this step as a bacteriophage stock solution. Store the stock at 4°C over a small volume of chloroform.

6. Dispense 10 ml of a 2:1 slurry of DE52 resin into a centrifuge tube and sediment the resin by centrifugation at 500g (2000 rpm in a Sorvall SS-34 rotor) for 5 minutes at room temperature. Remove the supernatant from the resin pellet and place the centrifuge tube on ice.

7. Resuspend the DE52 in the cleared TM and allow the bacteriophage particles to absorb to the resin by rocking the centrifuge tube for 3 minutes at room temperature.

8. Centrifuge the TM/DE52 slurry at 4000g (5800 rpm in a Sorvall SS-34 rotor) for 5 minutes. Carefully transfer the supernatant to a fresh centrifuge tube and repeat the centrifugation step. Discard the pellet after each centrifugation.

9. Transfer the supernatant from the second centrifugation to a fresh centrifuge tube. Extract the supernatant, which contains the bacteriophage λ particles, once with phenol:chloroform.

10. Transfer the aqueous phase, which contains the bacteriophage λ DNA, to a fresh polypropylene tube and add an equal volume of isopropanol. Store the mixture for 10 minutes at –70°C.

11. Collect the precipitated bacteriophage DNA by centrifugation at 16,500g (12,000 rpm in a Sorvall SS-34 rotor) for 20 minutes at 4°C.

12. Drain the isopropanol from the centrifuge tube and allow the pellet of DNA to dry in air.

13. Redissolve the DNA pellet in 2 ml of low-salt buffer.

14. Purify the bacteriophage DNA by chromatography on an Elutip-d column:

    a. Use a syringe to push 1–2 ml of high-salt buffer through the Elutip-d column.

    b. Push 5 ml of low-salt buffer through the column.

    c. Attach the 0.45-μm prefilter to the column and slowly push the DNA sample (Step 13) through the column.

    d. Rinse the column with 2–3 ml of low-salt buffer.

    e. Remove the prefilter and elute the DNA with 0.4 ml of high-salt buffer. Collect the eluate at this step in a 1.5-ml microfuge tube.

15. Add 1 ml of ethanol to the solution of eluted DNA, invert the tube several times, and incubate the mixture on ice for 20 minutes. Collect the precipitated DNA by centrifugation in a microfuge, discard the supernatant, and rinse the pellet of DNA with 0.5 ml of 70% ethanol. Discard the supernatant and allow the pellet of DNA to dry in the air. Dissolve the pellet of DNA in 50 μl of TE (pH 8.0).

    > Resuspend the DNA by tapping on the side of the tube. Try to avoid vortexing. If the DNA proves difficult to dissolve, incubate the tube for 15 minutes at 50ºC.

    > If minipreparations are working well, expect to isolate ~5 μg of purified bacteriophage DNA from 5×10^{10} infectious particles. It is possible to estimate the quantity of bacteriophage DNA present in a plate lysate or liquid culture lysate by direct agarose gel electrophoresis (please see Protocol 7).

    > For restriction analysis and agarose gel electrophoresis, digest a 5–10-μl aliquot of the resuspended DNA. If the DNAs are resistant to cleavage, treat them according to the method described on the following page in **ADDITIONAL PROTOCOL: REMOVING POLYSACCHARIDES BY PRECIPITATION WITH CTAB.**

ALTERNATIVE PURIFICATION METHODS

Hundreds of different methods are described in the literature to prepare small amounts of bacteriophage λ DNA from plate lysates or liquid cultures. Most of these are minor variations or elaborations of the basic techniques described in this protocol. The two problems that arise most frequently are poor yields of DNA and an inability to cleave the DNA with restriction enzymes. As discussed, the first of these problems is best solved by experimenting with the ratios of bacteriophage to host cells when setting up the plate lysates or liquid cultures. The second, which is more commonly encountered with plate lysates rather than liquid cultures, is often caused by polysaccharide inhibitors derived from the host bacteria and/or the agar. This problem can sometimes be solved by using agarose or agar from a different manufacturer or by substituting agarose for agar in the medium used to pour the plates. If the problem persists, the best course of action is to use a more elaborate scheme to purify the bacteriophage particles and the bacteriophage DNA. For example:

- Manfioletti and Schneider (1988) describe a variation of the above methods in which DEAE cellulose or triethyaminoethyl cellulose is first used to remove polyanions from the lysate. Proteinase K and EDTA are then used to release the DNA from the virus particles, and finally, the bacteriophage DNA is precipitated with hexadecyltrimethyl ammonium bromide (CTAB).

- The protonated form of DE52 can also be used as a chromatography resin to purify bacteriophage λ particles from liquid cultures or plate lysates (Helms et al. 1985, 1987). The negatively charged virus particles bind to the resin in low concentrations of Mg^{2+} and are eluted in buffers containing high concentrations of Mg^{2+}. The viral DNA is extracted by digesting the bacteriophage particles with proteinase K in the presence of a detergent such as SDS. The DNA is then precipitated with isopropanol.

- Several companies sell kits to prepare bacteriophage DNA from plate or liquid lysates. The Wizard kit marketed by Promega is fairly typical and involves digesting the lysate with nuclease to remove contaminating bacterial DNA and RNA, precipitating the bacteriophage particles from the supernatant with PEG or a resin, and finally purifying the viral DNA on another resin. These kits work well if the manufacturers' instructions are followed to the letter. However, like all commercial products, they are expensive and are therefore best used as a last resort if other methods fail.

ANALYSIS OF CLONES USING PCR

A simple approach to analyze cDNA clones is to use PCR to amplify the insert (please see Chapter 8, Protocol 12).

   If the oligonucleotide primers are well-designed, the amplified DNA can be digested with a restriction enzyme and ligated into a plasmid vector, or it can be cloned directly without restriction (please see Chapter 8, Protocol 5). With longer cDNA clones and genomic DNA inserts, three strategies should be considered. The first is to use a version of long PCR (Barnes 1994) to amplify the insert before analysis or subcloning (Chapter 8, Protocol 13). The second is to rescue the insert as a phagemid DNA (Short et al. 1988). This option requires that a bacteriophage vector with an integrated phagemid genome (e.g., Stratagene's λZAP or BRL's ZipLox vectors) be used in the construction of the original library. A third strategy is to digest the recombinant bacteriophage DNA with a restriction enzyme to release the foreign DNA from the λ arms and then to subclone the insert directly into a plasmid vector. In general, no purification of the restriction digest is required prior to ligation, since vector arm–plasmid ligation products are poor candidates for transformation of bacteria. When setting up the ligation reactions, aim for an equimolar molar ratio of insert to plasmid vector and use a high-frequency transformation protocol (please see Chapter 1) to introduce the DNA into *E. coli*. For large genomic DNA inserts of 15–20 kb, it is often necessary to screen colonies of transformed bacteria by hybridization, as the background of empty colonies can be high. Once the cDNA or genomic DNA insert is cloned into a high-copy-number plasmid vector, much larger quantities of DNA can be prepared for detailed restriction mapping, exon hunting, and DNA sequence analysis.

ADDITIONAL PROTOCOL: REMOVING POLYSACCHARIDES BY PRECIPITATION WITH CTAB

If the bacteriophage DNA preparations obtained in Protocols 23 and 24 are resistant to cleavage by restriction enzymes, the DNA can be purified further by precipitation with the cationic detergent hexadecyltrimethyl ammonium bromide (CTAB). This procedure efficiently removes polysaccharides, which are frequently the cause of the problem.

Additional Materials

CAUTION: Please see Appendix 12 for appropriate handling of materials marked with <!>.

Bacteriophage DNA
   Prepared as described in Protocol 23 or 24 of this chapter.
Chloroform:isoamyl alcohol (24:1, v/v) <!>
CTAB (10% v/v) in 0.7 M NaCl <!>
   Dissolve 4.1 g of NaCl in 80 ml of H_2O and slowly add 10 g of CTAB while heating the solution to 55°C and stirring. Adjust the final volume to 100 ml, and store above 15°C to prevent CTAB from precipitating.

   CTAB, also known as cetrimide, is available from Sigma. Please see the information panel on CTAB in Chapter 6.
NaCl (5 M)
TE (pH 7.6)
Water bath preset to 68°C

Method

1. Precipitate the bacteriophage DNA with ethanol and dissolve it in 300 μl of TE (pH 7.6).

    Resuspend the DNA by tapping on the side of the tube. Try to avoid vortexing. If the DNA proves difficult to dissolve, incubate the tube for 15 minutes at 50°C.

2. To the bacteriophage DNA pellet, add 50 μl of 5 M NaCl, followed by 40 μl of CTAB/NaCl solution. Incubate the DNA/CTAB/NaCl solution for 10 minutes at 68°C.

3. Purify the bacteriophage DNA by extraction with chloroform:isoamyl alcohol, and then centrifuge the emulsion for 3 minutes in a microfuge to separate the phases.

4. Transfer the (upper) aqueous phase to a fresh tube, and extract with phenol:chloroform.

5. Centrifuge the emulsion for 3 minutes in a microfuge to separate the phases.

6. Transfer the (upper) aqueous phase to a fresh tube, and precipitate the bacteriophage DNA with isopropanol at room temperature.

7. Resuspend the pellet of DNA in 100 μl of TE (pH 8.0).

    Resuspend the DNA by tapping on the side of the tube. Try to avoid vortexing. If the DNA proves difficult to dissolve, incubate the tube for 15 minutes at 50°C.

Protocol 24

Rapid Analysis of Bacteriophage λ Isolates: Purification of λ DNA from Liquid Cultures

Bacteriophage λ DNA may be purified easily from bacteriophage grown in liquid cultures as described here. The preceding protocol presented a method for purifying bacteriophage λ DNA from plate lysates. In general, bacteriophage λ does not grow as well in small liquid cultures as in plate lysates. The following method should therefore be used only with robust strains of the bacteriophage, such as λgt10, λgt11, λZAP, or ZipLox recombinants. For analyzing clones using PCR, please see the panel on ANALYSIS OF CLONES USING PCR in Protocol 23.

MATERIALS

CAUTION: Please see Appendix 12 for appropriate handling of materials marked with <!>.

Buffers and Solutions

Please see Appendix 1 for components of stock solutions, buffers, and reagents. Dilute stock solutions to the appropriate concentrations.

Chloroform <!>
Ethanol
High-salt buffer
    20 mM Tris-Cl (pH 7.4)
    1.0 M NaCl
    1 mM EDTA (pH 8.0)
Isopropanol
Low-salt buffer
    20 mM Tris-Cl (pH 7.4)
    0.2 M NaCl
    1 mM EDTA (pH 8.0)
Phenol:chloroform (1:1, v/v) <!>
SM
TE (pH 8.0)

Media

NZCYM medium

Centrifuges and Rotors

Sorvall SS-34 rotor or equivalent

Special Equipment

Borosilicate Pasteur pipette
Elutip-d columns (Schleicher & Schuell)
Water bath or heating block preset to 47ºC
Whatman DE52

DE52 is a preparation of DEAE-cellulose, an anion-exchange resin, that is used in this protocol to remove host DNA and RNA from plate or liquid lysates. A preswollen version of DE52 is available from Whatman and works exceedingly well in this protocol. For each 150-mm plate lysate to be purified, 10 ml of a 2:1 slurry of DE52 in LB medium is required.

Vectors and Bacterial Strains

Bacteriophage recombinant, grown as single well-isolated plaques on a lawn of bacteria

Prepared as described in Protocol 1 of this chapter.

E. coli strain, grown as well-isolated, single colonies on an agar plate

Inoculate a single colony of an appropriate *E. coli* strain into 25 ml of NZCYM medium and incubate overnight at 30ºC. Measure the OD_{600} of the overnight culture and calculate the number of cells/ml using the conversion factor: $1\ OD_{600} = 1 \times 10^9$ cells/ml.

Growth at 30ºC increases the chance that the cells will not have reached saturation during the overnight growth period. The amount of cell debris in the medium is therefore kept to a minimum. Bacteriophages added to a saturated culture can attach to the MalB protein present on cellular debris, leading to a non-productive infection.

METHOD

1. Use a borosilicate Pasteur pipette to pick a single well-isolated bacteriophage plaque into 1 ml of SM containing a drop of chloroform in a small sterile polypropylene tube. Store the suspension for 4–6 hours at 4ºC to allow the bacteriophage particles to diffuse from the top agarose.

2. In a 25-ml tube, mix 0.5 ml of the bacteriophage suspension (~3×10^6 bacteriophages) with 0.1 ml of an overnight culture of bacteria. Incubate the culture for 15 minutes at 37ºC.

    The yield of bacteriophage particles (and hence DNA) is greatly affected by the absolute amounts and relative amounts of bacteriophages and bacterial cells in the inoculum for the liquid lysate. When using an unfamiliar strain of *E. coli*, bacteriophage λ vector, or recombinant, it is best to set up a series of cultures containing different ratios of bacteria and bacteriophages. Prepare bacteriophage λ DNA from each of the resulting liquid lysates.

3. Add 4 ml of NZCYM medium, and incubate the culture for ~9 hours at 37ºC with vigorous agitation.

    The culture should clear, but very little debris should be evident.

    > If lysis does not occur or is incomplete, add an equal volume of prewarmed NZCYM medium to the cultures and continue incubation for a further 2–3 hours at 37ºC with vigorous agitation. This step will occasionally drive the culture to complete lysis (and produce a higher yield of bacteriophage DNA).
    >
    > Problems sometimes arise because minipreparations of bacteriophage DNA are contaminated by bacterial DNA or RNA. In this case, digest the culture lysate with DNase I before batch chromatography on DE52. To include this step, add crude pancreatic DNase I (please see Protocol 6) to a final concentration of 10 ng/ml before starting Step 4, and incubate the lysate for 30 minutes at 37ºC. Thereafter, continue with the remainder of the protocol. DNase treatment decreases the viscosity of the lysate and may enhance removal of *E. coli* genomic DNA and RNA by DEAE-cellulose chromatography.

4. Add 0.1 ml of chloroform to the culture and continue incubation for a further 15 minutes at 37ºC with vigorous agitation. Transfer the lysate to a 5-ml polypropylene centrifuge tube. Centrifuge at 800*g* (2600 rpm in a Sorvall SS-34 rotor) for 10 minutes at 4ºC.

5. Transfer the supernatant to a fresh tube, and remove the bacterial debris by centrifugation at 4000*g* (5800 rpm in a Sorvall SS-34 rotor) for 10 minutes at 4ºC. A small aliquot of cleared lysate can be set aside at this step as a bacteriophage stock solution. Store the stock at 4ºC over chloroform.

6. Dispense 10 ml of a 2:1 slurry of DE52 resin into a fresh centrifuge tube and sediment the resin by centrifugation at 500*g* (2000 rpm in a Sorvall SS-34 rotor) for 5 minutes at room temperature. Remove the supernatant from the resin pellet and place the centrifuge tube on ice.

7. Resuspend the DE52 in the cleared bacteriophage λ supernatant and allow the bacteriophage particles to absorb to the resin by rocking the centrifuge tube for 3 minutes at room temperature.

8. Centrifuge the bacteriophage λ supernatant/DE52 slurry at 4000*g* (5800 rpm in a Sorvall SS-34 rotor) for 5 minutes. Carefully transfer the supernatant to a fresh centrifuge tube and repeat the centrifugation step. Discard the pellet after each centrifugation.

9. Transfer the supernatant from the second centrifugation to a fresh centrifuge tube. Extract the supernatant, which contains the bacteriophage λ particles, once with phenol:chloroform.

10. Transfer the aqueous phase, which contains the bacteriophage λ DNA, to a fresh polypropylene tube and add an equal volume of isopropanol. Store the mixture for 10 minutes at −70ºC.

11. Collect the precipitated bacteriophage DNA by centrifugation at 16,500*g* (12,000 rpm in a Sorvall SS-34 rotor) for 20 minutes at 4ºC.

12. Drain the isopropanol from the centrifuge tube and allow the pellet of DNA to dry in the air.

13. Dissolve the DNA pellet in 2 ml of low-salt buffer.

14. Purify the bacteriophage DNA by chromatography on an Elutip-d column as described in Protocol 23.

15. Mix 1 ml of ethanol with the solution of eluted DNA and incubate the mixture on ice for 20 minutes. Collect the precipitated DNA by centrifugation in a microfuge, discard the supernatant, and rinse the pellet of DNA with 0.5 ml of 70% ethanol. Discard the supernatant and allow the ethanol to evaporate. Dissolve the damp pellet of DNA in 50 µl of TE (pH 8.0).

    Resuspend the DNA by tapping on the side of the tube. Try to avoid vortexing. If the DNA proves difficult to dissolve, incubate the tube for 15 minutes at 50ºC.

    If minipreparations are working well, expect to isolate ~5 µg of purified bacteriophage DNA from 5 x 10^{10} infectious particles. It is possible to estimate the quantity of bacteriophage DNA present in a plate lysate or liquid culture lysate by direct agarose gel electrophoresis (please see Protocol 7).

    For restriction analysis and agarose gel electrophoresis, digest a 5–10-µl aliquot of the resuspended DNA. If resistant to cleavage, treat the DNA samples according to the method described in **ADDITIONAL PROTOCOL: REMOVING POLYSACCHARIDES BY PRECIPITATION WITH CTAB** in Protocol 23.

BACTERIOPHAGES: HISTORICAL PERSPECTIVE

In 1909, Frederick William Twort was made Director of the Brown Animal Sanitary Institution in London, which had been set up ~40 years before as a hospital "for the care and treatment of Quadrupeds and Birds useful to Man." Twort, who had been trained as a microbiologist, had one scientific idea that he pursued all of his life — that pathogenic bacteria needed an "Essential Substance" for growth and vitality. Each organism required a different nutrient substance that was normally provided by the infected host. This was an important idea at the time, opening up an entire field of the nutritional requirements of bacteria and leading to the development of vaccines for pathogenic organisms that previously had been impossible to culture. In 1914, Twort set out to identify the elusive substance that would allow vaccinia virus to grow in vitro. At that time, smallpox vaccines were prepared in the skin of calves and were almost always contaminated with *Staphylococcus*. Twort wondered whether the contaminating bacteria might be the source of the essential substance for vaccinia. He plated the smallpox vaccine on nutrient agar slants and obtained large bacterial colonies of several colors. In addition, with the aid of a hand lens, he saw minute glassy areas that failed to grow when subcultured. He quickly realized that these were not degenerative changes but rather were the end stages of an acute infectious disease that destroyed the bacterial cells and could be artificially transmitted from one staphylococcal colony to another. In a publication in the *Lancet* in 1915, he called the contagion the Bacteriolytic Agent. Additional experiments proved that the agent could pass through porcelain filters and required bacteria for growth. Twort seems to have flirted with the idea that the Bacteriolytic Agent was vaccinia that invaded the bacteria in search of the Essential Substance.

Twort, like others, became interested in the possibility of using bacteriolytic agents to cure bacterial diseases of humans and animals. When this approach proved to be unsuccessful, Twort retreated to his original idea — that bacteriolytic agents required an additional factor of an exceptional nature to satisfy their fundamental physiological needs. However, his search for a substance that would allow viruses to grow apart from other forms of life was fruitless and his later research became decreasingly rational as he struggled to prove that bacteria evolved from viruses. Financial support for Twort's work had dwindled to almost nothing when, in 1944, the Brown Institution was destroyed by a bomb. This gave the University of London a long-sought opportunity to deprive Twort of his post and research facilities. He retired to live at Camberley, in a house appropriately called "The Wilderness."

In 1949, Twort wrote an embittered account of his experiences. By then, his work was largely forgotten and even the name Bacteriolytic Agent had been discarded in favor of Bacteriophage. By then, too, the physical nature of bacteriophages was understood: Their structures had been analyzed by electron microscopy, and quantitative assays of infectivity had been established. The ability to infect bacteria synchronously in a single-step growth experiment had opened the way to biochemical analysis of bacteriophage replication. The first bacteriophage mutants had been isolated, and genetic recombination had been demonstrated (Cairns et al. 1992). Finally, the ready emergence of bacterial mutants that were resistant to bacteriophage infection provided a rational explanation for the failure of bacteriophages as therapeutic agents. All this seems to have passed Twort by. He died in 1950, unaware of the impact of his early discovery and with his belief in an Essential Substance intact.

In 1917, two years after Twort's original publication, a French-Canadian, Felix D'Herelle, presented a paper to the Académie des Sciènces on a microorganism (Le Bactériophage) that could kill dysentery bacilli. Whether D'Herelle was aware of Twort's work has been a matter of speculation. D'Herelle vigorously denied knowledge of Twort's earlier discovery and made persistent attempts to claim priority for himself. For many years, therefore, lysis of bacteria by phages was diplomatically known as the Twort-D'Herelle phenomenon. D'Herelle was a more incisive thinker than Twort and quickly recognized that bacteriophages behaved as infectious particles that could be titrated by plaque formation. He went on to describe a three-step process for the life history of the bacteriophage (attachment, multiplication, and release) that is remarkably accurate and perceptive (D'Herelle 1926). However, like Twort, D'Herelle became fascinated by the idea that bacteriophages could be used to cure bacterial infections and over the years collected a large amount of anecdotal data in support of this idea. Unlike Twort, D'Herelle tended to discount facts that were inconvenient and to the end remained a flamboyant proselytizer of an idea that even Twort had long since abandoned.

For a more detailed account of D'Herelle's discovery of bacteriophages, written with the benefit of hindsight, please see D'Herelle (1949).

MINIMIZING DAMAGE TO LARGE DNA MOLECULES

Long molecules of high-molecular-weight DNA (>100 kb) are easily broken by shearing forces. Conventional methods of extracting and concentrating DNA, which include extraction with organic solvents and precipitation with ethanol or butanol, typically yield molecules smaller than 100 kb in size. Even linear DNA molecules as short as 50 kb — the size of the bacteriophage λ genome — can be broken by excessively rapid and prolonged pipetting and vigorous shaking.

Linear double-stranded DNA behaves in solution as a random coil that is stiffened by (1) stacking interactions between bases and (2) electrostatic repulsion between the regularly spaced negatively charged phosphates in the backbone. The rigidity of long DNA molecules leaves them vulnerable to shearing forces that cause double-stranded breaks, which occur most often in the center of the extended molecules. Velocity gradients strong enough to shear DNA are generated when solutions are agitated by vortexing or shaking, when solutions are drawn into or expelled from pipettes, or when long molecules of DNA are dissolved after precipitation by alcohols.

One way to minimize damage to DNA during transfer is simply to pour the solution from one container to another. However, this is not always feasible and is a risky business at the best of times. Solutions of high-molecular-weight DNA are viscous and tend to flow in one great lump rather than in a smooth controllable stream.

Wide-bore pipettes offer a safer method. These pipettes can be purchased commercially or fashioned as needed in the laboratory by cutting the tips from disposable plastic pipettes, blue pipette tips, or Pasteur pipettes. However, the small amount of negative pressure provided by rubber bulbs or a manual pipetting device may not be sufficient to retain extremely viscous solutions of DNA in the pipette. Electrically driven automatic pipettes (such as PipetteAids) are, therefore, preferred. The following are additional ways to minimize shearing.

- Stir rather than shake DNA solutions.
- Maintain a high DNA concentration.
- Use a buffer of high ionic strength to thereby reduce the electrostatic forces that confer stiffness upon large DNA molecules.
- Add condensing agents such as spermine or polylysine.
- Isolate and manipulate DNA inside agarose blocks (please see Chapter 5, Protocol 15). This method is not required when preparing genomic DNA for cloning in cosmids or bacteriophage λ vectors. However, it is the method of choice when preparing high-molecular-weight DNA for cloning in bacteriophage P1 vectors or when constructing bacterial and yeast artificial chromosomes.

IN VITRO PACKAGING

Packaging of bacteriophage λ DNA in vitro was initially developed by Becker and Gold (1975) using mixtures of extracts prepared from bacteria infected with strains of bacteriophage λ carrying mutations in genes required for the assembly of bacteriophage particles. The procedure has been modified and improved to the point where 2×10^9 pfu can be generated routinely in packaging reactions containing 1.0 µg of intact bacteriophage λ DNA. This high efficiency of packaging, coupled with the development of a large stable of bacteriophage λ vectors and the ability to screen libraries by hybridization or immunochemical methods, led to the dominance of these vectors in cDNA library construction in the 1980s. The increased use of bacteriophage λ as a cloning vector also led to the development of commercial packaging reactions. Today, the preparation of packaging reactions as described in the Second Edition of this manual is almost a lost art, even in the laboratories of experienced bacteriophage workers. Commercial packaging reactions work exceedingly well and are so reasonably priced that they have replaced homemade extracts in most routine cloning tasks. However, for specialized applications such as the construction of linking and jumping genomic DNA libraries (which use huge numbers of packaging reactions), it is worth taking the time to prepare home-brewed packaging extracts (Poustka 1993). Packaging extracts are prepared by one of two general strategies:

1. Expression of bacteriophage λ genes is induced in two separate lysogens that provide complementing components of the packaging reaction (e.g., please see Scalenghe et al. 1981). As a consequence of mutations in the prophage genomes, neither lysogen alone is capable of packaging exogenously added bacteriophage DNA. Extracts of each culture are prepared separately and blended at the bench into a mixture that contains all of the components necessary for packaging. The resulting packaging mixtures are efficient, typically yielding in excess of 10^9 pfu/μg of bacteriophage λ DNA, and essentially free from background (when assayed on appropriate hosts strains). Examples of commercially available, two-component systems are Gigapack II Gold (Stratagene) and the λ packaging system available from Life Technologies.

2. A single *E. coli* C bacteriophage λ lysogen is used to prepare an extract that contains all of the components necessary to package exogenously added viral DNA (Rosenberg 1987). One lysogen can be used to prepare packaging extracts for two reasons. First, the prophage carried in the lysogenic strain codes for all of the proteins needed for packaging. Second, the *cos* site of the prophage has been deleted. These features work together in the following manner. Induction of the lysogen results in the intracellular accumulation of all protein components needed for packaging, and complete preheads are formed. However, the next steps in the packaging process are the recognition of the *cos* sites on concatenated bacteriophage λ DNA by the bacteriophage A protein and the insertion of the bacteriophage λ genome into the prehead. The lack of the *cos* site in the prophage DNA prevents this step from occurring, and packaging is thus effectively halted at the prehead stage, even though all of the necessary components used later in the process are present. However, exogenous DNA with an active *cos* site can be inserted into the prehead, and the packaging process then leads to the production of an infectious bacteriophage particle. Extracts made in this way usually have a lower background of plaques than the classical binary mixtures, because the deletion of the *cos* site blocks packaging of endogenous bacteriophage λ DNA more completely than the mutations present in the binary strains. *E. coli* C was chosen as the lysogenic host to lessen the probability of recombination between cryptic bacteriophage λ prophages, which are known to be present in the genome of *E. coli* K, and the *cos*-deleted prophage. Furthermore, *E. coli* C lacks the *Eco*K restriction system (Rosenberg 1985). This system, like other restriction systems, cuts unmodified DNA in a sequence-specific manner and is also functional in packaging reactions in vitro. Thus, extracts prepared from cells of *E. coli* K have the potential to select against DNA that contains an unmodified *Eco*K recognition site. Because eukaryotic DNA used to construct libraries will not be protected from cleavage, clones that by chance contain an *Eco*K recognition site may be lost from the population during packaging. Reconstruction experiments show that bacteriophage λ DNA carrying an *Eco*K recognition site is packaged two- to sevenfold less efficiently in extracts derived from *E. coli* K than in extracts prepared from *E. coli* C (Rosenberg 1985).

The *E. coli* C restriction-modification systems express components (*mcrA /mcrB* and *mrr*) that digest DNA carrying methyl groups on cytosine and adenine residues. (e.g., please see Kretz et al. 1989; Kohler et al. 1990). Because most eukaryotic DNAs are methylated on these residues, packaging extracts from strains of *E. coli* carrying intact *mcr* and *mrr* systems select against methylated eukaryotic DNA sequences. However, the use of packaging extracts prepared from bacterial cells deficient in the *Eco*K, *mcr*, and *mrr* genes (genotype Δ[*mrr-hsd*RMS-*mcr*B]) effectively eliminates this problem (Kretz et al. 1989). For good measure, the *mcrF*- and *mrr*-encoded restriction systems have also been eliminated from the *E. coli* strains used to prepare some commercially available in vitro packaging extracts. Examples of commercially available single-component bacteriophage λ packaging extracts are the Gigapack III Gold from Stratagene, the MaxPlax packaging extract from Epicentre Technologies, and the Packagene extract from Promega.

REFERENCES

Albertsen H.M, Abderrahim H., Cann H.M., Dausset J., Le Paslier D., and Cohen D. 1990. Construction and characterization of a yeast artificial chromosome library containing seven haploid human genome equivalents. *Proc. Natl. Acad. Sci.* **87:** 4256–4260.

Amundsen S.K., Taylor A.F., Chaudhury A.M., and Smith G.R. 1986. *rec*D: The gene for an essential third subunit of exonuclease V. *Proc. Natl. Acad. Sci.* **83:** 5558–5562.

Appleyard R.K. 1954. Segregation of new lysogenic types during growth of a doubly lysogenic strain derived from *Escherichia coli* K12. *Genetics* **39:** 440–452.

Arber W., Enquist L., Hohn B., Murray N.E., and Murray K. 1983. Experimental methods for use with lambda. In *Lambda II* (ed. R.W. Hendrix et al.), pp. 433–466. Cold Spring Harbor Laboratory, Cold Spring Harbor, New York.

Bajorath J., Hinrichs W., and Saenger W. 1988. The enzymatic activity of proteinase K is controlled by calcium. *Eur. J. Biochem.* **176:** 441–447.

Bajorath J., Raghunathan S., Hinrichs W., and Saenger W. 1989. Long-range structural changes in proteinase K triggered by calcium ion removal. *Nature* **337:** 481–484.

Banuett F., Hoyt M.A., MacFarlane L., Echols H., and Herskowitz I. 1986. *hfl*B, a new *Escherichia coli* locus regulating lysogeny and the level of bacteriophage lambda cII protein. *J. Mol. Biol.* **187:** 213–224.

Barnes W.M. 1994. PCR amplification of up to 35-kb DNA with high fidelity and high yield from lambda bacteriophage templates. *Proc. Natl. Acad. Sci.* **91:** 2216–2220.

Beamer L.J. and Pabo C.O. 1992. Refined 1.8 Å crystal structure of the λ repressor-operator complex. *J. Mol. Biol.* **227:** 177–196.

Becker A. and Gold M. 1975. Isolation of the bacteriophage lambda A-gene protein. *Proc. Natl. Acad. Sci.* **72:** 581–585.

Becker A. and Murialdo H. 1990. Bacteriophage λ DNA: The beginning of the end. *J. Bacteriol.* **172:** 2819–2823.

Becker A., Marko M., and Gold M. 1977. Early events in the *in vitro* packaging of bacteriophage λ DNA. *Virology* **78:** 291–305.

Benton W.D. and Davis R.W. 1977. Screening lambda gt recombinant clones by hybridization to single plaques in situ. *Science* **196:** 180–182.

Betzel C., Pal G.P., and Saenger W. 1988. Three-dimensional structure of proteinase K at 0.15nm resolution. *Eur. J. Biochem.* **178:** 155–171.

Black L.W. 1988. DNA packaging in dsDNA bacteriophages. In *The bacteriophages* (ed. R. Calendar), vol. 2, pp. 321–373. Plenum Press, New York.

Blaisdell B.E., Rudd K.E., Matin A., and Karlin S. 1993. Significant dispersed recurrent DNA sequences in the *Escherichia coli* genome. Several new groups. *J. Mol. Biol.* **229:** 833–848.

Blattner F.R., Williams B.G., Blechl A.E., Denniston-Thompson K., Faber H.E., Furlong L.-A., Grunwald D.J., Kiefer D.O., Moore D.D., Schumm J.W., Sheldon E.L., and Smithies O. 1977. Charon phages: Safer derivatives of bacteriophage lambda for DNA cloning. *Science* **196:** 161–169.

Bode V.C. and Kaiser A.D. 1965. Repression of the cII and cIII cistrons of phage lambda in a lysogenic bacterium. *Virology* **25:** 111–121.

Bolivar F. and Backman K. 1979. Plasmids of *Escherichia coli* as cloning vectors. *Methods Enzymol.* **68:** 245–267.

Borck K., Beggs J.D., Brammar W.J., Hopkins A.S., and Murray N.E. 1976. The construction in vitro of transducing derivatives of phage lambda. *Mol. Gen. Genet.* **146:** 199–207.

Boyd J. 1951. 'Excessive dose' phenomenon in virus infections. *Nature* **167:** 1061–1062.

Boyer H.W. and Roulland-Dussoix D. 1969. A complementation analysis of the restriction and modification of DNA in *Escherichia coli. J. Mol. Biol.* **41:** 459–472.

Brakke M.K. 1958. Estimation of sedimentation constants of viruses by density-gradient centrifugation. *Virology* **6:** 96–114.

Brock T.D. 1990. Lysogeny. In *The emergence of bacterial genetics*, pp. 163–188. Cold Spring Harbor Laboratory Press, Cold Spring Harbor, New York.

Bullock W.O., Fernandez J.M., and Short J.M. 1987. Xl1-blue: A high efficiency plasmid transforming recA *Escherichia coli* strain with beta-galactosidase selection. *BioTechniques* **5:** 376–379.

Burland V., Plunkett III, G., Daniels D.L., and Blattner F.R. 1993. DNA sequence and analysis of 136 kilobases of the *Escherichia coli* genome: Organizational symmetry around the origin of replication. *Genomics* **16:** 551–561.

Cairns J., Stent G.S., and Watson J.D., eds. 1992. *Phage and the origins of molecular biology*, expanded edition. Cold Spring Harbor Laboratory Press, Cold Spring Harbor, New York.

Campbell A.M. 1962. Episomes (review). *Adv. Genet.* **11:** 101–145.

———. 1965. The steric effect in lysogenization by bacteriophage lambda. I. Lysogenization of a partially diploid strain of *Escherichia coli* K12. *Virology* **27:** 329–339.

———. 1993. Thirty years ago in *Genetics:* Prophage insertion into bacterial chromosomes. *Genetics* **133:** 433-437.

Casjens S. and Hendrix R. 1988. Control mechanisms in dsDNA bacteriophage assembly. In *The bacteriophages* (ed. R. Calendar), vol. 1, pp. 15–91. Plenum Press, New York.

Casjens S., Horn T., and Kaiser A.D. 1972. Head assembly steps controlled by genes *F* and *W* in bacteriophage λ. *J. Mol. Biol.* **64:** 551–563.

Chattoraj D.K. and Inman R.B. 1974. Location of DNA ends in P2, 186, P4 and lambda bacteriophage heads. *J. Mol. Biol.* **87:** 11–22.

Court D. and Sato K. 1969. Studies of novel transducing variants of lambda: Dispensability of genes *N* and *Q*. *Virology* **39:** 348–352.

Craig N.L. and Nash H.A. 1983. The mechanism of phage λ site-specific recombination: Site-specific breakage of DNA by Int topoisomerase. *Cell* **35:** 795–803.

Crouse G.F. 1985. Plasmids supplying the *Q-qut*-controlled *gam* function permit growth of lambda *red⁻ gam⁻* (Fec) bacteriophages on *rec*A hosts. *Gene* **40:** 151–155.

Cue D. and Feiss M. 1993. The role of *cos B*, the binding site for terminase, the DNA packaging enzyme of bacteriophage λ, in the nicking reaction. *J. Mol. Biol.* **234:** 594–609.

Daniels D.L., Schroeder J.L., Szybalski W., Sanger F., and Blattner F.R. 1983a. Appendix I: A molecular map of coliphage lambda. In *Lambda II* (ed. R.W. Hendrix et al.), pp. 469–517. Cold Spring Harbor Laboratory, Cold Spring Harbor, New York.

Daniels D.L., Schroeder J.L., Szybalski W., Sanger F., Coulson A.R., Hong G.F., Hill D.F., Petersen G.B., and Blattner F.R. 1983b. Appendix II: Complete annotated lambda sequence.

In *Lambda II* (ed. R.W. Hendrix et al.), pp. 519–676. Cold Spring Harbor Laboratory, Cold Spring Harbor, New York.

Das A. 1993. Control of transcription termination by RNA-binding proteins. *Annu. Rev. Biochem.* **62:** 893–930.

Davison J., Brunel F., and Merchez M. 1979. A new host-vector system allowing selection for foreign DNA inserts in bacteriophage λgtWES. *Gene* **8:** 69–80.

D'Herelle F. 1926. *The bacteriophage and its behavior.* Williams and Wilkins, Baltimore, Maryland.

———. 1949. The bacteriophage. *Science News* (Penguin Press, Harmondsworth, England) **14:** 44–59. .

Dove W.F. 1966. Action of the λ chromosome. I. Control of functions late in bacteriophage development. *J. Mol. Biol.* **19:** 187–201.

Dugaiczyk A., Boyer H.W., and Goodman H.M. 1975. Ligation of *EcoRI* endonuclease-generated DNA fragments into linear and circular structures. *J. Mol. Biol.* **96:** 171–184.

Dunn I.S. and Blattner F.R. 1987. Charons 36 to 40: Multienzyme, high capacity, recombination deficient replacement vectors with polylinkers and polystuffers. *Nucleic Acids Res.* **15:** 2677–2698.

Ebeling W., Hennrich N., Klockow M., Metz H., Orth H.D., and Lang H. 1974. Proteinase K from *Tritirachium album Limber.* *Eur. J. Biochem.* **47:** 91–97.

Echols H. 1980. Bacteriophage λ development. In *The molecular genetics of development* (ed. T. Leighton and W.F. Loomis, Jr.), pp. 1–16. Academic Press, New York.

Emmons S. 1974. Bacteriophage λ derivatives carrying two copies of the cohesive end site. *J. Mol. Biol.* **83:** 511–525.

Enquist L.W. and Weisberg R.A. 1976. The red plaque test: A rapid method for identification of excision defective variants of bacteriophage lambda. *Virology* **72:** 147–153.

Faulds D., Dower N., Stahl M.M., and Stahl F.W. 1979. Orientation-dependent recombinational hotspot activity in bacteriophage λ. *J. Mol. Biol.* **131:** 681–695.

Feiss M. 1986. Terminase and the recognition, cutting and packaging of λ chromosomes. *Trends Genet.* **2:** 100–104.

Feiss M. and Becker A. 1983. DNA packaging and cutting. In *Lambda II* (ed. R.W. Hendrix et al.), pp. 305–330. Cold Spring Harbor Laboratory, Cold Spring Harbor, New York.

Feiss M. and Campbell A. 1974. Duplication of the bacteriophage lambda cohesive end site: Genetic studies. *J. Mol. Biol.* **83:** 527–540.

Ferenci T. and Boos W. 1980. The role of the *Escherichia coli* lambda receptor in the transport of maltose and maltodextrins. *J. Supramol. Struct.* **13:** 101–116.

Fong R.S.-C., Woody S., and Gusssin G.N. 1993. Modulation of P_{RM} activity by the lambda P_R promoter in both the presence and absence of repressor. *J. Mol. Biol.* **232:** 792–804.

Frackman S., Siegele D.A., and Feiss M. 1984. A functional domain of bacteriophage λ terminase for prohead binding. *J. Mol. Biol.* **180:** 283–300.

Franklin N.C. 1971. Illegitimate recombination. In *The bacteriophage lambda* (ed. A.D. Hershey), pp. 175–194. Cold Spring Harbor Laboratory, Cold Spring Harbor, New York.

Friedman D.I., Obson E.R., Georgopoulos C., Tilly K., Herskowitz I., and Banuett F. 1984. Interactions of bacteriophage and host macromolecules in the growth of bacteriophage lambda. *Microbiol. Rev.* **48:** 299–325.

Friedman D.I. 1988. Regulation of phage gene expression by termination and antitermination of transcription. In *The bacteriophages* (ed. R. Calendar), vol. 2, pp. 263–319. Plenum Press, New York.

———. 1992. Interaction between bacteriophage λ and its *Escherichia coli* host. *Curr. Opin. Genet. Dev.* **2:** 727–738.

Frischauf A.M., Lehrach H., Poustka A., and Murray N. 1983. Lambda replacement vectors carrying polylinker sequences. *J. Mol. Biol.* **170:** 827–842.

Furth M.E. and Wickner S.H. 1983. Lambda DNA replication. In *Lambda II* (ed. R.W. Hendrix et al.), pp. 145–173. Cold Spring Harbor Laboratory, Cold Spring Harbor, New York.

Gingery R. and Echols H. 1967. Mutants of bacteriophage λ unable to integrate into the host chromosome. *Proc. Natl. Acad. Sci.* **58:** 1507–1514.

Gold M. and Becker A. 1983. The bacteriophage λ terminase: Partial purification and preliminary characterization of properties. *J. Biol. Chem.* **258:** 14619–14625.

Gottesman S., Gottesman M., Shaw J.E., and Pearson M.L. 1981. Protein degradation in *E. coli:* The *lon* mutation and bacteriophage lambda N and cII protein stability. *Cell* **24:** 225–233.

Gough J.A. and Murray N.E. 1983. Sequence diversity among related genes for recognition of specific targets in DNA molecules. *J. Mol. Biol.* **166:** 1–19.

Grayhack E.J., Yang X.J., Lau L.F., and Roberts J.W. 1985. Phage lambda gene Q antiterminator recognizes RNA polymerase near the promoter and accelerates it through a pause site. *Cell* **42:** 259–269.

Greenstein M. and Skalka A. 1975. Replication of bacteriophage λ DNA: *In vivo* studies of the interaction between the viral gamma protein and the host *recBC* DNAase. *J. Mol. Biol.* **97:** 543–549.

Grodzicker T., Arditti R.R., and Eisen H. 1972. Establishment of repression by lambdoid phage in catabolite activator protein and adenylate cyclase mutants of *Escherichia coli. Proc. Natl. Acad. Sci.* **69:** 366–370.

Guarente L., Nye J.S., Hochschild A., and Ptashne M. 1982. Mutant λ phage repressor with a specific defect in its positive control function. *Proc. Natl. Acad. Sci.* **79:** 2236–2239.

Gunkel F.A. and Gassen H.G. 1989. Proteinase K from *Tritirachium album* Limber. Characterization of the chromosomal gene and expression of the cDNA in *Escherichia coli. Eur. J. Biochem.* **179:** 185–194.

Gussin G.N., Johnson A.D., Pabo C.O., and Sauer R.T. 1983. Repressor and cro protein: Structure, function and role in lysogenization. In *Lambda II* (ed. R.W. Hendrix et al.), pp. 93–121. Cold Spring Harbor Laboratory, Cold Spring Harbor, New York.

Han J.H. and Rutter W.J. 1987. λgt22, an improved λ vector for the directional cloning of full-length cDNA. *Nucleic Acids Res.* **15:** 6304.

———. 1988. Isolation of intact mRNA and construction of full-length cDNA libraries: Use of a new vector λgt22, and primer-adapters for directional cDNA cloning. *Genet. Eng.* **10:** 195–219.

Harrison S.C. 1992. Molecular characteristics of the regulatory switch in phages 434 and λ. In *Transcriptional regulation* (ed. S.L. McKnight and K.R. Yamamoto), pp. 449–473. Cold Spring Harbor Laboratory Press, Cold Spring Harbor, New York.

Hawley D.K. and McClure W.R. 1983. The effect of lambda repressor mutation on the activation of transcription initiation from the lambda P_{RM} promoter. *Cell* **32:** 327–333.

Helms C., Dutchik J.E., and Olson M.V. 1987. A lambda DNA protocol based on purification of phage on DEAE-cellulose. *Methods Enzymol.* **153:** 69–82.

Helms C., Graham M.Y., Dutchik J.E., and Olson M.V. 1985. A

new method for purifying lambda DNA from phage lysates. *DNA* **4:** 39–49.

Henderson D. and Weil J. 1975. Recombination-deficient deletions in bacteriophage lambda and their interaction with *chi* mutations. *Genetics* **79:** 143–174.

Hendrix R.W. 1978. Symmetry mismatch and DNA packaging in large bacteriophages. *Proc. Natl. Acad. Sci.* **75:** 4779–4783.

Hendrix R.W., Roberts J.W., Stahl. F.W., and Weisberg R.A., eds. 1983. *Lambda II.* Cold Spring Harbor Laboratory, Cold Spring Harbor, New York.

Hershberger P.A., Mita B.C., Tripatara A., and deHaseth P.L. 1993. Interference by P_R-bound RNA polymerase with P_{RM} function *in vitro*. Modulation by the bacteriophage lambda cl protein. *J. Biol. Chem.* **268:** 8943–8948.

Herskowitz I. and Hagen D. 1980. The lysis-lysogeny decision of phage λ: Explicit programming and responsiveness. *Annu. Rev. Genet.* **14:** 399–445.

Higgins R.R., Lucko H.J., and Becker A. 1988. Mechanism of *cos* DNA cleavage by bacteriophage λ terminase: Multiple roles of ATP. *Cell* **54:** 765–775.

Hilz H., Wiegers U., and Adamietz P. 1975. Stimulation of proteinase K action by denaturing agents: Application to the isolation of nucleic acids and the degradation of 'masked' proteins. *Eur. J. Biochem.* **56:** 103–108.

Ho Y.S. and Rosenberg M. 1988. Structure and function of the transcription activator protein cII and its regulatory signals. In *The bacteriophages* (ed. R. Calendar), vol. 2, pp. 725–756. Plenum Press, New York.

Hochschild A. 1994. Transcriptional activation. How λ repressor talks to RNA polymerase. *Curr. Biol.* **4:** 440–442.

Hochschild A., Irwin N., and Ptashne M. 1983. Repressor structure and the mechanism of positive control. *Cell* **32:** 319–325.

Hoess R.H., Foeller C., Bidwell K., and Landy A. 1980. Site-specific recombination functions of bacteriophage λ: DNA sequence of regulatory regions and overlapping structural genes for Int and Xis. *Proc. Natl. Acad. Sci.* **77:** 2482–2486.

Hoheisel J.D., Nizetic D., and Lehrach H. 1989. Control of partial digestion combining the enzymes dam methylase and MboI. *Nucleic Acids Res.* **17:** 9571–9582.

Hohn B. 1979. *In vitro* packaging of λ and cosmid DNA. *Methods Enzymol.* **68:** 299–309.

———. 1983. DNA sequences necessary for packaging of bacteriophage λ DNA. *Proc. Natl. Acad. Sci.* **80:** 7456–7460.

Hohn B. and Murray K. 1977. Packaging recombinant DNA molecules into bacteriophage particles *in vitro*. *Proc. Natl. Acad. Sci.* **74:** 3259–3263.

Hong J.S., Smith G.R., and Ames B.N. 1971. Adenosine 3′:5′-cyclic monophosphate concentration in the bacterial host regulates the viral decision between lysogeny and lysis. *Proc. Natl. Acad. Sci.* **68:** 2258–2262.

Hoyt M.A., Knight D.M., Das A., Miller H.I., and Echols H. 1982. Control of phage lambda development by stability and synthesis of cII protein: Role of the viral cIII and host *hflA, himA* and *himD* genes. *Cell* **31:** 565–573.

Hsaio C.L. and Black L.W. 1977. DNA packaging and the pathway of bacteriophage T4 head assembly. *Proc. Natl. Acad. Sci.* **74:** 3652–3656.

Huynh T.V., Young R.A., and Davis R.W. 1985. Constructing and screening cDNA libraries in λgt10 and λgt11. In *DNA cloning: A practical approach* (ed. D.M. Glover), vol. 1, pp. 49–78. IRL Press, Oxford, United Kingdom.

Jany K.-D., Lederer G., and Mayer B. 1986. Amino acid sequence

of proteinase K from the mold *Tritirachium album Limber*. *FEBS Lett.* **199:** 139–144.

Jendrisak J., Young R.A., and Engel J.D. 1987. Cloning cDNA into λgt10 and λgt11. *Methods Enzymol.* **152:** 359–371.

Jerpseth B., Greener, A., Short J.M., Viola J., and Kretz P.L. 1992. XL1-Blue MRF E. *coli* cells: McrA⁻, McrCB⁻, McrF⁻, Mrr⁻, HsdR⁻derivative of XL1-Blue cells. *Strategies Newsletter* **5:** 81–83. Stratagene, La Jolla, California.

Johnson A.D., Meyer B.J., and Ptashne M. 1978. Mechanism of action of the cro protein of bacteriophage λ. *Proc. Natl. Acad. Sci.* **75:** 1783–1787.

———. 1979. Interactions between DNA-bound repressors govern regulation by the λ phage repressor. *Proc. Natl. Acad. Sci.* **76:** 5061–5065.

Joyner A., Isaacs L.N., Echols H., and Sly W.S. 1966. DNA replication and messenger RNA production after induction of wild-type lambda bacteriophage and lambda mutants. *J. Mol. Biol.* **19:** 174–186.

Kaiser D. 1955. A genetic study of the temperate coliphage λ. *Virology* **1:** 424–443.

Kaiser D., Syvanen M., and Masuda T. 1975. DNA packaging steps in bacteriophage lambda head assembly. *J. Mol. Biol.* **91:** 175–186.

Karn J., Brenner S., Barnett L., and Cesareni G. 1980. Novel bacteriophage λ cloning vector. *Proc. Natl. Acad. Sci.* **77:** 5172–5176.

Karn J., Matthes H.W., Gait M.J., and Brenner S. 1984. A new selective cloning vector, λ2001, with sites for *Xba*I, *Bam*HI, *Hin*dIII, *Eco*RI, *Sst*I and *Xho*I. *Gene* **32:** 217–224.

Khandjian E.W. 1987. Optimized hybridization of DNA blotted and fixed to nitrocellulose and nylon membranes. *BioTechnology* **5:** 165–167.

Kikuchi Y. and Nash H.A. 1979a. Integrative recombination of bacteriophage λ: Requirement for supertwisted DNA *in vivo* and characterization of Int. *Cold Spring Harbor Symp. Quant. Biol.* **43:** 1099–1109.

———. 1979b. Nicking-closing activity associated with bacteriophage λ *int* gene product. *Proc. Natl. Acad. Sci.* **76:** 3760–3764.

Kim S. and Landy A. 1992. Lambda Int protein bridges between higher order complexes at two distant chromosomal loci *attL* and *attR*. *Science* **256:** 198–203.

Klein B. and Murray K. 1979. Phage lambda receptor chromosomes for DNA fragments made with restriction endonuclease I of *Bacillus amyloliquefaciens* H. *J. Mol. Biol.* **133:** 289–294.

Kohler S.W., Provost G.S., Kretz P.L., Dycaico M.J., Sorge J.A., and Short J.M. 1990. Development of a short-term, in vivo mutagenesis assay: The effects of methylation on the recovery of a lambda phage shuttle vector from transgenic mice. *Nucleic Acids Res.* **18:** 3007–3013.

Kornberg A. and Baker T.A. 1992. *DNA replication*, 2nd edition. W.H. Freeman, New York.

Kourilsky P. 1973. Lysogenization by bacteriophage λ. I. Multiple infection and the lysogenic response. *Mol. Gen. Genet.* **122:** 183–195.

Kretz P.L., Reid C.H., Greener A., and Short J.M. 1989. Effect of lambda packaging extract *mcr* restriction activity on DNA cloning. *Nucleic Acids Res.* **17:** 5409.

Kuzminov A., Schabtach E., and Stahl F.W. 1994. Chi sites in combination with recA protein increase the survival of linear DNA in *Escherichia coli* by inactivating exoV activity of RecBCD nuclease. *EMBO J.* **13:** 2764–2776.

Lam S.T., Stahl M.M., McMilin K.D., and Stahl F.W. 1974. Rec-mediated recombinational hot spot activity in bacteriophage lambda. II. A mutation which causes hot spot activity. *Genetics* **77:** 425–433.

Landy A. 1989. Dynamic, structural and regulatory aspects of lambda site-specific recombination. *Annu. Rev. Biochem.* **58:** 913–949.

Lauer J., Shen C.K., and Maniatis T. 1980. The chromosomal arrangement of human α-like globin genes: Sequence homology and α-globin gene deletions. *Cell* **20:** 119–130.

Leder P., Tiemeier D., and Enquist L. 1977. EK2 derivatives of bacteriophage lambda useful in the cloning of DNA from higher organisms: The λ gt*WES* system. *Science* **196:** 175–177.

Lieb M. 1953a. Studies on lysogenization in *Escherichia coli*. *Cold Spring Harbor Symp. Quant. Biol.* **18:** 71–73.

———. 1953b. The establishment of lysogeny in *Escherichia coli*. *J. Bacteriol.* **65:** 642–651.

———. 1979. Heat-sensitive lambda repressors retain partial activity during bacteriophage infection. *J. Virol.* **32:** 162–166.

Little J.W. 1984. Autodigestion of lexA and phage lambda repressors. *Proc. Natl. Acad. Sci.* **81:** 1375–1379.

———. 1991. Mechanism of specificity lexA cleavage: Autodigestion and the role of RecA coprotease. *Biochimie* **73:** 411–421.

———. 1993. LexA cleavage and other self-processing reactions. *J. Bacteriol.* **175:** 4943–4950.

Loenen W.A.M. and Blattner F.R. 1983. Lambda charon vectors (Ch32, 33, 34 and 35) adapted for DNA cloning in recombination-deficient hosts. *Gene* **26:** 171–179.

Lwoff A. 1953. Lysogeny. *Bacteriol. Rev.* **17:** 269–337.

———. 1966. The prophage and I. In *Phage and the origins of molecular biology* (ed. J. Cairns et al.), pp. 88–99. Cold Spring Harbor Laboratory, Cold Spring Harbor, New York.

Lwoff A. and Gutmann A. 1950. Recherches sur un *Bacillus megatherium* lysogène. *Ann. Inst. Pasteur* **78:** 711–739.

MacKay D.J. and Bode V.C. 1976. Events in lambda injection between phage adsorption and DNA entry. *Virology* **72:** 154–166.

Mandal N.C. and Lieb M. 1976. Heat-sensitive DNA binding activity of the *cI* product of bacteriophage λ. *Mol. Gen. Genet.* **146:** 299–302.

Manfioletti G. and Schneider C. 1988. A new and fast method for preparing high quality lambda DNA suitable for sequencing. *Nucleic Acids Res.* **16:** 2873–2884.

Maniatis T., Hardison R.C., Lacy E., Lauer J., O'Connell C., Quon D., Sim G.K., and Efstratiadis A. 1978. The isolation of structural genes from libraries of eukaryotic DNA. *Cell* **15:** 687–701.

Marchal C. and Hofnung M. 1983. Negative dominance in gene *lamB*: Random assembly of secreted subunits issued from different polysomes. *EMBO J.* **2:** 81–86.

McDermit M., Pierce M., Staley D., Shimaji M., Shaw R., and Wulff D.L. 1976. Mutations masking the lambda *cin-1* mutation. *Genetics* **82:** 417–422.

Médigue C., Viari A., Hénaut A., and Danchin A. 1993. Colibri: A functional data base for the *Escherichia coli* genome. *Microbiol. Rev.* **57:** 623–654.

Meissner P.S., Sisk W.P., and Berman M.L. 1987. Bacteriophage λ cloning system for the construction of directional cDNA libraries. *Proc. Natl. Acad. Sci.* **84:** 4171–4175.

Meselson M. and Yuan R. 1968. DNA restriction enzyme from E. coli. *Nature* **217:** 1110–1114.

Meyer B.J., Maurer R., and Ptashne M. 1980. Gene regulation at the right operator (O_R) of bacteriophage λ. II. O_R1, O_R2, and O_R3: Their roles in mediating the effects of repressor and cro. *J. Mol. Biol.* **139:** 163–194.

Miller H.I. and Friedman D.I. 1977. Isolation of *Escherichia coli* mutants unable to support lambda integrative recombination. In *DNA insertion elements, plasmids and episomes* (ed. A.I. Bukhari et al.), pp. 349–356. Cold Spring Harbor Laboratory, Cold Spring Harbor, New York.

Miller H.I., Kikuchi A., Nash H.A., Weisberg R.A., and Friedman D.I. 1979. Site-specific recombination of bacteriophage lambda: The role of host gene products. *Cold Spring Harbor Symp. Quant. Biol.* **43:** 1121–1126.

Miller J.H. 1972. *Experiments in molecular genetics*. Cold Spring Harbor Laboratory, Cold Spring Harbor, New York.

Mizuuchi K., Gellert M., and Nash H.A. 1978. Involvement of supertwisted DNA in integrative recombination of bacteriophage lambda. *J. Mol. Biol.* **121:** 375–392.

Müller A., Hinrichs W., Wolf W.M., and Saenger W. 1994. Crystal structure of calcium-free proteinase K at 1.5Å resolution. *J. Biol. Chem.* **269:** 23108–23111.

Murialdo H. and Siminovitch L. 1972. The morphogenesis of phage lambda. V. Form-determining function of the genes required for the assembly of the head. *Virology* **48:** 824–835.

Murray N.E. 1983. Phage lambda and molecular cloning. In *Lambda II* (ed. R.W. Hendrix et al.), pp. 395–432. Cold Spring Harbor Laboratory, Cold Spring Harbor, New York.

———. 1991. Special uses of λ phage for molecular cloning. *Methods Enzymol.* **204:** 280–301.

Murray N.E. and Murray K. 1974. Manipulation of restriction targets in phage λ to form receptor chromosomes for DNA fragments. *Nature* **251:** 476–481.

Murray N.E., Brammar W.J., and Murray K. 1977. Lambdoid phages that simplify the recovery of *in vitro* recombinants. *Mol. Gen. Genet.* **150:** 53–61.

Nash H.A. 1990. Bending and supercoiling of DNA at the attachment site of bacteriophage lambda. *Trends Biochem. Sci.* **15:** 222–227.

Nash H.A. and Robertson C.A. 1981. Purification and properties of the *Escherichia coli* protein factor required for lambda integrative recombination. *J. Biol. Chem.* **256:** 9246–9253.

Nash H.A., Mizuuchi K., Weisberg R.A., Kikuchi Y., and Gellert M. 1977. Integrative recombination of bacteriophage lambda — The biochemical approach to DNA insertions. In *DNA insertion elements, plasmids and episomes* (ed. A.I. Bukhari et al.), pp. 363–373. Cold Spring Harbor Laboratory, Cold Spring Harbor, New York.

Neuhaus J.M. 1982. The receptor protein of phage lambda: Purification, characterization and preliminary electrical studies in planar lipid bilayers. *Ann. Microbiol.* **133:** 27–32.

Nichols B.P. and Donelson J.E. 1978. 178-Nucleotide sequence surrounding the *cos* site of bacteriophage λ DNA. *J. Virol.* **26:** 429–434.

Oliver D.B. and Goldberg E.B. 1977. Protection of parental T4 DNA from a restriction exonuclease by the product of gene 2. *J. Mol. Biol.* **116:** 877–881.

Oppenheim A.B., Kornitzer D., Altuvia S., and Court D.L. 1993. Posttranscriptional control of the lysogenic pathway in bacteriophage lambda. *Prog. Nucleic Acid Res. Mol. Biol.* **46:** 37–49.

Pabo C.O. and Lewis M. 1982. The operator-binding domain of λ repressor: Structure and DNA recognition. *Nature* **298:** 443–447.

Pabo C.O., Sauer R.T., Sturtevant J.M., and Ptashne M. 1979. The λ repressor contains two domains. *Proc. Natl. Acad. Sci.* **76:** 1608–1612.

Parris W., Davidson A., Keeler Jr., C.L., and Gold M. 1988. The *Nu1* subunit of bacteriophage λ terminase. *J. Biol. Chem.* **263:** 8413–8419.

Patterson T.A. and Dean M. 1987. Preparation of high titer lambda phage lysates. *Nucleic Acids Res.* **15:** 6298.

Postma P.W. 1987. Phosphotransferase system for glucose and other sugars. In Escherichia coli *and* Salmonella typhimurium. *Cellular and molecular biology* (ed. F.C. Neidhardt et al.), vol. 1, pp. 127–141. American Society for Microbiology, Washington, D.C.

Pourcel C. and Tiollais P. 1977. λ*plac*5 derivatives, potential vectors for DNA fragments cleaved by *Streptomyces stanfordii* restriction enzyme (*Sst*I). *Gene* **1:** 281–286.

Pourcel C., Marchal C., Louise A., Fritsch A., and Tiollais P. 1979. Bacteriophage lambda-*E. coli* K12 vector-host system for gene cloning and expression under lactose promoter control: I. DNA fragment insertion at the *lacZ EcoRI* restriction site. *Mol. Gen. Genet.* **170:** 161–169.

Poustka A. 1993. Construction and use of chromosome jumping libraries. *Methods Enzymol.* **217:** 358–378.

Ptashne M. 1986. *A genetic switch: Gene control and phage* λ. Blackwell Scientific, Palo Alto, California and Cell Press, Cambridge, Massachusetts.

———. 1992. *A genetic switch: Phage* λ *and higher organisms,* 2nd edition. Blackwell Scientific, Palo Alto, California and Cell Press, Cambridge, Massachusetts.

Raleigh E.A. and Wilson G. 1986. *Escherichia coli* K-12 restricts DNA containing 5-methylcytosine. *Proc. Natl. Acad. Sci.* **83:** 9070–9074.

Rambach A. and Tiollais P. 1974. Bacteriophage λ having *EcoRI* endonuclease sites only in the non-essential region of the genome. *Proc. Natl. Acad. Sci.* **71:** 3927–3930.

Richet E., Abcarian P., and Nash H.A. 1986. The interaction of recombination proteins with supercoiled DNA: Defining the role of supercoiling in lambda integrative recombination. *Cell* **46:** 1011–1021.

Roberts J.W. 1975. Transcription termination and late control in phage lambda. *Proc. Natl. Acad. Sci.* **72:** 3300–3304.

———. 1993. RNA and protein elements of *E. coli* and λ transcription antitermination complexes. *Cell* **72:** 653–655.

Roberts J.W. and Devoret R. 1983. Lysogenic induction. In *Lambda II* (ed. R.W. Hendrix et al.), pp. 123–144. Cold Spring Harbor Laboratory, Cold Spring Harbor, New York.

Rosenberg M., Court D., Shimatake H., Brady C., and Wulff D.L. 1978. The relationship between function and DNA sequence in an intercistronic regulatory region in phage lambda. *Nature* **272:** 414–423.

Rosenberg S.M. 1985. *EcoK* restriction during in vitro packaging of coliphage lambda DNA. *Gene* **39:** 313–315.

———. 1987. Improved in vitro packaging of lambda DNA. *Methods Enzymol.* **153:** 95–103.

Saigo K. and Uchida H. 1974. Connection of the right-hand terminus of DNA to the proximal end of the tail in bacteriophage lambda. *Virology* **61:** 524–536.

Sanger F., Coulson A.R., Hong G.F., Hill D.F., and Petersen G.B. 1982. Nucleotide sequence of bacteriophage λ DNA. *J. Mol. Biol.* **162:** 729–773.

Sauer R.T., Pabo C.O., Meyer B.J., Ptashne M., and Backman K.C. 1979. Regulatory functions of the λ repressor reside in the amino-terminal domain. *Nature* **279:** 396–400.

Scalenghe F., Turco E., Edstrom J.E., Pirotta V., and Melli M. 1981. Microdissection and cloning of DNA from a specific region of *Drosophila melanogaster* polytene chromosomes. *Chromosoma* **82:** 205–216.

Scherer G., Telford J., Baldari C., and Pirotta V. 1981. Isolation of cloned genes differentially expressed at early and late stages of *Drosophila* embryonic development. *Dev. Biol.* **86:** 438–447.

Schirmer T., Keller T.A., Wang Y.F., and Rosenbusch J.P. 1995. Structural basis for sugar translocation through maltoporin channels at 3.1Å resolution. *Science* **267:** 512–514.

Schwartz M. 1967. Sur l'existence chez *Escherichia coli* K12 d'une régulation commune à la biosynthèse des récepteurs du bactériophage λ et au métabolisme du maltose. *Ann. Inst. Pasteur* **113:** 685–704.

———. 1975. Reversible interaction between coliphage lambda and its receptor protein. *J. Mol. Biol.* **99:** 185–201.

Short J.M., Fernandez J.M., Sorge J.A., and Huse W.D. 1988. Lambda ZAP: A bacteriophage lambda expression vector with in vivo excision properties. *Nucleic Acids Res.* **16:** 7583–7600.

Siezen R.J. and Leunissen J.A. 1997. Subtilases: The superfamily of subtilisin-like serine proteases. *Protein Sci.* **6:** 501–523.

Siezen R.J., de Vos W.M., Leunissen J.A., and Dijkstra B.W. 1991. Homology modelling and protein engineering strategy of subtilases, the family of subtilisin-like serine proteinases. *Protein Eng.* **4:** 719–737.

Simmon V.F. and Lederberg S. 1972. Degradation of bacteriophage lambda deoxyribonucleic acid after restriction by *Escherichia coli* K-12. *J. Bacteriol.* **112:** 161–169.

Sippy J. and Feiss M. 1992. Analysis of a mutation affecting the specificity domain for prohead binding of the bacteriophage λ terminase. *J. Bacteriol.* **174:** 850–856.

Smith G.R. 1983. Chi hotspots of generalized recombination. *Cell* **34:** 709–710.

———. 1990. RecBCD enzyme. *Nucleic Acids Mol. Biol.* **4:** 78–98.

Smith G.R., Kunes S.M., Schultz D.W., Taylor A., and Triman K.L. 1981. Structure of Chi hotspots of generalized recombination. *Cell* **24:** 429–436.

Sorge J.A. 1988. Bacteriophage lambda cloning vectors. In *Vectors: A survey of molecular cloning vectors and their uses* (ed. R.L. Rodriguez and D.T. Denhardt), pp. 43–60. Butterworth, Boston, Massachusetts.

Stahl F.W., Crasemann J.M., and Stahl M.M. 1975. *Rec*-mediated recombinational hot spot activity in bacteriophage lambda III. Chi mutations are site mutations stmulating *Rec*-mediated recombination. *J. Mol. Biol.* **94:** 203–212.

Sternberg N. and Weisberg R. 1977. Packaging of coliphage λ DNA. II. The role of the gene *D* protein. *J. Mol. Biol.* **117:** 733–759.

Sternberg N., Tiemeier D., and Enquist L. 1977. *In vitro* packaging of a λ *Dam* vector containing *EcoRI* DNA fragments of *Escherichia coli* and phage P1. *Gene* **1:** 255–280.

Sussman R. and Jacob F. 1962. Sur un système de répression thermosensible chez le bactériophage d'*Escherichia coli*. *C.R. Acad. Sci.* **254:** 1517.

Szmelcman S. and Hofnung M. 1975. Maltose transport in *Escherichia coli* K-12: Involvement of the bacteriophage lambda receptor. *J. Bacteriol.* **124:** 112–118.

Taylor A.F. 1988. RecBCD enzyme of *Escherichia coli*. In *Genetic recombination* (ed. R. Kucherlapati and G.R. Smith), pp. 231–263. American Society for Microbiology, Washington, D.C.

Taylor A.F., Schultz D.W., Ponticelli A.S., and Smith G.R. 1985. RecBC enzyme nicking at Chi sites during DNA unwinding:

Location and orientation-dependence of the cutting. *Cell* **41:** 153–163.

Telander-Muskavitch K.M. and Linn S. 1981. *recBC*-like enzymes: Exonuclease V deoxyribonucleases. In *The enzymes,* 3rd edition (ed. P.D. Boyer), vol. 14, pp. 233–250. Academic Press, New York.

Thirion J.P. and Hofnung M. 1972. On some genetic aspects of phage λ resistance in *E. coli* K12. *Genetics* **71:** 207–216.

Thomas J.O. 1974. Chemical linkage of the tail to the right-hand end of bacteriophage lambda DNA. *J. Mol. Biol.* **87:** 1–9.

Thomas M., Cameron J.R., and Davis R.W. 1974. Viable molecular hybrids of bacteriophage λ and eukaryotic DNA. *Proc. Natl. Acad. Sci.* **71:** 4579–4583.

Thomas R. 1993. Bacteriophage λ: Transactivation, positive control and other odd findings. *BioEssays* **15:** 285–289.

Tsui L. and Hendrix R.W. 1980. Head-tail connector of bacteriophage lambda. *J. Mol. Biol.* **142:** 419–438.

Twort F.W. 1915. An investigation on the nature of ultra-microscopic viruses. *Lancet* **II:** 1241–1243.

———. 1949. The discovery of the bacteriophage. *Science News* (Penguin Press, Harmondsworth, England) **14:** 33–43.

Unger R.C. and Clark A.J. 1972. Interaction of the recombination pathways of bacteriophage λ and its host *Escherichia coli* K12. Effects on exonuclease V activity. *J. Mol. Biol.* **70:** 539–548.

Vande Woude G.F., Oskarsson M., Enquist L.W., Nomura S., Sullivan M., and Fischinger P.J. 1979. Cloning of integrated Moloney sarcoma proviral DNA sequences in bacteriophage lambda. *Proc. Natl. Acad. Sci.* **76:** 4464–4468.

Weigel P.H., Englund P.T., Murray K., and Old R.W. 1973. The 3′-terminal nucleotide sequences of bacteriophage lambda DNA. *Proc. Natl. Acad. Sci.* **70:** 1151–1155.

Weisberg R.A. and Landy A. 1983. Site-specific recombination in phage lambda. In *Lambda II* (ed. R.W. Hendrix et al.), pp. 211–250. Cold Spring Harbor Laboratory, Cold Spring Harbor, New York.

Werts C., Michel V., Hofnung M., and Charbit A. 1994. Adsorption of bacteriophage lambda on the LamB protein of *Escherichia coli* K-12: Point mutations in gene J of lambda responsible for extended host range. *J. Bacteriol.* **176:** 941–947.

Wiegers U. and Hilz H. 1971. A new method using "proteinase K" to prevent mRNA degradation during isolation from HeLa cells. *Biochem. Biophys. Res. Commun.* **44:** 513–519.

———. 1972. Rapid isolation of undegraded polysomal RNA without phenol. *FEBS Lett.* **23:** 77–82.

Williams B.G. and Blattner F.R. 1979. Construction and characterization of the hybrid bacteriophage lambda Charon vectors for DNA cloning. *J. Virol.* **29:** 555–575.

———. 1980. Bacteriophage lambda vectors for DNA cloning. *Genet. Eng.* **2:** 201–281.

Woo S.L. 1979. A sensitive and rapid method for recombinant phage screening. *Methods Enzymol.* **68:** 389–395.

Woo S.L., Dugaiczyk A., Tsai M.-J., Lai E.C., Catterall J.F., and O'Malley B.W. 1978. The ovalbumin gene: Cloning of the natural gene. *Proc. Natl. Acad. Sci.* **75:** 3688–3692.

Wood W.B. 1966. Host specificity of DNA produced by *Escherichia coli:* Bacterial mutations affecting the restriction and modification of DNA. *J. Mol. Biol.* **16:** 118–133.

Wu R. and Taylor E. 1971. Nucelotide sequence analysis of DNA. II. Complete nucleotide sequence of the cohesive ends of bacteriophage lambda DNA. *J. Mol. Biol.* **57:** 491–511.

Wulff D.L. and Rosenberg M. 1983. Establishment of repressor synthesis. In *Lambda II* (ed. R.W. Hendrix et al.), pp. 53–73. Cold Spring Harbor Laboratory, Cold Spring Harbor, New York.

Xu S.-Y. 1986. A rapid method for preparing phage lambda DNA from agar plate lysates. *Gene Anal. Tech.* **3:** 90–91.

Yagil E., Dower N.A., Chattoraj D., Stahl M., Pierson C., and Stahl F.W. 1980. Chi mutation in a transposon and the orientation dependence of Chi phenotype. *Genetics* **96:** 43–57.

Yamamoto K.R., Alberts B.M., Benzinger R., Lawhorne L., and Treiber G. 1970. Rapid bacteriophage sedimentation in the presence of polyethylene glycol and its application to large-scale virus purification. *Virology* **40:** 734–744.

Yarmolinsky M.B. 1971. Making and joining DNA ends. In *The bacteriophage lambda* (ed. A.D. Hershey), pp. 97–111. Cold Spring Harbor Laboratory, Cold Spring Harbor, New York.

Yarnell W.S. and Roberts J.W. 1992. The phage λ gene Q transcription antiterminator binds DNA in the late gene promoter as it modifies RNA polymerase. *Cell* **69:** 1181–1189.

Yeo A. and Feiss M. 1995. Specific interaction of terminase, the DNA packaging enzyme of bacteriophage λ, with the portal protein of the prohead. *J. Mol. Biol.* **245:** 141–150.

Young R. 1992. Bacteriophage lysis: Mechanisms and regulation. *Microbiol. Rev.* **56:** 430–481.

Young R.A. and Davis R.W. 1983a. Efficient isolation of genes by using antibody probes. *Proc. Natl. Acad. Sci.* **80:** 1194–1198.

———. 1983b. Yeast RNA polymerase II genes: Isolation with antibody probes. *Science* **222:** 778–782.

Zissler J. 1967. Integration-negative (*int*) mutants of phage λ. *Virology* **31:** 189.

Zissler J., Signer E., and Schaefer F. 1971. The role of recombination in growth of bacteriophage lambda. I. The gamma gene. In *The bacteriophage lambda* (ed. A.D. Hershey), pp. 455–475. Cold Spring Harbor Laboratory, Cold Spring Harbor, New York.

Chapter 3

Working with Bacteriophage M13 Vectors

RECOMBINANT FILAMENTOUS BACTERIOPHAGES are used to provide single-stranded copies of fragments of DNA cloned in other vectors. This approach is now commonly used in place of older physical and enzymatic techniques to separate the strands of segments of DNA. These single-stranded DNA fragments are used chiefly as templates for site-directed mutagenesis, sequencing of DNA fragments by the dideoxy chain-termination method, construction of subtractive cDNA libraries, and synthesis of strand-specific probes. Specialized M13 vectors can also be used for display of foreign peptides and proteins on the surface of the bacteriophage particles.

THE DISCOVERY OF MALE-SPECIFIC BACTERIOPHAGES

A search of New York City sewage (Loeb 1960) for viruses that grow only on male (F^+ and Hfr) strains of *Escherichia coli* resulted in the isolation of seven types of bacteriophages (f1 through f7). Most of these bacteriophages turned out to be small, spherical viruses that contain RNA as their genetic material (Loeb and Zinder 1961). f1, although clearly different from the others in buoyant density and antigenic structure, was not immediately studied because it made turbid plaques that were difficult to detect and count. However, the initial report of male-specific bacteriophages inspired other groups to search for additional viruses with a sex-specific host range. From this work emerged the male-specific bacteriophages M13 (Munich 13) (Hofschneider 1963) and fd (Marvin and Hoffman-Berling 1963). Early electron micrographs of fd phages showed spheres embedded in a matrix of tangled fibrous material, which was at first thought to be pili that had detached from the bacterial cell wall. However, during extensive attempts to clean the bacteriophage preparations, infectivity always remained associated with these long flexible rod-like structures. The conclusion that these filaments were, in fact, the bacteriophages was strengthened by the observations (1) that high titers of infectious virus were always highly viscous and (2) that the infectivity was very sensitive to shearing forces. Chemical analysis showed that the filaments contained DNA whose base composition was not consistent with Watson-Crick base pairing. In addition, the DNA showed anomalous hydrodynamic properties that were not understood at the time but are now easily interpretable as those expected of circular and linear single-stranded DNA molecules.

THE BIOLOGY OF FILAMENTOUS BACTERIOPHAGES

M13 is a member of a family of filamentous bacteriophages with single-stranded DNA genomes ~6400 bases in length. The genomes of M13 and its two closest relatives fd and f1 are organized identically, and their particles are similar in size and shape. The DNAs of these bacteriophages have been completely sequenced (fd, Beck et al. 1978; M13, van Wezenbeek et al. 1980; fl, Beck and Zink 1981). More than 98% of their nucleotide sequences are identical; the few sites of differences are scattered around the genome, mostly in the third position of redundant codons (Beck and Zink 1981). M13, fd, and fl actively complement and recombine with one another (Lyons and Zinder 1972) and may be regarded as identical for the purposes of the summary that follows. The genetic map of bacteriophage M13 is shown in Figure 3-1.

- M13 bacteriophages are filamentous particles that infect only male bacteria and do not lyse their hosts. Instead, they are released from infected cells even as the cells continue to grow and divide.

- During infection, the single-stranded bacteriophage genome is converted into a double-stranded, circular form called the replicative form (RF), which replicates as a Cairns or θ structure. The RF molecules then generate single-stranded plus (+)-strand progeny DNA molecules by a rolling-circle mechanism. RF molecules are also templates for transcription of M13 genes, of which there are 11.

- Three of the viral gene products (pII, pV, and pX) are involved in the replication of the viral DNA and five virally coded transmembrane proteins (pIII, pVI, pVII, pVIII, and pIX) make up the capsid.

- Progeny particles are formed by a concerted process in which coat proteins are mustered into the bacterial membrane where they are assembled around the (+)-strand progeny DNA molecules. The protein-DNA complex is extruded from the cell in the form of a filamentous virus particle. These two processes, secretion and assembly of the filamentous virus particle, occur simultaneously in a coordinated manner. The viral gene products pI, pI* (which is also known as pXI), and pIV are required for assembly of progeny bacteriophages, but do not become incorporated into particles.

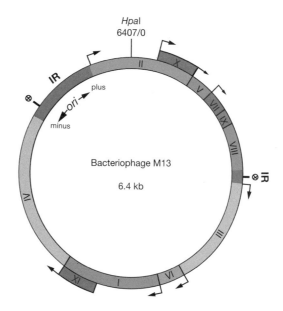

FIGURE 3-1 Genetic Map of Bacteriophage M13

Wild-type M13 is a single-stranded circular DNA, 6407 nucleotides in length. The nucleotides are numbered from a unique *Hpa*I site (van Wezenbeek et al. 1980). In the figure, the genes, which are all oriented in the same direction "clockwise," are numbered I to XI, the two intergenic regions are labeled IR, the major promoters are indicated with arrows, and the transcription terminators are marked with a cross in a circle. By convention, the viral DNA is called the (+) strand, which has the same sense as the viral mRNAs.

- All indispensable *cis*-acting elements of the M13 genome are sequestered into a 508-bp intergenic region, which has been cloned into plasmids. When cells transformed by these plasmids (or phagemids) are infected by a wild-type or mutant "helper" bacteriophage M13, single-stranded forms of the plasmid DNA are packaged into progeny particles.

- Because their genomes tend to be unstable, recombinant filamentous bacteriophages are not used for cloning and long-term propagation of segments of foreign DNA (please see Alting-Mees and Short 1993). Instead, they are used to provide single-stranded copies of fragments of DNA that have already been cloned in other vectors.

More than 90% of the bacteriophage M13 genome codes for protein products, and most of the 11 genes are separated by only a few nucleotides. The single-stranded genome encodes three classes of proteins: replication (pII, pV, and pX), morphogenetic (pI, pIV, and pXI), and structural (pIII, pVI, pVII, pVIII, and pIX) proteins. All structural proteins of the bacteriophage are inserted into the bacterial membrane prior to bacteriophage assembly (Endemann and Model 1995). For further details about the structures and functions of these proteins, please see Table 3-1.

A small noncoding region lies between genes VIII and III, whereas a more substantial noncoding region of 508 bp is located between genes II and IV. All of the vital *cis*-acting elements in the bacteriophage genome are condensed into this larger intergenic region, which contains sequences regulating packaging and orientation of the DNA within bacteriophage particles (Dotto et al. 1981b; Webster et al. 1981; Dotto and Zinder 1983), sites for the initiation and termination of synthesis of (+)-strand and minus (–)-strand DNA (please see Beck and Zink 1981; Dotto et al. 1983), and a signal for ρ-independent termination of transcription (see Konings and Schoenmakers 1978). Because these *cis*-acting elements are packed so tightly into a small region of DNA, they can easily be transferred en bloc to other types of cloning vehicles, such as plasmids.

TABLE 3-1 Summary of the Functions of Proteins Encoded by Bacteriophage M13

PROTEIN/ SIZE	FUNCTION
pI/348 residues	pI, which spans the inner membrane of M13-infected bacteria, interacts with the viral pIV and host-encoded thioredoxin and may also recognize the packaging signal in phage DNA, thereby initiating phage assembly. A smaller product, pXI, is produced by internal initiation of translation within the gene I transcript at methionine codon 241. pXI, which is also known as pI*, may be involved in forming the site for assembly of bacteriophage particles.
pII/410 residues	pII introduces a nick at a specific site in the intergenic region of the (+)-strand of RF DNA, initiating the rolling circle phase of replication, which generates (+)-strand progeny DNA molecules. pII also cleaves the single-stranded product of rolling circle replication into monomeric molecules that are packaged into progeny bacteriophage particles.
pIII/427 residues	pIII, a minor coat protein, is anchored to the membrane by a single membrane-spanning domain near the carboxyl terminus. As the M13 filament emerges from the infected cell, three to five copies of pIII are attached to the proximal tip of the bacteriophage particle. The proximal tip enters a new host first during infection and leaves the membrane last when progeny particles are extruded. pIII, which is associated with pVI at the proximal tip, is required for adsorption of the bacteriophage to the sex pili of new hosts and for penetration of the phage DNA. Fusion peptides in bacteriophage display libraries are located in the early mature region of pIII, near or immediately adjacent to the signal peptide cleavage site.
pIV/426 residues	pIV, a multimeric protein, may form a gated channel connecting the bacterial cytoplasm to the exterior. pIV, which is synthesized in large quantities in infected cells, interacts with pI and is required for the induction of the *E. coli psp* (phage shock protein) operon that occurs during M13 infection.
pV/87 residues	pV, an 87-amino-acid protein synthesized in large amounts in infected cells, binds strongly and in a cooperative manner to newly synthesized (+) strands. The resulting pV-DNA complexes move to specialized packaging sites on the bacterial membrane, where pV is stripped from the viral DNA and is recycled into the cell. In addition to DNA binding, pV also acts as a translational repressor by binding specifically to the leader sequences of viral mRNAs coding for gene II and other viral proteins. These two properties of pV work in combination to regulate both the expression and replication of the viral genome. When the intracellular concentration of pV reaches a critical level (10^5 to 10^6 molecules/cell/generation), the conversion of progeny (+) strands to double-stranded RF is suppressed, and the rolling circle phase of bacteriophage DNA replication therefore proceeds at an essentially constant pace.
pVI/112 residues	pVI is a minor coat protein of M13. A few molecules of pVI are located at the proximal end of the M13 filament, where they are associated with pIII. pVI is a membrane protein that is located in the cytoplasmic membrane before incorporation into virus particles.
pVII/33 residues	pVII is a coat protein that interacts with the packaging signal located in the intergenic region of M13 DNA. Five molecules of pVII are located at the end of the bacteriophage particle that emerges first from the infected cell.
pVIII/73 residues	pVIII, the major coat protein of M13, is synthesized as a preprotein known as "procoat," which binds to the inner surface of the plasma membrane and subsequently translocates as a loop structure across the membrane in the presence of a transmembrane potential. Particles of M13 contain ~2700 copies of the processed or mature 50-residue α-helical protein, arranged in a cylindrical sheath around the bacteriophage DNA.
pIX/32 residues	pIX is a minor coat protein of M13. Five copies of pIX are located at the end of the bacteriophage particle where assembly begins. Like pVII, pIX is a membrane protein that interacts with the packaging signal located in the intergenic region of M13 DNA.
pX	Translation of pX begins at the in-frame AUG triplet at codon 300 of pII. pX is therefore identical in sequence to the carboxy-terminal third of pII. pX, which is required for efficient accumulation of single-stranded DNA, is a powerful repressor of phage-specific DNA synthesis in vivo and is thought to limit the number of RF molecules in infected cells.
pXI (also known as pI*)	pXI, which spans the cytoplasmic membrane but lacks a cytoplasmic domain, is produced by internal initiation of translation within the gene I transcript at methionine codon 241. pXI may be involved in forming the site for assembly of bacteriophage particles.

For references, please see reviews by Makowski (1984), Webster and Lopez (1985), Model and Russel (1988), and Russel (1991, 1995).

Bacteria transformed by these phage-plasmid hybrids (which are known as phagemids) produce single-stranded versions of the plasmid DNA when infected with helper wild-type or mutant filamentous bacteriophages carrying replication-defective intergenic regions. For further details, please see the introduction to Protocol 8, which deals with phagemids.

The filamentous particles of M13 infect only bacterial strains that express sex pili encoded by an F factor. Adsorption of the virus to the bacterial cell requires interaction between a sex pilus and the viral minor coat protein pIII, three to five copies of which are located at one end of the filamentous rod (please see Table 3-1). The following events then occur: As the rod-shaped virus penetrates the pilus, pIII interacts with the host TolQ, TolR, and TolA proteins, which (1) mediate removal of the major coat protein and (2) allow the viral DNA to penetrate into the body of the bacterium (Webster 1991).

- The infecting (+)-strand single-stranded DNA is then converted into a double-stranded circular form, called RF DNA. Synthesis of the (−) strand is initiated by a 20-nucleotide RNA primer that is synthesized at a unique site on the viral DNA by *E. coli* RNA polymerase (Geider and Kornberg 1974; Higashitani et al. 1993). Transcription of viral genes begins at any one of a series of promoters in RF DNA and proceeds unidirectionally to one of two terminators, which are located immediately downstream from genes VIII and IV. This organization of promoters and terminators leads to gradients of transcription in which genes located closest to a termination site (e.g., gene VIII) are transcribed much more frequently than genes further upstream (e.g., gene II) (for a review of this and other aspects of the molecular biology of filamentous bacteriophages, please see Model and Russel 1988; Russel 1995).

- Amplification of the viral genome begins when the protein product of gene II introduces a nick at a specific site in the (+) strand of the parental RF DNA (Meyer et al. 1979). *E. coli* DNA polymerase I then adds nucleotides to the free 3′-hydroxyl terminus, progressively displacing the original (+) strand from the circular (−)-strand template (please see Figure 3-2).

- After the replication fork has completed a full circle, the displaced (+) strand is cleaved by the gene II protein, generating a unit-length viral genome that is then circularized (Horiuchi 1980). During the first 15–20 minutes of infection, these progeny (+) strands are converted by cellular enzymes to closed circular RF DNA molecules, which serve as templates for further rounds of transcription and synthesis of additional (+) strands.

- By the time 100–200 copies of the RF DNA have accumulated in the infected cell, there is enough single-stranded DNA-binding protein (the product of gene V) to repress translation, inter alia, of gene II mRNA (Model et al. 1982; Yen and Webster 1982; Zaman et al. 1990) and to bind strongly and cooperatively to the newly synthesized (+) strands, thereby preventing their conversion to RF DNA. DNA synthesis therefore becomes dedicated almost exclusively to the production of progeny viral strands (Salstrom and Pratt 1971; Mazur and Zinder 1975). In addition, pX and pV are powerful repressors of phage-specific DNA synthesis and are thought to limit the number of RF molecules in infected cells (Fulford and Model 1984, 1988; Guilfoyle and Smith 1994). As a consequence, both the number of RF DNA molecules in the infected cell and the rate of production of progeny (+) strands are kept within moderate limits (Mazur and Model 1973; Lerner and Model 1981).

The morphogenesis of filamentous bacteriophage particles is extraordinary. Unlike most other bacterial viruses, progeny particles are not assembled intracellularly. Instead, morphogenesis and secretion occur in a concerted fashion, so that nascent virus particles are assembled as they cross the inner and outer bacterial membranes of the host cell. The intracellular pV–viral DNA complexes are compact, rod-like structures (Gray 1989) that associate with specific assembly sites in the bacterial membrane (Lopez and Webster 1983, 1985). The signal for packaging — an

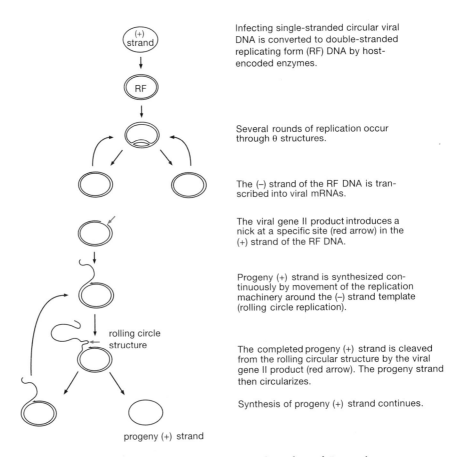

Infecting single-stranded circular viral DNA is converted to double-stranded replicating form (RF) DNA by host-encoded enzymes.

Several rounds of replication occur through θ structures.

The (–) strand of the RF DNA is transcribed into viral mRNAs.

The viral gene II product introduces a nick at a specific site (red arrow) in the (+) strand of the RF DNA.

Progeny (+) strand is synthesized continuously by movement of the replication machinery around the (–) strand template (rolling circle replication).

The completed progeny (+) strand is cleaved from the rolling circular structure by the viral gene II product (red arrow). The progeny strand then circularizes.

Synthesis of progeny (+) strand continues.

FIGURE 3-2 Replication of Bacteriophage M13 DNA in Infected Bacteria

The first four stages, up to the point where nicking of closed circular RF DNA begins, occur during the first 15–20 minutes of infection and result in the accumulation of 100–200 circular RF DNA molecules per cell. The subsequent production of single-stranded DNA is a continuous process that leads to morphogenesis of progeny particles.

inverted repeat located in the intergenic region of the bacteriophage DNA — protrudes from one end of the pV–viral DNA (Bauer and Smith 1988) and presumably initiates morphogenesis by interacting with the membrane-associated coat proteins, pVII and pIX. Assembly of virus particles is a repetitious process whereby the 1500 dimeric pV proteins are progressively removed from the (+) strand and replaced by capsid proteins as the nascent bacteriophage particle is extruded through the membranes of the infected cell. The finished viral filaments (illustrated in Figure 3-3), which are 100 times greater in length than in width, are extruded from the host cell without causing lysis or cell death (for reviews, please see Russel 1991, 1994, 1995).

Mature particles contain 5 of the 11 bacteriophage-encoded proteins (please see Table 3-1). At least four other proteins (pI, pIV, pXI, encoded by the virus, and thioredoxin, encoded by the host cell) are required for assembly and secretion.

Wild-type filamentous bacteriophages are long and flexible tubular structures, 880 nm in length and 6–7 nm in diameter (for reviews, please see Rasched and Oberer 1986; Russel 1991; Makowski 1994). A high-resolution X-ray crystallographic structure of the particles is not available, but models of the bacteriophage have been generated from fiber diffraction studies and solid-state nuclear magnetic resonance (NMR) (Opella et al. 1980; Banner et al. 1981; Glucksman et al. 1992; McDonnell et al. 1993; Marvin et al. 1994). The DNA at the core of the particles is coated by 2700 copies of an α-helical 50-residue protein, which is encoded by gene VIII. The cap or distal end of the nascent bacteriophage cylinder extruded from the membrane consists of five

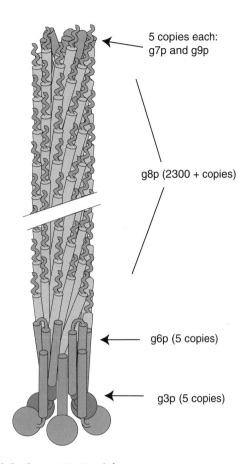

5 copies each:
g7p and g9p

g8p (2300 + copies)

g6p (5 copies)

g3p (5 copies)

FIGURE 3-3 Structural Model of an M13 Particle

M13 is a filamentous bacteriophage of the family Inoviridae. The native particle is ~900 nm long and 6.5 nm in diameter and is composed of the single-stranded circular viral DNA encapsulated by ~2300 copies of the major coat protein, the product of phage gene 8 (g8p), plus five copies each of four minor proteins. The single-stranded bacteriophage DNA extends along the axis of the phage particle, with the length of the DNA determining both the length of and the number of g8p in the virus particle. The minor phage proteins g7p and g9p are involved in the initiation of assembly and are required for particle stability. g3p is a 42,000-dalton protein attached to the virus particle by g6p and is responsible for binding to host cells. (Courtesy of Lee Makowski and Matt Ray.)

copies each of pVII and pIX, which interact with the packaging signal in the intergenic region. The tail or proximal end of the completed cylinder consists of a complex of three to five copies of pVI and pIII.

Because the viral genome is not inserted into a preformed structure, there is no strict limit to the size of the single-stranded DNA that can be packaged. Rather, the length of the filamentous particle varies according to the amount of DNA it contains. Particles longer than unit length and containing multiple copies of the viral genome are found in stocks of all filamentous viruses (Salivar et al. 1967; Scott and Zinder 1967; Pratt et al. 1969), and inserts of foreign DNA seven times longer than the wild-type viral genome have been cloned and propagated in M13 (Messing 1981).

The replication of the filamentous bacteriophages occurs in harmony with that of the host bacterium, and the infected cells are therefore not lysed but continue to grow (albeit at one half to three quarters of the normal rate) while producing several hundred virus particles per cell per generation (Marvin and Hohn 1969). This production leads to the accumulation of vast numbers of particles in the medium; the titer of bacteriophage from a culture of infected bacteria frequently exceeds 10^{12} pfu/ml.

BACTERIOPHAGE M13 AS A VECTOR

Because single-stranded DNA is a poor substrate for most restriction endonucleases and DNA ligases, double-stranded segments of foreign DNA are inserted in vitro into the RF of the bacteriophage DNA (please see the panel on ENGINEERING M13 AS A VECTOR). This double-stranded closed circular DNA can easily be purified from infected cells, manipulated in the same way as plasmid DNA, and then reintroduced into cells by standard transformation procedures. The double-stranded DNA then reenters the replication cycle, eventually generating progeny bacteriophage particles that contain only one of the two strands of the foreign DNA. The other strand of the DNA, the (–) strand, is never packaged.

ENGINEERING M13 AS A VECTOR

In 1963, when Peter-Hans Hofschneider described the isolation of Munich 13 from Bavarian sewage, the virus seemed to have few prospects. Indeed, research on M13 remained parochial until the early 1970s, when Joachim Messing, then a graduate student at the Max-Planck Institute in Munich, saw that the biological properties of the bacteriophage could be exploited for cloning and sequencing of foreign DNAs.

Messing reasoned that the length of the bacteriophage filaments reflected the size of the single-stranded DNA inside them. M13 might therefore be able to accommodate additional sequences of nonviral DNA in a manner that other single-stranded DNA viruses, such as the icosahedral φX174, could not. In addition, the single-stranded nature of the M13 genome made it ideal for use as a template in the recently described Sanger DNA sequencing method (Sanger et al. 1973). However, turning these properties into an advantage required solutions to some serious problems. In 1974, the restriction map of M13 was rudimentary, the locations of its genes were vague, and, worst of all for Messing, the restriction enzymes and DNA ligases required to solve these difficulties and to construct vectors were not commercially available. Messing (1991, 1993, 1996) has described in some detail the bootstrapping and borrowing that eventually allowed him to insert into M13 the genetic element that has been the key to the success of all subsequent vectors of the mp series: a 789-bp fragment of DNA encoding the control region of the wild-type *lac* operon and the first 146 amino acids of β-galactosidase. The resulting recombinant M13mp1 (for Max-Planck Institute), which carried the *lac* sequences inserted into a *Hae*III site in the intergenic region of the bacteriophage, was viable and expressed an α-complementing fragment of β-galactosidase in infected cells (Messing et al. 1977; Gronenborn and Messing 1978).

Messing deliberately chose a strain of male host cells carrying an F´ plasmid encoding a mutant of β-galactosidase lacking amino acids 11–41. This defective polypeptide can associate with the 146-residue amino-terminal fragment of β-galactosidase encoded by M13mp1 to form an enzymatically active protein. M13mp1 will therefore form deep-blue plaques when plated on hosts carrying the appropriate F´ episome on medium containing IPTG (isopropyl-β-D-thiogalactoside, a gratuitous inducer of the β-galactosidase gene) and X-gal (5-bromo-4-chloro-3-indolyl-β-D-galactoside, a chromogenic substrate). (For additional historical details, please see the information panels on X-GAL and α-COMPLEMENTATION in Chapter 1.) Insertion of foreign DNA into the *lacZ* region of M13mp1 usually eliminates α-complementation and gives rise to recombinants that form pale blue or colorless plaques (Gronenborn and Messing 1978). Messing was therefore able to develop a histochemical test to distinguish between M13 recombinants that carried a piece of foreign DNA and empty vectors that did not.

Messing's next task was to equip the *lac* region of M13mp1 with restriction sites suitable for cloning. The *lac* fragment contained no useful restriction sites and few sequences that could be easily converted into one. During a trip to California, however, Messing learned that the chemical mutagen nitrosomethylurea would efficiently promote the conversion of guanine residues to thymine. Gronenborn and Messing (1978) therefore treated M13mp1 with nitrosomethylurea and screened for infectious RF molecules that were linearized by *Eco*RI. In this way, they were able to isolate a bacteriophage (M13mp2) that carried an *Eco*RI site at codon six of the β-galactosidase gene as a consequence of a G to T transition. Messing quickly realized that in-frame insertions of synthetic linkers into the newly created *Eco*RI site retained their ability to synthesize an α-complementing fragment of β-galactosidase in infected cells. This observation was turned to great advantage during the course of the succeeding 15 years, when Messing and his co-workers equipped a succession of mp vectors with a wide variety of multiple cloning sites (e.g., please see Messing 1979; Messing et al. 1981; Yanisch-Perron et al. 1985; Vieira and Messing 1987, 1991). These embellishments, combined with an already powerful set of biological properties, provided M13 vectors with decisive practical advantages for site-directed mutagenesis, subtractive hybridization, and shotgun DNA sequencing.

Three types of M13 vectors have been described that differ in the location of the cloning site:

- **Cloning into the large intergenic region:** All genes of filamentous bacteriophages are essential, and vectors must therefore carry a full complement of coding sequences. However, segments of foreign DNA may be inserted into the 508-bp intergenic region located between genes II and IV (Messing et al. 1977; Gronenborn and Messing 1978). Insertion of foreign DNA segments within this intergenic region can severely affect the replication of the bacteriophage genome (Dotto and Zinder 1984a). Fortunately, most vectors used to clone foreign DNA sequences carry mutations (in gene II or V) that partially compensate for the disruption of the *cis*-acting elements (Dotto and Zinder 1984b).

  A majority of vectors in current use adhere closely to the theme established by the M13mp series, differing chiefly in the number and variety of restriction sites that can accept DNA fragments. Typically, M13 vectors appear as pairs (e.g., M13mp18 and M13mp19) that vary only in the orientation of the nonsymmetrical polycloning region within the *lacZ* region. After cleavage of the RF DNAs with two different restriction enzymes, M13mp18 and M13mp19 cannot recircularize easily unless a double-stranded foreign DNA fragment with compatible termini is present in the ligation mixture. This fragment will be inserted in opposite orientations in the two vectors. Thus, one of the two strands of the fragment will be attached to the (+) strand of M13mp18, and the complementary strand will be attached to the (+) strand of M13mp19. The progeny of the M13mp18 recombinant will therefore contain one strand of the foreign DNA, and the progeny of the M13mp19 recombinant will contain the other (complementary) strand. Consequently, by using M13mp18 and M13mp19 as dual vectors, it is possible to use a single primer ("universal primer") to determine the sequence of nucleotides on opposite strands from each end of the inserted DNA and to generate probes that are complementary to only one strand or the other of the foreign DNA.

  The *lacZ* fragments used in the construction of bacteriophage M13 vectors have also been inserted into a deleted version of pBR322, creating a family of plasmid vectors (pUC vectors) that contain a variety of commonly used cloning sites. These vectors are especially useful because they (1) can participate in α-complementation and (2) carry the same constellation of restriction sites in the polycloning site as the analogous vectors of the mp series. Thus, fragments of foreign DNA can be moved between M13mp vectors and pUC vectors with great ease. In addition, the intergenic region of M13 is now a standard fixture of most plasmid vectors, which can therefore be used as conventional plasmids or as phagemids.

  > The original *lacZ* fragment carried in the mp series of M13 vectors and in pUC plasmids is derived from the wild-type *lac* operon and does not carry the *uv5* mutation and is therefore sensitive to catabolite repression.

- **Cloning into the small intergenic region:** The smaller intergenic region between genes VIII and III has also served as the cloning site for another series of vectors (Barnes 1979, 1980). In addition, a number of vectors carry other selectable markers (antibiotic resistance; *hisD*) that may be destroyed by insertion of a foreign DNA sequence (e.g., please see Barnes 1979; Herrmann et al. 1980; Zacher et al. 1980). Unfortunately, these systems require the establishment of colonies of infected cells that must be screened by replica plating, a much slower and more tedious process than visual examination of plaques.

- **Cloning into gene X:** If overproduced, gene X protein completely blocks phage-specific DNA synthesis (Fulford and Model 1988). A bacteriophage vector called M13-100 carries a supernumerary copy of gene X in the large intergenic region of M13 (Guilfoyle and Smith 1994). Expression of the gene is driven by the T7 promoter and therefore occurs only in host cells, such as JM109(DE), that express T7 RNA polymerase. When foreign DNA sequences are cloned into the supernumerary copy of gene X, the gene is inactivated and the resulting recombinants can therefore replicate on JM109(DE) cells, which, of course, are nonpermissive hosts for empty vectors. This elegant system, which was developed to reduce the cost and manual labor of screening large numbers of plaques by histochemical staining, has not been widely adopted.

BACTERIAL HOSTS FOR BACTERIOPHAGE M13 VECTORS

Because M13 enters the host cell through sex pili encoded by an F factor, only male bacteria are used to propagate the virus. Infections can be established in female cells if the bacteriophage DNA is introduced by transfection. However, the progeny particles produced by the transfected cells are unable to infect other cells in the culture, and the yields of virus are consequently very low.

Bacterial strains carrying F′ plasmids and a number of genetic markers useful in work with M13 vectors have been constructed by Messing and his co-workers (Yanisch-Perron et al. 1985). The following are the most important of these markers:

- **lacZΔM15:** A deletion mutant that lacks the sequences of the *lacZ* gene coding for the amino-terminal portion of β-galactosidase (Beckwith 1964). The peptide expressed by ΔM15 can take part in α-complementation (Ullmann et al. 1967; Ullmann and Perrin 1970). Many hosts for bacteriophage M13 vectors carry this deleted version of the *lacZ* gene on an F′ plasmid.

- **Δ(lac-proAB):** A deletion of the chromosomal segment that spans the *lac* operon and neighboring genes coding for enzymes involved in proline biosynthesis. Bacterial hosts carrying this marker are unable to use lactose as a carbon source and require proline for growth, unless *proAB* is present on an F′ plasmid.

- **lacI^q:** A mutant of the *lacI* gene that synthesizes approximately tenfold more repressor than wild type (Müller-Hill et al. 1968). This overproduction of repressor suppresses still further the already low level of transcription of the *lac* operon in the absence of inducer. Thus, synthesis of potentially toxic proteins is minimized when foreign coding sequences are placed under the control of the *lacZ* promoter in cells carrying a *lacI^q* mutation. When the host cells carrying a *lacI^q* mutation are grown in glucose, catabolite repression reduces the level of transcription across the intergenic region from the *lacZ* promoter, and so potentiates the production of single-stranded DNA. In most of the strains used in cloning with M13 vectors, *lacI^q* is carried with *lacZ*ΔM15 (see above) on an F′ plasmid.

- **proAB:** The region of the bacterial chromosome that encodes enzymes involved in proline biosynthesis. The *proAB* genes are often carried on an F′ plasmid, which can then complement proline prototrophy in a host with a (*lac-proAB*) deletion. When such cells are grown in media lacking proline, the maintenance of the F′ plasmid in the host can be guaranteed.

- **traD36:** A mutation that suppresses conjugal transfer of F factors (Achtman et al. 1971). This marker was required by the National Institutes of Health (NIH) guidelines that were extant many years ago. The guidelines are no longer in force, but the marker lingers on in several of the bacterial strains dating from that era.

- **hsdR17 *and* hsdR4:** Mutations that lead to loss of restriction, but not modification, by the type I restriction/modification system of *E. coli* strain K. Unmodified DNA cloned directly into M13 vectors and propagated in bacterial strains carrying this mutation will be modified and therefore protected against restriction if the vector is subsequently introduced into an *hsd$^+$* strain of *E. coli* K.

- **mcrA *and* mrr:** Mutations that lead to loss of restriction of methylated DNA and therefore enhance the cloning of genomic DNA in bacteriophage M13 vectors.

- **recA1:** The *recA* gene of *E. coli* codes for a DNA-dependent ATPase that is essential for genetic recombination in *E. coli* (for review, please see Radding 1982). Strains that carry the *recA1* mutation are defective in recombination and therefore have two advantages. First, plasmids propagated in these strains remain as monomers and do not form multimeric circles (Bedbrook and Ausubel 1976). Second, segments of foreign DNA propagated in M13 vectors may experience fewer deletions in *recA⁻* strains (Yanisch-Perron et al. 1985).

- **supE:** An amber suppressor that inserts glutamine at UAG codons. At one time, the NIH guidelines required bacteriophage M13 vectors to carry an amber mutation. This requirement has long since been dropped, and most vectors in common use today do not carry such mutations. However, many of the strains of *E. coli* that are used as hosts were developed when the guidelines were still in force. These strains and many of their derivatives carry a suppressor that allows the growth of vectors carrying certain amber mutations.

Table 3-2 contains a summary of strains of *E. coli* commonly used to propagate M13 vectors and recombinants, and Figure 3-4 displays the polycloning sites in many vectors.

CHOOSING AND MAINTAINING A SUITABLE STRAIN OF *E. COLI*

As mentioned above, infection of *E. coli* by bacteriophage M13 and its close relatives requires an intact F pilus. To ensure that bacteria used for propagating bacteriophage M13 maintain the F′ plasmid encoding the pilus structure, one of two positive selection strategies may be used:

- In all strains of *E. coli* commonly used for propagation of male-specific bacteriophages, the F′ plasmid carries genes encoding enzymes involved in proline biosynthesis (*proAB⁺*). Because these genes have been deleted from the host chromosome, only those bacteria that carry the F′ plasmid will be proline prototrophs and hence be able to form colonies on media lacking proline (e.g., M9 minimal medium). Bacterial strains grow much more slowly on minimal media than on rich media and do not survive prolonged periods of storage at 4ºC. For this reason, it is important to prepare fresh cultures of host bacteria every few days on M9 minimal agar plates, using a master stock stored at –70ºC as inoculum (please see below).

- Some but not all F′ plasmids carry a gene encoding resistance to an antibiotic, usually kanamycin or tetracycline. Only cells that maintain the F′ plasmid will grow in media containing the appropriate antibiotic. Using this selection eliminates the need to use minimal media, thereby greatly speeding the work of the laboratory.

Whatever the selection used to maintain the F′ plasmid, master stocks of F′ strains of *E. coli* used for propagation and plating of M13 should be stored at –70ºC in LB medium containing 15% glycerol. The choice of bacterial strain should, however, not be dictated by the type of selection used to maintain the F′ plasmid. Of much greater importance are the chromosomal markers carried by the strain, which can greatly influence the stability and yield of M13 recombinants and the purity of the single-stranded DNA templates prepared from infected cells. The following are two types of strain-dependent problems commonly encountered when cloning in filamentous bacteriophage vectors:

- ***Deletion of part of the foreign DNA segment.*** DNA cloned into the intergenic region of filamentous bacteriophages tends to be unstable. The larger the cloned segment, the greater the rate at which deletions occur. This problem can be minimized (although never completely

TABLE 3-2 Bacterial Strains Used to Propagate Bacteriophage M13 Vectors

PHENOTYPE	RELEVANT GENOTYPE	STRAIN	USES	REFERENCE
	$supE$ $\Delta(lac\text{-}proAB)$ F'$traD36$ $proAB^+$ $lacI^q$ $lacZ\Delta M15$	JM101[a]	permissive for vectors carrying amber mutations	Messing (1979)
r_k^-	$supE$ $\Delta(lac\text{-}proAB)$ $hsdR4$ F'$traD36$ $proAB^+$ $lacI^q$ $lacZ\Delta M15$	JM105	permissive for vectors carrying amber mutations; will modify but not restrict transfected DNA	Yanisch-Perron et al. (1985)
r_k^-	$supE$ $\Delta(lac\text{-}proAB)$ $hsdR17$ F'$traD36$ $proAB^+$ $lacI^q$ $lacZ\Delta M15$	JM107[b]	permissive for vectors carrying amber mutations; will modify but not restrict transfected DNA	Yanisch-Perron et al. (1985)
r_k^- Rec$^-$	$supE$ $\Delta(lac\text{-}proAB)$ $hsdR17$ $recA1$ F'$traD36$ $proAB^+$ $lacI^q$ $lacZ\Delta M15$	JM109[b,c]	permissive for vectors carrying amber mutations; will modify but not restrict transfected DNA RecA$^-$ strain	Yanisch-Perron et al. (1985)
r_k^- Dam$^-$	$supE$ $\Delta(lac\text{-}proAB)$ $hsdR17$ dam F'$traD36$ $proAB^+$ $lacI^q$ $lacZ\Delta M15$	JM110	permissive for vectors carrying amber mutations; will modify but not restrict transfected DNA; will not modify $BclI$ sites	Yanisch-Perron et al. (1985)
r_k^- r_m^-	$supE$ $\Delta(lac\text{-}proAB)$ $hsd\Delta5$ F'$traD36$ $proAB^+$ $lacI^q$ $lacZ\Delta M15$	TG1	permissive for vectors carrying amber mutations; will not modify or restrict transfected DNA	Gibson (1984)
r_k^- r_m^- Rec$^-$	$supE$ $\Delta(lac\text{-}proAB)$ $hsd\Delta5$ $\Delta(srl\text{-}recA)306$::Tn$10(tet^r)$ F'$traD36$ $proAB^+$ $lacI^q$ $lacZ\Delta M15$	TG2	permissive for vectors carrying amber mutations; will not modify or restrict transfected DNA; RecA$^-$ strain	M. Biggin (pers. comm.)
(Tet^r) r_k^- Rec$^-$	$supE^+$ lac^- $hsdR17$ $recA1$ F'$ProAB^+$ $lacI^q$ $lacZ\Delta M15$ Tn10 (Tet^r)	XL1-Blue	permissive for vectors carrying amber mutations; will modify but not restrict transfected DNA; RecA$^-$ strain	Bullock et al. (1987)
	$\Delta(lac\text{-}proAB)$ F'$traD36$ $proAB^+$ $lacI^q$	XS127	used for growth of phagemids	Levinson et al. (1984)

r$_k^-$ Rec$^-$ Kan$^+$	hsdR recA1 F' kan	XS101	used for growth of phagemids; will modify but not restrict transfected DNA; RecA$^-$ strain; carries episome conferring resistance to kanamycin	Levinson et al. (1984)
r$_k^-$	supE Δ(lac-proAB) F'ProAB$^+$ lacI^q lacZΔM15	71/18	used for growth of phagemids	Dente et al. (1983)
r$_k^-$	supE Δ(lac-proAB) hsdR4 F'traD36 proAB$^+$ lacI^q lacZΔM15	KK2186	permissive for vectors carrying amber mutations; will modify but not restrict transfected DNA	Zargusky and Berman (1984)
Rec$^-$	Δ(lac-proAB) Δ(srl-recA) 306::Tn10(tet) (φ80lacZΔM15) F'traD36 proAB$^+$ lacI^q lacZΔM15	MV1184[d]	used to propagate pUC118/pUC119; used to obtain single-stranded copies of phagemids; RecA$^-$ strain	Vieira and Messing (1987)
Mcr$^-$	supE Δ(lac-proAB) Δ(mcrB-hsdSM)5 F'proAB lacI^q lacZΔM15	NM522	used for growth of phagemids; enhanced cloning of methylated genomic DNA	Gough and Murray (1983)
r$_k^-$ r$_m^-$ Rec$^-$ Mcr$^-$	Δ(lac-pro AB)Δ(recA 1398) Δ(mrr-hsd RMS-mcrBC) mcrA deoR rpsL srl$^-$)	DH11S	used for growth of phagemids; RecA$^-$ strain; enhanced cloning of methylated genomic DNA; enhanced uptake of large plasmids	Lin et al. (1992)
r$_k^-$ r$_m^-$ Rec$^-$ Mcr$^-$	supE recA1 Δ(mcrA)183 Δ(mcr CB$^-$ hsd SMR-mrr)173 F'proAB lacI^q lacZΔM15 Tn10(tet')	XLI-Blue MRF'	used for growth of phagemids; RecA$^-$ strain; enhanced cloning of methylated genomic DNA	Jerpseth et al. (1992)

[a] JM103 (Messing et al. 1981) is a restrictionless derivative of JM101 that has been used to propagate bacteriophage M13 recombinants. However, some cultivars of JM103 have lost the *hsdR4* mutation (Felton 1983) and are lysogenic for bacteriophage P1 (which codes for its own restriction/modification system). JM103 is therefore no longer recommended as a host for bacteriophage M13 vectors. Strain KK2186 (Zagursky and Berman 1984) is genetically identical to JM103 except that it is nonlysogenic for bacteriophage P1.

[b] JM106 and JM108 are identical to JM107 and JM109, respectively, except that they do not carry an F' episome. These strains will not support the growth of bacteriophage M13 but may be used to propagate plasmids. However, JM106 and JM108 do not carry the *lacI*^{q} marker (normally present on the F' episome) and are therefore unable effectively to suppress the synthesis of potentially toxic products encoded by foreign DNA sequences cloned into plasmids carrying the *lacZ* promoter.

[c] JM108 and JM109 are defective for synthesis of bacterial cell walls and form mucoid colonies on minimal media. This trait does not affect their ability to support the growth of bacteriophage M13.

[d] The original strain of MV1184, constructed by M. Volkert (pers. comm.), did not carry an F' episome. However, the strain of MV1184 distributed by the Messing laboratory clearly carries an F' episome. It is therefore advisable to check strains of MV1184 on their arrival in the laboratory for their ability to support the growth of male-specific bacteriophages.

M13mp7/pUC7
7237/2674

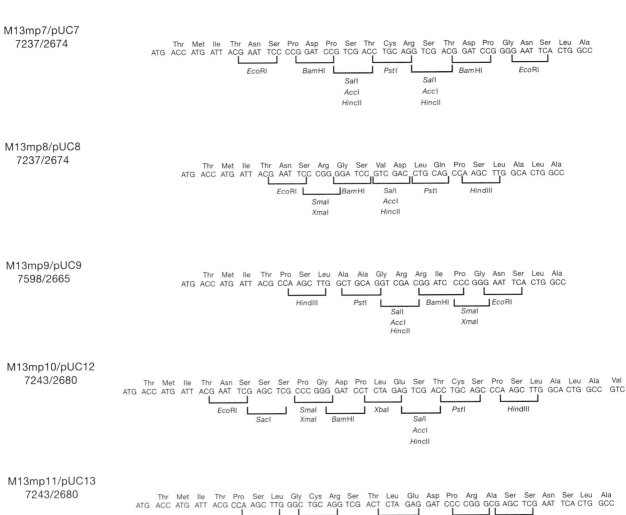

M13mp8/pUC8
7237/2674

M13mp9/pUC9
7598/2665

M13mp10/pUC12
7243/2680

M13mp11/pUC13
7243/2680

M13mp18/pUC18
7249/2686

M13mp19/pUC19
7249/2686

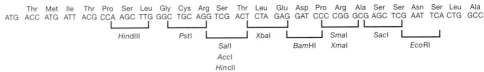

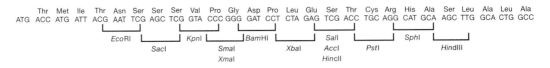
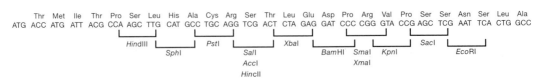

FIGURE 3-4 Multiple Cloning Sites in Bacteriophage M13 and Phagemid Vectors

Shown are the positions of restriction sites in the multiple cloning sites of commonly used bacteriophage M13 vectors and their corresponding pUC plasmids. The numbers beneath the names of the vectors are their approximate sizes (in nucleotides). The polycloning regions of the corresponding phagemids are virtually identical.

pCR 2.1
3900

```
              Thr  Met  Ile  Pro  Ser  Leu  Val  Pro  Ser  Ser  Asp  Pro  Leu  Val  Thr  Ala  Ala  Ser  Val  Leu  Glu  Phe  Gly  Leu  Gly
         ATG  ACC  ATG  ATT  CCA  AGC  TTG  GTA  CCG  AGC  TCG  GAT  CCA  CTA  GTA  ACG  GCC  GCC  AGT  GTG  CTG  GAA  TTC  GGC  TTA*  GCC
                             └── HindIII ──┘ └─ KpnI ─┘ └─ SacI ─┘ └─ BamHI ─┘ └─ SpeI ─┘                         └─ EcoRI ─┘
```

```
              Glu  Phe  Cys  Arg  Tyr  Pro  Ser  His  Trp  Arg  Pro  Leu  Glu  His  Ala  Ser  Arg  Gly  Pro  Asn  Ser  Pro  Tyr  Ser
              GAA  TTC  TGC  AGA  TAT  CCA  TCA  CAC  TGG  CGG  CCG  CTC  GAG  CAT  GCA  TCT  AGA  GGG  CCC  AAT  TCG  CCC  TAT  AGT
              └── EcoRI ──┘   └──── EcoRV ────┘                        └── AvaI ──┘      └── XbaI ──┘
                                                                       └── XhoI ──┘
```

pBluescript II SK (+/-)
2961

```
              Met  Thr  Met  Ile  Thr  Pro  Ser  Ala  Gln  Leu  Thr  Leu  Thr  Lys  Gly  Asn  Lys  Ser  Trp  Ser  Ser  Thr  Ala  Val
         G  GAA  ACA  GCT  ATG  ACC  ATG  ATT  ACG  CCA  AGC  GCG  CAA  TTA  ACC  CTC  ACT  AAA  GGG  AAC  AAA  AGC  TGG  AGC  TCC  ACC  GCG  GTG
                                                                                                                    └── SacI ──┘
```

```
         Ala  Ala  Ala  Leu  Glu  Leu  Val  Asp  Pro  Pro  Gly  Cys  Arg  Asn  Leu  Ile  Ser  Ser  Leu  Ser  Ile  Pro  Ser  Thr  Ser  Arg  Gly
         GCG  GCC  GCT  CTA  GAA  CTA  GTG  GAT  CCC  CCG  GGC  TGC  AGG  AAT  TCG  ATA  TCA  AGC  TTA  TCG  ATA  CCG  TCG  ACC  TCG  AGG  GGG
                        └─ XbaI ─┘ └─ SpeI ─┘ └─ BamHI ─┘ └── SmaI ──┘ └─ PstI ─┘ └── EcoRI ──┘        └── HindIII ──┘      └─ SalI ─┘ └── XhoI ──┘
                                                           └── XmaI ──┘                                                      Acc I
                                                                                                                             HincII
```

```
         Gly  Pro  Val  Pro  Asn  Ser  Pro  Tyr  Ser  Glu  Ser  Tyr  Tyr  Ala  Arg  Ser  Leu  Ala  Val  Val  Leu  Gln
         GGC  CCG  GTA  CCC  AAT  TCG  CCC  TAT  AGT  GAG  TCG  TAT  TAC  GCG  CGC  TCA  CTG  GCC  GTC  GTT  TTA  CAA
                   └── KpnI ──┘
```

pBluescript II KS (+/-)
2961

```
              Met  Thr  Met  Ile  Thr  Pro  Ser  Ala  Gln  Leu  Thr  Leu  Thr  Lys  Gly  Asn  Lys  Ser  Trp  Val  Pro  Gly  Pro
         G  GAA  ACA  GCT  ATG  ACC  ATG  ATT  ACG  CCA  AGC  GCG  CAA  TTA  ACC  CTC  ACT  AAA  GGG  AAC  AAA  AGC  TGG  GTA  CCG  GGC  CCC
                                                                                                               └── KpnI ──┘
```

```
         Pro  Ser  Arg  Ser  Thr  Val  Ser  Ile  Ser  Leu  Ile  Ser  Asn  Ser  Sys  Ser  Pro  Gly  Asp  Pro  Leu  Val  Leu  Glu  Arg  Pro  Pro  Pro  Arg
         CCC  TCG  AGG  TCG  ACG  GTA  TCG  ATA  AGC  TTG  ATA  TCG  AAT  TCC  TGC  AGC  CCG  GGG  GAT  CCA  CTA  GTT  CTA  GAG  CGG  CCG  CCA  CCG  CGG
         └── XhoI ──┘ └─ SalI ─┘          └── HindIII ──┘       └── EcoRI ──┘ └─ PstI ─┘ └── SmaI ──┘ └── BamHI ──┘ └─ SpeI ─┘ └─ XbaI ─┘
                      Acc I
                      HincII
```

```
         Trp  Ser  Ser  Asn  Ser  Pro  Tyr  Ser  Glu  Ser  Tyr  Tyr  Ala  Arg  Ser  Leu  Ala  Val  Val
         TGG  AGC  TCC  AAT  TCG  CCC  TAT  AGT  GAG  TCG  TAT  TAC  GCG  CGC  TCA  CTG  GCC  GTC  GTT
              └── SacI ──┘
```

pGL2
5789

```
         ATC  AAT  GTA  TCT  TAT  GGT  ACT  GTA  ACT  GAG  CTA  ACA  TAA  CCC  GGG  AGG  TAC  CGA  GCT  CTT  ACG  CGT  GCT  AGC  TCG  AGA  TCT
                                                                       └── SmaI ──┘ └── KpnI ──┘ └── SacI ──┘ └── MluI ──┘ └── XhoI ──┘ └── BglII
                                                                        └─ XmaI ─┘                                         └── NheI ──┘
```

```
                        Met  Glu  Asp  Ala  Lys  Asn  Ile  Lys  Lys
         AAG  TAA  GCT  TGG  CAT  TCC  GGT  ACT  GTT  GGT  AAA  ATG  GAA  GAC  GCC  AAA  AAC  ATA  AAG  AAA
              └── HindIII ──┘
```

pβgal
7486

```
         ATC  AAT  GTA  TCT  TAT  GGT  ACT  GTA  ACT  GAG  CTA  ACA  TAA  CCC  GGG  AGG  TAC  CGA  GCT  CTT  ACG  CGT  GCT  AGC  TCG  AGA  TCT
                                                                       └── SmaI ──┘ └── KpnI ──┘ └── SacI ──┘ └── MluI ──┘ └── XhoI ──┘ └── BglII
                                                                        └─ XmaI ─┘                                         └── NheI ──┘
```

```
                                                                                          Met  Ser  Phe  Thr  Leu  Thr  Asn  Lys
         AAG  TAA  GCT  TGG  GGG  ATC  GAA  AGA  GCC  TGC  TAA  AGC  AAA  AAA  GAA  GTC  ACC  ATG  TCG  TTT  ACT  TTG  ACC  AAC  AAG
              └── HindIII ──┘
```

FIGURE 3-4 *(See facing page for legend.)*

eliminated) (1) by using strains of bacteria that carry *recA* mutations and (2) taking care never to propagate the bacteriophage by serial growth of infected cells in liquid culture. Instead, stocks of recombinant bacteriophages stored at –70ºC should be plated on an appropriate host, and bacteria from the center of a single well-isolated plaque should be used to establish a small-scale culture. This culture should provide sufficient quantities of single-stranded DNA or double-stranded RF DNA for most purposes. The culture should be grown for the shortest possible time (usually 4–8 hours, depending on the vector and the strain of *E. coli*) and should not be used as a stock to seed further cultures. Please see the information panel on GROWTH TIMES.

- ***Insertion of the foreign DNA in only one orientation.*** Quite frequently, a given vector will carry a specific segment of foreign DNA far more readily in only one of the two possible orientations. This phenomenon occurs because sequences on opposite strands of the foreign DNA interfere to different extents with the functioning of the vector's intergenic region. This problem can sometimes be avoided by inserting the foreign DNA at a different site within the polycloning site, by changing hosts strains, or by using a combination of restriction enzymes that allow directional cloning. However, if bacteriophage M13 vectors are forced to propagate unwelcome sequences of foreign DNA, the resulting recombinants are often unstable and give rise to progeny that carry deleted or rearranged versions of the foreign sequences. Under these circumstances, a better alternative is to propagate the foreign DNA in plasmid vectors that carry an origin of replication derived from a filamentous bacteriophage. Vectors of this type (phagemids) are discussed in detail in the introduction to Protocol 8. For the moment, however, it is worthwhile pointing out that phagemids are not a universal panacea: The quantities of single-stranded DNA produced by phagemids vary from one host strain to another and are often low.

In summary, the yield and stability of recombinants constructed in bacteriophage M13 and phagemid vectors are influenced by several variables: the structure and size of the foreign DNA, the type of vector, and the properties of the host strain, including its efficiency of transformation and ability to produce high yields of single-stranded DNA. The best course of action, therefore, is to try several combinations of vector and host cell. Start by using standard host strains such as TG1 or XL1-Blue. If problems arise, switch to a host cell such as DH11S that contains several additional genetic markers (please see Table 3-2). DH11S carries mutations in (1) the *recA* gene to enhance stability of inserts, (2) the restriction systems that attack methylated mammalian genomic DNA, and (3) the *deo*^{r} gene that increases the efficiency of transformation by larger plasmids (Lin et al. 1992).

In this chapter, we describe methods for the propagation of bacteriophage M13, the uses of bacteriophage M13 vectors, the preparation of double-stranded DNAs from infected cells and single-stranded DNAs from virus particles, and methods to characterize bacteriophage recombinants. Methods for the use and propagation of phagemids complete the chapter.

Once upon a time an honest fellow had the idea that men drowned in water only because they were possessed with the idea of gravity. If they were to knock this idea out of their heads, say by stating it a superstition, a religious idea, they would be sublimely resilient against any danger from water. His whole life long he fought against the illusion of gravity, of whose harmful results all statistics brought him new and manifold evidence.

Karl Marx, preface to *The German Ideology* (Vol I. 1845–1846)

Protocol 1

Plating Bacteriophage M13

A PLAQUE OF BACTERIOPHAGE M13 DERIVES FROM INFECTION of a single bacterium by a single virus particle. The progeny particles infect neighboring bacteria, which in turn release another generation of daughter virus particles. If the bacteria are growing in semisolid medium (e.g., containing agar or agarose), then the diffusion of the progeny particles is limited. Because cells infected with bacteriophage M13 have a longer generation time than uninfected *E. coli*, plaques appear as areas of slower-growing cells on a faster-growing lawn of bacterial cells. Bacteriophage M13 plaques are therefore turbid, in contrast to the clear plaques of viruses such as the T bacteriophages that lyse the bacterial host. Very clear "plaques" are most likely to be small air bubbles trapped in the soft agar during mixing prior to plating.

Minimal (M9) agar plates can be used to advantage for plaque formation by bacteriophage M13. Not only are plaques formed on minimal media easier to see than those on richer media, but infected cultures established from a plaque formed on minimal medium are unlikely to contain a significant number of female cells. Plaques formed on richer medium (YT or LB) may be overgrown by auxotrophic female cells that are resistant to infection by bacteriophage M13. Fortunately, the danger is slight since the spontaneous loss of F′ plasmids from bacteria grown for a limited period in rich medium is rarely high enough to cause problems. Because plaques form more rapidly on richer medium than on minimal medium, we recommend that YT or LB medium be used for routine plating of bacteriophage M13 stocks.

Bacteriophage M13 can be propagated by infecting a susceptible strain of *E. coli* and plating the infected cells in soft agar. After 4–8 hours, "plaques," or zones of slowed cellular growth, are readily detectable in the top agar. Infection is carried out with either a bacteriophage stock or freshly picked plaques and freshly grown colonies of the appropriate strain of *E. coli*.

MATERIALS

CAUTION: Please see Appendix 12 for appropriate handling of materials marked with <!>.

Buffers and Solutions

Please see Appendix 1 for components of stock solutions, buffers, and reagents. Dilute stock solutions to the appropriate concentrations.

IPTG solution (20% w/v)
X-gal solution (2% w/v) <!>

Media

LB agar plates containing tetracycline or kanamycin
These plates are needed only if a tetracycline-resistant strain of *E. coli*, such as XL1-Blue, or a kanamycin-resistant strain of *E. coli*, such as XL1-Blue MRF′ Kan, is used to propagate the virus.

or

Supplemented M9 minimal agar plates
When using *E. coli* strains that carry a deletion of the proline biosynthetic operon ($\Delta[lac$-$proAB]$) in the bacterial chromosome and the complementing *proAB* genes on the F′ plasmid, use supplemented M9 minimal medium.

LB or YT medium

LB or YT medium agar plates containing 5 mM MgCl$_2$

LB or YT medium top agar or agarose containing 5 mM MgCl$_2$
The addition of Mg^{2+} (5 mM) to media (Reddy and McKenney 1996) is reported to improve the yield of bacteriophage M13 cultures infected at low multiplicity.

Special Equipment

Heating block or water bath preset to 47ºC
Ice-water bath

Vectors and Bacterial Strains

Bacteriophage M13 stock in LB or YT medium
or

Bacteriophage M13 plaque in 1 ml of LB or YT medium
Medium from a fully grown liquid culture of bacteria infected with bacteriophage M13 contains between 10^{10} and 10^{12} pfu/ml. A bacteriophage M13 plaque contains between 10^6 and 10^8 pfu.

E. coli *F′ strain, prepared as a master culture*
Preparation of a master culture is described in Chapter 1, Protocol 1. For a list of *E. coli* strains suitable for the propagation of bacteriophage M13, please see Table 3-2 in the introduction to this chapter.

METHOD

1. Streak a master culture of a bacterial strain carrying an F′ plasmid onto either a supplemented minimal (M9) agar plate or an LB plate containing tetracycline (XL1-Blue) or kanamycin (XL1-Blue MRF′ Kan). Incubate the plate for 24–36 hours at 37ºC.

2. To prepare plating bacteria, inoculate 5 ml of LB or YT medium in a 20-ml sterile culture tube with a single, well-isolated colony picked from the agar plate prepared in Step 1. Agitate the culture for 6–8 hours at 37ºC in a rotary shaker. Chill the culture in an ice bath for 20 minutes and then store it at 4ºC. These plating bacteria can be stored for periods of up to 1 week at 4ºC.

   ▲ IMPORTANT Do not grow the cells to saturation, as this will increase the risk of losing the pili encoded by the F′ plasmid.

3. Prepare sterile tubes (13 x 100 mm or 17 x 100 mm) containing 3 ml of melted LB or YT medium top agar or agarose, supplemented with 5 mM $MgCl_2$. Allow the tubes to equilibrate to 47°C in a heating block or water bath.

4. Label a series of sterile tubes (13 x 100 mm or 17 x 100 mm) according to the dilution factor and amount of bacteriophage stock to be added (please see Step 5), and deliver 100 µl of plating bacteria from Step 2 into each of these tubes.

5. Prepare tenfold serial dilutions (10^{-6} to 10^{-9}) of the bacteriophage stock in LB or YT medium. Dispense 10 µl or 100 µl of each dilution to be assayed into a sterile tube containing plating bacteria from Step 4. Mix the bacteriophage particles with the bacterial culture by vortexing gently.

    Unlike bacteriophage λ, M13 adsorbs rapidly to bacteria; there is thus no need to incubate the plating bacteria with the bacteriophage suspension before adding top agar.

6. Add 40 µl of 2% X-gal solution and 4 µl of 20% IPTG solution to each of the tubes containing top agar. Immediately pour the contents of one of these tubes into one of the infected cultures. Mix the culture with the agar/agarose by gently vortexing for 3 seconds, and then pour the mixture onto a labeled plate containing LB or YT agar medium supplemented with 5 mM $MgCl_2$ and equilibrated to room temperature. Swirl the plate gently to ensure an even distribution of bacteria and top agar.

    Work quickly so that the top agar spreads over the entire surface of the agar before it sets.

7. Repeat the addition of top agar with X-gal and IPTG for each tube of infected culture prepared in Step 5.

8. Replace the lids on the plates and allow the top agar/agarose to harden for 5 minutes at room temperature. Wipe excess condensation off the lids with Kimwipes. Invert the plates and incubate them at 37°C.

    Pale blue plaques begin to appear after 4 hours. The color gradually intensifies as the plaques enlarge. Development of both plaques and color is complete after 8–12 hours of incubation. The blue color will intensify further if the plates are placed for several hours at 4°C or examined against a canary yellow background.

Protocol 2

Growing Bacteriophage M13 in Liquid Culture

STOCKS OF BACTERIOPHAGE M13 ARE USUALLY GROWN in liquid culture. The infected bacteria do not lyse but instead grow at a slower than normal rate to form a dilute suspension. The inoculum of bacteriophage is almost always a freshly picked plaque or a suspension of bacteriophage particles obtained from a single plaque. Infected cells contain up to 200 copies of double-stranded RF DNA and extrude several hundred bacteriophage particles per generation. Thus, a 1-ml culture of infected cells can produce enough double-stranded viral DNA (1–2 μg) for restriction mapping and recovery of cloned DNA inserts and sufficient single-stranded DNA (~5–10 μg) for site-directed mutagenesis, DNA sequencing, or synthesis of radiolabeled probes. The titer of bacteriophages in the supernatant from infected cells is so high (~10^{12} pfu/ml) that a small aliquot serves as a permanent stock of the starting plaque. Alternatively, larger volumes of the supernatant can be used to scale up the production of virus, RF DNA, and single-stranded DNA (please see Protocol 5).

Most manipulations involving bacteriophage M13, including preparation of viral stocks and isolation of single- and double-stranded DNAs, begin with small-scale liquid cultures. Typically, a plaque is picked from an agar plate and added to a 1–2-ml aliquot of medium containing uninfected *E. coli* cells. After a 4–6-hour period of growth (please see the information panel on GROWTH TIMES), the titer of bacteriophage particles in the medium reaches ~10^{12} pfu/ml, which is sufficient for the subsequent isolation of viral DNA or for storage as a stock solution.

MATERIALS

Media

LB medium containing tetracycline or kanamycin
> These media are needed only if a tetracycline-resistant strain of *E. coli*, such as XL1-Blue, or a kanamycin-resistant strain of *E. coli*, such as XL1-Blue MRF′ Kan, is used to propagate the virus.

or

Supplemented M9 minimal medium
> When using *E. coli* strains that carry a deletion of the proline biosynthetic operon (Δ[*lac-proAB*]) in the bacterial chromosome and the complementing *proAB* genes on the F′ plasmid, use supplemented M9 minimal medium.

YT or LB medium

2x YT medium containing 5 mM MgCl₂

Special Equipment

Sterile toothpicks or Inoculating needles or Glass capillary tubes (50 μl)

Vectors and Bacterial Strains

Bacteriophage M13 plaques plated onto an agar or agarose plate

For methods to produce bacteriophage M13 plaques in top agar or agarose, please see either Protocol 1 or 6 of this chapter.

E. coli F´ strain, grown as well-isolated colonies on an agar plate

For a list of *E. coli* strains suitable for the propagation of bacteriophage M13, please see Table 3-2 in the introduction to this chapter.

Streak a master culture of an appropriate host onto an M9 minimal agar plate or, for antibiotic-resistant strains, onto an LB plate containing the appropriate antibiotic. Incubate for 24–36 hours at 37°C. Bacteriophage M13 single-stranded DNA to be used as a template for oligonucleotide-directed mutagenesis should be propagated in *E. coli* F´ strains bearing mutations in the *dut* and *ung* genes. For a detailed protocol for growth of bacteriophage in these strains, please see Chapter 13, Protocol 1.

METHOD

1. Inoculate 5 ml of supplemented M9 medium (or, for antibiotic-resistant strains, LB medium with the appropriate antibiotic) with a single freshly grown colony of *E. coli* carrying an F´ plasmid. Incubate the culture for 12 hours at 37°C with moderate shaking.

   Avoid growing the culture to stationary phase, which increases the risk of losing the pili encoded by the F´ plasmid.

2. Transfer 0.1 ml of the *E. coli* culture into 5 ml of 2x YT medium containing 5 mM $MgCl_2$. Incubate the culture for 2 hours at 37°C with vigorous shaking.

3. Dilute the 5-ml culture into 45 ml of 2x YT containing 5 mM $MgCl_2$ and dispense 1-ml aliquots into as many sterile tubes (13 x 100 mm or 17 x 100 mm) as there are plaques to be propagated. Dispense two additional aliquots for use as positive and negative controls for bacteriophage growth. Set these cultures aside for use at Step 7.

4. Dispense 1 ml of YT or LB medium into sterile 13 x 100-mm tubes. Prepare as many tubes as there are plaques. Dispense two additional aliquots for use as positive and negative controls for bacteriophage growth.

5. Prepare a dilute suspension of bacteriophage M13 by touching the surface of a plaque with the end of a sterile inoculating needle and immersing the end of the needle into the YT or LB medium. Pick one blue M13 plaque as a positive control for bacteriophage growth. Also pick an area of the *E. coli* lawn from the plate that does not contain a plaque as a negative control. Please see the panel on **PICKING PLAQUES** on the following page.

6. Allow the suspension to stand for 1–2 hours at room temperature to allow the bacteriophage particles to diffuse from the agar.

   An average plaque contains between 10^6 and 10^8 pfu. The suspension of bacteriophage particles can be stored indefinitely in LB medium at 4°C or –20°C without loss of viability.

7. Use 0.1 ml of the bacteriophage suspension (Step 6) as an inoculum to infect 1-ml cultures of *E. coli* (Step 3) for isolation of viral DNA. Incubate the inoculated tubes for 5 hours at 37°C with moderate shaking.

   Alternatively, transfer a plaque directly into the *E. coli* culture: Touch the surface of the chosen plaque with the end of a sterile inoculating needle, and immediately immerse the end of the needle into the tube containing the 2x YT medium (Step 3). Shake the tube vigorously to dislodge small fragments of agar (or agarose).

   ▲ IMPORTANT To minimize the possibility of selecting deletion mutants, grow cultures infected with recombinant M13 bacteriophages for the shortest time that will produce a workable amount of single-stranded DNA (usually 5 hours). For additional information, please see the information panel on **GROWTH TIMES**.

PICKING PLAQUES

Bacteriophage M13 can diffuse considerable distances through top agar. To minimize the possibility of cross contamination, pick plaques that are well separated (ideally by ~0.5 cm) from their nearest neighbors. Do not pick plaques that have been grown for more than 16 hours at 37°C or stored for extended periods at 4°C. The following are several alternative methods for picking plaques:

- Use an inoculating loop or sterile applicator stick.

- Attach a bulb to a sterile, disposable Pasteur or capillary pipette and stab through the plaque into the underlying agar. Then expel the plug of agar from the pipette into the liquid culture.

- Touch the surface of the plaque with a sterile toothpick, and then drop the toothpick into the liquid culture. This method violates the rules of sterile technique, since a nonsterile hand has held the toothpick. However, in practice, few problems arise, perhaps because the "dirty" end of the toothpick usually does not come into contact with the medium. This method may be used when picking plaques that will be used immediately (e.g., to generate templates for sequencing), but it is not recommended when picking plaques that will be stored for long periods of time or that will be used to make master stocks of valuable recombinants.

- Attach a sterile 50-μl glass capillary tube to a mouth pipette plugged with cotton. Core the plaque with the capillary tube and use gentle suction to dislodge the plug containing the plaque from the plate. Expel the core into the aliquot of 2x YT medium containing bacteria.

---

8. Transfer the culture to a sterile microfuge tube and centrifuge at maximum speed for 5 minutes at room temperature. Transfer the supernatant to a fresh microfuge tube without disturbing the bacterial pellet.

9. Transfer 0.1 ml of the supernatant to a sterile microfuge tube.

    This high-titer stock can be stored indefinitely at 4°C or –20°C without loss of infectivity.

10. Use the remaining 1 ml of the culture supernatant to prepare single-stranded bacteriophage DNA (Protocol 4). Use the bacterial cell pellet to prepare double-stranded RF DNA (Protocol 3).

    Alternatively, the culture supernatant may be stored at 4°C for large-scale preparation of M13 (Protocol 5).

Protocol 3

Preparation of Double-stranded (Replicative Form) Bacteriophage M13 DNA

Bacteria infected with bacteriophage M13 contain the double-stranded RF of the viral DNA and extrude virus particles containing single-stranded progeny DNA into the medium. The double-stranded RF DNA can be isolated from small cultures of infected cells using methods similar to those used to purify plasmid DNA. Several micrograms of RF DNA can be isolated from a 1–2-ml culture of infected cells, which is enough for subcloning and restriction enzyme mapping.

Minipreparations or midipreparations (described in Chapter 1, Protocols 1 and 2) for plasmid purification may be used to prepare RF DNA. The method described here was devised by Birnboim and Doly (1979) and subsequently modified by Ish-Horowicz and Burke (1981). It was originally used to isolate closed circular plasmid and cosmid DNAs from bacterial cultures. Bacteriophage M13 RF DNA prepared with this method generally is used in two ways:

- To confirm the presence of a desired insert in the bacteriophage M13 vector by restriction analysis and Southern hybridization of recombinant bacteriophage RF DNA.

- To recover double-stranded DNA from recombinant bacteriophage M13 clones that have been subjected to site-directed mutagenesis (Chapter 13, Protocol 2). The mutated DNA can then be subcloned into a bacterial or eukaryotic expression vector.

Preparations of bacteriophage M13 RF DNA are rarely as clean as small-scale preparations of plasmid DNA. The former are often contaminated with single-stranded viral DNA that can confuse the pattern of DNA fragments obtained by digestion with restriction enzymes. This problem can be alleviated by analyzing in parallel an aliquot of RF DNA that has not been digested. Linear and circular single-stranded viral DNAs (which usually appear as fuzzy bands migrating faster than the double-stranded RF DNA) are not cleaved by most of the restriction enzymes commonly used for cloning in bacteriophage M13. Fragments of double-stranded DNA with recessed 3′ termini can also be distinguished from single-stranded DNAs by end-labeling using the Klenow fragment of *E. coli* DNA polymerase I (please see Chapter 10, Protocol 7).

MATERIALS

CAUTION: Please see Appendix 12 for appropriate handling of materials marked with <!>.

Buffers and Solutions

Please see Appendix 1 for components of stock solutions, buffers, and reagents. Dilute stock solutions to the appropriate concentrations.

Alkaline lysis solution I
Alkaline lysis solution II
Prepare fresh for each use from standard stocks; use at room temperature.
Alkaline lysis solution III
Ethanol
Phenol:chloroform (1:1, v/v) <!>
TE (pH 8.0) containing 20 µg/ml RNase A

Enzymes and Buffers

Restriction endonucleases

Gels

Agarose gel (0.8%) cast in 0.5x TBE, containing 0.5 µg/ml ethidium bromide <!>
Please see Step 13.

Vectors and Bacterial Strains

E. coli *culture infected with bacteriophage M13*
Prepared as described in Protocol 2 of this chapter.

METHOD

Lysis of the Infected Cells

1. Centrifuge 1 ml of the M13-infected cell culture at maximum speed for 5 minutes at room temperature in a microfuge to separate the infected cells from the medium. Transfer the supernatant to a fresh microfuge tube and store at 4ºC. Keep the infected bacterial cell pellet on ice.

   The supernatant contains M13 bacteriophage housing single-stranded DNA. If desired, prepare M13 DNA from this supernatant at a later stage (Protocol 4).

2. Centrifuge the bacterial cell pellet for 5 seconds at 4ºC and remove residual medium with an automatic pipetting device.

3. Resuspend the cell pellet in 100 µl of ice-cold Alkaline lysis solution I by vigorous vortexing.

   Make sure that the bacterial pellet is completely dispersed in Alkaline lysis solution I. Vortexing two microfuge tubes simultaneously with their bases touching increases the rate and efficiency with which the bacterial pellets are resuspended.

   Some strains of bacteria shed cell-wall components into the medium that can inhibit the action of restriction enzymes. This problem can be avoided by resuspending the bacterial cell pellet in 0.5 ml of STE (0.1 M NaCl, 10 mM Tris-Cl [pH 8.0], 1 mM EDTA [pH 8.0]) before Step 3 and centrifuging again. After removal of the STE, resuspend the pellet in Alkaline lysis solution I as described above.

   Some protocols for the preparation of bacteriophage M13 RF DNA include digestion of the cell walls with lysozyme. This step is generally not necessary but does no harm. To include this step, add 90 µl of Alkaline lysis solution I to the bacterial cell pellet and resuspend the cells by vortexing. To the resuspended cells, add 10 µl of Alkaline lysis solution I containing freshly prepared 10 mg/ml lysozyme. Mix the components by tapping the side of the tube and incubate on ice for 5 minutes. Continue with Step 4.

4. Add 200 µl of freshly prepared Alkaline lysis solution II to the tube. Close the tube tightly and mix by inverting the tube rapidly five times. *Do not vortex.* Store the tube on ice for 2 minutes after mixing.

5. Add 150 µl of ice-cold Alkaline lysis solution III to the tube. Close the tube to disperse Alkaline lysis solution III through the viscous bacterial lysate by inverting the tube several times. Store the tube on ice for 3–5 minutes.

6. Centrifuge the bacterial lysate at maximum speed for 5 minutes at 4ºC in a microfuge. Transfer the supernatant to a fresh tube.

Purification of RF Bacteriophage M13 DNA

7. Add an equal volume of phenol:chloroform. Mix the organic and aqueous phases by vortexing and then centrifuge the tube at maximum speed for 2–5 minutes. Transfer the aqueous (upper) phase to a fresh tube.

8. Precipitate the double-stranded DNA by adding 2 volumes of ethanol. Mix the contents of the tube by vortexing and then allow the mixture to stand for 2 minutes at room temperature.

9. Recover the DNA by centrifugation at maximum speed for 5 minutes at 4ºC in a microfuge.

10. Remove the supernatant by gentle aspiration. Stand the tube in an inverted position on a paper towel to allow all of the fluid to drain away. Remove any drops of fluid adhering to the walls of the tube.

    This step can be conveniently accomplished with a disposable pipette tip attached to a vacuum line. Use a gentle vacuum and touch the tip to the surface of the liquid. Keep the tip as far away from the pellet of nucleic acid as possible as the fluid is withdrawn from the tube. Use the pipette tip to vacuum the walls of the tube to remove any adherent droplets of fluid.

    > An additional ethanol precipitation step here helps to ensure that the double-stranded DNA is efficiently cleaved by restriction enzymes.
    >
    > - Dissolve the pellet of RF DNA in 100 µl of TE (pH 8.0).
    >
    > - Add 50 µl of 7.5 M ammonium acetate (please see Appendix 1), mix well, and add 300 µl of ice-cold ethanol.
    >
    > - Store the tube for 15 minutes at room temperature or overnight at –20°C and then collect the precipitated DNA by centrifugation at maximum speed for 5–10 minutes at 4°C in a microfuge. Remove the supernatant by gentle aspiration.
    >
    > - Rinse the pellet with 250 µl of ice-cold 70% ethanol, centrifuge again for 2–3 minutes, and discard the supernatant.
    >
    > - Allow the pellet of DNA to dry in the air for 10 minutes and then dissolve the DNA as described in Step 12.

11. Add 1 ml of 70% ethanol at 4ºC and centrifuge again for 2 minutes. Remove the supernatant as described in Step 10, and allow the pellet of nucleic acid to dry in the air for 10 minutes.

12. To remove RNA, resuspend the pellet in 25 µl of TE (pH 8.0) with RNase. Vortex briefly.

13. Analyze the double-stranded RF DNA by digestion with appropriate restriction endonucleases followed by electrophoresis through an agarose gel.

    The yield of RF DNA expected from 1 ml of an infected bacterial culture is usually several micrograms, which is enough for 5–10 restriction digests.

Protocol 4

Preparation of Single-stranded Bacteriophage M13 DNA

BACTERIOPHAGE M13 SINGLE-STRANDED DNA IS PREPARED from virus particles secreted by infected cells into the surrounding medium. The filamentous virus is first concentrated by precipitation with polyethylene glycol (PEG) in the presence of high salt. Subsequent extraction with phenol releases the single-stranded DNA, which is then collected by precipitation with ethanol. The resulting preparation is pure enough to be used as a template for DNA sequencing by the dideoxy chain termination method (Chapter 12, Protocol 3 or 4), for oligonucleotide-directed mutagenesis (Chapter 13, Protocol 1), or for synthesis of radioactive probes (Chapter 9, Protocols 4 and 5). The following protocol, adapted from Sanger et al. (1980) and Messing (1983), is the simplest and most widely used method for preparing single-stranded DNA from a small number of bacteriophage M13 isolates. A yield of 5–10 μg of single-stranded DNA/ml of infected cells may be expected from recombinant bacteriophages bearing inserts of 300–1000 nucleotides. This amount is enough for 10–20 cycle-sequencing reactions or 5–10 Sequenase reactions (Chen et al. 1991; Halloran et al. 1993).

The standard method for purification of bacteriophage M13 DNA described in this protocol is not appropriate for large-scale sequencing projects, which typically require many thousands of DNA templates. For a method to produce these templates in large numbers, see Chapter 12, Protocol 2.

MATERIALS

CAUTION: Please see Appendix 12 for appropriate handling of materials marked with <!>.

Buffers and Solutions

Please see Appendix 1 for components of stock solutions, buffers, and reagents. Dilute stock solutions to the appropriate concentrations.

Chloroform <!>
  Please see note at Step 7.
Ethanol
Phenol <!>
Polyethylene glycol 8000 (20% w/v PEG 8000) <!> *in 2.5 M NaCl*
  Please see the information panel on **POLYETHYLENE GLYCOL**.

Sodium acetate (3 M, pH 5.2)
Sucrose gel-loading buffer
TE (pH 8.0)

Gels

Agarose gel (1.2%), cast in 0.5x TBE and containing 0.5 µg/ml ethidium bromide <!>
Please see Step 13.

Nucleic Acids and Oligonucleotides

Single-stranded bacteriophage M13 vector of recombinant DNA
Use preparations of bacteriophage M13 DNA of known concentration as controls during gel electrophoresis. Please see Step 13.

Special Equipment

Multitube vortexing machine (optional)

Vectors and Bacterial Strains

E. coli *cultures infected with bacteriophage M13*
Prepare an infected culture as described in Protocol 2. These cultures should be infected with both the hoped-for recombinant bacteriophage and a control culture infected with nonrecombinant bacteriophage. Please see note to Step 4. To minimize the possibility of selecting deletion mutants, grow culture infected with recombinant M13 bacteriophages for the shortest possible time required to achieve an adequate yield (≤5 hours). For further details, please see the information panel on GROWTH TIMES.

Bacteriophage M13 single-stranded DNA to be used as a template for certain types of oligonucleotide-directed mutagenesis should be propagated in *E. coli* F′ strains bearing mutations in the *dut* and *ung* genes. For a detailed protocol for bacteriophage growth in these strains, please see Chapter 13, Protocol 1.

E. coli *cultures, uninfected*
Prepare a mock-infected culture by picking an area of the *E. coli* lawn from the plate that does not contain a plaque as a negative control. Use this culture to monitor the recovery of bacteriophage M13 particles. Please see Step 4.

METHOD

Precipitation of Bacteriophage Particles with PEG

1. Transfer 1 ml of the infected and uninfected cultures to separate microfuge tubes and centrifuge the tubes at maximum speed for 5 minutes at room temperature. Transfer each supernatant to a fresh microfuge tube at room temperature.

    If desired, set aside 0.1 ml of the supernatant as a master stock of the bacteriophage particles.

2. To the supernatant add 200 µl of 20% PEG in 2.5 M NaCl. Mix the solution well by inverting the tube several times, followed by gentle vortexing. Allow the tube to stand for 15 minutes at room temperature.

    Make sure that all of the dense PEG/NaCl solution is mixed with the infected cell medium.

3. Recover the precipitated bacteriophage particles by centrifugation at maximum speed for 5 minutes at 4ºC in a microfuge.

4. Carefully remove all of the supernatant using a disposable pipette tip linked to a vacuum line or a drawn-out Pasteur pipette attached to a rubber bulb. Centrifuge the tube again for 30 seconds and remove any residual supernatant.

   > A tiny, pinhead-sized, pellet of precipitated bacteriophage particles should be visible at the bottom of the tube. No pellet should be visible in the negative control tube in which a portion of the uninfected *E. coli* lawn was inoculated. If no bacteriophage pellet is visible, it is unlikely that sufficient single-stranded DNA will be obtained to justify proceeding further. In this case, the best course of action is to pick more recombinant plaques, using them to infect cultures at different multiplicities, and then to grow the infected cultures for longer periods of time (6–12 hours). Remember, however, that longer growth periods can result in deletions and rearrangements in the cloned insert DNA (please see Protocol 2). Also be sure that true plaques (not air bubbles) were picked.

Extraction of Single-stranded DNA with Phenol

5. Resuspend the pellet of bacteriophage particles in 100 μl of TE (pH 8.0) by vortexing.

   > The best method to accomplish resuspension is to allow the bacteriophage pellet to soak in the TE buffer for 15–30 minutes at room temperature. Subsequent low-speed vortexing will dissolve the now clear pellet. It is important to resuspend the bacteriophage pellet completely to allow efficient extraction of the single-stranded DNA by phenol in the next step. A multitube vortexing machine saves time and effort when multiple samples are processed.

6. To the resuspended pellet add 100 μl of equilibrated phenol. Mix well by vortexing for 30 seconds. Allow the sample to stand for 1 minute at room temperature, and then vortex for another 30 seconds.

7. Centrifuge the sample at maximum speed for 3–5 minutes at room temperature in a microfuge. Transfer as much as is easily possible of the upper, aqueous phase to a fresh microfuge tube.

   > To facilitate separation of the phases, add 30 μl of silicone lubricant (Phase-Lock Gel, 5′→3′). This step sometimes improves yields but is generally not necessary. Do not try to transfer all of the aqueous phase. Much cleaner preparations of single-stranded DNA are obtained when ~5 μl of the aqueous phase is left at the interface.

   > The templates prepared with a single phenol extraction are adequate for most purposes (including DNA sequencing), and there is generally no need to use other extraction steps. However, contamination of the bacteriophage pellet with components in the PEG/NaCl supernatant in Step 3 can affect the reproducibility of the dideoxy sequencing reactions and can reduce the length of reliable sequence to 300 bases per reaction or less. These problems can be avoided by taking special care to extract all traces of supernatant material from the microfuge tube. To this end, some investigators either (i) add 100 μl of chloroform to each tube after Step 6 and re-vortex the tubes before separating the phases by centrifugation or (ii) transfer the aqueous phase to a fresh tube as described in Step 7, and then extract the aqueous phase once with 100 μl of chloroform. Separate the phases by centrifugation and transfer the aqueous phase to a fresh tube.

Precipitation of the Bacteriophage DNA with Ethanol

8. Recover the M13 DNA by standard precipitation with ethanol in the presence of 0.3 M sodium acetate. Vortex briefly to mix, and incubate the tubes for 15–30 minutes at room temperature or overnight at –20ºC.

   > The aqueous phase of the phenol extraction may be cloudy upon transfer to the fresh microfuge tube, but it should clear up when the sodium acetate solution is added.

Precipitation of the single-stranded DNA can also be accomplished by adding 300 μl of a 25:1 mixture of absolute ethanol:3 M sodium acetate (pH 5.2) followed by an incubation for 15 minutes at room temperature. This alteration saves independent pipetting of the sodium acetate and ethanol and can speed up the step when large numbers of single-stranded DNAs are being purified.

M13 DNAs can be stored in ethanol at –20ºC for several months.

9. Recover the precipitated single-stranded bacteriophage DNA by centrifugation at maximum speed for 10 minutes at 4ºC in a microfuge.

10. Remove the supernatant by gentle aspiration, being careful not to disturb the DNA pellet (which is often only visible as a haze on the side of the tube). Centrifuge the tube again for 15 seconds and remove any residual supernatant.

11. Add 200 μl of cold 70% ethanol and centrifuge at maximum speed for 5–10 minutes at 4ºC. Immediately remove the supernatant by gentle aspiration.

    ▲ IMPORTANT At this stage, the pellet is not firmly attached to the wall of the tube. It is therefore important to work quickly and carefully to avoid losing the DNA.

12. Invert the open tube on the bench for 10 minutes to allow any residual ethanol to drain and evaporate. Dissolve the pellet in 40 μl of TE (pH 8.0). Warm the solution to 37ºC for 5 minutes to speed dissolution of the DNA. Store the DNA solutions at –20ºC.

    The yield of single-stranded DNA is usually 5–10 μg/ml of the original infected culture.

13. Estimate the DNA concentration of a few of the samples by mixing 2-μl aliquots of the DNA from Step 12 each with 1 μl of sucrose gel-loading buffer. Load the samples into the wells of a 1.2% agarose gel cast in 0.5x TBE and containing 0.5 μg/ml ethidium bromide. As controls, use varying amounts of M13 DNA preparations of known concentrations. Examine the gel after electrophoresis for 1 hour at 6 V/cm. Estimate the amount of DNA from the intensity of the fluorescence.

    Usually 2–3 μl of a standard bacteriophage M13 DNA preparation is required for each set of four dideoxy cycle sequencing reactions using dye primers.

Protocol 5

Large-scale Preparation of Single-stranded and Double-stranded Bacteriophage M13 DNA

T HIS PROTOCOL, A SCALED-UP VERSION OF PROTOCOLS 3 AND 4, is used chiefly to generate large stocks of double-stranded DNA of strains of bacteriophage M13 that are routinely used as cloning vectors in the laboratory. Large amounts of single-stranded bacteriophage DNAs are needed for specialized purposes, for example, when a particular recombinant is to be used many times to generate radiolabeled probes or to construct large numbers of site-directed mutants. Most importantly, perhaps, large-scale preparations of both double- and single-stranded DNAs can be divided into small aliquots and used as standardized controls in dideoxy sequencing reactions and transfections by everyone in the laboratory.

In general, the yields of double- and single-stranded viral DNAs are not as high as those obtained from small-scale (1–2 ml) cultures of bacteriophage M13. The problems encountered with this method are similar to those outlined in Protocols 3 and 4.

MATERIALS

CAUTION: Please see Appendix 12 for appropriate handling of materials marked with <!>.

Buffers and Solutions

Please see Appendix 1 for components of stock solutions, buffers, and reagents. Dilute stock solutions to the appropriate concentrations.

Ethanol
NaCl (solid)
Phenol <!>
Phenol:chloroform (1:1, v/v) <!>
Polyethylene glycol (20% w/v PEG 8000) <!> in H_2O
Sodium acetate (3 M, pH 5.2)
STE
TE (pH 8.0)
Tris-Cl (10 mM, pH 8.0)

Gels

Agarose gels (0.8%) cast in 0.5x TBE, containing 0.5 μg/ml ethidium bromide <!>
Please see Steps 6 and 17.

Media

LB or YT medium containing 5 mM $MgCl_2$
Transfer 250 ml of the medium into a 2-liter flask and warm to 37ºC before Step 2.

Centrifuges and Rotors

Sorvall GSA rotor or equivalent
Sorvall SS-34 rotor or equivalent

Special Equipment

Corex centrifuge tubes (30 ml)
Silicon rubber band
Sterile culture tubes (13 x 100 mm or 17 x 100 mm)

Additional Reagents

Step 5 of this protocol requires the reagents listed in Protocols 3, 8, 9, and 10 of Chapter 1.

Vectors and Bacterial Strains

E. coli F´ plating bacteria

Please see Table 3-2 for a list of *E. coli* strains suitable for the propagation of bacteriophage M13. Pick a single colony of an appropriate host from a freshly streaked M9 minimal agar plate (or from an LB plate containing tetracycline or kanamycin for XL1-Blue strains) into 5 ml of LB in a 20-ml sterile culture tube. Incubate the culture for 6–8 hours at 37ºC with moderate agitation. The aim here is to avoid growing the culture to stationary phase, which increases the risk of losing the pili encoded by the F´ plasmid.

Bacteriophage M13 single-stranded DNA to be used as a template for certain types of oligonucleotide-directed mutagenesis should be propagated in *E. coli* F´ strains bearing mutations in the *dut* and *ung* genes. For a detailed protocol for medium-scale growth of bacteriophage in these strains, please see Chapter 13, Protocol 1.

Bacteriophage M13 Stock

Prepared as described in Protocol 2 of this chapter.

METHOD

Preparation of Bacteriophage M13 RF DNA

1. Transfer 2.5 ml of plating bacteria (please see Protocol 1) to a sterile tube (13 x 100 mm or 17 x 100 mm). Add 0.5 ml of bacteriophage M13 stock (~5 x 10^{11} pfu) and mix by tapping the side of the tube. Incubate the infected cells for 5 minutes at room temperature.

2. Dilute the infected cells into 250 ml of fresh LB or YT medium containing 5 mM MgCl$_2$ prewarmed to 37ºC in a 2-liter flask. Incubate for 5 hours at 37ºC with constant, vigorous shaking.

3. Harvest the infected cells by centrifugation at 4000g (5000 rpm in a Sorvall GSA rotor) for 15 minutes at 4ºC. Recover the supernatant, which may be used for large-scale preparations of single-stranded bacteriophage M13 DNA, as described in Steps 7–17 below.

4. Resuspend the bacterial pellet in 100 ml of ice-cold STE. Recover the washed cells by centrifugation at 4000g (5000 rpm in a Sorvall GSA rotor) for 15 minutes at 4ºC.

5. Isolate the bacteriophage M13 closed circular RF DNA by the alkaline lysis method (please see Chapter 1, Protocol 3). Scale up the volumes of lysis solutions appropriately. Purify the DNA either by precipitation with PEG, by column chromatography, or by equilibrium centrifugation in CsCl-ethidium bromide gradients.

6. Measure the concentration of the DNA spectrophotometrically and confirm its integrity by agarose gel electrophoresis. Store the closed circular DNA in small (1–5 μg) aliquots at –20ºC.

   The yield of RF DNA expected from 250 ml of infected cells is ~200 μg.

Preparation of Single-stranded Bacteriophage M13 DNA

7. To isolate single-stranded DNA from the bacteriophage particles in the infected cell medium, transfer the 250-ml supernatant from Step 3 to a 500-ml beaker containing a magnetic stirring bar.

8. Add 10 g of PEG and 7.5 g of NaCl to the supernatant. Stir the solution for 30–60 minutes at room temperature.

    Do not stir for longer periods of time or at lower temperature because undesired bacterial debris may precipitate.

9. Collect the precipitate by centrifugation at 10,000*g* (7800 rpm in a Sorvall GSA rotor) for 20 minutes at 4ºC. Invert the centrifuge bottle for 2–3 minutes to allow the supernatant to drain, and then use Kimwipes to remove the last traces of supernatant from the walls and neck of the bottle.

    Avoid touching the thin whitish film of precipitated bacteriophage particles on the side and bottom of the centrifuge bottle.

10. Add 10 ml of 10 mM Tris-Cl (pH 8.0) to the bottle. Swirl the solution in the bottle and use a Pasteur pipette to rinse the sides of the bottle thoroughly. When the bacteriophage pellet is dissolved, transfer the solution to a 30-ml Corex centrifuge tube.

11. To the bacteriophage suspension, add an equal volume of equilibrated phenol, seal the tube with a silicon rubber stopper, and mix the contents by vortexing vigorously for 2 minutes.

12. Centrifuge the solution at 3000*g* (5000 rpm in a Sorvall SS-34 rotor) for 5 minutes at room temperature. Transfer the upper aqueous phase to a fresh tube and repeat the extraction with 10 ml of phenol:chloroform.

    If there is a visible interface between the organic and aqueous layers, then extract the aqueous supernatant once more with chloroform.

13. Transfer equal amounts of the aqueous phase to each of two 30-ml Corex tubes. Add 0.5 ml of 3 M sodium acetate (pH 5.2) and 11 ml of ethanol to each tube. Mix the solutions well and then store them for 15 minutes at room temperature.

14. Recover the precipitate of single-stranded DNA by centrifugation at 12,000*g* (10,000 rpm in a Sorvall SS-34 rotor) for 20 minutes at 4ºC. Carefully remove all of the supernatant.

    Most of the precipitated DNA will collect in a thin film along the walls of the centrifuge tubes. To avoid discarding the DNA accidentally, it is best to mark the outside of the tubes with a permanent marker and to place the tubes in the centrifuge rotor with the marks facing outward from the axis of rotation.

15. Add 30 ml of 70% ethanol at 4ºC to each tube, and centrifuge at 12,000*g* (10,000 rpm in a Sorvall SS-34 rotor) for 10 minutes at 4ºC. Carefully remove as much of the supernatant as possible, invert the tubes to allow the last traces of supernatant to drain away from the precipitate, and wipe the neck of the tubes with Kimwipes.

    Make sure that the precipitate does not slide out of the tubes.

16. Allow the residual ethanol to evaporate at room temperature. Dissolve the pellets in 1 ml of TE (pH 8.0). Store the DNA at –20ºC.

17. Measure the concentration of the DNA spectrophotometrically and confirm its integrity by agarose gel electrophoresis. Store the closed circular DNA in small (10–50 µg) aliquots at –20ºC.

    The yield of single-stranded DNA expected from 250 ml of infected culture is 250 µg to 1 mg.

Protocol 6

Cloning into Bacteriophage M13 Vectors

Cloning fragments of foreign DNA into bacteriophage M13 vectors takes little effort:

- Ligate double-stranded segments of DNA with blunt or cohesive termini into compatible sites in double-stranded M13 RF DNAs.

- Use the products of the ligation reaction to transform competent male *E. coli* cells, which are plated in top agar containing IPTG and X-gal.

- Pick and propagate blue (nonrecombinant) and white (recombinant) plaques appearing after 6–8 hours as described in Protocol 2.

This blue-white test is an excellent indicator, but it is not infallible: Rare recombinant viruses retain the ability to generate blue plaques. On analysis, the segment of foreign DNA in these anomalous recombinants is generally found to be very small — perhaps <100 bases — and inserted in-frame into the *lacZ* sequences of the vector (e.g., please see Close et al. 1983). The resulting fusion peptide retains sufficient α-complementing activity to generate a blue plaque in media containing IPTG and X-gal.

Although there is no limit in theory to the size of the fragment of foreign DNA that can be carried in bacteriophage M13 recombinants, there are restrictions in practice: Larger segments of foreign DNA are far more likely to suffer deletions and rearrangements than smaller fragments. For this reason, it is best wherever possible to clone into bacteriophage M13 pieces of foreign DNA that are no more than 1000 bases in length. In addition, the central regions of larger fragments may lie outside the range that can be reached in DNA sequencing reactions primed by the universal "forward" and "reverse" sequencing primers. Limit the opportunities for deletion and other rearrangements of cloned DNAs as follows:

- Keep the fragments of foreign DNA as small as the experiment will allow.

- Do not propagate recombinant bacteriophages for more than one or two serial passages in culture.

- Recover double-stranded DNA fragments from M13 recombinants as soon as possible after site-directed mutagenesis.

Described below are three different methods commonly used to construct bacteriophage M13 recombinants.

- *Cloning by ligation of insert to linearized vector.* A site within the multiple cloning region of the vector is cleaved with a single restriction enzyme, and the resulting linear DNA is ligated with a three- to fivefold molar excess of foreign DNA that has compatible termini. No effort is made to reduce the background of nonrecombinant viruses formed by recircularization of the vector or to suppress the formation of chimeric clones. This method is best suited to cloning a single segment of DNA — perhaps purified from a gel — in preparation for site-directed mutagenesis, DNA sequencing, or synthesis of radiolabeled probes.

  Recombinant bacteriophages made in this way can in theory carry the foreign DNA sequences in two possible orientations. Sometimes, however, it happens that most of the population of recombinants carry the insert in the same orientation. This phenomenon occurs because sequences on opposite strands of the foreign DNA interfere to varying extents with the functioning of the intergenic region. The problem can be overcome by cloning the foreign DNA at a different site within the multiple cloning site or by using a combination of restriction enzymes that will allow directional cloning (please see below). Alternatively, a reversal experiment can be attempted in which RF DNA from the original recombinant is digested with the restriction enzyme used for cloning, religated, and used to transform *E. coli*. Screening of the resulting white plaques may yield clones carrying the insert in the opposite orientation. In general, however, it is not advisable to force bacteriophage M13 vectors to propagate unwelcome sequences of foreign DNA. The resulting recombinants are often unstable and give rise to progeny that carry deleted or rearranged versions of the foreign sequences. A possible solution to this problem is to propagate the foreign DNA in plasmid vectors that carry an origin of replication derived from a filamentous bacteriophage (phagemids; please see Protocol 8).

- *Treatment of vector DNA with alkaline phosphatase.* After linearization with a single restriction enzyme, the vector is dephosphorylated to reduce its ability to recircularize during ligation and to increase the proportion of recombinant clones (please see Chapter 1, Protocol 20, and Chapter 9, Protocol 13). This is the method of choice when the amount of foreign DNA is limiting or when ligating blunt-ended DNA fragments into bacteriophage M13 vectors, for example, when creating libraries of M13 subclones for sequencing (please see Chapter 12, Protocol 1).

- *Forced or directional cloning.* The multiple cloning site of the vector can be cleaved with two different restriction enzymes, generating molecules with incompatible termini that do not need to be dephosphorylated before use. The vector is ligated to a one- to threefold molar excess of foreign DNA whose termini are compatible with those of the vector. This strategy works well when cloning a single segment of foreign DNA in a desired orientation within M13. However, it is clearly unsuitable for the construction in M13 of libraries of large DNAs cloned in YACs, P1 vectors, or cosmids. Directional cloning may also prove to be a liability when single-stranded templates are used to determine the sequence of a segment of foreign DNA or to generate radiolabeled strand-specific probes. If a "universal primer" is used in the reaction, the sequences obtained will be restricted to the 200–700 nucleotides of foreign DNA immediately downstream from the primer-binding site; radioactive probes will correspond to only one of the strands of the foreign DNA. One solution to this problem is to insert the foreign DNA separately into each member of a pair of bacteriophage M13 vectors (e.g., M13mp18 and M13mp19) that carry the polycloning site in opposite orientations. Single-stranded templates prepared from these recombinants will yield the terminal sequences of each of the two strands of the foreign DNA; radiolabeled probes can be generated that will hybridize specifically to one strand or the other of the foreign DNA.

MATERIALS

CAUTION: Please see Appendix 12 for appropriate handling of materials marked with <!>.

Buffers and Solutions

Please see Appendix 1 for components of stock solutions, buffers, and reagents. Dilute stock solutions to the appropriate concentrations.

ATP (10 mM)
Ethanol
IPTG (20% w/v)
Phenol:chloroform (1:1, v/v) <!>
Sodium acetate (3 M, pH 5.2)
TE (pH 7.6 and pH 8.0)
X-gal (2% w/v) <!>

Enzymes and Buffers

Bacteriophage T4 DNA ligase
Restriction endonucleases
  The choice of restriction enzymes to be used in Steps 1 and 6 depends on the cloning strategy.

Gels

Agarose gels (0.8%) cast in 1x TBE, containing 0.5 μg/ml ethidium bromide <!>
  Please see Steps 2, 6, and 9.

Nucleic Acids and Oligonucleotides

Foreign DNA
  Individual fragments of foreign DNA to be cloned in M13 vectors are usually derived from a larger segment of DNA that has already been cloned and characterized in another vector. For methods to construct M13 libraries of DNA segments cloned in YACs or other genomic vectors, please see Chapter 12, Protocol 1.
Test DNA
  Please see note at Step 7.

Media

YT or LB agar plates
YT or LB medium
YT or LB top agar or agarose

Special Equipment

Culture tubes (5 ml or 15 ml, e.g., Falcon 2054 or 2006, Becton Dickinson), chilled to 0°C
Heating block preset to 47°C
Ice-water bath
Water baths preset to 12–16°C and 42°C

Additional Reagents

Step 4 of this protocol requires the reagents listed in Chapter 1, Protocol 20.

Vectors and Bacterial Strains

Bacteriophage M13 vector DNA (RF)
  A large number of bacteriophage M13 vectors, equipped with a wide variety of cloning sites, are available from both commercial and academic sources (please see Figure 3-4 and Appendix 3).

E. coli *competent cells of an appropriate strain carrying an F´ plasmid*

> Competent cells may be prepared in the laboratory as described in Chapter 1, Protocol 25 or purchased from commercial suppliers.

E. coli *F´ plating bacteria*

> Plating bacteria may be prepared in the laboratory as described in Protocol 1 or purchased from commercial suppliers.

METHOD

Preparation of Vector DNA

1. Digest 1–2 µg of the bacteriophage M13 vector RF DNA to completion with a three- to five-fold excess of the appropriate restriction enzyme(s). Set up a control reaction containing M13 RF DNA but no restriction enzyme(s).

2. At the end of the incubation period, remove a small sample of DNA (50 ng) from each of the reactions and analyze the extent of digestion by electrophoresis through an 0.8% agarose gel. If digestion is incomplete (i.e., if any closed circular DNA is visible), add more restriction enzyme(s) and continue the incubation.

   > Preparations of M13 RF DNA can contain significant amounts of single-stranded M13 DNA, which are visible as fuzzy, faster-migrating bands in agarose gel electrophoresis. Because single-stranded DNA is not cleaved efficiently by most restriction enzymes, the appearance and mobility of these bands should be identical in the control and test lanes.

3. When digestion is complete, purify the M13 DNA by extraction with phenol:chloroform followed by standard precipitation with ethanol in the presence of 0.3 M sodium acetate (pH 5.2). Dissolve the DNA in TE (pH 8.0) at a concentration of 50 µg/ml.

4. If required, dephosphorylate the linearized vector DNA by treatment with calf alkaline phosphatase or shrimp alkaline phosphatase. At the end of the dephosphorylation reaction, inactivate the alkaline phosphatase by heat and/or by digestion with proteinase K, followed by extraction with phenol:chloroform (for details, please see Chapter 1, Protocol 20).

5. Recover the linearized M13 DNA as outlined in Step 3. Dissolve the dephosphorylated DNA in TE (pH 7.6) at a concentration of 50 µg/ml.

Preparation of Foreign DNA to be Cloned

6. Generate individual restriction fragments of foreign DNA by cleavage with the appropriate restriction enzymes and purify them by agarose gel electrophoresis. Dissolve the final preparation of foreign DNA in TE (pH 7.6) at a concentration of 50 µg/ml.

Ligation

When ligating DNAs with complementary cohesive termini, please follow Steps 7–9 below. For methods to set up blunt-ended ligation reactions, please see Chapter 1, Protocol 19.

7. In a microfuge tube (Tube A), mix together ~50 ng of vector DNA and a one- to fivefold molar excess of the target (foreign) DNA fragment(s). The combined volume of the two

DNAs should not exceed 8 μl. If necessary, add TE (pH 7.6) to adjust the volume to 7.5–8.0 μl. As controls, set up three ligation reactions containing:

Tube	DNA
B	the same amount of vector DNA, but no foreign DNA
C	the same amount of vector DNA and a one- to fivefold molar excess of the target DNA fragment(s)
D	the same amount of vector DNA together with an equal amount by weight of a test DNA that has been successfully cloned into bacteriophage M13 on previous occasions

As a test DNA, we routinely use a standard preparation of bacteriophage λ DNA cleaved with restriction enzymes that recognize tetranucleotide sequences and generate termini that are complementary to the M13 vectors to be used.

8. Add 1 μl of 10x ligation buffer and 1 μl of 10 mM ATP to all four reactions (Tubes A–D).

   Omit ATP if using a commercial buffer that contains ATP.

9. Add 0.5 Weiss unit of bacteriophage T4 DNA ligase to Tubes A, B, and D. Mix the components by gently tapping the side of each tube for several seconds. Incubate the ligation reactions for 4–16 hours at 12–16ºC.

   At the end of the ligation reaction, analyze 1 μl of each ligation reaction by electrophoresis through an 0.8% agarose gel. Bands of circular recombinant molecules containing vector and fragment(s) of foreign DNA should be visible in the test reaction (Tube A) but not in the control (Tube C).

   After ligation, the reactions may be stored at –20ºC until transformation.

Transformation

10. Prepare and grow an overnight culture of plating bacteria (please see Protocol 1) in YT or LB medium at 37ºC with constant shaking.

11. Remove from the –70ºC freezer an aliquot of frozen competent cells of the desired strain carrying an F′ plasmid, allow the cells to thaw at room temperature, and then place them on ice for 10 minutes.

12. Transfer 50–100 μl of the competent F′ bacteria to each of 16 sterile 5-ml culture tubes (Falcon 2054, Becton Dickinson) that have been chilled to 0ºC.

    Tubes other than Falcon 2054 (Becton Dickinson) may be used in the plating reaction, but in this case, it will be necessary to adjust the time and temperature of heat shock. For example, if 15-cm plates are preferred for some reason, larger tubes (17 x 150 mm) should be used (e.g., Falcon 2006, Becton Dickinson). Falcon 2006 tubes require 2 minutes of heat shock (Step 15) and larger amounts of top agar, 2% X-gal, and 20% IPTG (7 ml, 120 μl, and 20 μl, respectively).

13. Immediately add 0.1-, 1.0-, and 5-μl aliquots of the ligation reactions and controls (Tubes A–D) to separate tubes of competent cells. Mix the DNAs with the bacteria by tapping the sides of the tubes gently for a few seconds. Store on ice for 30–40 minutes. Include two transformation controls, one containing 5 pg of bacteriophage M13 RF DNA and the other containing no added DNA.

14. While the ligated DNA is incubating with the competent cells, prepare a set of 16 sterile culture tubes containing 3 ml of melted YT or LB top agar. Store the tubes at 47ºC in a heating block or water bath until needed in Step 16.

15. Transfer the tubes containing the competent bacteria and DNA to a water bath equilibrated to 42°C. Incubate the tubes for exactly 90 seconds. Immediately return the tubes to an ice-water bath.

> In this protocol, all of the transfected cultures of competent *E. coli* cells are exposed to heat shock simultaneously. An alternative is to administer heat shock to each culture in turn and thus avoid leaving the cells on ice. In this approach, the plating cells, X-gal, and IPTG are added to the top agar/agarose during the heat shock step. At the end of the heat shock, the top agar/agarose, plating cells, X-gal, etc., are immediately mixed with the transfected cells and poured directly onto an agar plate. This approach requires careful timing and exact knowledge of the length of time required for each step.

Plating the Transformed Cells

16. Add 40 µl of 2% X-gal, 4 µl of 20% IPTG, and 200 µl of the overnight culture of *E. coli* cells (Step 10) to the tubes containing the melted top agar prepared in Step 14, and mix the contents of the tubes by gentle vortexing for a few seconds. Transfer each sample of the transformed bacteria to the tubes. Cap the tubes and mix the contents by gently inverting the tubes three times. Pour the contents of each tube in turn onto a separate labeled LB agar plate. Swirl the plate to ensure an even distribution of bacteria and top agar.

> It may be difficult to obtain an even distribution of the top agar across the agar plate, especially when larger plates (15-cm diameter) are used for the first time. The speed with which the top agar solidifies can be decreased (thereby allowing more time for the swirling step) by preheating the agar plates for 30–60 minutes at 37°C before the plating step. Top agar that is hotter than 47°C will kill the competent bacteria (and dramatically decrease the transfection frequency!).

17. Close the plates and allow the top agar to harden for 5 minutes at room temperature. Use a Kimwipe to remove any condensation from the top of the plate, invert the plates, and incubate at 37°C.

> Plaques will be fully developed after 8–12 hours. Plaques formed by nonrecombinant bacteriophage M13 will be deep blue; those formed by recombinants will be colorless in most cases. For details on efficiencies and expected results, please see Table 3-3.

TABLE 3-3 Typical Transformation Results Using a Frozen Preparation of Competent Cultures of *E. coli* Strain TG1

RF DNA	NUMBER OF PLAQUES/µg VECTOR DNA	
	BLUE	WHITE
Closed circular	3×10^7	$3 \times 10^{3\,a}$
Linearized by cleavage with one restriction enzyme	1×10^5	$\sim 5 \times 10^4$
Linearized by cleavage with one restriction enzyme and self-ligated	2×10^7	$\sim 1 \times 10^4$
Linearized by cleavage with one restriction enzyme, phosphatase-treated, and self-ligated	3×10^4	$\sim 5 \times 10^4$
Cleaved by two different restriction enzymes	$<5 \times 10^3$	$\sim 1 \times 10^4$
Linearized by cleavage with one restriction enzyme and ligated in the presence of molar excess of foreign DNA cleaved with a compatible restriction enzyme	$\sim 1 \times 10^5$	$\sim 4 \times 10^6$
Cleaved by two different restriction enzymes and ligated in the presence of molar excess of foreign DNA carrying compatible termini	$<5 \times 10^3$	$\sim 2 \times 10^6$

The method used to prepare the competent cells can dramatically influence the number of bacteriophage M13 plaques. The frequencies in the above table are those obtained using preparations of competent bacterial cells that produce ~10^7 plaques/µg of RF DNA. Lower or higher transfection efficiencies will require more or less of the ligation reaction to obtain equivalent numbers of recombinant plaques. For example, if electroporation is used (Chapter 1, Protocol 26), then the ligation reactions should be diluted substantially (10^{-1} to 10^{-3}) to obtain well-separated plaques.

[a]The small proportion of colorless plaques is formed by spontaneous mutants that have lost the ability to accomplish α-complementation.

Protocol 7

Analysis of Recombinant Bacteriophage M13 Clones

Several methods are used to analyze the size and orientation of foreign DNA sequences carried in M13 recombinants.

- screening *lac*⁻ (white) bacteriophage M13 plaques by hybridization (please see the panel on **ALTERNATIVE PROCOTOL: SCREENING BACTERIOPHAGE M13 PLAQUES BY HYBRIDIZATION** at the end of this protocol)

- analysis of *lac*⁻ plaques by PCR (please see Chapter 8, Protocol 7)

- analysis of small-scale RF DNA preparations (Protocol 3) by restriction enzyme digestion, gel electrophoresis, and Southern hybridization

- electrophoretic analysis of the size of single-stranded DNA in putative recombinant clones (this protocol)

In this protocol, recombinant bacteriophage M13 clones carrying sequences of foreign DNA longer than 200–300 nucleotides are detected by gel electrophoresis of single-stranded DNA released from infected bacteria into the surrounding medium.

MATERIALS

CAUTION: Please see Appendix 12 for appropriate handling of materials marked with <!>.

Buffers and Solutions

Please see Appendix 1 for components of stock solutions, buffers, and reagents. Dilute stock solutions to the appropriate concentrations.

SDS (2% w/v)
20x SSC
Sucrose gel-loading buffer

Gels

Agarose gel (0.7%) cast in 0.5x TBE, containing 0.5 µg/ml ethidium bromide <!>
Please see Step 4.

Nucleic Acids and Oligonucleotides

Single-stranded recombinant bacteriophage M13 DNA

Choose previously characterized recombinants that carry foreign sequences of known size to use as positive controls during gel electrophoresis. Please see Step 4 note.

Special Equipment

Water bath preset to 65°C

Additional Reagents

Step 1 of this protocol requires the reagents listed in Protocol 2 of this chapter.
Step 7 of this protocol may require the reagents listed in Chapter 2, Protocols 21 and 22.

Vectors and Bacterial Strains

Bacteriophage M13 recombinants plaques in top agarose

Prepared as described in Protocol 6 of this chapter.

Bacteriophage M13 nonrecombinant vector, grown as well-isolated plaques in top agarose

Prepared as described in Protocol 1 of this chapter.

E. coli F´ strain

For a listing of strains suitable for the propagation of bacteriophage M13, please see Table 3-2 in the introduction to this chapter.

METHOD

1. Prepare stocks of putative recombinant bacteriophages from single plaques, grown in an appropriate F´ host, as described in Protocol 2.

   As controls, prepare stocks of several nonrecombinant bacteriophages (picked from well-isolated dark blue plaques).

2. Use a micropipettor with a sterile tip to transfer 20 μl of each of the supernatants into a fresh microfuge tube. Store the remainder of the supernatants at 4°C until needed.

3. To each 20-μl aliquot of supernatant, add 1 μl of 2% SDS. Tap the sides of the tubes to mix the contents, and then incubate the tubes for 5 minutes at 65°C.

4. To each tube, add 5 μl of sucrose gel-loading buffer. Again mix the contents of the tubes by tapping and then analyze each sample by electrophoresis through an 0.7% agarose gel. Run the gel at 5 V/cm. As positive controls, use single-stranded DNA preparations of previously characterized M13 recombinants that carry foreign sequences of known size.

   Electrophoresis at low voltage eliminates problems associated with salt fronts created in the gel by the large volume of sample.

5. When the bromophenol blue has traveled the full length of the gel, photograph the DNA under UV illumination.

6. Compare the electrophoretic mobilities of the single-stranded DNAs liberated from the putative recombinants with those of the DNAs liberated from the control nonrecombinant bacteriophages.

   The single-stranded DNAs of recombinants carrying sequences of foreign DNA longer than 200–300 nucleotides migrate slightly more slowly than empty vector through 0.7% agarose gels. Once recombinants of the desired size have been identified, single-stranded DNAs can be prepared from supernatants stored at 4°C (Step 2).

7. If necessary, confirm the presence of foreign DNA sequences by transferring single-stranded DNAs from the gel to a nitrocellulose or nylon membrane (please see Chapter 2, Protocol 21)

and hybridizing to an appropriate radiolabeled probe (please see Chapter 2, Protocol 22). Soak the gel in 10 volumes of 20x SSC for 45 minutes, and then transfer the DNA directly to the membrane.

> There is no need to denature the DNA by soaking the gel in alkali.

> Southern blotting using oligonucleotide probes is particularly useful in identifying recombinants carrying different strands of a target DNA.

ALTERNATIVE PROTOCOL: SCREENING BACTERIOPHAGE M13 PLAQUES BY HYBRIDIZATION

Bacteriophage M13 plaques can be screened by hybridization to ^{32}P-labeled probes by following essentially the same methods devised for screening bacteriophage λ.

Method

1. Transfer the bacteriophage DNA to a nitrocellulose or nylon filter as described in Chapter 2, Protocol 21.

2. After removing the filter from the surface of the agar or agarose, allow it to dry (DNA side up) at room temperature.

   > The single-stranded bacteriophage M13 DNA transferred to the filter does not need to be denatured with alkali.

3. Bake the filter under vacuum for 2 hours at 80°C or autoclave for 3 minutes, or, in the case of nylon filters, expose to UV irradiation to fix the DNA to the filter (please see Chapter 2, Protocol 21).

4. Hybridize the immobilized DNAs to an appropriate ^{32}P-labeled DNA probe as described in Chapter 2, Protocol 22.

   > Double-stranded DNA probes will hybridize to all M13 recombinants that carry the target sequence irrespective of the orientation of the segment of foreign DNA within the vector. Single-stranded probes will hybridize only to recombinants that carry complementary sequences attached to the (+) strand of M13 bacteriophage DNA.

   > If the filter is treated with alkali, as in conventional Benton-Davis screening of plaques, double-stranded M13 RF DNA released from the infected bacteria will be denatured. Both the (+) and (–) strands of M13 recombinants therefore become available for hybridization. Since the amount of (+) strand attached to the filter is much greater than the amount of RF DNA, single-stranded probes complementary to the (+) strand will generate a much stronger hybridization signal than probes complementary to the (–) strand. A weak hybridization signal with a single-stranded probe usually results from hybridization of the probe to denatured M13 RF DNA in plaques that contain the insert in the opposite orientation. This difference in intensity of hybridization has been used as a method to assay the orientation of cloned inserts (Picken 1990).

Protocol 8

Producing Single-stranded DNA with Phagemid Vectors

Phagemids felicitously combine features of plasmids and filamentous bacteriophages. Stripped to their bare essentials, these vectors are conventional high-copy-number plasmids that carry a modified version of the major intergenic region of a filamentous bacteriophage (please see Table 3-4). This region (508 bp in its wild-type form) encodes no proteins but contains all of the *cis*-acting sequences that are indispensable for initiation and termination of viral DNA synthesis and for morphogenesis of bacteriophage particles.

TABLE 3-4 Phagemids

PLASMID	INTERGENIC REGION	HELPER VIRUS	HOST BACTERIA[a]	REFERENCE
pEMBL (derived from pUC8)	f1	IR1, an interference-resistant variant of f1[b]	71/18	Dente et al. (1983)
pRSA101 (derived from π VX[c])	M13	a variant of M13 resistant to interference by plasmids containing the M13 intergenic region	XS127, XS101	Levinson et al. (1984)
pUC118/119 (derived from pUC18/19)	M13	M13K07 carries a mutated version of gene II that works less well on its own intergenic region than on that cloned in pUC118/119	MV1184	Vieira and Messing (1987)
pBluescript	f1	M13K07	XL1-Blue	Short et al. (1988)
pBluescript II SK +/−	f1	R408 or M13K07	XL1-Blue MRF′	Short et al. (1988)
pBS +/−	f1	R408 or M13K07	XL1-Blue MRF′	Alting-Mees and Short (1989)
pBC SK +/−	f1	R408 or M13K07	XL1-Blue MRF′	Alting-Mees and Short (1989)
pGEM 11Zf(t)	f1	M13K07 or R408	DH11S, JM109	
pGEM 13Zf(t)	f1	M13K07 or R408	DH11S, JM109	

Other more complicated phagemid systems have been devised (e.g., please see Geider et al. 1985; Mead et al. 1985; Peeters et al. 1986).
[a]Please see Table 3-2.
[b]Enea and Zinder (1982).
[c]Seed (1983).

Segments of foreign DNA can be cloned in phagemids and propagated as plasmids in the usual way. However, when a male strain of *E. coli* carrying a phagemid is infected with a suitable filamentous bacteriophage, the mode of replication of the phagemid changes in response to gene products expressed by the incoming virus. The gene II protein encoded by the helper virus introduces a nick at a specific site in the intergenic region of the phagemid and hence initiates rolling circle replication (Beck and Zink 1981; Dotto et al. 1981a), which generates copies of one strand of the plasmid DNA. These single-stranded copies of the plasmid DNA are packaged into progeny bacteriophage particles, which are then extruded into the medium (Dotto et al. 1981b; Dente et al. 1983; Levinson et al. 1984; Zagursky and Berman 1984; Geider et al. 1985; Mead et al. 1985). The secreted particles can easily be recovered by precipitation with polyethylene glycol and the single-stranded DNA purified by extraction with phenol (Protocol 4).

Single-stranded DNAs produced by phagemids are used for the same purposes as single-stranded DNAs of bacteriophage M13 recombinants: for DNA sequencing, for the synthesis of strand-specific radiolabeled probes, for subtractive hybridization, and for oligonucleotide-directed mutagenesis. In addition, phagemid vectors can be used in appropriate strains of *E. coli* (e.g., BW313) to produce single-stranded DNAs that contain uracil in place of a proportion of the thymine residues. These uracil-substituted DNAs are excellent substrates for certain types of oligonucleotide-directed mutagenesis (please see Chapter 13, Protocol 1; McClary et al. 1989).

Phagemids have several attractive features that overcome problems commonly encountered with cloning in bacteriophage M13, including:

- a positive selectable marker that can be used to select bacteria transformed by the phagemid

- higher yields of double-stranded DNA

- elimination of the time-consuming process of subcloning DNA fragments from plasmids to filamentous bacteriophage vectors

- a significant reduction in the frequency and extent of deletions and rearrangements in single-stranded DNA

- the ability to allow segments of DNA several kilobases in length to be isolated in single-stranded form

In addition, it is possible to construct a complete expression cassette in a phagemid, containing, for example, a strong promoter, the gene or cDNA of interest, and a transcription terminator (e.g., please see Kunapuli and Colman 1993). Expression phagemids of this type can be isolated in single-stranded DNA form, subjected to site-directed mutagenesis, and then used to transform *E. coli* or yeast for phenotypic expression.

IMPROVEMENTS IN PHAGEMIDS AND HELPER VIRUSES

The first generation of vectors, the pEMBL vectors, gave phagemids a bad name because, after superinfection with a helper virus, the yield of single-stranded DNA was generally poor and was influenced by many factors, including the density of the culture at the time of infection, the multiplicity of infection, and the length of time after infection. Even when superinfection was carried out under optimal conditions, the yield of progeny virus all too often consisted predominantly of helper viruses rather then packaged single-stranded phagemid DNA. These problems were ameliorated by constructing helper viruses encoding a mutated version of gene II that preferentially activates the phagemid origin of replication (please see the panel on HELPER BACTERIOPHAGES). In addition, novel strains of *E. coli* have been engineered (e.g., DH11S, TG2, and MV1184) that are efficiently transformed by plasmids, are easily infected by commonly used helper viruses, and yield preparations of single-stranded phagemid DNA that are free from contamination with bacterial DNA and helper phages (e.g., please see Lin et al. 1992).

The particular strand of the foreign DNA that is packaged into the bacteriophage particles depends on its orientation in the polylinker site of the phagemid vector and on the orientation of the bacteriophage origin of DNA replication carried in the vector. As a consequence, most commercially available phagemid vectors (e.g., pBluescript II from Stratagene and pGEMZf from Promega) come in four chiralities in which the orientation of the polylinker sequence is opposite in one pair of vectors (e.g., pBluescript II SK and pBluescript II KS), and the orientation of the intergenic region is opposite in the other pair (e.g., pBluescript II SK [+] and pBluescript II SK [−]). The (+) and (−) orientations of the intergenic region allow the rescue by helper bacteriophages of sense and antisense single-stranded DNAs. For a list of phagemid vectors and helper bacteriophages, please see Table 3-4. For first-time users of phagemids, the safest choices for helper virus, phagemid vector, and host are a well-tested and reliable helper virus such as M13K07 and a dependable phagemid (e.g., one or more of the Stratagene SK or Promega pGemZ series) in an *E. coli* strain such as DH11S (Lin et al. 1992).

HELPER BACTERIOPHAGES

Several helper viruses have been engineered to maximize the yield of single-stranded phagemid DNA packaged into filamentous particles after superinfection of a phagemid-transformed culture. When working well, the ratio of phagemid to helper genomes in the bacteriophage particles released into the medium should be ~20:1. A small-scale (1.5 ml) culture should provide enough single-stranded phagemid DNA for four to eight sequencing reactions.

- **M13K07** is a derivative (Vieira and Messing 1987) of bacteriophage M13 that carries a plasmid origin of replication (derived from p15A), the kanamycin-resistance gene from the transposon Tn*903*, and a mutated version of gene II (derived from M13mp1), in which the G residue at 6125 has been replaced by a T (Vieira and Messing 1987). When M13K07 infects cells carrying phagemids, the incoming single-stranded DNA of the helper bacteriophage is converted by cellular enzymes to a double-stranded form that then uses the plasmid p15A origin to replicate. Because the accumulation of double-stranded M13K07 DNA does not require viral gene products, there is little opportunity for the resident phagemids to interfere with the early stages of replication of the incoming helper bacteriophage genome. With time, the pool of double-stranded M13K07 genomes expresses all of the proteins required to generate progeny single-stranded DNA. However, the mutated gene II product encoded by M13K07 interacts less efficiently with the bacteriophage origin of replication carried on its own genome (due to the insertion of *lacZ* sequences) than with the origin cloned into the phagemid vector (Vieira and Messing 1987). This preference results in the production of more (+) strands from the phagemid than from the helper virus and ensures that the virus particles produced by the cell contain a preponderance of single-stranded DNA derived from the phagemid. When M13K07 is grown in the absence of a phagemid vector (Steps 1–3 in this protocol), the mutant gene II protein interacts well enough with the disrupted origin of replication to produce sufficient bacteriophage for superinfection.

- **R408** is a derivative (Russel et al. 1986) of bacteriophage f1 from which an internal 24-bp segment of the signal required for packaging of bacteriophage particles has been deleted. The resulting helper bacteriophage packages single-stranded DNAs containing a complete packaging signal better than it packages its own single-stranded DNA. In addition to a modified packaging signal, R408 carries (1) a mutation known as IR1 that renders R408 insensitive to interference by defective viruses (Enea and Zinder 1982) and (2) the *gtrxA* mutation that improves the efficiency of bacteriophage assembly by altering an amino acid in a morphogenetic protein. Unlike M13K07, R408 does not carry an antibiotic resistance marker.

- **Other Helper Viruses:** Although M13K07 and R408 are the most widely used helper viruses, companies that sell phagemids may recommend other helper viruses, for example, ExAssist (Stratagene) and VCSM13, which is a derivative of M13K07 (Vieira and Messing 1987). However, both in our experience and that of others, the yield and proportion of filamentous particles containing single-stranded phagemid genomes are usually higher with M13K07 (e.g., please see Lin et al. 1992) than with other helper viruses.

MATERIALS

CAUTION: Please see Appendix 12 for appropriate handling of materials marked with <!>.

Buffers and Solutions

Please see Appendix 1 for components of stock solutions, buffers, and reagents. Dilute stock solutions to the appropriate concentrations.

Kanamycin (10 mg/ml)

Kanamycin is used in this protocol to ensure that all bacterial cells containing a phagemid genome are infected by the helper M13K07 bacteriophage. During propagation of M13K07 (e.g., Steps 1–3), there is selection for bacteriophage genomes that have lost the p15A origin and the Tn*903* transposon. For this reason, it is essential to include kanamycin in the medium used to prepare the stock of helper virus (Step 3).

SDS solution (2% w/v)

Sucrose gel-loading buffer

Gels

Agarose gel (0.7%) cast in 0.5x TBE, containing 0.5 μg/ml ethidium bromide <!>

Please see Step 12.

Media

Supplemented M9 minimal agar plates

When using *E. coli* strains that carry a deletion of the proline biosynthetic operon (Δ[*lac-proAB*]) in the bacterial chromosome and the complementing *proAB* genes on the F′ plasmid, use supplemented M9 minimal medium.

YT agar plates containing 60 μg/ml ampicillin

2x YT medium

2x YT medium containing 60 μg/ml ampicillin

2x YT medium containing 25 μg/ml kanamycin

The addition of Mg^{2+} (5 mM) to media (Reddy and McKenney 1996) is reported to improve the yield of bacteriophage M13 cultures infected at low multiplicity.

Special Equipment

Water bath preset to 65°C

Additional Reagents

Steps 2 and 5 of this protocol require the reagents listed in Protocol 1 of this chapter.

Step 14 of this protocol requires the reagents listed in Protocol 4 of this chapter.

Vectors and Bacterial Strains

Bacteriophage M13K07 (helper)

M13K07 may be obtained commercially (e.g., from Pharmacia or New England Biolabs) and propagated as described in Steps 1–3 below. Store stocks of helper virus at 4°C in growth medium or at –20°C in growth medium containing 50% (v/v) glycerol. M13K07 should not be used to superinfect cultures of *E. coli* JM109 transformed with phagemid vectors. For reasons that are not understood, this strain undergoes significant lysis when infected with M13K07. The recommended strain for M13K07 is DH11S (Lin et al. 1992).

E. coli F′ strain

For a listing of strains suitable for the propagation of bacteriophage M13, please see Table 3-2 in the introduction to this chapter.

In principle, it should be possible to produce bacteriophage particles that contain single-stranded copies of phagemid DNA in any male strain of *E. coli*. Unfortunately, the yield of single-stranded DNA can be greatly affected by the bacterial strain used to propagate the plasmid. For example, *E. coli* strains MV1184 (derived from JM83) and MV1190 (derived from JM101) produce satisfactory yields, whereas MV1304 (derived from JM105) does not. The biological reasons for varying yields are poorly understood. Several strains (MV1184, DH11S, XL1-Blue, XL1-Blue MRF´; for more complete details, please see Table 3-2) have been used by many laboratories and generally yield workable quantities of single-stranded phagemid DNAs (Vieira and Messing 1987; Lin et al. 1992). With all strains, maximum yields of phagemid DNA are obtained when infected cultures are well-aerated.

E. coli *strain DH11S*

DH11S (Lin et al. 1992) is available from Life Technologies. MV1184, a less-preferred option, can be obtained from J. Messing. Both strains should be plated on supplemented minimal agar plates.

E. coli *strain DH11S, transformed with bacteriophage M13 phagemid vector*

Transform *E. coli* with the phagemid vector as described in Protocol 6. The transformed strain may be propagated as a culture as described in Protocol 2.

E. coli *strain DH11S, transformed with bacteriophage M13 recombinant phagemid vector clone carrying foreign DNA*

Transform *E. coli* with the recombinant phagemid vector as described in Protocol 6. The transformed strain may be propagated as a culture as described in Protocol 2.

METHOD

Preparation of a High-titer Stock of Helper Bacteriophage

The key to success in using phagemids is to prepare a stock of helper virus whose titer is accurately known.

1. In 20 ml of 2x YT medium, establish a culture of *E. coli* strain DH11S from a single colony freshly picked from supplemented minimal agar plates. Incubate the culture at 37ºC with moderate agitation until the OD_{600} reaches 0.8.

2. Prepare a series of tenfold dilutions of bacteriophage M13K07 in 2x YT medium, and plate aliquots of the bacteriophage as described in Protocol 1 to obtain well-isolated plaques on a lawn of DH11S cells.

3. Pick well-separated, single plaques and place each plaque in 2–3 ml of 2x YT medium containing kanamycin (25 µg/ml) in a 15-ml culture tube. Incubate the infected cultures for 12–16 hours at 37ºC with moderate agitation (250 cycles/minute).

   ▲ IMPORTANT Use stocks of M13K07 derived from single freshly picked plaques in the following steps.

4. Transfer the infected cultures to 1.5-ml sterile microfuge tubes and centrifuge them at maximum speed for 2 minutes at 4ºC in a microfuge. Transfer the supernatants to fresh tubes and store them at 4ºC.

5. Measure the titer of each of the bacteriophage stocks by plaque formation (Protocol 1) on a strain of *E. coli* F´ (TG1, DH11S, NM522, or XL1-Blue) that supports the growth of bacteriophage M13.

   The titer of infectious bacteriophage particles in the stocks should be 10^{10} pfu/ml. Discard any stock with a lower titer.

Growth of Recombinant Phagemids with Helper Virus

6. Streak DH11S cells transformed by (i) the recombinant phagemid and (ii) the empty (parent) phagemid vector onto two separate YT agar plates containing 60 µg/ml ampicillin. Incubate the plates for 16 hours at 37ºC.

7. Pick (i) several colonies transformed by the recombinant phagemid and (ii) one or two colonies transformed by the parent vector into sterile 15-ml culture tubes that contain 2–3 ml of 2x YT medium containing 60 µg/ml ampicillin.

   > Because the variables that affect the yield of single-stranded DNA are poorly defined, pick multiple isolates from each phagemid recombinant to increase the chances of success.

8. To each culture, add M13K07 helper bacteriophage to achieve a final concentration of 2×10^7 pfu/ml. Incubate the cultures for 1.0–1.5 hours at 37ºC with strong agitation (300 cycles/minute).

   > The bacterial cultures should be only slightly turbid after this short incubation. If growth is too florid, dilute the cultures with prewarmed 2x YT medium until the turbidity is only just visible.

ALTERNATIVE PROCEDURES FOR SUPERINFECTION BY HELPER VIRUS

Using Neglected Colonies for Superinfection

The standard protocol works best with cultures established directly from freshly picked colonies of DH11S, i.e., colonies that have been grown for 18 hours or less and have not been stored at 4ºC. Colonies that have been stored at 4ºC or otherwise neglected need to be restored to full health before superinfection.

1. Inoculate 2 ml of 2x YT medium containing ampicillin (100 µg/ml) with a bacterial colony transformed by the recombinant plasmid.

2. Incubate the culture at 37ºC with strong agitation (300 cycles/minute) until the culture reaches saturation.

3. Dilute 20 µl of the saturated culture into 2 ml of 2x YT medium containing M13K07 helper bacteriophage at a concentration of 2×10^8 to 4×10^8 pfu/ml.

4. Incubate the culture for 1 hour at 37ºC with strong agitation. (Please see the note in Step 8 regarding turbidity at this stage.) Proceed as described in Steps 9–14 of the standard protocol.

Using Frozen Cultures for Superinfection

Some investigators find that the yield of single-stranded phagemid DNA is highest when a saturated culture of DH11S is used in Step 6. Saturated cultures may be prepared ahead of time and stored at –70ºC. Lin et al. (1992) recommend growing the cells containing the phagemid to saturation and then adding sterile glycerol to a final concentration of 20% (v/v). The cells are divided into small aliquots, quick-frozen in a dry ice–ethanol bath, and stored at –70ºC. Thawed cells (20 µl) are then used to inoculate 2 ml of 2x YT medium containing M13K07 helper bacteriophage. The optimum amount of helper bacteriophage should be determined empirically for each culture, but usually lies in the range of 10^7 to 4×10^8 pfu/ml. The infected cultures are grown at 37ºC with strong agitation (300 cycles/minute) until the OD_{600} reaches 0.5. Then proceed as described in Steps 9–14 of the standard protocol.

---

9. Add kanamycin to the cultures to a final concentration of 25 µg/ml. Continue incubation for a further 14–18 hours at 37ºC.

   > Because the bacteriophage M13K07 contains a kanamycin resistance gene, only those cells that are infected will survive the addition of this antibiotic in this step.

   > Other helper bacteriophages (e.g., R408) do not carry an antibiotic resistance marker. Check the genotype of the helper virus before adding antibiotic to the medium!

10. Transfer the cell suspensions to microfuge tubes and separate the bacterial cells from the growth medium by centrifugation at maximum speed for 5 minutes at room temperature in a microfuge. Transfer the supernatants to fresh tubes and store them at 4ºC.

Estimation of the Yield of Single-stranded Phagemid DNA by Gel Electrophoresis

11. Combine 40 µl of each supernatant with 2 µl of 2% SDS in 0.5-ml microfuge tubes. Mix the contents of the tubes by tapping and then incubate the tubes for 5 minutes at 65ºC.

    Alternatively, estimate the yield of virus particles containing single-stranded copies of the phagemid by infecting *E. coli* DH11S cells with dilutions of the supernatants (please see Protocol 1) and then plating the infected cells on YT agar containing ampicillin (60 µg/ml). The number of ampicillin-resistant colonies that arise after 24 hours incubation at 37ºC is a measure of the number of virus particles in the supernatant that contain single-stranded phagemid DNA. Supernatants that contain 2×10^{11} to 5×10^{11} cfu/ml will generate satisfactory yields of purified single-stranded phagemid DNA.

12. Add 5 µl of sucrose gel-loading buffer to each sample of the phagemid DNA, mix the samples, and load them into separate wells of an 0.7% agarose gel.

13. Carry out electrophoresis for several hours at 6 V/cm until the bromophenol blue has migrated approximately half the length of the gel. Examine and photograph the gel by UV light.

    Yields vary depending on the size and nature of foreign DNA in the phagemid, but are generally ~1 µg/ml of culture volume.

14. Isolate single-stranded phagemid DNA from the supernatants containing the largest amount of single-stranded DNA. Follow the steps outlined in Protocol 4, scaling up the volumes two- to threefold.

    In phagemids, as in bacteriophage M13 vectors, the yield of single-stranded DNA can vary over a five- to tenfold range depending on the size and nature of the foreign DNA. In general, the larger the fragment, the poorer the yield. Furthermore, for reasons that are not understood, foreign DNAs of equivalent size can suppress the yield of single-stranded DNA to varying extents. For example, most segments of yeast DNA seem to be amenable to propagation in phagemids, whereas human genomic DNAs of equivalent size may produce disappointing yields of single-stranded DNA. The orientation of both the foreign DNA insert and the bacteriophage origin of DNA replication in the phagemid vector can also dramatically affect yields. Thus, recloning a fragment in the opposite orientation or in a vector with the bacteriophage origin of replication in the opposite orientation will sometimes solve a problem of low yields.

GROWTH TIMES

Deletion or rearrangement of part of the foreign DNA segment can be a problem with some bacteriophage M13 clones. The larger the insert, the greater the rate at which deletions occur. This problem can be minimized (although not eliminated) by taking care never to propagate the bacteriophage by serial growth of infected cells in liquid culture. Instead, stocks of recombinant bacteriophages stored at –20ºC should be plated on an appropriate host, and a single, well-isolated plaque be used to establish a small-scale culture. This culture should provide enough single-stranded DNA (Protocol 4) for most purposes. The culture should be grown for the shortest possible time (5 hours is usually optimal) and not be used to seed further cultures. Recombinant bacteriophages carrying larger segments of foreign DNA almost always grow more slowly than those carrying smaller inserts. Cultures of these slower-growing recombinants may require up to 8 hours of incubation to produce a satisfactory yield of single-stranded DNA. Deletion of foreign DNA sequences confers a selective advantage that is frequently strong enough to result in the elimination of bacteria synthesizing the original recombinant within a few serial passages. Recombinant bacteriophages that harbor DNA inserts with long tracts of a single nucleotide (such as a segment of a eukaryotic cDNA containing the 3′ poly(A) sequence or a fragment of DNA containing multiple copies of a short repeated sequence) are very susceptible to rearrangement. These bacteriophages should be grown for the shortest possible periods of time and never for more than 8 hours.

POLYETHYLENE GLYCOL

Polyethylene glycol (PEG) is a straight-chain polymer of a simple repeating unit $H(OCH_2 CH_2)_n OH$. PEG is available in a range of molecular weights whose names reflect the number (n) of repeating units in each molecule. In PEG 400, for example, $n = 8–9$, whereas in PEG 4000, n ranges from 68 to 84.

PEG induces macromolecular crowding of solutes in aqueous solution (Zimmerman and Minton 1993) and has a range of uses in molecular cloning, including:

- Precipitation of DNA molecules according to their size (Lis and Schleif 1975a,b; Ogata and Gilbert 1977; Lis 1980).
- Precipitation and purification of bacteriophage particles (Yamamoto et al. 1970).
- Increasing the efficiency of reassociation of complementary chains of nucleic acids during hybridization, blunt-end ligation of DNA molecules, and end-labeling of DNA with bacteriophage T4 polynucleotide kinase (Zimmerman and Minton 1993).
- Fusion of cultured cells with each other or with bacterial protoplasts (Schaffner 1980; Rassoul-zadegan et al. 1982).

REFERENCES

Achtman M., Willetts N., and Clark A.J. 1971. Beginning a genetic analysis of conjugational transfer determined by the F factor in *Escherichia coli* by isolation and characterization of transfer-deficient mutants. *J. Bacteriol.* **106:** 529–538.

Alting-Mees M.A. and Short J.M. 1989. pBluescript II: Gene mapping vectors. *Nucleic Acids Res.* **17:** 9494.

———. 1993. Polycos vectors: A system for packaging filamentous phage and phagemid vectors using lambda phage packaging extracts. *Gene* **137:** 93–100.

Banner D.W., Nave C., and Marvin D.A. 1981. Structure of the protein and DNA in fd filamentous bacteriophages. *Nature* **289:** 814–816.

Barnes W.M. 1979. Construction of an M13 histidine-transducing phage: A single-stranded cloning vehicle with one *Eco*RI site. *Gene* **5:** 127–139.

———. 1980. DNA cloning with single-stranded phage cloning vectors. *Genet. Eng.* **2:** 185–200.

Bauer M. and Smith G.P. 1988. Filamentous phage morphogenetic signal sequence and orientation of DNA in the virion and gene-V protein complex. *Virology* **167:** 166–175.

Beck E. and Zink B. 1981. Nucleotide sequence and genome organization of filamentous bacteriophages f1 and fd. *Gene* **16:** 35–58.

Beck E., Sommer R., Auerswald E.A., Kurz C., Zink B., Osterburg G., Schaller H., Sugimoto K., Sugisaki H., Okamoto T., and Takanami M. 1978. Nucleotide sequence of bacteriophage fd DNA. *Nucleic Acids Res.* **5:** 4495–4503.

Beckwith J.R. 1964. Deletion analysis of *lac* operator region in *Escherichia coli. J. Mol. Biol.* **8:** 427–430.

Bedbrook J.R. and Ausubel F.M. 1976. Recombination between bacterial plasmids leading to the formation of plasmid multimers. *Cell* **9:** 707–716.

Birnboim H.C. and Doly J. 1979. A rapid extraction procedure for screening recombinant plasmid DNA. *Nucleic Acids Res.* **7:** 1513–1523.

Bullock W.O., Fernandez J.M., and Short J.M. 1987. XL1-Blue: A high efficiency plasmid transforming recA *Escherichia coli* strain with beta-galactosidase selection. *BioTechniques* **5:** 376–379.

Chen E.Y., Kuang W.J., and Lee A.L. 1991. Overview of manual and automated DNA sequencing by the dideoxy chain termination method. *Methods* **3:** 3–19.

Close T.J., Christmann J.L., and Rodriguez R.L. 1983. M13 bacteriophage and pUC plasmids containing DNA inserts but still capable of β-galactosidase α-complementation. *Gene* **23:** 131–136.

Dente L., Cesareni G., and Cortese R. 1983. pEMBL: A new family of single-stranded plasmids. *Nucleic Acids Res.* **11:** 1645–1655.

Dotto G.P. and Zinder N.D. 1983. The morphogenetic signal of bacteriophage f1. *Virology* **130:** 252–256.

———. 1984a. Reduction of the minimal sequence for initiation of DNA synthesis by qualitative or quantitative changes of an initiator protein. *Nature* **311:** 279–280.

———. 1984b. Increased intracellular concentration of an initiator protein markedly reduces the minimal sequence required for initiation of DNA synthesis. *Proc. Natl. Acad. Sci.* **81:** 1336–1340.

Dotto G.P., Enea V., and Zinder N.D. 1981a. Gene II of phage f1: Its functions and products. *Proc. Natl. Acad. Sci.* **78:** 5421–5424.

———. 1981b. Functional analysis of bacteriophage f1 intergenic region. *Virology* **114:** 463–473.

Dotto G.P., Horiuchi K., Jakes K.S., and Zinder N.D. 1983. Signals for the initiation and termination of synthesis of the viral strand of bacteriophage f1. *Cold Spring Harbor Symp. Quant. Biol.* **47:** 717–722.

Endemann H. and Model P. 1995. Location of filamentous phage minor coat proteins in phage and in infected cells. *J. Mol. Biol.* **250:** 496–506.

Enea V. and Zinder N.D. 1982. Interference-resistant mutants of phage f1. *Virology* **122:** 222–226.

Felton J. 1983. M13 host strain JM103 contains two restriction systems. *BioTechniques* **1:** 42–43.

Fulford W. and Model P. 1984. Gene X of bacteriophage f1 is required for phage DNA synthesis. Mutagenesis of in-frame overlapping genes. *J. Mol. Biol.* **78:** 137–153.

———. 1988. Regulation of bacteriophage f1 DNA replication. I. New functions for genes II and X. *J. Mol. Biol.* **203:** 49–62.

Geider K. and Kornberg A. 1974. Conversion of the M13 viral single-strand to the double-stranded replicative form by purified proteins. *J. Biol. Chem.* **249:** 3999–4005.

Geider K., Hohmeyer C., Haas R., and Meyer T.F. 1985. A plasmid cloning system utilizing replication and packaging functions of the filamentous bacteriophage fd. *Gene* **33:** 341–349.

Gibson T.J. 1984. "Studies on the Epstein-Barr virus genome." Ph.D. thesis, Cambridge University, England.

Glucksman M.J., Bhattacharjee S., and Makowski L. 1992. Three-dimensional structure of a cloning vector. X-ray diffraction studies of filamentous bacteriophage M13 at 7 Å resolution. *J. Mol. Biol.* **226:** 455–470.

Gough J.A. and Murray N.E. 1983. Sequence diversity among related genes for recognition of specific targets in DNA molecules. *J. Mol. Biol.* **166:** 1–19.

Gray C.W. 1989. Three-dimensional structure of complexes of single-stranded DNA-binding proteins with DNA. IKe and fd gene 5 proteins form left-handed helices with single-stranded DNA. *J. Mol. Biol.* **208:** 57–64.

Gronenborn B. and Messing J. 1978. Methylation of single-stranded DNA in vitro introduces new restriction endonclease cleavage sites. *Nature* **272:** 375–377.

Guilfoyle R.A. and Smith L.M. 1994. A direct selection strategy for shotgun cloning and sequencing in the bacteriophage M13. *Nucleic Acids Res.* **22:** 100–107.

Halloran N., Du Z., and Wilson R.K. 1993. Sequencing reactions for the applied biosystems 393A Automated DNA Sequence. *Methods Mol. Biol.* **23:** 297–315.

Herrmann R., Neugebauer E., Pirkl E., Zentgraf H., and Schaller H. 1980. Conversion of bacteriophage fd into an efficient single-stranded DNA vector system. *Mol. Gen. Genet.* **177:** 231–242.

Higashitani N., Higashitani A., and Horiuchi K. 1993. Nucleotide sequence of the primer RNA for DNA replication of filamentous bacteriophages. *J. Virol.* **67:** 2175–2181.

Hofschneider P.-H. 1963. Untersuchungen über 'kleine' *E. coli* K-12 Bacteriophagen M12, M13, und M20. *Z. Naturforsch.* **18:** 203–205.

Horiuchi K. 1980. Origin of DNA replication of bacteriophage f1 as the signal for termination. *Proc. Natl. Acad. Sci.* **77:** 5226–5229.

Ish-Horowicz D. and Burke J.F. 1981. Rapid and efficient cosmid cloning. *Nucleic Acids Res.* **9:** 2989–2998.

Jerpseth B., Greener A., Short J.M., Viola J., and Kretz P.L. 1992. XL1-Blue MRF $E. coli$ cells: McrA$^-$, McrCB$^-$, McrF$^-$, Mrr$^-$, HsdR$^-$ derivative of XL1-Blue cells. *Strategies Newsletter* **5:** 81–83. Stratagene, La Jolla, California.

Konings R.N.H. and Schoenmakers J.G.G. 1978. Transcription of the filamentous phage genome. In *The single-stranded DNA phages* (ed. D.T. Denhardt et al.), pp. 507–530. Cold Spring Harbor Laboratory, Cold Spring Harbor, New York.

Kunapuli S.P. and Colman R.W. 1993. Two new phagemid vectors for site-directed mutagenesis and expression in *E. coli*. *BioTechniques* **3:** 332, 336–338.

Lerner T.J. and Model P. 1981. The "steady-state" of coliphage f1: DNA synthesis late in infection. *Virology* **115:** 282–294.

Levinson A., Silver D., and Seed B. 1984. Minimal size plasmids containing an M13 origin for production of single-stranded transducing particles. *J. Mol. Appl. Genet.* **2:** 507–517.

Lin J.-J., Smith M., Jessee J., and Bloom F. 1992. DH11S: An *Escherichia coli* strain for preparation of single-stranded DNA from phagemid vectors. *BioTechniques* **12:** 718–721.

Lis J.T. 1980. Fractionation of DNA fragments by polyethylene glycol induced precipitation. *Methods Enzymol.* **65:** 347–352.

Lis J.T. and Schleif R. 1975a. Size fractionation of double-stranded DNA by precipitation with polyethylene glycol. *Nucleic Acids Res.* **2:** 383–389.

———. 1975b. The regulatory region of the L-arabinose operon: Its isolation on a 1000 base-pair fragment from DNA heteroduplexes. *J. Mol. Biol.* **95:** 409–416.

Loeb T. 1960. Isolation of a bacteriophage specific for the F$^+$ and Hfr mating types of *Escherichia coli* K12. *Science* **131:** 932–933.

Loeb T. and Zinder N.D. 1961. A bacteriophage containing RNA. *Proc. Natl. Acad. Sci.* **47:** 282–289.

Lopez J. and Webster R.E. 1983. Morphogenesis of filamentous bacteriophage f1: Orientation of extrusion and production of polyphage. *Virology* **127:** 177–193.

———. 1985. Assembly site of bacteriophage f1 corresponds to adhesion zones between the inner and outer membrane of the host. *J. Bacteriol.* **163:** 1270–1274.

Lyons L.B. and Zinder N.D. 1972. The genetic map of the filamentous bacteriophage f1. *Virology* **49:** 45–60.

Makowski L. 1984. Structural diversity in filamentous bacteriophages. In *Biological macromolecules and assemblies. I. Virus structures* (ed. F.A. Jurnak and A. MacPherson), pp. 203–253. Wiley, New York.

———. 1994. Phage display: Structure assembly and engineering of filamentous bacteriophage M13. *Curr. Opin. Struct. Biol.* **4:** 225–230.

Marvin D.A. and Hoffman-Berling H. 1963. Physical and chemical properties of two new small bacteriophages. *Nature* **197:** 517–518.

Marvin D.A. and Hohn B. 1969. Filamentous bacterial viruses. *Bacteriol. Rev.* **33:** 172–209.

Marvin D.A., Hale R.D., Nave C., and Citterich M.H. 1994. Molecular models and structural comparisons of native and mutant class I filamentous bacteriophages Ff (fd, f1, M13), If1 and IKe. *J. Mol. Biol.* **235:** 260–286.

Mazur B.J. and Model P. 1973. Regulation of coliphage f1 single-stranded DNA synthesis by a DNA-binding protein. *J. Mol. Biol.* **78:** 285–300.

Mazur B.J. and Zinder N.D. 1975. The role of gene V protein in f1 single-strand synthesis. *Virology* **68:** 490–502.

McClary J.A, Witney F., and Geisselsoder J. 1989. Efficient site-

directed in vitro mutagenesis using phagemid vectors. *BioTechniques* **7:** 282–289.

McDonnell P.A., Shon K., Kim Y., and Opella S.J. 1993. fd coat protein structure in membrane environments. *J. Mol. Biol.* **223:** 447–463.

Mead D.A., Szczesna-Skorupa E.S., and Kemper B. 1985. Single-stranded DNA SP6 promoter plasmids for engineering mutant RNAs and proteins: Synthesis of a "stretched" pre-proprathyroid hormone. *Nucleic Acids Res.* **13:** 1103–1118.

Messing J. 1979. A multipurpose cloning system based on the single-stranded DNA bacteriophage M13. *Recomb. DNA Tech. Bull.* **2:** 43–48.

———. 1981. M13mp2 and derivatives: A molecular cloning system for DNA sequencing, strand-specific hybridization and in vitro mutagenesis. In *Recombinant DNA: Proceedings of the 3rd Cleveland Symposium on Macromolecules* (ed. A.G. Walton), pp. 22–36. Elsevier, Amsterdam, The Netherlands.

———. 1983. New M13 vectors for cloning. *Methods Enzymol.* **101:** 20–78.

———. 1991. Cloning in M13 phage or how to use biology at its best. *Gene* **100:** 3–12.

———. 1993. M13 cloning vehicles. Their contribution to DNA sequencing. *Methods Mol. Biol.* **23:** 9–22.

———. 1996. Cloning single-stranded DNA. *Mol. Biotechnol.* **5:** 39–47.

Messing J., Crea R., and Seeburg P.H. 1981. A system for shotgun sequencing. *Nucleic Acids Res.* **9:** 309–321.

Messing J., Gronenborn B., Müller-Hill B., and Hofschneider P.H. 1977. Filamentous coliphage M13 as a cloning vehicle: Insertion of a *Hind*II fragment of the *lac* regulatory region in M13 replicative form *in vitro*. *Proc. Natl. Acad. Sci.* **74:** 3642–3246.

Meyer T.F., Geider K., Kurz C., and Schaller H. 1979. Cleavage site of bacteriophage fd gene II-protein in the origin of viral strand replication. *Nature* **278:** 365–367.

Model P. and Russel M. 1988. Filamentous bacteriophage. In *The bacteriophages* (ed. R. Calendar), vol. 2, pp. 375–456. Plenum Press, New York.

Model P., McGill C., Mazur B., and Fulford W.D. 1982. The replication of bacteriophage f1: Gene V protein regulates the synthesis of gene II protein. *Cell* **29:** 329–335.

Müller-Hill B., Crapo L., and Gilbert W. 1968. Mutants that make more *lac* repressor. *Proc. Natl. Acad. Sci.* **59:** 1259–1264.

Ogata R. and Gilbert W. 1977. Contacts between the lac repressor and the thymines in the lac operator. *Proc. Natl. Acad. Sci.* **74:** 4973–4976.

Opella S.J., Cross T.A., DiVerdi J.A., and Sturm C.F. 1980. Nuclear magnetic resonance of the filamentous bacteriophage fd. *Biophys. J.* **32:** 531–548.

Peeters B.P.H., Schoenmakers J.G.G., and Konings R.N.H. 1986. Plasmid pKUN9, a versatile vector for the selective packaging of both DNA strands into single-stranded DNA-containing phage-like particles. *Gene* **41:** 39–46.

Picken R.N. 1990. Method for the direct detection of both orientations of an insert in M13. *BioTechniques* **9:** 412–413.

Pratt D., Tzagaloff H., and Beaudoin J. 1969. Conditional lethal mutants of the small filamentous coliphage M13. II. Two genes for coat proteins. *Virology* **39:** 42–53.

Radding C.M. 1982. Homologous pairing and strand exchange in genetic recombination. *Annu. Rev. Genet.* **16:** 405–437.

Rasched I. and Oberer E. 1986. Ff coliphages: Structural and functional relationships. *Microbiol. Rev.* **50:** 401–427.

Rassoulzadegan M., Binetruy B., and Cuzin F. 1982. High frequency of gene transfer after fusion between bacteria and eukaryotic cells. *Nature* **295:** 257–259.

Reddy P. and McKenney K. 1996. Improved method for the production of M13 phage and single-stranded DNA for DNA sequencing. *BioTechniques* **20:** 854–860.

Russel M. 1991. Filamentous phage assembly. *Mol. Microbiol.* **5:** 1607–1613.

———. 1994. Phage assembly: A paradigm for bacterial virulence factor export? *Science* **265:** 612–614.

———. 1995. Moving through the membrane with filamentous phages. *Trends Microbiol.* **3:** 223–228.

Russel M., Kidd S., and Kelley M.R. 1986. An improved filamentous helper phage for generating single-stranded plasmid DNA. *Gene* **45:** 333–338.

Salivar W.O., Henry T.J., and Pratt D. 1967. Purification and properties of diploid particles of coliphage M13. *Virology* **32:** 41–51.

Salstrom J.D. and Pratt D. 1971. Role of coliphage M13 gene 5 in single-stranded DNA production. *J. Mol. Biol.* **61:** 489–501.

Sanger F., Coulson A.R., Barrell B.G., Smith A.J., and Roe B.A. 1980. Cloning in single-stranded bacteriophage as an aid to rapid DNA sequencing. *J. Mol. Biol.* **143:** 161–178.

Sanger F., Donelson J.E., Coulson A.R., Kossel H., and Fischer H. 1973. Use of DNA polymerase I primed by a synthetic oligonucleotide to determine a nucleotide sequence in phage f1 DNA. *Proc. Natl. Acad. Sci.* **70:** 1209–1213.

Schaffner W. 1980. Direct transfer of cloned genes from bacteria to mammalian cells. *Proc. Natl. Acad. Sci.* **77:** 2163–2167.

Scott J.R. and Zinder N.D. 1967. Heterozygotes of phage f1. In *The molecular biology of viruses* (ed. J.S. Colter and W. Paranchych), pp. 212–281. Academic Press, New York.

Seed B. 1983. Purification of genomic sequences from bacteriophage libraries by recombination and selection in vivo. *Nucleic Acids Res.* **11:** 2427–2445.

Short J.M., Fernandez J.M., Sorge J.A., and Huse W.D. 1988. λZAP: A bacteriophage λ expression vector with *in vivo* excision properties. *Nucleic Acids Res.* **16:** 7583–7600.

Ullmann A. and Perrin D. 1970. Complementation in β-galactosidase. In *The lactose operon* (ed. J.R. Beckwith and D. Zipser), pp. 143–172. Cold Spring Harbor Laboratory, Cold Spring Harbor, New York.

Ullmann A., Jacob F., and Monod J. 1967. Characterization by *in vitro* complementation of a peptide corresponding to an operator-proximal segment of the β-galactosidase structural gene of *Escherichia coli*. *J. Mol. Biol.* **24:** 339–343.

van Wezenbeek P.M.G.F., Hulsebos T.J.M., and Schoenmakers J.G.G. 1980. Nucleotide sequence of the filamentous bacteriophage M13 DNA genome: Comparison with phage fd. *Gene* **11:** 129–148.

Vieira J. and Messing J. 1987. Production of single-stranded plasmid DNA. *Methods Enzymol.* **153:** 3–11.

———. 1991. New pUC-derived cloning vectors with different selectable markers and DNA replication origins. *Gene* **100:** 189–194.

Webster R.E. 1991. The tol gene products and the import of macromolecules into *Escherichia coli*. *Mol. Microbiol.* **5:** 1005–1011.

Webster R.E. and Lopez J. 1985. Structure and assembly of the class I filamentous bacteriophages. In *Virus structure and assembly* (ed. S. Casjens), pp. 235–267. Jones and Bartlett, Boston, Massachusetts.

Webster R.E., Grant R.A., and Hamilton L.A.W. 1981. Orientation of the DNA in the filamentous bacteriophage f1. *J. Mol. Biol.* **152:** 357–374.

Yamamoto K.R., Alberts B.M., Benzinger R., Lawhorne L., and Treiber G. 1970. Rapid bacteriophage sedimentation in the presence of polyethylene glycol and its application to large-scale virus purification. *Virology* **40:** 734–744.

Yanisch-Perron C., Vieira J., and Messing J. 1985. Improved M13 phage cloning vectors and host strains: Nucleotide sequences of the M13mp18 and pUC19 vectors. *Gene* **33:** 103–119.

Yen T.S.B. and Webster R.E. 1982. Translational control of bacteriophage f1 gene II and gene X proteins by gene V protein. *Cell* **29:** 337–345.

Zacher III, A.N., Stock III, C.A., Golden II, J.W., and Smith G.P. 1980. A new filamentous phage cloning vector: fd-tet. *Gene* **9:** 127–140.

Zagursky R.J. and Berman M.L. 1984. Cloning vectors that yield high levels of single-stranded DNA for rapid DNA sequencing. *Gene* **27:** 183–191.

Zaman G.J.R., Schoenmakers J.G.G., and Konings R.N.H. 1990. Translational regulation of M13 gene II protein by its cognate single-stranded DNA binding protein. *Eur. J. Biochem.* **189:** 119–124.

Zimmerman S.B. and Minton A.P. 1993. Macromolecular crowding: Biochemical, biophysical and physiological consequences. *Annu. Rev. Biophys. Biomol. Struct.* **22:** 27–65.

Chapter 4

Working with High-capacity Vectors

THE REASON THAT WE KNEW SO LITTLE FOR SO LONG OF THE HUMAN GENOME is its immense scale: 3 billion or more base pairs containing ~1 million exons grouped into an estimated 40,000 to 60,000 genes distributed among 23 pairs of chromosomes. However, if current estimates are correct, we have moved in less than 50 years from the discovery of the structure of DNA in 1953 to

TABLE 4-1 High-capacity Vectors for Genomic Cloning

Vector	Capacity (kb)	Replicon	Host	Copy Number	Introduction into Cells	Screening for Recombinants	Recovery of Cloned DNA
Cosmid	30–45	colE1	*E. coli*	high	transduction	not necessary	alkaline extraction
P1	70–100	P1	*E. coli*	1 (amplifiable)	transduction	*sacB*	alkaline extraction
PAC	130–150	P1	*E. coli*	1	electroporation	*sacB*	alkaline extraction
BAC	120–300	F	*E. coli*	1	electroporation	α-complementation	alkaline extraction
YAC	250–400	ARS	yeast	1	transformation	*ade2*	pulse-field gels

the elucidation of the complete sequence of the human genome in the year 2000. That we have learned so much about the human genome during the last decade is in part due to the development of a series of vectors with the capacity to propagate large segments of genomic DNA. These vectors have been instrumental in the rapid assembly of overlapping arrays of individual clones (contigs) in which each recombinant contains a piece of genomic DNA that partially overlaps DNA carried by its neighbor. Such physical maps grant access to genes that in their entirety may sprawl over several hundred kilobases; they fuel DNA sequencing mills; and they provide points through which physical and genetic maps may be riveted together.

There are five major types of high-capacity vectors. Because physical maps of eukaryotic chromosomes are built by linking together overlapping clones, it might seem that the vector with the largest capacity would be preferred for construction of framework maps. However, it turns out that each vector has its own set of advantages and disadvantages (please see below and Table 4-1), and, in consequence, physical maps of chromosomal regions are typically constructed from a mosaic of DNA fragments cloned in different vectors.

- *Yeast artificial chromosomes (YACs)* are linear DNA molecules whose architecture mimics that of authentic yeast chromosomes (Burke et al. 1987). Recombinant YACs are created by ligating large fragments of genomic DNA to two "arms" of a YAC vector, and the ligation mixture is then introduced into yeast by transformation. Each of the arms carries a selectable marker, as well as appropriately oriented DNA sequences that function as telomeres. In addition, one of the two arms carries centromeric DNA segments and an origin of replication (also called an autonomously replicating sequence or ARS). In recombinant YACs, therefore, a segment of foreign genomic DNA becomes flanked on one side by a centromere, an origin of replication, and a selectable marker and on the other side by the second selectable marker. Yeast transformants that have taken up and stably maintained an artificial chromosome are identified as colonies on selective agar plates.

  Most YAC vectors in current use are designed to allow facile distinction between clones that are empty and those that carry inserts of genomic DNA (please see Figure 4-1). For example, in several YAC vectors, insertion of DNA into the cloning site interrupts a suppressor tRNA gene and results in the formation of red rather than white colonies by yeast strains that carry an ochre mutation in the *ade2* gene. Because YACs have no packaging constraints that limit their cloning capacity, the average size of the inserts is determined chiefly by the quality of the preparation of genomic DNA. Most YAC libraries contain between 250 kb and 400 kb of foreign DNA per clone. However, libraries of mammalian genomic DNA have been constructed containing clones whose size exceeds 1 Mb.

- *Bacterial artificial chromosomes (BACs)* are circular DNA molecules that carry an antibiotic resistance marker, a stringently controlled replicon derived from the F factor (fertility factor) of *Escherichia coli* (Shizuya et al. 1992), an ATP-driven helicase (*repE*) to facilitate DNA replication, and three loci (*parA*, *parB*, and *parC*) to ensure accurate partitioning of low-copy-number plasmids to daughter cells. Segments of foreign genomic DNA are ligated to the ~7-

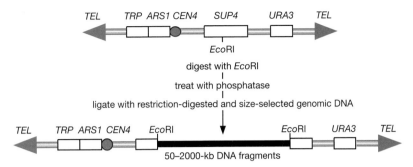

FIGURE 4-1 Cloning in YAC Vectors

The genome of the YAC vector includes two selectable markers (*TRP* and *URA*), an autonomously repli-cating sequence (*ARS1*), a centromere (*CEN4*), a suppressor tRNA gene (*SUP4*), and telomeric sequences (*TEL*) at the termini.

kb BAC vector in vitro, and the ligation mixture is introduced by electroporation into well-characterized recombination-deficient strains of *E. coli*, where they become established as sin-gle-copy plasmids.

The first generation of BAC vectors (Shizuya et al. 1992) carried no markers that could be used to distinguish between antibiotic-resistant bacterial colonies carrying recombinants and those carrying empty vectors. Newer BAC vectors allow screening by α-complementation to identify recombinants with inserts and are equipped with sites to facilitate recovery and manipulation of cloned DNAs (see Figure 4-2) (Kim et al. 1996; Asakawa et al. 1997). BACs, like YACs and PACs (P1 artificial chromosomes), have no packaging contraints and there is no fixed limit to the size of genomic DNA that they can accept. The median size of clones in most

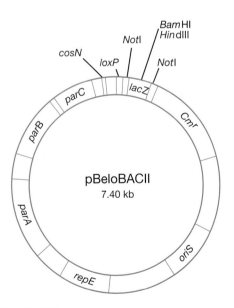

FIGURE 4-2 Diagram of pBeloBACII

The circular vector contains genes *parA*, *parB*, and *parC* derived from the fertility factor (F factor) of *E. coli* to ensure that the low-copy-number plasmid is accurately partitioned to daughter cells during division of its bacterial host. In addition, the vector carries genes (*oriS* and *repC*) involved in initiation and orientation of DNA replication; a chloramphenicol resistance gene (*Cm*^r); an element (*lacZ*) that allows color-based iden-tification of recombinants; *loxP* and *cosN* sites that facilitate recovery of cloned sequences; and restriction sites that can be used to clone large fragments of genomic DNA.

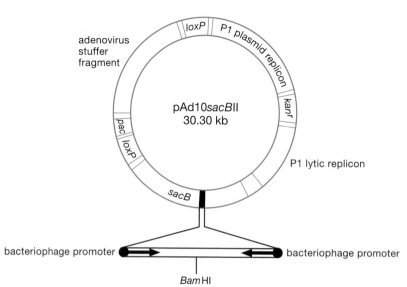

FIGURE 4-3 **Diagram of pAd10*sacB*II**

The left-hand side of the circular vector contains two *loxP* sites, a plasmid origin of DNA replication, a minimal signal (*pac*) for packaging into P1 particles, and a stuffer fragment derived from adenovirus DNA. The right-hand side contains a kanamycin resistance gene (*kan*ʳ): a replicon (P1 plasmid replicon) derived from bacteriophage P1 that allows the vector to replicate as a low-copy-number plasmid in *E. coli*; an inducible replicon (P1 lytic replicon) that can be used to increase the copy number of the plasmid; and a selectable marker (*sacB*) containing a cloning site (*Bam*HI) flanked by promoters derived from bacteriophages SP6 and T7.

BAC libraries is ~120 kb, whereas the largest individual recombinant BACs contain ~300 kb of genomic DNA.

- ***Bacteriophage P1 vectors*** contain many *cis*-acting elements derived from bacteriophage P1 and will accommodate fragments of genomic DNA between 70 kb and 100 kb (Figure 4-3) (Sternberg 1990, 1992, 1994). In this system, linear recombinant molecules consisting of genomic and vector sequences are packaged in vitro into bacteriophage P1 particles, which have a total capacity (vector plus insert) of 115 kb. After injection into a strain of *E. coli* expressing Cre recombinase, the linear DNA molecules are circularized by recombination between two *loxP* sites present in the vector. The vector carries, in addition, a general selectable marker (*kan*ʳ), a positive selection marker (*sacB*) for clones that carry inserts of foreign DNA, and a P1 plasmid replicon, which maintains the circular recombinant plasmids at ~1 copy per cell. A second P1 replicon (the P1 lytic replicon), under the control of the inducible *lac* promoter, can be used to amplify the plasmid before isolation of DNA.

- ***P1 artificial chromosomes*** combine the best features of P1 vectors and BACs, including the positive selection marker (*sacB*) and the plasmid and lytic replicons of bacteriophage P1 (please see Figure 4-4). However, instead of packaging ligation products into bacteriophage particles, and instead of using site-specific recombination at *cre-loxP* sites to generate plasmid molecules, circular recombinant PACs generated during ligation in vitro are introduced into *E. coli* by electroporation and are then maintained as single-copy plasmids (Ioannou et al. 1994). The inserts in PAC-based libraries of human genomic DNA range in size from 60 kb to 150 kb (Ioannou et al. 1994; Strong et al. 1997).

- ***Cosmids,*** the oldest of the five types of vectors used for analysis of complex genomes (Collins and Hohn 1978), also have the smallest capacity: 43–45 kb of foreign DNA stretches cosmids to their limit. Cosmid vectors are conventional plasmids that contain one or two copies of a

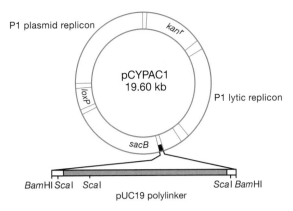

FIGURE 4-4 Diagram of pCYPAC1

The vector contains a subset of the genetic elements contained in pAd10*sacB*II (Figure 4-3), a kanamycin resistance gene (*kan*^r), a *loxP* site, a replicon (P1 plasmid replicon) derived from bacteriophage P1 that allows the vector to replicate as a low-copy-number plasmid in *E. coli*; an inducible replicon (P1 lytic replicon) that can be used to increase the copy number of the plasmid; and a selectable marker (*sacB*) containing a variety of cloning sites.

small region of bacteriophage λ DNA—the cohesive end site (*cos*)—which contains all of the *cis*-acting elements required for packaging of viral DNA into bacteriophage λ particles (please see Figure 4-5) (for review, please see Hohn 1979; Hohn et al. 1988). Linear concatenated DNA substrates, suitable for packaging in vitro, are generated by ligating restriction fragments containing a *cos* sequence to each end of a genomic DNA molecule. During packaging, the two flanking *cos* sequences are cleaved by the bacteriophage λ *ter* function to generate a linear molecule with termini that are complementary to one another but not identical (Feiss et al. 1983; please see the panel on λ TERMINASE in the introduction to Chapter 2). After injection into susceptible bacterial cells, the complementary termini anneal to one another and are sealed by the host's DNA ligase, generating circular DNA molecules carrying a colicin E1 (colE1) plasmid replicon and a selectable marker. Bacterial colonies selected on plates containing the appropriate antibiotic carry multiple copies of recombinant cosmids.

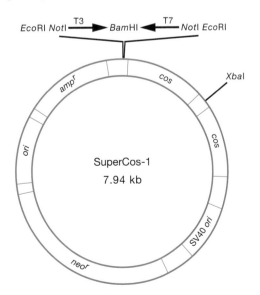

FIGURE 4-5 Diagram of SuperCos-1 (Stratagene)

This cosmid vector contains two *cos* sites separated by a unique *Xba*I restriction site, an SV40 origin of replication (SV40 *ori*), two antibiotic resistance genes (*neo*^r and *amp*^r), a colE1 origin of replication (*ori*), and a cloning site flanked by bacteriophage promoters.

CONSTRUCTING LIBRARIES OF GENOMIC DNA

Genomic libraries are constructed by cloning segments of DNA generated by partial digestion of high-molecular-weight genomic DNA with restriction enzymes (Maniatis et al. 1978). In some cases, these fragments are fractionated by preparative gel electrophoresis or density gradient centrifugation to select those of a size suitable for insertion into the vector.

In theory, every DNA sequence in the target genome should be proportionally represented in a library of recombinant clones. In practice, this ideal is never realized. Instead, in libraries of complex genomes, some DNA sequences are missing entirely and others may be overrepresented to varying degrees. Such bias is the inevitable result of the methods that are used to construct genomic libraries.

Gaps in coverage arise in part because there is no truly random method to shear complex genomes, irrespective of their sequence and base composition. Since genomic libraries are typically generated by partial digestion of high-molecular-weight DNA, the composition of the resulting population of size-selected fragments depends on the distribution of restriction sites within the genomic DNA and on the relative rates at which these sites are cleaved. Unfortunately, the distribution of restriction sites is far from normal and the efficiency of digestion at different sites is influenced by surrounding sequences (for review, please see Brooks 1987). Regions rich in restriction sites tend to be underrepresented because they are quickly reduced to an unacceptably small size. Conversely, impoverished regions may be excluded because they generate fragments that are too large. For theoretical treatment of these problems, please see Seed (1982), Seed et al. (1982), and Tang and Waterman (1990). Although there is no general solution, juggling with digestion conditions can sometimes be used to correct underrepresentation of specific sequences in genomic libraries (e.g., please see Wong et al. 1993).

Gaps in coverage are inevitable because libraries are at best a statistical sampling of a population of restriction fragments. The size and number of these "statistical" gaps depend on the number of genome equivalents carried in the entire library (please see the panel on GENOMIC LIBRARIES). For example, a cosmid library of human genomic DNA consisting of 75,000 clones of ~40-kb DNA fragments would contain a total of 3×10^9 bp of human DNA, or one haploid equivalent. Even if the 40-kb cloned fragments were generated by entirely random cleavage of the original DNA preparation, and even if the packaging of these fragments into bacteriophage heads were also entirely random, the library would be far from complete. In this case, the probability that any DNA sequence of interest would not be represented in the library is ~37%. This problem can be ameliorated by increasing the depth of coverage of the library. For example, in a library of 750,000 cosmids that covers the genome ten times, there is an ~99.995% chance that

---

GENOMIC LIBRARIES

The probability that any given DNA sequence will be represented in a genomic library can be calculated from the equation

$$N = \frac{\ln(1-P)}{\ln(1-f)}$$

where P is the desired probability, f is the fractional proportion of the genome in a single recombinant, and N is the necessary number of clones in the library (Clarke and Carbon 1976). For example, to achieve a 99% probability ($P = 0.99$) of having a given DNA sequence represented in a library of 17-kb fragments of mammalian DNA (3×10^9) bp

$$N = \frac{\ln(1-0.99)}{\ln\left(1 - \frac{1.7 \times 10^4}{3 \times 10^9}\right)} = 8.1 \times 10^5$$

For more detailed mathematical treatments of genomic library construction and probability calculations, please see Seed (1982) and Seed et al. (1982).

the human DNA sequence of interest would be represented at least once. Unfortunately, because some genomic clones replicate better than others, additional bias in representation may occur as the library is replicated and expanded. Finally, because cloned sequences may undergo rearrangements during passage, there is no guarantee that any given recombinant clone isolated from a genomic library would necessarily carry an accurate copy of the corresponding genomic sequence.

Knowing that genomic libraries are always imperfect, pessimists and purists might throw up their hands and say "Enough." However, given the size, quality, number, depth of coverage, and proven performance of currently available libraries, optimists and pragmatists can remain confident knowing that the odds of isolating the desired genomic clones are stacked very much in their favor.

CHOOSING AMONG VECTORS

The major variables that influence the choice of a vector for construction of genomic libraries are the size of the target region and the capacity of the vector, the ease of screening libraries, whether the vector is designed to facilitate chromosome walking, whether cloned DNA sequences can easily be purified and recovered, and, finally, whether instability of cloned sequences is likely to be a problem.

Size of the Target Region

If the target region of the genome is very small (<50 kb), then bacteriophage λ or cosmids are the vectors of choice for the construction of genomic libraries. Unless the investigator works on an esoteric organism or wants to construct a library from a particular mutant strain, there is a good chance that a suitable cosmid library of genomic DNA already exists. If such a library is not available, well-defined cosmid vectors, highly efficient packaging mixtures, and suitable strains of *E. coli* are readily available from commercial sources. Preparation of the necessary high-molecular-weight genomic DNA should be within the capacity of any experienced laboratory (please see Chapter 6).

If the region of interest is too large to fit into a single cosmid or if there is good reason to believe that the region may be difficult to clone, a possible alternative is bacteriophage P1, PAC, or BAC libraries. Genomic libraries of many species are now available in these vectors. For a listing of companies that provide libraries and various cloning services, please see the information panel on **LARGE-FRAGMENT CLONING PRODUCTS AND SERVICES**. Although screening of existing libraries is straightforward, and generation of small P1 libraries is well within the capacity of most laboratories, de novo construction of large genomic libraries in P1 vectors remains a difficult undertaking. This is because the efficiency of packaging of DNA into bacteriophage P1 particles is relatively low and preparation of sufficient quantities of 75–90-kb fragments of genomic DNA is laborious. Until the efficiency (and cost) of P1 packaging improves, the PAC system may be a more reasonable alternative because it requires no experience with bacteriophage P1 or specialized reagents such as packaging mixtures.

If the region of interest is >250 kb in size, then YACs are the vectors of choice. However, as with bacteriophage P1, construction of new large genomic libraries in YAC vectors is probably best left to experts.

The Ease of Screening Libraries

For cloning of small (<50 kb) sequences, genomic libraries in cosmid or bacteriophage λ vectors are generally prepared and maintained as a single pool of clones that are plated anew when screening by conventional hybridization. However, this process is too laborious and expensive for the construction of regional maps and contigs. More and more, genomic libraries are being maintained as two-dimensional arrays that can be screened for specific sequences, either by conventional hybridization with single-copy probes (for review, please see Bentley and Dunham 1995) or as pools in microtiter dishes that can be screened by polymerase chain reaction (PCR)-based protocols. In the latter case, a pair of oligonucleotide primers, designed to amplify a specific target segment of DNA, are used to screen pools of clones. The number of clones in the pools decreases with each round of screening until the clone of interest is identified (Green and Olson 1990; Anand et al. 1991; for review, please see Evans et al. 1992; also see the panel on ARRAYED LIBRARIES). Reference libraries constructed in high-capacity vectors such as bacteriophage P1, BAC, and YAC are archived in this way as a resource that can be used by many groups (e.g., please see Francis et al. 1994; Shepherd et al. 1994; Zehetner and Lehrach 1994). Copies of the libraries are maintained at Human Genome Centers in the United States, Europe, Asia and Australiasia, and some libraries may be accessible through commercial screening companies (please see Table 4-2 and the information panel on LARGE-FRAGMENT CLONING PRODUCTS AND SERVICES).

Chromosome Walking

Chromosomal regions or individual genes that are too large to be isolated as a single segment of DNA can be cloned by chromosome walking as a series of overlapping fragments. In this technique, a segment of nonrepetitive DNA isolated from one end of a cloned segment of genomic DNA is used to rescreen the library for additional recombinant clones containing overlapping

---

ARRAYED LIBRARIES

The idea of storing libraries as individually picked clones in microtiter dishes goes back to the very early days of cloning when the few available cDNA libraries were small in size and high in value. Transformed bacterial clones carrying recombinant plasmids were picked from the initial selective plates and transferred to wells of microtiter dishes containing liquid medium. Arraying libraries in this fashion eliminated competition between clones, reduced contamination by molds, and facilitated storage, replication, and screening.

The major disadvantage of arrayed libraries is the sheer number of clones that must be picked and stored in microtiter plates in order to accommodate a representative set. In the case of cDNA libraries, arraying is only worthwhile when a particular cDNA library is to be screened many times (Lennon and Lehrach 1991). However, arraying is certainly a cost-effective method for storing libraries of genomic DNA that have been constructed in "difficult" vectors such as YACs, BACs, and bacteriophage P1. Some YAC libraries are arrayed in microtiter dishes at a density of 1 clone/well, and others are arrayed as pools of specific size. P1 libraries are often stored as pools of 10–20 clones/well. The work involved in picking recombinant clones by hand and transferring them one at a time into microtiter dishes is formidable in its scale and depressing in its nature. However, several research groups and commercial companies have developed mechanical colony and plaque pickers that considerably ease the effort required to establish arrayed libraries. Furthermore, the use of higher-density arrays that compress several hundred clones onto a microscope slide reduces storage space at –70ºC (please see Appendix 10).

Arraying P1, BAC, and YAC genomic libraries has four advantages that together outweigh the problems of picking and storage.

- Each clone has a specific set of coordinates (dish number, row, and column) and can therefore be easily located and recovered. This feature is especially important when several laboratories are working on the same set of arrayed clones, since sharing of clones merely involves sharing of coordinates within the reference library.

- The arrayed format allows libraries to be screened in a combinatorial fashion. Individual clones are pooled into overlapping N-dimensional sets, which are then screened hierarchically by hybridization or PCR. The pattern of positive and negative results obtained from these pools can then be deciphered to identify the location of an individual clone that carries the sequences of interest (Kwiatkowski et al. 1990; Barillot et al. 1991; Amemiya et al. 1992). Once the appropriate pools are established, this combinatorial approach can greatly reduce the amount of labor involved in screening genomic libraries with many different probes. For example, in the scheme devised by Barillot et al. (1991), only 258 pools and 282 tests are needed to screen the 72,000 clones of a human genomic YAC library.

- The arrayed format naturally leads to an elimination of redundancy and a detection of overlapping clones during screening. Since a clone is always at the same address, its detection by two different probes is immediately obvious.

- The ordered layout of the library allows simple robotic devices to carry out many of the routine steps involved in the replication and screening.

TABLE 4-2 Widely Used Large-insert Human Genomic Libraries

Library and Characteristics	Contact Information
CEPH Mega YAC Library[a] Number of clones: 23,808 Average insert length: 918 kb Genome equivalents: ~7 Estimated chimera frequency: 30–40% Constructed in yeast strain AB1380 using 46, XY cell line DNA Cohen et al. (1993)	Fondation Jean Dausset–CEPH (clones) E-mail: yac_manager@cephb.fr URL: http://www.cephb.fr/services/ Research Genetics, Inc. (screening resources and clones) Fax: (205) 536-9016 E-mail: info@resgen.com URL: http://www.resgen.com Genome Systems, Inc. (screening resources and clones) Fax: (314) 692-0044 E-mail: sales@genomesystems.com URL: http://www.genomesystems. com HGMP Resource Centre (screening resources and clones) E-mail: biohelp@hgmp.mrc.ac.uk URL: http://www.hgmp.mrc.ac.uk
Human PAC Library Number of clones: ~500,000 Average insert length: 115 kb Genome equivalents: ~20 Estimated chimera frequency: <5% Constructed in PAC vector pCYPAC-1 using HSF7 fibroblast cell line DNA Ioannou et al. (1994)	Roswell Park Cancer Institute Contact: Pieter deJong E-mail: pieter@dejong.med.buffalo.edu URL: http://bacpac.med.buffalo.edu Research Genetics, Inc. (screening resources and clones) Fax: (205) 536-9016 E-mail: info@resgen.com URL: http://www.resgen.com Genome Systems, Inc. (screening resources and clones) Fax: (314) 692-0044 E-mail: sales@genomesystems.com URL: http://www.genomesystems. com HGMP Resource Centre (screening resources and clones) E-mail: biohelp@hgmp.mrc.ac.uk URL: http://www.hgmp.mrc.ac.uk
CIT Human BAC Library Number of clones: total ~680,000 (segment B: ~74,000, segment C: ~216,000, segment D: –390,000) Average insert length: ~130 kb Genome equivalents: ~30 Estimated chimera frequency: <5% Constructed with DH10B/r using XY-fibroblast cell line DNA Shizuya et al. (1992)	Research Genetics, Inc. (screening resources, services, clones, and other specialized services) Fax: (205) 536-9016 E-mail: info@resgen.com URL: http://www.resgen.com
RPCI-11 Human BAC Library Number. of clones: ~437,000 (four subsets with ~109,000 clones) Average insert length: ~175 kb Genome equivalents: 25 Estimated chimera frequency: <5% Constructed in BAC vector pBACe3.6 using male blood lymphocyte DNA K. Osoegawa et al. (unpubl.)	Roswell Park Cancer Institute (screening resources and clones) E-mail: pieter@dejong.med.buffalo.edu URL: http://bacpac.med.buffalo.edu Research Genetics, Inc. (screening resources, services, and clones) Fax: (205) 536-9016 E-mail: info@resgen.com URL: http://www.resgen.com

The libraries listed here are widely used by the human genome research community. Several other large-insert human libraries are available through the Roswell Park Cancer Institute, Research Genetics, Genome Systems, and the HGMP Resource Centre. Additional large-insert libraries are available from at least one of these suppliers for baboon, mouse, rat, dog, zebrafish, pufferfish (*Fugu* and *Spheroides*), maize, *Arabidopsis*, *Drosophila*, filaria, mosquito, *C. elegans*, *C. briggsae*, *Chlamydomonas*, *Cryptospordium*, and *Halobacterium*.

[a]Copies of this library are maintained by many laboratories in the United States but are generally not available for outside screening. Copies for redistribution were sent to: Eric Lander, Fax: (617) 252-1933 (for U.S. distribution); Hans Lehrach, Fax: (49) (30) 8413 1380 (Berlin); M. Muramatsu, Fax: (81) (298) 36-9140 (Japan); Y. Nakamura, Fax: (81) (3) 3918-0342 (Japan); Z. Chen, Fax: (86) (21) 3180-300 (China).

(Reprinted, with permission, from *Current Protocols in Human Genetics* [ed. N.C. Dracopoli et al.] 1994 [©Wiley, New York].)

sequences. The new set of clones is then mapped and the sequences furthest away from the starting point are used to screen the library for a third time. This process (walking) is repeated until the entire region of interest has been recovered in a series of overlapping clones.

Most vectors used in recent years to construct genomic libraries carry promoters for bacteriophage-encoded RNA polymerases in regions immediately flanking the foreign DNA. This advance, and the development of PCR methods that use oligonucleotide cassettes, "vectorette" or "splinkerette," to amplify insert sequences immediately adjacent to each vector arm, has greatly simplified the task of generating end-specific probes (for reviews, please see Arnold and Hodgson 1991; Hengen 1995; Ogilvie and James 1996). However, chromosome walking remains a laborious process. High-capacity vectors that accommodate large segments of DNA are greatly preferred because they decrease the number of steps that are required to complete a chromosomal walk.

Recovery of Cloned Sequences

Cosmids, bacteriophage P1, PAC, and BAC clones can be separated easily from *E. coli* chromosomal DNA by alkaline extraction. However, recovery of pure YACs from *Saccharomyces cerevisiae* is a major problem because there is no simple method to separate YAC DNA from the background of natural yeast chromosomal DNA. Purifying inserts of mammalian genomic DNA from YACs usually requires pulsed-field gel electrophoresis (PFGE) and/or direct subcloning of the entire yeast genome into bacteriophage λ or cosmid vectors. The subclones carrying mammalian sequences are then identified by their ability to hybridize to repetitive DNA probes.

Stability of Cloned Sequences

Serious concerns have been raised over the years about the fidelity and stability of genomic sequences cloned in cosmids and YACs. In the case of cosmids, rearrangement of cloned DNA occurs because the recombinants are carried at high copy number in *E. coli*, a situation that often favors the emergence of shorter, deleted clones that can replicate faster than their parent. Genomic sequences cloned in YACs also undergo rearrangements, but for a different reason. Unlike cosmids, YACs do not exclude one another during transformation, and it is fairly common to find two or more YACs coexisting in the same cell. This provides opportunities for recombination between repetitive DNA sequences in the genomic DNA of different YACs. The products of this type of rearrangement are chimeric inserts that consist of DNA from two different chromosomal regions. More than 40% of the clones in YAC libraries may be chimeric, as judged from fluorescent in situ hybridization of individual YAC clones to spreads of mammalian chromosomes (Green et al. 1991; Selleri et al. 1992) or from characterizing subcloned YAC ends (Nagaraja et al. 1994).

Summary

In summary, no single genomic vector is ideal for all purposes (please see Table 4-1, p. 4.2) and no single genomic library contains a perfect representation of the genome from which it is derived. For some investigators, the best option will be to screen a copy of an existing arrayed or pooled genomic library; for others, the only way forward may be to generate their own libraries; for an increasing number, the best course is to use the services of commercial organizations such as Genome Systems Inc., who, for a fee, will use oligonucleotides provided by the investigator to screen BAC and YAC libraries for clones that contain the desired sequences. Cloners who take pride in doing everything for themselves should take solace from the fact that it is considerably less expensive and by far quicker to use a commercial service than to set up screening of large-insert libraries in the laboratory. With these considerations in mind, we describe in this chapter methods for the construction and screening of cosmid libraries containing genomic DNA inserts, and the manipulation of individual bacteriophage P1, BAC, and YAC clones containing a gene or region of interest.

Protocol 1

Construction of Genomic DNA Libraries in Cosmid Vectors

ESSENTIALLY THE SAME PROCEDURES ARE USED TO CONSTRUCT genomic DNA libraries in both bacteriophage λ and cosmid vectors. In each system, segments of eukaryotic DNA are ligated in vitro to vector DNA, forming concatemers that can be packaged into bacteriophage λ particles. Libraries constructed in λ vectors are stored and propagated as infectious recombinant bacteriophages (please see Chapter 2). In cosmid cloning, however, bacteriophage particles generated by in vitro packaging serve merely as Trojan horses that deliver recombinant DNA molecules efficiently into bacteria, where the DNA circularizes and is propagated as large plasmids (please see Figure 4-6). Because cosmids are subject to the same packaging constraints as bacteriophage λ vectors and because cosmid vectors are typically ~5–7 kb in size, recombinant cosmids can contain no less than ~28 kb and no more than ~45 kb of foreign genomic DNA. Genomic fragments of a size appropriate for cloning are generally obtained by partial digestion of high-molecular-weight chromosomal DNA with a restriction enzyme that recognizes a 4-bp sequence and generates a cohesive terminus. The enzymes most widely used for this purpose are *MboI* and *Sau*3AI, which generate DNA fragments that can be cloned into a *Bam*HI site.

The aim when constructing a genomic DNA library in cosmids should be to generate recombinants in numbers sufficient to encompass five to seven equivalents of the target genome. A good cosmid library of a mammalian genome, with a haploid complement of ~3×10^9 bp of DNA, should therefore contain ≥500,000 individual transformants (please see the introduction to this chapter). Once created, the library is generally amplified and then stored frozen either as a single pool of transformed bacteria that is plated afresh for screening (Protocol 3), as a population of transformed colonies on nitrocellulose filters or LB-glycerol plates (Hanahan and Meselson 1980), or as an array of single or pooled transformants in wells of microtiter plates (Protocol 4) (Evans et al. 1992). Alternatively, and less frequently, the recombinant cosmids are rescued from the population of primary transformants by transduction and maintained as a stock of transducing bacteriophage particles.

Cosmid vectors can contain either one or two *cos* sites. Cloning into older, single *cos* vectors requires many steps, including the isolation of fragments of genomic DNA of the appropriate size (please see Figure 4-7). Because of the inefficiency of this and several other steps, generating representative libraries of complex genomes in single *cos* vectors has always been a challenging task.

A great improvement in cosmid design came with the inclusion of two *cos* sites in the vector (Bates and Swift 1983). These dual *cos* vectors have a singular advantage: They no longer require fractionation of partial digests of genomic DNA before ligation and packaging. Figure 4-8 shows how a cosmid vector with two *cos* sites (in this example, SuperCos-1; Evans et al. 1989) can be used to generate genomic libraries.

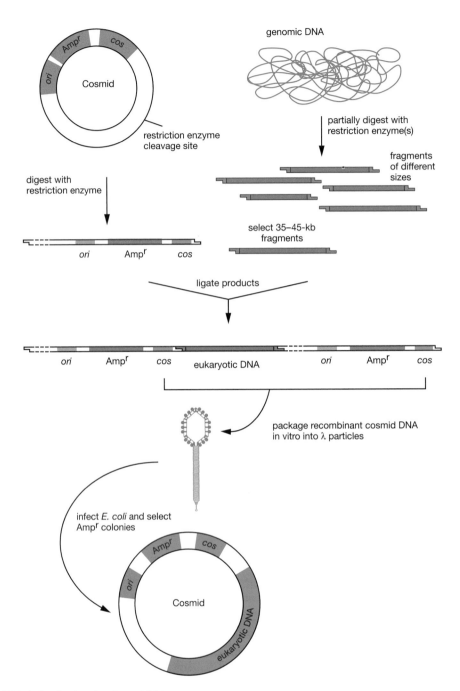

FIGURE 4-6 Cloning in Cosmid Vectors

Shown in diagrammatic form are the steps involved in cloning in cosmid vectors. The steps are discussed in detail in the text.

In vectors such as SuperCos-1, two *cos* sites are separated by a recognition site for a restriction enzyme that cleaves the vector only once (in this case, *Xba*I). The vector arms are prepared by first digesting the DNA with *Xba*I and then removing the 5′-terminal phosphate residues from the linearized cosmid by treatment with alkaline phosphatase. In a second digestion, the linearized double *cos* vector is digested with *Bam*HI to produce two arms, each of which carries a *cos* site. The two arms are then ligated to partially digested genomic DNA, generating, inter alia, molecules in which the two *cos* sites are oriented in the same manner and separated by eukaryotic DNA inserts.

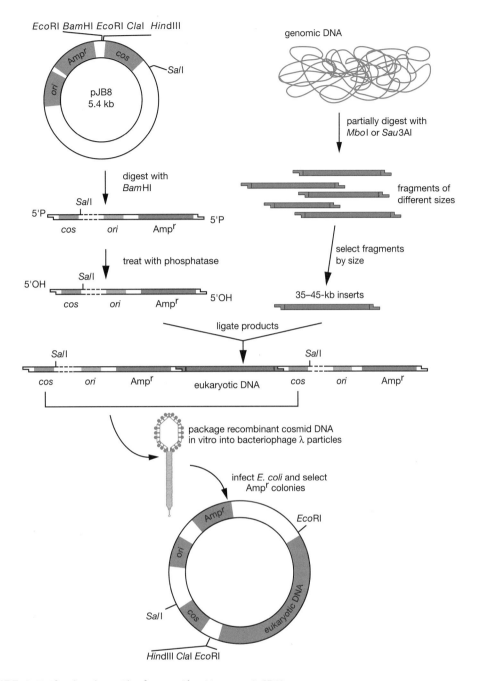

FIGURE 4-7 Cloning into Single *cos* Site Vectors (pJB8)

The DNA of cosmid pJB8 is digested with *Bam*HI and dephosphorylated with alkaline phosphatase to yield a vector with protruding 5´ termini that can be ligated to 35–45-kb fragments of eukaryotic DNA generated by partial digestion with *Mbo*I or *Sau*3AI. The resultant concatemers serve as substrate for in vitro packaging of bacteriophage λ particles. Following introduction into *E. coli*, the cosmid DNA recircularizes and replicates in the form of a large plasmid. The plasmid contains the β-lactamase gene that confers resistance to ampicillin on the host bacterium.

Although at best, only 50% of the concatemers can have the correct arrangement of *cos* sites, such molecules are packaged into bacteriophage λ heads with very high efficiency, provided they are between 35 kb and 52 kb in length (Feiss et al. 1977). When all is working well, between 10^5 and

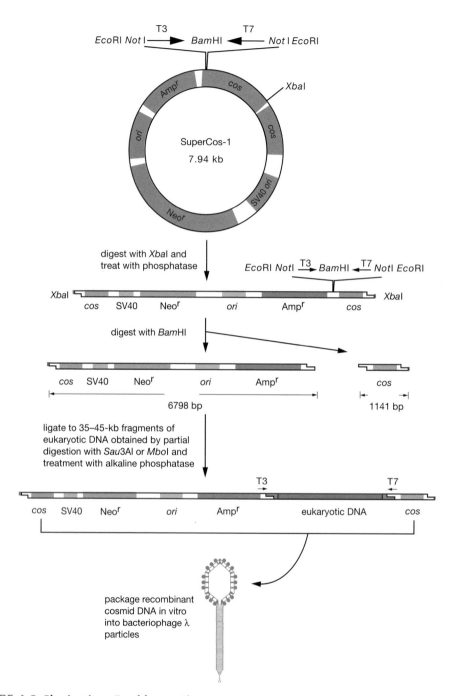

FIGURE 4-8 Cloning into Double *cos* Site Vectors (SuperCos-1)

Following digestion with *Xba*I and treatment with alkaline phosphatase, the cosmid DNA is further digest-ed with *Bam*HI to separate the *cos* sequences that are now carried on separate fragments. The resulting cosmid DNA is ligated to dephosphorylated fragments of eukaryotic DNA obtained by partial digestion with *Mbo*I and treatment with alkaline phosphatase. These eukaryotic fragments carry termini that are compatible only with the *Bam*HI cohesive termini of the vector. The concatenated DNA is then packaged into bacteriophage λ particles that are used to infect a *recA⁻* strain of *E. coli*.

2×10^7 transformed colonies are generated per microgram of genomic DNA (Bates 1987; Evans et al. 1992). With this level of efficiency, only 5 μg of partially digested genomic DNA is needed to generate a library that is a reasonable representation of a mammalian genome.

During ligation, there is a risk that smaller fragments of eukaryotic DNA in the preparation will ligate to one another and to the cosmid vector producing recombinants that contain sequences derived from two or more noncontiguous segments of the genome. A population of DNA fragments with an average size of 42 kb will contain many molecules that are shorter than the mean. Although these shorter molecules may comprise only a fraction of the total weight of the DNA, they make a more substantial contribution to the number of molecules in the population. As the kinetics of ligation are determined by the concentration of reactive termini of DNA, these smaller molecules become preferentially incorporated into concatemers, which may be of a size suitable for packaging in vitro. Three methods are available to reduce the number of undesirable chimeric clones in cosmid libraries:

- As described in the following protocol, the partially digested genomic DNA may be treated with alkaline phosphatase before ligation.

- The cohesive ends of the genomic and cosmid DNAs may be partially filled so that they ligate only to each other and not to themselves (Hung and Wensink 1984; Zabarovsky and Allikmets 1986; Loftus et al. 1992). In this technique, genomic DNA is partially digested with *Mbo*I (GATC) and cosmid arms are prepared by cleavage with *Sal*I (G TCGAC). The cohesive termini generated by *Mbo*I and *Sal*I are not normally compatible, but partial filling of the recessed 3′ termini in controlled reactions using the Klenow fragment of *E. coli* DNA polymerase I generates complementary termini and simultaneously destroys the ability of the original termini to self-anneal (please see Figure 4-9). Partial filling of the recessed termini therefore suppresses self-ligation and prevents formation of chimeric molecules of genomic DNA.

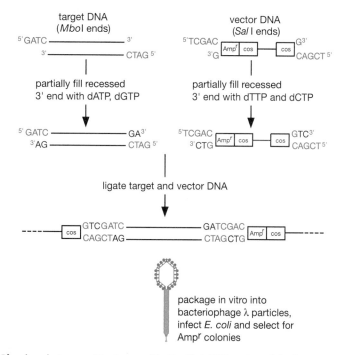

FIGURE 4-9 Cloning into *cos* Vectors with Partial Filling in of Ends

The strategy illustrated in this diagram allows the conversion of noncompatible termini of target and vector to compatible termini. Fragments of target DNA generated by digestion with *Mbo*I are partially filled with dATP, resulting in fragments carrying a 5′ overhang of "GA." Similarly, vector DNA digested with *Sal*I is filled with dTTP and dCTP to generate termini, now complementary to the ends of the target fragments, carrying the 5′ overhang of "TC." The ligated product is packaged into bacteriophage λ particles and used to infect an appropriate strain of *E. coli*.

- The partially digested genomic DNA can be fractionated according to size by agarose gel electrophoresis or centrifugation through sucrose or NaCl gradients before ligation to the cosmid arms. However, because of the inevitable losses associated with these techniques, sizing of partial digestion products can be used only when high-molecular-weight genomic DNA is available in abundance. Even then, most laboratories have difficulty in recovering sufficient DNA of the proper size for cloning. For this reason, sizing is nowadays the least favored of the three available options to reduce the number of chimeric clones in cosmid libraries.

A great variety of cosmid vectors are available, many of them carrying specialized functions. Among these are selectable genes for drug resistance, which may be used to establish mammalian cell lines that have incorporated cosmid sequences after transfection. Other features include bacteriophage promoters for the production of RNA probes complementary to the termini of the cloned genomic DNA sequences, recognition sites for restriction enzymes that cleave mammalian DNA very rarely (e.g., *Not*I, *Sal*I, *Sac*II, *Pac*I; please see Table 4-3) and may allow the cloned segment to be isolated from the cosmid in one piece, sequences that facilitate homologous recombination between cosmids, multiple cloning sites, and replicons of several different types. For examples of these vectors, please see the Appendix 3 and Hohn et al. (1988).

TABLE 4-3 Frequency of Restriction Endonuclease Sites in the Human Genome

ENZYME	SEQUENCE	AVERAGE FRAGMENT SIZE (KB)	ESTIMATED NUMBER OF SITES
*Apa*I	GGGCC	2	1.5×10^6
*Asc*I	GGCGCGCC	80	3.75×10^4
*Avr*II	CCTAGG	8	3.75×10^5
*Bam*HI	GGATCC	5	6×10^5
*Bgl*I	GCCN$_5$GGC	3	1×10^6
*Bgl*II	AGATCT	3	1×10^6
*Bss*HII	GCGCGC	10	3×10^5
*Dra*I	TTTAAA	2	1.5×10^6
*Eag*I	CGGCCG	10	3×10^5
*Eco*RI	GAATTC	5	6×10^5
*Hind*III	AAGCTT	4	7.5×10^5
*Nae*I	GCCGGC	4	7.5×10^5
*Nar*I	GGCGCC	4	7.5×10^5
*Nhe*I	GCTAGC	10	3×10^5
*Not*I	GCGGCCGC	100	3×10^4
*Pac*I	TTAATTAA	60	5×10^4
*Pme*I	GTTTAAAC	70	4.3×10^4
*Rsr*I	CGGWCCG	60	5×10^4
*Sac*I	GAGCTC	3	1×10^6
*Sac*II	CCGCGG	6	5×10^5
*Sal*I	GTCGAC	20	1.5×10^5
*Sbf*I	CCTGCAGG	15	2×10^5
*Sfi*I	GGCCN$_5$GGCC	30	1×10^5
*Sgr*AI	CRCCGGYC	70	4.3×10^4
*Sma*I	CCCGGG	4	7.5×10^5
*Spe*I	ACTAGT	10	3×10^5
*Sph*I	GCATGC	6	5×10^5
*Srf*I	GCCCGGGC	50	6×10^4
*Ssp*I	AATATT	2	1.5×10^6
*Swa*I	ATTTAAAT	30	1×10^5
*Xba*I	TCTAGA	5	6×10^5
*Xho*I	CTCGAG	7	4.3×10^5

Adapted with permission, 1998/99 New England Biolabs Catalog (©NEB).

The following protocol, describing the construction of a genomic DNA library, has been written with SuperCos-1 in mind. However, the procedure can easily be adapted for use with other cosmid vectors that contain two *cos* sites (e.g., please see Evans et al. 1989) and for use with different combinations of restriction enzymes. Procedures for screening libraries are presented in Protocol 2, and for amplifying libraries in Protocols 3 and 4.

MATERIALS

CAUTION: Please see Appendix 12 for appropriate for appropriate handling of materials marked with <!>.

Buffers and Solutions

Please see Appendix 1 for components of stock solutions, buffers, and reagents. Dilute stock solutions to the appropriate concentrations.

Chloroform <!>
10x Dephosphorylation buffer (CIP buffer)
Ethanol
Phenol:chloroform (1:1, v/v) <!>
SM
Sodium acetate (3 M, pH 5.2)
TE (pH 8.0)

Enzymes and Buffers

Bacteriophage T4 DNA ligase
Calf intestinal phosphatase (CIP)
Restriction endonucleases: BamHI, MboI, XbaI
Restriction endonucleases that cleave cosmid vector but not the genomic insert DNA

Gels

Agarose gels (0.7%) cast in 0.5x TBE, containing 0.5 μg/ml of ethidium bromide <!>
Please see Step 24.
Agarose gel (0.8%) cast in 0.5x TBE, containing 0.5 μg/ml of ethidium bromide
Please see Steps 2 and 8, and the panel following Step 6.
Pulsed-field gels (or 0.5% agarose gels)
Please see Steps 10, 11, and 26, and the panel on **PULSED-FIELD GEL ELECTROPHORESIS** on the following page.

Media

TB agar plates containing 25 μg/ml kanamycin
TB medium
TB medium containing 25 μg/ml kanamycin

Nucleic Acids and Oligonucleotides

Control DNA: bacteriophage λ DNA digested with HindIII
Control DNA: superhelical SuperCos-1 DNA
High-molecular-weight genomic DNA
Linearized plasmid in 1x dephosphorylation buffer
Please see the panel after Step 6.
Marker DNA: linear bacteriophage λ DNA

Special Equipment

Water baths preset to 16°C and 65°C

Additional Reagents

Step 10 of this protocol requires the reagents listed in Chapter 2, Protocol 17.

Step 23 of this protocol requires the reagents listed in Chapter 1, Protocol 1.

Vectors and Bacterial Strains

Bacteriophage λ packaging mixtures

Packaging mixtures may be purchased in a kit form from any of several companies (e.g., Gigapack III XL Packaging Extract, Stratagene). Please see note to Step 19 and the information panel on **IN VITRO PACKAGING** in Chapter 2.

Bacteriophage λ stock

Please see panel following Step 6.

E. coli *plating bacteria of the appropriate strain for titering packaged cosmid (e.g., XL1-Blue, ED8767, NM554, DH5αMCR)*

For a complete listing of appropriate strains, please see Appendix 3.

SuperCos-1 DNA (Stratagene)

PULSED-FIELD GEL ELECTROPHORESIS

PFGE is the preferred method to measure the size of an insert in a high-capacity vector. After digestion with a restriction enzyme (e.g., *Not*I), the DNA fragments are separated by pulsed-field electrophoresis through a 1% agarose gel. Transverse alternating field electrophoresis (TAFE, please see Chapter 5, Protocol 17) resolves DNA fragments between 50 kb and 500 kb in a program in which switch times are ramped from 7 to 50 seconds/pulse at 9 V/cm for 20–24 hours at 15°C (Shizuya et al. 1992). Alternatively, a CHEF hexagonal array system can be used with switch times ramping from 1 to 150 seconds/pulse at 9 V/cm for 20 hours at 15°C (Zimmer and Verrinder Gibbins 1997). For additional information on PFGE, please see Chapter 5.

METHOD

Linearization and Dephosphorylation of SuperCos-1 DNA

1. Combine 20 μg of SuperCos-1 DNA with 50 units of *Xba*I in a volume of 200 μl of 1x *Xba*I digestion buffer and incubate the reaction mixture for 2–3 hours at 37°C.

2. After 2 hours of incubation, transfer an aliquot (~1 μl) of the reaction mixture to a fresh tube. Analyze the aliquot of cosmid DNA by electrophoresis through an 0.8% agarose gel, using as controls (i) 50–100 ng of superhelical SuperCos-1 DNA and (ii) 50–100 ng of a bacteriophage λ DNA digested with *Hin*dIII.

   If the digestion with the restriction enzyme is complete, all of the superhelical SuperCos-1 DNA will have been converted to a linear 7.9-kb fragment of DNA.

   If superhelical or nicked forms of SuperCos-1 DNA are still visible, add 10 more units of *Xba*I to the digest and continue incubation at 37°C until the reaction has gone to completion.

   If the *Xba*I digestion is not complete, the library will contain a significant number of colonies generated by concatemerization of the vector.

3. Extract the digestion reaction once with phenol:chloroform and once with chloroform.

4. Transfer the aqueous phase to a fresh tube and recover the linearized cosmid DNA by standard precipitation with ethanol and subsequent washing in 70% ethanol. Store the open tube

in an inverted position on a bed of paper towels to allow the ethanol to drain and evaporate. Dissolve the damp pellet of DNA in 180 μl of H_2O. Remove a 100-ng aliquot of the DNA for use as a control (please see the panel on DEPHOSPHORYLATION REACTIONS).

> In some cosmid vectors (e.g., 2CRB), the two *cos* sites are separated by cleavage with a restriction enzyme that creates blunt ends. In this case, dephosphorylation of the linearized vector (Step 5) is no longer necessary. This is because concatemerization of the vector can be suppressed very effectively by including high concentrations of ATP (5 mM) in the ligation buffer (Ferretti and Sgaramella 1981). Dephosphorylation of the genomic DNA must still be carried out to prevent creation of chimeric clones.

5. Add 20 μl of 10x dephosphorylation buffer to the remainder of the DNA solution. Add 0.1 unit of CIP and incubate the reaction for 30 minutes at 37ºC. Add a second aliquot (0.1 unit) of CIP and continue digestion for an additional 30 minutes. Transfer the reaction to a water bath set at 65ºC and incubate for 30 minutes to inactivate CIP. Remove two 100-ng aliquots of the DNA for use as controls (please see the panel on DEPHOSPHORYLATION REACTIONS).

6. Extract the reaction mixture once with phenol:chloroform and once with chloroform. Recover the linearized, dephosphorylated SuperCos-1 DNA by standard precipitation with ethanol and subsequent washing in 70% ethanol. Dissolve the damp pellet of DNA in 180 μl of H_2O.

DEPHOSPHORYLATION REACTIONS

Successful construction of a genomic library in double *cos* vectors requires that the linearized vector be completely dephosphorylated. Unfortunately, there is no simple way to monitor the progress of the dephosphylation reaction catalyzed by alkaline phosphatases. However, since DNA molecules lacking 5´-terminal phosphate residues cannot be ligated together, the success or failure of the dephosphorylation reaction can be assessed by testing whether the linearized DNA can serve as a substrate in ligation reactions catalyzed by bacteriophage T4 DNA ligase. The outcome of the ligation reaction can be checked either by agarose gel electrophoresis (please see below) or by comparing the efficiency with which dephosphorylated and phosphorylated cosmid DNAs can, after ligation, transform *E. coli*. Dephosphorylation should reduce the efficiency of transformation by at least 100-fold.

1. At the completion of Step 4, transfer a 100-ng aliquot of *Xba*I-digested DNA to a fresh microfuge tube (Tube 1).

2. At the completion of Step 5, transfer two 100-ng aliquots of *Xba*I-digested/CIP treated vector DNA to separate microfuge tubes (Tubes 2 and 3).

3. To all three tubes, add 18 μl of H_2O followed by 2 μl of 10x ligase buffer.

4. To Tubes 1 and 2, add 0.2 Weiss units of bacteriophage T4 DNA ligase. Incubate all three tubes for 3 hours at room temperature.

5. Analyze the DNAs by electrophoresis through an 0.8% agarose gel.

The DNA digested with *Xba*I alone (Tube 1) should ligate to itself, forming dimers, closed circular monomers, and higher-order multimers. After removal of 5´-terminal phosphate residues, the DNA should no longer be capable of ligation (Tube 2) and should therefore display an electrophoretic pattern similar to that of the DNA of Tube 3 (no ligase control). If any ligation products are visible in the DNA of Tube 2, the dephosphorylation reaction (Step 5) must be repeated.

Isolation of the Cosmid Arms

7. Transfer an aliquot of the dephosphorylated DNA (50–100 ng) to a fresh microfuge tube and store it on ice. Add 20 μl of 10x *Bam*HI restriction buffer to the remainder of the desphosphorylated DNA. Add 40 units of *Bam*HI and incubate the reaction for 2–3 hours at 37ºC.

8. After 2 hours of incubation, remove a second aliquot of DNA to a separate microfuge tube. Analyze both aliquots of DNA by agarose gel electrophoresis. After digestion with *Bam*HI, the

linear 7.9-kb fragment of dephosphorylated SuperCos-1 DNA should be quantitatively cleaved into two DNA fragments of ~1.1 and ~6.8 kb.

> If traces of the 7.9-kb DNA are still visible, add 10 more units of *Bam*HI to the digest and continue incubation at 37ºC until the reaction has gone to completion.

9. Extract the digestion reaction once with phenol:chloroform and once with chloroform. Recover the DNA by standard precipitation with ethanol followed by washing with 70% ethanol. Dissolve the damp pellet of DNA in 20 μl of H₂O and store the solution at 4ºC until needed.

Partial Digestion of High-molecular-weight Genomic DNA

10. Establish the conditions for partial digestion of a 30-μg sample of high-molecular-weight genomic DNA with *Mbo*I. The aim is to establish conditions that produce the highest yield of DNA fragments with a modal size of 38–52 kb.

> For guidance in establishing conditions for partial digestion of genomic DNA, please see Chapter 2, Protocol 17. The progress of the digestion can be followed by PFGE or, less desirably, by electrophoresis through a 0.5% agarose gel using as markers (i) unit-length bacteriophage λ DNAs and/or (ii) multimers of bacteriophage λ DNA ligated at the *cos* site and then partially digested with a restriction enzyme that cleaves the linear λ DNA once. The 0.5% agarose gels are very sloppy and are best poured and run at 4ºC at low voltage (1–2 V/cm) for long periods of time (15–24 hours).
>
> When only small amounts of the genomic DNA are available (e.g., when constructing libraries of flow-sorted chromosomes or gel-purified YAC DNAs), conditions for partial digestion can be established in small-scale reactions containing 50–100 ng of genomic DNA and different amounts (0.0005–0.001 unit) of restriction enzyme. After digestion for 15 minutes, aliquots (10–20 ng) of each reaction are analyzed by PFGE and Southern blotting with a repetitive DNA probe. For further details, please see Longmire et al. (1993).

11. Using the conditions for partial digestion established in Step 10, set up three large-scale reactions each containing 100 μg of high-molecular-weight genomic DNA and amounts of *Mbo*I that bracket the optimal concentration, as determined in Step 10. At the end of the incubation period, check the size of an aliquot of each partially digested DNA by agarose gel electrophoresis, as described in the note to Step 10.

12. Pool the two samples of partially digested genomic DNA that contain the highest amounts of DNA in the 38–52-kb range. Extract the pooled DNAs once with phenol:chloroform and once with chloroform. Recover the DNA by standard precipitation with ethanol and subsequent washing in 70% ethanol. Dissolve the damp pellet of DNA in 180 μl of TE (pH 8.0).

> Resuspension is best accomplished by allowing the DNA pellet to soak in TE overnight at 4ºC. Do not vortex the DNA. Instead, mix the DNA by gently tapping the sides of the tube (please see the information panel on **MINIMIZING DAMAGE TO LARGE DNA MOLECULES** in Chapter 2). If only small amounts of DNA are available, as is the case when constructing cosmid libraries from flow-sorted eukaryotic chromosomes or from purified YACs, then, instead of ethanol precipitation, purify the DNA by drop dialysis against TE (pH 8.0) with floating membranes, as described in Protocol 5.

Dephosphorylation of High-molecular-weight Genomic DNA

13. To the resuspended partially digested genomic DNA, add 20 μl of 10x dephosphorylation buffer and 2 units of CIP. Immediately withdraw a sample of DNA for use as a control:

    a. Remove an aliquot of the reaction containing 0.1–1.0 μg of DNA to a small (0.5 ml) microfuge tube containing 0.3 μg of a linearized plasmid in 1x dephosphorylation buffer (e.g., pUC cleaved with *Bam*HI).

b. Set up a second control that contains 0.3 µg of the same linearized plasmid in 10 µl of 1x dephosphorylation buffer.

> Do not add CIP to this control.

c. Follow the instructions in Steps 14–16.

14. Incubate the large-scale dephosphorylation reaction and the two controls for 30 minutes at 37°C. Then transfer the three reactions to a water bath set at 65°C and incubate them for 30 minutes to inactivate CIP.

15. Cool the reactions to room temperature. Purify the DNAs by extracting once with phenol:chloroform and once with chloroform. Recover the DNA by standard precipitation with ethanol and subsequent washing in 70% ethanol.

> If only small amounts (<1 µg) of genomic DNA are present in the test dephosphorylation reaction, dialyze the extracted DNA against TE (pH 7.6) with floating membranes as described in the panel on **ADDITIONAL PROTOCOL: PURIFICATION OF HIGH-MOLECULAR-WEIGHT DNA BY DROP DIALYSIS** in Protocol 5.

16. Dissolve the two control DNAs in 10 µl of 1x ligation buffer. Add 0.1 Weiss unit of bacteriophage T4 DNA ligase to each tube and incubate them for 3 hours at room temperature. Examine the ligated DNAs by agarose gel electrophoresis.

> There should be no evidence of ligation in the control reaction containing genomic and plasmid DNAs that was subject to phosphatase treatment, whereas the untreated plasmid DNA should be converted to multimers and closed circular molecules.

17. Allow the DNA in the large-scale reaction to dissolve overnight at 4°C in a small volume of H_2O. Aim for a final concentration of ~500 µg of DNA/ml. Estimate the concentration of DNA by agarose gel electrophoresis, or better, by measuring A_{260}.

Ligation of Cosmid Arms to Genomic DNA: Packaging and Plating Recombinants

18. Set up a series of ligation reactions (final volume 20 µl) containing:

cosmid arms DNA (Step 9)	2 µg
dephosphorylated genomic DNA (Step 17)	0.5, 1, or 2.5 µg
10x ligation buffer	2 µl
bacteriophage T4 DNA ligase	2 Weiss units

Incubate the ligation reactions for 12–16 hours at 16°C.

> When using vectors in which the two *cos* sites are separated by cleavage with a restriction enzyme that creates blunt ends, the ligation buffer should be supplemented with ATP to a final concentration of 5 mM. This addition inhibits ligation of blunt ends (Ferretti and Sgaramella 1981) and thereby suppresses concatemerization of the vector.

19. Package 5 µl of each of the ligation reactions in bacteriophage λ particles (equivalent to 0.5 µg of vector arms) using a commercial packaging kit and following the conditions recommended by the supplier. After packaging, add 500 µl of SM and 20 µl of chloroform to the reactions and then store the diluted reactions at 4°C.

> The size of the inserts that can be cloned in cosmids is affected by the method used to prepare packaging extracts (Bates and Swift 1983). Ideally, extracts used to package cosmids should be prepared using a buffer that contains spermidine but not putrescine. When putrescine is omitted from the packaging extract and the packaging reaction, the system exhibits selectivity in the size of DNA molecules that are packaged. Thus, DNA that is 80% of wild-type bacteriophage DNA in length is packaged 200-fold less efficiently than wild-type bacteriophage λ DNA itself. In the absence of putrescine, cosmids that contain large inserts (~45 kb) will be preferentially packaged. For unknown reasons, possibly because of a shortage of *ter* function, some preparations of packaging extracts that work well with bacteriophage λ DNA are not suitable for packaging cosmids. Some

commercially available packaging extracts, such as the Gigapack III XL extract from Stratagene, are better than others for construction of cosmid libraries.

20. Measure the titer of the packaged cosmids in each of the packaging reactions by transduction into an appropriate *E. coli* host. Mix 0.1 ml of a 10^{-2} dilution of an aliquot of each reaction with 0.1 ml of SM and 0.1 ml of fresh plating bacteria. Allow the bacteriophage particles containing the recombinant cosmids to adsorb by incubating the infected bacterial cultures for 20 minutes at 37°C. Add 1 ml of TB medium and continue the incubation for a further 45 minutes at 37°C to allow expression of the kanamycin resistance gene in the SuperCos-1 vector.

    Store the remainder of the packaging mixtures at 4°C until Steps 21–24 have been completed (2–3 days).

    The ability of a strain of *E. coli* to be infected efficiently with bacteriophage λ should always be tested before it is used to propagate the cosmid library. This control is best done by measuring the infectivity of a bacteriophage λ stock of known titer on the plating bacteria.

21. Spread 0.5 ml and 0.1 ml of the bacterial culture onto TB agar plates containing kanamycin (25 μg/ml). After incubating the plates overnight at 37°C, count the number of bacterial colonies.

    Each microgram of ligated cosmid-eukaryotic DNA should yield between 10^5 and 10^7 bacterial colonies.

22. Pick 12 individual colonies and grow small-scale (2.5 ml) cultures in TB containing 25 μg/ml kanamycin for periods of no longer than 6–8 hours. Shake the cultures vigorously during incubation.

    For unknown reasons, the yield of some recombinant cosmids is poor when cultures of the host bacteria are grown to late log phase.

Isolation and Analysis of Recombinant Cosmids: Validation of the Library

23. Isolate cosmid DNA from 1.5 ml of each of the 12 small-scale bacterial cultures using the alkaline lysis method, described in Chapter 1, Protocol 1.

    For some applications, it may be necessary to purify minipreparations of cosmid DNA further. For details, please see the panel on CLEANING UP COSMID DNA.

24. Digest 2–4 μl of each of the DNA preparations with restriction enzymes (e.g., *Not*I and *Sal*I) that cleave the cosmid vector but are unlikely to cleave the cloned insert of genomic DNA. Analyze the sizes of the resulting fragments by electrophoresis through a 0.7% agarose gel.

    Use as markers linear bacteriophage λ DNA and *Hin*dIII fragments of bacteriophage λ DNA, which can be prepared easily in the laboratory and are also available commercially.

25. Calculate the proportion of colonies that carry inserts.

26. Estimate the average size of the inserts by isolating a few dozen clones and measuring the size of inserts by PFGE (for details, please see Chapter 5, Protocol 17 or 18).

27. Calculate the "depth" of the library, i.e., how many genome equivalents it contains (please see the panel on GENOMIC LIBRARIES, in the chapter introduction).

    If the library is satisfactory in size and quality, proceed to plate and screen the library by hybridization (Protocol 2) or, alternatively, to amplify and store the library (Protocols 3 and 4)

    If difficulties are encountered during construction of the library, try to work out the most likely reasons for the failure of the experiment. For example, a high proportion of "empty" clones might indicate that the vector DNA was not completely dephosphorylated (Step 5). A disappointingly small number of recombinants might indicate that insufficient amounts of genomic DNA or cosmid arms were present in the ligation reaction or that packaging of concatemers into bacteriophage λ particles was inefficient.

CLEANING UP COSMID DNA

Small-scale preparations of cosmid DNA are sometimes not suitable for use as a template for in vitro transcription by bacteriophage DNA-dependent RNA polymerases, for labeling with biotin- or digoxigenin-modified dNTPs, or for use as a probe in fluorescent in situ hybridization (FISH) experiments. Additional purification steps are required for these and other fastidious techniques:

1. Extract the DNA once with phenol:chloroform and once with chloroform.

2. Collect the DNA by standard precipitation with ethanol and subsequent washing in 70% ethanol.

3. Dissolve the DNA in 100 μl of TE (pH 7.6) and then precipitate the DNA again by adding NaCl and PEG 8000 to final concentrations of 0.4 M and 6.5% (w/v), respectively. Incubate the reaction for 2 hours at 0°C.

4. Collect the DNA by standard ethanol precipitation and subsequent washing in 70% ethanol. Dissolve the damp pellet of DNA in a small volume of DEPC-treated H_2O.

Protocol 2

Screening an Unamplified Cosmid Library by Hybridization: Plating the Library onto Filters

Dense populations of bacterial colonies transformed by cosmids may be screened by hybridization using a method originally devised for mass screening of plasmid-transformed colonies (Hanahan and Meselson 1980). The following protocol is a variant of the original method (DiLella and Woo 1987; please see Chapter 1, Protocol 30), adapted for plating and screening unamplified libraries. Colonies may be plated onto either nitrocellulose or nylon filters. In certain cases, it may be desirable to amplify the library before screening. Methods for amplification of cosmid libraries are given in Protocols 3 and 4.

MATERIALS

Media

TB agar plates (150 mm) containing 25 µg/ml kanamycin
TB medium

Special Equipment

Glass plates (thick)
  Sterilize *two* plates by swabbing with ethanol and allowing them to dry in a laminar flow hood.
Hypodermic needle (17 gauge)
Nitrocellulose or Nylon filters (137 mm), sterile
Whatman No. 1 filter papers, sterile

Additional Reagents

Step 16 of this protocol requires the reagents listed in Chapter 1, Protocols 31 and 32.

Vectors and Bacterial Strains

Bacteriophage λ packaging reaction
  Please see Protocol 1, Step 19 of this chapter.
E. coli *plating bacteria of the appropriate strain (e.g., XL1-Blue, ED8767, NM554, DH5αMCR)*
  For a complete listing of appropriate strains, please see Appendix 3.

METHOD

Transformation of *E. coli* by Cosmid DNA Packaged in Bacteriophage λ Particles

1. Calculate the volume of the packaging reaction (Protocol 1, Steps 20–21) that will generate 30,000–50,000 transformed bacterial colonies.

2. Set up a series of sterile test tubes containing this volume of packaging reaction and 0.2 ml of plating bacteria.

   The actual number of tubes to set up for plating the packaging reaction depends on the genome size, average size of fragments cloned, and the coverage of the genome required to find the particular clone of interest. In most cases, 15–20 tubes should be sufficient. For a further discussion of this issue, please refer to the chapter introduction and the panel on GENOMIC LIBRARIES (p. 4.6).

3. Incubate the tubes for 20 minutes at 37°C.

4. To each tube, add 0.5 ml of TB. Continue the incubation for a further 45 minutes.

5. Place sterile filters onto a series (equal in number to the series of tubes in Step 2) of 150-mm TB agar plates containing kanamycin (25 μg/ml).

6. Use a sterile spreader to smear the contents of each tube over the surface of a filter on an agar plate. After the inoculum has been absorbed into each filter, transfer the plates to a 37°C incubator for several hours to overnight (12–15 hours).

   Try to avoid spreading the inoculum within 3 mm of the edge of the master filters.

   Transformed colonies first become visible on the master filters after 8–10 hours of incubation. The plates are usually incubated for a total of 12–15 hours before the colonies are screened by hybridization to a radiolabeled probe.

7. Place a sterile, numbered 137-mm filter on a fresh TB agar plate containing kanamycin (25 μg/ml).

   Filters may be numbered using a soft-lead pencil. This filter will become a replica of one of the master filters.

8. Place a sterile Whatman No. 1 filter on a thick, sterile glass plate.

9. Use blunt-ended forceps to remove the replica filter from the fresh TB agar plate (Step 7) and place it on the Whatman No. 1 filter.

10. Again use forceps to remove a master filter now carrying transformed colonies from its TB agar plate (Step 6) and place it, colony side down, exactly on top of the numbered replica filter on the Whatman No. 1 filter. Cover the two filters with another sterile Whatman No. 1 filter.

11. Place a second sterile glass plate on top of the stack of filters. Press the plates together.

12. Remove the upper glass plate and the upper Whatman No. 1 filter. Use a 17-gauge hypodermic needle to key the two nitrocellulose or nylon filters to each other by making a series of holes (~5 will do), placed asymmetrically around the edge of the filters.

Growth of the Replica Filters

13. Peel the two nitrocellulose or nylon filters apart, and working quickly, replace them on their TB agar plates containing kanamycin (25 μg/ml).

14. Incubate the master and replica filters for a few hours at 37°C, until the bacterial colonies are 0.5–1.0 mm in diameter.

15. Seal the master plates in Parafilm and store them at 4ºC in an inverted position.

16. Lyse the colonies on the replica filter (Chapter 1, Protocol 31), and process the filters for hybridization to radiolabeled probes (Chapter 1, Protocol 32).

    Replica filters can be used to replicate the library again or may be stored frozen at –70ºC.

- Labeled probes used for screening must be free of plasmid vector sequences and bacteriophage λ *cos* sequences. Otherwise, every recombinant cosmid will hybridize to the probe.

- Because of their lower copy number, cosmids generate weaker hybridization signals than plasmids. Care must therefore be taken to reduce the level of nonspecific background hybridization to a minimum. This is best done by using Church buffer (please see recipe below) as a solvent for hybridization and, if necessary, including a competitor DNA in the hybridization mixture (usually 50 µg/ml of denatured *E. coli* DNA).

Church Buffer
BSA (1%)
EDTA (1 mM)
Phosphate buffer (0.5 M)*
SDS (7%)

*Phosphate buffer (2 M) (pH 7.2) is made up by dissolving 142 g of $Na_2HPO_4 \cdot 7H_2O$ in 999 ml of H_2O and adding 1 ml of 85% (w/v) H_3PO_4.

- The genomic DNA of most species contains amounts of repetitive sequences that can cause enormous problems in hybridization experiments and chromosome walking experiments. For example, a radiolabeled probe containing an *Alu* sequence will hybridize to the majority of recombinants in a cosmid library of human genomic DNA. Repetitive elements are also present in mRNAs, albeit at lower frequency (e.g., please see Yamamoto et al. 1984). When using a cloned segment of genomic DNA or cDNA to screen a cosmid library, first ascertain whether the probe contains repetitive elements. This is best done by hybridizing the radiolabeled probe to a Southern blot of genomic DNA. If highly repetitive sequences are present, the autoradiograph will display a complex series of bands or a continuous smear of hybridization along the length of the gel track.

ADDITIONAL PROTOCOL: REDUCING CROSS-HYBRIDIZATION

Cross-hybridization between repetitive DNAs can be substantially reduced by prehybridizing the radiolabeled probe with a competitor DNA. The following protocol is designed for use with human genomic DNA and may be readily modified for use with DNA from other species. Commercial preparations of DNA enriched for repetitive sequences (e.g., $C_o t1$ DNAs from Life Technologies) may be used in place of total placental DNA in this protocol.

Additional Materials

Ethanol
Plasmid pBLUR8
Solution A
    0.9 M NaCl
    50 mM sodium phosphate (pH 8.0)
    5 mM EDTA
    0.1% (w/v) SDS
Solution B
    50 mM sodium phosphate (pH 8.0)
    5 mM EDTA
    0.1% (w/v) SDS
Sonicator, probe or bath type
TE (pH 7.6)
Total human genomic DNA
Water baths preset to 42°C and boiling

Method

1. In 10 ml of TE (pH 7.6), dissolve 25 mg of total human genomic DNA and 50 mg of the plasmid pBLUR8 that contains a member of the *Alu* family of repetitive DNAs (Deininger et al. 1981).

2. Sonicate the DNA mixture to an average length of 50–100 bp using a probe or bath type sonicator (please see Appendix 8).

   Store the blocking mixture in 1-ml aliquots at 4°C.

3. To set up a hybridization reaction, add 100 μl of blocking mixture (from Step 2) to the radiolabeled probe. Denature the mixture of probe and blocking DNAs by heating to 100°C for 5 minutes, and then plunge the tube into ice water.

4. To the hybridization reaction, add 20 μl of Solution A. Mix well, and add 600 μl of ice-cold ethanol.

5. Collect the precipitated nucleic acids by centrifugation at maximum speed for 10 minutes in a microfuge, and allow the pellet to dry in the air until no more traces of ethanol are visible. Dissolve the damp pellet in Solution B. Incubate the mixture for 10 minutes at 42°C to allow the repetitive DNA sequences to reanneal.

6. Immediately add the partially annealed mixture of radiolabeled probe and blocking solution to hybridization buffer and continue with the standard protocol for in situ hybridization of colonies to radiolabeled probes (Chapter 1, Protocol 32).

Protocol 3

Amplification and Storage of a Cosmid Library: Amplification in Liquid Culture

Overenthusiastic amplification of cosmid libraries is not recommended, because it inevitably results in a distorted representation of the original genome. Faster-growing clones become overrepresented; unstable clones undergo rearrangement (please see the panel on DEALING WITH UNSTABLE RECOMBINANT COSMID CLONES); slow-growing clones may disappear completely from the library.

Undesirable though it may be, amplication is generally necessary and sometimes unavoidable. For example, if the library is to be screened with several different probes and transported to other laboratories, or if there is a chance that the library will be used for chromosome walking, then the library must be expanded and copied several times. This protocol and Protocol 4 describe several options for amplification and storage of cosmid libraries. Amplification of the library during growth in TB medium is presented here, whereas Protocol 4 deals with amplification during growth on filters or on plates. (An alternative means of cosmid library amplification and storage is outlined in the panel on AMPLIFICATION BY RESCUING COSMID DNA IN TRANSDUCING PARTICLES OF BACTERIOPHAGE λ at the end of this protocol.) In our hands, the method of amplification in liquid culture introduces less distortion of cosmid libraries than any other method, perhaps because the shock to the host cells associated with plating is avoided. This experience is documented by Longmire et al. (1993), who report that plating cosmid libraries on filters reduces the complexity of the library.

DEALING WITH UNSTABLE RECOMBINANT COSMID CLONES

Repeated sequences, palindromic sequences, and methylated bases can all trigger rearrangement of genomic DNAs cloned in cosmids. The first outward sign of rearrangement is usually the appearance of extra bands, often in submolar amounts, in restriction digests of a cosmid. Although there is no guaranteed cure for instability, two methods are available to ameliorate the problem:

- If the problematic cosmid is between 38 kb and 52 kb in size, it can be transferred to a different host strain by packaging in vitro using commercial packaging extracts (Yokobata et al. 1991) or by packaging in vivo using a helper bacteriophage (Vollenweider et al. 1980; Little and Jackson 1987). In both cases, improvements in stability have been reported.

- Cosmid DNA, isolated from a series of individual bacterial colonies, can be analyzed by digestion with restriction enzymes. In many cases, some colonies will be identified that contain a high proportion of full-length cosmid DNAs. These intact molecules can be transferred to a new bacterial strain by electroporation or rescued with high efficiency by in vitro packaging and then transferred to a different strain.

Strains of E. coli that have been reported to improve stability of individual cosmids include DH5αMCR and NM554.

MATERIALS

Buffers and Solutions

Glycerol

Media

TB agar plates containing 25 μg/ml kanamycin
TB medium
TB medium containing 25 μg/ml kanamycin

Centrifuges and Rotors

Sorvall GSA rotor or equivalent

Special Equipment

Freezing vials

Additional Reagents

Step 9 of this protocol requires reagents listed in Protocol 2 of this chapter.
Step 9 of this protocol also requires the reagents listed in Chapter 1, Protocols 31 and 32.

Vectors and Bacterial Strains

Bacteriophage λ packaging reaction
Please see Protocol 1, Step 19 of this chapter.

E. coli *plating bacteria of the appropriate strain (e.g., XL1-Blue, ED8767, NM554, DH5αMCR)*
For a complete listing of appropriate strains, please see Appendix 3.

METHOD

Preliminary Growth

1. Calculate the volume of the packaging reaction (Protocol 1, Steps 20–21) that will generate 30,000–50,000 transformed bacterial colonies.

2. Set up a series of sterile test tubes and into each tube deliver 0.2 ml of plating bacteria followed by the volume of packaging reaction determined in Step 1.

   The actual number of tubes to set up for plating the packaging reaction depends on the genome size, average size of fragments cloned, and the coverage of the genome required to find the particular clone of interest. In most cases, 15–20 tubes should be sufficient. For a further discussion of this issue, please refer to the chapter introduction and the panel on **GENOMIC LIBRARIES** (p. 4.6).

3. Incubate the tubes for 20 minutes at 37ºC.

   Large amounts of packaging mixture can inhibit attachment of the bacteriophage particles to the plating bacteria. If the concentration of packaged bacteriophages is low ($<10^4$ transducing units/ml of packaging mixture), use more plating bacteria, e.g., 5 ml/ml of packaging reaction. After incubating the cells for 20 minutes at 37ºC, recover the bacteria by centrifugation at 5000g (6500 rpm in a Sorvall SS-34 rotor) for 10 minutes at 4ºC. Resuspend the cells in 0.5 ml of TB and proceed to Step 4.

4. Add 0.5 ml of TB to each tube. Continue incubation for a further 45 minutes.

Amplification in TB Medium Containing 25 μg/ml Kanamycin

5. Inoculate 0.25-ml aliquots of each culture of infected cells into 100-ml volumes of TB medium containing 25 μg/ml kanamycin in 250-ml flasks.

6. Incubate the inoculated cultures with vigorous shaking at 37°C until the cells reach an optimal density of 0.5–1.0 OD_{600}.

7. Pool the cultures and recover the cells by centrifugation at 5000*g* (5500 rpm in a Sorvall GSA rotor) for 15 minutes at 4°C. Resuspend the cells in a volume of TB that is equal to 0.1x the volume of the original pooled cultures.

   Cosmid DNA can be isolated (please see Step 23 in Protocol 1) from aliquots of cells taken before the addition of glycerol. This stock of DNA can be used as a template in PCR to determine whether a particular DNA sequence of interest is present in the library (please see Chapter 8).

8. Add sterile glycerol to the cell suspension to a final concentration of 15% (v/v). Mix the suspension well by inverting the closed tube several times. Dispense aliquots (0.5–1.0 ml) of the bacterial suspension into sterile vials. Store the tightly closed vials at –70°C.

9. To screen the library, thaw an aliquot of frozen cells rapidly at 37°C and plate 30,000–50,000 bacteria onto each of a series of numbered filters as described in Protocol 2 beginning with Step 5. Proceed with lysing the colonies on the replica filters (Chapter 1, Protocol 31) and processing the filters for hybridization to labeled probes (Chapter 1, Protocol 32).

   Once some likely clones of interest are identified by hybridization, they may be further analyzed by restriction enzyme digestion (please see the panel on CONSTRUCTING RESTRICTION MAPS OF RECOMBINANT PLASMIDS in Protocol 4).

AMPLIFICATION BY RESCUING COSMID DNA IN TRANSDUCING PARTICLES OF BACTERIOPHAGE λ

Because circular cosmid molecules carried in bacterial cells contain a *cos* sequence, they can be efficiently packaged into bacteriophage λ particles. When cosmid-containing bacteria are infected with bacteriophage λ (or when a resident prophage is induced), the *cos* site in the cosmid DNA is cleaved by the bacteriophage λ terminase function (*ter*). The linearized cosmid DNA is then packaged into the heads of newly formed bacteriophage λ particles, which can be readily isolated, stored for long periods of time, and used at the investigator's convenience to transduce the cosmid genome into other bacterial strains. Although this method of storage is in little use today, the ability to rescue the cosmid DNA in the form of bacteriophage particles provides a convenient method to amplify cosmid libraries. For a transduction protocol, please see Sambrook et al. (1989; pages 3.52–3.53).

Protocol 4

Amplification and Storage of a Cosmid Library: Amplification on Filters

IN THIS METHOD OF AMPLIFICATION, DISTORTION OF THE LIBRARY is rarely a problem: At no stage are mixed populations of bacteria containing different recombinant cosmids grown in competition with one another. However, amplification is tedious and is sometimes compromised by the loss of colonies that do not grow after storage of the master filters. An alternative method is provided for amplification on TB plates (please see the panel on ALTERNATIVE PROTOCOL: AMPLIFICATION ON PLATES at the end of this protocol). This alternative amplification protocol is vulnerable to the loss of cosmid clones that grow poorly. The best of all options may be to obtain a cosmid library that has been arrayed in microtiter plates; such libraries may then be used to generate high-density arrays (for review, please see Evans et al. 1992).

For the vast majority of laboratories, arraying is not a realistic option. However, arrayed libraries are becoming available to an increasing extent from commercial sources. In addition, copies of arrayed libraries are stored in most of the major academic Genome Centers in the United States and Europe and in some commercial organizations. Access to these libraries is sometimes possible by setting up appropriate collaborative arrangements.

MATERIALS

Media

TB agar plates (150 mm) containing 25 µg/ml kanamycin
TB medium

Special Equipment

Nitrocellulose or Nylon filters (137 mm), detergent-free, sterile

Additional Reagents

Step 7 of this protocol requires reagents listed in Protocol 2 of this chapter.
Step 8 of this protocol requires the reagents listed in Chapter 1, Protocols 31 and 32.

Vectors and Bacterial Strains

Bacteriophage λ packaging reaction
Please see Protocol 1, Step 19 of this chapter.
E. coli plating bacteria of the appropriate strain (e.g., XL1-Blue, ED8767, NM554, DH5αMCR)
For a complete listing of appropriate strains, please see Appendix 3.

METHOD

Preliminary Growth

1. Calculate the volume of the packaging reaction (Protocol 1, Steps 20–21) that will generate 30,000–50,000 transformed bacterial colonies.

2. Set up a series of sterile test tubes and into each tube deliver 0.2 ml of plating bacteria followed by the volume of packaging reaction determined in Step 1.

   The actual number of tubes to set up for plating the packaging reaction depends on the genome size, average size of fragments cloned, and the coverage of the genome required to find the particular clone of interest. In most cases, 15–20 tubes should be sufficient. For a further discussion of this issue, please refer to the chapter introduction and the panel on GENOMIC LIBRARIES (p. 4.6).

3. Incubate the tubes for 20 minutes at 37ºC.

   Large amounts of packaging mixture can inhibit attachment of the bacteriophage particles to the plating bacteria. If the concentration of packaged bacteriophages is low ($<10^4$ transducing units/ml of packaging mixture), use more plating bacteria, e.g., 5 ml/ml of packaging reaction. After incubating the cells for 20 minutes at 37ºC, recover the bacteria by centrifugation at 5000g (5500 rpm in a Sorvall SS-34 rotor) for 10 minutes at 4ºC. Resuspend the cells in 0.5 ml of TB and proceed to Step 4.

4. Add 0.5 ml of TB to each tube. Continue incubation for a further 45 minutes.

Amplification on Filters

5. Place sterile, numbered filters onto a series (equal in number to the series of tubes in Step 2) of 150-mm TB agar plates containing kanamycin (25 µg/ml).

   Filters may be numbered using a soft-lead pencil.

6. Use a sterile spreader to smear the contents of each tube over the surface of a filter on an agar plate. After the inoculum has absorbed into each filter, transfer the plates to a 37ºC incubator for several hours to overnight (12–15 hours).

   Try to avoid spreading the inoculum within 3 mm of the edge of the master filters.

   Transformed colonies first become visible on the master filters after 8–10 hours of incubation. The plates are usually incubated for a total of 12–15 hours before the colonies are screened by hybridization to a radiolabeled probe.

7. Make a replica of each of the master filters as described beginning with Step 7 of Protocol 2. Store the filters at –70ºC.

8. To screen the library, thaw the replica filters and proceed with lysing the colonies on the filters (Chapter 1, Protocol 31) and processing the filters for hybridization to labeled probes (Chapter 1, Protocol 32).

   Once some likely clones of interest are identified by hybridization, they may be further analyzed by restriction enzyme digestion (please see the panel on CONSTRUCTING RESTRICTION MAPS OF RECOMBINANT COSMIDS).

CONSTRUCTING RESTRICTION MAPS OF RECOMBINANT COSMIDS

Several strategies are available to construct low-resolution restriction maps of segments of genomic DNA cloned in cosmids:

- The cloning sites of many cosmid vectors are flanked by restriction sites for enzymes that cleave mammalian DNA infrequently (e.g., *Sac*II, *Sal*I, *Pac*I, and *Not*I). Digestion with these enzymes, singly or in combination, will generally yield a small number of DNA fragments that can be ordered into a map.

- If a restriction enzyme is identified that releases the insert from the vector but does not cleave within it, then a second strategy becomes available in cosmid vectors such as SuperCos-1. In vectors of this type, the promoters for the bacteriophage T3 and T7 RNA polymerases are located between the *Bam*HI cloning site and the flanking *Not*I restriction sites. Restriction sites can be mapped by releasing the insert with *Not*I, setting up partial digestion with restriction enzymes, and analyzing the products by Southern hybridization using an oligonucleotide probe complementary to either the bacteriophage T3 or the bacteriorphage T7 promoter sequence. A ladder of hybridizing bands is detected on the autoradiogram, with the smallest band generated by cleavage at the site nearest one of the termini of the cloned genomic fragment and progressively larger bands generated by cleavage at sites increasingly distant from the end. The difference in size between adjacent bands is a measure of the distance between restriction sites. This rapid mapping approach is a variation on the strategy originally developed by Smith and Birnstiel (1976).

- A similar method takes advantage of the ability of the terminase enzyme of bacteriophage λ to recognize and cleave at *cos* sites (Rackwitz et al. 1985). Cleavage of cosmid DNA in vitro with terminase yields a linear molecule carrying protruding single-stranded termini, 12 nucleotides in length (Wu and Taylor 1971). Partial digestion reactions can then be carried out as described above to map the sites of cleavage of other restriction enzymes. In single *cos* vectors, the terminase-digested DNA can be end-labeled with [α-^{32}P]dNTPs and the Klenow fragment of *E. coli* DNA polymerase I (please see Chapter 9, Protocol 10) before partial digestion with the restriction enzyme. In double *cos* vectors, the two *cos* sites can be distinguished by end labeling with different [α-^{32}P]dNTPs (Wu and Taylor 1971). Alternatively, oligonucleotide probes specific for the left *cos* site or right *cos* site can be used as probes in Southern hybridizations (Rackwitz et al. 1984).

ALTERNATIVE PROTOCOL: AMPLIFICATION ON PLATES

Additional Materials

Freezing vials
Glycerol
Step 10 of this protocol requires the reagents listed in Protocol 2 of this chapter and in Chapter 1, Protocols 31 and 32.
TB medium containing 25 µg/ml kanamycin

Method

1. Follow Steps 1 through 3 of Protocol 4.

2. Add 0.5 ml of TB to each tube. Continue incubation for a further 45 minutes.

3. Use a sterile spreader to smear the contents of each tube over the surface of a TB agar plate containing kanamycin (25 µg/ml), and transfer the plates to a 37°C incubator for several hours to overnight (12–15 hours).

4. When the transformed bacterial colonies reach 0.1–0.2 mm in diameter, scrape them from each plate in turn into separate 10-ml aliquots of TB containing kanamycin (25 µg/ml).

5. Rinse each plate with an additional 5 ml of TB containing kanamycin (25 µg/ml), to ensure complete recovery of the bacteria. Pool the bacterial suspensions obtained from different plates.

6. Vortex the pooled suspension to disperse clumps of bacteria. Measure the exact volume of the suspension.

7. To the suspension, add sterile glycerol to a final concentration of 15% (v/v). Mix the suspension well by inverting the closed tube several times. Dispense aliquots (0.5–1.0 ml) of the bacterial suspension into sterile vials. Store the tightly closed vials overnight at –70°C.

8. The next day, remove an aliquot of the bacterial suspension from the freezer and thaw it rapidly at 37°C. Make a series of tenfold dilutions of the suspension in TB. Spread duplicate 0.1-ml aliquots of each dilution onto TB plates containing kanamycin (25 µg/ml). Incubate the plates overnight at 37°C.

9. Count the number of colonies and calculate the number of viable cells/ml of original suspension.
   The titer of the library should remain constant for at least 1 year during storage at –70°C.

10. To screen the library, thaw an aliquot of the suspension rapidly at 37°C and plate 30,000–50,000 bacteria onto each of a series of numbered filters as described in Protocol 2 beginning with Step 5. Proceed with lysing the colonies on the replica filters (Chapter 1, Protocol 31) and processing the filters for hybridization to labeled probes (Chapter 1, Protocol 32).

Protocol 5

Working with Bacteriophage P1 and Its Cloning Systems

Bacteriophage P1 was discovered in the same year as bacteriophage λ (Bertani 1951). Although both bacteriophages are temperate in their natural hosts, their histories in the laboratory could hardly be more different. Almost immediately after its discovery, bacteriophage λ was quickly adopted by the influential laboratories of the time as the type-species for molecular studies of lysogenic bacteriophages. The 30-year effort to understand its intricate control circuits became a lodestone for generations of graduate students and postdoctoral fellows. By the early 1970s, a huge amount of knowledge had been harvested and, as a consequence, bacteriophage λ was the natural first choice as a vector to clone fragments of genomic DNA.

It was to be another 20 years before the first bacteriophage P1 vector was developed as part of a deliberate effort to create a cloning vehicle that could efficiently propagate larger (90–100 kb) fragments of genomic DNA (Sternberg 1990). By then, it had become clear that the assembly of sets of large contiguous sequences (contigs) and the construction of physical maps of mammalian genomes could not readily be achieved with libraries constructed in either bacteriophage λ or cosmid vectors. Efforts to produce contigs longer than several hundred kilobases generally failed because of the slow rate of chromosome walking imposed by the small size of inserts in bacteriophage λ clones, by rearrangement of cloned genomic sequences during propagation of cosmids, or because of gaps in coverage in both kinds of libraries. YAC vectors (Burke et al. 1987) had their own sets of problems, chiefly, the high frequency of chimeric clones and the difficulty in manipulating and isolating YACs in a background of yeast genomic DNA.

THE DESIGN OF P1 VECTORS

By contrast to bacteriophage λ, where vectors evolved from the work of many hundreds of investigators in traditional academic instituions, bacteriophage P1 vectors were the product of a single laboratory, that of Nat Sternberg at the Dupont Merck Pharmaceutical Company, located in the then wilderness of Wilmington, Delaware. Sternberg's goal was to "develop a system that would generate libraries that exhibit the desirable features of cosmid and YAC libraries but minimize their deficiencies." The resulting P1 cloning system, which is full of ingenious ideas, draws deeply on the biology of bacteriophage P1 (please see the panel on THE LIFE CYCLE OF BACTERIOPHAGE P1) but is similar in principle to cloning in cosmids:

- Genomic DNA is partially digested with a restriction enzyme such as *Sau*3AI, and molecules 70–100 kb in length are then purified by sucrose density centrifugation or pulsed-field gel electrophoresis.

- The fragments of genomic DNA are ligated to a vector that contains various genetic elements derived from P1 and a plasmid replicon/partition system.

- Linear recombinant molecules are packaged in vitro into bacteriophage P1 particles.

- The packaged DNA is transfected into bacteria where it circularizes and replicates autonomously under the control of the single-copy P1 plasmid replicon.

- The plasmid can be amplified to high copy number by adding isopropyl-β-D-5-thiogalactoside (IPTG), which induces replication from the P1 lytic replicon (please see Step 1 of this protocol).

Although simple in principle, this scheme requires P1 vectors equipped with many accessory elements that assure a high efficiency of cloning and recovery of unrearranged genomic DNA

THE LIFE CYCLE OF BACTERIOPHAGE P1

- The DNA molecules extracted from a population of infectious P1 particles are ~110 kb in length, double-stranded, linear, terminally redundant, and circularly permuted. The nonredundant DNA sequences are ~90 kb in length.

- After injection into a permissive, recombination-proficient host, homologous recombination between the 10-kb redundant terminal sequences generates nonredundant circular DNA genomes, ~100 kb in length. In a *rec⁻* host, circularization can still occur if the viral DNAs contain *loxP* sites in the terminally redundant regions. *loxP* sites are 34-bp sequences that are substrates for the virally encoded Cre recombinase (please see the information panel on **CRE-*loxP***).

- Depending on the physiological state of the host cell, either the circularized viral DNA can enter a lysogenic state and become a prophage in which lytic functions are repressed by the viral cI repressor or it can unfurl the much larger set of viral functions required for lytic infection.

- In P1 lysogens, the viral DNA is maintained as a single-copy plasmid that replicates via the R replicon, which consists of an origin of replication and DNA encoding an essential replication protein (RepA) with its associated control region. Adjacent to the replicon is a 2.7-kb partitioning element (*par*) that ensures faithful segregation of the daughter prophage molecules at cell division.

- Lytic infection proceeds when the concentration of cI repressor is insufficient to establish or maintain the lysogenic state. DNA replication, which is driven by the lytic or L replicon, occurs first in Cairns or θ structures but soon switches to a rolling circle mechanism, which produces head-to-tail tandemly repeated copies of the viral DNA. These concatemeric molecules are the templates for packaging into bacteriophage particles.

- Precursor head structures (proheads) bind to the concatemeric viral DNA at a specific 162-bp site (*pac*) that is cleaved by the P1-encoded pacase and two *E. coli* DNA-binding proteins, IHF and HU. Starting from the newly created end, the viral DNA is packaged unidirectionally until the prohead is full. The packaged DNA is then cleaved from the remainder of the concatemer by a sequence-independent cutting reaction and a second round of packaging is initiated from the end created by the "headful" cutting reaction.

- Because bacteriophage P1 heads can accommodate 110 kb of DNA, whereas the P1 genome is only 100 kb in length, the DNA packaged into each prohead is terminally redundant. Since the headful cutting reaction moves progressively along the viral genome, the population of packaged molecules is circularly permuted.

- Lytic infection of laboratory strains of *E. coli* with bacteriophage P1 generates 100–200 progeny particles per cell. Lysis of the infected cell requires expression of virally encoded lysis genes and occurs after ~60 minutes.

For references and further details, please see the comprehensive review of bacteriophage P1 biology by Yarmolinsky and Sternberg (1988). The detailed mechanism of cleavage at the *pac* site is discussed by Black (1989) and Skorupski et al. (1992, 1994).

from transformed bacteria. For the last several years, the vectors of choice for construction of genomic libraries have been pAd10*sacB*II (please see Figure 4-3, p. 4.4) and its derivatives (Pierce et al. 1992a; for reviews, please see Pierce and Sternberg 1992; Sternberg 1992, 1994; Shepherd and Smoller 1994). These vectors, which contain a marker that allows positive selection of recombinants (*sacB*⁻; please see below), have allowed the construction of genomic libraries of sufficient complexity to cover mammalian genomes with redundancy required for chromosome mapping and isolation of genes. The following are the chief features of the circular pAd10*sacB*II molecule (please see Figure 4-3):

- The vector is divided into two domains by *loxP* recombination sites (Hoess and Abremski 1984). The *loxP* sequences are substrates for the P1-encoded Cre recombinase, which can be used in vitro or in vivo to divide the vector into two circular plasmids (Abremski et al. 1983).

- The domain on the left-hand side of the vector contains:

  1. A colE1 replicon derived from pBR322.

  2. The minimal P1 packaging site (162 bp) (*pac*) (Bächi and Arber 1977), within the coding sequence of the *pacA* gene (Skorupski et al. 1992).

  3. An 11-kb stuffer fragment of adenovirus DNA whose insertion into a *Sca*I site has inactivated an *amp*ʳ gene while leaving intact the *Sca*I site immediately clockwise to *pac*. The stuffer fragment has a purely passive function: to fill the phage head when the insert DNA is of insufficient size (Sternberg et al. 1990).

- The "*kan*" domain on the right-hand side of the vector contains:

  1. The kanamycin gene from Tn*903*.

  2. The unit copy P1 plasmid replicon and a partition system *par*. The basic P1 replicon maintains P1 plasmids in *E. coli* at about one copy per host chromosome.

  3. A synthetic replicon, consisting of the lytic P1 replicon whose activity is driven by the *lac* promoter. The replicon is inactive in bacteria expressing the *lac* repressor but can be brought to life by adding the inducer IPTG to the medium. The plasmid DNA is then rapidly amplified (within 30 minutes) from a copy number of ~1 to ~20 copies per cell (Sternberg and Cohen 1989).

  4. A *tet*ʳ gene that has been deliberately inactivated by insertion of the *sacB* gene from *Bacillus amyloliquefaciens. sacB* encodes an exoenzyme, levan sucrase, which catalyzes the hydrolysis of sucrose. When expressed in *E. coli*, the SacB enzyme generates levan, which acculumates in the periplasmic space, with lethal effects (Gay et al. 1983, 1985; Tang et al. 1990). Expression of *sacB* in pAd10*sacB*II is controlled by a synthetic near-consensus *E. coli* promoter that overlaps with a consensus P1 *cI* repressor/operator site (Eliason and Sternberg 1987). The *sacB* gene is therefore repressed in cells that express the *cI* repressor, allowing the efficient production of vector DNA.

CLONING INTO P1 VECTORS

P1 libraries are typically generated by cloning into the P1 vector pAd10*sacB*II (please see Figure 4-10). Cloning DNA into the *Bam*HI site of the *sacB* gene interrupts expression of levan sucrase and permits growth of plasmid-containing cells in the presence of 5% sucrose. This disruption provides a 50–75-fold discrimination of P1 clones that contain inserts from those that do not contain inserts (Pierce et al. 1992a; Ioannou et al. 1994). The *Bam*HI cloning site is flanked by bacteriophage T7 and SP6 promoters to facilitate the synthesis of RNA probes from the termini of cloned DNA and by rare restriction sites that allow easy recovery of cloned DNA fragments.

The steps involved in generating libraries in pAd10*sacB*II are shown diagrammatically in Figure 4-10. The complete nucleotide sequence of the *sacB*II *kan* domain of pAd10*sacB*II cloning vector is available (Pan et al. 1994; Genbank numbers L19899, L119900, and L19898). We have not

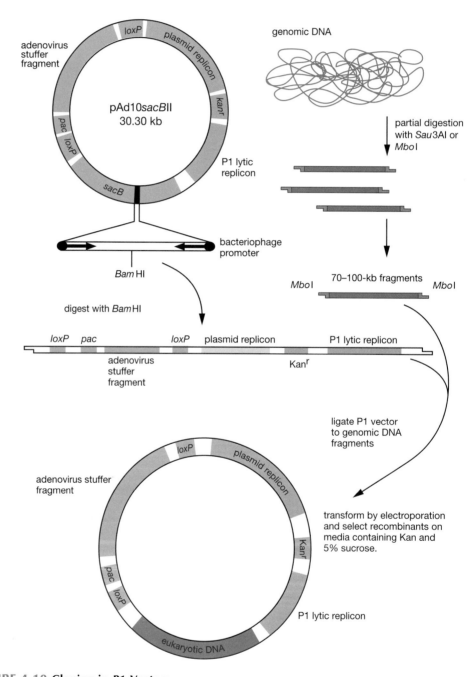

FIGURE 4-10 **Cloning in P1 Vectors**

P1 vector DNA, digested with *Bam*HI, is ligated to 70–100-kb fragments of eukaryotic DNA obtained by partial digestion with *Mbo*I or *Sau*3A. The resulting products are packaged into bacteriophage P1 heads, and the recombinant virus particles are introduced into an appropriate host and selected as described in the text.

TABLE 4-4 Screening Facilities for YAC, PAC, and P1 Libraries

SCREENING CENTER	SCREENING SERVICES	CONTACT
Genome Systems, Inc. St. Louis, Missouri	PCR	E-mail: sales@genomesystems.com URL: http://www.genomesystems.com
Research Genetics, Inc.	PCR, high-density membrane hybridization	E-mail: info@resgen.com URL: http://www.resgen.com
Leiden YAC Center The Netherlands	PCR, high-density membrane hybridization	
Pavia YAC Center Italy	PCR, high-density grid screening	
CEPH Paris	PCR	E-mail: yac_manager@cephb.fr URL: http://www.cephb.fr/services
UK HGMP Resource Center London, England	PCR, high-density grid screening	E-mail: biohelp@hgmp.mrc.ac.uk URL: http://www.hgmp.mrc.ac.uk
ICRF London, England	Filter hybridization	

(Reprinted, with permission, from *Current Protocols in Human Genetics* [ed. N.C. Dacopoli et al.] 1994 [©Wiley, New York].)

provided a protocol for construction of a P1 library; the process is sufficiently complex that few investigators actually create their own libraries. For a listing of the facilities that provide available libraries, please see Table 4-2 (p. 4.3), and for contacts for facilities that provide screening options for the library, please see Table 4-4.

The Organization and Screening of Genomic Libraries Constructed in P1 Vectors

Libraries in P1 vectors have been constructed using genomic DNA isolated from fission yeast (Hoheisel et al. 1993), *Drosophila* (Smoller et al. 1991, 1994; Hartl et al. 1994), pine (Gorman et al. 1992), mouse (Pierce et al. 1992a,b; Sternberg 1994; Francis et al. 1994), and human (Sternberg et al. 1990; Francis et al. 1994; Shepherd et al. 1994; Tanahashi 1994). In addition, a human genomic library has been constructed in a smaller derivative of pAd10*sacB*II, pCYPAC1, which was developed for electroporation of circular ligation products, rather than packaging and Cre-mediated recombination (Ioannou et al. 1994).

Most P1 libraries are arrayed, either as individual clones or, more commonly, as pools of clones in the wells of microtiter dishes. In the latter case, the pools are screened by PCR in a top-down approach (Green and Olson 1990; Pierce et al. 1992b). Individual clones, picked at random from the library, are pooled in various combinations of increasing complexity and screened for the presence of the desired target sequence. For example, the murine genomic P1 libraries described by Pierce et al. (1992a) and Sternberg (1994) are initially screened in six pools of 25,000 clones each. When a positive pool is identified, a second round of screening is carried out on 10 subpools, each containing 2500 clones. The third and final round of screening is carried out on 10 subsub pools containing 350–500 clones each. Once a positive third-level pool is identified, the desired clone is identified by colony hybridization. The plasmid DNA can then be amplified and isolated by standard methods, e.g., alkaline DNA extraction (Shepherd and Smoller 1994).

Although arrayed P1 libraries containing multiple clones per well can be screened efficiently, pooling of clones also carries risks. Because individual clones grow at different rates, there is a danger that slow-growing recombinants may be lost from the pools (Shepherd et al. 1994; Shovlin 1996). This possibility has led to the suggestion that libraries should be plated or maintained in a one-clone-per-well format. However, screening such a library is beyond the capacity of most laboratories. For a full discussion of the advantages and disadvantages of pooled, arrayed P1 libraries, please see Shepherd and Smoller (1994).

THE PAC CLONING SYSTEM

The PAC system combines the features of P1 vectors and bacterial artificial chromosomes (BAC). The PAC vector is derived from pAd10*sac*BII by deletion of the adenovirus stuffer and insertion of a pUC-based plasmid. These changes increase the yield of vector and reduce the toxicity of the SacBII protein in the absence of sucrose. The PAC vector retains all of the other features of pAd10*sac*BII, including the positive selection system and the two P1-encoded replicons. However, instead of packaging and site-specific recombination, recombinant PACs are introduced into *E. coli* by electroporation. The inserts in a PAC-based library of human genomic DNA range in size from 130 kb to 150 kb (Ioannou et al. 1994).

ADVANTAGES AND DISADVANTAGES OF THE P1 AND PAC CLONING SYSTEMS

By contrast to cosmids and bacteriophage λ, a single P1 or PAC clone of genomic DNA is long enough to span the average mammalian gene, including introns and controlling elements. In theory at least, it should be possible to transfect such long DNA molecules into appropriate lines of mammalian cells and obtain expression of the target gene in its natural setting of 5′ and 3′ sequences. However, the existing P1 and PAC libraries are constructed in vectors that lack reporter genes and selectable markers for mammalian cells. At present, therefore, it is necessary to retrofit individual PAC and P1 clones containing the gene of interest with cassettes carrying the relevant markers and reporters (Chatterjee and Sternberg 1996; Mejia and Monaco 1997).

In addition to functional analysis of particular genes, P1 and PAC clones are used increasingly to generate contigs and to construct physical maps of genomic regions. In general, genomic sequences cloned in P1 and PAC vectors exhibit lower rates of rearrangement and chimerism (1–2%) (Sternberg 1994) than YACs. In addition, they are considerably more tolerant of repetitive and palindromic genomic sequences that are underrepresented or absent from YAC and cosmid libraries. The bacteriophage promoters flanking the cloned genomic DNA in pAd10*sac*BII facilitate the production of probes that can be used to build contigs by chromosome walking and to bridge gaps in cosmid and YAC contigs.

The chief disadvantage of the bacteriophage P1 system lies in the difficulty of constructing large libraries that cover the genome to a depth sufficient for chromosome walking. This remains a challenge even for laboratories such as those descended from Sternberg's that know the system intimately. Although packaging extracts are commercially available, a better option for most investigators is to use commercial bacteriophage P1 libraries, even though their depth of coverage (~3-fold) is generally smaller than one might wish.

Several companies and genome centers now offer services in which preexisting bacteriophage P1 and PAC libraries are screened for a gene of interest (please see Table 4-4). To take advantage of the service, an investigator typically submits proof that a pair of oligonucleotide primers can be used in a PCR to detect a particular target gene. The company then screens one or more P1 libraries to identify clones harboring the target gene, and aliquots of the *E. coli* cultures harboring the recombinant P1 or PAC clone(s) identified in the PCR screen are then returned to the investigator. At this point, the investigator carries out a detailed characterization of the target gene or region of DNA identified by the service.

WORKING WITH BACTERIOPHAGE P1 AND PAC CLONES

The following protocol describes methods for recovery and purification of recombinant clones of closed circular bacteriophage P1 or PAC DNAs from bacteria. These methods are longer and somewhat more complicated than the techniques used to isolate cosmid DNA. The reason for this is that the large P1 or PAC DNAs are sensitive to shearing forces, which necessitates certain precautions during handling, including the use of wide-bore pipette tips to transfer DNAs and drop dialysis to exchange buffers. In addition, because P1 and PAC recombinants are maintained at much lower copy number than cosmids and plasmids, more stringent methods of purification are required to obtain clean DNA. Low yields, the presence of contaminating *E. coli* chromosomal DNA, and poor results in subsequent molecular cloning reactions are the typical outcomes of quick and dirty P1 purifications. This protocol, derived from Pierce and Sternberg (1992) and from methods supplied by David Smoller of Genome Systems, Inc., generally yields P1 DNA that is efficiently digested with many different restriction enzymes, is readily ligated, serves as a good template for DNA sequencing and amplification with thermostable DNA polymerases, and is an efficient template for in vitro transcription assays using bacteriophage RNA polymerases.

MATERIALS

CAUTION: Please see Appendix 12 for appropriate handling of materials marked with <!>.

Buffers and Solutions

Please see Appendix 1 for components of stock solutions, buffers, and reagents. Dilute stock solutions to the appropriate concentrations.

Ammonium acetate (0.5 M)
Ethanol
IPTG (1 mM)
  Optional, please see note to Step 1.
Isopropanol
MgCl$_2$ (1 mM)
Phenol:chloroform (1:1, v/v) <!>
Polyethylene glycol (40% w/v PEG 8000 solution) <!>
  Please see the information panel on **POLYETHYLENE GLYCOL** in Chapter 1.
Sodium acetate (0.3 M, pH 5.2)
Solutions for DNA isolation:
  Alkaline lysis solution I
  Alkaline lysis solution II
    Solution II should be freshly prepared and used at room temperature.
  Alkaline lysis solution III
TE (pH 8.0)
TE (pH 8.0) containing 20 µg/ml RNase

Enzymes and Buffers

Restriction endonucleases

Gels

Pulsed-field gels (or 0.5% agarose gels)
  Please see Step 15 below and the panel on **PULSED-FIELD GEL ELECTROPHORESIS** in Protocol 1.

Media

LB medium containing 25 µg/ml kanamycin
Optional, use with IPTG in Step 1.
TB medium containing 25 µg/ml kanamycin

Centrifuges and Rotors

Sorvall SS-34 rotor or equivalent

Special Equipment

Corex centrifuge tubes (30 ml)
Water bath preset to 65°C

Vectors and Bacterial Strains

E. coli *strain transformed with a nonrecombinant bacteriophage P1 or PAC vector (culture)*
E. coli *strain transformed with a recombinant bacteriophage P1 or PAC vector (culture)*

METHOD

Preparation of Recombinant P1 or PAC DNA

1. Transfer 10 ml of TB containing 25 µg/ml kanamycin into each of two 50-ml Falcon tubes or Erlenmeyer flasks. Inoculate one tube with a single colony of bacteria containing the recombinant P1 or PAC. Inoculate the other tube with a single colony of bacteria transformed by the vector alone. Grow the cultures to saturation, with vigorous shaking for 12–16 hours at 37ºC.

   The addition of IPTG (1 mM) to cultures of cells carrying P1 recombinants inactivates the *lac* repressor and leads to induction of the P1 lytic replicon, which results in an increase in the copy number of the plasmid DNA from 1 to ~20 copies/cell. However, there are indications that amplification in the presence of IPTG can lead to instability in P1 recombinants that carry repetitive sequences of genomic DNA (Sternberg 1994). Most investigators therefore avoid the amplification step completely or induce the cultures only for short periods of time (2–3 hours). In the latter case, comparison of the restriction maps of clones before and after amplification with IPTG is recommended.

   For induction with IPTG, cultures are grown in LB containing 25 µg/ml kanamycin until the OD_{600} reaches ~0.8, at which point IPTG is added to a final concentration of 0.5–1 mM. The cells are incubated for a further 3 hours at 37ºC and then harvested.

2. Transfer each culture to a 15-ml centrifuge tube. Harvest the cells by centrifugation at 3500*g* (5400 rpm in a Sorvall SS-34 rotor) for 5 minutes at 4ºC. Resuspend each cell pellet in 3 ml of sterile H_2O and repeat the centrifugation step.

3. Resuspend each cell pellet in 2 ml of Alkaline lysis solution I and place on ice.

4. Add 3 ml of Alkaline lysis solution II, and gently invert the tube several times to mix the solutions. Transfer the tube to an ice bath for 10 minutes.

   ▲IMPORTANT Because recombinant P1 and PAC clones are large enough to be sensitive to shearing, keep vortexing, pipetting, and shaking to a minimum during the isolation of DNA. Wherever possible, transfer by pouring the DNA from one tube to another. When pipetting cannot be avoided, use wide-bore pipette tips. Please see the information panel on MINIMIZING DAMAGE TO LARGE DNA MOLECULES in Chapter 2.

5. Add 3 ml of ice-cold Alkaline lysis solution III to each cell suspension, and mix the solution by gently inverting the tube several times. Store the tube on ice for 10 minutes.

6. Pellet the cellular debris by centrifugation at 12,000*g* (10,000 rpm in a Sorvall SS-34 rotor) for 10 minutes at 4°C.

7. Decant the supernatant (~7 ml) into a 30-ml Corex centrifuge tube and add an equal volume of isopropanol. Mix the solutions by gently inverting the tube several times and collect the precipitated nucleic acids by centrifugation at 12,000*g* (10,000 rpm in a Sorvall SS-34 rotor) for 10 minutes at 4°C.

8. Remove the supernatant by gentle aspiration. Invert the tube on a Kimwipe tissue until the last drops of fluid have drained away. Use a Pasteur pipette attached to a vacuum line to remove any drops remaining attached to the wall of the tube. Dissolve the pellet of nucleic acids in 0.4 ml of 0.3 M sodium acetate (pH 5.2). Heat the solution to 65°C briefly (for a few minutes) to assist in dissolving the nucleic acids.

Purification of Recombinant P1 or PAC DNA

9. Transfer the DNA solution to a microfuge tube. Extract the solution once with an equal volume of phenol:chloroform. Separate the aqueous and organic phases by centrifugation at maximum speed for 5 minutes at room temperature in a microfuge. Transfer the upper aqueous phase to a fresh microfuge tube.

10. Add 1 ml of ice-cold ethanol. Mix the solutions by inverting the tube several times. Collect the precipitated DNA by centrifugation at maximum speed for 10 minutes at 4°C. Rinse the DNA pellet with 0.5 ml of 70% ethanol and centrifuge again for 2 minutes.

11. Carefully remove the supernatant. Store the open inverted tube at room temperature until no more traces of ethanol are visible. Add 0.4 ml of TE plus RNase to the pellet and place the closed tube at 37°C. Periodically during the next 15 minutes, shake the tube gently to assist in dissolving the DNA. Continue the incubation for a total of 2 hours.

12. Add 4 μl of 1 M MgCl$_2$ and 200 μl of 40% PEG solution. Mix well and collect the precipitated DNA by centrifugation at maximum speed for 15 minutes at 4°C in a microfuge.

13. Remove the supernatant by aspiration and resuspend the pellet in 0.5 ml of 0.5 M ammonium acetate. Add 1 ml of ethanol, mix the solutions by inverting the tube several times, and collect the precipitate by centrifugation at maximum speed for 15 minutes at 4°C in a microfuge.

14. Decant the supernatant and rinse the pellet twice with 0.5 ml of ice-cold 70% ethanol. Store the open inverted tube at room temperature until no more traces of ethanol are visible. Resuspend the damp pellet in 50 μl of TE (pH 8.0).

    The yield of DNA varies between 2 μg and 5 μg per 10 ml of uninduced overnight culture.

15. For restriction enzyme analysis, digest 5–15 μl (~1 μg) of resuspended DNA and analyze the products either by 0.5% agarose gel electrophoresis or by PFGE.

    Larger amounts of DNA are used in the enzymatic reactions to achieve adequate molar concentrations of substrate.

ADDITIONAL PROTOCOL: PURIFICATION OF HIGH-MOLECULAR-WEIGHT DNA BY DROP DIALYSIS

If high-molecular-weight (e.g., bacteriophage P1 or PAC) DNA will be used as a template in DNA sequencing reactions, or if restriction enzymes fail to digest the DNA to completion, then low-molecular-weight contaminants should be removed by drop dialysis.

Additional Materials

Millipore Series V membranes (13-mm-diameter discs) pore size 0.025 μm
P1 DNA (prepared in Step 14 above)

Method

1. Spot the remainder of the bacteriophage P1 DNA from Step 14 above in the center of a Millipore Series V membrane, floating shiny side up on 10 ml of sterile H_2O in a 90-mm-diameter Petri dish.

2. Dialyze the DNA for 10 minutes.

3. Remove the drop to a clean microfuge tube and use aliquots of the dialyzed DNA for restriction enzyme digestion and/or DNA sequencing.

ALTERNATIVE PROTOCOL: PURIFICATION OF HIGH-MOLECULAR-WEIGHT CIRCULAR DNA BY CHROMATOGRAPHY ON QIAGEN RESIN

Qiagen resins have been used successfully to purify circular high-molecular-weight DNA (e.g., bacteriophage P1 DNA; e.g., please see Pierce and Sternberg 1992; MacLaren and Clarke 1996). However, this protocol will not work for linear high-molecular-weight DNA, which binds irreversibly to the column.

CAUTION: Please see Appendix 12 for appropriate handling of materials marked with <!>.

Additional Materials

Cheesecloth
E. coli host strain carrying P1 recombinant
Elution buffer
> *50 mM Tris-Cl (pH 8.1–8.2)*
> *1.4 M NaCl*
> *15% (v/v) ethanol*

Lysozyme
> *Dissolve solid lysozyme at a concentration of 10 mg/ml in 10 mM Tris-Cl (pH 8.0) just before using.*

Qiagen-tip 500 or 2500 column with appropriate buffers (e.g., P3 and QBT, supplied in Qiagen kit).
Sorvall GSA rotor or equivalent
TB medium containing 25 µg/ml kanamycin
Wash buffer
> *50 mM MOPS-KOH* <!> *(pH 7.5–7.6)*
> *0.75 M NaCl*
> *15% (v/v) ethanol*
> *When making this buffer, adjust the pH of a MOPS/NaCl solution before adding the ethanol.*

Method

1. Grow an overnight culture of the appropriate host strain carrying the P1 recombinant clone in 500 ml of TB containing 25 µg/ml kanamycin.

2. Recover the cells by centrifugation at 5000g (5500 rpm in a Sorvall GSA rotor) and digest them using lysozyme at a final concentration of 1 mg/ml and the modified alkaline procedure described in the Qiagen literature. After the addition of chilled P3 buffer and incubation on ice for 20 minutes, centrifuge the lysate at 15,000g (9600 rpm in a Sorvall GSA rotor) for 30 minutes at 4ºC.

3. Promptly transfer the supernatant to a fresh tube, and filter the supernatant through several layers of cheesecloth.

4. Equilibrate a Qiagen-tip column with 10 ml of QBT buffer (supplied in Qiagen kit).

5. Apply the filtered lysate from Step 3 to the column.

6. Wash the column with 30 ml of wash buffer.
   Do not wash the column with more than 30 ml of this buffer.

7. Elute the P1 DNA from the column with 15 ml of elution buffer.

8. Precipitate the eluted DNA with 0.7 volume of isopropanol. Collect the precipitated DNA by centrifugation at 10,000g (12,000 rpm in a Sorvall SS-34 rotor) for 30 minutes at 4ºC.

9. Rinse the pellet with 70% ethanol. Remove as much ethanol as possible, and resuspend the DNA in 200 µl of TE (pH 8.0).

10. Analyze samples of the DNA (2.0 µl or ~1 µg) by restriction enzyme digestion and electrophoresis through a conventional agarose gel or a pulsed-field agarose gel.

Protocol 6

Transferring Bacteriophage P1 Clones between *E. coli* Hosts

THE YIELD AND QUALITY OF BACTERIOPHAGE P1 DNA OBTAINED from different strains of *E. coli* vary depending on the genotype of the host bacterium and the particular sequence of foreign DNA carried in the recombinant. Problems with low yield or poor quality can sometimes be overcome by transferring the P1 or PAC recombinant into a strain of *E. coli* that does not express Cre recombinase (e.g., NS3516; Sternberg et al. 1994). Two methods are commonly used to transfer recombinant P1 clones from one host strain to another:

- ● ***Transduction*** of the P1 recombinant plasmid involves superinfection of the strain originally carrying the P1 clone with wild-type P1 bacteriophage. During the ensuing cycle of lytic infection, the P1 plasmid is packaged into P1 particles, which can be used to infect another strain of *E. coli*. Transformed cells containing the P1 clone in plasmid form are then selected on plates containing kanamycin. Stocks of wild-type P1 bacteriophage, together with protocols for transduction, are often supplied by commercial companies as part of their service to screen P1 libraries.

- ● ***Electroporation*** of purified P1 DNA into a different strain of host cells is a simple method, but some of the recombinant genomes may suffer deletions during electroporation. The restriction patterns of the original recombinant and DNAs from a series of independent transformants should be compared to identify clones that have not suffered rearrangements during electroporation.

The following protocol for transfer of P1 clones by electroporation was supplied by Ray MacDonald (University of Texas Southwestern Medical Center, Dallas) and describes the electroporation of a commercially available strain of *E. coli* (JS-5, Bio-Rad). In the MacDonald laboratory, the yields of bacteriophage P1 DNA were increased as much as tenfold after transfer into strains JS-5 or DH10B from NS3529. Similar results have been reported after transfer into *E. coli* strain NS3516 (MacLaren and Clarke 1996).

MATERIALS

Enzymes and Buffers

Restriction endonucleases

Gels

Agarose gel
Please see Step 10.

Media

LB agar plates containing 25 µg/ml kanamycin
SOC medium
Warm the SOC medium to 37ºC before use.
TB medium containing 25 µg/ml kanamycin

Special Equipment

Equipment for electroporation
Please see Chapter 1, Protocol 26.

Additional Reagents

Step 9 of this protocol requires reagents listed in Protocol 5 of this chapter.

Vectors and Bacterial Strains

Closed circular recombinant P1 DNA
Prepared as described in Protocol 5 of this chapter.
E. coli *strain (e.g., DH10B) as frozen electrocompetent cells*
Please see Chapter 1, Protocol 26.

METHOD

1. Dilute 2–3 µg of P1 plasmid DNA to a concentration of 60 ng/µl in sterile H_2O. Set up a control lacking P1 DNA (sterile H_2O only), and carry the control through the electroporation procedure in parallel with the DNA sample.

2. Thaw vials of electrocompetent cells on ice and prechill 0.1-cm electroporation cuvettes.

    For information on electroporation, please see Chapter 1, Protocol 26.

3. Combine 20 µl of cells and 1 µl of P1 DNA in the cold cuvette.

4. Set the electroporation device to 1.8 kV, 200 ohms, and 25 µF.

5. Shock the cells. The optimum time constant is usually ~5 milliseconds.

6. Immediately add 0.5 ml of prewarmed (37ºC) SOC medium to the cell suspension. Transfer the suspension to a culture tube and incubate the suspension for 1 hour at 37ºC with moderate agitation.

7. Plate 100-µl aliquots of the cell suspensions on LB plates containing 25 µg/ml kanamycin. Incubate the plates overnight at 37ºC.

    The control plates (no P1 DNA) should remain sterile; plates from the culture treated with P1 DNA should contain several hundred transformed colonies.

8. Transfer 10–12 colonies into separate 11-ml aliquots of TB containing 25 µg/ml kanamycin. Incubate the cultures overnight at 37ºC with vigorous agitation.

9. Prepare P1 DNA as described in Protocol 5.

    The remainder of the overnight cultures can be stored at –80ºC in TB/kanamycin containing 30% (v/v) glycerol.

10. Perform digestions with several different restriction endonucleases and compare the patterns of the newly isolated DNAs with that of the original recombinant by agarose gel electrophoresis.

Protocol 7

Working with Bacterial Artificial Chromosomes

BACTERIAL ARTIFICIAL CHROMOSOMES, OR BACS, ARE SYNTHETIC VECTORS based on the fertility (F) factor of *E. coli*. Among the properties that make the F factor so attractive as a high-capacity vector for genomic DNA are the following:

- A low copy number (1–2 molecules/cell; Frame and Bishop 1971) and the presence of two genes (*parA* and *parB*) ensure the accurate partitioning of F-factor DNA molecules to daughter cells during cell division. *parB* is also responsible for excluding extraneous F plasmids from cells. This combination of low copy number and an insulated environment limits the opportunities for intermolecular recombination between plasmid molecules within cells. In practical terms, this limitation means that recombinant BACs display a lower level of rearrangement and chimerism of foreign DNA sequences than YACs.

- It has the ability to propagate very large segments of DNA. Naturally occurring F factors can carry up to one quarter of the *E. coli* chromosome without strain or instability.

- It is easy to manipulate. Because of its closed circular nature, F-factor DNA can be isolated from *E. coli* by straightforward, familiar techniques such as alkaline lysis, isopycnic centrifugation in CsCl-ethidium bromide gradients, and spun column chromatography through resins (Zimmer and Verrinder Gibbins 1997). Sufficient BAC DNA can usually be obtained from a 5-ml bacterial culture for restriction analysis, PCR, and fluorescent in situ hybridization.

For more information on F factors, please see the panel on **F FACTORS**.

BAC CLONING VECTORS

The features described here were exploited by Mel Simon and colleagues in the early 1990s to develop BAC vectors that contain, in addition to *parA* and *parB*, genes (*oriS* and *repE*) involved in the initiation and orientation of F-factor DNA replication. The vectors (~7.4 kb in length) are also equipped with a polycloning sequence and a selectable marker (chloramphenicol resistance). Newer BAC vectors contain additional elements that (1) allow color-based identification (*lacZ*, α-complementation) of recombinants carrying inserts and (2) contain elements to facilitate recovery and manipulation of cloned DNAs (Kim et al. 1996; Asakawa et al. 1997) (please see Figure 4-2 in the introduction to this chapter).

F FACTORS

Fertility or F factors were discovered through the independent work of Cavalli-Sforza (1950) and Hayes (1952) on the unidirectional transfer of chromosomal markers during conjugal mating of *E. coli*. The ability to serve as a donor of chromosomal markers (the F^+ character) was transferred to recipient cells (F^-) with very high efficiency (Cavalli-Sforza et al. 1953; Hayes 1953), suggesting that conjugative transfer required a transmissible fertility factor, which was designated F. We now know that this original F-factor plasmid was a naturally occurring variant that could integrate into the host chromosome and transfer genetic markers at an abnormally high frequency. The development of conjugative transfer of markers was therefore advanced several years by this happy chance.

The F factor of *E. coli* is an ~100-kb plasmid encoding more than 60 proteins involved in replication, partition, and conjugation (for review, please see Willetts and Skurray 1987). Usually carried in the form of a double-stranded, closed circular DNA (1–2 copies/cell), the F factor can nevertheless integrate at random into at least 30 sites on the *E. coli* chromosome (for review, please see Low 1987). Cells carrying F, either episomally or in an integrated state, express up to three hair-like F pili, which are flexible hollow cylinders ~8 nm in diameter with a 2-nm axial lumen. The pili are composed largely of a single protein, pilin, which is the processed product of the plasmid *traA* gene (for reviews, please see Ippen-Ihler and Minkley 1986; Paranchych and Frost 1988). F-pili not only are required for productive physical contact between donor and recipient cells, but also provide sites for the attachment of male-specific, filamentous bacteriophages such as M13 and fd (for more information, please see the introduction to Chapter 3).

CONSTRUCTION OF GENOMIC LIBRARIES IN BAC VECTORS

Genomic libraries are constructed in BAC vectors essentially the same way as in PAC vectors (please see Figure 4-11). In brief, closed circular vector DNA is linearized by digestion with a restriction enzyme, treated with alkaline phosphatase and ligated to genomic DNA that has been partially digested with an appropriate restriction enzyme, and fractionated by PFGE. To prevent formation of chimeric clones, the ligation reaction contains a tenfold molar excess of vector DNA. The ligation products are introduced into *E. coli* by electroporation, and transformants are selected on agar plates containing chloramphenicol, IPTG, and X-gal. White colonies carrying recombinant BACs are transferred to a second plate containing the same additives to confirm the color selection. White colonies are again picked and arrayed in the wells of microtiter plates. These steps are described in more detail in papers describing the establishment of libraries of genomic DNA of various species (e.g., human, Shizuya et al. 1992; Kim et al. 1996; sorghum, Woo et al. 1994; rice, Wang et al. 1995; bovine, Cai et al. 1995; chicken, Zimmer and Verrinder Gibbins 1997).

Unlike bacteriophage λ, cosmid, and bacteriophage P1 vectors, BACs have no packaging limitations, and recombinants may contain segments of genomic DNA that exceed 300 kb in size (Shizuya et al. 1992). However, the average size of the inserts in many BAC libraries is considerably smaller, between 100 kb and 140 kb (Kim et al. 1996). Nevertheless, libraries with much larger inserts can be generated by careful sizing of the genomic DNA before cloning and by optimizing conditions for electroporation that favor transformation of *E. coli* with very large plasmids (Zimmer and Verrinder Gibbins 1997). To prevent intrachromosomal recombination between repetitive sequences commonly found in eukaryotic DNAs, BACs are propagated in recombination-defective hosts such as *E. coli* DH10B (*mcrA* Δ[*mrr-hsd RMS-mcrBC] recA1*). Large plasmid DNAs can be introduced into this strain with high efficiency by electroporation (Sheng et al. 1995), a property that facilitates both construction of libraries and retrofitting of individual BAC recombinants with accessory elements that facilitate manipulation of large cloned DNAs (Mejia and Monaco 1997).

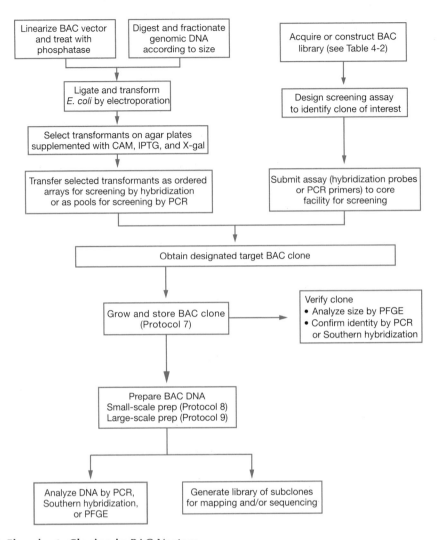

FIGURE 4-11 Flowchart: Cloning in BAC Vectors

SCREENING BAC LIBRARIES

Genomic libraries constructed in BACs are routinely gridded into ordered arrays for screening by hybridization, or they are combined into bins, pools, and subpools for rapid screening by PCR. Many of these arrayed libraries are not readily available from academic sources but are instead maintained by commercial companies such as Research Genetics, Inc., or Genome Systems, Inc. (please see Table 4-2). For most investigators, it is by far less expensive and faster to obtain recombinant BAC clones from these commercial suppliers than to construct their own libraries. In most cases, a hybridization probe or a pair of oligonucleotides specific for the chromosomal region of interest is sent to a commercial supplier, who screens genomic BAC libraries of the appropriate species and returns individual positive clones as transformed bacteria or BAC DNA. In our experience, at least 50% of these positive clones actually contain the region of interest, in all or part. The remainder are false positives of one sort or another. For this reason, it is essential to confirm by independent methods the identity and chromosomal location of newly isolated BAC clones. These methods include PCR analysis with multiple primer pairs, DNA sequencing, Southern hybridization with more than one probe, genetic mapping by analysis of radiation hybrid panels, and physical mapping by fluorescent in situ hybridization (for a more detailed discussion of these techniques, please see Green et al. 1997–1999).

BAC DNA is generally isolated from individual clones of transformed *E. coli* by alkaline lysis and may be further purified by column chromatography. Depending on the size and nature of the insert, a 5.0-ml culture of transformed bacterial cells will yield 0.1–0.4 µg of BAC DNA, suitable for analytical restriction enzyme digestions, PCR, and Southern blotting (Protocol 8). More extensive characterization (e.g., detailed restriction mapping, DNA sequencing, or subcloning) requires purification of BAC DNA from larger-scale cultures (250–500 ml) by column chromatography (Protocol 9). In this and the following two protocols, we outline methods for the propagation and storage of BAC-transformed bacteria and the isolation of BAC DNA.

WHEN A NEW BAC APPEARS IN THE LABORATORY

BACs are supplied by commercial companies as purified DNA or as cultures of transformed bacteria. In general, BACs should be maintained as frozen, transformed bacteria and not as stocks of DNA. DNA stored at 4ºC is susceptible to degradation by contaminating enzymes; DNA stored at –20ºC is damaged by freezing and thawing.

MATERIALS

CAUTION: Please see Appendix 12 for appropriate handling of materials marked with <!>.

Buffers and Solutions

Please see Appendix 1 for components of stock solutions, buffers, and reagents. Dilute stock solutions to the appropriate concentrations.

LB freezing buffer

Enzymes and Buffers

Restriction endonucleases
Please see Step 5. Choose restriction endonucleases appropriate for measuring insert size in BACs.

Gels

Equipment for pulsed-field gel electrophoresis
Please see the panel on **PULSED-FIELD GEL ELECTROPHORESIS** in Protocol 1.

Media

LB agar plates containing 12.5 µg/ml chloramphenicol <!>
LB medium containing 12.5 µg/ml chloramphenicol
Dissolve solid chloramphenicol in ethanol to a final concentration of 34 mg/ml. Prepare and add the chloramphenicol just before use.

Special Equipment

Equipment for electroporation (optional)
Required only if the BAC isolate is supplied as purified DNA (please see Step 1). Please see Chapter 1, Protocol 26.

Additional Reagents

Step 4 of this protocol requires reagents listed in Protocol 8 of this chapter.
Step 5 of this protocol requires either reagents listed in Chapter 8, Protocol 12 or reagents listed in Chapter 6, Protocol 10.

Vectors and Bacterial Strains

BAC DNA
or
Culture of E. coli *strain transformed with BAC isolate*
E. coli *strain (e.g., DH10B) as frozen electrocompetent cells*
Required only if the BAC isolate is supplied as purified DNA. Please see Chapter 1, Protocol 26.

METHOD

1. Prepare fresh BAC transformants.

    IF THE BAC IS SUPPLIED IN THE FORM OF DNA

    a. Transform *E. coli* (strain DH10B) with BAC DNA by electroporation.

        Because the efficiency of transformation by large BACs decreases dramatically as a function of the voltage applied during electroporation, it is best to set up a series of electroporation reactions at voltages ranging from 13 kV/cm to 25 kV/cm (Sheng et al. 1995; Zimmer and Verrinder Gibbins 1997).

    b. Plate 2.5, 25, and 250 μl of each batch of electroporated bacteria onto LB agar plates containing 12.5 μg/ml chloramphenicol. Incubate the plates for 16–24 hours at 37°C.

    IF THE BAC IS SUPPLIED AS A TRANSFORMED BACTERIAL STOCK

    a. Streak the culture without delay onto LB agar plates containing 12.5 μg/ml chloramphenicol.

    b. Incubate the plates for 12–16 hours at 37°C.

2. Select 12 individual transformants and inoculate these into 5-ml aliquots of LB medium containing chloramphenicol (12.5 μg/ml). Grow the cultures overnight at 37°C with vigorous shaking.

3. Use a loopful of each 5-ml culture to set up cultures of the 12 transformants in LB freezing medium. When these cultures have grown, transfer them to a –20°C freezer for storage.

4. Purify the BAC DNA from 4.5 ml of each 5-ml culture from Step 2, as described in Protocol 8.

5. Analyze the BAC DNA.

    a. Confirm by PCR that the BACs contain the chromosomal region of interest (please see Chapter 8, Protocol 12) or Southern hybridization (please see Chapter 6, Protocol 10).

    b. Measure the size of the inserts by digestion with restriction enzymes and PFGE.

6. On the basis of the results, select one or more of the BACs for further analysis.

Protocol 8

Isolation of BAC DNA from Small-scale Cultures

S~MALL AMOUNTS OF BAC DNAS ARE PREPARED~ from 5-ml cultures of BAC transformed cells. DNA is isolated by an adaptation of the alkaline lysis method described in Chapter 1, Protocol 1. The yield of the preparation is 0.1–0.4 µg of BAC DNA, which is suitable for analysis by restriction enzyme digestion, PCR, or Southern blotting.

MATERIALS

CAUTION: Please see Appendix 12 for appropriate handling of materials marked with <!>.

Buffers and Solutions

Please see Appendix 1 for components of stock solutions, buffers, and reagents. Dilute stock solutions to the appropriate concentrations.

Ethanol

Isopropanol

Solutions for DNA isolation:

    Alkaline lysis solution I, ice cold

    Alkaline lysis solution II

        Solution II should be freshly prepared and used at room temperature.

    Alkaline lysis solution III, ice cold

        Place the solution on ice just before use.

STE solution, ice cold

    Place the solution on ice just before use.

TE (pH 8.0)

Enzymes and Buffers

Restriction endonucleases

Gels

Equipment for pulsed-field gel electrophoresis

    Please see the panel on **PULSED-FIELD GEL ELECTROPHORESIS** in Protocol 1.

Media

LB medium containing 12.5 µg/ml chloramphenicol <!>

    Dissolve solid chloramphenicol in ethanol to a final concentration of 34 mg/ml. Prepare and add the chloroamphenicol just before use.

Nucleic Acids and Oligonucleotides

DNA markers for pulsed-field gel electrophoresis

    Obtain megabase markers from Life Technologies or use BACs whose sizes have been previously established.

Centrifuges and Rotors

Sorvall SS-34 rotor or equivalent

Special Equipment

Chromatography resin

Chromatography resin may be required to facilitate restriction endonuclease digestion of BAC DNA (please see Step 9). Resins can be purchased from Qiagen Inc. (Qiaprep Spin Plasmid MiniPrep kit works very nicely) or from Genome Systems, Inc. (KB-100 columns).

Vectors and Bacterial Strains

E. coli *strain transformed with BAC isolate*

Please see Protocol 7 of this chapter.

METHOD

1. Prepare 5-ml cultures of BAC-transformed *E. coli* in LB medium containing 12.5 μg/ml chloramphenicol, and grow the cultures overnight at 37ºC with vigorous shaking.

2. Collect the bacterial cells by centrifugation at 2000*g* (4100 rpm in a Sorvall SS-34 rotor) for 5 minutes at 4ºC. Decant the medium carefully and remove any residual drops by aspiration.

3. Add 5 ml of ice-cold STE to each tube, and resuspend the bacterial pellet by pipetting. Recover the cells by centrifugation as in Step 2.

   Cleaner preparations of BAC DNA are obtained if the cells are washed briefly in ice-cold STE at this stage.

4. Resuspend the cells in 200 μl of ice-cold Alkaline lysis solution I. Transfer the cells to an ice-cold microfuge tube. Place the tube on ice.

   The cell suspension may be gently vortexed to break up clumps of cells.

5. Add 400 μl of freshly prepared Alkaline lysis solution II to the tube. Gently invert the closed tube several times. Place the tube on ice.

6. Add 300 μl of ice-cold Alkaline lysis solution III to the tube. Gently invert the closed tube several times. Place the tube on ice for 5 minutes.

7. Remove the precipitated cell debris by centrifugation at maximum speed for 5 minutes at 4ºC in a microfuge. Decant the supernatant into a fresh microfuge tube. Add 900 μl of isopropanol at room temperature and mix the contents of the tube by gentle inversion.

8. Immediately collect the precipitated nucleic acids by centrifugation at maximum speed for 5 minutes at room temperature in a microfuge. Discard the supernatant and carefully rinse the pellet with 1 ml of 70% ethanol. Centrifuge the tube for 2 minutes at room temperature and remove the ethanol by aspiration. Allow the pellet of nucleic acid to dry in the air for 5–10 minutes. Dissolve the damp pellet in 50 μl of TE (pH 8.0).

   The usual yield of BAC DNA from a 5-ml culture is 0.1–0.4 μg.

9. Digest the BAC DNA with restriction endonucleases.

   Occasional preparations are resistant to cleavage and must be purified further by column chromatography on Qiagen resin or KB-100 columns. In each case, follow the manufacturer's directions precisely.

10. Analyze the digested BAC DNA by PFGE, using DNA markers of an appropriate size.

Protocol 9

Isolation of BAC DNA from Large-scale Cultures

EXTENSIVE ANALYSIS OF BAC RECOMBINANTS, including detailed restriction mapping, DNA sequencing, or subcloning, requires more DNA than is provided by a small-scale culture (Protocol 8). In this protocol, the isolation procedure is scaled up to accommodate large-scale cultures carrying a recombinant BAC. The average yield from a 500-ml culture of BAC-transformed cells is 20–25 μg of BAC DNA. The DNA may be further purified by column chromatography.

MATERIALS

CAUTION: Please see Appendix 12 for appropriate handling of materials marked with <!>.

Buffers and Solutions

Please see Appendix 1 for components of stock solutions, buffers, and reagents. Dilute stock solutions to the appropriate concentrations.

Ethanol

Isopropanol

Phenol:chloroform (1:1, v/v) <!>

Solutions for DNA isolation:

Alkaline lysis solution I, ice cold

For large-scale preparations of BAC DNA, sterile Alkaline lysis solution I should be supplemented just before use with DNase-free RNase at a concentration of 100 μg/ml.

Alkaline lysis solution II

Solution II should be freshly prepared and used at room temperature.

Alkaline lysis solution III, ice cold

Place the solution on ice just before use.

STE solution, ice cold

Place the solution on ice just before use.

TE (pH 8.0)

Enzymes and Buffers

Lysozyme

Restriction endonucleases

Nucleic Acids and Oligonucleotides

DNA markers for pulsed-field gel electrophoresis

Obtain megabase markers from Life Technologies or use BACs whose sizes have been previously established.

Gels

Equipment for pulsed-field gel electrophoresis
Please see the panel on **PULSED-FIELD GEL ELECTROPHORESIS** in Protocol 1.

Media

LB medium containing 12.5 µg/ml chloramphenicol <!>
Dissolve solid chloramphenicol in ethanol to a final concentration of 34 mg/ml. Prepare and add the chloroamphenicol just before use.

Centrifuges and Rotors

Sorvall GSA rotor or equivalent, with Oakridge tubes (Nalgene)

Special Equipment

Chromatography resin
Chromatography resin may be required to facilitate restriction endonuclease digestion of BAC DNA (please see Step 13). Resins can be purchased from Qiagen Inc. or from Genome Systems, Inc. (KB-100 columns).

Vectors and Bacterial Strains

E. coli strain transformed with BAC isolate
Please see Protocol 7 of this chapter. Prepare a fresh overnight culture; please see Step 1.

METHOD

1. Inoculate 500 ml of LB medium containing 12.5 µg/ml of chloramphenicol with 50 µl of a saturated overnight culture of BAC-transformed cells. Incubate the 500-ml culture for 12–16 hours at 37ºC with vigorous agitation (300 cycles/minute) until the cells reach saturation.

2. Harvest the cells from the culture by centrifugation at 2500*g* (3900 rpm in a Sorvall GSA rotor) for 15 minutes at 4ºC. Pour off the supernatant, and invert the open centrifuge bottle to allow the last drops of the supernatant to drain away.

3. Resuspend the bacterial pellet in 100 ml of ice-cold STE. Collect the bacterial cells by centrifugation as described in Step 2.

   If necessary, the washed cell pellet may be stored for several days in the sealed centrifuge bottle at –20ºC.

4. Resuspend the bacterial pellet in 24 ml of Alkaline lysis solution I containing DNase-free RNase (100 µg/ml). Add lysozyme to a final concentration of 1 mg/ml.

   Make sure that the cells are completely resuspended and that the suspension is free of clumps.

5. Add 24 ml of freshly prepared Alkaline lysis solution II. Close the top of the centrifuge bottle and mix the contents thoroughly by gently inverting the bottle several times. Incubate the bottle for 5 minutes on ice.

6. Add 24 ml of ice-cold Alkaline lysis solution III. Close the top of the centrifuge bottle and mix the contents gently but thoroughly by swirling the bottle until there are no longer two distinguishable liquid phases. Place the bottle on ice for 5 minutes.

7. Centrifuge the bacterial lysate at 15,000*g* (9600 rpm in a Sorvall GSA rotor) for 10 minutes at 4ºC. At the end of the centrifugation step, decant the clear supernatant into a polypropylene centrifuge bottle. Discard the pellet remaining in the centrifuge bottle.

   The failure to form a compact pellet after centrifugation is usually a consequence of inadequate mixing of the bacterial lysate with Alkaline lysis solution III (Step 6). If the bacterial debris does not form a tightly packed pellet, centrifuge again at 15,000*g* for a further 15 minutes, and then transfer as much of the supernatant as possible to a fresh tube.

8. Add an equal volume of phenol:chloroform. Mix the aqueous and organic phases by gently inverting the tube several times. Separate the phases by centrifugation at 3000*g* (4300 rpm in a Sorvall GSA rotor) for 15 minutes at room temperature.

9. Use a wide-bore pipette to transfer the aqueous layer to a fresh centrifuge bottle and add an equal volume of isopropanol. Invert the bottle several times to mix well.

10. Mark the tube on one side and place it in a centrifuge rotor with the marked side facing away from the center of the rotor. Marking in this way will aid in the subsequent identification of the nucleic acid pellet. Recover the precipitated nucleic acids by centrifugation at 15,000*g* (9600 rpm in a Sorvall GSA rotor) for 15 minutes at *room temperature.*

    ▲IMPORTANT Salt may precipitate if centrifugation is carried out at 4ºC.

11. Decant the supernatant carefully, and invert the bottle on a paper towel to allow the last drops of supernatant to drain away. Rinse the pellet and the walls of the bottle with 20 ml of 70% ethanol at room temperature. Drain off the ethanol, and place the inverted tube on a pad of paper towels for a few minutes at room temperature to allow the ethanol to evaporate.

    ▲WARNING The DNA pellet is easily dislodged and lost at this step.

12. Gently dissolve the pellet of BAC DNA in 0.2 ml of TE (pH 8.0). Assist in the dissolution of the DNA by tapping the sides of the bottle rather than vortexing. Measure the concentration of DNA by absorption spectroscopy (please see Appendix 8).

    The average yield of BAC DNA is 20–25 μg per 500-ml culture.

13. Digest the BAC DNA with restriction endonucleases.

    Occasional preparations are resistant to cleavage and must be purified further by column chromatography on Qiagen resin or KB-100 columns. In each case, follow the manufacturer's directions precisely.

14. Analyze the digested BAC DNA by PFGE, using DNA markers of an appropriate size.

Protocol 10

Working with Yeast Artificial Chromosomes

UNTIL THE MID 1980S, NO TECHNIQUES WERE AVAILABLE to isolate, propagate, and analyze coherent large segments of genomic DNA. Before then, detailed physical and functional studies were of necessity carried out on segments of DNA of a size that could fit into the shells of bacteriophage λ or cosmid vectors. Two separate advances were required to break free from this constraint: the widespread acceptance of PFGE as a method to separate large DNA molecules (please see the introduction to Chapter 5) and the development of yeast artificial chromosomes (YACs) as vehicles to clone and propagate much larger segments of genomic DNA. The basic theory of YACs was first published in 1983 (Murray and Szostak 1983), but the importance of the technique was not fully realized until David Burke, working in Maynard Olson's group, developed YAC vectors that were capable of propagating several hundred kilobases of DNA and showed that they could be used to generate entire libraries of mammalian genomic DNA (please see Burke et al. 1987).

Construction of genomic libraries in YACs is time-consuming, expensive, and demanding, requiring not only expertise in handling large DNA molecules, but also familiarity with the genetics and molecular biology of a different type of microbial host, *S. cerevisiae*. Furthermore, efficient storage of genomic YAC libraries involves arraying clones into the wells of microtiter plates, whereas library screening often necessitates generating a hierarchy of pools of YAC clones from within the library. This combination of skills and resources—manipulation of fragile molecules of DNA, fluency in yeast genetics, and access to robotic devices—is rarely found in a single laboratory. The construction of new YAC libraries is therefore best left to specialists, whereas screening of existing YAC libraries is generally carried out in collaboration with Genome Centers or, with increasing frequency, on a commercial basis. YAC libraries of the genomes of many species are now available from these sources (e.g., please see Burke 1991; van Ommen 1992; see also Table 4-2 in the introduction to this chapter).

YAC Cloning Vectors

Modern YAC vectors are mosaics of *cis*-acting components and functional units drawn from several different organisms. They are propagated as conventional plasmids in *E. coli* and are con-

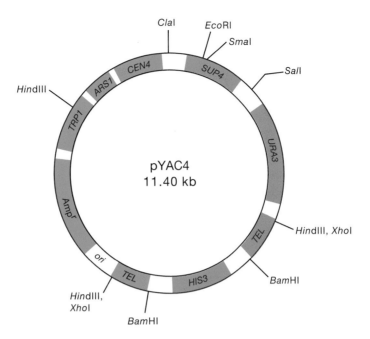

FIGURE 4-12 pYAC4

The general features important for construction of YAC libraries are depicted: the arrangement of genes in the circular vector, as well as important sequence elements, and key restriction sites (for further details, please see Burke et al. 1987; Burke and Olson 1991).

verted into two arms by restriction enzyme cleavage during the cloning process. Genomic YAC libraries are created in vitro by inserting very high-molecular-weight segments of genomic DNA between these two arms, generating linear molecules whose structure and topology resemble that of an authentic yeast chromosome. Because YAC vectors contain elements required for autonomous replication, for segregation of chromosomes between daughter cells, and for chromosome stability, recombinant YACs introduced into *S. cerevisiae* become part of the organism's complement of chromosomes.

An example of a vector (pYAC4) belonging to the commonly used pYAC series is shown in Figure 4-12. For descriptions of other vectors of this series, please see Reeves et al. (1992). Vectors of the pYAC series contain the following:

- Two sets of telomeric repeat (*TEL*) sequences, separated by a stuffer fragment, are required for the formation of stable chromosome ends. In most YAC vectors, the telomeric sequences are derived from *Tetrahymena*. Before cloning, the vector DNA is digested with *Bam*HI to release the stuffer fragment carrying the *HIS3* gene, which encodes imidazoleglycerolphosphate (IGP) dehydratase, an enzyme that catalyzes a step in the histidine biosynthetic pathway.

- A cloning site located within the *SUP4* gene that upon cleavage separates the vector DNA into two arms. The *SUP4* gene product (a tRNA) suppresses a mutation at the *ade* locus of appropriate strains of yeast, resulting in a change in the color of colonies from red to white in the presence of limiting concentrations of adenine. Transformants carrying recombinant YACs, in which the *SUP4* gene is interrupted by insertion, grow as red colonies (Hieter et al. 1985) (please see the panel on SCREENING YAC RECOMBINANTS on the following page).

SCREENING YAC RECOMBINANTS

The *ade2* allele contains a nonsense mutation that can be suppressed by *SUP4* carried in YAC vectors such as pYAC4. Cloning sites for the vector lie within the *SUP4* gene. If no insert is present in the YAC vector, the *SUP4* gene is intact (active) and the *ade2* mutation is suppressed. Transformants carrying this parent vector grow as white colonies on acid-hydrolyzed casein (AHC) medium. Conversely, if an insert is present in the pYAC4 vector, then the *SUP4* gene is inactivated and the nonsense mutation in the *ade2* allele prevents synthesis of the phosphoribosylaminoimidazole carboxylase enzyme in the host. In the absence of this enzyme, phosphoribosylglycinamidine accumulates in the yeast, which grow as red or pink colonies, depending on the amount of enzyme that builds up. The use of this simple color screen was initially reported in the late 1950s by Herschel Roman (1957), a leading light in corn and yeast genetics. Since that time, the scheme has been used with great elegance to monitor gene recombination events (Fogel et al. 1981) and to examine chromosome instability (Hieter et al. 1985; Koshland et al. 1985).

The left arm contains:

- One of the telomeric sequences.

- A centromeric (*CEN4*) sequence that attaches to the mitotic spindle and is required for efficient segregation of chromosomes between daughter cells. This segment of DNA also maintains the artificial chromosome at a copy number of one in the cell.

- An autonomously replicating sequence (*ARS1*) that contains signals required for bidirectional replication of DNA in yeast.

- An ampicillin resistance marker and the colE1 origin of replication for propagation of the vector in *E. coli*.

- An auxotrophic marker, *TRP1*, that confers on *trp* auxotrophs of *S. cerevisiae* the ability to grow on media lacking tryptophan.

The right arm contains:

- The second telomeric sequence.

- An auxotrophic marker, *URA3*, that confers on *ura* auxotrophs of *S. cerevisiae* the ability to grow on media lacking uracil.

CONSTRUCTION OF GENOMIC LIBRARIES IN YAC VECTORS

High-molecular-weight genomic DNA is extracted from the target organism and partially digested with a restriction enzyme that generates cohesive termini compatible with those of the cloning site in the YAC vector. The DNA is fractionated by PFGE to remove fragments <200 kb in size before ligation to a large molar excess of dephosphorylated vector (Anand et al. 1990). The recipient yeast strain, auxotrophic for uracil and tryptophan, is grown in rich medium and converted to spheroplasts by digestion of cell walls with lyticase or Zymolyase. The spheroplasts are transformed with the products of the ligation reaction in the presence of polyamines (to prevent degradation of DNA; Larin et al. 1991) and plated in agar medium lacking uracil and tryptophan. After regeneration of the cell walls, the transformed cells form colonies that carry a recombinant YAC and are prototrophic for uracil and tryptophan. Regeneration of transformed colonies is generally carried out in 2% sodium alginate in the presence of Ca^{2+}, which ensures that the colonies grow on the surface of the plate (Lai and Cantrell 1989).

For more information on construction of YAC libraries, please see Burke et al. (1987), Albertsen et al. (1990), Feingold et al. (1990), McCormick et al. (1990), Schlessinger (1990), Burke and Olson (1991), Anand (1992), Reeves et al. (1992), Riley et al. (1992), and Ramsay (1994). Yeast strains commonly used to construct and propagate YAC libraries are described by Reeves et al. (1992).

CHARACTERIZATION OF YAC LIBRARIES

The quality and complexity of a YAC library are generally assessed by isolating a few dozen random clones and measuring the size of the inserts by PFGE. The depth of coverage may then be calculated by multiplying the average insert size (in kb) by the number of full clones in the library and dividing the product by the size of the genome (also in kb). A library containing four genome equivalents is required to cover 95% of the genomic DNA sequence (Riley et al. 1992; please see the panel on GENOMIC LIBRARIES in the introduction to this chapter).

All YAC libraries contain chimeric clones, whose inserts consist of more than one fragment of genomic DNA (please see Problems with YACs below). Chimerism is best detected by fluorescent in situ hybridization of individual YACs to preparations of metaphase chromosomes (e.g., please see Lichter and Ward 1990; Wada et al. 1990; Montanaro et al. 1991). If positive signals are detected at more than one chromosomal location, the original YAC must be a composite of DNA sequences from different genomic regions.

SCREENING OF YAC LIBRARIES

In earlier times, unordered YAC libraries were screened by hybridization of radiolabeled probes to the DNA of lysed transformed colonies immobilized on filters (Little et al. 1989; Traver et al. 1989). Today, transformants are generally picked, either manually or by robot, and assembled into ordered arrays in the wells of microtiter dishes. Copies of the arrayed library may be stored at –70ºC, replicated at high density to membranes as needed, and screened by hybridization (Brownstein et al. 1989; Anand et al. 1990; Bentley et al. 1992). Alternatively, the arrayed transformants may be organized into a hierarchy of pools that can be screened by multiple rounds of PCR. The number of individual clones decreases with every round of screening (Anand et al. 1990, 1991; Green and Olson 1990; Barillot et al. 1991; MacMurray et al. 1991). For an overall scheme for the construction of libraries in YAC vectors, please see Figure 4-13, and for special considerations of YAC libraries, please see the following section on Problems with YACs.

PROBLEMS WITH YACS

Small Inserts

Many of the early YAC libraries contained inserts whose average size was only 100–200 kb, not much bigger than a P1 or PAC clone. This problem was overcome by using PFGE rather than sucrose gradient centrifugation to fractionate the genomic DNA before cloning, by devising gentle methods to prepare and manipulate large fragments of genomic DNA, and by including polyamines and/or high-molecular-weight carrier DNA in the ligation and transformation reactions. Carrier DNA, whose ends are incompatible with those of the cloning vector, increases the viscosity of the solution and thereby offers passive protection to the target DNA molecules against damage by shearing.

Instability and Rearrangement of Cloned Genomic Sequences

Instability usually results in the appearance of submolar bands of DNA of lower molecular weight when YACs from individual clones are analyzed by PFGE. These deletions, which range in size from a few kilobases to >250 kb, are generated both during the transformation process and dur-

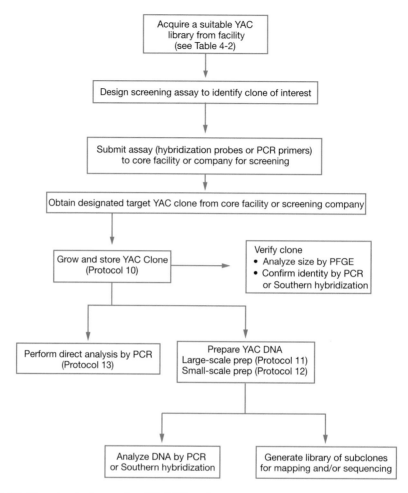

FIGURE 4-13 Flowchart: Screening YAC Libraries

ing subsequent mitotic growth of transformants (Kouprina et al. 1994). One cause of the instability is recombination between repetitive sequences in the cloned DNA, which can be suppressed to some extent by transforming a strain of yeast that is recombination-deficient (Vilageliu and Tyler-Smith 1992; Ling et al. 1993).

Chimerism

Chimeric YACs are artifacts in which DNA fragments from distant regions of the target genome become joined together and propagated in a single YAC. Chimeras can be generated either during in vitro ligation of genomic DNA to YAC arms or, more rarely, by mitotic recombination between different YAC clones introduced into the same yeast spheroplast by cotransformation (Heale et al. 1994). Depending on the methods used to construct YAC libraries, between 10% and 60% of clones may be chimeric.

Purification of YACs

A major problem is that YAC clones are carried at low copy number and cannot easily be separated from authentic yeast chromosomes. Purification of intact YAC clones can be achieved only by PFGE. Alternatively, the cloned segment of genomic DNA can be recovered in fragmented form by subcloning the total DNA extracted from an individual yeast transformant into cosmid or bacteriophage vectors. Subclones carrying genomic sequences are then identified, for example, by hybridization to probes containing highly repetitive segments of mammalian DNA (please see Subcloning Genomic DNA Sequences Cloned in YACs, page 4.64).

MAPPING GENOMIC INSERTS CLONED IN INDIVIDUAL YACs

In most cases, screening a YAC genomic library will yield several positive clones carrying overlapping inserts that span the region corresponding to the probe. These clones should be checked for chimerism, and their sizes should be measured by PFGE. Groups of YACs can sometimes be aligned by their content of polymorphic markers, by their content of recognition sites for rare restriction enzymes, or, more frequently, by DNA fingerprinting. The latter is best carried out by digesting the total DNA (yeast plus YAC) isolated from each of the positive clones with several restriction enzymes. The products of the digestion are analyzed by Southern hybridization using repetitive DNA as a probe (e.g., *Alu* DNA in the case of YACs containing human sequences, and LINE DNA in the case of mouse).

Clones to be analyzed in detail should be mapped with additional restriction enzymes. This can be done by partial digestion and Southern hybridization using probes specific to the pBR322 sequences in the left and right arms of the YAC vector. Most restriction sites can be mapped from both ends of the YAC, enabling sites to be located with accuracy (Schlessinger 1990). Because yeast DNA is unmethylated, the restriction map of the YAC will not necessarily correspond to that of the homologous region of genomic DNA.

RESCUING THE TERMINI OF GENOMIC DNAs CLONED IN YACs

Several well-validated techniques exist to identify and subclone the ends of genomic sequences cloned in YACs. All of these techniques take advantage of the YAC vector sequences that lie immediately proximal to the cloned DNA. For example, the left arm of pYAC4 and its derivatives contain the pBR322 origin of replication and a selectable marker. The genomic sequences immediately adjacent to the left arm can therefore be recovered by end-rescue subcloning (Burke et al. 1987; Garza et al. 1989; McCormick et al. 1989). Alternatively, libraries of subclones can be screened by hybridization using probes specific for the plasmid sequences carried in the right and left ends of the vector (Bellane-Chantelot et al. 1991).

Among the PCR-based methods that can be used to amplify and clone genomic sequences adjacent to the left and right arms are inverse PCR, which uses vector sequences in outward orientation as primers (Ochman et al. 1988; Triglia et al. 1988; Silverman et al. 1989), and vectorette or bubble PCR, which uses an oligonucleotide cassette as a primer (Riley et al. 1990, 1992). Vectorette PCR is the better method since it not only amplifies insert sequences immediately proximal to each arm, but also provides templates for DNA sequencing (Anand 1992). Vectorette PCR is described in greater detail in Protocol 14.

RETROFITTING YACs

An advantage of YACs over other genomic vectors is the ability to accommodate the complete sequences of large mammalian genes. This has led to the growing use of YACs as vehicles to transfect mammalian cells (for reviews, please see Gnirke and Huxley 1991; Huxley 1994) and to generate transgenic animals, in which for some, the YACs complement mutations in mouse chromosomal genes (for reviews, please see Capecchi 1993; Forget 1993; Montoliu et al. 1993, 1994; Peterson 1997).

The efficient introduction of YACs into mammalian cells in tissue culture requires the presence of a dominant selectable marker in the YAC vector that can be used to select rare transformed cells. Many of the older YAC vectors do not carry a suitable selectable marker. However, recombinant YACs carrying the gene of interest can be retrofitted with a selectable marker such as neomycin resistance by homologous recombination in yeast cells. Similarly, homologous recombination can be used to introduce specific mutations at defined sites in segments of genomic DNA cloned in YACs (for review, please see Huxley 1994; Monaco and Larin 1994).

The methods used for transfer of YACs into cultured mammalian cells include fusion with yeast spheroplasts, calcium phosphate precipitation, electroporation, lipofection, and microinjection of total yeast DNA or YAC DNA, purified by PFGE (for review, please see Huxley 1994; Montoliu et al. 1994).

SUBCLONING GENOMIC DNA SEQUENCES CLONED IN YACs

The genome of wild-type haploid *S. cerevisiae* consists of 12,057,495 bp of DNA packaged into 16 chromosomes (please see http://genome-www.stanford.edu/Saccharomyces/). The presence of an extra chromosome in the form of a YAC increases the size of the genome by 1–2 Mb or less. A bacteriophage λ library of just 2500 clones with inserts of ~20 kb will therefore provide a theoretical fourfold coverage of the genome of the host yeast and its artificial chromosome. Between 1% and 10% of the clones will contain foreign DNA sequences. These can be recognized by their ability to hybridize to mammalian probes containing highly repetitive DNA sequences. Cloning of yeast plus YAC DNA into cosmid or bacteriophage λ vectors is generally used to isolate a region of the YAC DNA containing a desired DNA element (promoter, exon, etc.) or to provide templates for the construction of high-resolution restriction maps.

An entirely different strategy is required when YACs are subcloned into plasmid or bacteriophage M13 vectors for DNA sequencing. In this case, the aim is to produce YAC DNA that is free of contaminating yeast sequences. The YAC DNA must therefore be purified by PFGE and then sheared into fragments of suitable size either by sonication or by nebulization. The termini of the sheared DNA molecules are repaired, and the fragments are fractionated according to size and ligated into the desired vector. The proportion of clones containing yeast sequences is greatly reduced if the YAC DNA is subjected to two cycles of purification by PFGE.

A major difficulty is to obtain sufficient, purified YAC DNA to generate libraries with reasonable depth of coverage. However, efficient methods have been described to construct in bacteriophage M13 and plasmid vectors one- to fivefold deep libraries of segments of gel-purified YAC DNA (Chen et al. 1993; Vaudin et al. 1995). Overlapping sequences obtained from single sequencing reactions of subclones chosen at random from these libraries can be used to construct small contigs, which then can be confirmed and extended by further rounds of directed sequencing.

WHEN A NEW YAC APPEARS IN THE LABORATORY

The following protocol describes how to make an initial analysis and how to store newly received YAC clones. YAC clones are usually shipped by screening companies as slant cultures of *S. cerevisiae* harboring the YAC of interest. Most YAC libraries are constructed in pYAC4 or a YAC vector derived from it. Because these vectors confer prototrophy to tryptophan and uracil, they are propagated in a yeast strain that is auxotrophic for these markers. The cultures of *S. cerevisiae* should therefore be plated on agar media lacking uracil and tryptophan (please see the panel on YEAST MEDIA). Cultures should be dealt with immediately upon arrival.

Subsequent protocols in this chapter describe the growth of *S. cerevisiae* and preparation of DNA (Protocol 11), preparation of DNA from small-scale cultures (Protocol 12), and direct analysis of yeast colonies by PCR (Protocol 13).

YEAST MEDIA

This protocol recommends the use of rich YPD medium to propagate YAC-bearing yeast strains before isolation of genomic DNA. Because YPD contains uracil and tryptophan, there is no selection for retention of the YAC. However, provided the culture is grown for a short period of time (overnight) and that the yeast strain grows well, there is little danger of selecting variants that have lost their YAC. However, when working with a strain that grows slowly, either because of the particular YAC carried or because of the genotype of the host, it is a good idea to grow the yeast in uracil tryptophan drop-out medium (also known as ⁻Ura ⁻Trp drop-out medium, referring to minimal medium lacking uracil and tryptophan) or acid-hydrolyzed casein (AHC) medium to apply selection for the retention of YAC DNA.

Some strains of yeast harboring YAC clones grow better in AHC medium (Burke and Olson 1991). This is a complete medium containing adenine, which inhibits the reversion of *ade* mutants. Adenine is added at either a low concentration (20 mg/liter) or a high concentration (100 mg/liter) depending on the experiment. Low concentrations are used in the initial construction of YAC libraries to select for insert-containing YAC vectors. High concentrations of adenine are used when a YAC strain is to be grown for DNA isolation.

MATERIALS

Buffers and Solutions

Please see Appendix 1 for components of stock solutions, buffers, and reagents. Dilute stock solutions to the appropriate concentrations.

Glycerol (30% v/v) in YPD medium

Gels

Equipment for pulsed-field gel electrophoresis
Please see the panel on **PULSED-FIELD GEL ELECTROPHORESIS** in Protocol 1.

Media

Selective medium
Please see the panel on **YEAST MEDIA**.
YPD agar plates
YPD medium

Special Equipment

Vials (2 ml)

Additional Reagents

Step 3 of this protocol requires reagents listed in Chapter 6, Protocol 7.
Step 4 of this protocol requires reagents listed in Chapter 5, Protocol 17 or 18.
Step 5 of this protocol requires either reagents listed in Chapter 6, Protocol 10, or reagents listed in Chapter 8, Protocol 12.

Vectors and Yeast Strains

S. cerevisiae carrying recombinant YAC clone
These are most often obtained from a screening company. Please see Appendix 3.

METHOD

1. Immediately upon the arrival of clones in the laboratory, streak the cultures onto selective media and incubate for 48 hours at 30°C to obtain single colonies.

    Yeast colonies may be analyzed directly by PCR (please see Protocol 13).

2. Transfer each of 6–12 individual colonies into 10 ml of YPD medium. Incubate the cultures with vigorous agitation (300 cycles/minute) at 30°C overnight. The cells should reach saturation (OD_{600}= 2.0–3.0, ~3 x 10^7 cells/ml) during this time.

3. Extract yeast DNA from 9 ml of each of the cultures following the steps described in Chapter 6, Protocol 7.

    Store the unused portions of the cultures at 4°C.

4. Analyze the size of the YAC in each of the DNA preparations by PFGE.

5. Confirm by either Southern hybridization (please see Chapter 6, Protocol 10) or PCR (please see Chapter 8, Protocol 12) that the target sequence is present in the YAC DNA.

6. If the results are satisfactory, i.e., if the cultures contain YACs of the same size, if there is no sign of instability or rearrangement, and if the target sequences are present, then choose one or two of the cultures for long-term storage (please see the panel on **STORAGE OF YEAST CULTURES**).

STORAGE OF YEAST CULTURES

Yeast cultures can be stored indefinitely at –70°C in growth medium containing 15% (v/v) glycerol (Well and Stewart 1973). For storage:

1. Prepare 2-ml vials containing 0.5 ml of sterile 30% (v/v) glycerol in YPD medium.

2. Add 0.5 ml of the yeast culture and mix the contents of the tube by gentle vortexing.

3. Transfer the vials to –70°C.

    Yeast can be recovered from storage by transferring a small frozen sample to a YPD agar plate.

    ▲ WARNING Yeast cultures lose viability if stored at temperatures higher than –55°C.

Protocol 11

Growth of *S. cerevisiae* and Preparation of DNA

T HE FOLLOWING PROTOCOL DESCRIBES METHODS FOR ISOLATION of total DNA from a strain of *S. cerevisiae* carrying a recombinant YAC. This method is appropriate for preparing DNA that will be subjected to regular agarose gel electrophoresis, Southern blotting, subcloning, genomic library construction, PCR, or other methods that do not require intact high-molecular-weight DNA. If the DNA is used in PFGE, follow the preparation method given in Chapter 5, Protocol 14. The small-scale preparation of YAC DNA is presented in Protocol 12 of this chapter. Because the linear YAC DNAs are sensitive to shearing forces, pipettes with wide-bore tips should be used to transfer DNAs. Drop dialysis should be used to exchange buffers. The expected yield from a 10-ml culture is 2–4 µg of yeast DNA.

MATERIALS

CAUTION: Please see Appendix 12 for appropriate handling of materials marked with <!>.

Buffers and Solutions

Please see Appendix 1 for components of stock solutions, buffers, and reagents. Dilute stock solutions to the appropriate concentrations.

Ammonium acetate (10 M)
Ethanol
Phenol:chloroform (1:1, v/v) <!>
TE (pH 8.0)
TE (pH 8.0) containing 20 µg/ml RNase
Triton/SDS solution

Media

YPD medium
Please see the panel on **YEAST MEDIA** in Protocol 10.

Centrifuges and Rotors

Sorvall SS-34 rotor or equivalent

Special Equipment

Glass beads

Acid-washed glass beads should be used (e.g., Sigma). Unwashed beads are *not* recommended.

Vectors and Yeast Strains

Yeast colony carrying the YAC clone of interest

METHOD

Growth of Cells

1. Inoculate a yeast colony containing the YAC clone of interest into 10 ml of YPD medium and incubate overnight with shaking at 30ºC.

   The cells should reach saturation (OD_{600} = 2.0–3.0, ~3 x 10^7 cells/ml) during this time.

   If the DNA to be extracted will be used in PFGE, follow the steps described in Chapter 5, Protocol 14.

2. Collect the cells by centrifugation at 2000g (4100 rpm in a Sorvall SS-34 rotor) for 5 minutes.

3. Remove the medium, replace with 1 ml of sterile H_2O, and resuspend the cells by gentle vortexing.

4. Collect the cells by centrifugation as in Step 2.

5. Remove the wash, resuspend cells in 0.5 ml of sterile H_2O, and transfer to a sterile 1.5-ml microfuge tube.

6. Collect the cells by centrifugation at maximum speed for 5 seconds at room temperature in a microfuge, and remove the supernatant.

Extraction of DNA

7. Add 0.2 ml of Triton/SDS solution to the cells and resuspend the cell pellet by tapping the side of the tube.

8. Add 0.2 ml of phenol:chloroform and 0.3 g of glass beads to the cells, and vortex the cell suspension for 2 minutes at room temperature. Add 0.2 ml of TE (pH 8.0), and mix the solution by vortexing briefly.

9. Separate the organic and aqueous phases by centrifugation at maximum speed for 5 minutes at room temperature in a microfuge. Transfer the aqueous upper layer to a fresh microfuge tube, taking care to avoid carrying over any of the material at the interface.

Isolation of DNA

10. Add 1 ml of ethanol to the aqueous solution, cap the centrifuge tube, and gently mix the contents by inversion.

11. Collect the precipitated DNA by centrifugation at maximum speed for 2–5 minutes at 4°C in a microfuge. Remove the supernatant with a drawn out Pasteur pipette. Centrifuge the tube briefly (2 seconds) and remove the last traces of ethanol from the bottom of the tube.

12. Resuspend the nucleic acid pellet in 0.4 ml of TE (pH 8.0) with RNase and incubate the solution for 5 minutes at 37°C.

13. Add to the solution an equal volume of phenol:chlorofom and extract the RNase-digested solution, mixing by inversion rather than vortexing. Separate the aqueous and organic phases by centrifugation at maximum speed for 5 minutes at room temperature in a microfuge and transfer the aqueous layer to a fresh microfuge tube.

14. Add 80 µl of 10 M ammonium acetate and 1 ml of ethanol to the aqueous layer. Mix the solution by gently inversion and store the tube for 5 minutes at room temperature.

15. Collect the precipitated DNA by centrifugation for 5 minutes in a microfuge. Decant the supernatant and rinse the nucleic acid pellet with 0.5 ml of 70% ethanol. Centrifuge at maximum speed for 2 minutes and remove the ethanol rinse with a drawn out Pasteur pipette. Centrifuge the tube briefly (2 seconds) and remove the last traces of ethanol from the bottom of the tube. Allow the pellet of DNA to dry in the air for 5 minutes and then dissolve the pellet in 50 µl of TE (pH 8.0).

    The preparation should contain 2–4 µg of yeast DNA.

    At this stage, the DNA can be analyzed by PCR and Southern hybridization and may be used to generate libraries of subclones for DNA sequencing or other purposes.

Protocol 12

Small-scale Preparations of Yeast DNA

YEAST DNA IS PREPARED BY DIGESTION OF THE CELL WALL and lysis of the resulting spheroplasts with SDS. This method reproducibly yields several micrograms of yeast DNA that can be efficiently cleaved by restriction enzymes and used as a template in PCR. Note that the following protocol (Protocol 13) describes a method for analyzing yeast colonies directly by PCR, without purifying yeast DNA. An alternative method for preparing yeast DNA is given in Chapter 6, Protocol 7.

MATERIALS

Buffers and Solutions

Please see Appendix 1 for components of stock solutions, buffers, and reagents. Dilute stock solutions to the appropriate concentrations.

Isopropanol
Potassium acetate (5 M)
SDS (10% w/v)
Sodium acetate (3 M, pH 7.0)
Sorbitol buffer
TE (pH 7.4)
TE (pH 8.0) containing 20 μg/ml RNase
Yeast resuspension buffer

Enzymes and Buffers

Zymolyase 100T

Media

YPD medium
Please see the panel on YEAST MEDIA in Protocol 10.

Centrifuges and Rotors

Sorvall SS-34 rotor or equivalent

Special Equipment

Water bath preset to 65ºC

Vectors and Yeast Strains

Yeast cells

4.70

METHOD

Growth of Cells and Extraction of DNA

1. Set up 10-ml cultures of yeast in YPD medium. Incubate the cultures overnight at 30ºC with moderate agitation.

2. Transfer 5 ml of the cells to a centrifuge tube. Collect the cells by centrifugation at 2000*g* (4100 rpm in a Sorvall SS-34 rotor) for 5 minutes. Store the unused portion of the culture at 4ºC.

3. Resuspend the cells in 0.5 ml of sorbitol buffer. Transfer the suspension to a microfuge tube.

4. Add 20 µl of a solution of Zymolyase 100T (2.5 mg/ml in sorbitol buffer), and incubate the cell suspension for 1 hour at 37ºC.

5. Collect the cells by centrifugation in a microfuge for 1 minute. Remove the supernatant by aspiration.

6. Resuspend the cells in 0.5 ml of yeast resuspension buffer.

7. Add 50 µl of 10% SDS. Close the top of the tube and mix the contents by rapidly inverting the tube several times. Incubate the tube for 30 minutes at 65ºC.

8. Add 0.2 ml of 5 M potassium acetate and store the tube for 1 hour on ice.

Isolation of DNA

9. Pellet the cell debris by centrifugation at maximum speed for 5 minutes at 4ºC in a microfuge.

10. Use a wide-bore pipette tip to transfer the supernatant to a fresh microfuge tube at room temperature.

11. Precipitate the nucleic acids by adding an equal volume of room-temperature isopropanol. Mix the contents of the tube and store it for 5 minutes at room temperature.

    ▲IMPORTANT Do not allow the precipitation reaction to proceed for >5 minutes.

12. Recover the precipitated nucleic acids by centrifugation at maximum speed for 10 *seconds* in a microfuge. Remove the supernatant by aspiration and allow the pellet to dry in the air for 10 minutes.

13. Dissolve the pellet in 300 µl of TE (pH 8.0) containing 20 µg/ml pancreatic RNase. Incubate the digestion mixture for 30 minutes at 37ºC.

14. Add 30 µl of 3 M sodium acetate (pH 7.0). Mix the solution and then add 0.2 ml of isopropanol. Mix once again and recover the precipitated DNA by centrifugation at maximum speed for 20 seconds in a microfuge.

15. Remove the supernatant by aspiration and allow the pellet to dry in the air for 10 minutes. Dissolve the DNA in 150 µl of TE (pH 7.4).

Protocol 13

Analyzing Yeast Colonies by PCR

THERE IS NO NEED TO PURIFY DNA FROM YEAST FOR ANALYSIS in PCR. The following protocol, which uses crude lysates of individual yeast colonies as templates for amplification, is used to ascertain whether DNA sequences of interest are present in YACs. The method can also be used to check whether genetic manipulations in yeast, e.g., gene disruptions, have been successful. For additional details on performing PCR, please see Chapter 8, Protocol 1.

- As in all PCR amplifications, it is essential to include appropriate negative controls, e.g., reactions to which no yeast material is added and reactions containing wild-type yeast that does not carry a YAC.

- Positive controls include yeast strains already carrying the DNA sequence targeted for amplification and/or reconstruction reactions containing wild-type yeast colonies and 10–100 pg of plasmid DNA containing the target DNA sequence.

MATERIALS

CAUTION: Please see Appendix 12 for appropriate handling of materials marked with <!>.

Buffers and Solutions

Please see Appendix 1 for components of stock solutions, buffers, and reagents. Dilute stock solutions to the appropriate concentrations.

10x Colony PCR buffer
    0.125 M Tris-Cl (pH 8.5)
    0.56 M KCl
dNTP solution (10 mM) containing all four dNTPs (pH 8.0; PCR grade)
$MgCl_2$ (25 mM)

Enzymes and Buffers

Taq DNA polymerase
    Please see the information panel on *TAQ DNA POLYMERASE* in Chapter 8.

Gels

Agarose or Polyacrylamide gel <!>
    Please see Step 4.

Nucleic Acids and Oligonucleotides

Oligonucleotide primers

The oligonucleotides should be 20–24 nucleotides in length, specific for the target DNA sequences, free of potential secondary structures, and contain no less than 10 and no more than 15 G and C residues. For advice on the design of oligonucleotide primers used in PCR, please see the introduction to Chapter 8.

Marker DNA

Special Equipment

Microfuge tubes (0.5 ml)

Use thin-walled amplification tubes designed for use in a thermal cycler.

Thermal cycler programmed with desired amplification protocol

If the thermal cycler is not equipped with a heated lid, use either mineral oil or paraffin wax to prevent evaporation of liquid from the reaction mixture during PCR.

Vectors and Yeast Strains

Yeast strain carrying recombinant YAC of interest

METHOD

1. In a sterile 0.5-ml microfuge tube, mix in the following order:

10x colony PCR buffer	2 µl
25 mM $MgCl_2$	1.2 µl
10 mM dNTPs	0.4 µl
oligonucleotide primers	10 pmoles of each primer
Taq polymerase	5 units (0.2 µl)
H_2O	to 20 µl

2. Use a disposable yellow pipette tip to transfer a small amount of a yeast colony (0.10–0.25 µl) to the reaction mixture.

   It is important not to be too greedy when sampling the yeast colony because cell wall components inhibit the PCR.

3. Transfer the PCR tube to the thermocycler, programmed as follows, and start the program.

Cycle Number	Denaturation	Annealing	Polymerization
1	4 min at 95ºC		
2–35	1 min at 95ºC	1 min at 55ºC	1 min at 72ºC
Last			10 min at 72ºC

   These times are suitable for 50-µl reactions assembled in thin-walled 0.5-ml tubes and incubated in thermal cyclers such as the Perkin-Elmer 9600 or 9700, Master cycler (Eppendorf), and PTC 100 (MJ Research). Times and temperatures may need to be adapted to suit other types of equipment and reaction volumes.

4. Analyze the products of the PCR by electrophoresis through an agarose or polyacrylamide gel, using markers of suitable size.

   If amplification of the target sequence is weak or erratic, repeat the reactions using a polymerization temperature 2–3ºC below the calculated melting temperature of the oligonucleotide primer that is richer in A+T. (For methods to calculate melting temperatures of oligonucleotide duplexes, please see the information panel on **MELTING TEMPERATURES** in Chapter 10.) If the results are still unsatisfactory, convert the yeast cells to spheroplasts by removing the cell walls with Zymolyase 100T before beginning the protocol. This takes only 1 hour and almost always clears up any problems. Alternatively, grow 10-ml liquid (YPD) cultures of the colonies under test and make small-scale preparations of yeast DNA (please see Protocol 12).

Protocol 14

Isolating the Ends of Genomic DNA Fragments Cloned in High-capacity Vectors: Vectorette Polymerase Chain Reactions

MANY EUKARYOTIC GENES, AND CERTAINLY MOST CHROMOSOMES, encompass more DNA than can be accommodated within a single recombinant. For this reason, it is often necessary to establish an overlapping set of cloned DNAs that can be ordered into a contiguous sequence (contig) spanning a large gene or region of interest. A convenient method for identifying members of a contig is to screen genomic libraries by hybridization or PCR, using probes or primers derived from the extreme 5′ and 3′ ends of an initial isolate. These probes identify sets of recombinants that overlap with the termini of the original isolate and extend in both directions along the chromosome. The process of end-recovery and screening is repeated until the entire region of interest has been captured.

Extension of clones into contigs requires genomic libraries that are deep in coverage and free from large gaps. However, the success of the method also depends on the efficient characterization of the 5′ and 3′ termini of large, nonchimeric, genomic clones whose DNA sequence is unknown. A number of techniques have been devised to facilitate this process and to obviate the need to clone the junctions between vector and cloned DNAs:

- *In vitro transcription.* Many bacteriophage λ and cosmid vectors, and some BAC vectors, contain promoters for bacteriophage DNA-dependent RNA polymerases adjacent to their cloning sites. These can be used to transcribe the terminal sequences of the cloned genomic fragment, as described in Chapter 9, Protocol 6. The RNA can be used directly as hybridization probes or sequenced and used to generate oligonucleotide primers.

- *Inverse PCR.* To prepare the DNA for inverse PCR, the initial clone is digested with a restriction enzyme that cleaves at a specific site within the vector DNA and at one or more sites within the cloned DNA sequence, and the resulting fragments are circularized. Sequences located at the terminus of the cloned segment thereby become flanked by vector DNA whose sequence is known. Amplification is carried out using two oligonucleotide primers that anneal to the vector and point away from each other (please see Figure 4-14). Inverse PCR (Ochman et al. 1988; Triglia et al. 1988), when working at its best, has sufficient sensitivity and specificity to, for example, amplify the termini of YAC clones in preparations of total yeast genomic DNA (Silverman et al. 1989; Arveiler and Porteous 1991). However, success with inverse PCR is not easily achieved: The critical circularization step is difficult to control and the circular DNA templates must be of a size that can be amplified efficiently.

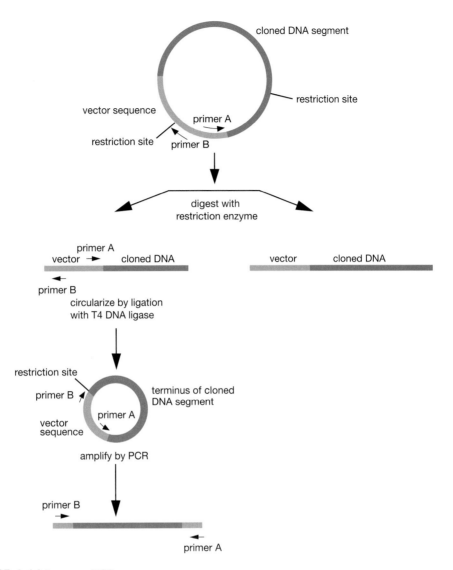

FIGURE 4-14 Inverse PCR

The strategy for inverse PCR is described in the accompanying text.

- ***PCR using repetitive or random primers.*** A variety of methods have been devised that use one vector-specific primer and a second primer that is either specific for highly repetitive elements such as *Alu* or LINE (long interspersed nuclear element) sequences (Nelson et al. 1989) or of random sequence (Wesley et al. 1994). Success in both cases depends on the serendipitous occurrence of repetitive elements or priming sequences in the correct orientation within 1–2 kb of the appropriate terminus of the cloned genomic fragment.

- ***TAIL PCR.*** Thermal asymmetric interlaced (TAIL) PCR may be used to amplify the insert ends from YAC or P1 clones (Liu and Whittier 1995) or, with some modification, to recover and amplify genomic sequences flanking T-DNA and transposon insertions (Liu et al. 1995). The strategy for TAIL PCR relies upon the use of nested, sequence-specific primers (derived from the cloning vector or insertion element) in conjunction with a short arbitrary degenerate primer of low melting temperature. Alternating cycles of high and low stringency during the reaction allow the preferential amplification of the target sequences.

  • *PCR using synthetic oligonucleotide cassettes.* In these techniques, cloned DNA sequences are amplified using one primer complementary to sequences in the vector and a second primer that recognizes an oligonucleotide cassette ligated to a nearby restriction site in the foreign DNA (for review, please see Rosenthal 1992). The best of these techniques are vectorette PCR (Riley et al. 1990; Allen et al. 1994) and single-site PCR (MacGregor and Overbeek 1991), which are described in the following protocol.

In both vectorette PCR (Figure 4-15) and single-site PCR (Figure 4-16), the DNA to be amplified is first digested with a restriction enzyme that cleaves within the cloned DNA. The restriction enzyme must not cleave between the priming site on the vector and the cloned sequences, and it should produce a junction fragment of a suitable size for amplification (typically 200–2000 bp). In pYAC4, suitable enzymes that do not cleave between the vector-specific priming site and the cloning site are *Rsa*I, *Pvu*II, and *Stu*I. However, because the detailed distribution of restriction sites in the cloned DNA is usually unknown, it may be best to test several enzymes to find one that generates a target fragment whose size is optimal for PCR. After digestion, a synthetic oligonucleotide casette is ligated to the ends of the cleaved DNA, and purified products of ligation are amplified using a vector-specific primer and a primer that is complementary to one strand of the attached cassette.

Vectorette and single-site PCRs differ in the design of the cassettes that are attached to the digested DNA. In single-site PCR, a single-stranded oligonucleotide is ligated to the ends of the fragments of cleaved DNA. Amplification is primed by a locus-specific oligonucleotide that binds specifically to the flanking vector sequences and a second oligonucleotide that has the same sequence as the synthetic single-stranded termini (Figure 4-16). Extension from the locus-specific oligonucleotide in the first cycle of PCR provides a complementary sequence to which the second primer can bind (for review, please see Rosenthal 1992).

Vectorettes can be amplified only if they are attached to the DNA of interest, in this case, the junction fragment between the vector and the cloned DNA. The vectorette is only partially double-stranded and contains a central mismatched region (Riley et al. 1990; Allen et al. 1994). The priming oligonucleotide has the same sequence as one of the strands in the mismatched region and therefore has no complementary sequence until the first cycle of PCR is completed. This cycle is primed by the oligonucleotide that binds specifically to the flanking vector sequences (Figure 4-15). Thus, although vectorettes can ligate to themselves and to all fragments of DNA with compatible termini, only DNA containing both the flanking vector sequences and the vectorette can be amplified. For reviews of vectorettes, please see Arnold and Hodgson (1991), Hengen (1995), McAleer et al. (1996), and Ogilvie and James (1996).

Theoretically, in both vectorette PCR and single-site PCR, only the end fragment from the starting clone will amplify. However, in practice, there is often more than one product due to priming on imperfectly matched templates. In addition, illegitimate products may arise from repair of recessed termini of vectorette and cloned DNA fragments (Tadokoro et al. 1992). After denaturation, these termini can anneal to form primer:templates that may be extended in subsequent cycles of the PCR. The synthesis of unwanted amplification products may be suppressed by the use of primers with a relatively high content of G+C (54–58%) and high annealing temperatures (65–67ºC) or by the use of improved vectorettes—splinkerettes—containing hairpin structures rather than mismatches (Devon et al. 1995).

Both vectorette and single-site PCRs have been used successfully to recover the termini of genomic DNAs cloned into YACs, using total yeast DNA as a substrate for library construction (e.g., please see McAleer et al. 1996; Ogilvie and James 1996). Vectorette and single-site PCR methods are also useful for isolating DNA that lies adjacent to a cloned DNA or known DNA

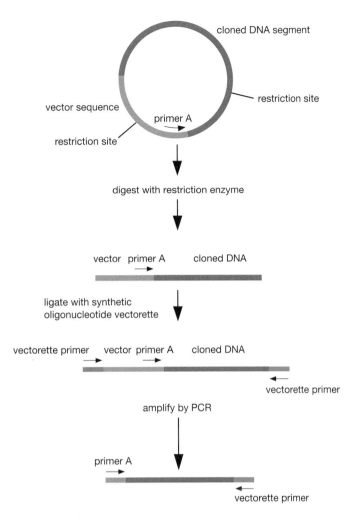

FIGURE 4-15 Vectorette Scheme

The strategy for identifying the ends of cloned fragments using the vectorette scheme for PCR is described in the text.

sequence. For example, sequences flanking an integrated transgene (MacGregor and Overbeek 1991; Allen et al. 1994) or a retrovirus have been isolated by these procedures. Finally, both techniques can be used to recover sequences from uncloned mammalian genomic DNA. However, success is often elusive and requires the use of size-fractionated DNA templates or nested primer pairs to provide sufficient product for cloning, sequencing, or hybridization (please see the panel on **ENHANCEMENTS OF VECTORETTE REACTIONS WHEN USING GENOMIC DNA TEMPLATES** at the end of this protocol).

No comparison of the efficiencies of the two methods has been published. However, single-site PCR is the simpler and less expensive option, requiring fewer steps and synthetic oligonucleotides. Below, we describe a protocol for single-site PCR that works well in our hands. The method may be easily adapted to vectorette PCR by changing the oligonucleotide cassette. For details of vectorettes that may be used to recover the terminal sequences of pYAC4, please see Riley et al. (1990), McAleer et al. (1996), and Ogilvie and James (1996). Vectorettes are available commercially from Genosys Biotechnology (Woodlands, Texas).

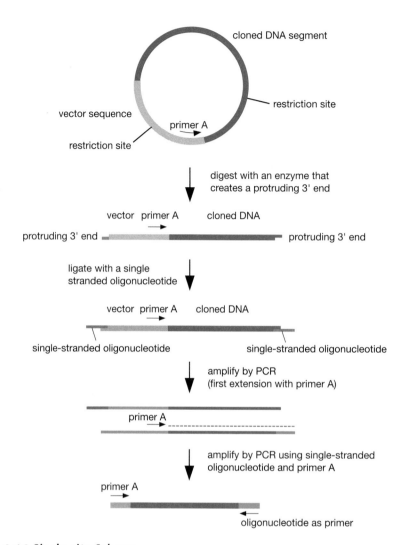

FIGURE 4-16 Single-site Scheme

The strategy for using single-site PCR to identify the ends of cloned fragments is described in the text.

MATERIALS

CAUTION: Please see Appendix 12 for appropriate handling of materials marked with <!>.

Buffers and Solutions

Please see Appendix 1 for components of stock solutions, buffers, and reagents. Dilute stock solutions to the appropriate concentrations.

10x Amplification buffer
dNTP solution (1 mM) containing all four dNTPs (pH 8.0; PCR grade)
Ethanol
Phenol:chloroform (1:1, v/v) <!>
Sodium acetate (3 M, pH 5.2)
10x T4 DNA ligase buffer

Enzymes and Buffers

Bacteriophage T4 DNA ligase
Restriction endonucleases PstI or NsiI
Thermostable DNA polymerase

Gels

Agarose gels
Please see Steps 1 and 8.

Nucleic Acids and Oligonucleotides

Oligonucleotide cassette (5.0 OD$_{260}$/ml [~8.5 µM]) in TE (pH 7.6)
5´CATGCTCGGTCGGGATAGGCACTGGTCTAGAGGGTTAGGTTCCTGCTACATCTCCAGCCTTGCA3´

This 64-nucleotide single-stranded cassette is designed for ligation to target DNAs carrying termini generated by *Pst*I or *Nsi*I. The four 3´-terminal nucleotides (underlined) are complementary to the protruding termini of fragments of DNA generated by cleavage with these enzymes. If another restriction enzyme is used, the nucleotides at the 3´ end of the linker must be changed so as to complement the protruding terminus generated by the enzyme.

Before use, the oligonucleotide should be purified by C$_{18}$ chromatography or electrophoresis through a 12% polyacrylamide gel, as outlined in Chapter 10, Protocol 1. The 5´ terminus of the oligonucleotide should not be phosphorylated.

Oligonucleotide (linker) primer (5.0 OD$_{260}$/ml [~17 µM]) in TE (pH 7.6)
5´CATGCTCGGTCGGGATAGGCACTGGTCTAGAG3´

This oligonucleotide is identical in sequence to the 32 nucleotides at the 5´ end of the oligonucleotide cassette and is used as an amplimer in the PCR.

There is no need to purify or phosphorylate the deprotected oligonucleotide before use. Dissolve the oligonucleotide in TE (pH 7.6) at a concentration of 5.0 OD$_{260}$/ml solution (~17 µM).

Sequence-specific oligonucleotide (vector) primer (5.0 OD$_{260}$/ml [~17 µM]) in TE (pH 7.6)
This primer is complementary to the vector when terminal sequences of a cloned segment of DNA are to be amplified or to cloned DNA sequences when a neighboring segment of genomic DNA is to be recovered. The primer should be 28–32 nucleotides in length and its predicted melting temperature should be approximately equal to that of the 32-nucleotide oligonucleotide primer. For sequences of primers specific for the left and right arms of pYAC4, please see McAleer et al. (1996).

There is no need to purify or phosphorylate the deprotected oligonucleotide before use. Dissolve the oligonucleotide in TE (pH 7.6) at a concentration of 5.0 OD$_{260}$/ml solution (~17 µM).

Template DNAs: recombinant BAC, YAC, or cosmid DNA
YACs can either be embedded in an agarose plug (2 µg in 100-µl plug) or in solution. Unless the yeast strain is carrying more than one YAC, there is no need to purify YAC DNA by PFGE before use in vectorette or single-site PCR.

DNAs should be purified by column chromatography using, e.g, Qiagen resin or GeneClean II (please see Chapter 1, Protocol 9), and resuspended at a concentration of 1 µg/µl in TE (pH 7.6).

Special Equipment

Barrier tips for automatic pipettes
Microfuge tubes (0.5 ml), thin-walled for amplification
Positive displacement pipette
Thermal cycler programmed with desired amplification protocol
If the thermal cycler is not equipped with a heated lid, use either mineral oil or paraffin wax to prevent evaporation of liquid from the reaction mixture during PCR.
Water bath or cooling block preset to 15°C

METHOD

1. Digest ~5 µg of template DNA with *Pst*I or *Nsi*I. Check a small aliquot of the reaction by agarose gel electrophoresis to ensure that all of the DNA has been cleaved.

2. Extract the reaction mixture with phenol:chloroform, and recover the DNA by standard precipitation with ethanol and subsequent washing in 70% ethanol. Store the open tube in an inverted position on a bed of paper towels to allow the last traces of ethanol to evaporate, and then dissolve the damp pellet of DNA in 50 µl of H$_2$O.

3. In a sterile 0.5-ml microfuge tube, mix in the following order:

10x T4 DNA ligase buffer	10 μl
digested template DNA	20 μl
oligonucleotide cassette, 5.0 OD$_{260}$/ml	2 μl
T4 bacteriophage DNA ligase, 5 Weiss units/μl	2 μl
H$_2$O	to 100 μl

    Set up three control reactions as described above but without template DNA in one tube, without linker oligonucleotide in another, and without T4 DNA ligase in the third.

4. Incubate the test ligation reaction and controls for 12–16 hours at 15ºC.

5. In a sterile 0.5-ml microfuge tube, mix in the following order:

10x amplification buffer	2 μl
1 mM solution of four dNTPs (pH 7.0)	2 μl
linker primer oligonucleotide, 5.0 OD$_{260}$/ml	1 μl
vector primer oligonucleotide, 5.0 OD$_{260}$/ml	1 μl
test DNA ligation reaction, from Step 4	1 μl
thermostable DNA polymerase, 5.0 units/μl	0.5 μl
H$_2$O	to 20 μl

    Set up three control PCRs that contain 1 μl of the control ligation reactions instead of the test ligation reaction.

6. If the thermocycler is not fitted with a heated lid, overlay the reaction mixtures with 1 drop (~50 μl) of light mineral oil to prevent evaporation of the samples during repeated cycles of heating and cooling. Alternatively, place a bead of wax into the tube if using a hot-start approach.

7. Place the PCR tubes in the thermocycler, programmed as follows, and start the amplification program.

Cycle Number	Denaturation	Annealing	Polymerization
1	2 min at 95ºC		
2–35	30 sec at 94ºC	30 sec at 60ºC	3 min at 72ºC
Last			5 min at 72ºC

8. Analyze aliquots (25%) of each amplification reaction on an agarose gel.

    A prominent DNA product visible by ethidium bromide staining should be present in the PCR containing the products of the test ligation. This DNA should be absent from the control reactions. The size of the product depends on the distance between the vector primer and the first cleavage site in the cloned insert. For *Pst*I and *Nsi*I, the amplified product is typically between 0.5 kb and 2 kb.

    PCR products spanning the junction of genomic and vector sequences should, in most cases, be cleaved within the cloning site by one or more restriction enzymes. In pYAC4, for example, the amplified DNA should contain an *Eco*RI site that divides the vector sequences from the cloned genomic sequences. Confirmation that the PCR product is correct can therefore be obtained by digestion with *Eco*RI, agarose gel electrophoresis, and Southern blotting, using an oligonucleotide primer specific to the appropriate YAC arm as probes.

    The amplified DNA can be sequenced directly, cloned, radiolabeled by random hexamer priming or PCR, and even used as a transcription template if a bacteriophage promoter is added to the linker or is present in the amplified segment of vector DNA.

ENHANCEMENTS OF VECTORETTE REACTIONS WHEN USING GENOMIC DNA TEMPLATES

If amplification is inefficient and/or if more than one amplification product is detected, repeat the protocol using one or more of the enhancements outlined below. These are particularly useful when the concentration of target sequences is low, e.g., when using total eukaryotic DNA as a template rather than an individual clone of genomic DNA.

- In a preliminary experiment, determine the size of the desired DNA fragment by Southern hybridization using a probe derived from the neighboring, known DNA sequence. Then fractionate the digested DNA by agarose gel electrophoresis in readiness for Step 2 (please see Chapter 5, Protocol 1).

- After Step 1, heat the digested template DNA for 10 minutes at 65°C to melt any annealed complexes that may have formed.

- After Step 3, remove excess oligonucleotide cassette by spun column chromatography.

- Increase the time of the denaturation step in the first cycle of PCR to 10 minutes. This change ensures complete inactivation of the T4 DNA ligase and guarantees that all template DNAs are fully denatured. Thorough denaturation prevents end repair of recessed 3´ termini and therefore suppresses unwanted PCR products (please see protocol introduction).

- Use hot-start PCR, in which the thermostable DNA polymerase is denied access to the template before complete denaturation (for details, please see Chapter 8 introduction).

- Use a nested vector primer(s) to enhance specificity and yield. This enhancement requires the synthesis of an additional vector primer, which can be used either in an additional amplification reaction or be added to the initial amplification after 5–10 cycles. Alternatively, the products of the initial PCR can be fractionated by electrophoresis through an agarose gel and analyzed by Southern hybridization, using the nested primer as a probe. A second PCR can then be performed using as templates DNAs of the appropriate size.

- The addition of Perfect Match (Stratagene) to a concentration of 0.1 units/μl of reaction mixture may sometimes help to reduce the number of nonspecific PCR products (McAleer et al. 1996).

- The use of GC-Melt (CLONTECH) may improve the efficiency of the PCR.

CRE-*loxP*

The genome of bacteriophage P1 is both circularly permuted and terminally redundant. The genetic map, however, is linear (Scott 1968; Walker and Walker 1975, 1976). This paradox was resolved by the discovery that P1 contains a recombinational hot spot, *loxP* (locus of crossing-over [X] in P1), that defines the ends of the genetic map (Sternberg et al. 1978, 1983); recombination at this site is mediated by a single phage-encoded protein, Cre (*c*yclization *re*combination protein) (Sternberg et al. 1986). The *loxP-cre* system is necessary for cyclization of linear P1 DNA, which occurs within the first minutes after infection of *E. coli* (Segev et al. 1980; Segev and Cohen 1981; Hochman et al. 1983). Interestingly, because of the constraints imposed by the packaging process, only one in every four or five bacteriophage particles contains a DNA molecule with *loxP* sites in its terminally redundant regions (please see Figure 4-17). Only this subset of bacteriophage genomes are substrates for the *cre-loxP* system and only these bacteriophage genomes are capable of circularization and replication in *recA*-deficient strains of *E. coli* (for review, please see Yarmolinsky and Sternberg 1988). The 34-bp *loxP* site consists of two 13-bp inverted repeats separated by an 8-bp spacer (Hoess et al. 1982).

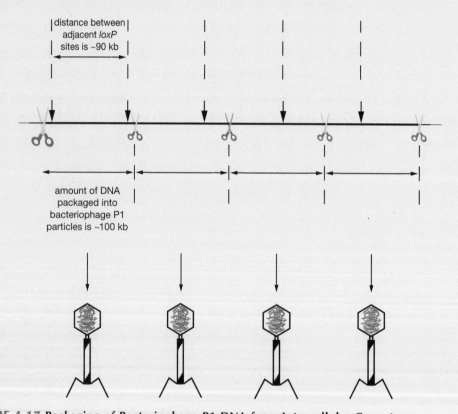

distance between adjacent *loxP* sites is ~90 kb

amount of DNA packaged into bacteriophage P1 particles is ~100 kb

FIGURE 4-17 Packaging of Bacteriophage P1 DNA from Intracellular Concatemers

The substrate for packaging is a linear concatemer of DNA (shown in bold), in which the individual P1 genomes are arranged in a head-to-tail tandem. Packaging is initiated at a site (*pac*, shown as large scissors) that lies ~5 kb from the nearest *loxP* site. Other *pac* sites (small scissors) in the concatemer are not used. Packaging occurs by a unidirectional processive "headful" mechanism in which successive 100-kb segments of DNA are reeled into the bacteriophage prohead. Because the size of the bacteriophage P1 genome is ~90 kb, whereas the capacity of the prohead is ~100 kb, the DNA packaged into each bacteriophage particle is terminally redundant. Because of this redundancy, the first bacteriophage particle to be formed from each concatemer contains two *loxP* sites. The DNA of this bacteriophage can therefore be cyclized by Cre recombinase after injection into a new bacterial cell. Approximately four bacteriophages are packaged from each concatemer. However, only one of these virions contains *loxP* sites in its terminally redundant regions.

FIGURE 4-18 Structure of the 34-bp *loxP* Site

The 34-bp *loxP* site consists of two perfect inverted repeats 13 bp in length (shown within arrows), separated by an 8-bp spacer. Vertical arrows mark the locations of the sites cleaved by the Cre protein on the upper and lower strands of DNA. By convention, the nucleotides in the *loxP* site are numbered from the center of the spacer (*vertical line*). Base pairs to the left are given leftward positive (+) numbers; base pairs to the right are given negative (–) numbers.

Recombination at the *loxP* site is catalyzed by Cre, a 343-amino-acid recombinase protein encoded by the *cre* gene of P1 (Sternberg et al. 1986) that is a member of the Int family of recombinases (Argos et al. 1986). Each *loxP* site consists of two nonidentical Cre-binding domains, composed of one of the 13-bp repeats and the adjacent 4 bp of spacer. The most distal 2 bp of each inverted repeat can be modified without altering recombination frequency: Larger deletions, however, generate recombinant products with abnormal topology (Abremski and Hoess 1985). At saturation, two molecules of Cre bind to a complete *loxP* site (one Cre molecule per inverted repeat) (Mack et al. 1992). The Cre-*loxP* complex then synapses with a second *loxP* site, which can be located on the same molecule of DNA or another. Whether or not the second *loxP* site is also occupied by Cre is not known (Mack et al. 1992). Strand exchange between the synapsed *loxP* partners is initiated following asymmetric cleavage of DNA in the spacer region (please see Figures 4-18 and 4-19). Because of the asymmetry of the spacer, recombination between *loxP* sites located on the same DNA molecule has a polarity: Recombination between *loxP* sites that are in the same orientation results in excision of the DNA between the two sites, whereas recombination between sites that are in the opposite orientation causes inversion of the intervening DNA (Abremski et al. 1983). Thus, linear plasmid DNAs containing directly repeated *loxP* sites are cyclized in *E. coli* strains expressing Cre. In addition, *cre*[+] strains of *E. coli* can efficiently excise and circularize segments of DNA that are flanked by *loxP* sites in large linear genomes (Sauer and Henderson 1988a).

Vectors Containing Cre-*loxP* Sites

Several groups have constructed bacteriophage λ vectors whose arms have unique restriction sites positioned between two *loxP* sites (e.g., please see Palazzolo et al. 1990; Elledge et al. 1991; Brunelli and Pall 1993; Holt and May 1993). A number of different specialized plasmids have been inserted into these vectors that contain *cis*-acting sequences required for high-level expression of cloned cDNAs in *E. coli* (Palazzolo et al. 1990) and yeast (Elledge et al. 1991; Brunelli and Pall 1993, 1994). Bacteriophage λ expression vectors of this type have two advantages: (1) automatic subcloning, in which Cre-mediated recombination can be used to convert the DNA lying between the *loxP* sites into an autonomously replicating plasmid that (2) is equipped with the controlling elements required to express cloned DNAs in both yeast and *E. coli*.

In the case of λYES vectors (Elledge et al. 1991), which are available from CLONTECH, phages are used to infect a strain of *E. coli* (BNN132) that expresses both λ repressor and Cre protein but does not express the P1 restriction-modification system. The λ repressor ensures that the infecting phage enters the lysogenic pathway, whereas the Cre protein causes excision of the plasmid portion of the vector. This automatic subcloning system is extremely efficient with ~50% of the infecting phage giving rise to ampicillin-resistant colonies. λEXlox (available commercially from Novagen) and λZipLox (available from Life Technologies) also work efficiently as automatic subcloning vectors (Palazzolo et al. 1990; D'Alessio et al. 1992). A potential advantage of these vectors is that the excised plasmids carry a bacteriophage f1 origin of replication and can function as phagemids.

Vectors with properties similar to those of λYES are available that are suitable for construction of genomic libraries (Holt and May 1993). These vectors are useful chiefly for constructing genomic libraries of yeast, *Aspergillus*, and other eukaryotes whose genes are comparatively small and relatively free from

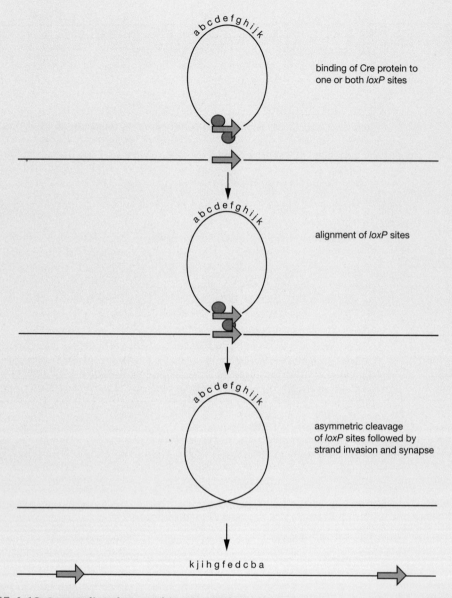

FIGURE 4-19 Cre-mediated Recombination at *loxP* Sites

Please see the text for details.

introns. In such cases, the genomic inserts rescued by automatic subcloning can be used to isolate extragenic suppressor mutations.

Rescue of plasmids from λ Cre-*loxP* vectors requires a source of Cre protein (such as *E. coli* strain BNN132, see above). However, there is some evidence that the presence of this protein suppresses the yield of multicopy plasmids carrying a *loxP* site and that plasmids with large cDNA inserts may be prone to deletion during propagation in *cre*+ strains of *E. coli*. It is therefore advisable to move the rescued plasmids as quickly as possible into a strain of *E. coli* that does not express Cre (Palazzolo et al. 1990).

Site-specific Integration and Excision of Transgenes Mediated by the Cre-*loxP* System

The Cre protein can catalyze recombination events not only in *E. coli,* but also in yeast (Sauer 1987) and mammalian cells (Sauer 1987; Sauer and Henderson 1988b; Fukushige and Sauer 1992). Thus, the Cre recombinase can both drive site-specific integration of plasmids into the chromosomes of yeast and mammalian cells and catalyze precise excision of DNA segments flanked by *loxP* sites (see Figure 4-19). The integration event results from recombination between a plasmid-borne *loxP* site and a second *loxP* site that has been installed into the eukaryotic genome. The Cre protein can be supplied either from a cloned copy of the *cre* gene or, in the case of cultured mammalian cells, by using lipofection to introduce the purified recombinase (Baubonis and Sauer 1993). The latter method, although perhaps not everyone's cup of tea, has the advantage of (1) preventing integration of a transfected *cre* gene and (2) confining Cre-mediated recombination to a particular window of time. Extended expression of Cre results in a second round of recombination that removes the targeting vector from the chromosome. As far as is known, the genomes of yeast and mouse cells do not contain any *loxP* sites. Furthermore, the expression of Cre is not toxic to eukaryotic cells, nor does it affect the development, growth, or fertility of transgenic mice that carry the *cre* gene under the control of the mouse metallothionein I promoter or a cytomegalovirus promoter (Lakso et al. 1992; Orban et al. 1992). (Note: The *cre* gene lacks an optimal initiation signal for translation in mammalian cells [Kozak 1986, 1987]. Changing the –3 nucleotide from T to G results in a substantial increase in recombination ability in transfected mammalian cells [Sauer and Henderson 1990].)

Excision of chromosomal DNA segments flanked by *loxP* sites occurs with higher efficiency than integration of *loxP* plasmids into chromosomal *loxP* sites. By crossing genetically engineered strains of mice containing *loxP* sites at chosen chromosomal locations with transgenic animals that express Cre, the Cre-*loxP* system can be used to generate null alleles (Gu et al. 1994) and to activate oncogenes in a tissue-specific and developmentally regulated manner (Lakso et al. 1992). Other possible uses include the generation of specific chromosomal inversions and deletions, the ablation of specific cell lineages, and the generation of mice hemizygous for particular genes in preselected tissues.

The Cre-*loxP* system is not unique. Several other recombinase/target combinations are known that are capable of directing recombination events in a defined spatial and temporal fashion in eukaryotic organisms. These include the (1) the FLP recombinase of *Saccharomyces cerevisiae* that can catalyze recombination in both cultured mammalian cells and *Drosophila* and (2) the pSR1 recombinase of *Zygosaccharomyces rouxii* that can function efficiently in *S. cerevisiae* (Matsuzaki et al. 1990) However, at present, none of these site-specific recombination systems are as well developed as Cre-*loxP*.

LARGE-FRAGMENT CLONING PRODUCTS AND SERVICES

Company	Products/Services	YAC Products[a]			BAC Products			Custom Services (AC)[a]		
		Vec.	Lib.	Iso. Kits	Vec.	Lib.	Iso. Kits	Iso.	Lib. Constr.	Lib. Scr.
Ana-Gen Technologies Inc. Tele: 800-654-4671 Web Site: www.ana-gen.com	Custom services							√		
AutoGen Tele: 800-654-4671 Web Site: www.autogen.com	AutoGen 740, 850, 850 Alpha			√			√			
CLONTECH Laboratories Inc. Tele: 800-662-2566 Web Site: www.clontech.com	NucleoBond Plasmid Kits			√			√			
Commonwealth Biotechnologies Inc. Tele: 800-735-9224 Web Site: www.cbi-biotech.com	Custom services							√	√	
CPG Inc. Tele: 800-362-2740 Web Site: www.cpg-biotech.com	DNA-Pure Yeast Genomic Kit			√						
Genome Systems Inc Tele: 800-430-0030 Web Site: www.genomesystems.com	P1 & PAC Plasmid Purification Kit						√			
	BAC Large Plasmid Purification Kit pBeloBAC11				√					
	YAC/BAC filter screening sets		√			√				
	Custom service								√	√
Life Technologies Inc. Tele: 800-828-6686 Web Site: www.lifetech.com	CONCERT High Purity Plasmid Purification System						√			
Princeton Separations Inc. Tele: 800-223-0902 Web Site: www.prinsep.com	PSI CLONE BAC DNA Kit						√			
QIAGEN Tele: 800-426-8157 Web Site: www.qiagen.com	QIAGEN Large-Construct Kit R.E.A.L. Prep 96 Plasmid and BioRobot Kits						√			
Research Genetics Inc. Tele: 800-533-4363 Web Site: www.resgen.com	pBeloBAC11				√					
	BAC/YAC libraries		√			√				
	Custom services							√	√	√
Sigma Tele: 800-325-3010 Web Site: www.sigma-aldrich.com	pYAC4	√								
Tetra-Link International Tele: 800-747-5170, Web Site: www.tetra-link.com	TrueBlue-BAC				√					

Reprinted, with permission, from J.D. Cortese (The Scientist 13[24]: 28 [1999]).

[a](Vec.) vectors; (Lib.) libraries; (Iso. Kits) isolation kits; (Lib. Const.) library construction; (Lib. Scr.) library screening.

REFERENCES

Abremski K. and Hoess R. 1985. Phage P1 Cre-*loxP* site-specific recombination. Effects of DNA supercoiling on catenation and knotting of recombinant products. *J. Mol. Biol.* **184:** 211–220.

Abremski K., Hoess R., and Sternberg N. 1983. Studies on the properties of P1 site-specific recombination: Evidence for topological unlinked products following recombination. *Cell* **32:** 1301–1311.

Albertsen H.M., Abderrahim H., Cann H.M., Dausset J., Le Paslier D., and Cohen D. 1990. Construction and characterization of a yeast artificial chromosome library containing seven haploid human genome equivalents. *Proc. Natl. Acad. Sci.* **87:** 4256–4260.

Allen M.J., Collick A., and Jeffreys A.J. 1994. Use of vectorette and subvectorette PCR to isolate transgene flanking DNA. *PCR Methods Appl.* **4:** 71–75.

Amemiya C.T., Alegria-Hartman M.J., Aslanidis C., Chen C., Nikolic J., Gingrich J.C., and de Jong P.J. 1992. A two-dimensional YAC pooling strategy for library screening via STS and *Alu*-PCR methods. *Nucleic Acids Res.* **20:** 2559–2563.

Anand R. 1992. Yeast artificial chromosomes (YACs) and the analysis of complex genomes. *Trends Biotechnol.* **10:** 35–40.

Anand R., Riley J.H., Butler R., Smith J.C., and Markham A.F. 1990. A 3.5 genome equivalent multi access YAC library: Construction, characterisation, screening and storage. *Nucleic Acids Res.* **18:** 1951–1956.

Anand R., Ogilvie D., Butler R., Riley J.H., Finiear R.S., Powell S.J., Smith J.C., and Markham A.F. 1991. A yeast artificial chromosome contig encompassing the cystic fibrosis locus. *Genomics* **9:** 124–130.

Argos P., Landy A., Abremski K., Egan J.B., Haggard-Ljungquist E., Hoess R.H., Kahn M.L., Kalionis B., Narayana S.V., Pierson L.S.D. et al. 1986. The integrase family of site-specific recombinases: Regional similarities and global diversity. *EMBO J.* **5:** 433–440.

Arnold C. and Hodgson I.J. 1991. Vectorette PCR: A novel approach to genomic walking. *PCR Methods Appl.* **1:** 39–42.

Arveiler B. and Porteous D.J. 1991. Amplification of end fragments of YAC recombinants by inverse-polymerase chain reaction. *Technique* **3:** 24–28.

Asakawa S., Abe I., Kudoh Y., Kishi N., Wang Y., Kubota R., Kudoh J., Kawasaki K., Minoshima S., and Shimuzu N. 1997. Human BAC library: Construction and rapid screening. *Gene* **191:** 69–79.

Bächi B. and Arber W. 1977. Physical mapping of *Bgl*II, *Bam*HI, *Eco*RI, *Hin*dIII and *Pst*I restriction fragments of bacteriophage P1 DNA. *Mol. Gen. Genet.* **153:** 311–324.

Barillot E., Lacroix B., and Cohen D. 1991. Theoretical analysis of library screening using an N-dimensional pooling strategy. *Nucleic Acids Res.* **19:** 6241–6247.

Bates P. 1987. Double *cos* site vectors: Simplified cosmid cloning. *Methods Enzymol.* **153:** 82–94.

Bates P.F. and Swift R.A. 1983. Double *cos* site vectors: Simplified cosmid cloning. *Gene* **26:** 137–146.

Baubonis W. and Sauer B. 1993. Genomic targeting with purified Cre recombinase. *Nucleic Acids Res.* **21:** 2025–2029.

Bellane-Chantelot C., Barillot E., Lacroix B., Le Paslier D., and Cohen D. 1991. A test case for physical mapping of human genome by repetitive seqeunce fingerprints: Construction of a physical map of a 420 kb YAC subcloned into cosmids.

Nucleic Acids Res. **19:** 505–510.

Bentley D.R. and Dunham I. 1995. Mapping human chromosomes. *Curr. Opin. Genet. Dev.* **5:** 328–334.

Bentley D.R., Todd C., Collins C., Holland J., Dunham I., Hassock S., Bankier A., and Gianelli F. 1992. The development and application of automated gridding for the efficient screening of yeast and bacterial ordered libraries. *Genomics* **12:** 534–541.

Bertani G. 1951. Studies in lysogenesis. I. The mode of phage liberation by lysogenic *Escherichia coli. J. Bacteriol.* **62:** 293–300.

Black L.W. 1989. DNA packaging in dsDNA bacteriophages. *Annu. Rev. Microbiol.* **43:** 267–292.

Brooks J.E. 1987. Properties and uses of restriction endonucleases. *Methods Enzymol.* **152:** 113–129.

Brownstein B.H., Silverman G.A., Little R.D., Burke D.T., Korsmeyer S.J., Schlessinger D., and Olson M.V. 1989. Isolation of single-copy human genes from a library of yeast artificial-chromosome clones. *Science* **244:** 1348–1351.

Brunelli J.P. and Pall M.L. 1993. A series of yeast/*Escherichia coli* lambda expression vectors designed for directional cloning of cDNAs and *cre/lox*-mediated plasmid excision. *Yeast* **9:** 1309–1318.

———. 1994. Lambda/plasmid vector construction by in vivo *cre/lox*-mediated recombination. *BioTechniques* **16:** 1060–1064.

Burke D.T. 1991. The role of yeast artificial chromosome clones in generating genome maps. *Curr. Opin. Genet. Dev.* **1:** 69–74.

Burke D.T. and Olson M.V. 1991. Preparation of clone libraries in yeast artificial chromosome vectors. *Methods Enzymol.* **194:** 251–270.

Burke D.T., Carle G.F., and Olson M.V. 1987. Cloning of large segments of exogenous DNA into yeast by means of artificial chromosome vectors. *Science* **236:** 806–812.

Cai L., Taylor J.F., Wing R.A., Gallagher D.S., Woo S.-S., and Davis S.K. 1995. Construction and characterization of a bovine bacterial artificial chromosome library. *Genomics* **29:** 413–425.

Capecchi M. 1993. Mouse genetics. YACs to the rescue. *Nature* **362:** 205–206.

Cavalli-Sforza L.L. 1950. La sessualita nei bateri. *Boll. Inst. Sieroter. Milan* **29:** 281–289.

Cavalli-Sforza L., Lederberg J., and Lederberg E. 1953. An infective factor controlling sex compatibility in *B. coli. J. Gen. Microbiol.* **8:** 89–103.

Chatterjee P.K. and Sternberg N.L. 1996. Retrofitting high molecular weight DNA cloned in P1: Introduction of reporter genes, markers selectable in mammalian cells and generation of nested deletions. *Genet. Anal.* **13:** 33–42.

Chen E.Y., Schlessinger D., and Kere J. 1993. Ordered shotgun sequencing, a strategy for integrated mapping and sequencing of YAC clones. *Genomics* **17:** 651–656.

Clarke L. and Carbon J. 1976. A colony bank containing synthetic Col E1 hybrid plasmids representative of the entire *E. coli* genome. *Cell* **9:** 91–99.

Cohen D., Chumakov I., and Weissenbach J. 1993. A first generation physical map of the human genome. *Nature* **366:** 698–701.

Collins J. and Hohn B. 1978. Cosmids: A type of plasmid gene-cloning vector that is packageable *in vitro* in bacteriophage λ heads. *Proc. Natl. Acad. Sci.* **75:** 4242–4246.

D'Alessio J.M., Bebee R., Hartley J.L., Noon M.C., and Polayes D.

1992. Lambda ZipLox: Automatic subcloning of cDNA. *Focus* (Life Technologies) **14:** 76–79.

Deininger P.L., Jolly D.J., Rubin C.M., Friedmann T., and Schmid C.W. 1981. Base sequence studies of 300 nucleotide renatured repeated human DNA clones. *J. Mol. Biol.* **151:** 17–33.

Devon R.S., Porteous D.J., and Brookes A.J. 1995. Splinkerettes — Improved vectorettes for greater efficiency in PCR walking. *Nucleic Acids Res.* **23:** 1644–1645.

DiLella A.G. and Woo S.L.C. 1987. Cloning large segments of genomic DNA using cosmid vectors. *Methods Enzymol.* **152:** 199–212.

Eliason J.L. and Sternberg N. 1987. Characterization of the binding sites of cI repressor of bacteriophage P1: Evidence for multiple asymmetric sites. *J. Mol. Biol.* **198:** 281–293.

Elledge S.J., Mulligan J.T., Ramer S.W., Spottswood M., and Davis R.W. 1991. Lambda YES: A multifunctional cDNA expression vector for the isolation of genes by complementation of yeast and *Escherichia coli* mutations. *Proc. Natl. Acad. Sci.* **88:** 1731–1735.

Evans G.A., Lewis K., and Rothenberg B.E. 1989. High efficiency vectors for cosmid microcloning and genomic analysis. *Gene* **79:** 9-20

Evans G.A., Snyder K., and Hermanson G.G. 1992. Use of cosmids and arrayed clone libraries for genome analysis. *Methods Enzymol.* **216:** 530–548.

Feingold J.M., Ogden S.D., and Denny C.T. 1990. Streamlined approach to creating yeast artificial chromosome libraries from specialized cell sources. *Proc. Natl. Acad. Sci.* **87:** 8637–8641.

Feiss M., Fisher R.A., Crayton M.A., and Egner C. 1977. Packaging of the bacteriophage lambda chromosome: Effect of chromosome length. *Virology* **77:** 281–293.

Feiss M., Widner W., Miller G., Johnson G., and Christiansen S. 1983. Structure of the bacteriophage-lambda cohesive end site — Location of the sites of terminase binding (*cosB*) and nicking (*cosN*). *Gene* **24:** 207–218.

Ferretti L. and Sgaramella V. 1981. Temperature dependence of the joining by T4 DNA ligase of termini produced by type II restriction endonucleases. *Nucleic Acids Res.* **9:** 85–93.

Fogel S., Mortimer R.K., and Lusnak K. 1981. Mechanisms of meiotic gene conversion, or "Wanderings on a foreign strand." In *The molecular biology of the yeast* Saccharomyces: *Life cycle and inheritance* (ed. J.N. Strathern et al.), pp. 289–339. Cold Spring Harbor Laboratory, Cold Spring Harbor, New York.

Forget B.G. 1993. YAC transgenes: Bigger is probably better. *Proc. Natl. Acad. Sci.* **90:** 7909–7911.

Frame R. and Bishop J.O. 1971. The number of sex-factors per chromosome in *Escherichia coli*. *Biochem. J.* **121:** 93–103.

Francis F., Zehetner G., Hoglund M., and Lehrach H. 1994. Construction and preliminary analysis of the ICRF human P1 library. *Genet. Anal. Tech. Appl.* **11:** 148–157.

Fukushige S. and Sauer B. 1992. Genomic targeting with a positive-selection *lox* integration vector allows highly reproducible gene expression in mammalian cells. *Proc. Natl. Acad. Sci.* **89:** 7905–7909.

Garza D., Ajioka J.W., Burke D.T., and Hartl D.L. 1989. Mapping the *Drosophila* genome with yeast artificial chromosomes. *Science* **246:** 641–646.

Gay P., Le Coq D., Steinmetz M., Berkelman T., and Kado C.I. 1985. Positive selection procedure for entrapment of insertion sequence elements in gram-negative bacteria. *J. Bacteriol.* **164:** 918–921.

Gay P., Le Coq D., Steinmetz M., Ferrari E., and Hoch J.A. 1983.

Cloning the structural gene *sacB*, which codes for the exoenzyme levan sucrase of *Bacillus subtilis*: Expression of the gene in *Escherichia coli*. *J. Bacteriol.* **153:** 1424–1431.

Gnirke A. and Huxley C. 1991. Transfer of the human HPRT and GART genes from yeast to mammalian cells by microinjection of DNA. *Somat. Cell Mol. Genet.* **17:** 573–580.

Gorman S.W., Roberts-Oehlschlager S.L., Cullis C.A., and Teasdale R.D. 1992. Producing a P1 bacteriophge library from pine: Isolation and cloning of very high molecular weight DNA. *BioTechniques* **12:** 722–727.

Green E.D. and Olson M.V. 1990. Systematic screening of yeast artificial chromosome libraries by use of the polymerase chain reaction. *Proc. Natl. Acad. Sci.* **87:** 1213–1217.

Green E.D., Riethman H.C., Dutchik J.E., and Olson M.V. 1991. Detection and characterization of chimeric yeast artificial-chromosome clones. *Genomics* **11:** 658–669.

Green E.D., Birren B., Klapholz S., Myers R.M., and Heiter P., eds. 1997–1999. *Genome analysis: A laboratory manual*, vols. 1–4. Cold Spring Harbor Laboratory Press, Cold Spring Harbor, New York.

Gu H., Marth J.D., Orban P.C., Mossmann H., and Rajewsky K. 1994. Deletion of a DNA polymerase β gene segment in T cells using cell-type specific gene targeting. *Science* **265:** 103–106.

Hanahan D. and Meselson M. 1980. Plasmid screening at high colony density. *Gene* **10:** 63–67.

Hartl D.L., Nurminsky D.I., Jones R.W., and Lozovskaya E.R. 1994. Genome structure and evolution in *Drosophila*: Application of the framework P1 map. *Proc. Natl. Acad. Sci.* **91:** 6824–6829.

Hayes W. 1952. Recombination in *Bact. coli* K-12: Unidirectional transfer of genetic material. *Nature* **169:** 118–119.

———. 1953. Observations on a transmissible agent determining sexual differentiation in *B. coli*. *J. Gen. Microbiol.* **8:** 72–88.

Heale S.M., Stateva L.I., and Oliver S.G. 1994. Introduction of YACs into intact yeast cells by a procedure which shows low levels of recombinogenicity and co-transformation. *Nucleic Acids Res.* **22:** 5011–5015.

Hengen P.N. 1995. Vectorette, splinkerette and boomerang DNA amplification. *Trends Biochem. Sci.* **20:** 372–373.

Hieter P., Mann C., Snyder M., and Davis R.W. 1985. Mitotic stability of yeast chromosomes: A colony color assay that measures nondisjunction and chromosome loss. *Cell* **40:** 381–392.

Hochman L., Segev N., Sternberg N., and Cohen G. 1983. Site-specific recombinational circularization of bacteriophage P1 DNA. *Virology* **131:** 11–17.

Hoess R.H. and Abremski K. 1984. Interaction of the bacteriophage P1 recombinase Cre with the recombining site *lox*P. *Proc. Natl. Acad. Sci.* **81:** 1026–1029.

Hoess R.H., Ziese M., and Sternberg N. 1982. P1 site-specific recombination: Nucleotide sequence of the recombining sites. *Proc. Natl. Acad. Sci.* **79:** 3398–3402.

Hoheisel J.D., Maier E., Mott R., McCarthy L., Grigoriev A.V., Schalkwyk L.C., Nizetic D., Francis F., and Lehrach H. 1993. High resolution cosmid map and P1 maps spanning the 14 Mb genome of the fission yeast *S. pombe*. *Cell* **73:** 109–120.

Hohn B. 1979. In vitro packaging of lambda and cosmid DNA. *Methods Enzymol.* **68:** 299–309.

Hohn B., Koukolikova-Nicola Z., Lindenmaier W., and Collins J. 1988. Cosmids. *Bio/Technology* **10:** 113–127.

Holt C.L. and May G.S. 1993. A novel phage lambda replacement Cre-*lox* vector that has automatic subcloning capabilities.

Gene **133:** 95–97.

Hung M.-C. and Wensink P.C. 1984. Different restriction enzyme-generated sticky DNA ends can be joined in vitro. *Nucleic Acids Res.* **12:** 1863–1874.

Huxley C. 1994. Transfer of YACs to mammalian cells and transgenic mice. *Genet. Eng.* **16:** 65–91.

Ioannou P.A., Amemiya C.T., Garnes J., Kroisel P.M., Shizuya H., Chen C., Batzer M.A., and de Jong P.J. 1994. A new bacteriophage P1-derived vector for the propagation of large human DNA fragments. *Nat. Genet.* **6:** 84–89.

Ippen-Ihler K. and Minkley Jr., N.G. 1986. The conjugation system of F, the fertility factor of *Escherichia coli. Annu. Rev. Genet.* **20:** 593–624.

Kim U.J., Birren B.W., Slepak T., Mancino V., Boysen C., Kang H.L., Simon M.I., and Shizuya H. 1996. Construction and characterization of a human bacterial chromosome library. *Genomics* **34:** 213–218.

Koshland D., Kent J.C., and Hartwell L.H. 1985. Genetic analysis of the mitotic transmission of minichromosomes. *Cell* **40:** 393–403.

Kouprina N., Eldarov M., Moyzis R., Resnick M., and Larionov V. 1994. A model system to assess the integrity of mammalian YACs during transformation and propagation in yeast. *Genomics* **21:** 7–17.

Kozak M. 1986. Influences of mRNA secondary structure on initiation by eukaryotic ribosomes. *Proc. Natl. Acad. Sci.* **83:** 2850–2854.

———. 1987. An analysis of 5′-noncoding sequences from 699 vertebrate messenger RNAs. *Nucleic Acids Res.* **15:** 8125–8148.

Kwiatkowski Jr., T.J., Zoghbi H.Y., Ledbetter S.A., Ellison K.A., and Chinault A.C. 1990. Rapid identification of yeast artificial chromosome clones by matrix pooling and crude lysate PCR. *Nucleic Acids Res.* **18:** 7191–7192.

Lai E. and Cantrell C. 1989. Rapid colony screening of YAC libraries by using alginate as matrix support. *Nucleic Acids Res.* **17:** 8008.

Lakso M., Sauer B., Mosinger Jr., B., Lee E.J., Manning R.W., Yu S.H., Mulder K.L., and Westphal H. 1992. Targeted oncogene activation by site-specific recombination in transgenic mice. *Proc. Natl. Acad. Sci.* **89:** 6232–6236.

Larin Z., Monaco A.P., and Lehrach H. 1991. Yeast artificial chromosome libraries containing large inserts from mouse and human DNA. *Proc. Natl. Acad. Sci.* **88:** 4123–4127.

Lennon G.G. and Lehrach H. 1991. Hybridization analyses of arrayed cDNA libraries. *Trends Genet.* **7:** 314–317.

Lichter P. and Ward D.C. 1990. Is non-isotopic *in situ* hybridization finally coming of age? *Nature* **345:** 93–94.

Ling L.L., Ma N.S., Smith D.R., Miller D.D., and Moir D.T. 1993. Reduced occurrence of chimeric YACs in recombination-deficient hosts. *Nucleic Acids Res.* **21:** 6045–6046.

Little P.F.R. and Jackson I.J. 1987. Application of plasmids containing promoters specific for phage-encoded RNA polymerases. In *DNA cloning: A practical approach* (ed. D.M. Glover), vol. 3, pp. 1–18. IRL Press, Oxford, United Kingdom.

Little R.D., Porta G., Carle G.F., Schlessinger D., and D'Urso M. 1989. Yeast artificial chromosomes with 200- to 800-kilobase inserts of human DNA containing HLA, V kappa, 5S, and Xq24-Xq28. *Proc. Natl. Acad. Sci.* **86:** 1598–1602.

Liu Y.-G. and Whittier R.F. 1995. Thermal asymmetric interlaced PCR: Automatable amplification and sequencing of insert end fragments from P1 and YAC clones for chromosome walking. *Genomics* **25:** 674–681.

Liu Y.-G., Mitsukawa N., Oosumi T., and Whittier R.F. 1995.

Efficient isolation and mapping of *Arabidopsis thaliana* T-DNA insert junctions by thermal asymmetric interlaced PCR. *Plant J.* **8:** 457–463.

Loftus M.G., Foster L.M., and Ross I.K. 1992. A rapid method for cosmid cloning. *BioTechniques* **12:** 172–176.

Longmire J.L., Brown N.C., Meincke L.J., Campbell M.L., Albright K.L., Fawcett J.J., Campbell E.W., Moyzis R.K., Hildebrand C.E., Evans G.A. et al. 1993. Construction and characterization of partial digest DNA libraries made from flow-sorted human chromosome 16. *Genet. Anal. Tech. Appl.* **10:** 69–76.

Low K.B. 1987. Hfr strains of *Escherichia coli* K-12. In Escherichia coli *and* Salmonella typhimurium (ed. F.C. Neidhardt et al.), vol. 2, pp. 1134–1137. American Society for Microbiology, Washington, D.C.

MacGregor G.R. and Overbeek P.A. 1991. Use of a simplified single-site PCR to facilitate cloning of genomic DNA sequences flanking a transgene integration site. *PCR Methods Appl.* **1:** 129–135.

Mack A., Sauer B., Abremski K., and Hoess R. 1992. Stoichiometry of the Cre recombinase bound to the *lox* recombining site. *Nucleic Acids Res.* **20:** 4451–4455.

MacLaren D.C. and Clarke S. 1996. Rapid mapping of genomic P1 clones: The mouse L-isoaspartyl/D-aspartyl methyltransferase gene. *Genomics* **35:** 299–307.

MacMurray A.J., Weaver A., Shin H.-S., and Lander E.S. 1991. An automated method for DNA preparation from thousands of YAC clones. *Nucleic Acids Res.* **19:** 385–390.

Maniatis T., Hardison R.C., Lacy E., Lauer J., O'Connell C., Quon D., Sim G.K., and Efstratiadis A. 1978. The isolation of structural genes from libraries of eucaryotic DNA. *Cell* **15:** 687–701.

Matsuzaki H., Nakajima R., Nishiyama J., Araki H., and Oshima Y. 1990. Chromosome engineering in *Saccharomyces cerevisiae* by using a site-specific recombination system of a yeast plasmid. *J. Bacteriol.* **172:** 610–618.

McAleer M.A., Coffey A., and Dunham I. 1996. DNA rescue by the vectorette method. *Methods Mol. Biol.* **65:** 201–208.

McCormick M.K., Antonarakis S.E., and Hieter P. 1990. YAC cloning of DNA embedded in an agarose matrix. *Genet. Anal. Tech. Appl.* **7:** 114–118.

McCormick M.K., Shero J.H., Cheung M.C., Kan Y.W., Hieter P.A., and Antonarakis S.E. 1989. Construction of human chromosome 21-specific yeast artificial chromosome library. *Proc. Natl. Acad. Sci.* **86:** 9991–9995.

Mejia J.E. and Monaco A.P. 1997. Retrofitting vectors for *Escherichia coli*-based artificial chromosomes (PACs and BACs) with markers for transfection studies. *Genome Res.* **7:** 179–186.

Monaco A.P. and Larin Z. 1994. YACs, BACs, PACs and MACs: Artificial chromosomes as research tools. *Trends Biotechnol.* **12:** 280–286.

Montanaro V., Casamassimi A., D'Urso M., Yoon J.-Y., Freije W., Schlessinger D., Muenke M., Nussbaum R.L., Saccone S., Maugeri S., Santoro A.M., Motta S., and Della Valle G. 1991. In situ hybridization to cytogenetic bands of yeast artificial chromosome covering 50% of human Xq24-Xq28 DNA. *Am. J. Hum. Genet.* **48:** 183–194.

Montoliu L., Schedl A., Kelsey G., Zentgraf H., Lichter P., and Schütz G. 1994. Germ line transmission of yeast artificial chromosomes in transgenic mice. *Reprod. Fertil. Dev.* **6:** 577–584.

Montoliu L., Schedl A., Kelsey G., Lichter P., Larin Z., Lehrach H., and Schütz G. 1993. Generation of transgenic mice with yeast artificial chromosomes. *Cold Spring Harbor Symp. Quant. Biol.* **58:** 55–62.

Murray A.W. and Szostak J.W. 1983. Construction of artificial chromosomes in yeast. *Nature* **305:** 189–193.

Nagaraja R., Kere J., MacMillan S., Masisi M.J., Johnson D., Molini B.J., Halley G.R., Wein K., Trusgnich M., Eble B. et al. 1994. Characterization of 4 human YAC libraries for clone size, chimerism and X-chromosome sequence representation. *Nucleic Acids Res.* **22:** 3406–3411.

Nelson D.L., Ledbetter S.A., Corbo L., Victoria M.F., Ramirez-Solis R., Webster T.D., Ledbetter D.H., and Caskey C.T. 1989. *Alu* polymerase chain reaction: A method for rapid isolation of human-specific sequences from complex DNA sources. *Proc. Natl. Acad. Sci.* **86:** 6686–6690.

Ochman H., Gerber A.S., and Hartl D.L. 1988. Genetic applications of an inverse polymerase chain reaction. *Genetics* **120:** 621–623.

Ogilvie D.J. and James L.A. 1996. End rescue from YACs using the vectorette. *Methods Mol. Biol.* **54:** 131–138.

Orban P.C., Chui D., and Marth J.D. 1992. Tissue- and site-specific DNA recombination in transgenic mice. *Proc. Natl. Acad. Sci.* **89:** 6861–6865.

Palazzolo M.J., Hamilton B.A., Ding D.L., Martin C.H., Mead D.A., Mierendorf R.C., Raghavan K.V., Meyerowitz E.M., and Lipshitz H.D. 1990. Phage lambda cDNA cloning vectors for subtractive hybridization, fusion-protein synthesis and Cre-loxP automatic plasmid subcloning. *Gene* **88:** 25–36.

Pan H.-Q., Wang Y.-P., Chissoe S.L., Bodenteich A., Wang Z., Iyer K., Clifton S.W., Crabtree J.S., and Roe B.A. 1994. The complete nucleotide sequences of the SacBII Kan domain of the P1 pAD10-SacBII cloning vector and three cosmid cloning vectors: pTCF, svPHEP, and LAWRIST16. *Genet. Anal. Tech. Appl.* **11:** 181–186.

Paranchych W. and Frost L.S. 1988. The physiology and biochemistry of pili. *Adv. Microb. Physiol.* **29:** 53-114.

Peterson K.R. 1997. Production and analysis of transgenic mice containing yeast artificial chromosomes. *Genet. Eng.* **19:** 235-255.

Pierce J.C. and Sternberg N.L. 1992. Using the bacteriophage P1 system to clone high molecular weight genomic DNA. *Methods Enzymol.* **216:** 549-574.

Pierce J.C., Sauer B., and Sternberg N. 1992a. A positive selection vector for cloning high molecular weight DNA in the bacteriophage P1 system: Improved cloning efficiency. *Proc. Natl. Acad. Sci.* **89:** 2056–2060.

Pierce J.C., Sternberg N., and Sauer B. 1992b. A mouse genomic library in the bacteriophage P1 cloning system: Organization and characterization. *Mamm. Genome* **3:** 550–558.

Rackwitz H.R., Zehetner G., Frischauf A.M., and Lehrach H. 1984. Rapid restriction mapping of DNA cloned in lambda phage vectors. *Gene* **30:** 195–200.

Rackwitz H.R., Zehetner G., Murialdo H., Delius H., Chai J.H., Poustka A., Frischauf A., and Lehrach H. 1985. Analysis of cosmids using linearization by phage lambda terminase. *Gene* **40:** 259–266.

Ramsay M. 1994. Yeast artificial chromosome cloning. *Mol. Biotechnol.* **1:** 181–201.

Reeves R.H., Pavan W.J., and Hieter P. 1992. Yeast artificial chromosome modification and manipulation. *Methods Enzymol.* **216:** 584–603.

Riley J.H., Ogilvie D., and Anand R. 1992. Construction, characterization and screening of YAC libraries. In *Techniques for*

analysis of complex genomes (ed. R. Anand), pp. 59–80. Academic Press, London, United Kingdom.

Riley J., Butler R., Ogilvie D., Finniear R., Jenner D., Powell S., Anand R., Smith J.C., and Markham A.F. 1990. A novel rapid method for the isolation of terminal sequences from yeast artificial chromosome (YAC) clones. *Nucleic Acids Res.* **18:** 2887–2890.

Roman H. 1957. Studies of gene mutation in *Saccharomyces. Cold Spring Harbor Symp. Quant. Biol.* **21:** 175–185.

Rosenthal A. 1992. PCR amplification techniques for chromosome walking. *Trends Biotechnol.* **10:** 44–48.

Sambrook J., Fritsch E., and Maniatis T. 1989. *Molecular cloning: A laboratory manual,* 2nd edition. Cold Spring Harbor Laboratory Press, Cold Spring Harbor, New York.

Sauer B. 1987. Functional expression of the cre-lox site-specific recombination system in the yeast *Saccharomyces cerevisiae. Mol. Cell. Biol.* **7:** 2087–2096.

Sauer B. and Henderson N. 1988a. Site-specific DNA recombination in mammalian cells by the Cre recombinase of bacteriophage P1. *Proc. Natl. Acad. Sci.* **85:** 5166–5170.

———. 1988b. The cyclization of linear DNA in *Escherichia coli* by site-specific recombination. *Gene* **70:** 331–341.

———. 1990. Targeted insertion of exogenous DNA into the eukaryotic genome by the Cre recombinase. *New Biol.* **2:** 441–449.

Schlessinger D. 1990. Yeast artificial chromosomes: Tools for mapping and analysis of complex genomes. *Trends Genet.* **6:** 248–258.

Scott J.R. 1968. Genetic studies on bacteriophage P1. *Virology* **36:** 564–574.

Seed B. 1982. Theoretical study of the fraction of a long-chain DNA that can be incorporated in a recombinant DNA partial-digest library. *Biopolymers* **21:** 1793–1810.

Seed B., Parker R.C., and Davidson N. 1982. Representation of DNA sequences in recombinant DNA libraries prepared by restriction enzyme partial digestion. *Gene* **19:** 201–209.

Segev N. and Cohen G. 1981. Control of circularization of bacteriophage P1 DNA in *Escherichia coli. Virology* **114:** 333–342.

Segev N., Laub A., and Cohen G. 1980. A circular form of bacteriophage P1 DNA made in lytically infected cells of *Escherichia coli.* Characterization and kinetics of formation. *Virology* **101:** 261–271.

Selleri L., Eubanks J.H., Giovannini M., Hermanson G.G., Romo A., Djabali M., Maurer S., McElligott D.L., Smith M.W., and Evans G.A. 1992. Detection and characterization of "chimeric" yeast artificial chromosome clones by fluorescent in situ suppression hybridization. *Genomics* **14:** 536–541.

Sheng Y., Mancina V., and Birren B. 1995. Transformation of *Escherichia coli* with large DNA molecules by electroporation. *Nucleic Acids Res.* **23:** 1990–1996.

Shepherd N.S. and Smoller D. 1994. The P1 vector system for the preparation and screening of genomic libraries. *Genet. Eng.* **16:** 213–228.

Shepherd N.S., Pfrogner B.D., Coulby J.N., Ackerman S.L., Vaidyanathan G., Sauer R.H., Balkenhol T.C., and Sternberg N. 1994. Preparation and screening of an arrayed human genomic library generated with the P1 cloning system. *Proc. Natl. Acad. Sci.* **91:** 2629–2633.

Shizuya H., Birren B., Kim U.J., Mancino V., Slepak T., Tachiiri Y., and Simon M. 1992. Cloning and stable maintenance of 300-kilobase-pair fragments of human DNA in *Escherichia coli* using an F-factor-based vector. *Proc. Natl. Acad. Sci.* **89:** 8794–8797.

Shovlin C.L. 1996. Streamlined procedures for screening a P1 library. *BioTechniques* **21:** 388–390.

Silverman G.A., Ye R.D., Pollock K.M., Sadler J.E., and Korsmeyer S.J. 1989. Use of yeast artificial chromosome clones for mapping and walking within human chromosome segment 18q21.3. *Proc. Natl. Acad. Sci.* **86:** 7485–7489.

Skorupski K., Sauer B., and Sternberg N. 1994. Faithful cleavage of the P1 packaging site (*pac*) requires two phage proteins, PacA and PacB, and two *Escherichia coli* proteins, IHF and HU. *J. Mol. Biol.* **243:** 268–282.

Skorupski K., Pierce J.C., Sauer B., and Sternberg N. 1992. Bacteriophage P1 genes involved in the recognition and cleavage of the phage packaging site (*pac*). *J. Mol. Biol.* **223:** 977–989.

Smith H.O. and Birnstiel M.L. 1976. A simple method for DNA restriction site mapping. *Nucleic Acids Res.* **3:** 2387–2398.

Smoller D.A., Petrov D., and Hartl D.L. 1991. Characterization of a bacteriophage P1 library containing inserts of *Drosophila* DNA of 75–100 kilobase pairs. *Chromosoma* **100:** 487–494.

Smoller D.A., Kimmerly W.J., Hubbard O., Ericsson C., Martin C.H., and Palazzolo M.J. 1994. A role for the P1 cloning system in genome analysis. In *Automated DNA sequencing and analysis techniques* (ed. M.D. Adams et al.), pp. 89–101. Academic Press, London, United Kingdom.

Sternberg N. 1990. Bacteriophage-P1 cloning system for the isolation, amplification, and recovery of DNA fragments as large as 100 kilobase pairs. *Proc. Natl. Acad. Sci.* **87:** 103–107.

———. 1992. Cloning high molecular weight DNA fragments by the bacteriophage P1 system. *Trends Genet.* **8:** 11–16.

———. 1994. The P1 cloning system: Past and future. *Mamm. Genome* **5:** 397–404.

Sternberg N. and Cohen G. 1989. Genetic analysis of the lytic replicon of bacteriophage PI. II. Organization of the replicon elements. *J. Mol. Biol.* **207:** 111–133.

Sternberg N., Hoess R., and Abremski K. 1983. The P1 *lox*-Cre site-specific recombination system: Properties of *lox* sites and biochemistry of *lox*-Cre interactions. *UCLA Symp. Mol. Cell. Biol. New Ser.* **10:** 671–684.

Sternberg N., Ruether J., and deRiel K. 1990. Generation of a 50,000-member human DNA library with an average insert size of 75–100 kbp in a bacteriophage P1 cloning vector. *New Biol.* **2:** 151–162.

Sternberg N., Smoller D., and Braden T. 1994. Three new developments in P1 cloning. Increased cloning efficiency, improved clone recovery, and a new P1 mouse library. *Genet. Anal. Tech. Appl.* **11:** 171–180.

Sternberg, N., Austin S., Hamilton D., and Yarmolinsky M. 1978. Analysis of bacteriophage P1 immunity by using lambda-P1 recombinants constructed in vitro. *Proc. Natl. Acad. Sci.* **75:** 5594–5598.

Sternberg N., Sauer B., Hoess R., and Abremski K. 1986. Bacteriophage P1 *cre* gene and its regulatory region. Evidence for multiple promoters and for regulation by DNA methylation. *J. Mol. Biol.* **187:** 197–212.

Strong S.J., Ohta Y., Litman G.W., and Amemiya C.T. 1997. Marked improvement of PAC and BAC cloning is achieved using electroelution of pulsed-field gel-separated partial digests of genomic DNA. *Nucleic Acids Res.* **25:** 3959–3961.

Tadokoro K., Oki N., Fijii H., Ohshima A., Inoue T., and Yamada M. 1992. Genomic organization of the human WT1 gene. *Jpn. J. Cancer Res.* **83:** 1198–1203.

Tanahashi H. 1994. Analysis of human chromosome 21q: Isolation of linking clones and generation of STSs, and construction of P1 phage library. *Nippon Rinsho* **52:** 515–525.

Tang B. and Waterman M.S. 1990. The expected fraction of clonable genomic DNA. *Bull. Math. Biol.* **52:** 455–475.

Tang L.B., Lenstra R., Bochert T.V., and Nagarajan V. 1990. Isolation and characterization of levansucrase-encoding gene from *Bacillus amyloliquefaciens*. *Gene* **96:** 89–93.

Traver C.N., Klapholz S., Hyman R.W., and Davis R.W. 1989. Rapid screening of a human genome library in yeast artificial chromosomes for single copy sequences. *Proc. Natl. Acad. Sci.* **86:** 5898–5902.

Triglia T., Peterson M.G., and Kemp D.J. 1988. A procedure for in vitro amplification of DNA sequences that lie outside the boundaries of known sequences. *Nucleic Acids Res.* **16:** 8186.

van Ommen G.-J. 1992. First report of the HUGO YAC committee. In *Genome priority reports: Chromosome coordinating meeting* (ed. A.J. Cuticchia et al.), vol. 1, pp. 885–888. Karger, Basel, Switzerland.

Vaudin M., Roopra A., Hillier L., Brinkman R., Sulston J., Wilson R.K., and Waterston R.H. 1995. The construction and analysis of M13 libraries prepared from YAC DNA. *Nucleic Acids Res.* **23:** 670–674.

Vilageliu L. and Tyler-Smith C. 1992. Structural instability of YAC clones and the use of recombination-deficient host strains. In *Techniques for the analysis of complex genomes* (ed. R. Anand), pp. 93–112. Academic Press, London, United Kingdom.

Vollenweider H.J., Fiandt M., Rosenvold E.C., and Szybalski W. 1980. Packaging of plasmid DNA containing the cohesive ends of coliphage lambda. *Gene* **9:** 171–174.

Wada M., Little R.D., Abidi F., Porta G., Labella T., Cooper T., Della Valle G., D'Urso M., and Schlessinger D. 1990. Human Xq24-Xq28: Approaches to mapping with yeast artificial chromosomes. *Am. J. Hum. Genet.* **46:** 95–106.

Walker Jr., D.H. and Walker J.T. 1975. Genetic studies of coliphage P1. I. Mapping by use of prophage deletions. *J. Virol.* **16:** 525–534.

———. 1976. Genetic studies of coliphage P1. II. Relatedness to P7. *J. Virol.* **19:** 271–274.

Wang G.-L., Holsten T.E., Song W.-Y., Wang H.P., and Ronald P.C. 1995. Construction of a rice bacterial artificial chromosome library and identification of clones linked to the Xa-21 disease resistance locus. *Plant J.* **7:** 525–533.

Well A.M. and Stewart G.G. 1973. Storage of brewing yeasts by liquid nitrogen refrigeration. *Appl. Microbiol.* **26:** 577.

Wesley C.S., Myers M.P., and Young M.W. 1994. Rapid sequential walking from termini of cosmid, P1 and YAC inserts. *Nucleic Acids Res.* **22:** 538–539.

Willetts N. and Skurray R. 1987. Structure and function of the F factor and mechanisms of conjugation. In Escherichia coli *and* Salmonella typhimurium (ed. F.C. Neidhardt et al.), vol. 2, pp. 1110–1133. American Society for Microbiology, Washington, D.C.

Wong P., Myal Y., Shui R., and Tenniswood M. 1993. Identification and cloning of a new category of DNA fragments which are poorly represented in human genomic libraries. *Biochem. Biophys. Res. Commun.* **190:** 453–461.

Woo S.-S., Jiang J., Gill B.S., Paterson A.H., and Wing R.A. 1994. Construction and characterization of a bacterial artificial chromosome library of sorghum bicolor. *Nucleic Acids Res.* **22:** 4922–4931.

Wu R. and Taylor E. 1971. Nucleotide sequence analysis of DNA. II. Complete nucleotide sequence of the cohesive ends of bacteriophage lambda DNA. *J. Mol. Biol.* **57:** 491–511.

Yamamoto T., Davis C.G., Brown M.S., Schneider W.J., Casey M.L., Goldstein J.L., and Russell D.W. 1984. The human LDL receptor: A cysteine-rich protein with multiple *Alu* sequences in its mRNA. *Cell* 39: 27–38.

Yarmolinsky M.B. and Sternberg N. 1988. Bacteriophage P1. In *The bacteriophages* (ed. R. Calendar), vol. 1, pp. 291–438. Plenum Press, New York.

Yokobata K., Trenchak B., and de Jong P.J. 1991. Rescue of unstable cosmids by in vitro packaging. *Nucleic Acids Res.* **19**: 403–404.

Zabarovsky E.R. and Allikmets R.L. 1986. An improved technique for the efficient construction of gene libraries by partial filling in of cohesive ends. *Gene* **42**: 119–123.

Zehetner G. and Lehrach H. 1994. The reference library system-sharing biological material and experimental data. *Nature* **367**: 489–491.

Zimmer R. and Verrinder Gibbins A.M. 1997. Construction and characterization of a large-fragment chicken bacterial artificial chromosome library. *Genomics* **42**: 217–226.

Chapter 5

Gel Electrophoresis of DNA and Pulsed-field Agarose Gel Electrophoresis

5.1

ELECTROPHORESIS THROUGH AGAROSE OR POLYACRYLAMIDE GELS lies near the heart of molecular cloning and is used to separate, identify, and purify DNA fragments. The technique is simple, rapid to perform, and capable of resolving fragments of DNA that cannot be separated adequately by other procedures, such as density gradient centrifugation. Furthermore, the location of DNA within the gel can be determined directly by staining with low concentrations of fluorescent intercalating dyes, such as ethidium bromide or SYBR Gold; bands containing as little as 20 pg of double-stranded DNA can be detected by direct examination of the gel in UV. If necessary, these bands of DNA can be recovered from the gel and used for a variety of purposes.

Agarose and polyacrylamide gels can be poured in a variety of shapes, sizes, and porosities and can be run in a number of different configurations. The choices within these parameters depend primarily on the sizes of the fragments being separated. Polyacrylamide gels are most effective for separating small fragments of DNA (5–500 bp). Their resolving power is extremely high, and fragments of DNA that differ in size by as little as 1 bp in length or by as little as 0.1% of their mass can be separated from one another. Although they can be run very rapidly and can accommodate comparatively large quantities of DNA, polyacrylamide gels have the disadvantage of being more difficult to prepare and handle than agarose gels. Polyacrylamide gels are run in a vertical configuration in a constant electric field.

Agarose gels have a lower resolving power than polyacrylamide gels, but they have a greater range of separation. DNAs from 50 bp to several megabases in length can be separated on agarose gels of various concentrations and configurations. Small DNA fragments (50–20,000 bp) are best resolved in agarose gels run in a horizontal configuration in an electric field of constant strength and direction. Under these conditions, the velocity of the DNA fragments decreases as their length increases and is proportional to electric field strength (McDonell et al. 1977; Fangman 1978; Calladine et al. 1991). However, this simple relationship breaks down once the size of DNA fragments exceeds a maximum value, which is defined chiefly by the composition of the gel and the strength of the electric field (Hervet and Bean 1987). This limit of resolution is reached when the radius of gyration of the linear DNA duplex exceeds the pore size of the gel. The DNA can then no longer be sieved by the gel according to its size but must instead migrate "end-on" through the matrix as if through a sinuous tube. This mode of migration is known as "reptation." Several mathematical descriptions of reptation have been published previously (please see Lerman and Frisch 1982; Lumpkin and Zimm 1982; Stellwagen 1983; Edmondson and Gray 1984; Slater and Noolandi 1985, 1986; Lalande et al. 1987).

The greater the pore size of the gel, the larger the DNA that can be sieved. Thus, agarose gels cast with low concentrations of agarose (0.1–0.2% w/v) are capable of resolving extremely large DNA molecules (Fangman 1978; Serwer 1980). However, such gels are extremely fragile and must be run for several days. Even then, they are incapable of resolving linear DNA molecules larger than 750 kb in length. The importance of this limitation becomes apparent with the realization that a single genetic locus (e.g., the human dystrophin locus) may occupy several thousand kilobases (several megabases) of DNA and that DNA molecules in the individual chromosomes of lower eukaryotes may be 7000 kb or more in length.

A solution to this problem was found in 1984, when Schwartz and Cantor reported the development of pulsed-field gel electrophoresis (PFGE). In this method, alternating orthogonal electric fields are applied to a gel. Large DNA molecules become trapped in their reptation tubes every time the direction of the electric field is altered and can make no further progress through the gel until they have reoriented themselves along the new axis of the electric field. The larger the DNA molecule, the longer the time required for this realignment. Molecules of DNA whose reorientation times are less than the period of the electric pulse will therefore be fractionated according to size. The limit of resolution of PFGE depends on several factors, including:

- the degree of uniformity of the two electric fields

- the absolute lengths of the electric pulses

- the angles between the two electric fields

- the relative strength of the electric field

The original PFGE method described by Schwartz and Cantor (1984) was capable of resolving DNAs up to 2000 kb in length. However, as a consequence of improvements to the technique, resolution of DNA molecules larger than 6000 kb can now be achieved. These developments mean that PFGE can be used to determine the size of bacterial genomes and the numbers and sizes of chromosomes of simpler eukaryotes (e.g., *Neurospora crassa*, *Saccharomyces cerevisiae*, and *Schizosaccharomyces pombe*). For all organisms, from bacteria to humans, PFGE is used to study genome organization and to clone and analyze large fragments.

EARLY ANALYSIS OF DNA USING ELECTROPHORESIS

The idea of using electrophoresis through a supporting matrix to analyze DNA came from Vin Thorne, a biochemist/virologist who in the mid-1960s was working at the Institute of Virology in Glasgow. Thorne was interested in finding better ways to characterize the multiple forms of DNA that could be extracted from purified particles of polyomavirus. He reasoned that a combination of frictional and electrical forces would allow separation of DNA molecules that differed in shape or size. Using electrophoresis through agar gels, he was able to separate superhelical, nicked, and linear forms of polyomavirus DNA that had been radiolabeled with [^{3}H]thymidine (Thorne 1966, 1967). In those days, viral and mitochondrial DNAs were the only intact genomes that could be prepared in pure form. Thorne's work therefore attracted little general interest until the early 1970s when restriction enzymes opened the possibility of analyzing larger DNAs, and a way was found to detect small quantities of nonradioactive DNA in gels.

The notion of using ethidium bromide to stain unlabeled DNA in gels seems to have occurred independently to two groups. The procedure used by Aaij and Borst (1972) involved immersing the gel in concentrated dye solution and a lengthy destaining process to reduce the background fluorescence. At Cold Spring Harbor Laboratory, a group of investigators had found that *Haemophilus parainfluenzae* contained two restriction activities and were attempting to separate the enzymes by ion-exchange chromatography. Searching for ways to assay column fractions rapidly, they decided to stain agarose gels containing fragments of SV40 DNA with low concentrations of ethidium bromide. They soon realized that the dye could be incorporated into the gel and running buffer without significantly affecting the migration of linear DNA fragments through the gel. The technique described in their paper (Sharp et al. 1973) is still widely used in an essentially unaltered form today.

Between 1972 and 1975, there was a vast increase in the use of agarose gels as investigators mapped cleavage sites on their favorite DNAs with the rapidly expanding suite of restriction enzymes. In those days, gels were cast in sawn-off glass pipettes and were run vertically in electrophoresis tanks attached to homemade Heathkit power packs. Each DNA sample was analyzed on a separate little cylindrical gel. The first modern electrophoresis apparatus was developed by Walter Schaffner, who was then a graduate student at Zurich. Realizing that the electrical resistance of an agarose gel is essentially the same as that of the surrounding buffer, Schaffner constructed horizontal tanks to hold submerged gels that could accommodate more than a dozen samples. Schaffner distributed the plans for these machines to anyone who asked for them. Once people got over their incredulity that his machines actually worked, cylindrical gels cast in little glass tubes rapidly disappeared, and the newer "submarine" gels took hold.

Protocol 1

Agarose Gel Electrophoresis

A GAROSE IS A LINEAR POLYMER COMPOSED OF ALTERNATING RESIDUES of D- and L-galactose joined by α-(1→3) and β-(1→4) glycosidic linkages. The L-galactose residue has an anhydro bridge between the three and six positions (please see Figure 5-1). Chains of agarose form helical fibers that aggregate into supercoiled structures with a radius of 20–30 nm. Gelation of agarose results in a three-dimensional mesh of channels whose diameters range from 50 nm to >200 nm (Norton et al. 1986; for review, please see Kirkpatrick 1990).

Commercially prepared agarose polymers are believed to contain ~800 galactose residues per chain. However, agarose is not homogeneous: The average length of the polysaccharide chains varies from batch to batch and from manufacturer to manufacturer. In addition, lower grades of agarose may be contaminated with other polysaccharides, as well as salts and proteins. This variability can affect the gelling/melting temperature of agarose solutions, the sieving of DNA, and the ability of the DNA recovered from the gel to serve as a substrate in enzymatic reactions. These potential problems can be minimized by using special grades of agarose that are screened for the presence of inhibitors and nucleases and for minimal background fluorescence after staining with ethidium bromide.

THE RATE OF MIGRATION OF DNA THROUGH AGAROSE GELS

The following factors determine the rate of migration of DNA through agarose gels:

- **The molecular size of the DNA.** Molecules of double-stranded DNA migrate through gel matrices at rates that are inversely proportional to the $\log_{10}$ of the number of base pairs (Helling et al. 1974). Larger molecules migrate more slowly because of greater frictional drag and because they worm their way through the pores of the gel less efficiently than smaller molecules.

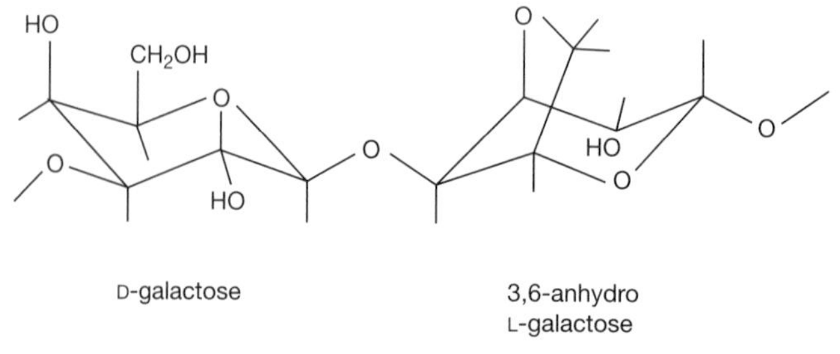

D-galactose   3,6-anhydro
                           L-galactose

FIGURE 5.1 Chemical Structure of Agarose

Buffer: 0.5x TBE, 0.5 µg/ml ethidium bromide,
electrophoresis 1 V/cm for 16 hours

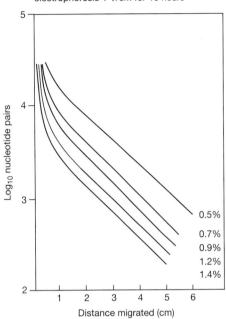

FIGURE 5-2 The Relationship between the Size of DNA and Its Electrophoretic Mobility

- *The concentration of agarose.* A linear DNA fragment of a given size migrates at different rates through gels containing different concentrations of agarose (please see Figure 5-2). There is a linear relationship between the logarithm of the electrophoretic mobility of the DNA (µ) and the gel concentration (ι) that is described by the equation:

$$\log \mu = \log \mu_{0} - K_{r}\iota$$

where μ_{0} is the free electrophoretic mobility of DNA and K_{r} is the retardation coefficient, a constant related to the properties of the gel and the size and shape of the migrating molecules.

- *The conformation of the DNA.* Superhelical circular (form I), nicked circular (form II), and linear (form III) DNAs migrate through agarose gels at different rates (Thorne 1966, 1967). The relative mobilities of the three forms depend primarily on the concentration and type of agarose used to make the gel, but they are also influenced by the strength of the applied current, the ionic strength of the buffer, and the density of superhelical twists in the form I DNA (Johnson and Grossman 1977). Under some conditions, form I DNA migrates faster than form III DNA; under other conditions, the order is reversed. In most cases, the best way to distinguish between the different conformational forms of DNA is simply to include in the gel a sample of untreated circular DNA and a sample of the same DNA that has been linearized by digestion with a restriction enzyme that cleaves the DNA in only one place.

- *The presence of ethidium bromide in the gel and electrophoresis buffer.* Intercalation of ethidium bromide causes a decrease in the negative charge of the double-stranded DNA and an increase in both its stiffness and length. The rate of migration of the linear DNA-dye complex through gels is consequently retarded by a factor of ~15% (Sharp et al. 1973).

- *The applied voltage.* At low voltages, the rate of migration of linear DNA fragments is proportional to the voltage applied. However, as the strength of the electric field is raised, the mobility of high-molecular-weight fragments increases differentially. Thus, the effective range

TABLE 5-1 Properties of Different Types of Agaroses

TYPE OF AGAROSE	GELLING TEMPERATURE (°C)	MELTING TEMPERATURE (°C)	COMMERCIAL NAMES
Standard agaroses			
low EEO	35–38	90–95	SeaKem LE (BioWhittaker)
isolated from *Gelidium* spp.			Agarose-LE (USB)
			Low EEO Agarose (Stratagene)
			Molecular Biology Certified Grade (Bio-Rad)
Standard agaroses			
low EEO	40–42	85–90	SeaKem HGT (BioWhittaker)
isolated from *Gracilaria* spp.			Agarose-HGT (USB)
High-gel-strength agaroses	34–43	85–95	FastLane (BioWhittaker)
			SeaKem Gold (BioWhittaker)
			Chromosomal Grade Agarose (Bio-Rad)
Low melting/gelling temperature (modified) agaroses			
low melting	25–35	63–65	SeaPlaque (BioWhittaker)
	35	65	NuSieve GTG (BioWhittaker)
ultra-low melting	8–15	40–45	SeaPrep (BioWhittaker)
Low-viscosity, low melting/gelling temperature agaroses			
	25–30	70	InCert (BioWhittaker)
	38	85	NuSieve 3:1 (BioWhittaker)
	30	75	Agarose HS (BioWhittaker)

of separation in agarose gels decreases as the voltage is increased. To obtain maximum resolution of DNA fragments >2 kb in size, agarose gels should be run at no more than 5–8 V/cm.

- *The type of agarose.* The two major classes of agarose are standard agaroses and low-melting-temperature agaroses (Kirkpatrick 1990). A third and growing class consists of intermediate melting/gelling temperature agaroses, exhibiting properties of each of the two major classes. Within each class are various types of agaroses that are used for specialized applications, please

TABLE 5-2 Range of Separation of DNA Fragments through Different Types of Agaroses

AGAROSE (%)	SIZE RANGE OF DNA FRAGMENTS RESOLVED BY VARIOUS TYPES OF AGAROSES			
	STANDARD	HIGH GEL STRENGTH	LOW GELLING/MELTING TEMPERATURE	LOW GELLING/MELTING TEMPERATURE LOW VISCOSITY
0.3				
0.5	700 bp to 25 kb			
0.8	500 bp to 15 kb	800 bp to 10 kb	800 bp to 10 kb	
1.0	250 bp to 12 kb	400 bp to 8 kb	400 bp to 8 kb	
1.2	150 bp to 6 kb	300 bp to 7 kb	300 bp to 7 kb	
1.5	80 bp to 4 kb	200 bp to 4 kb	200 bp to 4 kb	
2.0		100 bp to 3 kb	100 bp to 3 kb	
3.0			500 bp to 1 kb	500 bp to 1 kb
4.0				100 bp to 500 bp
6.0				10 bp to 100 bp

see Tables 5-1 and 5-2 and the accompanying panel, CLASSES OF AGAROSE AND THEIR PROP-
ERTIES.

- *The electrophoresis buffer.* The electrophoretic mobility of DNA is affected by the composition
  and ionic strength of the electrophoresis buffer. In the absence of ions (e.g., if water is substituted for electrophoresis buffer in the gel or in the reservoirs), electrical conductivity is minimal

---

CLASSES OF AGAROSE AND THEIR PROPERTIES

- *Standard (high-melting-temperature) agaroses* are manufactured from two species of seaweed: *Gelidium*
  and *Gracilaria*. These agaroses differ in their gelling and melting temperatures, but, for practical purposes,
  agaroses from either source can be used to analyze and isolate fragments of DNA ranging in size from 1
  kb to 25 kb. Several commercial grades of agaroses have been tested that (1) display minimal background
  fluorescence after staining with ethidium bromide, (2) are free of DNase and RNase, (3) display minimal
  inhibition of restriction endonucleases and ligase, and (4) generate modest amounts of electroendo-osmot-
  ic flow (EEO; please see below).

    Newer types of standard agarose combine high gel strength with low EEO, allowing gels to be cast with
    agarose concentrations as low as 0.3%. These gels can be used in conventional electrophoresis to separate
    high-molecular-weight DNA (up to 60 kb). At any concentration of these new agaroses, the speed of migra-
    tion of the DNA is increased by 10–20% over that achieved using the former standard agaroses, depending
    on buffer type and concentration. This increase can lead to significant savings of time in PFGE of megabase-
    sized DNA.

- *Low melting/gelling temperature agaroses* have been modified by hydroxyethylation and therefore melt at
  temperatures lower than those of standard agaroses. The degree of substitution determines the exact melting and gelling temperature. Low melting/gelling temperature agaroses are used chiefly for rapid recovery
  of DNA, as most agaroses of this type melt at temperatures (~65ºC) that are significantly lower than the
  melting temperature of duplex DNA. This feature allows for simple purification, enzymatic processing
  (restriction endonuclease digestion/ligation) of DNA; and allows bacterial transformation with nucleic acids
  directly in the remelted gel. As is the case with standard agaroses, manufacturers provide grades of low-
  melting-temperature agaroses that have been tested to display minimal background fluorescence after
  staining with ethidium bromide, to be free of DNase and RNase activity, and to display minimal inhibition
  of restriction endonucleases and ligase. Low-melting-temperature agaroses not only melt, but also gel at
  low temperatures. This property allows them to be held as liquids in the 30–35ºC range, so that cells can
  be embedded without damage. This treatment is useful in preparing and embedding chromosomal DNA
  in agarose blocks before analysis by PFGE (please see Protocols 13 and 14).

    Chemically modified agarose has significantly more sieving capacity than an equivalent concentration
    of standard agarose (please see Tables 5-1 and 5-2). This finding has been exploited to make agaroses that
    approach polyacrylamide in their resolving power and are therefore useful for separation of polymerase chain
    reaction (PCR) products, small DNA fragments, and small RNAs <1 kb. It is now possible to resolve DNA
    down to 4 bp and to separate DNAs in the 200–800-bp range that differ in size by 2% (please see Table 5-2).

    Because of the variation in products from manufacturer to manufacturer, it is advisable to read the sup-
    plier's catalog to obtain more precise information about specific brands of agarose.

- *Electroendo-osmosis.* In agarose gels, the speed at which nucleic acids migrate toward the positive electrode is affected by a electroendo-osmosis. This process is due to ionized acidic groups (usually sulfate)
  attached to the polysaccharide matrix of the agarose gel. The acidic groups induce positively charged coun-
  terions in the buffer that migrate through the gel toward the negative electrode, causing a bulk flow of liquid that migrates in a direction opposite to that of the DNA.

    The higher the density of negative charge on the agarose, the greater the EEO flow and the poorer the
    separation of nucleic acid fragments. Retardation of small DNA fragments (<10 kb) is minor, but larger
    DNA molecules can be significantly retarded, especially in PFGE. To avoid problems, it is best to purchase
    agarose from reputable merchants and to use types of agarose that display low levels of EEO. Agaroses that
    are sold as "zero" EEO are undesirable for two reasons: They have been chemically modified by adding
    positively charged groups, which neutralize the sulfated polysaccharides in the gel but may inhibit subse-
    quent enzyme reactions, and they have been adulterated by adding locust bean gum, which retards expul-
    sion of water from the gel (Kirkpatrick 1990).

and DNA migrates slowly, if at all. In buffer of high ionic strength (e.g., if 10x electrophoresis buffer is mistakenly used), electrical conductance is very efficient and significant amounts of heat are generated, even when moderate voltages are applied. In the worst case, the gel melts and the DNA denatures. For details of commonly used electrophoresis buffers, please see Table 5-3.

ELECTROPHORESIS BUFFERS

Several different buffers are available for electrophoresis of native, double-stranded DNA. These contain Tris-acetate and EDTA (pH 8.0; TAE) (also called E buffer), Tris-borate (TBE), or Tris-phosphate (TPE) at a concentration of ~50 mM (pH 7.5–7.8). Electrophoresis buffers are usually made up as concentrated solutions and stored at room temperature (please see Table 5-3).

All of these buffers work well, and the choice among them is largely a matter of personal preference. TAE has the lowest buffering capacity of the three and will become exhausted if electrophoresis is carried out for prolonged periods of time. When this happens, the anodic portion of the gel becomes acidic and the bromophenol blue migrating through the gel toward the anode changes in color from bluish-purple to yellow. This change begins at pH 4.6 and is complete at pH 3.0. Exhaustion of TAE can be avoided by periodic replacement of the buffer during electrophoresis or by recirculation of the buffer between the two reservoirs. Both TBE and TPE are slightly more expensive than TAE, but they have significantly higher buffering capacity. Double-stranded linear DNA fragments migrate ~10% faster through TAE than through TBE or TPE; the resolving power of TAE is slightly better than TBE or TPE for high-molecular-weight DNAs and worse for low-molecular-weight DNAs. This difference probably explains the observation that electrophoresis in TAE yields better resolution of DNA fragments in highly complex mixtures such as mammalian DNA. For this reason, Southern blots used to analyze complex genomes are generally derived from gels prepared in and run with TAE as the electrophoresis buffer. The resolution of supercoiled DNAs is better in TAE than in TBE.

TABLE 5-3 Electrophoresis Buffers

BUFFER	WORKING SOLUTION	STOCK SOLUTION/LITER
TAE	1x 40 mM Tris-acetate 1 mM EDTA	50x 242 g of Tris base 57.1 ml of glacial acetic acid 100 ml of 0.5 M EDTA (pH 8.0)
TPE	1x 90 mM Tris-phosphate 2 mM EDTA	10x 108 g of Tris base 15.5 ml of phosphoric acid (85%, 1.679 g/ml) 40 ml of 0.5 M EDTA (pH 8.0)
TBE[a]	0.5x 45 mM Tris-borate 1 mM EDTA	5x 54 g of Tris base 27.5 g of boric acid 20 ml of 0.5 M EDTA (pH 8.0)

[a]TBE is usually made and stored as a 5x or 10x stock solution. The pH of the concentrated stock buffer should be ~8.3. Dilute the concentrated stock buffer just before use and make the gel solution and the electrophoresis buffer from the same concentrated stock solution. Some investigators prefer to use more concentrated stock solutions of TBE (10x as opposed to 5x). However, 5x stock solution is more stable because the solutes do not precipitate during storage. Passing the concentrated buffer stocks through a 0.45-μm filter can prevent or delay formation of precipitates.

TABLE 5-4 6x Gel-loading Buffers

BUFFER TYPE	6X BUFFER	STORAGE TEMPERATURE
I	0.25% bromophenol blue 0.25% xylene cyanol FF 40% (w/v) sucrose in H_2O	4°C
II	0.25% bromophenol blue 0.25% xylene cyanol FF 15% Ficoll (Type 400; Pharmacia) in H_2O	room temperature
III	0.25% bromophenol blue 0.25% xylene cyanol FF 30% glycerol in H_2O	4°C
IV	0.25% bromophenol blue 40% (w/v) sucrose in H_2O	4°C

GEL-LOADING BUFFERS

Gel-loading buffers are mixed with the samples before loading into the slots of the gel. These buffers serve three purposes: They increase the density of the sample, ensuring that the DNA sinks evenly into the well; they add color to the sample, thereby simplifying the loading process; and they contain dyes that, in an electric field, move toward the anode at predictable rates. Bromophenol blue migrates through agarose gels ~2.2-fold faster than xylene cyanol FF, independent of the agarose concentration. Bromophenol blue migrates through agarose gels run in 0.5x TBE at approximately the same rate as linear double-stranded DNA 300 bp in length, whereas xylene cyanol FF migrates at approximately the same rate as linear double-stranded DNA 4 kb in length. These relationships are not significantly affected by the concentration of agarose in the gel over the range of 0.5–1.4%. Which type of loading dye to use is a matter of personal preference; various recipes are presented in Table 5-4.

MATERIALS

CAUTION: Please see Appendix 12 for appropriate handling of materials marked with <!>.

Buffers and Solutions

Please see Appendix 1 for components of stock solutions, buffers, and reagents. Dilute stock solutions to the appropriate concentrations.

Agarose solutions (Tables 5-1 and 5-2)
Agarose gels are cast by melting the agarose in the presence of the desired buffer until a clear, transparent solution is achieved. The melted solution is then poured into a mold and allowed to harden. Upon hardening, the agarose forms a matrix, the density of which is determined by the concentration of the agarose. For rapid analysis of DNA samples, the use of a minigel is recommended (please see the panel on **ELECTROPHORESIS THROUGH MINIGELS** below Step 13).

Electrophoresis buffer (usually 1x TAE or 0.5x TBE)
Please see Table 5-3 for recipes.

Ethidium bromide <!> or SYBR Gold staining solution <!>
For a discussion of staining DNA in agarose gels, please see Protocol 2.

6x Gel-loading buffer
Please see Table 5-4 for recipes.

Nucleic Acids and Oligonucleotides

DNA samples

DNA size standards

Samples of DNAs of known size are typically generated by restriction enzyme digestion of a plasmid or bacteriophage DNA of known sequence. Alternatively, they are produced by ligating a monomer DNA fragment of known size into a ladder of polymeric forms. Size standards for both agarose and polyacrylamide gel electrophoresis may be purchased from commercial sources or they can be prepared easily in the laboratory. It is a good idea to have two size ranges of standards, including a high-molecular-weight range from 1 kb to >20 kb and a low-molecular-weight range from 100 bp to 1000 bp. A stock solution of size standards can be prepared by dilution with a gel-loading buffer and then used as needed in individual electrophoresis experiments.

Special Equipment

Equipment for agarose gel electrophoresis

Clean, dry horizontal electrophoresis apparatus with chamber and comb, or clean dry glass plates with appropriate comb.

Gel-sealing tape

Common types of lab tape, such as Time tape or VWR lab tape, are appropriate for sealing the ends of the agarose gel during pouring.

Microwave oven or Boiling water bath

Power supply device capable of up to 500 V and 200 mA.

Water bath preset to 55°C

METHOD

1. Seal the edges of a clean, dry glass plate (or the open ends of the plastic tray supplied with the electrophoresis apparatus) with tape to form a mold (Figure 5-3). Set the mold on a horizontal section of the bench.

2. Prepare sufficient electrophoresis buffer (usually 1x TAE or 0.5x TBE) to fill the electrophoresis tank and to cast the gel.

   It is important to use the same batch of electrophoresis buffer in both the electrophoresis tank and the gel. Small differences in ionic strength or pH create fronts in the gel that can greatly affect the mobility of DNA fragments. When measuring the sizes of unknown DNAs, ensure that all samples are applied to the gel in the same buffer. The high concentrations of salt in certain restriction enzyme buffers (e.g., *Bam*HI and *Eco*RI) retard the migration of DNA and distort the electrophoresis of DNA in the adjacent wells.

3. Prepare a solution of agarose in electrophoresis buffer at a concentration appropriate for separating the particular size fragments expected in the DNA sample(s): Add the correct amount of powdered agarose (please see Table 5-5) to a measured quantity of electrophoresis buffer in an Erlenmeyer flask or a glass bottle.

   The buffer should occupy less than 50% of the volume of the flask or bottle.

   The concentrations of agarose required to separate DNAs in different size ranges is given in Table 5-2. DNAs differing in size by only a few base pairs can be separated when certain high-resolution agaroses (e.g., MetaPhor agarose, BioWhittaker) are used to cast the gel. Alternatively, modified polysaccharides (commerically available) can be added to regular agarose to enhance separation. This substance, used at a concentration of 0.5–2.0% (w/v), together with agarose, increases resolution, renders the cast gel more clear, and increases the strength of the gel.

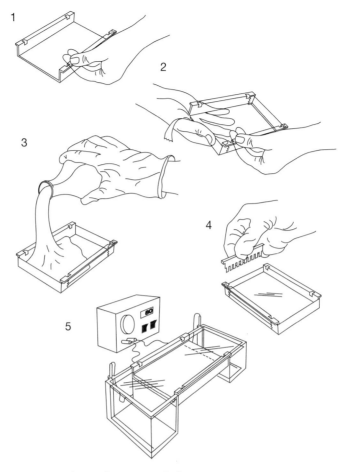

FIGURE 5-3 Pouring a Horizontal Agarose Gel

4. Loosely plug the neck of the Erlenmeyer flask with Kimwipes. If using a glass bottle, make certain the cap is loose. Heat the slurry in a boiling-water bath or a microwave oven until the agarose dissolves.

> ▲ WARNING The agarose solution can become superheated and may boil violently if it is heated for too long in the microwave oven.

> Heat the slurry for the minimum time required to allow all of the grains of agarose to dissolve. Undissolved agarose appears as small "lenses" or translucent chips floating in the solution. Wear an oven mitt and carefully swirl the bottle or flask from time to time to make sure that any unmelted grains of agarose sticking to the walls enter the solution. Longer heating times are required to dissolve higher concentrations of agarose completely. Check that the volume of the solution has not been decreased by evaporation during boiling; replenish with H_2O if necessary.

5. Use insulated gloves or tongs to transfer the flask/bottle into a water bath at 55ºC. When the molten gel has cooled, add ethidium bromide to a final concentration of 0.5 μg/ml. Mix the gel solution thoroughly by gentle swirling.

> ▲ IMPORTANT SYBR Gold should not be added to the molten gel solution. Please see Protocol 2 for further discussion.

> When preparing gels in plastic (lucite) trays, it is important to cool the melted agarose solution to <60ºC before casting the gel. Hotter solutions warp and craze the trays. At one time, solutions con-

TABLE 5-5 Range of Separation in Gels Containing Different Amounts of Standard Low-EEO Agarose

AGAROSE CONCENTRATION IN GEL (% [W/V])	RANGE OF SEPARATION OF LINEAR DNA MOLECULES (kb)
0.3	5–60
0.6	1–20
0.7	0.8–10
0.9	0.5–7
1.2	0.4–6
1.5	0.2–3
2.0	0.1–2

taining high concentrations of agarose (2% or above) were stored at 70ºC to prevent premature gelling. However, this treatment has become unnecessary because of improvements in the methods used to purify and prepare standard agaroses.

6. While the agarose solution is cooling, choose an appropriate comb for forming the sample slots in the gel. Position the comb 0.5–1.0 mm above the plate so that a complete well is formed when the agarose is added to the mold.

> Most apparatuses have side walls or outside "legs" that allow appropriate placement of the comb. If this is not the case, and if the comb is too close to the glass plate, the base of the well may tear when the comb is withdrawn, causing samples to leak between the gel and the glass plate. This problem is more common when low concentrations of agarose (<0.6%) or low-gelling-temperature agarose are used.

7. Pour the warm agarose solution into the mold.

> The gel should be between 3 mm and 5 mm thick. Check that no air bubbles are under or between the teeth of the comb. Air bubbles present in the molten gel can be removed easily by poking them with the corner of a Kimwipe.
>
> When preparing gels that contain low concentrations of agarose (<0.5%), first pour a supporting gel (1% agarose) without wells. Allow this gel to harden at room temperature on the glass plate or plastic tray, and then pour the lower-percentage gel directly on top of the supporting gel. Stacking the gels in this way reduces the chance that the lower-percentage gel will fracture during subsequent manipulations (e.g., photography and processing for Southern hybridization). Make sure that both gels are made from the same batch of buffer and contain the same concentration of ethidium bromide. Gels cast with low-melting-temperature agarose and gels that contain less than 0.5% agarose can also be chilled to 4ºC and run in a cold room to reduce the chance of fracture.

8. Allow the gel to set completely (30–45 minutes at room temperature), then pour a small amount of electrophoresis buffer on the top of the gel, and carefully remove the comb. Pour off the electrophoresis buffer and carefully remove the tape. Mount the gel in the electrophoresis tank.

9. Add just enough electrophoresis buffer to cover the gel to a depth of ~1 mm.

> It is not necessary to prerun an agarose gel before the samples are loaded.

10. Mix the samples of DNA with 0.20 volume of the desired 6x gel-loading buffer (please see Table 5-4).

> The maximum amount of DNA that can be applied to a slot depends on the number of fragments in the sample and their sizes. The minimum amount of DNA that can be detected by photography of ethidium-bromide-stained gels is ~2 ng in a 0.5-cm-wide band (the usual width of a slot). More sensitive dyes such as SYBR Gold can detect as little as 20 pg of DNA in a band. If there is more than 500 ng of DNA in a band of 0.5 cm, the slot will be overloaded, resulting in trailing, smiling, and smearing — problems that become more severe as the size of the DNA increases. When simple populations of DNA molecules (e.g., bacteriophage λ or plasmid DNAs) are to be analyzed, 100–500 ng of DNA should be loaded per 0.5-cm slot. When the sample consists of a very large number of DNA fragments of different sizes (e.g., restriction digests of mammalian DNA), however, it is possible to load 20–30 μg of DNA per slot without significant loss of resolution.

The maximum volume of solution that can be loaded is determined by the dimensions of the slot. (A typical slot [0.5 x 0.5 x 0.15 cm] will hold about 40 µl). Do not overfill a slot with a DNA sample solution. To reduce the possibility of contaminating neighboring samples, it is best to make the gel a little thicker or to concentrate the DNA by ethanol precipitation rather than to fill the slot completely.

11. Slowly load the sample mixture into the slots of the submerged gel using a disposable micropipette, an automatic micropipettor, or a drawn-out Pasteur pipette or glass capillary tube. Load size standards into slots on both the right and left sides of the gel.

    For many purposes, it is not necessary to use a fresh pipette tip for every sample as long as the tip is thoroughly washed with buffer from the anodic chamber between samples. However, if the gel is to be analyzed by Southern hybridization or if bands of DNA are to be recovered from the gel, it is sensible to use a separate pipette tip for every sample.

12. Close the lid of the gel tank and attach the electrical leads so that the DNA will migrate toward the positive anode (red lead). Apply a voltage of 1–5 V/cm (measured as the distance between the positive and negative electrodes). If the leads have been attached correctly, bubbles should be generated at the anode and cathode (due to electrolysis), and within a few minutes, the bromophenol blue should migrate from the wells into the body of the gel. Run the gel until the bromophenol blue and xylene cyanol FF have migrated an appropriate distance through the gel.

    The presence of ethidium bromide allows the gel to be examined by UV illumination at any stage during electrophoresis. The gel tray may be removed and placed directly on a transilluminator. Alternatively, the gel may be examined using a hand-held source of UV light. In either case, turn off the power supply before examining the gel!

    During electrophoresis, the ethidium bromide migrates toward the cathode (in the direction opposite to that of the DNA). Electrophoresis for protracted periods of time can result in the loss of significant amounts of ethidium bromide from the gel, making detection of small fragments difficult. In this case, restain the gel by soaking it for 30–45 minutes in a solution of ethidium bromide (0.5 µg/ml) as described in Protocol 2.

13. When the DNA samples or dyes have migrated a sufficient distance through the gel, turn off the electric current and remove the leads and lid from the gel tank. If ethidium bromide is present in the gel and electrophoresis buffer, examine the gel by UV light and photograph the gel as described in Protocol 2 and as shown in Figure 5-4. Otherwise, stain the gel by immersing it in electrophoresis buffer or H_2O containing ethidium bromide (0.5 µg/ml) for 30–45 minutes at room temperature or by soaking in a 1:10,000-fold dilution of SYBR Gold stock solution in electrophoresis buffer.

    For further details on staining and photography of DNA in gels, please see Protocol 2.

ELECTROPHORESIS THROUGH MINIGELS

During the last several years, methods have been developed for analyzing small quantities of DNA very rapidly using agarose minigels. Several types of miniature electrophoresis tanks are manufactured commercially, typically as smaller versions of the companies' larger electrophoresis models. Each gel slot holds 3–12 µl of sample, depending on the thickness of the gel and the width of the teeth of the comb. Usually, 10–100 ng of DNA in the gel-loading buffer of choice is applied to a slot. The gel is then run for 30–60 minutes at high voltage (5–20 V/cm) until the bromphenol blue and xylene cyanol FF have migrated the appropriate distance. The gel is then photographed as described in Protocol 2.

Minigels are particularly useful when a rapid answer is required before the next step in a cloning protocol can be undertaken. Because the wells are smaller and the gels thinner, less DNA than normal is required for visualization. In addition, because the gels can be prepared in advance and run rapidly, and because they require smaller amounts of reagents, there are considerable savings in both time and money. Many investigators prepare one gel at the beginning of the week, and use it over and over again through the course of an experiment. Thus, a particular set of samples may be loaded, run out onto the gel, and visualized. The gel then may be "erased" by running the samples off the gel into the buffer. Note that minigels are best suited for the analysis of small DNA fragments (<3 kb). Larger fragments resolve poorly because of the high voltages that are generally used and the comparatively short length of the gel.

Protocol 2

Detection of DNA in Agarose Gels

NUCLEIC ACIDS THAT HAVE BEEN SUBJECTED TO ELECTROPHORESIS through agarose gels may be detected by staining and visualized by illumination with 300-nm UV light. Methods for staining and visualization of DNA using either ethidium bromide or SYBR Gold are described here; for further details on detection of nucleic acids, please see the discussion on the Quantitation of Nucleic Acids in Appendix 8.

STAINING DNA IN GELS USING ETHIDIUM BROMIDE

The most convenient and commonly used method to visualize DNA in agarose gels is staining with the fluorescent dye ethidium bromide (Sharp et al. 1973), which contains a tricyclic planar group that intercalates between the stacked bases of DNA. Ethidium bromide binds to DNA with little or no sequence preference. At saturation in solutions of high ionic strength, approximately one ethidium molecule is intercalated per 2.5 bp (Waring 1965). After insertion into the helix, the dye lies perpendicular to the helical axis and makes van der Waals contacts with the base pairs above and below. The fixed position of the planar group and its close proximity to the bases cause dye bound to DNA to display an increased fluorescent yield compared to that of dye in free solution. UV radiation at 254 nm is absorbed by the DNA and transmitted to the dye; radiation at 302 nm and 366 nm is absorbed by the bound dye itself. In both cases, the energy is re-emitted at 590 nm in the red-orange region of the visible spectrum (LePecq and Paoletti 1967). Because the fluorescent yield of ethidium bromide–DNA complexes is ~20–30-fold greater than that of unbound dye, bands containing as little as ~10 ng of DNA can be detected in the presence of free ethidium bromide (0.5 µg/ml) in the gel.

> Ethidium bromide was synthesized in the 1950s in an effort to develop phenanthridine compounds as effective trypanocidal agents. Ethidium emerged from the screening program with flying colors. It was 10–50-fold more effective against trypanosomes than the parent compound, was no more toxic to mice, and, unlike earlier phenanthridines, did not induce photosensitization in cattle (Watkins and Woolfe 1952). Ethidium bromide is still used for the treatment and prophylaxis of trypanomiasis in cattle in tropical and subtropical countries.

Ethidium bromide can be used to detect both single- and double-stranded nucleic acids (both DNA and RNA). However, the affinity of the dye for single-stranded nucleic acid is relatively low and the fluorescent yield is comparatively poor. In fact, most fluorescence associated with staining single-stranded DNA or RNA is attributable to binding of the dye to short intrastrand duplexes in the molecules. For additional details on ethidium bromide, please see the information panel on **ETHIDIUM BROMIDE** in Chapter 1.

Ethidium bromide is prepared as a stock solution of 10 mg/ml in H_2O, which is stored at room temperature in dark bottles or bottles wrapped in aluminum foil. The dye is usually incorporated into agarose gels and electrophoresis buffers at a concentration of 0.5 µg/ml. Note that polyacrylamide gels cannot be cast with ethidium bromide because it inhibits polymerization of the acrylamide. Acrylamide gels are therefore stained with the ethidium solution after the gel has been run (please see Protocol 10).

Although the electrophoretic mobility of linear double-stranded DNA is reduced by ~15% in the presence of the dye, the ability to examine the agarose gels directly under UV illumination during or at the end of the run is a great advantage. However, sharper DNA bands are obtained when electrophoresis is carried out in the absence of ethidium bromide. Thus, when an accurate size of a particular fragment of DNA is to be established (e.g., when a restriction endonuclease map is being determined for a fragment of DNA), the agarose gel should be run in the absence of ethidium bromide and stained after electrophoresis is complete. Staining is accomplished by immersing the gel in electrophoresis buffer or H_2O containing ethidium bromide (0.5 µg/ml) for 30–45 minutes at room temperature. Destaining is not usually required. However, detection of very small amounts (<10 ng) of DNA is made easier if the background fluorescence caused by unbound ethidium bromide is reduced by soaking the stained gel in H_2O or 1 mM $MgSO_4$ for 20 minutes at room temperature.

STAINING DNA IN GELS USING SYBR GOLD

SYBR Gold is the trade name of a new ultrasensitive dye with high affinity for DNA and a large fluorescence enhancement upon binding to nucleic acid. The quantum yield of the SYBR Gold–DNA complex is greater than that of the equivalent ethidium bromide–DNA complex and the fluorescence enhancement is >1000 times greater. As a result, <20 pg of double-stranded DNA can be detected in an agarose gel (up to 25 times less than the amount visible after ethidium bromide staining). In addition, staining of agarose or polyacrylamide gels with this dye can reveal as little as 100 pg of single-stranded DNA in a band or 300 pg of RNA. SYBR Gold shows maximum excitation at 495 nm and has a secondary excitation peak at 300 nm. Fluorescent emission occurs at 537 nm. For additional details on SYBR Gold, please see the panel below.

SYBR GOLD

SYBR Gold is a proprietary fluorescent unsymmetrical cyanine dye, sold by Molecular Probes, that is used to stain single- and double-stranded nucleic acids in gels. Although far more expensive, SYBR Gold has several advantages over phenanthridine dyes such as ethidium bromide. It is more sensitive and can be used to stain both DNA and RNA in conventional neutral polyacrylamide and agarose gels and in gels containing denaturants, such as urea, glyoxal, and formaldehyde. When excited by standard transillumination at 300 nm, SYBR Gold gives rise to bright gold fluorescent signals that can be captured on conventional black and white Polaroid film or on charged couple device (CCD)-based image detection systems. Gels are stained with SYBR Gold after electrophoresis is complete. The level of background fluorescence is so low that no destaining is required. The stained nucleic acid can be transferred directly to membranes for northern or Southern hybridization. SYBR Gold may be removed from nucleic acids recovered from gels by ethanol precipitation.

SYBR Gold is supplied as a 10,000x concentrate in anhydrous dimethylsulfoxide (DMSO). The high cost of the dye precludes its use for routine staining of gels. However, the dye may be cost-effective as an alternative to using radiolabeled DNAs in techniques such as single-strand conformation polymorphism (SSCP) and denaturing gradient gel electrophoresis (DGGE).

SYBR Gold is used to stain DNA by soaking the gel, after separation of the DNA fragments, in a 1:10,000-fold dilution of the stock dye solution. SYBR Gold should not be added to the molten agarose or to the gel before electrophoresis, because its presence in the hardened gel will cause severe distortions in the electrophoretic properties of the DNA and RNA.

The greatest sensitivity is obtained when the gel is illuminated with UV light at 300 nm. Photography is carried out as described below with green or yellow filters. The dye is sensitive to fluorescent light, and working solutions containing SYBR Gold (1:10,000 dilution of the stock solution supplied by Molecular Probes) should be freshly made daily in electrophoresis buffer and stored at room temperature.

PHOTOGRAPHY OF DNA IN GELS

Photographs of ethidium-bromide-stained gels may be made using transmitted or incident UV light (please see Figure 5-4). Most commercially available devices (transilluminators) emit UV light at 302 nm. The fluorescent yield of ethidium bromide–DNA complexes is considerably greater at this wavelength than at 366 nm and slightly less than at short-wavelength (254 nm) light. However, the amount of nicking of the DNA is much less at 302 nm than at 254 nm (Brunk and Simpson 1977).

Today, images of ethidium-bromide-stained gels may be captured by integrated systems containing light sources, fixed-focus digital cameras, and thermal printers. The CCD cameras of these systems use a wide-angle zoom lens (f = 75 mm) that allows the detection of very small amounts of ethidium-bromide-stained DNA (0.01–0.5 ng is claimed). In the more advanced systems, gel images are directly transmitted to a computer and visualized in real time. The image can be manipulated on screen with respect to field, focus, and cumulative exposure time prior to printing. Individual images can be printed, saved, and stored electronically in several file formats and further manipulated with image analysis software programs. The average file size for a stained agarose gel image is ~0.3 Mb; thus, extensive archiving requires large-capacity storage systems. Although individual printouts cost only a few pennies compared to ~1 dollar for a Polaroid photograph (please see below), the hardware for a minimum integrated system can cost several thousand dollars and considerably more for a setup with a large assortment of accessories. Vendors that sell gel documentation systems include Alpha Innotech (San Leandro, California), Fotodyne (Hartland, Wisconsin), and Stratagene (La Jolla, California).

Although the results obtained with these documentation systems are entirely satisfactory for immediate analysis, the printed images fade during storage and are devoid of esthetic appeal. More pleasing and durable results are obtained from highly sensitive Polaroid film Type 57 or 667 (ASA 3000). With an efficient UV light source (>2500 mW/cm^2), a Wratten 22A (red/orange) filter, and a good lens (f = 135 mm), an exposure of a few seconds is sufficient to obtain images of bands containing as little as 10 ng of DNA. With a long exposure time and a strong UV light source, the fluorescence emitted by as little as 1 ng of ethidium-bromide-stained DNA can be recorded on film. For detection of extremely faint DNA bands stained with this dye, a lens with a shorter focal length (f = 75 mm) should be used in combination with a conventional wet-process film (e.g., Kodak no. 4155). This setup allows the lens to be moved closer to the gel, concentrates the image on a smaller area of film, and allows for flexibility in developing and printing the image.

A further 10–20-fold increase in the sensitivity of conventional photography can be obtained by staining DNA with SYBR Gold (Molecular Probes). Of course, the price of this

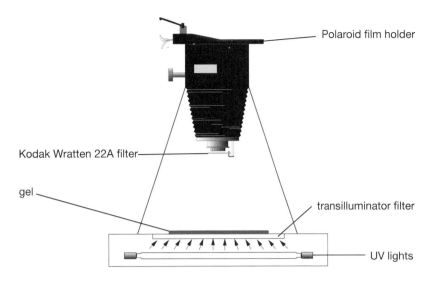

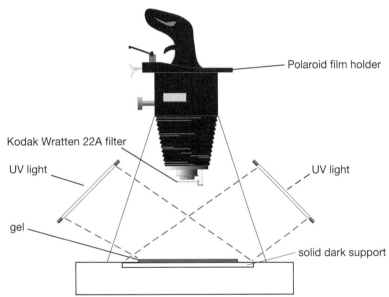

FIGURE 5-4 Photography of Gels by Ultraviolet Illumination

The top diagram shows the arrangement of the UV light source, the gel, and the camera that is used for photography by transmitted light. The bottom diagram shows the arrangement that is used for photography by incident light.

increase in sensitivity is steep: 10 liters of working solution of SYBR Gold stain costs more than 100 dollars, whereas the same amount of ethidium bromide costs ~5 cents. Detection of DNAs stained with this dye requires the use of a yellow or green gelatin or cellophane filter (S-7569, available from Molecular Probes or Kodak) with the camera and illumination with 300-nm UV light.

Protocol 3

Recovery of DNA from Agarose Gels: Electrophoresis onto DEAE-cellulose Membranes

Many methods have been developed over the years to recover DNA from agarose and polyacrylamide gels. Even now, scarcely an issue of technically oriented molecular cloning journals is printed without some variation on this general procedure. Despite the plethora of methods, none of these have proven satisfactory in all hands. The problems associated with the efficient recovery of DNA from agarose gels include:

- *DNA recovered from agarose gels is frequently difficult to ligate, digest, or radiolabel.* This difficulty is usually caused by charged polysaccharide inhibitors in the eluted DNA. In the past, most grades of agarose were contaminated with poorly characterized polysaccharides, which are extracted from the gel along with the DNA. These substances are potent inhibitors of many of the enzymes commonly used in molecular cloning. Although improvements in the quality of agarose have reduced this problem considerably, there are still occasions when DNA is recovered in a nonreactive form.

- *Inefficient recovery of large fragments of DNA.* The efficiency with which DNA is recovered from agarose gels is a function of its molecular weight. Although most methods give reasonable yields of DNA fragments that are <5 kb in length (>50%), none of them are entirely satisfactory for the recovery of larger fragments. As the size of the DNA fragments increases, the yield progressively decreases, especially when the DNA is purified by methods that involve binding to a solid matrix such as a diethylaminoethyl (DEAE)-cellulose membrane. Larger fragments bind more tenaciously to such supports and are more difficult to elute.

- *Inefficient recovery of small amounts of DNA.* The smaller the amount of DNA in the band, the lower the yield of purified fragments. In some methods, the loss of material is so great that it is not worthwhile to attempt to recover bands that contain <500 ng of DNA.

- *Inability to recover a number of different fragments simultaneously.* Several of the techniques are labor-intensive and consist of many individual manipulations. The number of fragments that can be processed at any one time is therefore limited.

In this protocol, DNA is recovered from an agarose gel by electrophoresis onto a positively charged DEAE-cellulose membrane. Fragments of DNA are first separated by electrophoresis through an agarose gel of the appropriate concentration. A slit is then cut in the gel immediately ahead of the DNA band(s) of interest, and a sliver of DEAE-cellulose membrane is inserted into the slit. The method can also be adapted for eluting DNA from a slice of polyacrylamide gel by introducing the polyacrylamide slice into the slit in an agarose gel, just ahead of the DEAE-cellulose membrane. Electrophoresis is continued until all of the DNA in the band has been collected onto the membrane. The membrane is then removed from the slit and washed free of contaminants in a buffer of low ionic strength. The DNA is finally eluted from the membrane in a buffer of high ionic strength. The DNA recovered from the membrane is of high purity and can be used for the most demanding tasks (e.g., transformation of mammalian cell lines).

The following method is based on the procedure of Girvitz et al. (1980), who used a dialysis membrane to trap bands of DNA. The original procedure was later modified by Dretzen et al. (1981), who replaced the dialysis membrane with DEAE paper (the recovery of DNA is much more efficient when a DEAE membrane is used). However, because DNAs larger than 5 kb are eluted from the positively charged membrane with progressively decreasing efficiency, the method is unsuitable for DNA fragments larger than ~10 kb in size. Electrophoresis onto a DEAE-cellulose membrane cannot be used to isolate single-stranded DNAs, which bind tenaciously to the membrane.

The protocols in the following pages describe methods for extracting and purifying DNA from agarose and polyacrylamide gels that have worked well in several laboratories and, in our hands, are consistent and reliable.

- Electrophoresis onto a DEAE-cellulose membrane (this protocol) is a relatively simple technique that can be performed simultaneously on many samples and consistently gives high yields of fragments between 500 bp and 5 kb in length.

- Electroelution into dialysis bags (Protocol 4) is an inconvenient but effective technique for the recovery of large fragments of DNA (>5 kb in length) and can be used to elute DNA from polyacrylamide gels. Purification of DNA recovered from gels by anion-exchange chromatography (Protocol 5) is an efficient but labor-intensive procedure.

- The recovery of DNA from gels cast with low-melting-temperature agarose (Protocols 6 and 7) can be less reproducible than other methods but has the advantage that certain enzyme reactions (e.g., digestion with restriction enzymes and ligation) can be carried out directly in the melted gel.

- DNA may also be recovered from agarose gels by adsorbtion onto glass beads (please see the panel on **ALTERNATIVE PROTOCOL: RECOVERY OF DNA FROM AGAROSE GELS USING GLASS BEADS** in Protocol 6).

MATERIALS

CAUTION: Please see Appendix 12 for appropriate handling of materials marked with <!>.

Buffers and Solutions

Please see Appendix 1 for components of stock solutions, buffers, and reagents. Dilute stock solutions to the appropriate concentrations.

Ammonium acetate (10 M)
DEAE high-salt elution buffer
    50 mM Tris-Cl (pH 8.0)
    1 M NaCl
    10 mM EDTA (pH 8.0)

DEAE low-salt wash buffer
  50 mM Tris-Cl (pH 8.0)
  0.15 M NaCl
  10 mM EDTA (pH 8.0)
EDTA (10 mM, pH 8.0)
Ethanol
6x Gel-loading buffer
  For a list of gel-loading buffers and recipes, please see Table 5-4 in Protocol 1.
NaOH (0.5 N) <!>
Phenol:chloroform (1:1, v/v) <!>
Sodium acetate (3 M, pH 5.2)
TE (pH 8.0)

Enzymes and Buffers

Restriction endonucleases

Gels

Agarose gels, containing 0.5 μg/ml ethidium bromide <!>
  Prepare gels containing a concentration of agarose (Protocol 1) appropriate for separating the fragments in the DNA sample. One of the gels is used for isolation of DNA and the other is used for analysis of the DNA recovered from the gel.

Nucleic Acids and Oligonucleotides

DNA sample
DNA standards
RNA, yeast carrier tRNA
  Optional: Use to improve recovery of DNA during precipitation. Please see Step 10.
  Prepare a solution containing yeast tRNA (Boehringer Mannheim or Sigma) at a concentration of 10 mg/ml in sterile TE (pH 7.6), 0.1 M NaCl. Extract the solution twice with phenol (equilibrated in Tris-Cl at pH 7.6) and twice with chloroform. Precipitate the RNA with 2.5 volumes of ethanol at room temperature, and recover the RNA by centrifugation at 5000*g* (6500 rpm in a Sorvall SS-34 rotor) for 15 minutes at 4ºC. Dissolve the pellet of RNA at a concentration of 10 mg/ml in sterile TE (pH 7.6). Store the carrier RNA in small aliquots at –20ºC.

Special Equipment

DEAE-cellulose membranes
  These membranes can be obtained from Schleicher & Schuell (NA-45) or from Whatman.
Ultraviolet lamp, hand-held, long-wavelength (302 nm) <!>
Water bath preset to 65ºC

METHOD

1. Digest an amount of DNA that will yield at least 100 ng of the fragment(s) of interest. Separate the fragments by electrophoresis through an agarose gel of the appropriate concentration that contains 0.5 μg/ml ethidium bromide, and locate the band of interest with a hand-held, long-wavelength UV lamp.

   Excitation of the ethidium bromide–DNA complex may cause photobleaching of the dye and single-strand breaks. Use of a light source that emits at 302 nm instead of 254 nm will minimize both effects.

2. Use a sharp scalpel or razor blade to make an incision in the gel directly in front of the leading edge of the band of interest and ~2 mm wider than the band on each side.

   If DNA is to be eluted from an entire lane of an agarose gel (e.g., a restriction digest of mammalian genomic DNA), make the incision in the gel *parallel* to the lane of interest and place a single long piece of DEAE-cellulose membrane (prepared as in Step 3) into the incision. *Reorient* the gel so that the DNA can be transferred electrophoretically from the gel to the membrane. After electrophoresis, remove the membrane and cut it into segments. Elute DNA of the desired size from the appropriate segment(s) of the membrane as described in Steps 7–11.

3. Wearing gloves, cut a piece of DEAE-cellulose membrane that is the same width as the incision and slightly deeper (1 mm) than the gel. Soak the membrane in 10 mM EDTA (pH 8.0) for 5 minutes at room temperature. To activate the membrane, replace the EDTA with 0.5 N NaOH, and soak the membrane for a further 5 minutes. Wash the membrane six times in sterile H$_2$O.

   Do not use larger pieces of membrane than necessary, as this excess reduces the efficiency with which DNA can be eluted.

   The strips may be stored at 4ºC in sterile H$_2$O for several weeks after they have been activated.

4. Use blunt-ended forceps or tweezers to hold apart the walls of the incision on the agarose gel and insert the membrane into the slit. Remove the forceps and close the incision, being careful not to trap air bubbles.

   Minimize the chance of contamination with unwanted species of DNA by either

   - cutting out a segment of gel containing the band of interest and transfering it to a hole of the appropriate size cut in another region of the gel far from any other species of DNA

     or

   - inserting a second piece of membrane above the band of interest to trap unwanted species of DNA

5. Resume electrophoresis (5 V/cm) until the band of DNA has just migrated onto the membrane. Follow the progress of the electrophoresis with a hand-held, long-wavelength (302 nm) UV lamp.

   Electrophoresis should be continued for the minimum time necessary to transfer the DNA from the gel to the membrane. Extended electrophoresis can result in cross-contamination with other DNA fragments (see above) or unnecessary accumulation of contaminants from the agarose.

6. When all of the DNA has left the gel and is trapped on the membrane, turn off the electric current. Use blunt-ended forceps to recover the membrane and rinse it in 5–10 ml of DEAE low-salt wash buffer at room temperature to remove any agarose pieces from the membrane.

   Do not allow the membrane to dry; otherwise, the DNA becomes irreversibly bound.

7. Transfer the membrane to a microfuge tube. Add enough DEAE high-salt elution buffer to cover the membrane completely. The membrane should be crushed or folded gently, but not tightly packed. Close the lid of the tube and incubate it for 30 minutes at 65ºC.

   Check the tube from time to time to ensure that the membrane does not expand above the level of the buffer.

8. While the DNA is eluting from the membrane, photograph the gel as described in Protocol 2 to establish a record of which bands were isolated.

9. Transfer the fluid from Step 7 to a fresh microfuge tube. Add a second aliquot of DEAE high-salt elution buffer to the membrane, and incubate the tube for a further 15 minutes at 65ºC. Combine the two aliquots of DEAE high-salt elution buffer.

   Check under UV illumination that the membrane no longer contains a visible smear of ethidium-bromide-stained DNA. Discard the used membrane.

10. Extract the high-salt eluate once with phenol:chloroform. Transfer the aqueous phase to a fresh microfuge tube, and add 0.2 volume of 10 M ammonium acetate and 2 volumes of ethanol at 4ºC. Store the mixture for 10 minutes at room temperature, and recover the DNA by centrifugation at maximum speed for 10 minutes at room temperature in a microfuge. Carefully rinse the pellet with 70% ethanol, store the open tube on the bench for a few minutes to allow the ethanol to evaporate, and then redissolve the DNA in 3–5 µl of TE (pH 8.0).

    The addition of 10 µg of carrier RNA before precipitation may improve the recovery of small amounts of DNA. However, before adding the RNA, make sure that the presence of RNA will not compromise any subsequent enzymatic reactions in which the DNA is used as a substrate or template.

11. If exceptionally pure DNA is required (e.g., for microinjection of fertilized mouse eggs or electroporation of cultured cells), reprecipitate the DNA with ethanol as follows.

    a. Suspend the DNA in 200 µl of TE (pH 8.0), add 25 µl of 3 M sodium acetate (pH 5.2), and precipitate the DNA once more with 2 volumes of ethanol at 4ºC.

    b. Recover the DNA by centrifugation at maximum speed for 5–15 minutes at 4ºC in a microfuge.

    c. Carefully rinse the pellet with 70% ethanol. Store the open tube on the bench for a few minutes to allow the ethanol to evaporate, and then dissolve the DNA in 3–5 µl of TE (pH 8.0).

12. Check the amount and quality of the DNA by gel electrophoresis. Mix a small aliquot (~10–50 ng) of the final preparation of the fragment with 10 µl of TE (pH 8.0), and add 2 µl of the desired gel-loading buffer (please see Table 5-4 in Protocol 1). Load and run an agarose gel of the appropriate concentration, using as markers restriction digests of known quantities of the original DNA and the appropriate DNA size standards. The isolated fragment should comigrate with the correct fragment in the restriction digest. Examine the gel carefully for the presence of faint fluorescent bands that signify the presence of contaminating species of DNA.

    It is often possible to estimate the amount of DNA in the final preparation from the relative intensities of fluorescence of the fragment and the markers.

Protocol 4

Recovery of DNA from Agarose and Polyacrylamide Gels: Electroelution into Dialysis Bags

T HIS TECHNIQUE (MCDONELL ET AL. 1977) ALLOWS THE RECOVERY in high yield of double-strand-ed DNAs of a wide range of sizes from slices of agarose and polyacrylamide gels. The method is somewhat tedious, requiring the insertion of individual gel slices into dialysis bags and is there-fore inefficient when recovering large numbers of fragments. However, electroelution works well and is the technique of first resort should difficulties arise with other methods.

MATERIALS

CAUTION: Please see Appendix 12 for appropriate handling of materials marked with <!>.

Buffers and Solutions

Please see Appendix 1 for components of stock solutions, buffers, and reagents. Dilute stock solutions to the appropriate concentrations.

Ethanol

Ethidium bromide <!> or SYBR Gold staining solution <!>

Phenol:chloroform (1:1, v/v) <!>

Sodium acetate (3 M, pH 5.2)

0.25x TBE electrophoresis buffer

For a list of recipes, please see Table 5-3 in Protocol 1.

Other electrophoresis buffers such as TAE (please see Table 5-3) or 0.5x TBE can be used for electroelu-tion of DNA fragments from agarose and polyacrylamide gels. Buffers are used at reduced strength (0.25–0.5x) to increase the rate at which the DNA migrates through the gel.

0.25x TBE electrophoresis buffer containing 0.5 μg/ml ethidium bromide <!>

Enzymes and Buffers

Restriction endonucleases

Gels

Agarose or polyacrylamide gel <!>

Prepare a gel containing a concentration of agarose (Protocol 1) or acrylamide (Protocol 9) appropriate for separating the fragments in the DNA sample.

Nucleic Acids and Oligonucleotides

> *DNA sample*

Special Equipment

> *Dialysis tubing, boiled*
>> For the preparation of dialysis tubing for use with DNA, please see Appendix 8 or use a commercial preparation of molecular biology grade dialysis tubing (e.g., Life Technologies).
>
> *Dialysis tubing clips*
>> Spectra Por closures from Spectrum Medical Industries.
>
> *Horizontal electrophoresis tank*
>
> *Ultraviolet lamp, hand-held, long-wavelength (302 nm)* <!>

Additional Reagents

> *Step 3 of this protocol requires reagents listed in Protocol 2 of this chapter.*
>
> *Step 10 of this protocol may require reagents listed in Protocol 5 of this chapter.*

METHOD

1. Digest an amount of the sample DNA that will yield at least 100 ng of the fragment(s) of interest. Separate the fragments by electrophoresis through an agarose or polyacrylamide gel of the appropriate concentration, stain with 0.5 µg/ml ethidium bromide or SYBR Gold, and locate the band(s) of interest with a hand-held, long-wavelength UV lamp.

   > Agarose gels may be cast with ethidium bromide or run and subsequently stained either with ethidium bromide or with SYBR Gold (please see Protocol 2). If the DNA is separated by electrophoresis through acrylamide, the gel is subsequently stained either with ethidium bromide or with SYBR Gold (please see Protocols 9 and 10). Excitation of the ethidium bromide–DNA complex may cause photobleaching of the dye and single-strand breaks. Use of a source that emits at 302 nm instead of 254 nm will minimize both effects.

2. Use a sharp scalpel or razor blade to cut out a slice of agarose or polyacrylamide containing the band of interest, and place it on a square of Parafilm wetted with 0.25x TBE. Cut the smallest slice of gel possible to reduce the amount of contamination of DNA with inhibitors, to minimize the distance the DNA need migrate to exit the gel, and to ensure an easy fit into the dialysis tubing on hand.

3. After excising the band, photograph the gel as described in Protocol 2 to establish a record of which band was removed.

4. Wearing gloves, seal one end of a piece of dialysis tubing with a secure knot. Fill the dialysis bag to overflowing with 0.25x TBE. Holding the neck of the bag and slightly squeezing the tubing to open it, use a thin spatula to transfer the gel slice into the buffer-filled bag.

5. Allow the gel slice to sink to the bottom of the bag. Squeeze out most of the buffer, leaving just enough to keep the gel slice in constant contact with the buffer. Place a dialysis clip just above the gel slice to seal the bag. Avoid trapping air bubbles and clipping the gel slice itself (Figure 5-5). Use a permanent felt-tipped marker to label the dialysis clip with the name of the DNA fragment.

6. Immerse the bag in a shallow layer of 0.25x TBE in a horizontal electrophoresis tank. Use a glass rod or pipette to prevent the dialysis bag from floating and to maintain the gel fragment in an orientation that is parallel to the electrodes. Pass an electric current through the bag (7.5

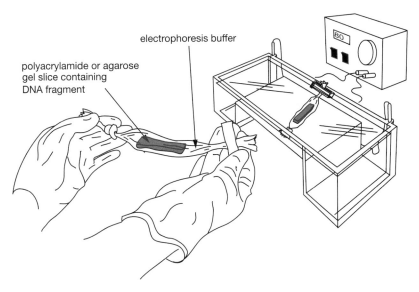

FIGURE 5-5 Electroelution of DNA from the Gel Slice

This method of recovering DNA from gels was originally described by McDonnell et al. (1977).

V/cm) for 45–60 minutes. Use a hand-held, long-wavelength UV lamp to monitor the movement of the DNA fragment out of the gel slice.

> If the dialysis bag containing the DNA fragment is subjected to an electric field for too short a period of time, not all of the DNA will migrate out of the gel slice and the yield will be reduced. Similarly, if the electrophoresis time is too long, the DNA becomes attached to the wall of the dialysis bag. Typically, 45–60 minutes at 7.5 V/cm in 0.25x TBE buffer is sufficient to electroelute ~85% of a DNA fragment of 0.1–2.0 kb from the gel slice. Other buffers, larger DNA fragments, and gels containing high concentrations of agarose require different electrophoresis times.

7. Reverse the polarity of the current for 20 seconds to release the DNA from the wall of the bag. Turn off the electric current and recover the bag from the electrophoresis chamber. Gently massage the bag to mix the eluted DNA into the buffer.

8. After the reverse electrophoresis, remove the dialysis clip, and transfer the buffer surrounding the gel slice to a plastic tube. Remove the gel slice from the bag and stain it as described in Step 9. Use a Pasteur pipette to wash out the empty bag with a small quantity of 0.25x TBE after the initial transfer, and add the wash to the tube.

9. Stain the gel slice by immersing it in 0.25x TBE containing ethidium bromide (0.5 µg/ml) for 30–45 minutes at room temperature. Examine the stained slice by UV illumination to confirm that all of the DNA has eluted.

10. Purify the DNA either by passage through DEAE-Sephacel (please see Protocol 5), by chromatography on commercial resins, or by extraction with phenol:chloroform and standard ethanol precipitation.

Protocol 5

Purification of DNA Recovered from Agarose and Polyacrylamide Gels by Anion-exchange Chromatography

DNA FRAGMENTS PURIFIED FROM AGAROSE GELS, generated by the polymerase chain reaction (PCR) (Chapter 8), or even produced by digestion with restriction enzymes, are often resistant to further enzymatic manipulation. The reasons for this resistance are manifold but are generally ascribed to the presence of "inhibitors." Purification of double-stranded DNA by ion-exchange chromatography on positively charged resins can be used to rid a sample of these poorly defined inhibitors. The negatively charged DNA is bound to a matrix, such as DEAE-Sephacel or DEAE-Sephadex in buffer of low ionic strength, the contaminants are washed away, and the DNA is then eluted from the matrix by raising the ionic strength of the buffer. Plasmid DNAs and single-stranded DNAs should not be purified on DEAE resins since they are difficult to elute once bound.

ALTERNATIVE RESINS

Disposable columns containing reversed-phase resins (e.g., Elutip-d columns, Schleicher & Schuell; NACS, Life Technologies), silica matricies (Wizard PCR Preps Resin, Promega; StrataClean Resin, Stratagene), or glass powder (e.g., Sephaglas, Pharmacia-LKB; GENECLEAN, Q•BIOgene) are available from several suppliers (for more information, please see Chapter 1, Protocol 9). These resins have different elution protocols that can vary dramatically from the method described in the current protocol. For example, double-stranded DNA is bound to glass powder at high ionic strength and eluted in low salt, exactly the opposite to anion-exchange chromatography. It is thus important to follow the instructions provided by the individual manufacturers of the different columns.

MATERIALS

CAUTION: Please see Appendix 12 for appropriate handling of materials marked with <!>.

Buffers and Solutions

Please see Appendix 1 for components of stock solutions, buffers, and reagents. Dilute stock solutions to the appropriate concentrations.

Ethanol

Isopropanol

Phenol:chloroform (1:1, v/v) <!>
TE (pH 7.6)
TE (pH 7.6) containing 0.1 M NaCl
TE (pH 7.6) containing 0.2 M NaCl
TE (pH 7.6) containing 0.3 M NaCl
TE (pH 7.6) containing 0.6 M NaCl
> These four buffers should be sterilized by autoclaving or filtration and stored at room temperature.

Nucleic Acids and Oligonucleotides

DNA samples in TE (pH 7.6)

Special Equipment

Column (small disposable) or Barrel of 2-cc syringe
> Small disposable columns are commercially available (e.g., Bio-Rad, Dispo Columns). However, the barrel of a 2-cc syringe containing a small circle of filter paper to retain the DEAE-Sephacel can also be used. If plastic columns are not available, a siliconized Pasteur pipette plugged with siliconized glass wool can be substituted. For advice on siliconizing glassware, please see Appendix 8.

Resin, preswollen DEAE-cellulose or DEAE-Sephacel
> DEAE-substituted celluloses are commercially available from several manufacturers, including Whatman (DE-52), Pharmacia-LKB, and Sigma. DEAE celluloses have been used to purify both proteins and nucleic acids for many years. They are typically obtained from manufacturers as preswollen resins, such as Whatman DE-52 and Pharmacia-LKB DEAE-Sephacel, in buffers that contain antibacterial agents (e.g., sodium azide, pyridine-*N*-oxide, and benzalkonium chloride). These substances are toxic and can inhibit enzymes. For this reason, it is important to equilibrate the DEAE resin with TE buffer containing 0.6 M NaCl as described in Step 1. Both DEAE-cellulose and DEAE-Sephacel can be sedemented in a microfuge, allowing batch elution methods to be used.

Additional Reagents

Step 10 of this protocol requires reagents listed in Protocol 12 of this chapter.

METHOD

1. Suspend the DEAE resin in 20 volumes of TE (pH 7.6) containing 0.6 M NaCl. Allow the resin to settle, and then remove the supernatant by aspiration. Add another 20 volumes of TE (pH 7.6) containing 0.6 M NaCl, and gently resuspend the resin. Allow the resin to settle once more, and then remove most of the supernatant by aspiration. Store the equilibrated resin at 4°C.

2. Pack 0.6 ml (sufficient to bind 20 μg of DNA) of the slurry of DEAE resin into a small column or into the barrel of a 2-cc syringe.

3. Wash the column as follows:
TE (pH 7.6) containing 0.6 M NaCl	3 ml
TE (pH 7.6)	3 ml
TE (pH 7.6) containing 0.1 M NaCl	3 ml

4. Mix the DNA (in TE at pH 7.6) with an equal volume of TE (pH 7.6) containing 0.2 M NaCl. Load the mixture directly onto the column. Collect the flow-through and reapply it to the column.

5. Wash the column twice with 1.5 ml of TE (pH 7.6) containing 0.3 M NaCl.

6. Elute the DNA with three 0.5-ml washes of TE (pH 7.6) containing 0.6 M NaCl.

7. Extract the eluate once with phenol:chloroform.

8. Divide the aqueous phase equally between two microfuge tubes, and add an equal volume of isopropanol to each tube. Store the mixtures for 15 minutes at room temperature, and then recover the DNA by centrifugation at maximum speed for 10 minutes at 4ºC in a microfuge.

9. Wash the pellets carefully with 70% ethanol, store the open tube on the bench for a few minutes to allow the ethanol to evaporate, and then redissolve the DNA in a small volume (3–5 μl) of TE (pH 7.6).

10. Check the amount and quality of the fragment by polyacrylamide or high-resolution agarose gel electrophoresis.

    a. Mix a small aliquot (~20 ng) of the final preparation of the fragment with 10 μl of TE (pH 8.0), and add 2 μl of the desired gel-loading buffer (please see Table 5-4).

    b. Load and run a polyacrylamide or high-resolution agarose gel of the appropriate concentration, using as markers restriction digests of known quantities of the original DNA. The isolated fragment should comigrate with the correct fragment in the restriction digest.

    c. Examine the gel carefully for the presence of faint fluorescent bands that signify the presence of contaminating species of DNA. It is often possible to estimate the amount of DNA in the final preparation from the relative intensities of fluorescence of the fragment and the markers.

       Only rarely is further purification of the recovered DNA required. The best option is to use chromatography on DEAE-Sephacel columns again, or to use any of a wide variety of specialty resins that are available commercially (please see Chapter 1, Protocol 9). Many of the specialty resins come in prepacked columns that are appropriate for purifying small amounts of DNA using a microfuge. Make sure that the resin chosen is appropriate for purifying linear DNA molecules as opposed to circular plasmids.

Protocol 6

Recovery of DNA from Low-melting-temperature Agarose Gels: Organic Extraction

A GAROSE THAT HAS BEEN MODIFIED BY HYDROXYETHYLATION, a substitution that reduces the number of intrastrand hydrogen bonds, melts and sets at lower temperatures than standard agaroses. The degree of substitution within the polysaccharide chain determines the exact melting and gelling temperature. These properties form the basis of techniques to recover and manipulate DNA fragments in gels (Wieslander 1979; Parker and Seed 1980). Many brands of low-melting-temperature agarose can be held as liquids in the 30–35°C range, so that enzymatic reactions (restriction endonuclease digestion/ligation) can be performed at a reasonable temperature without the agarose solidifying. In addition to enzymatic reactions, low melting/gelling temperature agaroses may be used for rapid recovery of DNA from gels and for bacterial transformation with nucleic acids in the remelted gel.

Because low-melting-temperature agarose remains fluid at 37°C, enzymatic manipulations such as ligation, synthesis of radioactive probes, and digestion with restriction enzymes can be carried out by adding portions of the melted gel slice containing the DNA of interest directly to the reaction mixture (Parker and Seed 1980; Struhl 1985). In general, however, polymerases, ligases, and restriction enzymes work less efficiently in the presence of melted gel than in conventional aqueous buffers. The magnitude of the decrease in enzymatic efficiency can be estimated by setting up control reactions containing different amounts of enzyme and (1) DNA fragments purified from conventional agarose gels (Protocols 3 and 4) or (2) DNA fragments extracted from low-melting-temperature gels (Protocols 6 and 7).

As is the case with standard agaroses used for preparative purposes, manufacturers provide grades of low-melting-temperature agaroses that have been tested to display minimal background fluorescence after staining with ethidium bromide, to be free of DNase and RNase activity, and to display minimal inhibition of restriction endonucleases and ligase.

In the current protocol, DNA fragments are separated according to size by electrophoresis through low-melting-temperature agarose, located by staining with ethidium bromide and UV light illumination, and then recovered by melting the agarose and extracting with phenol:chloroform. The protocol works best for DNA fragments ranging in size from 0.5 kb to 5.0 kb. Yields of DNA fragments outside this range are usually lower, but often are sufficient for many purposes.

An alternative method for recovering DNA from gels is described in the panel ALTERNATIVE PROTOCOL: RECOVERY OF DNA FROM AGAROSE GELS USING GLASS BEADS at the end of this protocol. Recovery by digestion with agarase is described in Protocol 7. A more detailed method for ligation in the presence of low-melting-temperature agarose is described in Chapter 1, Protocol 22.

MATERIALS

CAUTION: Please see Appendix 12 for appropriate handling of materials marked with <!>.

Buffers and Solutions

Please see Appendix 1 for components of stock solutions, buffers, and reagents. Dilute stock solutions to the appropriate concentrations.

Ammonium acetate (10 M)

Chloroform <!>

Ethanol

Ethidium bromide <!> or SYBR Gold staining solution <!>

For a discussion of staining agarose gels, please see Protocol 2.

6x Gel-loading buffer

For a list of gel-loading buffers and recipes, please see Table 5-4 in Protocol 1.

LMT elution buffer

20 mM Tris-Cl (pH 8.0)

1 mM EDTA (pH 8.0)

Phenol:chloroform (1:1, v/v) <!>

Phenol, equilibrated to pH 8.0 <!>

1x TAE electrophoresis buffer

For a list of electrophoresis buffers and recipes, please see Table 5-3 in Protocol 1.

TE (pH 8.0)

Gels

Agarose gel made with low-melting-temperature agarose

This agarose is available from numerous commercial manufacturers (please see Table 5-1 in Protocol 1). Prepare gels of a percentage of agarose appropriate for separating the fragments in the DNA sample. For details on preparing agarose gels, please see Protocol 1.

Nucleic Acids and Oligonucleotides

DNA sample

Centrifuges and Rotors

Sorvall SS-34 rotor or equivalent

Special Equipment

Ultraviolet lamp, hand-held, long-wavelength (302 nm) <!>

Water bath preset to 65°C

METHOD

1. Prepare a gel containing the appropriate concentration of low-melting-temperature agarose in 1xTAE buffer.

   There are several reasons to use TAE buffer instead of TBE buffer. In particular, borate ions inhibit ligation reactions and can interfere with subsequent purification of the eluted DNA fragment on glass beads (please see the panel on **ALTERNATIVE PROTOCOL: RECOVERY OF DNA FROM AGAROSE GELS USING GLASS BEADS**).

   Ethidium bromide may be added to the gel before casting (0.5 µg/ml) or the gel can be stained after the electrophoresis run with ethidium bromide or with SYBR Gold.

2. Cool the gel to room temperature, and then transfer it and its supporting glass plate to a horizontal surface in a gel box.

   The gel may be placed in a cold room to ensure complete setting.

3. Mix the samples of DNA with gel-loading buffer, load them into the slots of the gel, and carry out electrophoresis at 3–6 V/cm.

   DNA of a given size runs slightly faster through gels cast with low-melting-temperature agarose than through conventional agarose gels. For this reason, the voltage applied to low-melting-temperature agarose gels should be lower than that applied to standard agarose gels.

4. If needed, stain the agarose gel with ethidium bromide or with SYBR Gold as described in Protocol 2, and locate the DNA band of interest using a hand-held, long-wavelength (302 nm) UV lamp.

5. Use a sharp scalpel or razor blade to cut out a slice of agarose containing the band of interest and transfer it to a clean, disposable plastic tube.

   Cut the smallest slice of agarose possible to minimize the amount of contamination of DNA with inhibitors.

6. After cutting out the band, photograph the gel as described in Protocol 2 to record which band of DNA was removed.

7. Add ~5 volumes of LMT elution buffer to the slice of agarose, close the top of the tube, and melt the gel by incubation for 5 minutes at 65°C.

8. Cool the solution to room temperature, and then add an equal volume of equilibrated phenol. Vortex the mixture for 20 seconds, and then recover the aqueous phase by centrifugation at 4000*g* (5800 rpm in a Sorvall SS-34 rotor) for 10 minutes at 20°C.

   The white substance at the interface is agarose.

9. Extract the aqueous phase once with phenol:chloroform and once with chloroform.

10. Transfer the aqueous phase to a fresh centrifuge tube. Add 0.2 volume of 10 M ammonium acetate and 2 volumes of absolute ethanol at 4°C. Store the mixture for 10 minutes at room temperature, and then recover the DNA by centrifugation, for example, at 5000*g* (6500 rpm in a Sorvall SS-34 rotor) for 20 minutes at 4°C.

11. Wash the DNA pellet with 70% ethanol and dissolve in an appropriate volume of TE (pH 8.0).

    DNA purified from low-melting-temperature agarose gels is suitable for use in most enzymatic reactions of molecular cloning. Occasionally, more demanding experiments such as transfections, injections, or multifragment ligations require highly purified DNA. Fragments recovered from low-melting-temperature agarose can be purified by chromatography on small DEAE-Sephacel columns (please see Protocol 5) or any of a wide variety of specialty resins that are available commercially as prepacked columns (please see Chapter 1, Protocol 9). Make sure that the resin chosen is appropriate for purifying linear DNA molecules as opposed to circular plasmids.

ALTERNATIVE PROTOCOL: RECOVERY OF DNA FROM AGAROSE GELS USING GLASS BEADS

The recovery of DNA from low-melting-temperature agarose may also be achieved by adsorbing DNA in the melted gel slice to glass beads (or powder) in the presence of high salt. After washing, the DNA is eluted from the beads with a low-salt buffer. This method, although more rapid than organic extraction, may result in somewhat lowered yields. An alternative is to use a commercial kit (Qiaex gel extraction kit and GENECLEAN from Q·BIOgene). These commercial kits provide the necessary materials in prepackaged form.

Additional Materials

Glass beads suspension

In a microfuge tube, suspend 200 μl of acid-washed glass beads (0.2 mm) by vortexing in an equal volume of H_2O. Acid-washed glass beads may be purchased (e.g., from Sigma). Unwashed beads are not recommended.

Sodium iodide solution (6 M)

Dissolve 0.75 g of Na_2SO_3 in 40 ml of H_2O. To this solution add 45 g of sodium iodide and stir to dissolve. Filter the solution through Whatman paper or nitrocellulose and store in the dark (wrap in aluminum foil). The solution should remain stable for up to 2–3 months. If a precipitate is observed, discard the solution.

Wash solution

20 mM Tris-Cl (pH 7.4)

1 mM EDTA

100 mM NaCl

Add an equal volume of ethanol to this solution and store for 3–4 months at 0°C.

Method

1. Follow Steps 1 through 5 of Protocol 6, transferring the gel slice into a polypropylene tube in Step 5.

2. To the gel slice, add ~3–5 volumes of sodium iodide solution, and melt the agarose by incubating for 5 minutes at 55°C.

   Do not heat the solution longer than necessary to dissolve all of the agarose.

3. For DNA samples ≤5 μg, add 5 μl of glass beads. For DNA samples >5 μg, add an additional 2 μl/μg glass beads. Incubate the mixture for 5 minutes at room temperature with occasional shaking.

4. Centrifuge the mixture at maximum speed for 5 seconds in a microfuge, and discard the supernatant.

5. Wash the pellet three times with 500 μl of wash solution, and resuspend in TE (pH 8.0) at ~0.5 μg/μl.

6. Incubate the resuspended DNA/glass beads complex for 3 minutes at 45°C to elute the DNA from the beads.

7. Centrifuge the mixture at maximum speed for 1 minute in a microfuge, transfer the DNA-containing supernatant to a fresh tube, and store at 4°C.

Protocol 7

Recovery of DNA from Low-melting-temperature Agarose Gels: Enzymatic Digestion with Agarase

A N ENZYMATIC METHOD MAY BE USED TO RECOVER DNA from gels cast with low-melting-temperature agarose (Burmeister and Lehrach 1989). In this technique, the fragment containing the DNA is excised from the gel and digested with the enzyme agarase, which hydrolyzes the agarose polymer to disaccharide subunits. The released DNA is then purified by phenol extraction and ethanol precipitation. Because this method is extremely gentle, it is particularly useful for the recovery of high-molecular-weight DNAs extracted from pulsed-field agarose gels (Protocols 19 and 20). However, it also works well for recovery of smaller DNA fragments from agarose gels run in constant electrical fields.

MATERIALS

CAUTION: Please see Appendix 12 for appropriate handling of materials marked with <!>.

Buffers and Solutions

Please see Appendix 1 for components of stock solutions, buffers, and reagents. Dilute stock solutions to the appropriate concentrations.

Ethanol

Ethidium bromide <!> or SYBR Gold staining solution <!>

For a discussion of staining agarose gels, please see Protocol 2.

Gel equilibration buffer

10 mM Bis Tris-Cl (pH 6.5)
5 mM EDTA (pH 8.0)
0.1 M NaCl

Bis Tris-Cl, a component of gel equilibration buffer, is Bis(2-hydroxyethyl)iminotris(hydroxymethyl) methane hydrochloride. It is one of a large series of zwitterionic buffers developed in the mid 1960s by Norman Good and his colleagues in response to the need for compounds with strong buffering capacity at biologically relevant pHs (Good et al. 1966; Ferguson et al. 1980). The pK_a of Bis Tris-Cl is 6.5 at 25ºC, and it is effective as a buffer between pH 5.8 and 7.2 (please see Appendix 1).

NaCl (5 M)

Phenol, equilibrated to pH 8.0 <!>

TE (pH 8.0)

Enzymes and Buffers

Agarase

Agarase is available from a number of manufacturers (e.g., GELase from Epicenter Technologies, β-Agarase I from New England Biolabs, and β-Agarase I from Calbiochem).

Nucleic Acids and Oligonucleotides

DNA sample

Special Equipment

Dialysis tubing, boiled

For the preparation of dialysis tubing for use with DNA, please see Appendix 8 or use a commercial preparation of molecular biology grade dialysis tubing (e.g., Life Technologies).

Microdialysis system (Life Technologies)

Optional, please see Step 6.

Ultraviolet lamp, hand-held, long-wavelength (302 nm) <!>

Water baths preset to 40°C and 65°C

Additional Reagents

Step 1 of this protocol requires the reagents listed in Protocol 6 of this chapter.

METHOD

1. Follow Steps 1 through 4 of Protocol 6 to prepare a gel cast with low-melting-temperature agarose, to load the DNA sample, and to perform electrophoresis.

2. Excise a segment of gel containing the DNA of interest and incubate the gel slice for 30 minutes at room temperature in 20 volumes of gel equilibration buffer.

3. After cutting out the band, photograph the gel as described in Protocol 2 to record which band of DNA was removed.

4. Transfer the segment of gel to a fresh tube containing a volume of gel equilibration buffer approximately equal to that of the gel slice.

5. Melt the gel slice by incubation for 10 minutes at 65°C. Cool the solution to 40°C and add DNase-free agarase, using 1–2 units of agarase per 200-μl gel slice. Incubate the sample for 1 hour at 40°C.

   During this time, the agarose is digested to oligo- and disaccharides. If desired, the DNA solution may be used directly at this stage for ligation, restriction enzyme digestion, and transformation. Alternatively, the DNA may be purified further and concentrated as described in Step 6.

6. Purify and concentrate the DNA:

   TO PURIFY SMALL DNA FRAGMENTS (<20 KB)

   a. Extract the DNA solution twice with equilibrated phenol.

   b. After the second extraction, transfer the aqueous phase to a fresh tube and add 2 volumes of TE (pH 8.0).

      This step helps to prevent precipitation of oligosaccharides.

   c. Add 0.05 volume of 5 M NaCl followed by 2 volumes of ethanol. (Here, 1 volume is equal to the volume of DNA at the end of Step 6b.) Incubate the tube for 15 minutes at 0°C and then collect the precipitate by centrifugation at maximum speed for 15 minutes at 4°C in a microfuge.

d. Carefully remove the ethanol and add 0.5 ml of 70% ethanol at room temperature. Vortex the mixture and then centrifuge as described in Step c.

e. Remove the supernatant and store the open tube on the bench for a few minutes at room temperature to allow the ethanol to evaporate. Dissolve the DNA in an appropriate volume of TE (pH 8.0).

TO PURIFY LARGE DNA FRAGMENTS (>20 KB)

a. Transfer the agarase-digested sample to a dialysis bag, seal, and place the bag in a beaker or flask containing 100 ml of TE (pH 8.0).

b. Dialyze the sample for several hours at 4ºC.

> Alternatively, dialyze the solubilized gel against TE (pH 8.0) in a drop-dialysis apparatus (e.g., Microdialysis System, Life Technologies).

> To prevent shearing, larger DNA fragments should not be subjected to phenol extraction, vortexing, or ethanol precipitation (please see the information panel on **MINIMIZING DAMAGE TO LARGE DNA MOLECULES** in Chapter 2). The inclusion of 30 μM spermine and 70 μM spermidine in the dialysis buffer can enhance recovery of large DNA fragments (>15 kb).

Protocol 8

Alkaline Agarose Gel Electrophoresis

ALKALINE AGAROSE GELS ARE RUN AT HIGH PH, WHICH CAUSES EACH THYMIDINE and guanine residue to lose a proton, and thus prevents the formation of hydrogen bonds with their adenine and cytosine partners. The denatured DNA is maintained in a single-stranded state and migrates through an alkaline agarose gel as a function of its size. Other denaturants such as formamide and urea do not work well because they cause the agarose to become rubbery. Since their invention (McDonell et al. 1977), alkaline agarose gels have been used chiefly to

- measure the size of first and second strands of cDNA synthesized by reverse transcriptase (Chapter 11, Protocol 1)

- analyze the size of the DNA strand after digestion of DNA-RNA hybrids with nuclease S1 (Favaloro et al. 1980)

The use of alkaline agarose gel electrophoresis reached its maximum in the early 1980s when reagents and enzymes were less reliable than today and cloners were of necessity more vigilant about quality control. At that time, alkaline agarose electrophoresis was used routinely to

- check for nicking activity in enzyme preparations used for molecular cloning

- calibrate the reagents used in nick translation of DNA.

Nowadays, only the most compulsive investigators would use alkaline agarose electrophoresis to monitor the quality of enzymes. Nevertheless, the technique remains important because of its speed and accuracy in measuring the length of DNA strands in DNA-RNA hybrids and of first- and second-strand cDNAs.

HISTORICAL FOOTNOTE

Alkaline agarose electrophoresis was developed in Bill Studier's laboratory at Brookhaven National Laboratory as a replacement for laborious alkaline gradient centrifugation of bacteriophage T7 DNA. The first alkaline horizontal gels were equipped with agarose wicks, but later, Studier developed a gel box with removable slot-formers that allowed the gel to be poured, soaked, stained, and viewed in situ. This type of apparatus was simple to construct and became extremely popular for both alkaline and neutral electrophoreses in the years before commercially manufactured gel boxes became available.

Bromophenol blue is quickly bleached by incubation at high pH and is therefore unsatisfactory as a tracking dye in alkaline agarose gels. The superior qualities of bromocresol green were discovered in a systematic screen of an ancient collection of dyes languishing in the Brookhaven Laboratory chemical store.

MATERIALS

CAUTION: Please see Appendix 12 for appropriate handling of materials marked with <!>.

Buffers and Solutions

Please see Appendix 1 for components of stock solutions, buffers, and reagents. Dilute stock solutions to the appropriate concentrations.

Agarose

10x Alkaline agarose gel electrophoresis buffer

500 mM NaOH <!>

10 mM EDTA

Add 50 ml of 10 N NaOH and 20 ml of 0.5 M EDTA (pH 8.0) to 800 ml of H_2O and then adjust final volume to 1 liter. Dilute the 10x alkaline agarose gel electrophoresis buffer with H_2O to generate a 1x working solution immediately before use in Step 3 below. Use the same stock of 10x alkaline agarose gel electrophoresis buffer to prepare the alkaline agarose gel and the 1x working solution of alkaline electrophoresis buffer.

6x Alkaline gel-loading buffer

300 mM NaOH

6 mM EDTA

18% (w/v) Ficoll (Type 400, Pharmacia)

0.15% (w/v) bromocresol green

0.25% (w/v) xylene cyanol

Ethanol

Ethidium bromide <!> *or SYBR Gold staining solution* <!>

For a discussion of staining agarose gels, please see Protocol 2.

Neutralizing solution for alkaline agarose gels

1 M Tris-Cl (pH 7.6)

1.5 M NaCl

Sodium acetate (3 M, pH 5.2)

1x TAE electrophoresis buffer

For a list of electrophoresis buffers and recipes, please see Table 5-3 in Protocol 1.

Nucleic Acids and Oligonucleotides

DNA samples (usually radiolabeled) <!>

Special Equipment

Glass plate

Water bath preset to 55°C

Additional Reagents

Step 3 of this protocol requires the special equipment listed in Protocol 1 of this chapter.

NOTES

- Alkaline gels draw more current than neutral gels at comparable voltages and heat up during the run. Alkaline agarose electrophoresis should therefore be carried out at <3.5 V/cm. A glass plate placed on top of the gel after the run is started slows the diffusion of the bromocresol green dye out of the gel and prevents the gel from detaching and floating in the buffer.

- Partial base hydrolysis of the agarose causes single-stranded DNA to migrate as an uneven band, often at slower rates toward the bottom of the gel and at faster rates toward the top of the gel (Favaloro et al. 1980). If this is a problem, check the buffer to ensure that the final NaOH concentration is 50 mM; make sure that the gel solution is cooled to 60°C before adding the 10x alkaline agarose gel electrophoresis buffer, and cool the gel to room temperature before installing it in the electrophoresis tank and covering it with alkaline electrophoresis buffer.

- It is not strictly necessary to denature the DNA with base before electrophoresis. The exposure of the samples to the alkaline conditions in the gel is usually enough to render the DNA single-stranded.

METHOD

1. Prepare the agarose solution by adding the appropriate amount of powdered agarose (please see Protocol 1) to a measured quantity of H_2O in an Erlenmeyer flask or a glass bottle.

2. Loosely plug the neck of the Erlenmeyer flask with Kimwipes. When using a glass bottle, make sure that the cap is loose. Heat the slurry in a boiling-water bath or a microwave oven until the agarose dissolves.

   > Heat the slurry for the minimum time required to allow all of the grains of agarose to dissolve. Undissolved agarose appears as small "lenses" or translucent chips floating in the solution. Wearing an oven mitt, carefully swirl the bottle or flask from time to time to make sure that any grains sticking to the walls enter the solution. Check that the volume of the solution has not been decreased by evaporation during boiling; replenish with H_2O if necessary.

3. Cool the clear solution to 55°C. Add 0.1 volume of 10x alkaline agarose gel electrophoresis buffer, and immediately pour the gel as described in Protocol 1. After the gel is completely set, mount it in the electrophoresis tank and add freshly made 1x alkaline electrophoresis buffer until the gel is just covered.

   > Do not add ethidium bromide because the dye will not bind to DNA at high pH.

   > The addition of NaOH to a hot agarose solution causes hydrolysis of the polysaccharide. For this reason, the agarose is first melted in H_2O and then made alkaline by the addition of NaOH just before the gel is poured.

4. Collect the DNA samples by standard precipitation with ethanol. Dissolve the damp precipitates of DNA in 10–20 µl of 1x gel buffer. Add 0.2 volume of 6x alkaline gel-loading buffer.

   > Alternatively, if the volumes of the original DNA samples are small (<15 µl), add 0.5 M EDTA (pH 8.0) to a final concentration of 10 mM, followed by 0.2 volume of 6x alkaline gel-loading buffer.

   > It is important to chelate all Mg^{2+} with EDTA before adjusting the electrophoresis samples to alkaline conditions. In solutions of high pH, Mg^{2+} forms insoluble $Mg(OH)_2$ precipitates that entrap DNA.

5. Load the DNA samples dissolved in 6x alkaline gel-loading buffer into the wells of the gel as described in Protocol 1. Start the electrophoresis at <3.5 V/cm and, when the bromocresol green has migrated into the gel ~0.5–1 cm, turn off the power supply, and place a glass plate on top of the gel. Continue electrophoresis until the bromocresol green has migrated approximately two thirds of the length of the gel.

6. Process the gel according to one of the procedures described below, as appropriate for the goal of the experiment:

   ### SOUTHERN HYBRIDIZATION

   a. Soak the gel in neutralizing solution for 45 minutes at room temperature, and transfer the DNA to an uncharged nitrocellulose or nylon membrane as described in Chapter 6, Protocol 8.

      > Alternatively, transfer the DNA directly (without soaking the gel) from the alkaline agarose gel to a charged nylon membrane (please see Chapter 6, Protocol 8).

   b. Detect the target sequences in the immobilized DNA by hybridization to an appropriate labeled probe (please see Chapter 6, Protocol 10).

   ### STAINING

   a. Soak the gel in neutralizing solution for 45 minutes at room temperature.

   b. Stain the neutralized gel with 0.5 µg/ml ethidium bromide in 1x TAE or with SYBR Gold.

      > A band of interest can be sliced from the gel and subsequently eluted by one of the procedures described in Protocol 3 or 4.

AUTORADIOGRAPHY OF WET GELS: Follow one of the methods described in the panel below

---

ADDITIONAL PROTOCOL: AUTORADIOGRAPHY OF ALKALINE AGAROSE GELS

In many cases, DNA analyzed by alkaline agarose gel electrophoresis is labeled with ^{32}P, which can be detected by autoradiography. Drying the gel (please see below) greatly improves the sharpness of the autoradiographic image and slightly increases the sensitivity by reducing quenching. However, if there is sufficient radiolabel in the DNA and the sharpness of the bands is not a major concern, or if the DNA band is to be recovered from the gel, the gel can be autoradiographed without drying.

CAUTION: Please see Appendix 12 for appropriate handling of materials marked with <!>.

Additional Materials

Glass plate (the same size as the gel)
Hybridization bags
   Hybridization bags are available from Fisher or VWR; however, Seal-a-Meal bags from either Sears or Cheswick work just as well and are much less expensive alternatives.
Radiolabeled ink <!> or luminescent markers
Thermal sealer (e.g., Sears)
Trichloroacetic acid (7% TCA)
Whatman 3MM filter papers

Method

FOR AUTORADIOGRAPHY OF WET GELS

1. After completion of electrophoresis, place the gel on a glass plate.

2. Slide the gel and plate carefully into a thin plastic hybridization bag, squeeze the air from the bag, and seal the top of the bag in a heat sealer. Alternatively, wrap the gel and backing plate in Saran Wrap.

   The use of Saran Wrap is less satisfactory because radioactive fluid tends to ooze out of the wrap during autoradiography.

3. Apply adhesive labels marked with radioactive ink or luminescent markers to the outside of the plastic bag or Saran Wrap. Cover the labels with cellophane tape to prevent contamination of the film holder or intensifying screen.

4. In a darkroom, tape the sealed gel to a piece of X-ray film cut to the same size as the glass plate. Wrap the gel and film in light-tight aluminum foil.

   Do not use a metal film cassette; it may break the glass plate and crush the gel.

5. Expose the film for an appropriate period of time (for more information on autoradiography, please see Appendix 8).

   The band of interest can be sliced from the gel and subsequently eluted by one of the procedures described in Protocols 3 through 5.

FOR AUTORADIOGRAPHY OF DRIED GELS

1. Soak the gel in 7% TCA for 30 minutes at room temperature. Agitate the solution every few minutes to ensure that the gel remains covered with fluid.

2. Mount the gel on a glass plate and dry it for several hours under layers of paper towels weighted with another glass plate, or place the gel on two sheets of Whatman 3MM filter paper and dry it under vacuum on a gel dryer.

   Heat should not be used because the gel may melt.

3. Cover the dried gel with Saran Wrap and attach adhesive dot labels marked with radioactive ink or luminescent markers to align the film with the gel. Cover the labels with cellophane tape to prevent radioactive contamination of the film holder or intensifying screen.

4. Place the dried gel and film in a light-tight X-ray film holder. Expose the film to the gel for an appropriate length of time at room temperature or at –70°C with an intensifying screen (for more information on autoradiography, please see Appendix 8).

Protocol 9

Neutral Polyacrylamide Gel Electrophoresis

Cross-linked chains of polyacrylamide, introduced as matrices for electrophoresis by Raymond and Weintraub (1959), are used as electrically neutral matrices to separate double-stranded DNA fragments according to size and single-stranded DNAs according to size and conformation (please see Figure 5-6 and the panel on **POLYACRYLAMIDE**). Polyacrylamide gels have the following three major advantages over agarose gels: (1) Their resolving power is so great that they can separate molecules of DNA whose lengths differ by as little as 0.1% (i.e., 1 bp in 1000 bp). (2) They can accommodate much larger quantities of DNA than agarose gels. Up to 10 µg of DNA can be applied to a single slot (1 cm X 1 mm) of a typical polyacrylamide gel without significant loss of resolution. (3) DNA recovered from polyacrylamide gels is extremely pure and can be used for the most demanding purposes (e.g., microinjection of mouse embryos). The following are two types of polyacrylamide gels that are in common use.

- *Denaturing polyacrylamide gels* are used for the separation and purification of single-stranded fragments of DNA. These gels are polymerized in the presence of an agent (urea and/or, less frequently, formamide) that suppresses base pairing in nucleic acids. Denatured DNA migrates through these gels at a rate that is almost completely independent of its base composition and sequence. Among the uses of denaturing polyacrylamide gels are the isolation of radiolabeled DNA probes, analysis of the products of nuclease S1 digestions, and analysis of the products of DNA sequencing reactions. For methods of preparing and running denaturing polyacrylamide gels, please see Chapter 10, Protocol 1 and Chapter 12, Protocol 8.

- *Nondenaturing polyacrylamide gels* are used for the separation and purification of fragments of double-stranded DNA. As a general rule, double-stranded DNAs migrate through nondenaturing polyacrylamide gels at rates that are inversely proportional to the $\log_{10}$ of their size. However, electrophoretic mobility is also affected by their base composition and sequence, so that duplex DNAs of exactly the same size can differ in mobility by up to 10%. Nondenaturing polyacrylamide gels are used chiefly to prepare highly purified fragments of DNA (this protocol) and to detect protein-DNA complexes (please see Chapter 17).

Methods are presented here for preparing and running nondenaturing polyacrylamide gels (this protocol), for detection of DNA in these gels by staining (Protocol 10), and for autoradiography (Protocol 11). A more specialized application is described in Chapter 13, Protocol 8, in which polyacrylamide gels are used to detect conformational changes in single-stranded DNA resulting from the presence of mutation(s).

This protocol describes procedures for the preparation and casting of polyacrylamide gels, with subsequent assembly and processing for electrophoresis. The percentage of acrylamide

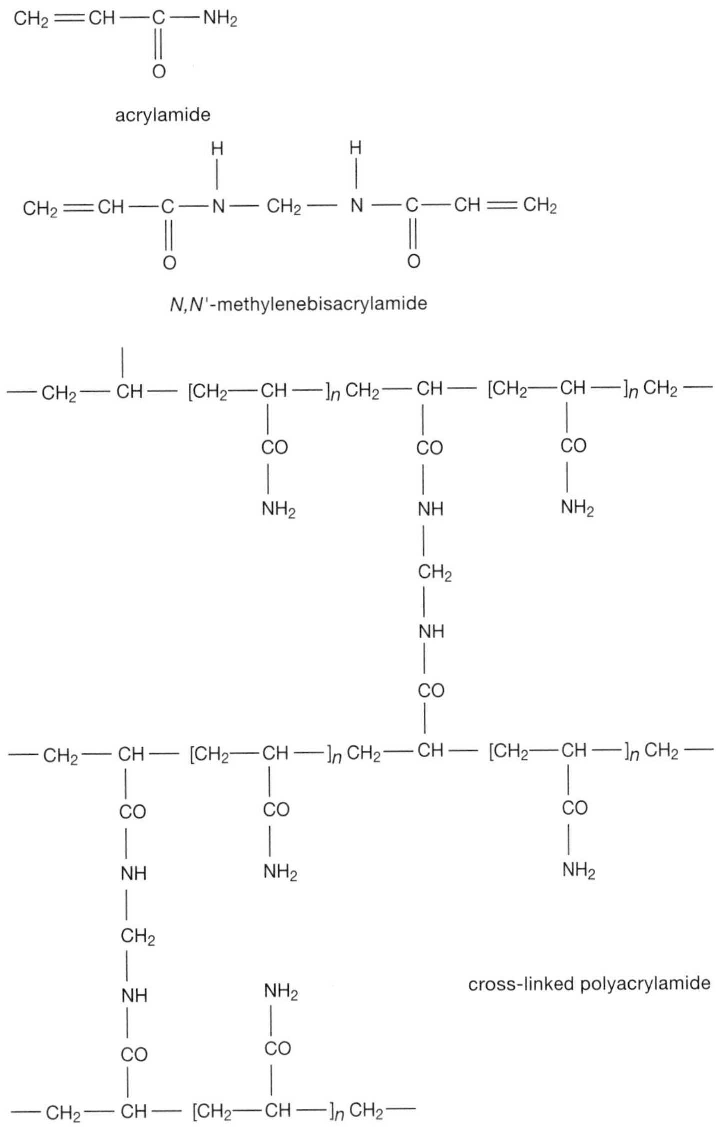

FIGURE 5-6 Structure of Polyacrylamide

Monomers of acrylamide are polymerized into long chains in a reaction initiated by free radicals. In the presence of N,N´-methylenebisacrylamide, these chains become cross-linked to form a gel. The porosity of the resulting gel is determined by the length of chains and degree of cross-linking that occurs during the polymerization reaction.

POLYACRYLAMIDE

In the presence of free radicals, which are usually generated by reduction of ammonium persulfate by TEMED (N,N´,N´-tetramethylethylene diamine), vinyl polymerization of acrylamide monomers results in the formation of linear chains of polyacrylamide. When bifunctional cross-linking agents (e.g., N,N´-methylenebisacrylamide) are included, the copolymerization reaction generates three-dimensional ribbon-like networks of cross-linked polyacrylamide chains with a statistical distribution of pore sizes. Because the mean diameter of the pores formed in these networks is determined by the concentrations of the acrylamide monomer and the bifunctional cross-linker, investigators can adjust the pore size and hence expand the separation range of the gel (Margolis and Wrigley 1975; Campbell et al. 1983; for review, please see Chiari and Righetti 1995). However, a number of other factors also affect the efficiency of separation, including gel thickness, Joulic heating, and electric field strength. Investigators who wish to optimize the separation of DNA fragments, should see Grossman et al. (1992), where these factors are analyzed in a systematic way.

monomer to be used in preparing the gel is determined by the size of DNA fragments to be resolved (please see Table 5-6). The cross-linker *N,N'*-methylenebisacrylamide is usually included at 1/30th the concentration of acrylamide monomer.

TABLE 5-6 Effective Range of Separation of DNAs in Polyacrylamide Gels

CONCENTRATION OF ACRYLAMIDE MONOMER (%)[a]	EFFECTIVE RANGE OF SEPARATION (bp)	XYLENE CYANOL FF[b]	BROMOPHENOL BLUE[b]
3.5	1000–2000	460	100
5.0	80–500	260	65
8.0	60–400	160	45
12.0	40–200	70	20
15.0	25–150	60	15
20.0	6–100	45	12

[a]*N,N'*-methylenebisacrylamide is included at 1/30th the concentration of acrylamide.
[b]The numbers given are the approximate sizes (in nucleotide pairs) of fragments of double-stranded DNA with which the dye comigrates.

TABLE 5-7 Volume of Reagents Used to Cast Polyacrylamide Gels

	REAGENTS TO CAST POLYACRYLAMIDE GELS OF INDICATED CONCENTRATIONS IN 1× TBE[a]			
POLYACRYLAMIDE GEL (%)	29% ACRYLAMIDE PLUS 1% *N,N'*-METHYLENEBISACRYLAMIDE (ml)	H₂O (ml)	5× TBE (ml)	10% AMMONIUM PERSULFATE (ml)
3.5	11.6	67.7	20.0	0.7
5.0	16.6	62.7	20.0	0.7
8.0	26.6	52.7	20.0	0.7
12.0	40.0	39.3	20.0	0.7
20.0	66.6	12.7	20.0	0.7

[a]Some investigators prefer to run acrylamide gels in 0.5x TBE. In this case, adjust the volumes of 5x TBE and H_2O accordingly.

TABLE 5-8 6× Gel-loading Buffers

BUFFER TYPE	6× BUFFER	STORAGE TEMPERATURE
I	0.25% bromophenol blue 0.25% xylene cyanol FF 40% (w/v) sucrose in H_2O	4°C
II	0.25% bromophenol blue 0.25% xylene cyanol FF 15% Ficoll (Type 400; Pharmacia) in H_2O	room temperature
III	0.25% bromophenol blue 0.25% xylene cyanol FF 30% glycerol in H_2O	4°C
IV	0.25% bromophenol blue 40% (w/v) sucrose in H_2O	4°C

MATERIALS

CAUTION: Please see Appendix 12 for appropriate handling of materials marked with <!>.

Buffers and Solutions

Please see Appendix 1 for components of stock solutions, buffers, and reagents. Dilute stock solutions to the appropriate concentrations.

Acrylamide:bisacrylamide (29:1) (% w/v) <!>

Stock solutions other than 29:1 (% w/v) acrylamide:bisacrylamide can be used to cast polyacrylamide gels. However, it is then necessary to recalculate the appropriate amount of stock solution to use. Gels can be cast with acrylamide solutions containing different acrylamide:bisacrylamide (cross-link) ratios, such as 19:1 and 37.5:1, in place of the 29:1 ratio recommended here. The mobility of DNA and dyes in such gels will be different from those given in this protocol.

▲ WARNING Wear gloves while working with acrylamide.

Ammonium persulfate (10% w/v) <!>

Ammonium persulfate is used as a catalyst for the copolymerization of acrylamide and bisacrylamide gels. The polymerization reaction is driven by free radicals that are generated by an oxido-reduction reaction in which a diamine (e.g., TEMED) is used as the adjunct catalyst (Chrambach and Rodbard 1972).

Ethanol

6x Gel-loading buffer

For a list of gel-loading buffers and recipes, please see Table 5-8.

KOH/methanol <!>

Siliconizing fluid (e.g., Sigmacote or Acrylease) (optional)

5x TBE electrophoresis buffer

For a list of recipes, please see Table 5-3 in Protocol 1.

Polyacrylamide gels are poured and run in 0.5x or 1x TBE at low voltage (1–8 V/cm) to prevent denaturation of small fragments of DNA by Joulic heating. Other electrophoresis buffers such as 1x TAE (please see Protocol 1) can be used, but they are not as good as TBE. The gel must be run more slowly in 1x TAE, which does not provide as much buffering capacity as TBE. For electrophoresis runs greater than 8 hours, we recommend that 1x TBE buffer be used to ensure that adequate buffering capacity is available throughout the run.

TEMED <!>

Electrophoresis grade TEMED is available from Bio-Rad, Sigma, and other suppliers. Store the solution at 4°C.

Nucleic Acids and Oligonucleotides

DNA samples

Special Equipment

Binder or "bulldog" paper clips (6–8, 2 inch/5 cm width)

Electrophoresis apparatus, glass plates, comb, and spacers

Some vertical electrophoresis tanks obtained from commercial sources are constructed to hold glass plates of varying sizes. Spacers (usually Teflon, sometimes Lucite) vary in thickness from 0.5 mm to 2.0 mm. The thicker the gel, the hotter it will become during electrophoresis. Overheating results in "smiling" bands of DNA and other problems. Thicker gels must be used when preparing large quantities of DNA (>1 µg/band); however, in general, thinner gels are preferred, as they produce the sharpest and flattest bands of DNA.

Gel-sealing tape

Common types of lab tape, such as Time tape or VWR lab tape, are appropriate for sealing the ends of the acrylamide gel during pouring.

Gel temperature-monitoring strips (optional)

These strips are thermochromic liquid crystal (TLC) indicators that change color as the temperature of the gel rises during electrophoresis. Temperature-monitoring strips are sold by several commercial companies, including BioWhittaker. Temperature-monitoring strips are not needed if an electrophoresis apparatus that has an in-built thermal sensor is used.

Micropipette with drawn-out plastic tip (e.g., Research Products International) or a Hamilton syringe
Petroleum jelly
Syringe (50 cc)

METHOD

Assembling the Apparatus and Preparing the Gel Solution

1. If necessary, clean the glass plates and spacers with KOH/methanol.

2. Wash the glass plates and spacers in warm detergent solution and rinse them well, first in tap water and then in deionized H$_2$O. Hold the plates by the edges or wear gloves, so that oils from the hands do not become deposited on the working surfaces of the plates. Rinse the plates with ethanol and set them aside to dry.

   The glass plates must be free of grease spots to prevent air bubbles from forming in the gel.

3. (*Optional*) Treat one surface of one of the two plates with siliconizing fluid (e.g., Sigmacote or Acrylease): Place the glass on a pad of paper in a chemical fume hood and pour a small quantity of siliconizing fluid onto the surface. Wipe the fluid over the surface of the plate with a pad of Kimwipes, and then rinse the plate in deionized H$_2$O. Dry the plate with paper towels.

   This treatment prevents the gel from sticking tightly to one plate and reduces the possibility that the gel will tear when the mold is dismantled after electrophoresis.

4. Assemble the glass plates with spacers:

   a. Lay the larger (or unnotched) plate flat on the bench and arrange the spacers at each side parallel to the two edges.

      Typically, the two plates are of slightly different size and one of them is notched.

   b. Apply minute dabs of petroleum jelly to keep the spacer bars in position during the next steps.

   c. Lay the inner (notched) plate in position, resting on the spacer bars.

   d. Clamp the plates together with binder or "bulldog" paper clips and bind the entire length of the two sides and the bottom of the plates with gel-sealing tape to make a watertight seal.

      Take particular care with the bottom corners of the plates, as these are the places where leaks often occur. An extra band of tape around the bottom of the plates can help to prevent leaks.

      There are many types of electrophoresis apparatuses available commercially, and the arrangement of the glass plates and spacers differs slightly from manufacturer to manufacturer. Whatever the design, the aim is to form a watertight seal between the plates and the spacers so that the unpolymerized gel solution does not leak out. Several manufacturers also sell precast polyacrylamide gels, which are foolproof but expensive and often can be used only in the manufacturer's gel apparatus.

5. Taking into account the size of the glass plates and the thickness of the spacers, calculate the volume of gel required. Prepare the gel solution with the desired polyacrylamide percentage according to Table 5-7, which gives the amount of each component required to make 100 ml.

6. (*Optional*) Place the required quantity of acrylamide:bis solution in a clean sidearm flask with a magnetic stir bar. De-aerate the solution by applying vacuum, gently at first. Swirl the flask during de-aeration until no more air bubbles are released.

   De-aeration of the acrylamide solution is not essential, but it does reduce the chance that air bubbles will form when thick gels (>1 mm) are poured, as well as reduce the amount of time required for polymerization.

Casting the Gel

7. Perform the following manipulations over a tray so that any spilled acrylamide:bis solution will not spread over the bench. Wear gloves. Work quickly to complete the gel before the acrylamide polymerizes.

    a. Add 35 μl of TEMED for each 100 ml of acrylamide:bis solution, and mix the solution by gentle swirling.

    > Vinyl polymerization of monomer to cross-linked polymer is 90% complete within 5–15 minutes. However, only a fraction of the bisacrylamide molecules become incorporated into cross-links. The rest of the molecules are quickly converted to a cyclic form by an intramolecular reaction between side chains.

    > Gels can be cast with as much as 1 μl of TEMED per milliliter of gel solution to increase the rate of polymerization.

    b. Draw the solution into the barrel of a 50-cc syringe. Invert the syringe and expel any air that has entered the barrel. Introduce the nozzle of the syringe into the space between the two glass plates. Expel the acrylamide gel solution from the syringe, filling the space almost to the top.

    > Keep the remaining acrylamide solution at 4ºC to reduce the rate of polymerization. If the plates have been well cleaned and well sealed, there should be no trapped air bubbles and no leaks. If air bubbles form, they can sometimes be coaxed to the top of the mold by gentle tapping or may be snagged with a bubble hook made of thin polypropylene tubing. If these methods fail, empty the gel mold, thoroughly clean the glass plates, and pour a new gel.

    c. Place the glass plates against a test tube rack at an angle of ~10º to the bench top.

    > This positioning decreases the chance of leakage and minimizes distortion of the gel.

8. As shown in Figure 12-9 in Chapter 12, immediately insert the appropriate comb into the gel, being careful not to allow air bubbles to become trapped under the teeth. The tops of the teeth should be slightly higher than the top of the glass. Clamp the comb in place with bulldog paper clips. If necessary, use the remaining acrylamide gel solution to fill the gel mold completely. Make sure that no acrylamide solution is leaking from the gel mold.

9. Allow the acrylamide to polymerize for 30–60 minutes at room temperature, adding more acrylamide:bis gel solution if the gel retracts significantly.

    > When polymerization is complete, a Schlieren pattern will be visible just beneath the teeth of the comb.

10. After polymerization is complete, surround the comb and the top of the gel with paper towels that have been soaked in 1x TBE. Then seal the entire gel in Saran Wrap and store it at 4ºC until needed.

    > Gels may be stored for 1–2 days in this state before they are used.

11. When ready to proceed with electrophoresis, squirt 1x TBE buffer around and on top of the comb and carefully pull the comb from the polymerized gel. Use a syringe to rinse out the wells with 1x TBE. Remove the gel-sealing tape from the bottom of the gel with a razor blade or scalpel.

    > Wash out the wells thoroughly as soon as the comb is removed. Otherwise, small amounts of acrylamide solution trapped by the comb will polymerize in the wells, producing irregularly shaped surfaces that give rise to distorted bands of DNA.

Loading the Samples and Running the Gel

12. Attach the gel to the electrophoresis tank, using large bulldog clips on the sides or clamps built into the apparatus. The notched plate should face inward toward the buffer reservoir.

13. Fill the reservoirs of the electrophoresis tank with electrophoresis buffer prepared from the same batch of 5x TBE used to cast the gel. Use a bent Pasteur pipette or syringe needle to remove any air bubbles trapped beneath the bottom of the gel.

    > It is important to use the same batch of electrophoresis buffer in both of the reservoirs and in the gel. Small differences in ionic strength or pH produce buffer fronts that can greatly distort the migration of DNA.

14. Use a Pasteur pipette or a syringe to flush out the wells once more with 1x TBE. Mix the DNA samples with the appropriate amount of 6x gel-loading buffer. Load the mixture into the wells using a Hamilton syringe or a micropipette equipped with a drawn-out plastic tip.

    > Usually, ~20–100 µl of DNA sample is loaded per well depending on the size of the slot. Do not attempt to expel all of the sample from the loading device, as this almost always produces air bubbles that blow the sample out of the well. In many cases, the same device can be used to load many samples, provided it is thoroughly washed between each loading. However, it is important not to take too long to complete loading the gel; otherwise, the samples will diffuse from the wells.

15. Connect the electrodes to a power pack (positive electrode connected to the bottom reservoir), turn on the power, and begin the electrophoresis run.

    > Nondenaturing polyacrylamide gels are usually run at voltages between 1 V/cm and 8 V/cm. If electrophoresis is carried out at a higher voltage, differential heating in the center of the gel may cause bowing of the DNA bands or even melting of the strands of small DNA fragments. Therefore, with higher voltages, gel boxes that contain a metal plate or extended buffer chamber should be used to distribute the heat evenly. Many types of gel apparatuses are equipped with thermal sensors that monitor the temperature of the gel during the run. These are particularly useful when striving to minimize variation from one gel run to the next. Alternatively, use a gel-temperature-monitoring strip.

16. Run the gel until the marker dyes have migrated the desired distance (please see Table 5-6). Turn off the electric power, disconnect the leads, and discard the electrophoresis buffer from the reservoirs.

17. Detach the glass plates, and use a scalpel or razor blade to remove the gel-sealing tape. Lay the glass plates on the bench (siliconized plate uppermost). Use a spacer or plastic wedge to lift a corner of the upper glass plate. Check that the gel remains attached to the lower plate. Pull the upper plate smoothly away. Remove the spacers.

    > Occasionally, the gel remains attached to the siliconized plate. In this case, turn the glass plates over and remove the nonsiliconized plate.

18. Use one of the methods described in Protocols 10 or 11 to detect the positions of bands of DNA in the polyacrylamide gel.

Protocol 10

Detection of DNA in Polyacrylamide Gels by Staining

UNLIKE AGAROSE GELS, POLYACRYLAMIDE GELS CANNOT BE CAST in the presence of ethidium bromide because the dye inhibits polymerization of the acrylamide. However, ethidium bromide can be used to stain the polyacrylamide gel after electrophoresis. Because polyacrylamide quenches the fluorescence of the dye, the sensitivity with which DNA can be detected is diminished.

The nucleic acid stain SYBR Gold (Molecular Probes) also can be used to stain a polyacrylamide gel after electrophoresis. It should not be incorporated into the gel at the time of polymerization, as incorporation into the polyacrylamide gel retards and distorts the migration of DNA.

Methylene blue staining, although somewhat less sensitive, provides a less expensive alternative to ethidium bromide or SYBR Gold.

MATERIALS

CAUTION: Please see Appendix 12 for appropriate handling of materials marked with <!>.

Buffers and Solutions

Please see Appendix 1 for components of stock solutions, buffers, and reagents. Dilute stock solutions to the appropriate concentrations.

Staining solution: ethidium bromide solution (0.5 μg/ml stock solution), SYBR Gold stock solution, or methylene blue solution (0.001–0.0025% in TAE buffer) <!>
For a discussion of staining DNA in gels, please see Protocol 2 and Appendix 9.

Gels

Polyacrylamide gel <!>
Prepare and run the gel as described in Protocol 9.

METHOD

1. Gently submerge the gel and its attached glass plate in the appropriate staining solution. Use just enough staining solution to cover the gel completely, and stain the gel for 30–45 minutes at room temperature.

Try to minimize the movement of the staining solution across the surface of the gel during staining. The aim is to keep the gel attached to its supporting glass plate. If the gel becomes completely detached, it can usually be rescued from the staining solution on a large glass plate and transferred to a shallow water bath. In most cases, the gel can then be carefully unfolded and restored to its original shape. To avoid problems, some investigators use a piece of plastic mesh (mesh size 1 cm, available from garden and hardware stores) to hold the gel in place during staining.

2. Remove the gel from the staining solution, using the glass plate as a support, rinse the gel with water, and carefully blot excess liquid from the surface of the gel with a pad of Kimwipes.

   ▲ IMPORTANT Do not use absorbent paper; it will stick to the gel.

3. Cover the gel with a piece of Saran Wrap. Smooth out any air bubbles or folds in the Saran Wrap with the broad end of a slot comb or a crumpled Kimwipe.

4. Place a piece of Saran Wrap on the surface of a UV transilluminator. Invert the gel, and place it on the transilluminator. Remove the glass plate, leaving the gel on the Saran Wrap.

5. Photograph the gel as described in Protocol 2.

   Note that ethidium bromide requires an orange filter and SYBR Gold requires a yellow or green filter. Maximum sensitivity with SYBR Gold staining is obtained by illuminating the gel from above (epi-illumination) with 254-nm wavelength UV light. Gels stained with methylene blue can be photographed with ordinary illumination and without a filter.

Protocol 11

Detection of DNA in Polyacrylamide Gels by Autoradiography

B ANDS OF RADIOACTIVE DNA SEPARATED BY ACRYLAMIDE GEL ELECTROPHORESIS may be detected by autoradiography. Analytical polyacrylamide gels containing radioactive DNA are usually fixed and dried before autoradiography. However, if bands of radioactive DNA are to be recovered from the gel (please see Protocols 4 and 12), the gel should generally not be fixed or dried. In this case, omit Steps 1–3, and proceed directly to Step 4 to process the gel for autoradiography.

MATERIALS

CAUTION: Please see Appendix 12 for appropriate handling of materials marked with <!>.

Buffer and Solutions

Please see Appendix 1 for components of stock solutions, buffers, and reagents. Dilute stock solutions to the appropriate concentrations.

Acetic acid (7% v/v) <!>

Gels

Polyacrylamide gel <!>
  Prepare and run the gel as described in Protocol 9 of this chapter.

Special Equipment

Commercial gel dryer (optional)
Plastic mesh piece (mesh size 1 cm, available from garden and hardware stores) (optional)
Radioactive ink or chemiluminescent markers <!>
Whatman 3MM filter paper

METHOD

1. Immerse the gel, together with its attached glass plate, in 7% acetic acid for 5 minutes. Remove the gel from the fixative by carefully lifting the glass plate from the fluid.

   Try to minimize the movement of fluid across the surface of the gel during fixation. The aim is to keep the gel attached to its supporting glass plate. If the gel becomes completely detached, it can usually be rescued from the acetic acid on a larger glass plate and transferred to a shallow water bath. In most cases, the gel can then be carefully unfolded and restored to its original shape. To avoid problems, some investigators use a piece of plastic mesh to hold the gel in place during fixation.

2. Rinse the gel briefly in deionized H_2O. Remove excess fluid from the surface of the gel with a pad of Kimwipes.

   ▲ IMPORTANT Do not use absorbent paper; it will stick to the gel.

3. (*Optional*) Dry the gel onto a piece of Whatman 3MM paper using a commercial gel dryer.

   Drying the gel is generally necessary only when the gel contains DNA labeled with weak β-emitting isotopes such as ^{35}S or such small amounts of ^{32}P-labeled DNA that long exposures (longer than 24 hours) are necessary to obtain an adequate autoradiographic image.

4. Wrap the gel, together with its supporting glass plate, in Saran Wrap. Smooth out any air bubbles or folds in the Saran Wrap with the broad end of a slot comb or a crumpled Kimwipe.

   If the DNA samples separated through the gel have been labeled with ^{35}S, it is better not to use Saran Wrap because the plastic film will block weak β particles. Make sure that the gel is very dry (in Step 3) and proceed to Step 5.

5. To align the gel and the film, attach adhesive dot labels marked with radioactive ink (please see Appendix 8) or with chemiluminescent markers to the surface of the Saran Wrap. Cover the radioactive ink labels with cellophane tape to prevent contamination of the film holder or intensifying screen.

6. Invert the gel and expose it to X-ray film (e.g., Kodak XAR-5 or equivalent) as follows:

   a. In a darkroom, tape the sealed gel to a piece of X-ray film cut to the same size as the glass plate.

      The plate serves as a weight to ensure good contact between the Saran Wrap and the X-ray film.

   b. Wrap the gel and film in light-tight aluminum foil.

      Do not use a metal film cassette; it may break the glass plate and crush the gel. If the gel has been dried onto a piece of Whatman 3MM paper (Step 3), a metal film cassette may be used.

   c. Expose the film for the appropriate period of time at room temperature or at –70ºC with or without an intensifying screen.

   d. Develop, fix, and dry the X-ray film as recommended by the manufacturer.

Protocol 12

Isolation of DNA Fragments from Polyacrylamide Gels by the Crush and Soak Method

THE STANDARD METHOD TO RECOVER DNA FROM POLYACRYLAMIDE GELS is the "crush and soak" technique originally described by Maxam and Gilbert (1977). The eluted DNA is generally free of contaminants that inhibit enzymes or that are toxic to transfected or microinjected cells. The method requires time but little labor and results in recovery of <30%–90% yield, depending on the size of the DNA fragment. It can be used to isolate both double- and single-stranded DNAs from neutral and denaturing polyacrylamide gels, respectively. The method is widely used to isolate synthetic oligonucleotides from denaturing polyacrylamide gels (please see Chapter 10, Protocol 1) and, occasionally, to recover end-labeled DNA for chemical DNA sequencing (please see Chapter 12, Protocols 8 and 9). DNA recovered from polyacrylamide gels by crushing and soaking is generally suitable for use as a hybridization probe, as a probe in gel-retention assays, or as a template in chemical sequencing and enzymatic reactions. The following procedure is a modification of the technique described by Maxam and Gilbert (1977, 1980). Faster methods to recover double-stranded DNA involve:

- embedding the piece of polyacrylamide containing the DNA of interest into a slit cut in an agarose gel, and then eluting the DNA onto a sliver of DEAE-cellulose membrane as described in Protocol 3

- electroeluting the DNA from the gel into a dialysis bag (Protocol 4)

MATERIALS

CAUTION: Please see Appendix 12 for appropriate handling of materials marked with <!>.

Buffers and Solutions

Please see Appendix 1 for components of stock solutions, buffers, and reagents.
Dilute stock solutions to the appropriate concentrations.

Acrylamide gel elution buffer
0.5 M ammonium acetate
10 mM magnesium acetate tetrahydrate
1 mM EDTA (pH 8.0)
0.1% (w/v) SDS (optional)

SDS improves the efficiency of recovery, most probably by blocking nonspecific adsorption of DNA to the walls of the tube. However, SDS is tenacious and difficult to remove from the eluted DNA, especially when purifying oligonucleotides on Sep-Pak columns. Perhaps the best advice is to use SDS only when attempting to recover very small amounts (<20 ng) of DNAs >1 kb in size, where recovery is already inefficient and further losses may prejudice the success of the experiment. This is not usually the case when purifying synthetic oligonucleotides, which are always relatively small and usually available in abundance.

Other buffers may be substituted for acrylamide gel elution buffer. For example, if the DNA fragment is radiolabeled and is to be used as a hybridization probe, hybridization buffer can be substituted.

Chloroform <!>

Ethanol

6x Gel-loading buffer

For a list of gel-loading buffers and recipes, please see Table 5-8 in Protocol 9.

Phenol:chloroform (1:1, v/v) <!>

Sodium acetate (3 M, pH 5.2)

TE (pH 8.0)

Gels

Polyacrylamide gel <!>

Prepare and run the gel as described in Protocol 9 of this chapter.

Please see Step 1.

Polyacrylamide gel or high-resolution agarose gel of the appropriate concentration

Prepare and run the gel as described in Protocols 9 and 1, respectively.

Please see Step 12.

Nucleic Acids and Oligonucleotides

DNA markers generated by restriction digests of known quantities of the DNA sample

DNA sample

Special Equipment

Column (disposable plastic) equipped with a frit (e.g., Quik-Sep columns, Isolabs, Inc.), or a syringe barrel containing a Whatman GF/C filter or packed siliconized glass wool

Rotating wheel/rotary platform in an incubator preset to 37°C

Ultraviolet lamp, hand-held, long-wavelength (302 nm)

Additional Reagents

Step 1 of this protocol requires the reagents listed in Protocol 9 of this chapter.

Step 1 of this protocol also requires the reagents listed in either Protocol 10 or 11 of this chapter.

METHOD

1. Carry out polyacrylamide gel electrophoresis of the DNA sample and markers as described in Protocol 9. Locate the DNA of interest by autoradiography (Protocol 11) or by examination of ethidium bromide- or SYBR Gold-stained gels in long-wavelength (302 nm) UV light (Protocol 10).

2. Use a clean sharp scalpel or razor blade to cut out the segment of the gel containing the band of interest, keeping the size of the polyacrylamide slice as small as possible. This can be achieved by any of the following methods:

   • While the DNA is illuminated with UV light, cut through both the gel and the Saran Wrap, and then peel the small piece of gel containing the DNA from the Saran Wrap.

- Use a permanent felt-tipped marker (e.g., Sharpie pen) to outline the DNA band on the back of the glass plate while the gel is illuminated from below with UV light. Invert the gel, remove the Saran Wrap, and cut out the band using the marker outline as a guide.

- In the case of a fragment of DNA identified by autoradiography, place the exposed autoradiographic film on the Saran Wrap and align it with the gel. Use a permanent marker to outline the position of the desired DNA fragment on the back of the glass plate. Remove the exposed film and Saran Wrap and cut out the band.

Photograph or autoradiograph the gel after the bands of DNA have been excised to produce a permanent record of the experiment.

3. Transfer the gel slice to a microfuge tube or a polypropylene tube. Use a disposable pipette tip or inoculating needle to crush the polyacrylamide gel against the wall of the tube.

    Alternatively, use a clean scalpel or razor blade to slice the gel into thin slivers prior to placement in the elution tube.

4. Calculate the approximate volume of the slice and add 1–2 volumes of acrylamide gel elution buffer to the microfuge tube.

5. Close the tube and incubate it at 37°C on a rotating wheel or rotary platform.

    At this temperature, small fragments of DNA (<500 bp) are eluted in 3–4 hours; larger fragments take 12–16 hours.

6. Centrifuge the sample at maximum speed for 1 minute at 4°C in a microfuge. Transfer the supernatant to a fresh microfuge tube, being extremely careful to avoid transferring fragments of polyacrylamide (a drawn-out Pasteur pipette works well).

7. Add an additional 0.5 volume of acrylamide gel elution buffer to the pellet of polyacrylamide, vortex briefly, and centrifuge again. Combine the supernatants.

8. (*Optional*) Remove any remaining fragments of polyacrylamide by passing the supernatant through a disposable plastic column equipped with a frit (e.g., Isolabs, Inc., Quick-Sep columns) or a syringe barrel plugged with a Whatman GF/C filter or siliconized glass wool.

    The eluted DNA can be extracted with phenol:chloroform and chloroform to remove SDS, which can inhibit subsequent enzymatic manipulation of the DNA. Precipitate the extracted DNA with ethanol as described in Step 9 and continue with the remainder of the protocol.

9. Add 2 volumes of ethanol at 4°C to the flow-through and store the solution on ice for 30 minutes. Recover the DNA by centrifugation at maximum speed for 10 minutes at 4°C in a microfuge.

    Even small quantities of DNA are efficiently precipitated by ethanol in this method, perhaps because of the presence of small amounts of polyacrylamide in the eluate (Gaillard and Strauss 1990). However, 10 µg of carrier RNA can be added before precipitation, which may improve even further the recovery of small amounts of DNA. Before adding the RNA, make sure that the presence of RNA will not compromise subsequent reactions with the DNA. (For preparation of carrier RNA, please see Protocol 3.)

10. Dissolve the DNA in 200 µl of TE (pH 8.0), add 25 µl of 3 M sodium acetate (pH 5.2), and again precipitate the DNA with 2 volumes of ethanol as described in Step 9.

11. Carefully rinse the pellet once with 70% ethanol, and dissolve the DNA in TE (pH 8.0) to a final volume of 10 µl.

12. Check the amount and quality of the fragment by polyacrylamide or high-resolution agarose gel electrophoresis:

    a. Mix a small aliquot (~20 ng) of the final preparation of the fragment with 10 µl of TE (pH 8.0), and add 2 µl of the desired gel-loading buffer (please see Table 5-4).

b. Load and run a polyacrylamide or high-resolution agarose gel of the appropriate concentration, using as markers restriction digests of known quantities of the original DNA. The isolated fragment should comigrate with the correct fragment in the restriction digest.

c. Examine the gel carefully for the presence of faint fluorescent bands that signify the presence of contaminating species of DNA. It is often possible to estimate the amount of DNA in the final preparation from the relative intensities of fluorescence of the fragment and the markers.

> Only rarely is further purification of the recovered DNA required. The best option is chromatography on DEAE-Sephacel columns (please see Protocol 5), or any of a wide variety of specialty resins that are available commercially (please see Chapter 1, Protocol 9). Many of the specialty resins come in prepacked columns that are appropriate for purifying small amounts of DNA using a microfuge. Make sure that the resin chosen is appropriate for purifying linear DNA molecules as opposed to circular plasmids.

Pulsed-field Gel Electrophoresis

ALL LINEAR DOUBLE-STRANDED DNA MOLECULES THAT ARE LARGER than a certain size migrate through agarose gels at the same rate. Above this critical length, the velocity of DNA molecules becomes almost independent of their size and depends chiefly on the strength of the electric field. In practical terms, this relationship means that DNAs greater than ~40 kb in length cannot be easily separated by applying a constant electrical field to horizontal agarose gels. This problem is solved by pulsed-field gel electrophoresis (Carle and Olson 1984, 1985; Schwartz and Cantor 1984; Carle et al. 1986; Chu et al. 1986), in which the electric field is switched periodically between two different directions with pulse times ranging from 0.1 to 1000 seconds or more. This method allows the separation of DNA molecules up to ~5 Mb in length. Fractionation occurs because the time required for a DNA molecule to change direction in response to the fluctuating electrical field depends on its size: Shorter molecules can reorient more quickly and can therefore move through the gel faster than longer molecules.

The general concept of PFGE apparatus design is shown schematically in Figure 5-7. This design, the original OFAGE (orthogonal field agarose gel electrophoresis) device of Carle and Olson (1984), is visually and conceptually simple. Two electrode pairs, A and B, are shown. When the A electrodes are activated, the negatively charged DNA migrates downward and to the right; when these electrodes are turned off, the B electrodes are activated, and the DNA now migrates downward and to the left. This regular alternation of A and B fields continues throughout the gel run and causes the DNA to follow a zigzag path as shown, with a net migration in the downward direction. Note that "pulsed" field electrophoresis is a slight misnomer; it is more accurately called "alternating" field electrophoresis. The interval at which the field direction is changed is termed the pulse time and may range from a few seconds to hours, with progressively larger DNA fragments resolving at longer pulse times.

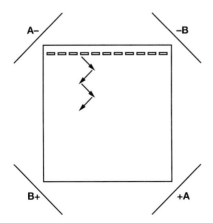

FIGURE 5-7 Concept of Pulsed-field Electrophoresis

An agarose gel is represented by the box; the series of short horizontal rectangles indicate the wells into which the DNA is loaded. A and B represent two sets of electrodes. When the A electrodes are activated, the DNA is driven anodically downward and to the right as indicated by the first arrow. When the A electrodes are turned off, the B electrodes are immediately activated. The DNA now moves downward and to the left. The path of a DNA molecule subjected to continued alternation of field direction is shown by the arrows.

As described earlier in the introduction to this chapter, the effect of alternating fields can be explained by considering that a DNA molecule stretches out and orients parallel to an electric field. It can then be moved through successive pores in the agarose gel by reptation. When the field direction changes, the DNA molecule must reorient before it can move in the new direction. As the field direction regularly changes, the DNA must regularly change directions. The larger the molecule, the more time required to reorient and turn corners, leaving proportionately less time (within each pulse) available to move in the new direction. For experiments illustrating this idea, please see Smith et al. (1989) and Schwartz and Koval (1989).

Schwartz et al. (1983) introduced the concept of field alternation in 1983 by demonstrating its effectiveness in separating the chromosomes of the yeast *Saccharomyces cerevisiae*. Within 1 year, two designs were proposed, using either two sets of diode arrays or two sets of linear electrodes (similar to that shown in Figure 5-7) to provide the alternating fields (Schwartz et al. 1983; Carle et al. 1986). Both separated molecules as large as 1500 kb. The major, and important, drawback to these designs, however, was that the electrode geometries produced nonhomogeneous electric fields (as can be inferred by inspection of Figure 5-7), causing lane-to-lane variations in the speed and trajectory of DNA fragments. For many applications, these distortions in the path hindered interpretation of band patterns. As a result, many different pulsed-field designs have been developed in attempts to generate uniform fields.

In the remainder of this chapter, we present protocols for extracting genomic DNA of very high molecular weight from lower and higher eukaryotes, a method to digest genomic DNA embedded in agarose and to generate size standards for use in PFGE, protocols for two different and popular forms of PFGE — TAFE and CHEF gels — and two methods for recovering DNA fragments from pulsed-field gels. These protocols were provided by Katheleen Gardiner (University of Colorado, Boulder).

TYPES OF APPARATUSES

Four popular designs are illustrated schematically in Figure 5-8 and are described below. (A note on nomenclature: Acronyms abound. They are used to refer to some specific aspect of the particular pulsed-field apparatus. Commercial development has added additional catchy names, e.g., TAFE for transverse alternating field electrophoresis.)

- ***The vertical pulsed field system*** (now called TAFE) (Gardiner and Patterson 1989): This apparatus (Figure 5-8A) is essentially a three-dimensional model of the original OFAGE (Figure 5-8). The gel stands upright between two linear electrode pairs and is supported by two thin plastic strips and the buoyancy of the buffer. DNA runs in a straight path in all lanes because the field is uniform across the gel; quite sharp bands are obtained, relating to the field gradient down the gel. The angle between the alternate fields is 110° at the wells, but it is much greater further down the gel.

- ***Field inversion (FIGE)*** (Carle et al. 1986; Turmel and Lalande 1988): This simplest of the pulsed-field designs (Figure 5-8B) uses a single pair of electrodes and a standard submarine agarose gel electrophoresis box. During the gel run, the field regularly inverts, first driving the DNA out of the wells and then back toward the wells. Thus, the angle between the fields is 180°. Either the forward pulse time or the forward field must be greater than the reverse for net forward migration of the DNA. To avoid anomalies in migration of fragments >600 kb, "ramping" is frequently used: The forward and reverse pulse times (and/or fields) are increased, either gradually or in a step fashion during the run.

- ***Rotating gels*** (Anand 1986; Southern et al. 1987): Instead of alternating the field direction, the gel (Figure 5-8D) is mounted on a rotating platform which then alternates between two ori-

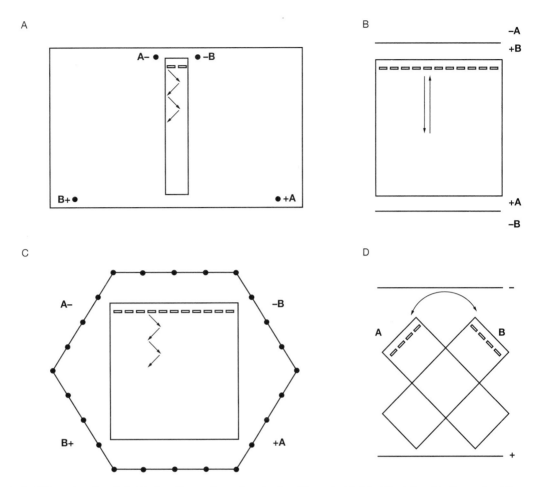

FIGURE 5-8 Pulsed-field Configurations Producing Electric Fields That Are Uniform in All Lanes of the Gel

Components of electrode sets, A and B, are represented as dots or lines. (*A*) The vertical pulsed-field system or transverse alternating fields (TAFE). (*B*) Field inversion. (*C*) Contour-clamped homogeneous electric field apparatus (CHEF). (*D*) Rotating apparatus (the gel alternates between positions A and B).

entations (120º apart) within a constant electric field. From the frame of reference of the DNA, this movement is the same as changing the field direction.

- *Contour-clamped homogeneous electric field* (CHEF) device (Chu et al. 1986; Orbach et al. 1988): A hexagonal array of point electrodes in a voltage divider circuit (Figure 5-8C) produces homogeneous fields (oriented at 120º) approximating those of pairs of infinitely long parallel electrodes. The electrophoresis device (Schwartz et al. 1989) uses an effective and simpler array of diodes. Clark et al. (1988) modified the CHEF system to use computer-controlled digital/analog converters at each electrode. This system retains the hexagonal array and can generate an essentially unlimited variety of field strengths and angles.

FACTORS AFFECTING RESOLUTION

All current PFGE designs, although differing in kind, number, and arrangement of electrodes, have eliminated major distortions, and all are capable of resolving fragments exceeding 6000 kb in size. Resolution in all systems also depends on the same set of electrophoretic parameters: pulse

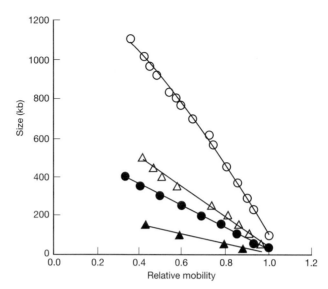

FIGURE 5-9 Effect of Pulse Time on Migration of DNA through a Pulsed-field Gel

Molecular weight vs. mobility is shown for bands of λ concatemers represented by triangles (4″ and 15″ pulse) or *S. cerevisiae* chromosomes represented by circles (15″ and 60″). (*Open circles*) 60″ 6 V/cm; (*closed circles*) 15″ 6 V/cm; (*open triangles*) 15″ 8 V/cm; (*closed triangles*) 4″ 6 V/cm.

time, field strength, temperature, buffer composition, type and concentration of agarose, and an obtuse angle between the fields (Olson 1989). In practice, most of these variables are generally kept constant, and the size range to be resolved is manipulated by increasing the pulse time to separate larger molecules and by decreasing it for smaller molecules.

Pulse Time

Figure 5-9 illustrates the relationship between molecular size and mobility (using λ concatemers and *S. cerevisiae* chromosomes as standards) for pulse times of 4″, 15″, and 60″. In each case, the relationship is linear through a range where excellent calculation of unknown fragment sizes would be possible. (This contrasts with standard electrophoresis where mobility of DNA molecules is inversely proportional to the log of their molecular weight.) Larger fragments run above the linear range, in the "compression zone," a broad band of material up to 1500–2000 kb in size. No inference regarding size can be made at any pulse time for any fragment in the compression zone. Fragments >2000 kb may be retained within the wells or may run in the "zone of no resolution" between the wells and the compression zone. In this latter case, "trapping" of the DNA in multiple pores of the agarose has prevented resolution (Olson 1989). Different conditions for separation in this size class are required (see below).

Voltage

Figure 5-9 also illustrates that if the pulse time is held constant (15″), increasing the field strength (from 6 to 8 V/cm) increases the size of the largest material resolved. Field strengths that are too high, however, result in trapping at progressively smaller fragment sizes. Thus, there is an upper limit to the speed with which PFGE separations can be carried out.

Voltage effects and trapping are particularly important considerations for resolution of >2000 kb. First, as expected from the results above, a long pulse time must be used. However, because the DNA is so very large, the voltage must also be lowered to prevent trapping. This in turn requires a further increase in the pulse time. Thus, to achieve resolution in the megabase range, long slow gel runs are required, ~1–2 V/cm, with a 30–90-minute pulse time, for several days. Such conditions resolve the chromosomes of *S. pombe, Candida albicans,* and *N. crassa,* which range from ~1600 kb to >6000 kb. Under these conditions, however, fragments of 2–1100 kb all migrate in a broad diffuse band, reminiscent of standard constant field electrophoresis. Long pulse times mimic constant electric fields from the viewpoint of smaller DNA fragments. There are conditions that separate the full range from 50 kb to 6000 kb on a single gel (Southern et al. 1987; Clark et al. 1988), but these generally sacrifice optimum resolution of all size classes.

Field Angle

The angle between fields is typically 110–120º, and it has been shown that varying the angle from 105º to 165º has small effects on performance (Birren et al. 1988). Effective use of a 90º field angle has been demonstrated by Bancroft and Wolk (1988). This system uses the following field pattern: downward, right, downward, left. Pulses in the right and left directions are at 90º to, and of twice the duration of, those in the downward direction. This straightforward system produces homogeneous fields and therefore (relatively) straight migration of the DNA.

Temperature

Unlike standard agarose gel electrophoresis, which is generally carried out at room temperature, PFGE is generally done at 4–15ºC. DNA migrates faster at higher temperatures; however, higher temperatures also cause trapping at lower fragment sizes and significant band broadening. Control of the temperature throughout the gel run also aids in controlling the reproducibility of the separations and the mobilities.

SPECIAL CONSIDERATIONS

DNA Preparation

Standard procedures for DNA isolation in solution are not appropriate for preparing DNA for PFGE analysis. To prevent shearing of the long DNA fragments, PFGE DNA is prepared by embedding live cells in agarose (Schwartz and Cantor 1984). Prior quantitation of cells is an important consideration, because the mobility of DNA in PFGE is more sensitive to concentration than it is on standard gels. Typical quantities of mammalian DNA loaded per lane on the latter range from 3 µg to 20 µg; on pulsed-field gels, amounts must be restricted to <1–2 µg to prevent anomalous slowing of migration.

Molecular-weight Markers

Lower eukaryotes, with their small genomes and small number of chromosomes, together with bacteriophage λ, have provided a valuable source of accurately sized standards in the size range required in PFGE.

- *50-kb ladder:* λ DNA (~50 kb), embedded in agarose, can be ligated to produce a mixture of monomers, dimers, trimers, etc. These concatemers separate on PFGE to produce a "ladder" of bands, each successive "rung" corresponding to a 50-kb increment. Ladders spanning 50–1000 kb (20 bands) can be formed (please see Protocol 16).

- ***200–2000-kb range:*** *S. cerevisiae* has 16 chromosomes ranging in size from ~200 kb to >2000 kb. These can be prepared intact from cells embedded in agarose. Different strains of *S. cerevisiae* will give slightly different patterns because of small variations in chromosome sizes. Fewer than 16 bands will be seen when two or more chromosomes are very close in size.

- ***Megabase range:*** *S. pombe* has three chromosomes, 3.5, 4.6, and 5.7 Mb in size. *C. albicans* and *N. crassa* also have chromosomes in this size class.

Restriction Enzymes

The ability to exploit the resolving power of PFGE depends on the ability to generate fragments reproducibly in the range of 100–1000 kb average size. Weil and McClelland (1989) have shown that in bacterial genomes of >45% G+C content, enzymes whose recognition sequence contains the tetranucleotide CTAG cut less than once in 100 kb. In those of <45% G+C, enzymes with recognition sites containing CCG and CGG cut less than once in 100 kb. Mammalian genomes are ~40% G+C and are depleted for the dinucleotide CpG (Swartz et al. 1962). Therefore, enzymes such as *Not*I, *Eag*I, *Sst*II, and *Bss*HII, with 8- and 6-bp G-C-rich recognition sequences, generate fragments in a complete digest averaging >500 kb (Swartz et al. 1962; Drmanac et al. 1986).

Miscellaneous

Several procedures require little or no modification for use with PFGE.

- ***Southern transfers:*** Capillary and alkaline transfer procedures are the same as those for standard gels, with the addition of a brief (3–20 minute) HCl acid treatment before the denaturation step. The acid treatment ensures depurination and sufficient breakage of the large fragments to allow their passive transfer from the gel.

- ***Agarose:*** The use of high-quality agarose is recommended for pulsed-field gels. For making plugs, low-melting-temperature agarose is required.

- ***Buffer:*** Standard Tris-borate buffer (TBE) is most widely used in PFGE.

- ***Preparative gels:*** Preparative electrophoresis using low-melting-temperature agarose is equally effective for the 50-kb to >1000-kb size range as it is for the standard <25-kb range.

Protocol 13

Preparation of DNA for Pulsed-field Gel Electrophoresis: Isolation of DNA from Mammalian Cells and Tissues

To avoid shearing during the extraction of large DNA molecules, cells are lysed in situ in an agarose plug (Schwartz and Cantor 1984) or a bead (Cook 1984). Most investigators now use agarose plugs because of their higher efficiency (Anand 1986). Intact cells or nuclei are resuspended in molten, low-melting-temperature agarose and solidified in blocks whose size matches the thickness of the loading slot of the gel. Depending on the organism, any of a variety of substances are infused into the plug to cause lysis of the cells and removal of proteins from the DNA. These procedures yield DNA that is both intact and susceptible to cleavage by restriction enzymes in situ. Following digestion with the appropriate restriction enzyme(s), the plug can be loaded directly into the well of a pulsed-field gel or it can be melted before loading. Procedures for the lysis of mammalian cells are described in this protocol; procedures for yeast are described in Protocol 14.

This protocol describes the preparation of samples from cultured cells and tissue samples. White blood cells isolated from patients or animals also can be used as a source of high-molecular-weight DNA for PFGE. If desired, DNA can be prepared from nuclei isolated from mammalian cells (please see Chapter 17, Protocol 1). However, it is our experience that no advantage is gained from preparing DNA from nuclei, as DNA isolated from intact cells is equally susceptible to cleavage by restriction enzymes.

MATERIALS

CAUTION: Please see Appendix 12 for appropriate handling of materials marked with <!>.

Buffers and Solutions

Please see Appendix 1 for components of stock solutions, buffers, and reagents. Dilute stock solutions to the appropriate concentrations.

EDTA (0.5 M, pH 8.0)
L buffer
  0.1 M EDTA (pH 8.0)
  0.01 M Tris-Cl (pH 7.6)
  0.02 M NaCl
  Store at 4ºC.

L buffer with proteinase K and Sarkosyl

Amend the L buffer to a final concentration of 1% (w/v) Sarkosyl. Store L buffer with Sarkosyl at room temperature, and add proteinase K to 0.1 mg/ml just before use. (For additional information, please see Appendix 4.)

Some investigators substitute 0.5 M EDTA/1% (w/v) SDS/2 mg/ml proteinase K for the L buffer containing Sarkosyl and proteinase K. However, using high concentrations of proteinase K can become expensive and is unnecessary.

Phosphate-buffered saline (PBS)

Use ice-cold PBS for all cell and tissue preparations, except white blood cells. In the latter case, the PBS should be at room temperature.

Red blood cell lysis buffer

155 mM NH_4Cl

0.1 mM EDTA

12 mM $NaHCO_3$

Use this buffer for the isolation of white blood cells.

TE (pH 7.6)

TE (pH 7.6) containing 40 μg/ml PMSF <!>

Purchase phenylmethylsulfonyl fluoride (PMSF) as a solid, and store at room temperature. Dissolve the appropriate amount in TE just before use.

Gels

Low-melting-temperature agarose (1%)

Use a grade of agarose that is suitable for PFGE (e.g., SeaPlaque GTG, BioWhittaker, or regular LMP, GIBCO-BRL).

Centrifuges and Rotors

Sorvall SS-34 rotor or equivalent

Special Equipment

Cheesecloth

Use for the preparation of fresh or frozen tissue samples.

Glass homogenizer with a tight-fitting pestle, chilled in ice

Use for the preparation of fresh tissue samples.

Hemocytometer

LeucoPrep cell separation tubes (Becton Dickinson)

Use for the isolation of white blood cells.

Mortar and pestle, chilled to –70ºC

Use for the preparation of frozen tissue samples.

Preformed Plexiglas molds (50–100 μl, Pharmacia or Bio-Rad), or a length of Tygon tubing (1/8 inch or 3.2-mm internal diameter), or a plastic syringe barrel (1 ml)

Please see Step 4.

Water baths preset to 42ºC and 50ºC

Cells and Tissues

Cell or tissue sample

This protocol describes methods for dealing with cultured cell lines, fresh or frozen tissue samples, or white blood cells.

METHOD

1. Prepare cells or tissue samples.

   ### FOR CULTURED CELLS

   a. Wash cells that have been growing in culture three times in ice-cold PBS.

   b. Harvest the cells by scraping into a small volume of ice-cold PBS using a sterilized rubber policeman. Collect the cells by low-speed centrifugation.

   c. Resuspend the cells at a concentration of $\sim 2 \times 10^7$ cells/ml in ice-cold L buffer.

   ### FOR FRESH TISSUE SAMPLES

   a. In a Petri dish, use a clean scalpel to mince freshly excised tissue into small cubes (1–2 mm^3) and then homogenize the cubes in ice-cold PBS in a chilled glass homogenizer with a tight-fitting pestle.

   b. Remove fragments of connective tissue by filtration through two layers of cheesecloth.

   c. Wash the suspended cells three times in ice-cold PBS and resuspend them at a concentration of 2×10^7 cells/ml in ice-cold L buffer.
      Use a hemacytometer to count the cells (please see Appendix 8).

   ### FOR FROZEN TISSUE SAMPLES

   a. Grind frozen tissue to a fine powder using a mortar and pestle chilled to –70ºC and suspend the powdered tissue in ice-cold PBS.

   b. Remove fragments of connective tissue by filtration through two layers of cheesecloth.

   c. Wash the suspended cells three times in ice-cold PBS and resuspend them at a concentration of 2×10^7 cells/ml in ice-cold L buffer.

   ### FOR WHITE BLOOD CELLS

   a. Fractionate 5–10 ml of starting blood by centrifugation in LeucoPrep cell separation tubes to grossly separate white and red blood cells.

   b. To the white blood cell layer (buffy coat) add 4 volumes of red blood cell lysis buffer and gently mix by two to three inversions of the tube.

   c. Incubate the cells in buffer for 5 minutes at room temperature, and then centrifuge the tube at 3000g (5000 rpm in a Sorvall SS-34 rotor) for 5 minutes at room temperature.

   d. Resuspend the pellet in 1 ml of PBS at room temperature.

2. Prepare a volume of 1% low-melting-temperature agarose in L buffer that is equal to the volume of the cell preparation in Step 1. Cool the melted agarose to 42ºC.

3. When the agarose has cooled to 42ºC, warm the cell suspension (Step 1) to the same temperature. Mix the melted agarose with the suspended cells. Stir the mixture with a sealed Pasteur pipette to ensure that the cells are evenly dispersed throughout the agarose.

4. Pipette or pour the molten mixture into preformed Plexiglas molds (50–100 µl, Pharmacia or Bio-Rad), or draw the mixture into an appropriate length of Tygon tubing (1/8-inch or 3.2-mm internal diameter), or a 1-ml plastic syringe barrel. Store the molds for 15 minutes at room temperature, and then transfer them to 4°C for 15–30 minutes.

5. When the agarose has set, gently collect the plugs from the Plexiglas molds or gently blow out the agarose from the Tygon tubing or syringe barrel into a Petri dish. Cut the cylindrical plugs into 1-cm sections.

   Each 1-cm length of agarose (45 µl) should contain ~0.5 x 10^6 cells and yield ~2–5 µg of DNA. Analysis of larger amounts of DNA in the individual lanes of a pulsed-field gel will distort the calculated molecular weights of the DNA fragments. The migration of large DNA fragments is significantly slowed when electrophoresis is carried out at high DNA concentrations. In turn, this slowing will lead to an overestimate of the size of an individual DNA fragment.

6. Transfer the plugs to 3 volumes of L buffer containing 0.1 mg/ml proteinase K and 1% (w/v) Sarkosyl. Incubate the plugs for 3 hours at 50°C. Replace the original digestion mixture with two volumes of fresh digestion mixture and continue the incubation for 12–16 hours at 50°C.

   Be as careful as possible not to scar the agarose plugs when changing buffer solutions.

   Some DNA isolation protocols include very long incubations (24–48 hours) at 50°C when treating the embedded cells with proteinase K in the presence of Sarkosyl. These extended incubation times are not required (Mortimer et al. 1990) and may lead to degradation of the high-molecular-weight DNA.

7. Incubate the plugs at room temperature in 50 volumes of TE (pH 7.6) with three to five changes of buffer over a period of 3 hours.

8. Remove the TE and replace with 2 volumes of TE (pH 7.6) containing 40 µg/ml PMSF. Incubate for 30 minutes at 50°C.

9. Incubate the plugs at room temperature in 50 volumes of TE (pH 7.6) with three to five changes of buffer over a period of 3 hours.

   The agarose plugs can be stored for several years in TE (pH 7.6) at 4°C. Plugs are best stored for longer periods of time in 0.5 M EDTA (pH 8.0) at 4°C. When mailed to other laboratories, plugs should be shipped at room temperature in tubes filled with 0.5 M EDTA (pH 8.0).

Protocol 14

Preparation of DNA for Pulsed-field Gel Electrophoresis: Isolation of Intact DNA from Yeast

Preparation of yeast DNA for electrophoresis requires that the cells first be treated enzymatically to break down the cell wall, and then resuspended in low-melting-temperature agarose plugs. The plugs are infused with lysis buffer and proteases to facilitate disruption of the cells and removal of proteins from the DNA. This method is a slight modification of that originally described by Schwartz and Cantor (1984) and can be used to prepare both high-molecular-weight yeast chromosomes as size markers and yeast artificial chromosomes (YACs).

CHROMOSOME SIZE IN YEASTS AND BACTERIA

The sizes of the chromosomes present in several species of bacteria and yeast (*S. cerevisiae* and *S. pombe*) have been determined. The sizes below are taken from Chu (1990a).

- **S. cerevisiae *(strain YNN 295):*** 245, 290, 370, 460, 580, 630, 700, 770, 800, 850, 945, 1020, 1200, 1570, and 2190 kb. YACs vary in size up to 2000 kb in the background of the native yeast chromosomes. Other yeast strains may have variations in chromosome size. In addition, chromosome XII varies in size between 2 and 3 Mb in different isolates of the YNN 295 strain. This chromosome contains ~1.1 Mb of low-copy-number DNA and variable numbers of tandem repeats encoding the rRNAs.

- **S. pombe:** 3500, 4600, and 5700 kb.

- **E. coli:** 4700 kb. This is a circular chromosome and must be linearized with low-dose γ irradiation before use as a size standard.

MATERIALS

CAUTION: Please see Appendix 12 for appropriate handling of materials marked with <!>.

Buffers and Solutions

Please see Appendix 1 for components of stock solutions, buffers, and reagents. Dilute stock solutions to the appropriate concentrations.

Cell wash buffer
0.01 M Tris-Cl (pH 7.6)
0.05 M EDTA (pH 8.0)
Store at room temperature.

EDTA (0.05 M, pH 8.0)

L buffer

    0.1 M EDTA (pH 8.0)

    0.01 M Tris-Cl (pH 7.6)

    0.02 M NaCl

    Store at 4°C.

L buffer with proteinase K and Sarkosyl

    Amend the L buffer to a final concentration of 1% (w/v) Sarkosyl. Store L buffer with Sarkosyl at room temperature, and add proteinase K to 0.1 mg/ml just before use.

TE (pH 7.6)

TE (pH 7.6) containing 40 μg/ml PMSF <!>

    Purchase PMSF as a solid, and store it at room temperature. Dissolve the appropriate amount of PMSF in TE just before use.

Yeast lysis buffer

    0.01 M Tris-Cl (pH 7.6)

    0.5 M EDTA (pH 8.0)

    β-mercaptoethanol (1% v/v) <!>

    Add β-mercaptoethanol just before use. Store the concentrated solution in a chemical fume hood.

Yeast cell wall digestion enzymes:

    Zymolyase 5000 (Kirin Breweries)

        Dissolve zymolyase at 2 mg/ml in 0.01 M sodium phosphate containing 50% glycerol just before use.

    or

    Lyticase (67 mg/ml) (Sigma)

        Dissolve at 67 mg/ml (900 units/ml) in 0.01 M sodium phosphate containing 50% glycerol just before use.

Gels

Low-melting-temperature agarose (1%)

    Use a grade of agarose that is suitable for PFGE (e.g., SeaPlaque GTG, BioWhittaker, or regular LMP, GIBCO-BRL).

Centrifuges and Rotors

Sorvall GSA rotor or equivalent

Special Equipment

Preformed Plexiglas molds (50–100 μl, Pharmacia or Bio-Rad), or a length of Tygon tubing (1/8-inch or 3.2-mm internal diameter), or a plastic syringe barrel (1 ml)

    Please see Step 6.

Cells and Tissues

Yeast suspension culture

    Prepare the yeast culture at a volume and cell density appropriate to yield the required number of plugs of embedded DNA.

METHOD

1. Collect yeast cells growing in suspension by centrifugation at 3000*g* (4300 rpm in a Sorvall GSA rotor) for 5 minutes at 4°C. Wash the cell pellet twice with cell wash buffer.

2. Resuspend the cells at a concentration of 3×10^9 cells/ml in 0.05 M EDTA (pH 8.0) at 0°C.

3. Prepare an equal volume of 1% low-melting-temperature agarose in L buffer. Cool the melted agarose to 42°C.

4. Add 75 µl of zymolyase or lyticase solution to the cell suspension of Step 2. Mix well.

5. Warm the cell suspension to 42°C. Mix 5 ml of the melted agarose with 5 ml of the suspended cells. Stir the mixture with a sealed Pasteur pipette to ensure that the cells are evenly dispersed throughout the agarose.

6. Pipette or pour the molten mixture into preformed Plexiglas molds (50–100 µl, Pharmacia or Bio-Rad), or draw the mixture into an appropriate length of Tygon tubing (3/32-inch internal diameter) or a 1-ml plastic syringe barrel. Store the molds for 15 minutes at room temperature, and then transfer them to 4°C for 15–30 minutes.

7. When the agarose has set, collect the plugs from the Plexiglas molds, or blow out the agarose from the Tygon tubing or syringe barrel into a Petri dish. Cut the cylindrical plugs into 1-cm blocks.

   Each block (50 µl) should contain ~5 µg of yeast chromosomal DNA.

8. Incubate the blocks in a chemical fume hood for 3 hours at 37°C in 3 volumes of yeast lysis buffer.

9. Add 3 volumes of L buffer containing 0.1 mg/ml proteinase K and 1% (w/v) Sarkosyl into a fresh Petri dish. Transfer the blocks to this buffer, and incubate them for 3 hours at 50°C. Replace the original digestion mixture with an equal volume of fresh digestion mixture and continue incubation for 12–16 hours at 50°C.

   Be as careful as possible not to scar the agarose plugs when changing buffer solutions.

10. Incubate the plugs at 50°C in 50 volumes of TE (pH 7.6) containing 40 µg/ml PMSF. After 1 hour, replace the original rinse buffer (TE containing PMSF) with an equal volume of fresh rinse buffer and continue incubation for another hour at 50°C.

11. Remove the rinse buffer (TE containing PMSF), replace with an equal volume of fresh TE (pH 7.6), and continue incubation for another hour at room temperature.

    The agarose plugs can be stored for several years in TE (pH 7.6) at 4°C. Plugs are best stored for longer periods of time in 0.5 M EDTA (pH 8.0) at 4°C. When mailed to other laboratories, plugs should be shipped at room temperature in tubes filled with 0.5 M EDTA (pH 8.0).

Protocol 15

Restriction Endonuclease Digestion of DNA in Agarose Plugs

GENOMIC DNA ISOLATED FROM MAMMALIAN, YEAST, OR BACTERIAL CELLS can be digested with restriction endonucleases by incubating agarose plugs containing the DNA in the presence of the desired endonuclease. The pores of the low-melting-temperature agarose plug are large enough to allow a restriction enzyme access to the substrate genomic DNA. After digestion, the DNA can be fractionated by PFGE and either isolated from the gel or analyzed by Southern blotting. This protocol describes the use of restriction enzymes to cleave genomic DNA in agarose plugs.

CHOOSING RESTRICTION ENDONUCLEASES FOR PFGE

Restriction endonucleases used in PFGE have several unique characteristics. First, they typically have one or more CpG dinucleotides in their recognition sequences. CpG dinucleotide sequences are rare in most eukaryotic genomes; thus, restriction enzymes that recognize this sequence cut the DNA infrequently. Furthermore, a majority of CpG sequences are methylated in mammalian DNAs, and most restriction enzymes with this dinucleotide in their recognition sequences will not cleave methylated DNA. However, CpG sequences located 5′ of many transcribed regions of the DNA are unmethylated (so-called *Hpa*II tiny fragment or HTF sequences, or CpG islands; Bird et al. 1985) and are thus cleaved by these enzymes. The arrangement of extensively methylated and unmethylated regions in the DNA of a particular organism or cell line leads to the generation of discrete DNA fragments after restriction enzyme digestion of a population of DNAs. The pattern of digestion can differ between cell types due to differential methylation of the DNA. Second, some of these restriction enzymes (*Not*I, *Sfi*I, *Asc*I, *Pac*I, *Pme*I) recognize and cleave 8-bp DNA sequences, again leading to infrequent cutting of DNA. Third, the enzymes must be of high purity and specific activity for use in PFGE. The presence of even trace nuclease impurities leads to smearing of the DNA in the gels and further compromises an already difficult method. Enzymes with low specific activity require the addition of too much enzyme or incubation times that are too long to be practical. A fourth consideration is cost. If a considerable excess of enzyme must be added to each plug to ensure complete digestion, then each experiment will be very expensive.

Table 5-9 gives examples of restriction enzymes that have proven useful in long-range mapping of genomic DNAs. The catalogs of restriction enzyme manufacturers often contain additional information regarding the ability of a given enzyme to cleave genomic DNA embedded in agarose. Keep in mind that the expected fragment sizes are averages. The exact distribution of sites

TABLE 5-9 Average Fragment Size Generated by Endonucleases

ENZYME	RECOGNITION SITE	EXPECTED AVERAGE FRAGMENT LENGTH (IN kb)[a]
*Asc*I	GGCGCGCC	n.d.[b]
*Bss*HII	GCGCGC	189
*Bst*BI	TTCGAA	10.9
*Eag*I	CGGCCG	149
*Fsp*I	TGCGCA	149
*Mlu*I	ACGCGT	132
*Not*I	GCGGCCGC	3000
*Nru*I	TCGCGA	100.5
*Pac*I	TTAATTAA	60
*Pme*I	GTTTAAAC	50
*Rsr*II	CGGA/TCCG	50
*Sst*II	CCGCGG	148.5
*Sal*I	GTCGAC	38.6
*Sfi*I	GGCCNNNNNGGCC	149
*Sma*I	CCCGGG	27.2
*Xho*I	CTCGAG	20.6

[a]Taken from Drmanac et al. (1986). See also Smith (1990).
[b]n.d. indicates not determined.

for a particular enzyme will vary depending on base composition, methylation status, localization within regions of the chromosome (e.g., within G bands vs. R bands), and the type of HTF/CpG island present in the immediate 5´-flanking region (Bird 1989).

The use of six to eight restriction enzymes is optimal for the determination of a locus map when combined with multiprobe Southern blotting. Each enzyme should be used singly and in all possible combinations to ensure accuracy. Intentional (and unintentional) partial digests with a limiting amount of restriction enzyme are also useful for generating a map. In species for which a large proportion of the genomic DNA has been sequenced, comparison of the expected and observed mapping results can reveal dynamic regions of a locus. For additional hints on the assembly of a long-range map of a genomic locus, please see Smith (1990) and Poustka (1990).

MATERIALS

Buffers and Solutions

Please see Appendix 1 for components of stock solutions, buffers, and reagents. Dilute stock solutions to the appropriate concentrations.

1x *Restriction enzyme buffer*

Prepare buffer according to the manufacturer's suggestions or purchase with restriction enzymes. Individual buffers should be supplemented with spermidine to enhance the efficiency of restriction digestion. High-salt buffers (containing 100–150 mM salt) should be supplemented to a final concentration of 10 mM spermidine, medium-salt buffers (50–100 mM salt) to 5 mM spermidine, and low-salt buffers (<50 mM salt) to 3 mM spermidine. It is best to supplement the buffers from a 0.1 M spermidine stock (dissolved in H$_2$O) just before use.

TE (pH 7.6)

Enzymes and Buffers

Restriction endonuclease(s)

For help in determining the appropriate restriction endonuclease(s) to use, please see the discussion on Choosing Restriction Endonucleases for PFGE in the introduction to this protocol.

Gels

Gel for pulsed-field electrophoresis

Prepare an appropriate PFGE gel according to the methods described in Protocol 17 (for TAFE) or Protocol 18 (for CHEF).

Nucleic Acids and Oligonucleotides

Genomic DNA embedded in low-melting-temperature agarose plugs

Please see Protocol 13 for the preparation of low-melting-temperature agarose plugs containing mammalian cell DNA or Protocol 14 for the preparation of plugs containing yeast DNA.

Special Equipment

Water bath preset to the optimum temperature for restriction endonuclease digestion

METHOD

1. If plugs have not been stored in TE (e.g., plugs received through the mail or those that have been stored in 0.5 M EDTA [pH 8.0]), incubate them in 50 volumes of TE (pH 7.6) for 30 minutes at room temperature. Transfer the plugs to 50 volumes of fresh TE (pH 7.6) and continue incubation for a further 30 minutes. Otherwise, proceed directly to Step 2.

2. Transfer the plugs to individual microfuge tubes, and add 10 volumes of the appropriate 1x restriction enzyme buffer to each tube. Incubate the tubes for 30 minutes at room temperature.

3. Remove the buffer and replace it with 2–3 volumes of fresh 1x restriction enzyme buffer. Add 20–30 units of the appropriate restriction enzyme to each tube, and incubate the tubes at the optimal temperature for the restriction enzyme: 3 hours if YAC DNA is used or 5– 6 hours if mammalian DNA is used.

   The restriction enzyme can be added in two aliquots, at the start of the incubation and at the midpoint, to enhance complete digestion.

4. If the DNA is to be digested with only one restriction enzyme, then soak the plugs in 20 volumes of TE (pH 7.6) at 4ºC. After 1 hour, proceed with Step 7. If the DNA is to be treated with more than one enzyme, skip the incubation in TE and proceed to Step 5.

   This treatment allows any salt in the restriction enzyme buffer to diffuse from the blocks.

5. If the DNA is to be digested with more than one restriction enzyme, reequilibrate the plug buffer before adding the second enzyme. To reequilibrate, use automatic pipetting devices to remove as much as possible of the first restriction enzyme buffer from each tube and replace it with 1 ml of TE (pH 7.6). Remove the TE and replace it with a fresh 1 ml of TE. Store the plug for 30–60 minutes at room temperature. Gently remove the TE buffer.

6. Add 10 volumes of the appropriate second 1x restriction enzyme buffer to each tube. Incubate the tubes for 30 minutes at room temperature. Repeat the restriction enzyme digestion as described in Step 3. Finally, soak each plug in 20 volumes of TE (pH 7.6) for 1 hour at 4ºC.

7. Use a disposable pipette tip to push the blocks directly into the slots of a pulsed-field gel, and separate the fragments of DNA by electrophoresis (Protocols 17 and 18).

Protocol 16

Markers for Pulsed-field Gel Electrophoresis

Bᴇᴄᴀᴜsᴇ ᴏꜰ ɪᴛs ᴄᴀᴘᴀᴄɪᴛʏ ᴛᴏ sᴇᴘᴀʀᴀᴛᴇ ᴇxᴛʀᴇᴍᴇʟʏ ʟᴀʀɢᴇ ᴍᴏʟᴇᴄᴜʟᴇs of DNA, PFGE requires markers of extremely high molecular weight. These may be obtained by extracting DNAs from bacteriophages such as T7 (40 kb), T2 (166 kb), and G (758 kb) according to the method of Lauer et al. (1977). However, a better series of markers, which are evenly spaced over a wider range of molecular weights, can be generated by ligation of bacteriophage λ DNA into a nested series of concatemers. The following procedure is an adaptation of the method described by Vollrath and Davis (1987). Yeast chromosomes, prepared as described in Protocol 14, may be used as even higher-molecular-weight markers.

This procedure yields a series of concatemers that contain up to 20 tandemly arranged copies of bacteriophage λ DNA. The viral DNA is readily ligated into concatemers by virtue of the 12-bp sticky ends or *cos* sites that occur at both ends of the bacteriophage genome. The size of intact bacteriophage λ DNA is 48.5 kb; thus, the individual concatenates are multiples of this length. Usually, 400–600 ng of the concatenated DNA is loaded onto a single lane (1 cm in length) of a TAFE (Protocol 17) or CHEF (Protocol 18) agarose gel.

The method given here is slow, but it produces a series of concatemers that contain approximately equal amounts of DNA.

MATERIALS

CAUTION: Please see Appendix 12 for appropriate handling of materials marked with <!>.

Buffers and Solutions

Please see Appendix 1 for components of stock solutions, buffers, and reagents.
Dilute stock solutions to the appropriate concentrations.

ATP (0.1 M)
Dithiothreitol (1 M)
EDTA (0.5 M, pH 8.0)
1x Ligation buffer with polyethylene glycol
    50 mM Tris-Cl (pH 7.6)
    1 mM ATP
    10 mM dithiothreitol
    10 mM MgCl$_2$
    2% PEG 8000 <!>

Low-melting-temperature (LMT) agarose buffer
　　100 mM Tris-Cl (pH 7.6)
　　20 mM MgCl$_2$
MgCl$_2$ (20 mM)
Polyethylene glycol (8% w/v PEG 8000 solution) <!>
TE (pH 7.6)

Enzymes and Buffers

Bacteriophage T4 DNA ligase

Gels

Low-melting-temperature agarose
　　Use a grade of agarose that is suitable for PFGE (e.g., SeaPlaque GTG, BioWhittaker).

Nucleic Acids and Oligonucleotides

Purified bacteriophage λ DNA
　　Please see Chapter 2, Protocols 11 and 12.

Special Equipment

Tygon tubing
　　Use tubing with a 3/32-inch internal diameter.
Water bath preset to 56°C

METHOD

1. Dissolve 0.1 g of low-melting-temperature agarose in 10 ml of LMT buffer by heating it in a boiling water bath or by microwaving. Cool the solution to 37°C.

2. Dissolve 10 μg of purified bacteriophage λ DNA in 172.5 μl of TE (pH 7.6) and heat the solution to 56°C for 5 minutes.

    This treatment denatures the cohesive termini of the bacteriophage λ DNA.

3. Cool the solution to 37°C, and rapidly add the following reagents in the order listed:

8% PEG 8000	62.5 μl
20 mM MgCl$_2$	5.0 μl
0.1 M ATP	5.0 μl
1 M dithiothreitol	5.0 μl
bacteriophage T4 DNA ligase	0.5 Weiss unit
1% LMT agarose solution (Step 1)	250 μl

    Polyethylene glycol acts like a crowding agent and increases the efficiency of ligation (please see the information panel on **CONDENSING AND CROWDING REAGENTS** in Chapter 1).

4. Draw the mixture into a short length of Tygon tubing, and chill the tubing on ice until the agarose has completely set.

5. Blow the agarose plug into a sterile, disposable plastic tube containing at least 3 volumes of 1x ligation buffer with polyethylene glycol.

    An alternative method to using Tygon tubing is to transfer the LMT solution from Step 3 directly to a disposable plastic tube. Allow the gel to harden and then add 3 volumes of 1x ligation buffer. Make sure to dislodge the agarose plug from the bottom of the tube to allow the ligation buffer equal access to the entire plug.

6. Incubate the plug in ligation buffer for 24 hours at room temperature and then transfer it to a tube containing 10 volumes of 20 mM EDTA (pH 8.0).

7. Incubate the plug in EDTA for 1 hour, then transfer the plug to a tube containing 10 volumes of fresh 20 mM EDTA (pH 8.0), and store at 4°C until needed for electrophoresis in Protocols 17 and 18.

Protocol 17

Pulsed-field Gel Electrophoresis via Transverse Alternating Field Electrophoresis Gels

GARDINER ET AL. (1986; GARDINER AND PATTERSON 1989) USED A GEL APPARATUS with platinum wire electrodes positioned on opposite sides of a vertically oriented gel to separate large DNA fragments. In this form of transverse alternating field electrophoresis (TAFE), the DNA moves first toward one set of electrodes and then toward the other as the electric fields are switched. The net result of the zigzag movements is a straight line from the loading well toward the bottom of the gel. Because all of the lanes in the gel are exposed to equivalent electric fields, there is no horizontal distortion of the DNA bands. As with other PFGE systems, the size of the molecules resolved at a given voltage is a function of the pulse time. Variation in these parameters allows the separation of DNAs ranging in size from 2 kb up to >6000 kb. TAFE gels are thus very versatile: They can be adapted to the analysis of almost any locus or gene, and they can be used to establish accurate long-range restriction maps and are especially good at resolving DNA fragments in the <1000-kb range. Resolution of larger DNA fragments using contour-clamped field electrophoresis (CHEF) gels is presented in Protocol 18. For a more detailed discussion on preparing and running agarose gels, please refer to the introduction to Protocol 1.

The following protocol, supplied by Tommy Hyatt and Helen Hobbs (University of Texas, Southwestern Medical Center, Dallas), describes the resolution of genomic DNA by TAFE, followed by blotting and detection by hybridization. Protocols 19 and 20 describe methods for isolating and recovering a particular DNA fragment resolved by PFGE.

PULSE TIMES IN TAFE GELS

In TAFE gels, voltage is applied to one set of electrodes for a period of time known as the pulse time and is then switched and applied to the other electrode pair for an equivalent time. In a TAFE apparatus in which the agarose gel is mounted in a vertical position, the resulting electric field moves through the thickness of the gel. The length of the pulse time determines the size range of DNA that is optimally resolved on the gel. Table 5-10 correlates pulse time with the fragment size range resolved. This table can be used with the protocol as a rough guide when setting up the initial TAFE gel experiments; the pulse time can then be customized to fit the needs of a particular experiment.

DNA fragments in the megabase range, such as the chromosomes of *S. pombe*, can also be resolved on TAFE gels but require a gel containing a low concentration of agarose (0.55%) and

TABLE 5-10 TAFE Gel Conditions for Separating DNAs of Various Sizes

SIZE RANGE (kb)	PULSE TIME (SECONDS)	TIME (HOURS)
5–50	1	10
20–100	3	10
50–250	10	14
100–400	20	14
200–1000	45	18
200–1600	70	20
Larger DNAs	see text	see text

the use of 2x TAFE gel buffer. A two-step electrophoresis program is run consisting of an initial electrophoresis of 12 hours of 30-minute pulses at 60 V, followed by a 60-hour run of 20-minute pulses at 50 V (K. Gardiner, pers. comm.).

The exact electrophoretic behavior of a DNA fragment in a TAFE gel is influenced by the electric field strength, pulse time, buffer concentration, temperature, and DNA topology. For a detailed analysis of how these parameters affect the migration of large DNAs in PFGE, please see Cantor et al. (1988) and Mathew et al. (1988a,b,c). In general, their conclusions are applicable to TAFE gels. However, a problem encountered during some TAFE gel experiments arises as a consequence of the vertical position of the agarose gel in the apparatus. If the gel box or the gel should warp, the DNA will be off-center in the electric field, causing the DNA to migrate out one face of the gel.

MATERIALS

CAUTION: Please see Appendix 12 for appropriate handling of materials marked with <!>.

Buffers and Solutions

Please see Appendix 1 for components of stock solutions, buffers, and reagents. Dilute stock solutions to the appropriate concentrations.

Denaturing buffer
  0.5 N NaOH <!>
  1.5 M NaCl
TAFE gel electrophoresis buffer containing 0.5 μg/ml ethidium bromide or an appropriate dilution of SYBR Gold <!>
  For a discussion of staining agarose gels, please see Protocol 2.
TAFE gel electrophoresis buffer
  20 mM Tris-acetate (pH 8.2)
  0.5 mM EDTA
  Use acetic acid to adjust the pH of the Tris solution to 8.2; use the free acid of EDTA, not the sodium salt. Concentrated solutions of TAFE buffer can also be purchased (e.g., from Beckman). A buffer of 0.045 M Tris-borate (pH 8.2) and 0.01 M EDTA has also been used successfully in this protocol.
  ▲ IMPORTANT The TAFE gel electrophoresis buffer must be cooled to 14°C before filling the gel apparatus.
TE (pH 8.0)

Gels

High-quality agarose
  It is essential to use a grade of agarose appropriate for PFGE. Many specialty agaroses are commercially available for this purpose (e.g., Seakem LE, BioWhittaker). We have had success with Agarose LE from Beckman in this protocol and with regular LMP agarose from Life Technologies.

Nucleic Acids and Oligonucleotides

DNA size standards
Please see Step 2. Standards can also be purchased from commercial manufacturers (e.g., New England Biolabs, Bio-Rad, or GIBCO-BRL).

Genomic DNA of interest
Please see Step 2.

Special Equipment

Circulating water bath
TAFE gels are run at 14°C and require a device that both circulates and cools the electrophoresis buffer. These devices are expensive (several thousand dollars each) and can be purchased either as part of the TAFE gel apparatus (commercially available) or as a separate piece of equipment (e.g., Lauda or Techne refrigeration immersion circulators or circulating baths).

TAFE gel apparatus
This apparatus is available commercially or can be constructed as described by Gardiner et al. (1986; Gardiner and Patterson 1989).

Water bath preset to 14°C
The water bath is required to cool the TAFE gel electrophoresis buffer before use.

Additional Reagents

Step 2 of this protocol requires the reagents listed in Protocols 13 or 14, 15, and 16 of this chapter.

Steps 9 and 10 of this protocol require the reagents listed in Chapter 6, Protocol 8.

Step 11 of this protocol requires the reagents listed in Chapter 6, Protocol 10.

METHOD

Separation of DNA Fragments by TAFE

1. Cast a 1% agarose gel in 1x TAFE gel buffer without ethidium bromide and allow the gel to set. Pour the gel with the same buffer solution to be used to fill the gel apparatus.

2. Prepare agarose plugs containing the DNA of interest (please see Protocol 13 for preparation of mammalian DNA or Protocol 14 for preparation of yeast DNA embedded in plugs) and carry out digestion with restriction enzymes as described in Protocol 15. Prepare and embed the appropriate DNA size standards as described in Protocols 14 and 16.

3. Rinse all of the plugs in 10 volumes of TE (pH 8.0) for 30 minutes with two changes of buffer.

4. Embed the digested and rinsed DNA plugs in individual wells of the gel. Seal the plugs in the wells with molten 1% agarose in 1x TAFE gel buffer.

5. Place the gel in the TAFE apparatus filled with 1x TAFE gel buffer previously cooled to 14°C.

6. Connect the gel apparatus to the appropriate power supply set to deliver 4-second pulses at a constant current of 170–180 mA for 30 minutes. This setting forces the DNA to enter the gel rapidly. After this time period, decrease the current input to 150 mA, change the pulse time to a setting optimum for the size range of DNAs to be resolved (please see Table 5-10 of this protocol), and continue electrophoresis for 12–18 hours.

   In a Tris-acetate/EDTA buffer, a pulse time of 15 seconds will separate DNA fragments in the 50–400-kb size range. This same range of fragments can be separated in the Tris-borate/EDTA buffer using a program of 8-second pulses at 350 mA for 12 hours followed by 15-second pulses at 350 mA for an additional 12 hours.

   The rapid electrophoresis of the DNA into the gel at the start of the run is optional. Some investigators skip this step and simply use one constant current and pulse time setting for the entire run.

7. Disconnect the power supply, dismantle the gel apparatus, and stain the gel in 1× TAFE buffer containing 0.5 μg/ml ethidium bromide or an appropriate dilution of SYBR Gold. Photograph the gel under UV light.

    The standard technique used to detect DNAs separated by PFGE is staining with ethidium bromide or SYBR Gold (please see Protocol 2). To facilitate the detection of minor species of DNA stained with ethidium bromide, the gels may be destained in H_2O for up to 1 hour before photography. For details of methods that can be used to maximize the photographic detection of DNA stained with these dyes, please see Protocol 2. Alternatively, these gels may be stained with a silver solution as described in the panel below.

ALTERNATIVE PROTOCOL: SILVER STAINING PFGE GELS

An alternative, more sensitive method for detecting DNA in TAFE or CHEF gels is to stain the gel with silver (Gardiner et al. 1986). Unfortunately, the staining procedure prevents subsequent transfer of the DNA to a membrane for hybridization analysis.

CAUTION: Please see Appendix 12 for appropriate handling of materials marked with <!>.

Additional Materials

Filter paper
Glutaraldehyde (3% v/v) in H_2O <!>
Weight (500 g)
Paper towels
Silver nitrate solution
    19 mM NaOH
    0.2 N NH_4OH
    0.1% (w/v) $AgNO_3$ <!>

Method

1. Dry the gel overnight between two sheets of filter paper and a 2-inch stack of paper towels weighed down with a 500-g mass.

2. Soak the dried gel in 100 ml of 3% (v/v) glutaraldehyde for 7 minutes at room temperature in a chemical fume hood.

3. Rinse the gel in H_2O, pour off the H_2O, and replace with 100 ml of freshly prepared silver nitrate solution. Leave the gel in this solution until the DNA bands are visible (typically 3–5 minutes).

4. Pour off the silver solution into a waste collection container and rinse the gel with H_2O for an extended period of time.

Denaturation and Transfer of DNA to a Nylon Membrane

8. Rinse the stained gel twice with H_2O. Pour off the second H_2O rinse and replace with denaturing buffer. Incubate with gentle shaking for 30 minutes. Change the denaturing buffer and incubate for an additional 30 minutes.

    In general, standard methods of Southern blotting as described in Chapter 6 (please see Protocols 8 and 9) can be used to detect hybridizing gene sequences in TAFE gels. Some investigators find that the very large DNA fragments typically analyzed by PFGE transfer to nylon membranes more efficiently after partial hydrolysis of the DNA by acid treatment. This treatment causes partial depurination and nicking of larger DNA fragments and in so doing enhances capillary transfer. To include an acid hydrolysis step, after the electrophoresis is complete, rinse the gel twice with H_2O in Step 8, pour off the second H_2O rinse, and replace with 25 mM HCl. Soak the gel with gentle agitation for 3–5 minutes. Rinse the gel with H_2O and continue with the denaturation protocol of Step 8 and onward.

    When acid treatments are used in the protocol, it is important to stain the agarose gel after transfer of the DNA to the nylon membrane. A slight residual smear of DNA should be visible. If no residual DNA is detected, then the acid treatment may have been too harsh (i.e., too long or too strong). Too much depurination and nicking increases the transfer of the DNA but also tends to reduce the intensity of subsequent hybridization signals.

9. Transfer the DNA directly to a nylon membrane by capillary blotting in denaturing buffer (for details, please see Chapter 6, Protocol 8).

   > Some investigators find that transfer of larger DNA fragments is enhanced when 6x SSC buffer is used in capillary blotting rather than the more standard 10x SSC solution.

10. After transfer, affix the DNA to the nylon membrane by baking for 2 hours at 80ºC, by UV cross-linking, or by microwaving.

11. Carry out prehybridization and hybridization with labeled probes in a formamide-containing buffer (for details, please see Chapter 6, Protocol 10).

    > We typically use ^{32}P-radiolabeled single-stranded bacteriophage M13 probes (please see Chapter 9, Protocol 5) at a concentration of 5×10^6 to 6×10^6 cpm/ml of hybridization buffer to detect a single-copy gene in a complex mammalian genome. A membrane hybridized for 12–16 hours in this fashion is washed in 500 ml of 2x SSC containing 1% (w/v) SDS for 15 minutes at room temperature, scrubbed gently with a sponge, then washed in 1 liter of 0.5x SSC containing 1% (w/v) SDS for 2 hours at 68ºC, and then subjected to autoradiography.

TROUBLESHOOTING

In general, the mark of a good electrophoretic run when separating mammalian genomic DNA digested with a restriction endonuclease is the presence of a constant smear of stained DNA extending from just below the well to the lower reaches of the gel. A concentration of DNA at the bottom of the gel is indicative of nonspecific degradation of the genomic DNA. This degradation is usually caused by contamination of the preparation with a nonspecific DNase, which is quiescent when the DNA is stored in TE, but is activated upon incubation in an Mg^{2+}-containing restriction enzyme buffer. Phenol:chloroform extraction of the DNA to remove the offending DNase is out of the question because the DNA is embedded in an agarose plug. However, retreatment of the plugs with proteinase K followed by the addition of PMSF as described for mammalian DNA in Protocol 13 (Steps 6–8) or for yeast DNA in Protocol 14 (Steps 9–11) can remove DNase from a batch of contaminated plugs. Along these lines, it is a good idea to check all preparations of agarose plugs prepared in this protocol by simply incubating the plug in the presence of a restriction buffer and absence of restriction enzyme. Thereafter, examine the DNA by separation through a TAFE gel in which 60-second pulse times are used over a 20-hour electrophoresis run. If the DNA in the plug is intact, then very little DNA will enter the gel during the electrophoresis. However, if there is a nonspecific DNase contaminant, a considerable amount of DNA will enter the gel and be visible after ethidium bromide staining.

If a focus of DNA is detected just below the well after restriction enzyme digestion and PFGE, then it may be assumed that the restriction enzyme did not digest the DNA to completion. Many of the restriction enzymes used in analyzing DNA by PFGE have strict buffer requirements for maximum activity. Make sure that the buffer recommended by the enzyme's manufacturer was used and that the digestion was carried out at the proper temperature. Alternatively, poor digestion by more than one enzyme can indicate a dirty DNA preparation. In this case as well, the contaminant may be removed by retreating the genomic DNA plugs with proteinase K and PMSF as described for mammalian DNA in Protocol 13 (Steps 6–8) or for yeast DNA in Protocol 14 (Steps 9–11).

Protocol 18

Pulsed-field Gel Electrophoresis via Contour-clamped Homogeneous Electric Field Gels

IN CONTOUR-CLAMPED HOMOGENEOUS ELECTRIC FIELD (CHEF) gels, the electric field is generated from multiple electrodes that are arranged in a square or hexagonal contour around the horizontal gel and are clamped to predetermined potentials (Chu et al. 1986; Vollrath and Davis 1987; Chu 1990a). A square contour generates electric fields that are oriented at right angles to each other; a hexagonal array of electrodes generates fields at angles of 120° or 60°, depending on the placement of the gel and the polarity of the electrodes. By using a combination of low field strengths (1.3 V/cm), low concentrations of agarose (0.6%), long switching intervals (1 hour), and extended periods of electrophoresis (130 hours), it is possible to resolve DNA molecules up to 5000 kb in length (Vollrath and Davis 1987). CHEF gels can be used to size DNA fragments accurately in genomic DNA and do not suffer from the problems of vertical gel positioning that are endemic to TAFE gels.

The following protocol, supplied by Elsy Jones (University of Texas Southwestern Medical Center, Dallas), describes the resolution of large genomic DNA molecules by CHEF gel electrophoresis, followed by blotting and detection by hybridization. Protocols 19 and 20 describe methods for isolating and recovering a particular DNA fragment resolved by PFGE.

CONDITIONS FOR CHEF ELECTROPHORESIS

The size range in which maximum resolution of DNA fragments is achieved on CHEF gels depends on the pulse time. In general, shorter pulse times are used to separate smaller DNA fragments and longer pulse times are used to separate larger DNAs. Table 5-11 presents empirically determined pulse and electrophoresis times for a given size range of DNAs using a CHEF apparatus from Bio-Rad. Other devices may yield slightly different separations for a given set of conditions.

The orientation of the electric field relative to the plane of the agarose gel, called the field angle, can be varied between 90° and 120°. In general, the smaller the field angle, the faster a DNA fragment of a given size migrates through the gel. Smaller angles (<105°) are best for resolving very large DNA fragments (>1000 kb), whereas larger angles are best for resolving smaller DNA fragments.

TABLE 5-11 Conditions for Separating DNAs of Various Sizes in CHEF Gels

% AGAROSE	SIZE RANGE (kb)	SWITCH TIMES	V/CM	TIME (HOURS)
1% Fast Lane	6–500	ramped, 3–80 seconds	6	18
	10–800	ramped, 6–80 seconds	6	20
	100–1000	60 seconds,	6	15
		then 90 seconds	6	9
0.8% Fast Lane	150–2000	ramped, 30–180 seconds	5	24

All gels are run in 0.5x TBE. When very high resolution is required in the 800–2000-kb range, a lower voltage and a longer run time than those indicated above are used. If the gels are cast with Seakem GTG agarose, add 10% to the electrophoresis time indicated.

The use of ramped switching permits greater resolution of DNA fragments within a given size range. In ramping, the switch time at the beginning of the electrophoresis run is different from that at the end of the run. Ramping decreases the occurrence of a peculiar phenomenon in the electrophoresis of large DNAs, in which very large fragments sometimes migrate faster than smaller DNAs (Carle et al. 1986; Chu 1990a).

MATERIALS

CAUTION: Please see Appendix 12 for appropriate handling of materials marked with <!>.

Buffers and Solutions

Please see Appendix 1 for components of stock solutions, buffers, and reagents. Dilute stock solutions to the appropriate concentrations.

Denaturing buffer
0.5 N NaOH
1.5 M NaCl

Ethidium bromide <!> (1 μg/ml) or an appropriate dilution of SYBR Gold <!>
For a discussion of staining agarose gels, please see Protocol 2.

0.5x TBE gel electrophoresis buffer
Please see Table 5-3 for 5x recipe.

Gels

High-quality agarose
The following agaroses from the BioWhittaker have been used successfully with this protocol:
- Seakem GTG Agarose
- Seakem Gold Agarose: A more expensive agarose that hardens into a stronger gel matrix than Seakem GTG agarose and reduces electrophoretic run times ~10% relative to Seakem GTG.
- Fast Lane Agarose: A high-grade agarose that is slightly less expensive than Seakem Gold and maintains the faster electrophoretic character of this agarose. Gels cast with Fast Lane agarose are not as tough as those made with Seakem Gold and must be handled with more care.

1% agarose gels resolve DNA fragments in a range of 10–1000 kb, whereas 0.8% agarose gels resolve DNA fragments larger than 1000 kb. For further details, please see above Conditions for CHEF Electrophoresis and Table 5-11.

Nucleic Acids and Oligonucleotides

DNA size standards
Please see Step 3. Standards can also be purchased from commercial manufacturers (e.g., New England Biolabs, Bio-Rad, or GIBCO-BRL).

Genomic DNA of interest
Please see Step 3.

Special Equipment

CHEF gel apparatus
The apparatus can be constructed as described by Chu (1990b) or purchased commercially. The following protocol was developed for use with either the CHEF DR or CHEF Mapper apparatus from Bio-Rad.

Circulating water bath
CHEF gels are run at 14ºC and require a device that both circulates and cools the electrophoresis buffer.

Water bath preset to 14ºC

Additional Reagents

Step 3 of this protocol requires the reagents listed in Protocosl 13 or 14, 15, and 16 of this chapter.

Steps 10 and 11 of this protocol require the reagents listed in Chapter 6, Protocol 8.

Step 12 of this protocol requires the reagents listed in Chapter 6, Protocol 10.

METHOD

Separation of DNA Fragments by CHEF

1. Cast an agarose gel of the appropriate concentration in 0.5x TBE buffer as described in Protocol 1. Use a bubble level to ensure that the casting tray is completely flat on the laboratory bench. Allow the gel to harden for 1 hour at room temperature.

2. Place the agarose gel in the CHEF apparatus, add enough 0.5x TBE to just cover the gel, and cool the remaining buffer to 14ºC.

3. Prepare agarose plugs containing the DNA of interest (please see Protocol 13 for preparation of mammalian DNA or Protocol 14 for preparation of yeast DNA embedded in plugs) and carry out digestion with restriction enzymes as described in Protocol 15. Prepare and embed the appropriate DNA size standards as described in Protocol 14 or 16.

4. Gently place the plugs in individual microfuge tubes and add 200 µl of 0.5x TBE to each. Incubate the plugs for 15 minutes at room temperature.

5. Embed the digested and rinsed DNA plugs in individual wells of the gel. Seal the plugs in the wells with the same solution of molten agarose used to pour the gel.

6. Allow the sealed plugs to harden in the gel for ~5 minutes, and then add additional 0.5x TBE buffer (previously cooled to 14ºC in Step 2) to the apparatus to cover the agarose gel completely.

7. Start the buffer circulating and begin the electrophoresis run using power supply settings as described in Table 5-11.

8. After electrophoresis, stain the gel in a 1 µg/ml solution of ethidium bromide or an appropriate dilution of SYBR Gold for 30 minutes at room temperature. Destain the gel in H_2O for 30 minutes and photograph the gel under UV light.

   For details of methods that can be used to maximize the photographic detection of DNA stained with these dyes, please see Protocol 2. If no transfer of the DNA to a membrane is planned, these gels may be stained with a silver solution as described in the panel on **ALTERNATIVE PROTO-COL: SILVER STAINING PFGE GELS** in Protocol 17.

Denaturation and Transfer of DNA to a Nylon Membrane

9. After photography, incubate the gel in 250 ml of denaturing buffer with gentle shaking for 30 minutes. Change the denaturing buffer and incubate for an additional 30 minutes.

10. Transfer the DNA directly to a nylon membrane by capillary blotting in denaturing buffer (for details, please see Chapter 6, Protocol 8).

    Enhanced transfer of larger DNA fragments has also been noted when 6x SSC buffer is used in capillary blotting rather than the more standard 10x SSC solution.

11. After transfer, affix the DNA to the nylon membrane by baking for 2 hours at 80°C, by UV cross-linking, or by microwaving.

12. Carry out prehybridization and hybridization with labeled probes in a formamide-containing buffer (for details, please see Chapter 6, Protocol 10).

    We typically use ^{32}P-radiolabeled single-stranded bacteriophage M13 probes (please see Chapter 9, Protocol 5) at a concentration of 5×10^6 to 6×10^6 cpm/ml of hybridization buffer to detect a single-copy gene in a complex mammalian genome. A membrane hybridized for 12–16 hours in this fashion is washed in 500 ml of 2x SSC containing 1% (w/v) SDS for 15 minutes at room temperature, scrubbed gently with a sponge, and then washed in 1 liter of 0.5x SSC containing 1% (w/v) SDS for 2 hours at 68°C, and then subjected to autoradiography.

Protocol 19

Direct Retrieval of DNA Fragments from Pulsed-field Gels

P REPARATIVE SCALE PFGE IN LOW-MELTING-TEMPERATURE AGAROSE (please see Protocols 17 and 18) is often used to isolate a large DNA fragment for subsequent manipulation. Size-fractionated DNAs can be digested with restriction endonucleases to generate a high-resolution cleavage map or to produce fragments for ligation into bacteriophage or plasmid vectors. Additionally, DNAs isolated from pulsed-field gels can be ligated directly into cosmid or yeast artificial chromosome (YAC) vectors, or if already cloned into YAC vectors, fractionated DNA can be injected into fertilized mouse embryos or transfected into murine embryonic stem cells. Working with size-fractionated high-molecular-weight DNAs requires that extra precautions be taken to maximize recovery of the desired DNA molecules and to avoid shearing the DNA. This protocol presents a method for the direct recovery of DNA from a low-melting-point PFGE. Protocol 20 first concentrates the fractionated DNA by electrophoresis into a high-percentage gel, followed by recovery of the DNA molecules. Both protocols rely on the use of agarase to release high-molecular-weight DNA enzymatically from agarose.

In this protocol, a gel slice containing a fragment of DNA resolved by PFGE is treated directly with agarase. The released DNA can be used as a substrate for ligation or restriction without further purification.

MATERIALS

CAUTION: Please see Appendix 12 for appropriate handling of materials marked with <!>.

Buffers and Solutions

Please see Appendix 1 for components of stock solutions, buffers, and reagents. Dilute stock solutions to the appropriate concentrations.

Ethidium bromide <!> (1 μg/ml) or an appropriate dilution of SYBR Gold <!>
For a discussion of staining agarose gels, please see Protocol 2.
Phenol:chloroform (1:1, v/v) (optional) <!>

Enzymes and Buffers

Agarase is available from a number of manufacturers (GELase from Epicenter Technologies, β-Agarase I from New England Biolabs, and β-Agarase I from Calbiochem). Use the buffer supplied with the enzyme. We recommend that all buffers be supplemented with 100 mM NaCl, 30 μM spermine, 70 μM spermidine to enhance recovery of the DNA.

Nucleic Acids and Oligonucleotides

DNA size standards

For the preparation of two different ranges of sizing standards, please see Protocols 14 and 16. Standards can also be purchased from commercial manufacturers (e.g., New England Biolabs, Bio-Rad, or GIBCO-BRL).

Genomic DNA embedded in low-melting-temperature agarose plugs

Please see Protocol 13 for preparation of mammalian DNA or Protocol 14 for preparation of yeast DNA embedded in plugs. Carry out digestion with restriction enzymes as described in Protocol 15 of this chapter.

Special Equipment

Water baths preset to 65–68°C and to temperature appropriate for agarase digestion

Additional Reagents

Steps 1 and 2 of this protocol require the reagents listed in Protocol 17 or 18 of this chapter.

METHOD

1. Prepare a preparative low-melting-point agarose PFGE that will provide optimum resolution of the DNA fragment or size fraction of interest.

2. Load the DNA size standards and single plugs of the digested genomic DNA in lanes located on both sides of the preparative slot. Load the preparative sample into the preparative slot. Carry out electrophoresis as described in Protocol 17 (for TAFE gel) or Protocol 18 (for CHEF gel).

    As many as 20 plugs containing DNA digested with a restriction enzyme can be loaded into a single "preparative" slot on the gel (van de Pol et al. 1990).

3. After electrophoresis, cut the lanes containing the size standards and single genomic DNA plugs from the gel and stain them with ethidium bromide or SYBR Gold for 30 minutes at room temperature. If necessary, destain the gel slices in H_2O for 30 minutes. Do not stain the preparative lane.

4. Examine the stained slices by UV illumination and make notches on the slices to mark the locations of markers flanking the position of DNA of interest.

5. Reassemble the gel with the lanes containing the stained size standards and single plugs and locate the approximate region of the unstained preparative lane containing the DNA of interest. Carefully excise this region with a clean razor blade, and transfer the gel slice to a snap-cap polypropylene tube.

    For long-term storage, the fragment should be placed in an airtight tube and stored at 4°C. Dot blotting or Southern blotting can be used to obtain a more precise determination of the location of the fragment of interest in the preparative gel (van de Pol et al. 1990).

6. Cover the gel fragment with agarase buffer, and incubate for 1 hour at room temperature with occasional agitation. Discard the buffer, and repeat the procedure twice more.

7. After the buffer exchange is complete, melt the agarose slice containing the fractionated DNA at 65–68°C. During the melting step, swirl the tube to ensure complete melting.

    Agarases digest denatured/melted agarose, not chunks of agarose.

8. Add an appropriate amount of agarase to the melted gel and digest the gel at the temperature recommended by the manufacturer.

   Digestions are usually carried out at temperatures between 37ºC and 45ºC and for times ranging from 1 hour to overnight.

9. After digestion, inactivate the agarase by heating (according to the manufacturer's instructions) or remove by phenol:chloroform extraction.

   Heat inactivation is preferred to avoid possible shearing of the DNA during extraction with organic solvents. Ligation or restriction enzyme digestion of the released DNA can be carried out in the presence of the agarose monomers produced by the agarase. Alternatively, the DNA can be precipitated in the presence of 0.3 M sodium acetate (pH 5.2) and 2 volumes of isopropanol.

Protocol 20

Retrieval of DNA Fragments from Pulsed-field Gels following DNA Concentration

DNA CONTAINED IN A SLICE OF LOW-MELTING-TEMPERATURE AGAROSE is first concentrated by electrophoresis into a high-percentage agarose gel, and then isolated by treatment with agarase. The resulting DNA preparation is purified by microdialysis. This method is especially useful if the size-fractionated DNA is to be injected into fertilized mouse eggs (Schedl et al. 1993) or used for transfection of murine embryonic stem cells (Choi et al. 1993).

The presence of spermine and spermidine in the buffers used in this protocol is crucial to obtaining high recoveries of high-molecular-weight biologically active DNA. Their use should be considered whenever large DNA fragments (>15 kb) are to be isolated from low-melting-temperature agarose. The direct retrieval of DNA from pulsed-field gels (without prior concentration) is described in Protocol 19.

MATERIALS

CAUTION: Please see Appendix 12 for appropriate handling of materials marked with <!>.

Buffers and Solutions

Please see Appendix 1 for components of stock solutions, buffers, and reagents. Dilute stock solutions to the appropriate concentrations.

Equilibration buffer
  1x TBE
  100 mM NaCl
  30 µM spermine
  70 µM spermidine

Ethidium bromide <!> *(1 µg/ml) or an appropriate dilution of SYBR Gold* <!>
  For a discussion of staining agarose gels, please see Protocol 2.

Injection/transfection buffer
  10 mM Tris-Cl (pH 7.5)
  0.1 mM EDTA
  100 mM NaCl
  30 µM spermine
  70 µM spermidine

Enzymes and Buffers

Agarase
  Agarase is available from a number of manufacturers (GELase from Epicenter Technologies, β-Agarase I from New England Biolabs, and β-Agarase I from Calbiochem). Use the buffer supplied with the enzyme.

It is critical that all buffers be supplemented with 100 mM NaCl, 30 μM spermine, and 70 μM spermidine to enhance recovery of the DNA.

Gels

NuSieve GTG Agarose minigel (5%)
Prepare the gel without a comb and in a taped gel mold.

Nucleic Acids and Oligonucleotides

DNA size standards
Please see Protocols 14 and 16 for the preparation of two different ranges of sizing standards. Standards can also be purchased from commercial manufacturers (e.g., New England Biolabs, Bio-Rad, or GIBCO-BRL).

Genomic DNA embedded in low-melting-temperature agarose plugs
Please see Protocol 13 for preparation of mammalian DNA or Protocol 14 for preparation of yeast DNA embedded in plugs. Carry out digestion with restriction enzymes as described in Protocol 15 of this chapter.

Special Equipment

Membranes for drop dialysis (0.05 μm pore size)
These membranes are available from Millipore.

Water baths preset to 65–68°C and to temperature appropriate for agarase digestion

Additional Reagents

Steps 1 and 2 of this protocol require the reagents listed in Protocol 17 or 18 of this chapter.

METHOD

1. Prepare a preparative low-melting-point agarose PFGE that will provide optimum resolution of the DNA fragment or size fraction of interest.

2. Load the DNA size standards and single plugs of the digested genomic DNA in lanes located on both sides of the preparative slot. Load the preparative sample into the preparative slot. Carry out electrophoresis as described in Protocol 17 (TAFE gel) or Protocol 18 (for CHEF gel).

    As many as 20 plugs containing DNA digested with a restriction enzyme can be loaded into a single "preparative" slot on the gel (van de Pol et al. 1990).

3. After electrophoresis, cut the lanes containing the size standards and single genomic DNA plugs from the gel and stain them with ethidium bromide or SYBR Gold for 30 minutes at room temperature. If necessary, destain the gel slices in H$_2$O for 30 minutes. Do not stain the preparative lane.

4. Examine the stained slices by UV illumination and make notches on the slices to mark the locations of markers flanking the position of DNA of interest.

5. Under normal illumination, reassemble the gel with the lanes containing the stained size standards and single plugs and locate the approximate region of the unstained preparative lane containing the DNA of interest. Carefully excise this region with a clean razor blade, and transfer the gel slice to a snap-cap polypropylene tube.

    For long-term storage, the fragment should be placed in an airtight tube and stored at 4°C. Dot blotting or Southern blotting can be used to obtain a more precise determination of the location of the fragment of interest in the preparative gel (van de Pol et al. 1990).

6. Equilibrate the gel slice containing the size-fractionated DNA in 40 ml of equilibration buffer for 20–30 minutes at room temperature. Agitate the mixture gently throughout this period.

7. Pour off the buffer and melt the gel slice at 65–68°C, gently swirling the tube periodically to ensure complete melting. Record the volume of the melted gel slice.

8. While the 5% NuSieve GTG minigel is still in the taped casting tray, slice off enough of the top of the gel to accommodate the volume of the melted gel slice that contains DNA.

9. Pour the melted gel slice into the casting tray and allow it to harden. Concentrate the size-fractionated DNA in the 5% gel by applying 60 V for 12 minutes per millimeter of low-melting-temperature gel.

   > For example, if the low-melting-temperature agarose portion of the gel is 10 mm long, apply a voltage across the gel for 120 minutes.

10. When electrophoresis is complete, slice a very thin section from the *center* of the gel and stain it with ethidium bromide. Determine how far into the gel the DNA has migrated (usually ~2 mm).

    > It is important to stain a sliver from the center of the gel as some smiling occurs during electrophoresis.

11. Remove the low-melting portion of the gel and trim as small a portion as possible of the 5% gel containing the concentrated DNA.

12. Equilibrate the gel slice containing the DNA in 12 ml of 1x agarase digestion buffer containing 100 mM NaCl, 30 μM spermine, and 70 μM spermidine. Incubate the gel slice in this buffer for 20 minutes at room temperature with gentle agitation.

13. Drain off the buffer, transfer the gel slice to a microfuge tube, and melt the DNA slice at 65–68°C. Transfer the melted gel to a water bath set at a temperature optimal for the agarase preparation (recommended by the manufacturer).

14. Incubate the melted gel slice for 15 minutes, and then add an appropriate amount of agarase to digest the starting volume of 5% gel.

    > Digestions are usually carried out at temperatures between 37°C and 45°C and for times ranging from 1 hour to overnight.

15. After digestion, centrifuge the tube at maximum speed for 5 minutes in a microfuge to pellet debris, and transfer the supernatant to a fresh microfuge tube.

16. Set up a drop dialysis of the supernatant using membranes with a 0.05-μm pore size:

    a. Spot the supernatant onto the center of the membrane, floating shiny side up on 100 ml of injection/transfection buffer.

       > One membrane can easily support 100 μl of supernatant.

    b. Dialyze for 1 hour at room temperature. Replace the original buffer with 100 ml of fresh injection/transfection buffer and dialyze for an additional hour.

    c. Transfer the DNA to a clean microfuge tube.

       > Drop dialysis removes the agarase enzyme and the digested carbohydrates released from the agarose.
       >
       > After drop dialysis, the concentration of the DNA can be estimated by gel electrophoresis.
       >
       > The DNA can be injected directly or combined with a lipofection reagent for transfection into cultured cells.

REFERENCES

Aaij C. and Borst P. 1972. The gel electrophoresis of DNA. *Biochim. Biophys. Acta* **269:** 192–200.

Anand R. 1986. Pulsed field gel electrophoresis: A technique for fractionating large DNA molecules. *Trends Genet.* **2:** 278–283.

Bancroft I. and Wolk C.P. 1988. Pulsed homogeneous orthogonal field gel electrophoresis (PHOGE). *Nucleic Acids Res.* **16:** 7405–7418.

Bird A.P. 1989. Two classes of observed frequency for rare-cutter sites in CpG islands. *Nucleic Acids Res.* **17:** 9485.

Bird A.P., Taggart M., Frommer M., Miller O.J., and Macleod D. 1985. A fraction of the mouse genome that is derived from islands of nonmethylated, CpG-rich DNA. *Cell* **40:** 91–99.

Birren B.W., Lai E., Clark S.M., Hood L., and Simon M.I. 1988. Optimized conditions for pulsed field gel electrophoretic separations of DNA. *Nucleic Acids Res.* **16:** 7563–7582.

Brunk C.F. and Simpson L. 1977. Comparison of various ultraviolet sources for fluorescent detection of ethidium bromide-DNA complexes in polyacrylamide gels. *Anal. Biochem.* **82:** 455–462.

Burmeister M. and Lehrach H. 1989. Isolation of large DNA fragments from agarose gels using agarase. *Trends Genet.* **5:** 41.

Calladine C.R., Collis C.M., Drew H.R., and Mott M.R. 1991. A sudy of electrophoretic mobility of DNA in agarose and polyacrylamide gels. *J. Mol. Biol.* **221:** 981–1005.

Campbell W.P., Wrigley C.W., and Margolis J. 1983. Electrophoresis of small proteins in highly concentrated and crosslinked polyacrylamide gradient gels. *Anal. Biochem.* **129:** 31–36.

Cantor C.R., Gaal A., and Smith C.L. 1988. High-resolution separation and accurate size determination in pulsed-field gel electrophoresis of DNA. 3. Effect of electrical field shape. *Biochemistry* **27:** 9216–9221.

Carle G.F. and Olson M.V. 1984. Separation of chromosomal DNA molecules from yeast by orthogonal-field-alternation gel electrophoresis. *Nucleic Acids Res.* **12:** 5647–5664.

———. 1985. An electrophoretic karyotype for yeast. *Proc. Natl. Acad. Sci.* **82:** 3756–3760.

Carle G.F., Frank M., and Olson M.V. 1986. Electrophoretic separations of large DNA molecules by periodic inversion of the electric field. *Science* **232:** 65–68.

Chiari M. and Righetti P.G. 1995. New types of separation matrices for electrophoresis. *Electrophoresis* **16:** 1815–1829.

Choi T.K., Hollenbach P.W., Pearson B.E., Ueda R.M., Weddell G.N., Kurahara C.G., Woodhouse C.S., Kay R.M., and Loring J.F. 1993. Transgenic mice containing a human heavy chain immunoglobulin gene fragment cloned in a yeast artificial chromosome. *Nat. Genet.* **4:** 117–123.

Chrambach A. and Rodbard D. 1972. Polymerization of polyacrylamide gels: Efficiency and reproducibility as a function of catalyst concentrations. *Sep. Sci.* **7:** 663–703.

Chu G. 1990a. Pulsed-field gel electrophoresis: Theory and practice. *Methods* **1:** 129–142.

———. 1990b. Apparatus for contour-clamped homogeneous electric fields. *Methods* **1:** 212–214.

Chu G., Vollrath D., and Davis R.W. 1986. Separation of large DNA molecules by contour-clamped homogeneous electric fields. *Science* **234:** 1582–1585.

Clark S.M., Lai E., Birren B.W., and Hood L. 1988. A novel instrument for separating large DNA molecules with pulsed homogeneous electric fields. *Science* **241:** 1203–1205.

Cook P.R. 1984. A general method for preparing intact nuclear DNA. *EMBO J.* **3:** 1837–1842.

Dretzen G., Bellard M., Sassone-Corsi P., and Chambon P. 1981. A reliable method for the recovery of DNA fragments from agarose and acrylamide gels. *Anal. Biochem.* **112:** 295–298.

Drmanac R., Petrovic M., Glisin V., and Crkvenjakov R. 1986. A calculation of fragment lengths obtainable from human DNA with 78 restriction enzymes: An aid for cloning and mapping. *Nucleic Acids Res.* **14:** 4691–4692.

Edmondson S.P. and Gray D.M. 1984. Analysis of the electrophoretic properties of double-stranded DNA and RNA in agarose gels at a finite voltage gradient. *Biopolymers* **23:** 2725–2742.

Fangman W.L. 1978. Separation of very large DNA molecules by gel electrophoresis. *Nucleic Acids Res.* **5:** 653–665.

Favaloro J., Treisman R., and Kamen R. 1980. Transcription maps of polyoma virus-specific RNA: Analysis by two-dimensional nuclease S1 gel mapping. *Methods Enzymol.* **65:** 718–749.

Ferguson W.J., Braunschweiger K.I., Braunschweiger W.R., Smith J.R., McCormick J.J., Wasmann C.C., Jarvis N.P., Bell D.H., and Good N.E. 1980. Hydrogen ion buffers for biological research. *Anal. Biochem.* **104:** 300–310.

Gaillard C. and Strauss F. 1990. Ethanol precipitation of DNA with linear polyacrylamide as carrier. *Nucleic Acids Res.* **18:** 378–383.

Gardiner K. and Patterson D. 1989. Transverse alternating field electrophoresis and applications to mammalian genome mapping. *Electrophoresis* **10:** 296–302.

Gardiner K., Laas W., and Patterson D. 1986. Fractionation of large mammalian DNA restriction fragments using vertical pulsed-field gradient gel electrophoresis. *Somat. Cell Mol. Genet.* **12:** 185–195.

Girvitz S.C., Bacchetti S., Rainbow A.J., and Graham F.L. 1980. A rapid and efficient procedure for the purification of DNA from agarose gels. *Anal. Biochem.* **106:** 492–496.

Good N.E., Winget G.D., Winter W., Connolly T.N., Izawa S., and Singh R.M.M. 1966. Hydrogen ion buffers for biological research. *Biochemistry* **5:** 467–177.

Grossman P.D., Menche S., and Hershey D. 1992. Quantitative analysis of DNA sequencing electrophoresis. *Genet. Anal. Tech. Appl.* **9:** 9–16.

Helling R.B., Goodman H.M., and Boyer H.W. 1974. Analysis of endonuclease R-*Eco*RI fragments of DNA from lambdoid bacteriophages and other viruses by agarose-gel electrophoresis. *J. Virol.* **14:** 1235–1244.

Hervet H. and Bean C.P. 1987. Electrophoretic mobility of lambda phage *Hin*dIII and *Hae*III DNA fragments in agarose gels: A detailed study. *Biopolymers* **26:** 727–742.

Johnson P.H. and Grossman L.I. 1977. Electrophoresis of DNA in agarose gels. Optimizing separations of conformational isomers of double- and single-stranded DNAs. *Biochemistry* **16:** 4217–4225.

Kirkpatrick F.H. 1990. Overview of agarose gel properties. *Curr. Commun. Cell Mol. Biol.* **1:** 9–22.

Lalande M., Noolandi J., Turmel C., Rousseau J., and Slater G.W. 1987. Pulsed-field electrophoresis: Application of a computer model to the separation of large DNA molecules. *Proc. Natl. Acad. Sci.* **84:** 8011–8015.

Lauer G.D., Roberts T.M., and Klotz L.C. 1977. Determination of the nuclear DNA content of *Saccharomyces cerevisiae* and implications for the organization of DNA in yeast chromosomes. *J. Mol. Biol.* **114:** 507–526.

LePecq J.B. and Paoletti C. 1967. A fluorescent complex between ethidium bromide and nucleic acids. Physical-chemical characterization. *J. Mol. Biol.* **27:** 87–106.

Lerman L.S. and Frisch H.L. 1982. Why does the electrophoretic mobility of DNA in gels vary with the length of the molecule? *Biopolymers* **21:** 995–997.

Lumpkin O.J. and Zimm B.H. 1982. Mobility of DNA in gel electrophoresis. *Biopolymers* **21:** 2315–2316.

Margolis J. and Wrigley C.W. 1975. Improvement of pore gradient electrophoresis by increasing the degree of cross-linking at high acrylamide concentrations. *J. Chromatogr.* **106:** 204–209.

Mathew M.K., Smith C.L., and Cantor C.R. 1988a. High-resolution separation and accurate size determination in pulsed-field gel electrophoresis of DNA. 1. DNA size standards and the effect of agarose and temperature. *Biochemistry.* **27:** 9204–9210.

———. 1988b. High-resolution separation and accurate size determination in pulsed-field gel electrophoresis of DNA. 2. Effect of pulse time and electric field strength and implications for models of the separation process. *Biochemistry* **27:** 9210–9216.

Mathew M.K., Hui C.-F., Smith C.L., and Cantor C.R. 1988c. High-resolution separation and accurate size determination in pulsed-field gel electrophoresis of DNA. 4. Influence of DNA topology. *Biochemistry* **27:** 9222–9226.

Maxam A.M. and Gilbert W. 1977. A new method for sequencing DNA. *Proc. Natl. Acad. Sci.* **74:** 560–564.

———. 1980. Sequencing end-labeled DNA with base-specific chemical cleavages. *Methods Enzymol.* **65:** 499–560.

McDonell M.W., Simon M.N., and Studier F.W. 1977. Analysis of restriction fragments of T7 DNA and determination of molecular weights by electrophoresis in neutral and alkaline gels. *J. Mol. Biol.* **110:** 119–146.

Mortimer R.K., Game J.C., Bell M., and Contopoulou C.R. 1990. Use of pulsed-field gel electrophoresis to study the chromosomes of *Saccharomyces* and other yeasts. *Methods* **1:** 169–179.

Norton I.T., Goodall D.M., Anstren K.R.J., Morris E.R., and Rees D.A. 1986. Dynamics of molecular organization in agarose sulfate. *Biopolymers* **25:** 1009–1030.

Olson M.V. 1989. Pulsed-field gel electrophoresis. *Genet. Eng.* **11:** 183–227.

Orbach M.J., Vollrath D., Davis R.W., and Yanofsky C. 1988. An electrophoretic karyotype of *Neurospora crassa. Nucleic Acids Res.* **8:** 1469–1473.

Parker R.C. and Seed B. 1980. Two-dimensional agarose gel electrophoresis. "SeaPlaque" agarose dimension. *Methods Enzymol.* **65:** 358–363.

Poustka A. 1990. Physical mapping by PFGE. *Methods* **1:** 204–211.

Raymond S. and Weintraub L. 1959. Acrylamide gel as a supporting medium for zone electrophoresis. *Science* **130:** 711–712.

Schedl A., Montoliu L., Kelsey G., and Schütz G. 1993. A yeast artificial chromosome covering the tyrosinase gene confers copy number-dependent expression in transgenic mice. *Nature* **362:** 258–261.

Schwartz D.C. and Cantor C.R. 1984. Separation of yeast chromosome-sized DNAs by pulsed field gradient gel electrophoresis. *Cell* **37:** 67–75.

Schwartz D.C. and Koval M. 1989. Conformational dynamics of individual DNA molecules during gel electrophoresis. *Nature* **338:** 520–522.

Schwartz D.C., Smith L.C., Baker M., and Hsu M. 1989. ED:

Pulsed electrophoresis instrument. *Nature* **342:** 575–576.

Schwartz D.C., Saffran W., Welsh J., Haas R., Goldenberg M., and Cantor C.R. 1983. New techniques for purifying large DNAs and studying their properties and packaging. *Cold Spring Harbor Symp. Quant. Biol.* **47:** 189–195.

Serwer P. 1980. Electrophoresis of duplex deoxyribonucleic acid in multiple-concentration agarose gels: Fractionation of molecules with molecular weights between 2×10^6 and 110×10^6. *Biochemistry* **19:** 3001–3004.

Sharp P.A., Sugden B., and Sambrook J. 1973. Detection of two restriction endonuclease activities in *Haemophilus parainfluenzae* using analytical agarose-ethidium bromide electrophoresis. *Biochemistry* **12:** 3055–3063.

Slater G.W. and Noolandi J. 1985. New biased-reptation model for charged polymers. *Phys. Rev. Lett.* **55:** 1579–1582.

———. 1986. On the reptation theory of gel electrophoresis. *Biopolymers* **25:** 431–454.

Smith D.R. 1990. Genomic long-range restriction mapping. *Methods* **1:** 195–203.

Smith S.B., Aldridge P.K., and Callis J.B. 1989. Observation of individual DNA molecules undergoing gel electrophoresis. *Science* **243:** 203–206.

Southern E.M., Anand R., Brown W.R.A., and Fletcher D.S. 1987. A model for the separation of large DNA molecules by crossed field gel electrophoresis. *Nucleic Acids Res.* **15:** 5925–5943.

Stellwagen N.C. 1983. Anomalous electrophoresis of deoxyribonucleic acid restriction fragments on polyacrylamide gels. *Biochemistry* **22:** 6186–6193.

Struhl K. 1985. A rapid method for creating recombinant DNA molecules. *BioTechniques* **3:** 452–453.

Swartz M.N., Trautner T.A., and Kornberg A. 1962. Enzymatic synthesis of deoxyribonucleic acid. XI. Further studies on nearest neighbor base sequences in deoxyribonucleic acids. *J. Biol. Chem.* **237:** 1961–1967.

Thorne H.V. 1966. Electrophoretic separation of polyoma virus DNA from host cell DNA. *Virology* **29:** 234–239.

———. 1967. Electrophoretic characterization and fractionation of polyoma virus DNA. *J. Mol. Biol.* **24:** 203–211.

Turmel C. and Lalande M. 1988. Resolution of *Schizosaccharomyces pombe* chromosomes by field inversion gel electrophoresis. *Nucleic Acids Res.* **16:** 4727.

van de Pol T.J.R., Cremers F.P.M., Brohet R.M., Wieringa B., and Ropers H.-H. 1990. Derivation of clones from the choroideremia locus by preparative field inversion gel electrophoresis. *Nucleic Acids Res.* **18:** 725–731.

Vollrath D. and Davis R.W. 1987. Resolution of DNA molecules greater than 5 megabases by contour-clamped homogeneous electric fields. *Nucleic Acids Res.* **15:** 7865–7876.

Waring M.J. 1965. Complex formation between ethidium bromide and nucleic acids. *J. Mol. Biol.* **13:** 269–282.

Watkins T.I. and Woolfe G. 1952. Effect of changing the quaternizing group on the trypanocidal activity of dimidium bromide. *Nature* **169:** 506.

Weil M.D. and McClelland M. 1989. Enzymatic cleavage of a bacterial genome at a 10-base-pair recognition site. *Proc. Natl. Acad. Sci.* **86:** 51–55.

Wieslander L. 1979. A simple method to recover intact high molecular weight RNA and DNA after electrophoretic separation in low gelling temperature agarose gels. *Anal. Biochem.* **98:** 305–309.

Chapter 6

Preparation and Analysis of Eukaryotic Genomic DNA

Cell DNA

I am the singular
in free fall.
I and my doubles
carry it all:

life's slim volume
spirally bound.
It's what I'm about,
it's what I'm around.

Presence and hungers
imbue a sap mote
with the world as they spin it.
I teach it by rote

but its every command
was once a miscue
that something rose to,
Presence and freedom

re-wording, re-beading
strains on a strand
making I and I more different
than we could stand.

Les Murray

DOUBLE-STRANDED DNA IS A REMARKABLY INERT CHEMICAL. Its potentially reactive groups are buried within the central helix, tied up in hydrogen bonds. Its base pairs are protected on the outside by a formidable casing of phosphates and sugars and are reinforced internally by strong stacking forces. With such robust shielding and scaffolding, DNA outlasts most other intracellular components in locations as disparate as modern day crime scenes and ancient burial sites. The same chemical durability endows libraries of genomic DNA with both permanence and value, thereby enabling genetic engineering and sequencing projects, both large and small.

Despite its chemical stability, double-stranded DNA is nevertheless physically fragile. Long and snaky, with little lateral stability, high-molecular-weight DNA is vulnerable to hydrodynamic shearing forces of the most modest kind (please see Table 12-1 in Chapter 12). Double-stranded DNA behaves in solution as a random coil that is stiffened by stacking interactions between the base pairs and electrostatic repulsion between the charged phosphate groups in the DNA backbone. Hydrodynamic flow — resulting from pipetting, shaking, or stirring — generates drag on the stiffened coil and has the capacity to shear both strands of the DNA. The longer the DNA molecule, the weaker the force required for breakage. Genomic DNA is therefore easy to obtain in fragmented form but becomes progressively more difficult to isolate as the desired molecular weight increases. DNA molecules >150 kb are prone to breakage by forces generated during procedures commonly used to isolate genomic DNA.

The method described in Protocol 1 involves digesting eukaryotic cells or tissues with proteinase K in the presence of EDTA (to sequester divalent cations and thereby inhibit DNases) and solubilizing membranes and denaturing proteins with a detergent such as SDS. The nucleic acids are then purified by phase extractions with organic solvents. Contaminating RNA is eliminated by digestion with an RNase, and low-molecular-weight substances are removed by dialysis. This method can be scaled to yield amounts of DNA ranging from less than ten to more than hundreds of micrograms of DNA. However, shearing forces are generated at every step, with the result that the DNA molecules in the final preparation rarely exceed 100–150 kb in length. DNA of this size is adequate for Southern analysis on standard agarose gels, as a template in polymerase chain reactions (PCRs), and for the construction of genomic DNA libraries in bacteriophage λ vectors.

The successful construction of libraries in higher-capacity vectors and the analysis of genomic DNA by pulsed-field gel electrophoresis require DNAs >200 kb in size, which are well beyond the reach of methods that generate significant hydrodynamic shearing forces. Protocol 2 describes a method for isolating and purifying DNA that generates molecules of a size suitable for these specialized purposes. An alternative method for preparing genomic DNA in agarose plugs is described in Chapter 5, Protocol 13.

In this chapter, we also describe ways to isolate genomic DNA from different samples of cells and tissues (Protocol 3) and from many samples grown in microtiter dishes (Protocol 4). Other protocols describe the preparation of DNA from mouse tails (Protocol 5), the rapid isolation of mammalian DNA (Protocol 6), and the rapid isolation of yeast DNA (Protocol 7). Finally, we describe how to analyze purified genomic DNAs by Southern blotting and hybridization (Protocols 8 through 10). Note also that a number of commercial kits are available for purifying genomic DNA.

Protocol 1

Isolation of High-molecular-weight DNA from Mammalian Cells Using Proteinase K and Phenol

T HIS PROCEDURE IS DERIVED FROM A METHOD ORIGINALLY described by Daryl Stafford and colleagues (Blin and Stafford 1976). It is the method of choice when large amounts of mammalian DNA are required, for example, for Southern blotting (Protocol 8) or for construction of genomic libraries in bacteriophage λ vectors (Chapter 2, Protocol 19). Approximately 200 μg of mammalian DNA, 100–150 kb in length, is obtained from 5×10^7 cultured aneuploid cells (e.g., HeLa cells). The usual yield of DNA from 20 ml of normal blood is ~250 μg.

All of the materials listed below are required for purification of mammalian genomic DNA, irrespective of the type of sample. Additional materials that are needed for particular types of samples are listed under the subheads for the four Step 1 methods: lysis of cells growing in monolayers, lysis of cells growing in suspension, lysis of tissue samples, and lysis of blood cells in freshly drawn or frozen samples.

MATERIALS

CAUTION: Please see Appendix 12 for appropriate handling of materials marked with <!>.

▲ WARNING Primate tissues and primary cultures of cells require special handling precautions.

Buffers and Solutions

Please see Appendix 1 for components of stock solutions, buffers, and reagents. Dilute stock solutions to the appropriate concentrations.

Ammonium acetate (10 M) (used as an alternative to dialysis, Step 9)

Dialysis buffer (used as an alternative to ethanol precipitation, Step 9)

    50 mM Tris-Cl (pH 8.0)

    10 mM EDTA (pH 8.0)

    Prepare four lots of 4 liters of dialysis solution and store at 4ºC.

Ethanol (used as an alternative to dialysis, Step 9)

Lysis buffer

    10 mM Tris-Cl (pH 8.0)

    0.1 M EDTA (pH 8.0)

    0.5% (w/v) SDS

    20 μg/ml DNase-free pancreatic RNase

    The first three ingredients of the lysis buffer may be mixed in advance and stored at room temperature. RNase is added to an appropriate amount of the mixture just before use. Adding RNase to the lysis buffer eliminates the need to remove RNA from semipurified DNA at a later stage in the preparation. Pancreatic RNase is not highly active in the presence of 0.5% SDS, but when added at high concentrations, it works well enough to degrade most of the cellular RNA.

Phenol, equilibrated with 0.5 M Tris-Cl (pH 8.0) <!>

▲ IMPORTANT The pH of the phenol must be ~8.0 to prevent DNA from becoming trapped at the interface between the organic and aqueous phases (please see Appendix 8).

TE (pH 8.0)

Tris-buffered saline (TBS)

Enzymes and Buffers

Proteinase K (20 mg/ml)

For this protocol, we recommend the use of a genomic grade proteinase K that has been shown to be free of DNase and RNase activity. Please see Appendix 4.

Gels

Pulsed-field gel (please see Chapter 5, Protocols 17 and 18) or Conventional horizontal 0.6% agarose gel (Chapter 5, Protocol 1)

Nucleic Acids and Oligonucleotides

Bacteriophage λ DNA, intact

Purify λ DNA as described in Chapter 2, Protocol 11 or 12. The DNA is used as a size standard during gel electrophoresis (please see Step 11).

Centrifuges and Rotors

Sorvall centrifuge with H1000B and SS-34 rotors (or their equivalents)

Special Equipment

Cut-off yellow tips

Cut-off yellow tips can be generated rapidly with a scissors or a dog nail clipper (e.g., Fisher 05-401A). Alternatively, the pointed ends of the tips can be removed with a sharp razor blade. The cut-off tips should be sterilized before use, either by autoclaving or by immersion in 70% alcohol for 2 minutes followed by drying in air. Alternatively, presterilized wide-bore tips can be purchased from a number of commercial companies (e.g., Bio-Rad).

Dialysis tubing clips

Spectra Por closures from Spectrum Medical Industries, Houston, Texas.

Rocking platform or Dialysis tubing

Prepared as described in Appendix 8.

Shepherd's crooks (used as an alternative to dialysis)

Shepherd's crooks are Pasteur pipettes whose tip has been sealed in the flame of a Bunsen burner and shaped into a U with a hemostat. Wear safety glasses while molding the Shepherd's crooks. For further information, please see Steps 5–7 of Protocol 3.

Spectrophotometer or Fluorometer

Tube mixer or Roller apparatus

Vacuum aspirator equipped with traps

Water bath, preset to 50°C

Wide-bore pipettes (0.3-cm diameter orifice)

Wide-bore pipettes are available from several manufacturers. However, standard glass pipettes can be used if they are autoclaved in the wrong orientation without cotton plugs.

Cells and Tissues

Monolayers or suspensions of mammalian cells, or fresh tissue, or blood samples

METHOD

Below are four alternative versions of Step 1 used to lyse different types of cells or tissue samples. Use the version appropriate for the material under study and then proceed to Step 2 on page 6.9.

Lysis of Cells Growing in Monolayers

> **Additional Materials**
>
> *Aspiration device attached to a vacuum line equipped with traps*
> *Bed of ice large enough to accommodate 10–12 culture dishes*
> *Erlenmeyer flask (50 or 100 ml)*
> *Rubber policeman*
> *Sorvall centrifuge, H1000B rotor (or equivalent) and centrifuge tubes cooled to 4°C*
> *Tris-buffered saline (TBS), ice cold*

1. Lyse cells growing in monolayer cultures.

> It is best to work with batches of 10–12 culture dishes at a time. Store the remaining culture dishes in the incubator until they are required.

a. Take one batch of culture dishes, containing cells grown to confluency, from the incubator and immediately remove the medium by aspiration. Working quickly, wash the monolayers of cells twice with ice-cold TBS. This is most easily accomplished by gently pipetting ~10 ml of TBS onto the first monolayer. Swirl the dish gently for a few seconds and then tip the fluid into a 2-liter beaker. Add another 10 ml of ice-cold TBS and store the dish on a bed of ice. Repeat the procedure until the entire batch of monolayers has been processed.

b. Tip the fluid from the first monolayer into the 2-liter beaker. Remove the last traces of TBS from the culture dish by aspiration. Add 1 ml of fresh ice-cold TBS and store the dish on a bed of ice. Repeat the procedure until the entire batch of monolayers has been processed.

c. Use a rubber policeman to scrape the cells from the first culture dish into the 1 ml of TBS. Use a Pasteur pipette to transfer the cell suspension to a centrifuge tube on ice. Immediately wash the culture dish with 0.5 ml of ice-cold TBS, and combine the washings with the cell suspension in the centrifuge tube. Process the remaining monolayers in the same way.

d. Recover the cells by centrifugation at 1500g (2700 rpm in a Sorvall H1000B rotor and swinging buckets) for 10 minutes at 4°C.

e. Resuspend the cells in 5–10 volumes of ice-cold TBS and repeat the centrifugation.

f. Resuspend the cells in TE (pH 8.0) at a concentration of 5×10^7 cells/ml. Transfer the solution to an Erlenmeyer flask.

> For 1 ml of cell suspension, use a 50-ml flask; for 2 ml, use a 100-ml flask, and so on. The density of cells grown as a monolayer culture (from Step a above) will vary with the cell type and culture conditions. As a rule of thumb, a confluent continuous culture (e.g., of HeLa or BHK cells) grown on a 90-mm culture dish contains on average 1×10^5 to 3×10^5 cells/cm^2.

g. Add 10 ml of lysis buffer for each milliliter of cell suspension. Incubate the suspension for 1 hour at 37°C, and then proceed immediately to Step 2 (p. 6.9).

> Make sure that the cells are well dispersed over the inner surface of the Erlenmeyer flask when the lysis buffer is added. This dispersal minimizes the formation of intractable clumps of DNA.

Lysis of Cells Growing in Suspension

Additional Materials

Aspiration device attached to a vacuum line equipped with traps
Erlenmeyer flask (50 or 100 ml)
Sorvall centrifuge, H100B rotor (or equivalent) and centrifuge tubes or bottles cooled to 4°C
TE (pH 8.0), ice-cold
Tris-buffered saline (TBS), ice cold

1. Lyse cells growing in suspension cultures.

   a. Transfer the cells to a centifuge tube or bottle and recover them by centrifugation at 1500g (2700 rpm in a Sorvall H100B rotor and swinging buckets) for 10 minutes at 4°C. Remove the supernatant medium by aspiration.

   b. Wash the cells by resuspending them in a volume of ice-cold TBS equal to the volume of the original culture. Repeat the centrifugation. Remove the supernatant by aspiration and then gently resuspend the cells once more in ice-cold TBS. Recover the cells by centrifugation.

   c. Remove the supernatant by aspiration and gently suspend the cells in TE (pH 8.0) at a concentration of 5 x 10^7 cells/ml. Transfer the suspension to an Erlenmeyer flask.

      For 1 ml of cell suspension, use a 50-ml flask; for 2 ml, use a 100-ml flask, and so on. The density of cells grown in suspension (from Step a) will vary with the cell type and culture conditions. As a rule of thumb, a saturated suspension culture of a continuous cell line (e.g., of HeLa or BHK cells) grown in a 1-liter culture contains on average 1 x 10^6 cells/ml.

   d. Add 10 ml of lysis buffer for each milliliter of cell suspension. Incubate the solution for 1 hour at 37°C and then proceed immediately to Step 2 (p. 6.9).

      Make sure that the cells are well dispersed over the inner surface of the Erlenmeyer flask when the lysis buffer is added. This dispersal minimizes the formation of intractable clumps of DNA.

Lysis of Tissue Samples

Because tissues generally contain large amounts of fibrous material, it is difficult to extract genomic DNA from them in high yield. The efficiency of extraction is greatly improved if the tissue is reduced to powder before homogenization in lysis buffer. If a large amount of fresh tissue (>1 g) is available, powdering can be accomplished with a Waring blender.

Additional Materials

Beaker (25 ml)
Liquid nitrogen <!>
Polypropylene centrifuge tube (50 ml; Falcon or equivalent)
Waring blender equipped with a stainless steel container
or
Mortar and pestle, prechilled with liquid nitrogen

   It is important to cool the mortar slowly by adding small amounts of liquid nitrogen over a period of time. Filling the mortar to the brim or suddenly immersing the grinding part of the pestle in liquid nitrogen can cause fracturing. Placing the mortar in an ice bucket filled with dry ice is a good way to precool the mortar before adding the liquid nitrogen. Be careful when grinding human and primate tissues as powdered aerosols are readily generated, especially when adding liquid nitrogen to the mortar.

1. Pulverize tissue samples.

   a. Drop ~1 g of freshly excised tissue into liquid nitrogen in the stainless-steel container of a Waring blender. Blend at top speed until the tissue is ground to a powder.

      Alternatively, smaller quantities of tissue can be snap-frozen in liquid nitrogen and then pulverized to a powder using a mortar and pestle precooled with liquid nitrogen.

   b. Allow the liquid nitrogen to evaporate, and add the powdered tissue little by little to ~10 volumes (w/v) of lysis buffer in a beaker. Allow the powder to spread over the surface of the lysis buffer, and then shake the beaker to submerge the material.

   c. When all of the material is in solution, transfer the suspension to a 50-ml centrifuge tube. Incubate the tube for 1 hour at 37ºC, and then proceed to Step 2 (p. 6.9).

Lysis of Blood Cells in Freshly Drawn or Frozen Samples

Additional Materials

Acid citrate dextrose solution B (ACD) (for freshly drawn or frozen blood samples)
   0.48% w/v citric acid
   1.32% w/v sodium citrate
   1.47% w/v glucose
Aspiration device attached to a vacuum line equipped with traps
EDTA (an alternative to ACD, for freshly drawn or frozen blood samples)
   ACD, an anticoagulant that is used when preparing genomic DNA from whole blood, is superior to EDTA in preserving high-molecular-weight DNA (Gustafson et al. 1987). However, blood is more frequently collected in commercially available tubes that contain measured amounts of EDTA as an anticoagulant. In most hospitals in the United States, blood collection tubes are conveniently color-coded to indicate which contain anticoagulants and which do not: Purple-topped tubes contain anticoagulant, usually dried EDTA, whereas yellow-topped tubes do not. In molecular cloning, the former (purple) are used to collect blood from which genomic DNA will be extracted, whereas the latter (yellow) are typically used to collect blood that will be used as a source of lymphocytes for immortalization with Epstein-Barr virus. Such immortalized cells provide a renewable resource from which large amounts of DNA can be isolated for later use in, for example, genetic studies.
Phosphate-buffered saline (PBS, for frozen blood samples)
Sorvall H1000B rotor (or equivalent) and centrifuge tubes cooled to 4ºC for freshly drawn blood samples
Sorvall SS-34 rotor (or equivalent) and centrifuge tubes cooled to 4ºC for frozen blood samples
Water bath, at room temperature

1. Collect blood cells from freshly drawn or frozen samples. Human blood must be collected by a trained phlebotomist under sterile conditions.

   TO COLLECT CELLS FROM FRESHLY DRAWN BLOOD

   a. Collect ~20 ml of fresh blood in tubes containing 3.5 ml of either acid citrate dextrose solution B (ACD) or EDTA (please see note to EDTA in the materials list).

      The blood may be stored for several days at 0ºC or indefinitely at –70ºC before the DNA is prepared. Blood should not be collected into heparin, which is an inhibitor of the polymerase chain reaction (Beutler et al. 1990).

   b. Transfer the blood to a centrifuge tube and centrifuge at 1300*g* (2500 rpm in a Sorvall H1000B rotor and 50-ml swinging buckets) for 15 minutes at 4ºC.

c. Remove the supernatant fluid by aspiration. Use a Pasteur pipette to transfer the buffy coat carefully to a fresh tube and repeat the centrifugation. Discard the pellet of red cells.

> The buffy coat is a broad band of white blood cells of heterogeneous density.

d. Remove residual supernatant from the buffy coat by aspiration. Resuspend the buffy coat in 15 ml of lysis buffer. Incubate the solution for 1 hour at 37°C, and proceed to Step 2.

To collect cells from frozen blood samples

a. Collect ~20 ml of fresh blood in tubes containing 3.5 ml of either acid citrate dextrose solution B (ACD) or EDTA (please see note to EDTA in the materials list).

> The blood may be stored for several days at 0°C or indefinitely at –70°C before the DNA is prepared.

b. Thaw the blood in a water bath at room temperature and then transfer it to a centrifuge tube. Add an equal volume of phosphate-buffered saline at room temperature.

c. Centrifuge the blood at 3500*g* (5400 rpm in a Sorvall SS-34 rotor) for 15 minutes at room temperature.

d. Remove the supernatant, which contains lysed red cells, by aspiration. Resuspend the pellet in 15 ml of lysis buffer. Incubate the solution for 1 hour at 37°C, and then proceed to Step 2.

Method Continues with Step 2 Below

Treatment of Lysate with Proteinase K and Phenol

2. Transfer the lysate to one or more centrifuge tubes that fit into a Sorvall SS-34 rotor, or equivalent. The tubes should not be more than one-third full.

3. Add proteinase K (20 mg/ml) to a final concentration of 100 μg/ml. Use a glass rod to mix the enzyme solution gently into the viscous lysate of cells.

4. Incubate the lysate in a water bath for 3 hours at 50°C. Swirl the viscous solution from time to time.

5. Cool the solution to room temperature and add an equal volume of phenol equilibrated with 0.1 M Tris-Cl (pH 8.0). Gently mix the two phases by slowly turning the tube end-over-end for 10 minutes on a tube mixer or roller apparatus. If the two phases have not formed an emulsion at this stage, place the tube on a roller apparatus for 1 hour.

> Blin and Stafford (1976) recommend the use of 0.5 M EDTA (pH 8.0) in the lysis buffer. However, the density of the buffer almost equals that of phenol, which makes separation of the phases difficult. The lysis buffer used here contains EDTA at a concentration of 0.1 M, which permits easier separation of the phenolic and aqueous phases while maintaining a high degree of protection against degradation of the DNA by nucleases and heavy metals.

6. Separate the two phases by centrifugation at 5000*g* (6500 rpm in a Sorvall SS-34 rotor) for 15 minutes at room temperature.

7. Use a wide-bore pipette (0.3-cm diameter orifice) to transfer the viscous aqueous phase to a fresh centrifuge tube.

   > When transferring the aqueous (upper) phase, it is essential to draw the DNA into the pipette very slowly to avoid disturbing the material at the interface and to minimize hydrodynamic shearing forces. If the DNA solution is so viscous that it cannot easily be drawn into a wide-bore pipette, use a long pipette attached to an aspirator to remove the organic (lower) phase as follows:
   >
   > i. Before starting, make sure that the vacuum traps are empty and secure, so that phenol cannot enter the vacuum system.
   >
   > ii. With the vacuum line closed, slowly lower the pipette to the bottom of the organic phase. Wait until the viscous thread of aqueous material detaches from the pipette, and then carefully open the vacuum line and gently withdraw all of the organic phase. Close the vacuum line and quickly withdraw the pipette through the aqueous phase. Immediately open the vacuum line to transfer the residual phenol into the trap.
   >
   > iii. Centrifuge the DNA solution at 5000*g* (6500 rpm in a Sorvall SS-34 rotor) for 20 minutes at room temperature. Protein and clots of DNA will sediment to the bottom of the tube. Transfer the DNA solution (the supernatant) into a 50-ml centrifuge tube, leaving behind the protein and clots of DNA.

8. Repeat the extraction with phenol twice more and pool the aqueous phases.

9. Isolate DNA by one of the following two methods.

TO ISOLATE DNA IN THE SIZE RANGE OF 150–200 KB

a. Transfer the pooled aqueous phases to a dialysis bag. Close the top of the bag with a dialysis tubing clip, allowing room in the bag for the sample volume to increase 1.5–2-fold during dialysis.

b. Dialyze the solution at 4°C against 4 liters of dialysis buffer. Change the buffer three times at intervals of ≥6 hours.

   > Because of the high viscosity of the DNA solution, dialysis generally takes ≥24 hours to complete.

TO ISOLATE DNA THAT HAS AN AVERAGE SIZE OF 100–150 KB

a. After the third extraction with phenol, transfer the pooled aqueous phases to a fresh centrifuge tube and add 0.2 volume of 10 M ammonium acetate. Add 2 volumes of ethanol at room temperature and swirl the tube until the solution is thoroughly mixed.

b. The DNA immediately forms a precipitate. Remove the precipitate in one piece from the ethanolic solution with a Shepherd's crook (a Pasteur pipette whose end has been sealed and shaped into a U; please see Steps 5–7 of Protocol 3). Contaminating oligonucleotides remain in the ethanolic phase.

c. If the DNA precipitate becomes fragmented, abandon the Shepherd's crook and collect the precipitate by centrifugation at 5000*g* (6500 rpm in a Sorvall SS-34) for 5 minutes at room temperature.

d. Wash the DNA precipitate twice with 70% ethanol, and collect the DNA by centrifugation as described in Step c.

e. Remove as much of the 70% ethanol as possible, using an aspirator. Store the pellet of DNA in an open tube at room temperature until the last visible traces of ethanol have evaporated.

   > Do not allow the pellet of DNA to dry completely; desiccated DNA is very difficult to dissolve.

    f. Add 1 ml of TE (pH 8.0) for each 0.1 ml of cells (Step 1). Place the tube on a rocking platform and gently rock the solution for 12–24 hours at 4°C until the DNA has completely dissolved. Store the DNA solution at 4°C.

10. Measure the concentration of the DNA.

It is often difficult to measure the concentration of high-molecular-weight DNA by standard methods such as absorbance at 260 nm. This is because the DNA solution is frequently nonhomogeneous and is usually so viscous that it is impossible to withdraw a representative sample for analysis. These problems can be minimized by withdrawing a large sample (10–20 μl) with an automatic pipetter equipped with a cut-off yellow tip. The sample is then diluted with ~0.5 ml of TE (pH 8.0) and vortexed vigorously for 1–2 minutes. The absorbance of the diluted sample can then be read at 260, 270, and 280 nm in the standard way.

A solution with an A_{260} of 1 contains ~50 μg of DNA/ml. Note that estimates of purity of nucleic acids based on OD_{260}:OD_{280} ratios are unreliable (Glasel 1995) and that estimates of concentration are inaccurate if the sample contains significant amounts of phenol. H_2O saturated with phenol absorbs with a characteristic peak at 270 nm and an OD_{260}:OD_{280} ratio of 2 (Stulnig and Amberger 1994). Nucleic acid preparations free of phenol should have OD_{260}:OD_{280} ratios of ~1.2. For further information, please see Appendix 8.

More accurate measurement of DNA concentrations can be made by fluorometry in the presence of fluorescent dyes such as SYBR Gold and Hoechst 33258, which bind DNA without intercalating and with specificity to double-stranded DNA (for further details, please see Appendix 8). For a method of fluorometric measurement of DNA concentrations using Hoechst 33258, please see the panel on **ADDITIONAL PROTOCOL: ESTIMATING THE CONCENTRATION OF DNA BY FLUOROMETRY** on the following page.

11. Analyze the quality of the preparation of high-molecular-weight DNA by pulsed-field gel electrophoresis (Chapter 5, Protocol 17 or 18) or by electrophoresis through a conventional 0.6% agarose gel (Chapter 5, Protocol 1). Use unit-length and/or linear concatemers of λ DNA as markers. A method to generate linear concatemers of λ DNA is described in Chapter 5, Protocol 16.

Do not be concerned if some of the DNA remains in the well, since DNA molecules >250 kb have difficulty entering the gel. This problem can usually be solved by embedding the DNA in a small amount of melted agarose (at 55°C) and transferring the molten solution to the well of a preformed agarose gel. The transfer should be done before the gel is submerged in electrophoresis buffer.

ADDITIONAL PROTOCOL: ESTIMATING THE CONCENTRATION OF DNA BY FLUOROMETRY

Measuring the concentration of DNA using fluorometry is more sensitive than spectrophotometry, allowing the detection of nanogram quantities of DNA. In this assay, DNA preparations of known and unknown concentrations are incubated with the fluorochrome Hoechst 33258. Absorption values for the unknown sample are compared with those observed for a known series, and the concentration of the unknown sample is estimated by interpolation.

Additional Materials

NaCl (4 M)

Sodium phosphate (0.5 M, pH 7.4)

Fluorometry buffer

    2 M NaCl

    50 mM sodium phosphate

    Prepare 500 ml and sterilize the solution by filtration through a 0.45-μm filter.

Hoechst 33258 dye (0.2 mg/ml in H_2O)

    The concentrated solution of dye can be stored at room temperature in a foil-wrapped test tube.

High-molecular-weight DNA solution, reference standard (100 μg/ml in TE)

    A DNA solution of known concentration is required to construct a standard curve. Because the binding of Hoechst 33258 dye to DNA is influenced by the base composition, the DNA used to construct the standard curve should be from the same species as the test sample.

Fluorometer, either fixed wavelength or scanning model

Method

1. Turn on the fluorometer 1 hour before the assay is carried out to allow the machine to warm up and stabilize.

   When bound to high-molecular-weight double-stranded DNA, Hoechst 33258 dye absorbs maximally at 365 nm and emits maximally at 458 nm.

2. Prepare an appropriate amount of diluted dye solution (50 μl of concentrated dye solution per 100 ml of fluorometry buffer). Each tube in the DNA assay requires 3 ml of diluted Hoechst 33258 dye solution. Transfer 3 ml of diluted dye solution to an appropriate number of clean glass tubes. Include six extra tubes for a blank and the standard curve.

3. Prepare a standard curve by adding 100, 200, 300, 400, and 500 ng of genomic DNA from the reference stock solution to individual tubes. Mix and read the absorbance on the prewarmed fluorometer of each tube immediately after addition of the DNA.

4. Add 0.1 μl (i.e., 1 μl of a 1:10 dilution), 1.0 μl, and 10 μl of the preparation of genomic DNA, whose concentration is being determined, to individual tubes containing diluted dye solution. Immediately read the fluorescence.

5. Construct a standard curve plotting fluorescence on the ordinate (*y* axis) and weight of reference DNA (in ng) on the abscissa (*x* axis). Estimate the concentration of DNA in the unknown sample by interpolation.

   If the reading for the unknown genomic DNA solution falls outside that of the standard curve, read the fluorescence of a more concentrated sample or make an appropriate dilution of the sample and repeat the assay.

   Binding of Hoechst 33258 is adversely influenced by pH extremes, the presence of detergents near or above their critical micellar concentrations, and salt concentrations above 3 M. If these conditions or reagents are used to prepare the genomic DNA and improbable results are obtained in the fluorometry assay, precipitate an aliquot of the DNA preparation with ethanol, rinse the pellet of nucleic acid in 70% ethanol, dissolve the dried pellet in TE, and repeat the assay.

   If the preparation of test DNA is highly viscous, sampling with standard yellow tips may be so inaccurate that the dilutions of unknown DNA will not track with the standard curve. In this case, the best solution is to withdraw two samples (10–20 μl) with an automatic pipetter equipped with a cut-off yellow tip. Each sample is then diluted with ~0.5 ml of TE (pH 8.0) and vortexed vigorously for 1–2 minutes. Different amounts of the diluted samples can then be transferred to the individual tubes containing diluted dye solution. The results obtained from the two sets of samples should be consistent.

   Use scissors or a dog nail clipper (e.g., Fisher) to generate cut-off yellow tips. Alternatively, the tips can be cut with a sharp razor blade. Sterilize the cut-off tips before use, either by autoclaving or by immersion in 70% alcohol for 2 minutes followed by drying in air. Presterilized, wide-bore tips can be purchased from a number of commercial companies (e.g., Bio-Rad).

   The assay can be used to measure the concentration of DNAs whose sizes exceed ~1 kb. Hoechst 33258 binds poorly to smaller DNA fragments.

Protocol 2

Isolation of High-molecular-weight DNA from Mammalian Cells Using Formamide

T HIS PROTOCOL IS A MODIFICATION OF THE PROCEDURE OF KUPIEC et al. (1987) and involves digestion of cells and tissues with proteinase K, dissociation of DNA-protein complexes (chromatin)
with high concentrations of formamide, and removal of the protease and organic solvent by
extensive dialysis through collodion bags. Formamide is an ionizing solvent that both dissociates
protein-DNA complexes and, subsequently, denatures the released proteins. However, it does not
significantly affect the activity of proteinase K. The genomic DNA prepared by this procedure is
large (>200 kb) and suitable for the construction of libraries in high-capacity vectors and for the
analysis of large DNA fragments by pulsed-field gel electrophoresis. The method has two disadvantages: (1) It requires more time than other procedures and (2) the concentration of DNA in
the final preparation is low (~10 µg/ml). Approximately 1 mg of high-molecular-weight DNA can
be prepared from 1×10^8 cultured aneuploid mammalian cells (e.g., HeLa cells).

MATERIALS

CAUTION: Please see Appendix 12 for appropriate handling of materials marked with <!>.

Buffers and Solutions

Please see Appendix 1 for components of stock solutions, buffers, and reagents.
Dilute stock solutions to the appropriate concentrations.

Dialysis buffer 1
20 mM Tris-Cl (pH 8.0)
0.1 M NaCl
10 mM EDTA (pH 8.0)
Prepare 6 liters of Dialysis buffer 1. Store at 4ºC.

Dialysis buffer 2
10 mM Tris-Cl (pH 8.0)
10 mM NaCl
0.5 mM EDTA (pH 8.0)
Prepare 6 liters of Dialysis buffer 2. Store at 4ºC.

Formamide denaturation buffer
> 20 mM Tris-Cl (pH 8.0)
> 0.8 M NaCl
> 80% (v/v) formamide <!>
>
> Many batches of reagent-grade formamide are sufficiently pure to be used without further treatment. However, if any yellow color is present, the formamide should be deionized (for protocol, please see Appendix 8).

TE (pH 8.0)

Gels

Pulsed-field gel (Chapter 5, Protocol 17 or 18) or 0.6% agarose gel

Nucleic Acids and Oligonucleotides

Linear monomers and concatemers of bacteriophage λ DNA (please see Chapter 5, Protocol 16)

Special Equipment

Blender with stainless steel container (for tissues)

Collodion Bags

> The pore size of these collodion bags is 8 nm, which is sufficient to allow denatured proteins of medium size to diffuse through the bags during dialysis. Collodion bags are supplied by Sartorius in 20% ethanol. Before use, they should be rinsed thoroughly in Dialysis buffer 2, and then immersed in 100 ml of the buffer for 30 minutes.

> Collodion bags are made from pyroxylin, which is chiefly nitrocellulose, dissolved in ethanol/ether. When the syrupy solution is spread thinly over a surface and allowed to evaporate, it leaves a tough, transparent film that can be molded into bags. For many years, liquid collodion was used as a solvent for wart and corn removers such as salicylic acid.

Cut-off yellow tips

> Cut-off yellow tips can be generated rapidly with a scissors or a dog nail clipper (Fisher 05-401A). Alternatively, the pointed ends of the tips can be removed with a sharp razor blade. The cut-off tips should be sterilized before use, either by autoclaving or by immersion in 70% alcohol for 2 minutes followed by drying in air. Presterilized, wide-bore tips can be purchased from a number of commercial companies (e.g., Bio-Rad).

Dialysis tubing clips

> Spectra Por closures from Spectrum Medical Industries, Houston, Texas.

Glass rod

Water bath or incubator preset to 15ºC

Water bath preset to 50ºC

Cells and Tissues

Monolayers or suspensions of mammalian cells, or fresh tissue, or blood samples

Additional Reagents

Materials and equipment used in Steps 1–4 of Protocol 1

> The materials and equipment required depend on the type of starting material: blood, cultured cells, or tissue (please see Protocol 1).

METHOD

1. Prepare lysates of cell suspensions (or frozen cell powders) as described in Steps 1–4 of Protocol 1.

2. Cool the solution containing lysed cells and lysis buffer to 15ºC. For every 1 ml of cell lysate, add 1.25 ml of formamide denaturation buffer, and mix the solution gently using a glass rod. Store the solution for 12 hours at 15ºC.

3. Pour the viscous solution into one or more collodion bags. Secure the open end of the bag with a dialysis clip and dialyze the solution for 45 minutes at 4ºC in 2 liters of Dialysis buffer 1. Replace the buffer with fresh Dialysis buffer 1 and continue the dialysis for at least 4 hours, followed by a further 4 hours in a third 2-liter aliquot of Dialysis buffer 1. Then dialyze the DNA against 2 liters of fresh Dialysis buffer 2, three times, for at least 4 hours each.

    Dialysis intervals should be 45 minutes for the first buffer change and 4 hours for all subsequent changes.

    A total dialysis time of 24 hours is required to remove proteins from the DNA effectively.

    For a description of a convenient and inexpensive device for holding the collodion bags, please see Kupiec et al. (1987).

4. Measure the concentration of the DNA.

    It is often difficult to measure the concentration of high-molecular-weight DNA by standard methods such as absorbance at 260 nm. This is because the DNA solution is nonhomogeneous and usually so viscous that it is impossible to withdraw a representative sample for analysis. These problems can be minimized by withdrawing a large sample (10–20 µl) with an automatic pipetter equipped with a cut-off yellow tip. The sample is then diluted with ~0.5 ml of TE (pH 8.0) and vortexed vigorously for 1–2 minutes. The absorbance of the diluted sample can then be read at 260, 270, and 280 nm in the standard way.

    A solution with a value of 1 (A_{260} measurement) contains ~50 µg of DNA/ml. Note that estimates of purity of nucleic acids based on OD_{260}:OD_{280} ratios are unreliable (Glasel 1995) and that estimates of concentration are inaccurate if the sample contains significant amounts of phenol. H_2O saturated with phenol absorbs with a characteristic peak at 270 nm and an OD_{260}:OD_{280} ratio of 2 (Stulnig and Amberger 1994). Nucleic acid preparations free of phenol (as in this protocol) should have OD_{260}:OD_{280} ratios of ~1.2. For further information, please see Appendix 8.

    More accurate measurement of DNA concentrations can be made by fluorometry in the presence of fluorescent dyes which bind DNA without intercalating and with specificity to double-stranded DNA. The most widely used dye for this purpose is Hoechst 33258, a bisbenzimidazole (for further details, please see Appendix 8). For a method of fluorometric measurement of DNA concentrations, please see the panel on **ADDITIONAL PROTOCOL: ESTIMATING THE CONCENTRATION OF DNA BY FLUOROMETRY** in Protocol 1.

5. Analyze the quality of the preparation of high-molecular-weight DNA by pulsed-field gel electrophoresis (Chapter 5, Protocol 17 or 18) or by electrophoresis through a conventional 0.6% agarose gel (Chapter 5, Protocol 1). Use unit-length and linear concatemers of λ DNA as markers (please see Chapter 5, Protocol 16). The genomic DNA should be more than 200 kb in size.

    Do not be concerned if some of the DNA remains in the well, since DNA molecules >250 kb have difficulty in entering the gel. This problem can usually be solved by embedding the DNA in a small amount of melted agarose (at 55ºC) and transferring the molten solution to the well of a preformed agarose gel. This transfer should be done before the gel is submerged in electrophoresis buffer.

CONCENTRATING SOLUTIONS CONTAINING HIGH-MOLECULAR-WEIGHT DNA

If the concentration of DNA in the preparation is too low to be workable, use a wide-bored pipette or cut-off yellow tip to transfer the DNA into a standard cellulose acetate dialysis bag (e.g., Spectra Por, m.w. cut-off 6000–8000 [VWR Scientific]) (for preparation of dialysis tubing, please see Appendix 8). Place the dialysis bag on a bed of solid sucrose (grade II, Sigma). Pack additional sucrose on top of the bag. This packing is best done at 4ºC, on a piece of aluminum foil spread on the bench in a cold room. Allow dialysis to proceed until the volume of the fluid in the dialysis bag has been reduced by a factor of 5–10. Rinse the outside of the bag with TE to remove all of the adherent sucrose. Gently massage the solution of DNA to one end of the bag and then clamp the tubing just above the level of the fluid with a dialysis clip. Dialyze the sample against 4 liters of TE (pH 8.0) for 16–24 hours with at least two changes of buffer.

This method works more efficiently than concentration in Centricon devices or in collodion bags and results in smaller losses of DNA.

Protocol 3

Isolation of DNA from Mammalian Cells by Spooling

THIS METHOD, ADAPTED FROM BOWTELL (1987), IS USED TO PREPARE DNA simultaneously from many different samples of cells or tissues. The key steps in the protocol are (1) precipitation of the genomic DNA at the interface between the cell lysate and a layer of ethanol, followed by (2) spooling of the precipitated DNA onto a Shepherd's crook. The DNA is then lifted from the ethanolic solution on the crook and dissolved in the aqueous buffer of choice. This method of collecting precipitates of high-molecular-weight DNA was first used in the 1930s (please see the information panel on SPOOLING DNA at the end of this chapter). Small fragments of DNA and RNA are not efficiently incorporated into the gelatinous spool. Although the DNA is generally too small (~80 kb) for efficient construction of genomic DNA libraries, it gives excellent results in Southern hybridizations and polymerase chain reactions and can be used to construct a size-fractionated library after limited digestion with a restriction enzyme. Cultured aneuploid mammalian cells (2.0×10^7, e.g., HeLa cells) yield 100 µg of DNA in a volume of ~1 ml.

MATERIALS

CAUTION: Please see Appendix 12 for appropriate handling of materials marked with <!>.

Buffers and Solutions

Please see Appendix 1 for components of stock solutions, buffers, and reagents. Dilute stock solutions to the appropriate concentrations.

Cell lysis solution
   6 M guanidinium hydrochloride <!>
   0.1 M sodium acetate (pH 5.5)
Ethanol (room temperature)
TE (pH 8.0)

Gels

Pulsed-field gel or 0.6% agarose gel

Nucleic Acids and Oligonucleotides

Linear monomers and concatemers of bacteriophage λ DNA (please see Chapter 5, Protocol 16)

Prepare λ DNA as described in Chapter 2, Protocol 11 or 12. The DNA is used as a size standard during gel electrophoresis.

Special Equipment

Kimwipes

Polypropylene tubes (50 ml)

Rocking platform

Shepherd's crooks (used as an alternative to dialysis)

Shepherd's crooks are Pasteur pipettes whose tip has been sealed in the flame of a Bunsen burner and shaped into a U with a hemostat. Wear safety glasses while molding the Shepherd's crooks.

Wide-bore pipettes (0.3-cm diameter orifice)

Wide-bore pipettes are available from several manufacturers. However, standard pipettes can be used if they are autoclaved in the wrong orientation without cotton-wool plugs.

Additional Reagents

Materials and equipment used in Step 1 of Protocol 1

The exact materials and equipment required will depend on the type of starting material: blood, cultured cells, or tissue (please see Protocol 1).

Cells and Tissues

Monolayers or suspensions of mammalian cells, fresh tissue, or blood samples

METHOD

1. Prepare cell suspensions (or frozen cell powders) as described in Step 1 of Protocol 1.

2. Lyse the cells by one of the following two methods.

   FOR LYSIS OF CELLS FROM SUSPENSIONS

   a. Transfer the cell suspensions to disposable 50-ml polypropylene centrifuge tubes.

   b. Add 7.5 volumes of cell lysis solution.

   FOR LYSIS OF CELLS FROM TISSUES

   a. Add the frozen cell powders little by little to ~7.5 volumes of cell lysis solution in beakers. Allow the powders to spread over the surface of the lysis solution, and then shake the beakers to submerge the material.

   b. When all of the material is in solution, transfer the solutions to centrifuge tubes.

3. Close the tubes and incubate them for 1 hour at room temperature on a rocking platform.

   Cells or tissue powders incubated with lysis solution as described in Steps 1–3 above can be stored for several months at 4ºC before extracting the genomic DNA.

4. Dispense 18 ml of ethanol at room temperature into each of a series of disposable 50-ml polypropylene centrifuge tubes. Use wide-bore pipettes to layer the cell suspensions carefully *under* the ethanol.

5. Recover the DNA from each tube by slowly stirring the interface between the cell lysate and the ethanol with a Shepherd's crook. The DNA will adhere to the crook, forming a gelatinous mass. Continue stirring until the ethanol and the aqueous phase are thoroughly mixed.

6. Transfer each Shepherd's crook, with its attached DNA, to a separate polypropylene tube containing 5 ml of ethanol at room temperature. Leave the DNA submerged in the ethanol until all of the samples have been processed.

7. Remove each crook, with its attached DNA, and allow as much ethanol as possible to drain away. By this stage, the DNA should have shrunk into a tightly packed, dehydrated mass; it is then possible to remove most of the free ethanol by capillary action by touching the U-shaped end of the crook to a stack of Kimwipes. Before all of the ethanol has evaporated from the DNA, transfer the crook into a fresh polypropylene tube containing 5 ml of ethanol at room temperature.

8. When all of the samples have been processed, again remove as much ethanol as possible (see Step 7).

    Do not allow the DNA pellets to dry completely or they will be very difficult to dissolve.

9. Transfer each pipette to a fresh polypropylene tube containing 1 ml of TE (pH 8.0). Allow the DNAs to rehydrate by storing the tubes overnight at 4ºC.

    Some DNAs may require 24–48 hours to rehydrate completely.

10. During rehydration, the DNAs become highly gelatinous but remain attached to their pipettes. Use fresh Shepherd's crooks as scrapers to free the pellets of DNA gently from their pipettes. Discard the pipettes, leaving the DNA pellets floating in the TE. Close the tubes and incubate them at 4ºC on a rocking platform until the pellets are completely dissolved (~24–48 hours).

    The level of contamination by RNA is kept within acceptable limits if 1.5 ml or more of lysis solution is used per 10^7 cells. However, the amount of RNA contaminating the DNA sample can be further reduced by adding RNase (final concentration of 1 µg/ml) to the solution DNA.

    The DNA prepared from homogenized tissues by this method often has a faint brownish-red color (presumably due to contamination with small amounts of hemoglobin). This contamination does not inhibit digestion with restriction enzymes.

11. Analyze an aliquot by pulsed-field gel electrophoresis (Chapter 5, Protocol 17 or 18) or by electrophoresis through a 0.6% agarose gel (Chapter 5, Protocol 1). Store the DNA at 4ºC.

    The DNA should be ~80 kb in size and should migrate more slowly than monomers of bacteriophage λ DNA.

    Because DNA made by this procedure is always contaminated with a small amount of RNA, it is necessary to estimate the concentration of DNA in the final preparation either by fluorometry (please see the panel on **ADDITIONAL PROTOCOL: ESTIMATING THE CONCENTRATION OF DNA BY FLUOROMETRY** in Protocol 1) or by gel electrophoresis and staining with ethidium bromide (Chapter 5, Protocol 2).

Protocol 4

Isolation of DNA from Mammalian Cells Grown in 96-well Microtiter Plates

T HE FOLLOWING PROTOCOL, FROM RAMÍREZ-SOLIS ET AL. (1992, 1993), describes a simple and efficient method for extracting genomic DNA from eukaryotic cells grown in the individual wells of microtiter plates. Each well yields sufficient genomic DNA for several standard polymerase chain reactions (PCRs) or for analysis in a single lane of a Southern hybridization. For a method optimizing the preparations of genomic DNA for use in PCR, please see the panel on **ADDITIONAL PROTOCOL: OPTIMIZING GENOMIC DNA ISOLATION FOR PCR** at the end of this protocol.

MATERIALS

Buffers and Solutions

Please see Appendix 1 for components of stock solutions, buffers, and reagents. Dilute stock solutions to the appropriate concentrations.

Cell lysis buffer
  10 mM Tris-Cl (pH 7.5)
  10 mM NaCl
  10 mM EDTA (pH 8.0)
  0.5% (w/v) Sarkosyl

Add proteinase K to the lysis buffer to a final concentration of 1 mg/ml just before use.

Sarkosyl, an anionic detergent, is usually supplied by the manufacturer as a 30% solution in H_2O. It is less prone than SDS to precipitate from solutions of high ionic strength. However, it is also a less effective detergent than SDS.

Ethanol
NaCl/ethanol solution
  Add 150 µl of 5 M NaCl per 10 ml of absolute ethanol. Store the NaCl/ethanol solution at –20ºC.
Phosphate-buffered saline (PBS)
Sucrose gel-loading buffer
TE (pH 8.0)

Enzymes and Buffers

Appropriate restriction enzymes
DNase-free RNase

Special Equipment

Aspiration device connected to a vacuum line fitted with traps

Multichannel pipettor, 8 or 12 channels

Rainin EDP-Plus M8 from Rainin Inc.

These devices aid the addition of multiple reagents to individual wells of microtiter plates. If PCR will be used to screen the cell cultures, use plugged pipette tips. The barrels of multichannel pipettes should be disassembled and cleaned before use.

Oven, preset to 60°C

The oven should be capable of maintaining a temperature of 60°C for 12–16 hours.

Rocking platform

Tupperware containers

These containers should be able to withstand extended incubations at 60°C.

Cells and Tissues

Cells growing in 96-cell plates

Cell cultures in individual flat-bottomed wells of 96-well tissue culture plates should be grown to confluence, or close to it. These plates are available from most suppliers of materials used for tissue culture. Label both the tops and the bottoms of the 96-well plates when working with more than one plate.

METHOD

1. Remove the medium from confluent cultures of cells growing in individual wells of 96-well plates by aspiration through a blue pipette tip or a Pasteur pipette.

   As long as care is taken to avoid touching the cell layer, there is generally no need to use a fresh pipette tip for each well.

2. Rinse the monolayers of cells in the individual wells twice with 100 µl of phosphate-buffered saline.

3. Use a multichannel pipettor to add 50 µl of cell lysis buffer to each well of the microtiter plate. Place several wet paper towels in a polypropylene box (e.g., a Tupperware box) and then stack the microtiter plates containing the lysis buffer and cells on top of the towels. Seal the box tightly with the lid.

4. Incubate the sealed box for 12–16 hours in a 60°C oven.

5. Remove the box from the oven, place the plates on a flat bench top, and allow them to cool for a few minutes before adding 100 µl of NaCl/ethanol solution per well. Store the plates for 30 minutes at room temperature without mixing. A stringy precipitate of nucleic acid should be visible at the end of the incubation.

6. Slowly invert each plate over a sink to decant the ethanolic solution. The precipitated nucleic acid should remain attached to the base of the wells. Place each plate in an upside down position on a bed of dry paper towels and allow the remaining ethanol to drain from the plate.

7. Add 150 µl of 70% ethanol to each well, being careful not to dislodge the precipitate of nucleic acid. Discard the 70% ethanol by inverting the plate as in Step 6. Blot the excess liquid on a bed of paper towels. Rinse the precipitates of DNA twice more with 70% ethanol.

8. Allow the plates to dry at room temperature until the last traces of ethanol have evaporated. If the genomic DNA is to be analyzed by PCR, then proceed to Step 9. If the DNA is to be analyzed by Southern hybridization, proceed to Steps 10, 11, and 12.

9. Add 30–50 µl of TE (pH 8.0) to each well and allow the DNA to dissolve during gentle rocking for 12–16 hours at room temperature.

    > Dissolution of the DNA can be accelerated by placing the microtiter dishes on the heating block of a thermal cycler that is programmed to cycle 10 times between 80°C and 50°C (1 minute at each temperature).

    > The DNA may now be used as template for standard PCR (please see Chapter 8, Protocol 1).

10. If the DNA is to be analyzed by Southern blotting, make up the following restriction enzyme mixture; 40 µl of the mixture will be required for each well.

H_2O	0.8 volume
10x restriction enzyme buffer	0.1 volume
DNase-free RNase	10 µg/ml

    Just before use, add 10 units of restriction enzyme for each 40 µl of mixture.

11. Use a multichannel pipettor to add 40 µl of the restriction enzyme mixture to each well. Mix the contents of the wells by pipetting up and down several times, taking care to avoid air bubbles. Incubate the reactions at the appropriate digestion temperature for 12–16 hours in a humidified sealed Tupperware box as described in Step 3.

12. Stop the reactions by adding 5–10 µl of sucrose gel-loading buffer and analyze the digested DNA by Southern blotting and hybridization as described in Protocols 8, 9, and 10.

ADDITIONAL PROTOCOL: OPTIMIZING GENOMIC DNA ISOLATION FOR PCR

Genomic DNA, isolated by the method given above, can be used as template in standard PCRs. However, for more demanding types of PCR (e.g., long PCR; see Chapter 8, Protocol 13), it is better to use a variation in which acetone and *N,N*-dimethylformamide are used to precipitate DNA in the 96-well plate (Udy and Evans 1994).

If the isolated DNAs will be used only as templates for PCR and not be analyzed by Southern hybridization, the cells in the wells of the microtiter plates can be lysed in a solution that is compatible with PCR. Lysis in such a buffer allows PCR to be carried out directly in the lysis solution and eliminates the need for ethanol precipitation and rinsing. The two protocols given below are robust and work well with a variety of thermostable DNA polymerases.

CAUTION: Please see Appendix 12 for appropriate handling of materials marked with <!>.

PROTOCOL A

Materials

PCR lysis solution A
> 67 mM Tris-Cl (pH 8.8)
> 16.6 mM ammonium sulfate
> 5 mM β-mercaptoethanol <!>
> 6.7 mM $MgCl_2$
> 6.7 μM EDTA (pH 8.0)
> 1.7 μM SDS
> 50 μg/ml proteinase K

Method

1. Remove the media from cultures of cells growing in 96-well plates.

2. Deliver 100 μl of PCR lysis solution A into each well and lyse the cells by incubation for 1 hour at 37°C, followed by a 10-minute incubation at 80°C to inactivate the proteinase K.

3. Use 5–25-μl aliquots of the DNA preparations as templates in PCRs.

PROTOCOL B (Köntgen and Stewart 1993)

Materials

PCR lysis solution B
> 10 mM Tris-Cl (pH 8.3)
> 50 mM KCl
> 2 mM $MgCl_2$
> 0.45% (v/v) Nonidet P-40
> 0.45% (v/v) Tween-20
> 20 μg/ml proteinase K

Lysate buffer
> 670 mM Tris-Cl (pH 8.8)
> 166 mM ammonium sulfate
> 1 mg/ml bovine serum albumin

Method

1. Remove the medium from cultures of cells growing in 96-well plates.

2. Deliver 50 μl of PCR lysis solution B into each well and lyse the cells by incubation overnight at 37°C, followed by a 30-minute incubation at 95°C to inactivate the proteinase K.

3. To each lysate add an equal volume of a lysate buffer.

4. Use 10–50-μl aliquots of the DNA preparations as templates in PCRs.

Protocol 5

Preparation of Genomic DNA from Mouse Tails and Other Small Samples

OVER THE YEARS, MANY PROTOCOLS FOR THE EXTRACTION OF DNA from mouse tails have been published, almost all of them descendants of the original method developed by Richard Palmiter and Ralph Brinster in 1985 (Palmiter et al. 1985). Palmiter's laboratory was in Seattle, while Brinster and his thousands of mice were 3000 miles away in Philadelphia. Brinster would snip fragments of tails from the mice, place them in a solution of SDS and proteinase K, and, in those pre-FedEx days, would ship them to Palmiter by U.S. Mail. After their 2–3-day journey at ambient temperature, the samples were extracted with phenol:chloroform, and the genomic DNA was recovered by precipitation with ethanol. Success with this method fortunately does not require entrusting semidigested mouse parts to the care of the U.S. postal system. Instead, the digestions can be more conveniently carried out overnight at 55ºC, without transportation. Each tail snippet generates 50–100 µg of DNA that can be used in dot or slot blotting to detect a transgene of interest, in Southern hybridization to detect DNA fragments that are <20 kb in size, and, more expediently, as a template in PCRs. This simple protocol continues to be used in hundreds of laboratories for genotyping transgenic and knock-out mice and for extracting DNA from small numbers of cultured cells or from fragments of tissue.

Two variants of the basic protocol are useful when processing very large numbers of samples. The method of Laird et al. (1991) omits extraction with phenol:chloroform, whereas the protocols described by Thomas et al. (1989) and Couse et al. (1994) use commercially available gel-barrier tubes to eliminate the tedious transfer of samples during serial extraction with organic solvents. These variations are described in the alternative protocols at the end this protocol.

MATERIALS

CAUTION: Please see Appendix 12 for appropriate handling of materials marked with <!>.

Buffers and Solutions

Please see Appendix 1 for components of stock solutions, buffers, and reagents. Dilute stock solutions to the appropriate concentrations.

Ethanol
Isopropanol
Phenol:chloroform:isoamyl alcohol (25:24:1 v/v) <!>
Phosphate-buffered saline

SNET
> 20 mM Tris-Cl (pH 8.0)
> 5 mM EDTA (pH 8.0)
> 400 mM NaCl
> 1% (w/v) SDS
> Sterilize the solution by filtration through a 0.45-μm nitrocellulose filter. Store the sterile solution in 50-ml aliquots at room temperature.

TE (pH 8.0)

Enzymes and Buffers

Proteinase K (20 mg/ml)
> Please see Appendix 4.

Centrifuges and Rotors

Sorvall H1000B and SH-3000 rotors or equivalents

Special Equipment

Polypropylene tubes (17 × 100 mm)
Rocking platform at room temperature and 4°C
Rocking platform or shaking incubator, preset to 55°C
Shepherd's crook (for a description, please see Steps 5–7 of Protocol 3)

Cells and Tissues

Cultured Cells

Monolayer cultures, grown to confluence or semiconfluence in 100-mm dishes, should be washed twice with ice-cold phosphate-buffered saline and then immediately lysed by addition of 1 ml of SNET containing 400 μg/ml proteinase K, as described in Step 1.

Cells growing in suspension should be recovered by centrifugation, washed twice in ice-cold phosphate-buffered saline, and then resuspended in TE (pH 8.0) at a concentration of 5×10^7/ml. Aliquots of the suspension (0.2 ml) are then transferred to a series of 17 × 100-mm Falcon polypropylene tubes and the cells are immediately lysed with SNET containing 400 μg/ml proteinase K, as described in Step 1.

Mouse tails or mouse tissue

Samples of mouse tails are generally cut from 10-day old suckling animals or at the time of weaning (~3 weeks of age). In the former case, the distal one third of the tail is removed and transferred into a microfuge. In the latter case, 6–10 mm of the tail is removed under anesthesia and transferred to a 17 × 100-mm Falcon polypropylene tube. Under rare circumstances, where obtaining a result rapidly is of paramount importance, the entire tail can be removed from newborn animals and transferred to a microfuge tube.

To isolate DNA from mouse tissue (other than tail snippets), transfer ~100 mg of the freshly dissected tissue to a 17 × 100-mm Falcon polypropylene tube.

Mouse tails or other tissues can be stored for a few weeks at –70°C in tightly closed tubes before adding SNET and proteinase K. However, it is better to proceed without delay to digest the samples with proteinase K (Steps 1 and 2). The completed digests can then be stored indefinitely at –20°C before phenol:chloroform extraction.

All experiments carried out on laboratory mice, including removing sections of tail, require prior authorization from the appropriate institutional ethics committee.

METHOD

1. Prepare the appropriate amount of lysis buffer (see Table 6-1) by adding proteinase K to a final concentration of 400 μg/ml in SNET. Add lysis buffer to the mouse tails or other tissues.

    This procedure also can be used to isolate DNA from monolayers of cultured mammalian cells. In this case, 1 ml of SNET containing 400 μg/ml proteinase K is added directly to 100-mm monolay-

TABLE 6-1 SNET Lysis Buffer Volumes

AGE OF MOUSE	AMOUNT OF TISSUE	TYPE OF TUBE	VOLUME OF SNET LYSIS BUFFER (ml)
Newborn	entire tail (1 cm)	microfuge	0.5
10 days old	distal one-third	microfuge	0.5
Weanling (3–4 weeks)	6–10-mm	17 x 100-mm polypropylene	4.0
Any age	100 mg of fresh tissue	17 x 100-mm polypropylene	4.0

ers that have been rinsed twice in phosphate-buffered saline. The viscous cell slurry is scraped from the dish with a rubber policeman, and transferred to a 17 x 100-mm polypropylene Falcon tube.

Cells growing in suspension that have been washed twice in phosphate-buffered saline are resuspended in TE and lysed with SNET containing 400 µg of proteinase K (1 ml per 10^9 cells).

2. Incubate the tube overnight at 55ºC in a horizontal position on a rocking platform or with agitation in a shaking incubator.

    It is important that the sample be mixed adequately during digestion. After overnight incubation, the tissue/tails should no longer be visible and the buffer should be a milky-gray.

3. Add an equal volume of phenol:chloroform:isoamyl alcohol, seal the top of the tube, and place it on a rocking platform for 30 minutes at room temperature.

    Protocols differ in their use of vortexing at various stages of the protocol. Some protocols state flatly not to vortex. Others say that vortexing ensures a greater yield of DNA composed of fragments up to 20 kb in length that can be detected by Southern hybridization, dot and slot blotting, and PCR analysis. If DNA of higher molecular weight is required, take care to minimize shearing forces (please see the information panel on **MINIMIZING DAMAGE TO LARGE DNA MOLECULES** in Chapter 2).

4. Separate the organic and aqueous phases by centrifugation. Centrifuge the samples in 17 x 100-mm polypropylene tubes at 666*g* (1800 rpm in a Sorvall H1000B rotor with swinging buckets or 1600 rpm in a Sorvall SH-3000 swinging bucket rotor) for 5 minutes at room temperature. Alternatively, for smaller sample volumes, centrifuge the samples in microfuge tubes at maximum speed for 5 minutes at room temperature in a microfuge. Transfer the upper aqueous phase to a fresh Falcon or microfuge tube.

5. Precipitate the DNA by adding an equal volume of isopropanol. Collect the precipitated DNA by centrifugation at 13,250*g* (8000 rpm in a Sorvall SH-3000 swinging bucket rotor or maximum speed in a microfuge) for 15 minutes at 4ºC.

6. Carefully remove the isopropanol. Rinse the pellet of DNA with 1 ml of 70% ethanol. If the pellets are loose, centrifuge the samples again for 5 minutes. Remove the 70% ethanol, and allow the pellets to dry in air for 15–20 minutes at room temperature.

    Do not allow the DNA pellets to dry completely or they will be very difficult to dissolve.

7. Dissolve the nucleic acid pellet by rocking it gently overnight in 0.5 ml of TE (pH 8.0) at 4ºC.

8. Transfer the solution to a microfuge tube and store it at room temperature.

    Between 100 µg and 250 µg of genomic DNA is typically isolated from 1 cm (~100 mg) of mouse tail.

    The addition of bovine serum albumin at a concentration of 100 µg/ml to restriction enzyme digests of genomic DNA prepared by this method will absorb residual SDS and reduce the possibility of incomplete digestions. If problems persist, re-extract the samples once more with phenol:chloroform and precipitate the DNA with 2 volumes of ethanol.

ALTERNATIVE PROTOCOL: ISOLATION OF DNA FROM MOUSE TAILS WITHOUT EXTRACTION BY ORGANIC SOLVENTS

Laird et al. (1991) describe a variation of the preceding protocol that does not require extraction with phenol:chloroform and can also be applied to mammalian cells grown in 24-well culture dishes.

Additional Materials

Mouse-tail lysis buffer I
  100 mM Tris-Cl (pH 8.5)
  5 mM EDTA (pH 8.0)
  200 mM NaCl
  0.2% (w/v) SDS
  100 µg/ml proteinase K

Method

1. Add 0.5 ml of Mouse-tail lysis buffer I to 1 cm of mouse tail in a microfuge tube.

2. Digest the tissue at 55°C as described in Step 2 of the main protocol.

3. Shake the digested sample vigorously, and centrifuge the tube at maximum speed for 10 minutes at room temperature in a microfuge to sediment undigested tissue.

4. Transfer the supernatant to a fresh microfuge tube containing 0.5 ml of isopropanol at room temperature. Mix the contents of the tube by inversion.

5. Fish out the stringy precipitate of DNA with a clean disposable micropipette tip or a Shepherd's crook. Briefly touch the precipitate to a Kimwipe to remove excess alcohol and then transfer the DNA to a fresh microfuge tube.

6. Store the open tube on the bench until the remaining alcohol has evaporated.

7. Dissolve the DNA in 200–500 µl of TE (pH 8.0), by rocking it gently overnight at 4°C.

   The yield of DNA usually varies from 5 to 12 µg/mm of mouse tail.

ALTERNATIVE PROTOCOL: ONE-TUBE ISOLATION OF DNA FROM MOUSE TAILS

Couse et al. (1994) have described a method based on earlier work of Thomas et al. (1989) that uses serial extractions with organic solvents to extract DNA from mouse tails; the same method can be applied to mammalian cells grown in 24-well culture dishes. Serial extractions usually require transfer of the aqueous phase to fresh tubes — a process that can be lengthy and boring. These disadvantages can be overcome by using serum separation tubes (SST), sold by Becton Dickinson. The tubes are made of a glass, with an inert gel plug at the base and a silicon rubber stopper. During centrifugation, the gel plug migrates to the top of the organic phase, trapping the cellular proteins and debris in the lower part of the tube and leaving the aqueous phase on the top of the plug. Serial extractions with organic solvents can be carried out in the same SST because the gel plug will always migrate during centrifugation to a position between the organic and aqueous phases.

Additional Reagents

   CAUTION: Please see Appendix 12 for appropriate handling of materials marked with <!>.

Ethanol
Chloroform <!>
Mouse-tail lysis buffer II
  50 mM Tris-Cl (pH 8.0)
  50 mM EDTA (pH 8.0)
  0.125% (w/v) SDS
  800 µg/ml proteinase K
Sodium acetate (3 M, pH 6.0)
SST tubes (Becton Dickinson)

Method

1. Add 1.0 ml of Mouse-tail lysis buffer II to 5 mm of mouse tail in an SST tube.

2. Digest the tissue overnight at 55°C as described in Step 2 of the main protocol.

(Continued on facing page.)

3. Add 1 ml of phenol:chloroform:isoamyl alcohol and mix the contents of the tube thoroughly by gentle inversion.

4. Centrifuge the tube at 2000*g* (3100 rpm in a Sorvall H1000B rotor) for 10 minutes at room temperature in a swinging bucket rotor. Repeat the centrifugation step if the aqueous phase is cloudy or if some of the protein interface remains trapped above the plug.

5. To the same tube, add 1 ml of chloroform and recentrifuge as described in Step 4.

6. Transfer 450-μl aliquots of the aqueous layer above the plug to two microfuge tubes containing 50 μl of 3 M sodium acetate (pH 6.0).

    The use of sodium acetate at pH 6.0, rather than pH 5.2, is unusual. EDTA is used in the lysis buffer at high concentration (100 mM) and will precipitate at low pH. This problem can best be avoided by maintaining a pH >6.0 and by working quickly during Steps 6 and 7. Alternatively, the concentration of EDTA in the lysis buffer may be reduced to 20 mM. However, this may not be enough to chelate all of the Mg^{2+} in the sample, leaving the DNA open to attack by DNases.

7. Add 2 volumes (0.9 ml) of ethanol (room temperature) to each tube. Working quickly, mix the contents of the tube by inversion and immediately centrifuge the tube at maximum speed for 5 minutes at room temperature in a microfuge.

8. Wash the pellets of DNA with 70% ethanol and recentrifuge. Remove the ethanolic solution by aspiration and leave the open tubes on the bench until any remaining ethanol has evaporated.

9. Dissolve the DNA in 250 μl of TE (pH 8.0) by rocking it gently overnight at 4°C.

    The yield of DNA is usually 10 μg/mm of mouse tail.

ALTERNATIVE PROTOCOL: DNA EXTRACTION FROM PARAFFIN BLOCKS

Archival tissue is often used as a source of DNA for the identification of mutations in human genetic diseases, in part because tissue samples are collected during a surgical operation and fixed, stained, and stored by pathologists. Although there are a number of publications that compare different methods for the extraction of DNA from paraffin blocks (e.g., please see Sepp et al. 1994), we have found that it is best to use one of the commercially available kits for DNA isolation from paraffin-embedded tissue. Kits from Intergen (EX-WAX DNA Extraction Kit) have proven to be efficient at extraction of DNA from tissues that have been embedded for as long as 17 years. Other investigators have reported the isolation of DNA from much older paraffin blocks. The extracted DNA is highly degraded and is useful only as a template in PCRs.

Protocol 6

Rapid Isolation of Mammalian DNA

M~AMMALIAN DNA PREPARED ACCORDING TO THIS PROTOCOL~ is 20–50 kb in size and suitable for use as a template in PCRs. The yields of DNA vary between 0.5 and 3.0 µg/mg tissue or 5 and 15 µg per 300 µl of whole blood.

MATERIALS

CAUTION: Please see Appendix 12 for appropriate handling of materials marked with <!>.

Buffers and Solutions

Please see Appendix 1 for components of stock solutions, buffers, and reagents. Dilute stock solutions to the appropriate concentrations.

Cell lysis buffer
  10 mM Tris-Cl (pH 8.0)
  1 mM EDTA (pH 8.0)
  0.1% (w/v) SDS
  Store the buffer at room temperature, but chill an aliquot to 0°C in readiness for Step 2.

Ethanol

Isopropanol

Potassium acetate solution
  60 ml of 5 M potassium acetate
  11.5 ml of glacial acetic acid <!>
  28.5 ml of H_2O
  The resulting solution is 3 M with respect to potassium and 5 M with respect to acetate.
  Store the buffer at room temperature.

Red blood cell lysis buffer
  20 mM Tris-Cl (pH 7.6)
  Store the buffer at room temperature.

TE (pH 7.6)

Enzymes and Buffers

DNase-free RNase (4 mg/ml)

Proteinase K (20 mg/ml)
  Optional, please see Step 3 and Appendix 4.

Special Equipment

Aspiration device connected to a vacuum line

Microfuge pestle
    This is available from Sigma in both hand-operated and motor-driven versions.

Mortar and pestle, prechilled with liquid nitrogen <!>

Water bath preset to either 55°C or 65°C

Cells and Tissues

Mammalian tissue or whole blood of interest

METHOD

1. Prepare tissue or whole blood for genomic DNA isolation.

   ### FOR TISSUE

   a. Dissect 10–20 mg of tissue.

   b. Either mince the tissue finely with a razor blade/scalpel or freeze the tissue in liquid nitrogen and then grind it to a powder in a mortar prechilled with liquid nitrogen, as described in Protocol 1.

   ### FOR BLOOD

   a. Transfer 300-μl aliquots of whole blood to each of two microfuge tubes. Add 900 μl of red blood cell lysis buffer to each tube and invert the capped tubes to mix the contents. Incubate the solution at room temperature for 10 minutes, occasionally inverting the tubes.

   b. Centrifuge the tubes at maximum speed for 20 seconds at room temperature in a microfuge.

   c. Discard all but 20 μl of each supernatant.

   d. Resuspend the pellets of white cells in the small amount of supernatant left in each tube. Combine the resuspended cell pellets in a single tube.

2. Transfer the minced tissue or the resuspended white blood cell pellets to a microfuge tube containing 600 μl of ice-cold cell lysis buffer. Homogenize the suspension quickly with 30–50 strokes of a microfuge pestle.
   The SDS will precipitate from the ice-cold cell lysis buffer producing a cloudy solution. This precipitation will not affect isolation of DNA.

3. (*Optional*) Add 3 μl of proteinase K solution to the lysate to increase the yield of genomic DNA. Incubate the digest for at least 3 hours but no more than 16 hours at 55°C.

4. Allow the digest to cool to room temperature and then add 3 μl of 4 mg/ml DNase-free RNase. Incubate the digest for 15–60 minutes at 37°C.

5. Allow the sample to cool to room temperature. Add 200 μl of potassium acetate solution and mix the contents of the tube by vortexing vigorously for 20 seconds.

6. Pellet the precipitated protein/SDS complex by centrifugation at maximum speed for 3 minutes at 4ºC in a microfuge.

   A pellet of protein should be visible at the bottom of the microfuge tube after centrifugation. If not, incubate the lysate for 5 minutes on ice and repeat the centrifugation step.

7. Transfer the supernatant to a fresh microfuge tube containing 600 μl of isopropanol. Mix the solution well and then recover the precipitate of DNA by centrifuging the tube at maximum speed for 1 minute at room temperature in a microfuge.

8. Remove the supernatant by aspiration and add 600 μl of 70% ethanol to the DNA pellet. Invert the tube several times and centrifuge the tube at maximum speed for 1 minute at room temperature in a microfuge.

9. Carefully remove the supernatant by aspiration and allow the DNA pellet to dry in air for 15 minutes.

10. Redissolve the pellet of DNA in 100 μl of TE (pH 7.6).

    The solubilization of the genomic DNA pellet can be faciltated by incubation for 16 hours at room temperature or for 1 hour at 65ºC.

Protocol 7

Rapid Isolation of Yeast DNA

Y EAST DNAS PREPARED ACCORDING THIS PROTOCOL can be used as templates in PCRs. Shuttle plasmids that replicate in both *Escherichia coli* and *Saccharomyces cerevisiae* can be extracted from yeast by this method and used to transform *E. coli*. The following protocol was provided by Peter Espenshade (University of Texas Southwestern Medical Center, Dallas). For an alternative method for preparing yeast DNA, please see Chapter 4, Protocol 12.

MATERIALS

CAUTION: Please see Appendix 12 for appropriate handling of materials marked with <!>.

Buffers and Solutions

Please see Appendix 1 for components of stock solutions, buffers, and reagents. Dilute stock solutions to the appropriate concentrations.

Ethanol
Phenol:chloroform (1:1, v/v) <!>
Sodium acetate (3 M, pH 5.2)
STES buffer
    0.2 M Tris-Cl (pH 7.6)
    0.5 M NaCl
    0.1 % (w/v) SDS
    0.01 M EDTA

    Store at room temperature.
TE (pH 7.6)

Special Equipment

Acid-washed glass beads (0.4 mm)
    Washed glass beads may be purchased, for example, from Sigma. Unwashed beads are not recommended.

Cells and Tissues

Yeast cells, freshly grown either as colonies on an agar plate or as an overnight culture

METHOD

1. Prepare the yeast cells for lysis.

   ### FOR YEAST COLONIES ON PLATES

   Use a sterile inoculating loop to transfer one or more large, freshly grown colonies to a microfuge tube containing 50 µl of STES buffer.

   ### FOR YEAST GROWN IN LIQUID CULTURE

   a. Transfer 1.5 ml from an overnight culture of yeast cells to a microfuge tube.

   b. Pellet the cells by centrifuging at maximum speed for 1 minute at room temperature in a microfuge.

   c. Remove the culture medium by aspiration and resuspend the pellet in 50 µl of STES buffer.

2. Add ~50 µl of acid-washed glass beads to each tube containing the resuspended yeast. Add 20 µl of TE (pH 7.6) to each tube.

3. Add 60 µl of phenol:chloroform, cap the tubes, and mix the organic and aqueous phases by vortexing for 1 minute.

4. Centrifuge the tubes at maximum speed for 5 minutes at room temperature in a microfuge.

5. Transfer the upper aqueous phase to a fresh microfuge tube. Collect the DNA by standard precipitation with ethanol for 15 minutes at 0°C.

6. Recover the precipitate of nucleic acids by centrifugation at maximum speed for 10 minutes at 4°C in a microfuge.

7. Remove the supernatant by aspiration and rinse the pellet with 100 µl of 70% ethanol in H_2O. Centrifuge the tubes at maximum speed for 1 minute at room temperature in a microfuge.

8. Remove the supernatant by aspiration and allow the pellet to dry in the air for 15 minutes. Redissolve the pellet in 40 µl of TE (pH 7.6).

   > Use 1–10 µl of the solution of DNA as template in PCRs. Shuttle plasmids can be recovered by transforming preparations of competent *E. coli* with 1 µl of the DNA.

Southern Hybridization

SOUTHERN TRANSFER AND HYBRIDIZATION (Southern 1975) is used to study how genes are organized within genomes by mapping restriction sites in and around segments of genomic DNA for
which specific probes are available. Genomic DNA is first digested with one or more restriction
enzymes, and the resulting fragments are separated according to size by electrophoresis through
a standard agarose gel. The DNA is then denatured in situ and transferred from the gel to a solid
support (usually a nylon or nitrocellulose membrane). The DNA attached to the membrane is
hybridized to a labeled DNA, RNA, or oligonucleotide probe, and bands complementary to the
probe are located by an appropriate detection system, for example, by autoradiography. By estimating the size and number of the bands generated after digestion of the genomic DNA with different restriction enzymes, singly or in combination, it is possible to place the target DNA within a context of restriction sites.

For 2 or 3 years after its introduction, the sensitivity of Southern blotting was barely sufficient to detect single-copy sequences in mammalian DNA, and the autoradiographs of the time
were so speckled and streaked with background (e.g., please see Botchan et al. 1976) that they certainly could not be published today. However, significant advances over the years in several areas
have brought increased sensitivity and reproducibility, so that immaculate results are now the
general rule rather than the rare exception. The most significant of these improvements is the use
of supported nylon membranes that are far more durable and have a higher binding capacity than
the original nitrocellulose membranes. In addition, DNA can now be covalently fixed to the membrane after transfer, eliminating problems caused by leaching of nucleic acids from nitrocellulose
membranes during incubation at elevated temperatures (Haas et al. 1972). Other advances
include

- More efficient methods of transfer of DNA from gel to membrane, downward capillary transfer (Lichtenstein et al. 1990; Chomczynski 1992), vacuum blotting (Medveczky et al. 1987;
  Olszewska and Jones 1988; Trnovsky 1992), bidirectional blotting (please see Protocol 9), and
  transfer in alkaline buffers (Reed and Mann 1985).

- Facile labeling of probes in vitro to higher specific activity (Feinberg and Vogelstein 1983,
  1984).

- More efficient blocking agents to prevent nonspecific attachment of radiolabeled probes to
  membranes (Church and Gilbert 1984).

- Use of sensitive phosphorimagers to capture images with high efficiency.

Many of these improvements have been incorporated into Protocols 8 and 9, which deal with transfer of DNA from gels to membranes, and Protocol 10, which describes hybridization of radiolabeled probes to immobilized DNAs. The techniques described are suitable for Southern analysis of restriction digests of mammalian genomic DNA but can easily be adapted to accommodate large DNA molecules separated by pulsed-field gels, as well as restriction digests of plasmids, cosmids, λ bacteriophages, bacterial artificial chromosomes (BACs), and yeast artificial chromosomes (YACs).

METHODS OF TRANSFERRING DNA FROM AGAROSE GELS TO SOLID SUPPORTS

The transfer of electrophoretically separated DNA from gels to two-dimensional solid supports is a key step in Southern hybridization. Described below are five methods to transfer fragments of DNA from agarose gels to solid supports (nitrocellulose or nylon membranes).

Upward Capillary Transfer

DNA fragments are carried from the gel in an upward flow of liquid and deposited on the surface of the solid support (Southern 1975). The liquid is drawn through the gel by capillary action that is established and maintained by a stack of dry absorbent paper towels (please see Figure 6-1). The rate of transfer of the DNA depends on the size of the DNA fragments and the concentration of agarose in the gel. Small fragments of DNA (<1 kb) are transferred almost quantitatively from a 0.7% agarose gel within 1 hour; larger fragments are transferred more slowly and less efficiently. For example, capillary transfer of DNAs >15 kb in length requires at least 18 hours, and even then the transfer is not complete. The efficiency of transfer of large DNA fragments is determined by the fraction of molecules that escape from the gel before it becomes dehydrated. As elution proceeds, fluid is drawn not only from the reservoir, but also from the interstices of the gel itself. This flow reduces the gel to a rubbery substance through which DNA molecules cannot easily pass. The problem of dehydration due to lengthy transfer can be alleviated by partial acid/base hydrolysis of the DNA before capillary transfer (Wahl et al. 1979; Meinkoth and Wahl 1984). The DNA in the gel is exposed to weak acid (which results in partial depurination), followed by strong base (which hydrolyzes the phosphodiester backbone at the sites of depurination). The resulting frag-

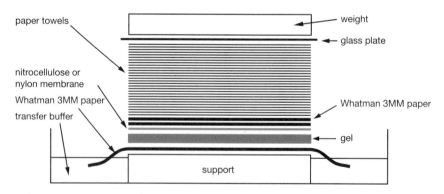

FIGURE 6-1 Upward Capillary Transfer of DNA from Agarose Gels

Buffer drawn from a reservoir passes through the gel into a stack of paper towels. DNA eluted from the gel by the moving stream of buffer is deposited onto a nitrocellulose or nylon membrane. A weight applied to the top of the paper towels helps to ensure a tight connection between the layers of material used in the transfer system.

ments of DNA (~1 kb in length) can then be transferred rapidly from the gel with high efficiency. The depurination reaction must not proceed too far; otherwise, the DNA will be cleaved into small fragments that are too short to bind efficiently to the solid support. Depurination/hydrolysis can also cause the bands of the final autoradiograph to assume a "fuzzy" appearance, presumably because of increased diffusion of DNA during transfer. Therefore, depurination/hydrolysis is recommended only when it is known ahead of time that the target DNA fragments will exceed 15 kb in length.

Downward Capillary Transfer

DNA fragments are carried in a downward direction in a flow of alkaline buffer and are deposited onto the surface of a charged nylon membrane. Various arrangements of wicks, reservoirs, and different formulations of transfer buffers have been described to achieve downward transfer (e.g., please see Lichtenstein et al. 1990; Chomczynski 1992). In our hands, the best results are achieved using 0.4 M NaOH and a setup in which the transfer buffer is drawn from reservoirs to the top of the gel through wicks and pulled through the gel by an underlying stack of paper towels (please see Figure 6-2) (Koetsier et al. 1993). Transfer of DNA fragments is rapid, and the intensity of signal is ~30% greater than can be achieved by conventional upward transfer. This improvement probably results from a more efficient migration of DNA fragments through the interstices of the gel, which is not under pressure from weights placed on top.

Simultaneous Transfer to Two Membranes

When the target DNA fragments are present in high concentration (e.g., in restriction digests of cloned DNAs), the capillary method can be used to transfer DNA simultaneously and rapidly

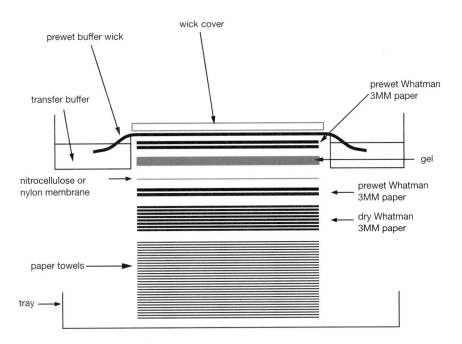

FIGURE 6-2 Downward Capillary Transfer

Alkaline transfer buffer is drawn from reservoirs to the top of the gel through wicks and sucked through the gel by an underlying stack of paper towels. DNA fragments are thus carried in a downward direction with the flow of buffer and are deposited onto the surface of a charged nylon membrane. (Adapted, with permission, from Koetsier et al. 1993.)

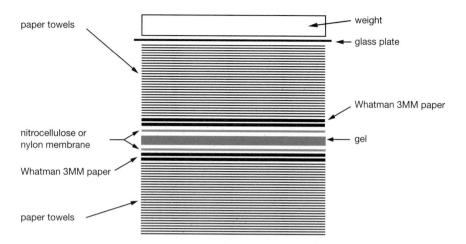

FIGURE 6-3 Capillary Transfer of DNA from Agarose Gels to Two Solid Supports Simultaneously

This procedure is appropriate for analyzing cloned DNAs and the genomes of simple organisms, but it is not sensitive enough to be used when analyzing complex mammalian genomes.

from a single gel to two nitrocellulose or nylon membranes (please see Figure 6-3). The only source of transfer buffer is the liquid trapped in the gel itself, and thus the efficiency of transfer is relatively poor. This method is not recommended when high sensitivity is required (e.g., detection of single-copy sequences in mammalian DNA), but it is perfectly adequate for Southern analysis of plasmids, bacteriophages, or cosmids or the genomes of simple organisms (e.g., *S. cerevisiae* and *Drosophila*) by Southern hybridization. Too little mammalian genomic DNA is transferred by this method to allow signal detection routinely.

Electrophoretic Transfer

This method is not practical when nitrocellulose is used as the solid support because of the high ionic strengths of the buffers that are required to bind nucleic acids to nitrocellulose. These buffers conduct electric current very efficiently, and it is necessary to use large volumes to ensure that the buffering power of the system does not become depleted by electrolysis. In addition, extensive external cooling is required to overcome the effects of ohmic heating.

Electrophoretic transfer has undergone a recent resurgence with the advent of charged nylon membranes and has become the method of choice for analysis of small fragments of DNA separated by electrophoresis through polyacrylamide gels (Stellwag and Dahlberg 1980; Church and Gilbert 1984). Nucleic acids as small as 50 bp will bind to charged nylon membranes in buffers of very low ionic strength (Reed and Mann 1985).

Although single-stranded DNA and RNA can be transferred directly, fragments of double-stranded DNA must first be denatured in situ as described in Protocol 8. The gel is then neutralized and soaked in electrophoresis buffer (e.g., 1x TBE; see Appendix 1) before being mounted between porous pads aligned between parallel electrodes in a large tank of buffer. The time required for complete transfer depends on the size of the fragments of DNA, the porosity of the gel, and the strength of the applied field. However, because even high-molecular-weight nucleic acids migrate relatively rapidly from the gel, depurination/hydrolysis is unnecessary and transfer is generally complete within 2–3 hours. Because electrophoretic transfer requires comparatively large electric currents, it is often difficult to maintain the electrophoresis buffer at a temperature compatible with efficient transfer of DNA. Many commercially available electrophoretic transfer machines are equipped with cooling devices, but others are effective only when used in a cold room.

Vacuum Transfer

DNA and RNA can be transferred rapidly and quantitatively from gels under vacuum. Several vacuum transfer devices are now commercially available in which the gel is placed in contact with a nitrocellulose or nylon membrane supported on a porous screen over a vacuum chamber. Buffer, drawn from an upper reservoir, elutes nucleic acids from the gel and deposits them on the membrane.

Vacuum transfer is more efficient than capillary transfer and is extremely rapid. DNAs that have been partially depurinated and denatured with alkali are quantitatively transferred within 30 minutes from gels of normal thickness (4–5 mm) and normal agarose concentration (<1%). If carried out carefully, vacuum transfer can result in a two- to threefold enhancement of the hybridization signal obtained from Southern transfers (Medveczky et al. 1987; Olszewska and Jones 1988).

All of the commercially available apparatuses work well as long as care is taken to ensure that the vacuum is applied evenly over the entire surface of the gel. Special care should be taken with the wells of horizontal agarose gels, which tend to break during preparation of the gel for transfer. If this occurs, the wells should be trimmed from the gel before transfer. (The wells need not be trimmed from the gel as long as they are unbroken.) It is also important not to apply too much vacuum during transfer. When the vacuum exceeds 60 cm of water, the gels become compressed and the efficiency of transfer is reduced.

MEMBRANES USED FOR SOUTHERN AND NORTHERN HYBRIDIZATION

For almost 20 years, the only available support for immobilization of DNA was nitrocellulose, which was first used in powder form (Hall and Spiegelman 1961) and later as sheets (Nygaard and Hall 1960; Gillespie and Spiegelman 1965; Southern 1975). Northern hybridization was initially carried out exclusively with RNA immobilized on activated cellulose papers (Alwine et al. 1977; Seed 1982a,b). However, it was soon realized that RNA denatured by glyoxal, formaldehyde, or methylmercuric hydroxide binds tightly to nitrocellulose. For several years, nitrocellulose therefore became the support of choice for both northern and Southern hybridization. Despite its evident success, nitrocellulose is not an ideal matrix for solid-phase hybridization.

- *Its capacity to bind nucleic acids is low* (~50–100 $\mu g/cm^2$) and varies according to the size of the DNA and RNA. In particular, nucleic acids <400 bases in length are retained inefficiently by nitrocellulose.

- *DNA and RNA are attached to nitrocellulose by hydrophobic interactions,* rather than covalent interactions, and therefore leach slowly from the matrix during hybridization and washing at high temperatures (Haas et al. 1972).

- *Nitrocellulose membranes become brittle during baking under vacuum at 80ºC,* which is usually an integral part of the process to immobilize nucleic acids. The friable membranes cannot subsequently survive more than one or two cycles of hybridization and washing at high temperatures. This problem can be alleviated but not completely solved by using supported membranes made from mixed ester nitrocellulose, which have a higher tensile strength.

- *Care is required in storing nitrocellulose membranes* if they are to be used successfully for nucleic acid hybridization and western blotting. When the humidity is high, the membrane will adsorb moisture from the air and expand, resulting in curling and wrinkling. When the humidity is low, nitrocellulose membranes will dry and become charged with static electricity. In this state, the membrane is prone to cracking and splitting and becomes very difficult to wet.

In most areas throughout the world, it is necessary to alter the conditions under which nitrocellulose is stored to suit seasonal changes in weather conditions. During the hot humid summers of New York, for example, nitrocellulose should be stored in a closed container over a dehydrating agent. In winter, the dehydrating agent is replaced by damp pads of paper. The aim is to have wrinkle-free membranes that wet evenly and quickly (30 seconds or less) and take on a bluish tinge when saturated with water.

The problems with nitrocellose were solved by the introduction of various types of nylon membranes that bind nucleic acids irreversibly, are far more durable than nitrocellulose membranes (Reed and Mann 1985), and can be repaired if damaged (Pitas 1989). Immobilized nucleic acids can be hybridized sequentially to several different probes without damaging the membrane. Furthermore, because nucleic acids can be immobilized on nylon in buffers of low ionic strength, transfer of nucleic acids from gels to nylon can be carried out electrophoretically. This method can be useful when capillary or vacuum transfer of DNA is inefficient, for example, when fragments of DNA are transferred from polyacrylamide gels.

Two types of nylon membranes are available commercially: unmodified (or neutral) nylon and charge-modified nylon, which carries amine groups and is therefore also known as positively charged or (+) nylon. Both types of nylon can bind single- and double-stranded nucleic acids, and retention is quantitative in solvents as diverse as water, 0.25 N HCl, and 0.4 N NaOH. Charge-modified nylon has a greater capacity to bind nucleic acids (please see Table 6-2), but it has a tendency to give increased levels of background, which results, at least in part, from nonspecific binding of negatively charged phosphate groups in DNA and RNA to the positively charged groups on the surface of the polymer. However, this problem can usually be controlled by using increased quantities of blocking agents in the prehybridization and hybridization steps.

Many different types of nylon membranes are available that vary in the extent and type of charge, the method used to apply it, and the density of the nylon mesh. Each manufacturer provides specific instructions for the transfer of nucleic acids to their particular product. These instructions should be followed exactly since they presumably have been shown to yield the best results.

TABLE 6-2 Properties of Membranes Used for Southern Blotting and Hybridization

PROPERTY	TYPE OF MEMBRANE		
	NITROCELLULOSE	NEUTRAL NYLON	CHARGED NYLON
Capacity (μg nucleic acid/cm^2)	80–120	~100	400–500
Size of nucleic acid required for maximal binding	>400 bp	>50 bp	>50 bp
Transfer buffer	high ionic strength at neutral pH	low ionic strength over a wide range of pH	
Immobilization	baking at 80ºC under vacuum for 2 hours	baking at 70ºC for 1 hour; no vacuum required *or* mild alkali *or* UV irradiation at 254 nm; damp membranes are generally exposed to 1.6 kJ/m^2; dried membranes require 160 kJ/m^2	
Commercial products		Hybond-N Gene-Screen	Hybond-N+ Zeta-Probe Nytran+ Gene-Screen Plus

Polyvinylidene difluoride (PVDF) membranes are not routinely used for northern or Southern transfers. However, PVDF membranes, by virtue of their higher mechanical strength and greater capacity to bind proteins, are preferred to nitrocellulose for western blotting. Nylon membranes should not be used for western blotting because the level of nonspecific absorption of immunological probes is unacceptably high.

Protocol 8

Southern Blotting: Capillary Transfer of DNA to Membranes

T HE PREPARATION OF GENOMIC DNA IS FIRST DIGESTED with one or more restriction enzymes and the resulting fragments are separated according to size by electrophoresis through a standard agarose gel. The DNA is then denatured in situ and transferred from the gel to a solid support (usually a nylon or nitrocellulose membrane). The relative positions of the DNA fragments are preserved during their transfer to the membrane. The DNA is then fixed to the membrane and prepared for hybridization as described in Protocol 10. An alternative method of simultaneous transfer is presented in Protocol 9. The procedure for upward transfer of DNA in Southern blotting is performed essentially as described for upward transfer of RNA in Chapter 7, Protocol 7.

SETTING UP RESTRICTION DIGESTIONS OF DNA FOR SOUTHERN ANALYSIS

The following are the cardinal points to remember when setting up restriction digests of genomic DNA for standard Southern analysis.

- *The amount of DNA digested must be sufficient to generate a signal.* For Southern analysis of mammalian genomic DNA, ~10 µg of DNA must be loaded into each slot of the gel when probes of standard length (>500 bp) and high specific activity (>10^9 cpm/µg) are used to detect single-copy sequences. Proportionately lower amounts of DNA may be used when the preparation of DNA contains higher molar concentrations of the sequences of interest.

- *The restriction enzymes used are likely to be informative.* For example, there is little point in digesting DNA whose median size is 50 kb with a restriction enzyme that cleaves on average every 100 kb. As a general rule, the median size of the DNA before digestion should be at least three times greater than the median size of fragments generated during the digestion. The frequency of cleavage by different restriction enzymes of various species of genomic DNAs is discussed in Chapter 4, Protocol 1 (please see Table 4-3).

- *The amount of DNA loaded into each lane of the gel is known with accuracy.* This does not necessarily mean that restriction digests must contain equal amounts of DNA. Measuring small volumes of extremely viscous preparations of high-molecular-weight genomic DNA is very difficult, and inaccuracies lead to overloading or underloading of lanes in the gel. If it is essential to analyze the same amount of DNA from multiple samples (e.g., when comparing genomic DNAs isolated from normal individuals and those affected with a genetic disease, or when attempting to determine the copy number of a gene), then it is best to digest a sufficiency of each of the DNAs without worrying too much about whether each digest contains the same amount of DNA. The exact concentration of DNA in each sample can be measured by fluorometry after digestion is complete before loading the agarose gel. A method for fluorometric determination of DNA concentration is given at the end of Protocol 1.

In many cases, the volumes of restriction digests are defined by the concentration of DNA in the preparations under analysis. The concentrations of DNA in preparations of high-molecular-weight mammalian genomic DNA are often so low that it is necessary to carry out restriction digests in large volumes. There is no reason why restriction digests of a comparative series of genomic DNAs need be carried out in equal volumes. As long as all digests are complete, the volume of each restriction digest is immaterial. After digestion, the fragments of DNA may be concentrated by precipitation with ethanol, measured by fluorometry, and then applied to the gel in a small volume of gel-loading buffer (see Step 2).

- ● ***The digests are complete.*** The chief problem encountered during digestion of high-molecular-weight DNA is unevenness of digestion caused by variations in the local concentrations of DNA. Clumps of DNA are relatively inaccessible to restriction enzymes and can be digested only from the exterior of the aggregate. To ensure homogeneous dispersion of the DNA:

  1. If possible, set up the reactions in a total volume of at least 45 µl. Before adding the restriction enzyme, store reactions at 4°C for several hours after dilution of the DNA and addition of 10x restriction enzyme buffer.

  2. Gently stir the DNA solution from time to time using a sealed glass capillary.

  3. After addition of the restriction enzyme (5 units/µg of DNA), gently stir the solution for 2–3 minutes at 4°C before warming the reaction to the appropriate temperature.

  4. After digestion for 15–30 minutes, add a second aliquot of restriction enzyme (5 units/µg of DNA) and stir the reaction as described above.

  5. Incubate the reaction at the appropriate temperature for 8–12 hours.

It is important to include controls to show whether digestion with the restriction enzyme(s) is complete and whether transfer and hybridization of the DNA have worked efficiently. This goal can be accomplished by setting up a series of digests containing high-molecular-weight genomic DNA and a very small amount of a plasmid carrying a sequence complementary to the probe (e.g., 10 µg of mammalian DNA and 10^{-5}, 10^{-6}, and 10^{-7} µg of plasmid). During digestion, the plasmid will be cleaved into a series of bands that may be invisible when the gel is examined by staining with ethidium bromide or SYBR Gold. However, fragments of the correct size should be detected by subsequent hybridization to the probe. To reduce the chance of accidental contamination and to minimize the possibility that the hybridization signal from the controls will obscure that from the test samples, the controls should be loaded into wells that lie toward one side of the gel, well away from the test samples of mammalian DNA.

MATERIALS

CAUTION: Please see Appendix 12 for appropriate handling of materials marked with <!>.

Buffers and Solutions

Please see Appendix 1 for components of stock solutions, buffers, and reagents. Dilute stock solutions to the appropriate concentrations.

Alkaline transfer buffer (for alkaline transfer to nylon membranes)
0.4 N NaOH <!>
1 M NaCl

Denaturation solution (for neutral transfer)
  1.5 M NaCl
  0.5 M NaOH <!>
HCl (0.2 N), for depurination of DNA <!>
  Optional, please see note to Step 6.
Neutralization buffer I (for transfer to uncharged membranes)
  1 M Tris (pH 7.4)
  1.5 M NaCl
Neutralization buffer II (for alkaline transfer to nylon membranes)
  0.5 M Tris-Cl (pH 7.2)
  1 M NaCl
Neutral transfer buffer, either 10x SSC or 10x SSPE
6x SSC
6x Sucrose gel-loading buffer
SYBR Gold <!> *or Ethidium bromide* <!>
TE (pH 8.0)

Enzymes and Buffers

Appropriate restriction enzymes

Gels

Agarose gel (0.7%) cast in 0.5x TBE or 1x TAE in the absence of ethidium bromide
  For analysis of mammalian genomic DNA, most investigators use large gels (20 x 20 x 0.5 cm) containing 20 standard slots large enough to hold ~50–60 μl. This capacity allows the entire digestion reaction to be loaded without spillage. The gel may be cast and run in the usual way in buffers containing 0.5 μg/ml ethidium bromide. However, a more accurate measurement of the size of DNA fragments may be obtained by staining the gel after electrophoresis with ethidium bromide or SYBR Gold. The inclusion of SYBR Gold in the gel matrix may cause distortion of the DNA bands and may retard the migration of the DNA fragments to varying degrees. Please see Chapter 5, Protocol 2 and Appendix 9.

Nucleic Acids and Oligonucleotides

DNA size markers
  Sets of size markers are available from many commercial manufacturers, or they can be prepared by digesting cloning vectors with appropriate restriction enzymes. We recommend using a 1-kb ladder (Life Technologies) in the lane closest to one side of the gel and a *Hin*dIII digest of bacteriophage λ DNA in the lane on the opposite side of the gel.

  Markers radiolabeled with ^{35}S or ^{33}P are not recommended because they usually require exposure times different from those optimal for the target bands.
Genomic DNA

Special Equipment

Cross-linking device (e.g., Stratalinker, Stratagene; GS Gene Linker, Bio-Rad), or Microwave oven, or Vacuum oven
Glass baking dishes
Glass rod
Large-bore yellow tips
  Large-bore yellow tips can be purchased or generated rapidly with a scissors or a dog nail clipper (Fisher 05-401A). Alternatively, the pointed ends of the tips can be removed with a sharp razor blade. The cut-off tips should be sterilized before use, either by autoclaving or by immersion in 70% alcohol for 2 minutes followed by -drying in air.
Neoprene stoppers

Nylon or nitrocellulose membrane

Please see discussion on Membranes Used for Southern and Northern Hybridization in the introduction to Protocols 8–10.

Plexiglas sheets or Glass plates

Rotary platform shaker

Thick blotting paper (e.g., Whatman 3MM, Schleicher & Schuell GB004, or Sigma QuickDraw)

Transparent ruler with fluorescent markings

The ruler is used to measure the distance traveled by the marker DNAs. A ruler placed alongside the gel during photography allows the distances traveled from the loading wells by DNA markers of known size to be measured on the photographic image and plotted graphically. The sizes of radiolabeled bands detected by hybridization can then be estimated by interpolation.

Weight (400 g)

METHOD

Digestion and Electrophoresis of the DNA

1. Digest an appropriate amount of genomic DNA with one or more restriction enzymes (please see the discussion on Setting up Restriction Digestions of DNA for Southern Analysis in the introduction to this protocol).

    Use large-bore yellow pipette tips to handle high-molecular-weight DNA.

2. If necessary, concentrate the DNA fragments at the end of the digestion by ethanol precipitation. Dissolve the DNAs in ~25 μl of TE (pH 8.0).

    Make sure that the ethanol is removed from the DNA solution before it is loaded on the gel. If significant quantities of ethanol remain, the DNA "crawls" out of the slot of the gel. Heating the solution of dissolved DNA to 70°C in an open tube for 10 minutes is usually sufficient to drive off most of the ethanol. This treatment also disrupts base pairing between cohesive termini of restriction fragments.

3. Measure the concentrations of the digested DNAs by fluorometry or by the ethidium bromide or SYBR Gold spot test (please see Appendix 8). Transfer the appropriate amount of each digest to a fresh microfuge tube. Add 0.15 volume of 6x sucrose gel-loading buffer and separate the fragments of DNA by electrophoresis through an agarose gel (for most genomic DNAs, a 0.7% gel cast in 0.5x TBE or 1x TAE may be used; please see Chapter 5, Protocol 1). Maintain a low voltage through the gel (about <1 V/cm) to allow the DNA to migrate slowly.

    If the digested DNAs have been stored at 4°C, they should be heated to 56°C for 2–3 minutes before they are applied to the gel. This heating disrupts any base pairing that may have occurred between protruding cohesive termini.

    Occasionally, problems arise during loading of the gel because the DNA solution will not sink to the bottom of the well. This floating occurs when very high-molecular-weight DNA is present at the end of the digest, for example, when the digest is incomplete or when mammalian DNA has been digested with enzymes such as *Not*I that generate very large fragments of DNA. To minimize the problem, make sure that the DNA is homogeneously dispersed, and load the samples very slowly into the wells of the gel. After loading, allow the gel to stand for a few minutes so that the DNA can diffuse evenly throughout the wells.

4. After electrophoresis is complete, stain the gel with ethidium bromide or SYBR Gold and photograph the gel as described in Chapter 5, Protocol 2. Place a transparent ruler alongside

the gel so that the distance that any band of DNA has migrated can be read directly from the photographic image.

> If desired, the gel may be stored at this stage before the DNA is denatured and transferred to the membrane. Wrap the gel in Saran Wrap and store it on a flat surface at 4ºC. Because the bands of DNA diffuse during storage, the gel should not be put aside for more than 1 day before being processed.

5. Denature the DNA and transfer it from the agarose gel to a nitrocellulose or a neutral or charged-nylon membrane using one of the methods described below.

Preparation of the Gel for Transfer

6. After fractionating the DNA by gel electrophoresis, transfer the gel to a glass baking dish. Use a razor blade to trim away unused areas of the gel, including the section of gel above the wells. Be sure to leave enough of the wells attached to the gel so that the positions of the lanes can be marked on the membrane after transfer of DNA. Cut off a small triangular piece from the bottom left-hand corner of the gel to simplify orientation during the succeeding operations.

> It is best to cut off the lanes containing the molecular-weight markers because probes may contain sequences complementary to some of the marker bands. The resulting pattern of bands appearing on the autradiogram is sometimes informative, but it is more often puzzling.
>
> If the fragments of interest are larger than ~15 kb, then transfer may be improved by nicking the DNA by brief depurination before denaturation (Wahl et al. 1979). Depurination lays the phosphate-sugar backbone of DNA open to subsequent cleavage by hydroxyl ions. After Step 6, soak the gel in several volumes of 0.2 N HCl until the bromophenol blue turns yellow and the xylene cyanol turns yellow/green. Immediately place the 0.2 N HCl in a hazardous-waste container and then rinse the gel several times with deionized H_2O.
>
> Because depurination depends on diffusion of H^+ ions into the gel, the DNA molecules at different levels within the agarose are depurinated at different rates and to different extents. The reaction is therefore difficult both to control and to reproduce and, if carried out too enthusiastically, can result in excessive fragmentation of DNA and a reduction in the strength of the hybridization signal. Therefore, depurination is best avoided when the size of the target fragments is <20 kb. However, for Southern analysis of higher-molecular-weight DNA separated by conventional or pulsed-field electrophoresis, depurination/nicking is advisable, if not essential.

7. Denature the DNA by soaking in a denaturing (alkaline) solution as follows:

For Transfer to Uncharged Membranes

a. Soak the gel for 45 minutes at room temperature in 10 gel volumes of denaturation solution with constant *gentle* agitation (e.g., on a rotary platform).

b. Rinse the gel briefly in deionized H_2O, and then neutralize it by soaking for 30 minutes at room temperature in 10 gel volumes of Neutralization buffer I with constant gentle agitation. Change the neutralization buffer and continue soaking the gel for a further 15 minutes.

For Transfer to Charged Nylon Membranes

a. Soak the gel for 15 minutes at room temperature in several volumes of alkaline transfer buffer with constant *gentle* agitation (e.g., on a rotary platform).

b. Change the solution and continue to soak the gel for a further 20 minutes with gentle agitation.

> If the gel floats to the surface of the liquid, weigh it down with several Pasteur pipettes.

Preparation of the Membrane for Transfer

8. Use a fresh scalpel or a paper cutter to cut a piece of nylon or nitrocellulose membrane ~1 mm larger than the gel in each dimension. Also cut two sheets of thick blotting paper to the same size as the membrane.

   ▲ IMPORTANT Use appropriate gloves and blunt-ended forceps (e.g., Millipore forceps) to handle the membrane. A membrane that has been touched by oily hands will not wet!

9. Float the membrane on the surface of a dish of deionized H_2O until it wets completely from beneath, and then immerse the membrane in the appropriate transfer buffer for at least 5 minutes. Use a clean scalpel blade to cut a corner from the membrane to match the corner cut from the gel.

   The rate at which different batches of nitrocellulose membranes wet varies enormously. If the membrane is not saturated after floating for several minutes on H_2O, it should be replaced with a new membrane, since the transfer of DNA to an unevenly wetted membrane is unreliable. The original membrane should be either discarded or autoclaved for 5 minutes between pieces of 3MM paper that are saturated with 2x SSC. This treatment usually results in complete wetting. The autoclaved membrane, sandwiched between the autoclaved 3MM papers saturated with 2x SSC, may be stored at 4°C in a sealed plastic bag until needed.

   Uneven wetting is not usually a problem with neutral or charged-nylon membranes.

Assembly of the Transfer Apparatus and Transfer of the DNA

Neutral transfer buffer (10x SSC or 10x SSPE) is used to transfer DNA to uncharged membranes. Alkaline transfer buffer (0.4 N NaOH with 1 M NaCl) is used to transfer DNA to charged nylon membranes.

10. While the DNA is denaturing, place a piece of thick blotting paper on a sheet of Plexiglas or a glass plate to form a support that is longer and wider than the gel. The ends of the blotting paper should drape over the edges of the plate. Place the support inside a large baking dish. The support can be placed on top of four neoprene stoppers to elevate it from the bottom of the dish. (For an example of a capillary blot, please see Figure 6-1.)

11. Fill the dish with the appropriate transfer buffer until the level of the liquid reaches almost to the top of the support. When the blotting paper on the top of the support is thoroughly wet, smooth out all air bubbles with a glass rod or pipette.

12. Remove the gel from the solution in Step 7 and invert it so that its underside is now uppermost. Place the inverted gel on the support so that it is centered on the wet blotting paper.

    Make sure that there are no air bubbles between the blotting paper and the gel.

13. Surround, but do not cover, the gel with Saran Wrap or Parafilm.

    This protective mask serves as a barrier to prevent liquid from flowing directly from the reservoir to paper towels placed on top of the gel. If these towels are not precisely stacked, they tend to droop over the edge of the gel and may touch the wick. This type of short-circuiting is a major cause of inefficient transfer of DNA from the gel to the membrane.

14. Wet the top of the gel with the appropriate transfer buffer. Place the wet membrane on top of the gel so that the cut corners are aligned. To avoid bubbles, touch one corner of the membrane to the gel and gently lower the membrane onto the gel. One edge of the membrane should extend just over the edge of the line of slots at the top of the gel.

    ▲ IMPORTANT Do not move the membrane once it has been applied to the surface of the gel. Make sure that there are no air bubbles between the membrane and the gel.

15. Wet the two pieces of thick blotting paper in the appropriate transfer buffer and place them on top of the wet membrane. Roll a pipette across the surface of the membrane to smooth away any air bubbles.

16. Cut or fold a stack of paper towels (5–8 cm high) just smaller than the blotting papers. Place the towels on the blotting papers. Put a glass plate on top of the stack and weigh it down with a 400-g weight.

    > The objective is to set up a flow of liquid from the reservoir through the gel and the membrane so that fragments of denatured DNA are eluted from the gel and are deposited on the membrane. The weight on the top of the gel should be heavy enough to ensure good contact between the various components of the blot, but light enough to prevent compressing the gel. Compression will squeeze liquid from the interstices of the gel, leaving a dehydrated matrix that greatly retards the movement of DNA and drastically reduces the efficiency of transfer from the gel to the membrane.

    > Intact, rather than cut or folded, paper towels can also be used in this setup, but only if the protective mask of Saran Wrap or Parafilm efficiently prevents seepage of buffer.

    > To prevent evaporation, some investigators wrap the entire transfer setup in Saran Wrap. Whether this is necessary seems somewhat doubtful.

17. Allow the transfer of DNA to proceed for 8–24 hours. Replace the paper towels as they become wet. Try to prevent the entire stack of towels from becoming wet with buffer.

18. Remove the paper towels and the blotting papers above the gel. Turn the gel and the attached membrane over and lay them, gel side up, on a dry sheet of blotting paper. Mark the positions of the gel slots on the membrane with a very soft lead pencil or a ballpoint pen.

19. Peel the gel from the membrane and discard the gel.

    > Instead of discarding the gel, it can be stained (45 minutes) in a 0.5 μg/ml solution of ethidium bromide in H_2O and visualized on a UV transilluminator to gauge the success of the DNA transfer. Note that the intensity of fluorescence will be quite low because any DNA remaining in the gel will have been denatured.

Fixation of the DNA to the Membrane

The sequence of steps from immobilization of DNA to the membrane to subsequent hybridization depends on the type of membrane, the method of transfer, and the method of fixation (please see Table 6-3). Because alkaline transfer results in covalent attachment of DNA to positively charged nylon membranes, there is no need to fix the DNA to the membrane before hybridization. DNA transferred to uncharged nylon membranes in neutral transfer buffer should be fixed to the membrane by baking under vacuum or heating in a microwave oven, or crosslinked to the membrane by UV irradiation.

TABLE 6-3 Fixing DNA to the Membrane for Hybridization

TYPE OF MEMBRANE	TYPE OF TRANSFER	METHOD OF FIXATION	SEQUENCE OF STEPS
Positively charged nylon	alkaline transfer	alkaline transfer	1. Soak membrane in Neutralization buffer II. 2. Proceed to prehybridization.
Uncharged nylon or positively charged nylon	neutral transfer	UV irradiation (please see Step 21 for details)	1. Soak membrane in 6x SSC. 2. Fix the DNA by UV irradiation. 3. Proceed to prehybridization.
Uncharged nylon or positively charged nylon	neutral transfer	baking in vacuum oven or microwave oven (please see Step 21 for details)	1. Soak membrane in 6x SSC. 2. Bake the membrane. 3. Proceed to prehybridization.

20. Soak the membrane in *one* of the following solutions as appropriate:

    For neutral transfer: 6x SSC for 5 minutes at room temperature.

    For alkaline transfer: Neutralization buffer II (0.5 M Tris-Cl [pH 7.2] with 1 M NaCl) for 15 minutes at room temperature.

    > This rinse removes any pieces of agarose sticking to the membrane and, in the latter case, also neutralizes the membrane.

21. Immobilize the DNA that has been transferred to uncharged membranes.

    > Because alkaline transfer results in covalent attachment of DNA to positively charged nylon membranes, there is no need for additional steps to fix the DNA to the membrane.

TO FIX BY BAKING IN A VACUUM OVEN

a. Remove the membrane from the 6x SSC and allow excess fluid to drain away. Place the membrane flat on a paper towel to dry for at least 30 minutes at room temperature.

b. Sandwich the membrane between two sheets of dry blotting paper. Bake for 30 minutes to 2 hours at 80ºC in a vacuum oven.

    > Overbaking can cause nitrocellulose membranes to become brittle. If the gel was not completely neutralized before the DNA was transferred, nitrocellulose membranes will turn yellow or brown during baking and chip very easily. The background of nonspecific hybridization also increases dramatically.

TO FIX BY BAKING IN A MICROWAVE OVEN

a. Place the damp membrane on a dry piece of blotting paper.

b. Heat the membrane for 2–3 minutes at full power in a microwave oven (750–900 W).

    > Proceed directly to hybridization (Protocol 10) or dry the membrane and store it between sheets of blotting paper until it is needed.

    > Baking nitrocellulose membranes in a microwave oven attenuates the signal in Southern hybridizations and is not recommended (Angeletti et al. 1995).

TO CROSS-LINK BY UV IRRADIATION

a. Place the damp membrane on a dry piece of blotting paper.

b. Irradiate at 254 nm to cross-link the DNA to the membrane (Khandjian 1987).

    > Immobilization of nucleic acids by UV irradiation can greatly enhance the hybridization signal obtained with some brands of *positively charged* nylon membranes (Khandjian 1987). However, for maximum effect, it is important to make sure that the membrane is not overirradiated. The aim is to form cross-links between a small fraction of the thymine residues in the DNA and positively charged amine groups on the surface of the membrane (Church and Gilbert 1984). Overirradiation results in the covalent attachment of a high proportion of the thymines, with consequent decrease in hybridization signal. Make sure that the side of the membrane carrying the DNA faces the UV light source. Most manufacturers advise that damp membranes be exposed to a total of 1.5 J/cm^2 and that dry membranes be exposed to 0.15 J/cm^2. However, we recommend carrying out a series of preliminary experiments to determine empirically the amount of irradiation required to produce the maximum hybridization signal.

22. Proceed directly to hybridization of immobilized DNA to a probe (Protocol 10).

    > Any membranes not used immediately in hybridization reactions should be thoroughly dried, wrapped loosely in aluminum foil or blotting paper, and stored at room temperature, preferably under vacuum.

Protocol 9

Southern Blotting: Simultaneous Transfer of DNA from a Single Agarose Gel to Two Membranes

DNA CAN BE SIMULTANEOUSLY TRANSFERRED FROM OPPOSITE SIDES of a single agarose gel to two membranes (please see Figure 6-3). This procedure is useful when the need arises to analyze the same set of restriction fragments with two different probes. Transfer of DNA fragments is rapid, but the efficiency is low because the agarose gel quickly becomes dehydrated as fluid is withdrawn from both sides. The method therefore works best when the target sequences are present in high concentration, for example, when analyzing cloned DNAs (plasmids, bacteriophages, cosmids, PACs, or BACs) or less complex genomes (e.g., those of *S. cerevisiae* or *Drosophila*). Too little mammalian genomic DNA is transferred to allow signals from single-copy sequences to be detected in a reproducible or timely fashion.

MATERIALS

CAUTION: Please see Appendix 12 for appropriate handling of materials marked with <!>.

Buffers and Solutions

Please see Appendix 1 for components of stock solutions, buffers, and reagents. Dilute stock solutions to the appropriate concentrations.

Denaturation solution
　1.5 M NaCl
　0.5 N NaOH <!>
HCl (0.2 N), for depurination of DNA <!>
　Optional, please see note to Step 6, Protocol 8.
Neutralization buffer
　1 M Tris (pH 7.4)
　1.5 M NaCl
Neutral transfer buffer (10x SSC)
6x SSC
6x Sucrose gel-loading buffer
SYBR Gold <!> *or Ethidium bromide* <!>

Enzymes and Buffers

Appropriate restriction enzymes

Gels

Agarose gel (0.7%) cast in 0.5x TBE or 1x TAE in the absence of ethidium bromide

The gel may be cast and run in the usual way in buffers containing 0.5 μg/ml ethidium bromide. However, a more accurate measurement of the size of DNA fragments may be obtained by staining the gel after electrophoresis with ethidium bromide or SYBR Gold. The inclusion of SYBR Gold in the gel matrix may cause distortion of the DNA bands and may retard the migration of the DNA fragments to varying degrees. Please see Appendix 8.

Nucleic Acids and Oligonucleotides

DNA size markers

Sets of size markers are available from many commercial manufacturers, or they can be prepared by digesting cloning vectors with appropriate restriction enzymes. We recommend using a 1-kb ladder (GIBCO-BRL) in the lane closest to one side of the gel and a *Hind*III digest of bacteriophage λ DNA in the lane on the opposite side of the gel.

Markers radiolabeled with ^{35}S or ^{33}P are not recommended because they usually require exposure times different from those optimal for the target bands.

Target DNA

Special Equipment

Cross-linking device (e.g., Stratalinker, Stratagene; GS Gene Linker, Bio-Rad), or Microwave oven, or Vacuum oven

Glass baking dishes

Glass plate

Nylon or nitrocellulose membranes

Please see discussion on Membranes Used in Southern and Northern Hybridization in the Introduction to Protocols 8–10.

Rotary platform shaker

Thick blotting paper (e.g., Whatman 3MM, Schleicher & Schuell GB004, or Sigma QuickDraw)

Transparent ruler with fluorescent markings

The ruler is used to measure the distance traveled by the marker DNAs. A ruler placed alongside the gel during photography allows the distances traveled from the loading wells by DNA markers of known size to be measured on the photographic image and plotted graphically. The sizes of radiolabeled bands detected by hybridization can then be estimated by interpolation.

Weight (400 g)

METHOD

1. Digest the DNA and fractionate it by gel electrophoresis according to Steps 1–3 of Protocol 8.

2. After fractionating the DNA by gel electrophoresis, stain the gel with ethidium bromide or SYBR Gold and photograph as described in Chapter 5, Protocol 2. Place a transparent ruler alongside the gel so that the distance that any band has migrated can be read directly from the photographic image. Prepare the gel for transfer under neutral conditions (Protocol 8, Steps 6–7).

3. Use a fresh scalpel or a paper cutter to cut two pieces of nylon or nitrocellulose membrane ~1–2 mm larger than the gel in each dimension. Cut a corner from the membranes to match the corner cut from the gel. Also cut four sheets of thick blotting paper to the same size as the membranes.

   ▲ IMPORTANT Use appropriate gloves and blunt-ended forceps (e.g., Millipore forceps) to handle the membranes. A membrane that has been touched by oily hands will not wet!

   To retain small fragments of DNA (<300 nucleotides), use nitrocellulose membranes with a small pore size (0.2 μm) or nylon membranes.

4. Float the membranes on the surface of a dish of deionized H_2O until they wet completely from beneath, and then immerse the membranes in 10x SSC for at least 5 minutes.

    The rate at which different batches of nitrocellulose membranes wet varies enormously. If the membrane is not saturated after floating for several minutes on H_2O, it should be replaced with a new membrane, since the transfer of DNA to an unevenly wetted membrane is unreliable. The original membrane should be either discarded or autoclaved for 5 minutes between pieces of 3MM paper saturated with 2x SSC. This treatment usually results in complete wetting of the membrane. The autoclaved membrane, sandwiched between the autoclaved 3MM papers saturated with 2x SSC, may be stored at 4ºC in a sealed plastic bag until needed.

5. Roll a moistened pipette over each layer as it is assembled to ensure that no air bubbles are trapped, especially between the membranes and the gel sides. Place one of the membranes on two pieces of dampened blotting paper. Lay the gel on top of the membrane, aligning the cut corner of the gel with the cut corner of the membrane. Without delay, place the second membrane on the other side of the gel, followed by two sheets of dampened blotting paper (please see Figure 6-3).

6. Transfer the entire sandwich of blotting papers, membranes, and gel onto a 2–4-inch stack of paper towels. Cover the sandwich with a second stack of paper towels. Put a glass plate on top of the entire stack and weigh it down with a 400-g weight.

7. After 2–4 hours, remove the paper towels and blotting papers. Transfer the gel and membrane sandwich to a dry sheet of blotting paper, and mark the approximate positions of the gel slots with a very soft lead pencil or a ballpoint pen.

8. Immobilize the DNA onto the membranes by completing Steps 19–21 of Protocol 8.

9. Proceed directly to hybridization of immobilized DNA to a probe (Protocol 10).

    Any membranes not used immediately in hybridization reactions should be thoroughly dry, wrapped loosely in aluminum foil or blotting paper, and stored at room temperature, preferably under vacuum.

Protocol 10

Southern Hybridization of Radiolabeled Probes to Nucleic Acids Immobilized on Membranes

THE STRENGTH OF THE HYBRIDIZATION SIGNAL OBTAINED IN SOUTHERN HYBRIDIZATION depends on a number of factors, including the proportion of immobilized DNA that is complementary to the probe, the size of the probe and its specific activity, and the amount of genomic DNA transferred to the membrane. Under the best conditions, the method is sufficiently sensitive to detect <0.1 pg of DNA complementary to a probe that has been radiolabeled with ^{32}P to high specific activity (>10^9 cpm/µg; please see Chapter 9). A sequence of 1000 bp that occurs only once in the mammalian genome (i.e., 1 part in 3 million) can be detected in an overnight exposure to conventional X-ray film (or 15–60 minutes on a phosphorimager) if 10 µg of genomic DNA is transferred to the membrane and hybridized to a probe several hundred nucleotides in length. Because the strength of the signal is proportional to the specific activity of the probe and inversely proportional to its length, Southern hybridization reaches the limits of its sensitivity when very short probes are used. To obtain a signal from single-copy genomic sequences with, for example, oligonucleotide probes, it is necessary to radiolabel to the highest specific activity possible (please see Chapter 10, Protocol 2 or 7), to increase the amount of target DNA on the membrane, and to expose the autoradiograph for several days, or the phosphorimager plate for many hours. For the detection of related but not identical sequences, please see the panel on **ADDITIONAL PROTOCOL: HYBRIDIZATION AT LOW STRINGENCY** at the end of this protocol.

Several methods are now available for nonradioactive labeling of DNA and RNA (for reviews, please see Guesdon 1992; Viale and Dell'Orto 1992; Mansfield et al. 1995; see also Chapter 9). Although these methods offer advantages such as long storage times and reduced exposure to radiation, they cannot yet be recommended for detection of single-copy sequences by Southern hybridization. The background is often high and, in many systems that utilize nonradioactive probes, the signal is not proportional to the amount of nucleic acid bound to the membrane. Worst of all, the detection of single-copy sequences in Southern analysis of mammalian DNAs lies at or just beyond the limit of sensitivity of most nonradioactive probes. Although nonradioactive labeling has improved dramatically during the past few years, it still has some way to go before it can be recommended for general use.

HYBRIDIZATION CHAMBERS

The first Southern hybridizations in the United States were carried out in a homemade hybridization device consisting of a rotating wheel housed within a 65°C oven that was kept under the back stairs in a lab at Cold Spring Harbor Laboratory. The precious nitrocellulose sheets were rolled up and inserted, together with the hybridization solution, into glass tubes that were sealed with a silicon rubber bung held in place with electrical tape. The tubes were then clamped to the wheel and left to rotate for 18 hours. The ancient, asbestos-lined oven door was always opened with trepidation since experience had shown that at least one of the tubes would break and that the bungs would pop from others. Of course, the oven and the wheel became encrusted with dried hybridization fluid and contaminated beyond redemption. Not surprisingly, successful experiments were few in number.

It was a great relief when Sears' Seal-A-Meal bags appeared on the scene some months later. Almost immediately, leaks were a thing of the past and the awful levels of background hybridization endemic to tightly rolled membranes were reduced to manageable proportions. For the next 10 years, when the results of Southern hybridizations were published at an average rate of >10,000 per year, hybridization in bags was the method of choice. Given the early frightening experience with hybridization ovens, it is understandable that their reappearance during the 1980s was greeted with some incredulity and suspicion. However, the machines available today from commercial manufacturers are a far cry from the gimcrack arrangements of the early investigators. The tubes are virtually leakproof and can be fitted with mesh to hold the rolls of the membrane apart and reduce background. Commercial rotating wheels have one additional advantage over Seal-A-Meal bags: They are less prone to leak when using hybridization buffers with high concentrations of SDS. Because plastic bags containing such buffers are very difficult to seal, the risk of leaks and contamination with radioactivity is increased.

MATERIALS

CAUTION: Please see Appendix 12 for appropriate handling of materials marked with <!>.

Buffers and Solutions

Please see Appendix 1 for components of stock solutions, buffers, and reagents. Dilute stock solutions to the appropriate concentrations.

Phosphate-SDS washing solution 1
40 mM sodium phosphate buffer (pH 7.2)
1 mM EDTA (pH 8.0)
5% (w/v) SDS
0.5% (w/v) Fraction-V-grade bovine serum albumin

Phosphate-SDS washing solution 2
40 mM sodium phosphate buffer (pH 7.2)
1 mM EDTA (pH 8.0)
1% (w/v) SDS

Prehybridization/hybridization solutions

Prepare the prehybridization solution appropriate for the task at hand. Approximately 0.2 ml of prehybridization solution is required for each square centimeter of membrane. Smaller volumes (~0.1 ml/cm^2) can be used when hybridizing in roller bottles. For advice on which solution to use, please see the introduction to Protocol 32 in Chapter 1.

Prehybridization/hybridization solution may be prepared with or without poly(A) RNA. When ^{32}P-labeled cDNA or RNA is used as a probe, poly(A) RNA may be included in prehybridization or hybridization solutions to prevent the probe from binding to thymidine-rich sequences commonly found in eukaryotic DNA. Poly(A) RNA should be added to aqueous and formamide hybridization buffers at a final concentration of 1 μg/ml.

Solution for hybridization in aqueous buffer
6x SSC (or 6x SSPE)
5x Denhardt's reagent
0.5% (w/v) SDS
1 μg/ml poly(A)
100 μg/ml salmon sperm DNA

6x SSPE contains EDTA, which is a better chelator of divalent metal ions (e.g., Mg^{2+}) than citrate, and in turn will more efficiently inhibit DNase activity that can decrease probe and target DNA concentrations. After thorough mixing, filter the solution through a 0.45-μm disposable cellulose acetate membrane (Schleicher & Schuell Uniflow syringe membrane or equivalent).

Solution for hybridization in formamide buffers

   6x SSC (or 6x SSPE)
   5x Denhardt's reagent
   0.5% (w/v) SDS
   1 μg/ml poly(A)
   100 μg/ml salmon sperm DNA
   50% (v/v) formamide <!>

After thorough mixing, filter the solution through a 0.45-μm disposable cellulose acetate membrane (Schleicher & Schuell Uniflo syringe membrane or equivalent). To decrease background when hybridizing under conditions of reduced stringency (e.g., 20–30% formamide), it is important to use formamide that is as pure as possible. Please see the information panel on **FORMAMIDE AND ITS USES IN MOLECULAR CLONING**.

Solution for hybridization in phosphate-SDS buffer

   0.5 M sodium phosphate (pH 7.2)
   1 mM EDTA (pH 8.0)
   7% (w/v) SDS
   1% (w/v) bovine serum albumin

Use an electrophoresis grade of bovine serum albumin. No blocking agents or hybridization rate enhancers are required with this particular prehybridization/hybridization solution.

Sodium phosphate (1 M, pH 7.2)

0.1x SSC

0.1x SSC with 0.1% (w/v) SDS

2x SSC with 0.1% (w/v) SDS

2x SSC with 0.5% (w/v) SDS

6x SSC or 6x SSPE

Nucleic Acids and Oligonucleotides

DNA immobilized on membrane

Poly(A) RNA (10 mg/ml) in sterile H_2O

Optional, for hybridization buffers. Prepare solution by dissolving poly(A) RNA in sterile H_2O and store in 100-μl aliquots.

Probe DNA or RNA <!>

For Southern analysis of mammalian genomic DNA, where each lane of the gel contains 10 μg of DNA, use 10–20 ng/ml radiolabeled probe (sp. act. $\geq 10^9$ cpm/μg). For Southern analysis of cloned DNA fragments, where each band of the restriction digest contains 10 ng of DNA or more, much less probe is required. When analyzing cloned DNA, hybridization is carried out for 6–8 hours using 1–2 ng/ml radiolabeled probe (sp. act. 10^6 to 10^9 cpm/μg). Labeling should be carried out according to the methods described in Chapter 9 or 10.

Salmon sperm DNA (~10 mg/ml)

Denatured fragmented salmon sperm DNA should be used at a concentration of 100 μg/ml in prehybridization and hybridization solutions involving essentially any type of hybridization experiment. To prepare:

   i.   Dissolve salmon sperm DNA (Sigma type III sodium salt) in H_2O at a concentration of 10 mg/ml. If necessary, stir the solution on a magnetic stirrer for 2–4 hours at room temperature to help the DNA to dissolve.

   ii. Adjust the concentration of NaCl to 0.1 M, and extract the solution once with phenol and once with phenol:chloroform.

   iii. Recover the aqueous phase, and shear the DNA by passing it 12 times rapidly through a 17-gauge hypodermic needle.

   iv. Precipitate the DNA by adding 2 volumes of ice-cold ethanol, recover by centrifugation, and dissolve at a concentration of 10 mg/ml in H_2O.

v. Determine the A_{260} of the solution and calculate the approximate concentration of the DNA.

vi. Boil the solution for 10 minutes and store at –20ºC in small aliquots. Just before use, heat the solution for 5 minutes in a boiling-water bath and chill quickly in ice water.

Special Equipment

Adhesive dots marked with radioactive ink <!> or Phosphorescent adhesive dots
Hybridization container
Incubator or commercial hybridization device preset to the appropriate temperature
Incubator or shaking water bath preset to 65ºC (for hybridization in phosphate-SDS buffer)
Water bath, boiling

METHOD

1. Float the membrane containing the target DNA on the surface of a tray of 6x SSC (or 6x SSPE) until the membrane becomes thoroughly wetted from beneath. Submerge the membrane for 2 minutes.

2. Prehybridize the membrane by one of the following methods.

FOR HYBRIDIZATION IN A HEAT-SEALABLE BAG

a. Slip the wet membrane into a heat-sealable bag (e.g., Sears Seal-A-Meal or equivalent), and add 0.2 ml of prehybridization solution for each square centimeter of membrane. Squeeze as much air as possible from the bag.

b. Seal the open end of the bag with a heat sealer and then make a second seal. Test the strength and integrity of the seal by gently squeezing the bag. Incubate the bag for 1–2 hours submerged in a water bath set to the appropriate temperature (68ºC for aqueous solvents; 42ºC for solvents containing 50% formamide; 65ºC for phosphate-SDS solvents).

FOR HYBRIDIZATION IN A ROLLER BOTTLE

a. Gently roll the wetted membrane into the shape of a cylinder and place it inside a hybridization roller bottle together with the plastic mesh provided by the manufacturer. Add 0.1 ml of prehybridization solution for each square centimeter of membrane. Close the bottle tightly.

b. Place the hybridization tube inside a prewarmed hybridization oven at the appropriate temperature (68ºC for aqueous solvents; 42ºC for solvents containing 50% formamide; 65ºC for phosphate-SDS solvents).

FOR HYBRIDIZATION IN A PLASTIC CONTAINER

a. Place the wetted membrane in a plastic (e.g., Tupperware) container, and add 0.2 ml of prehybridization solution for each square centimeter of membrane.

b. Seal the box with the lid and place the box on a rocking platform in an air incubator set at the appropriate temperature (68°C for aqueous solvents; 42°C for solvents containing 50% formamide; 65°C for phosphate-SDS solvents).

3. If the radiolabeled probe is double-stranded DNA, denature it by heating for 5 minutes at 100°C. Chill the probe rapidly in ice water.

   Alternatively, denature DNA probes by adding 0.1 volume of 3 N NaOH. After 5 minutes at room temperature, chill the probe to 0°C in an ice-water bath, and add 0.05 volume of 1 M Tris-Cl (pH 7.2) and 0.1 volume of 3 N HCl. Store the probe in ice water until it is needed.

   Single-stranded DNA and RNA probes need not be denatured.

4. To hybridize the probe to a blot containing genomic DNA, carry out one of the following methods.

   FOR HYBRIDIZATION IN A HEAT-SEALABLE BAG

   a. Working quickly, remove the bag containing the membrane from the water bath. Open the bag by cutting off one corner with scissors and pour off the prehybridization solution.

   b. Add the denatured probe to an appropriate amount of fresh prehybridization solution and deliver the solution into the bag. Squeeze as much air as possible from the bag.

   c. Reseal the bag with the heat sealer; make sure that as few bubbles as possible are trapped in the bag. To avoid radioactive contamination of the water bath, seal the resealed bag inside a second, noncontaminated bag. Incubate the bag submerged in a water bath set at the appropriate temperature for the required period of hybridization.

   FOR HYBRIDIZATION IN A ROLLER BOTTLE

   a. Pour off the prehybridization solution from the hybridization bottle and replace with fresh hybridization solution containing probe.

   b. Seal bottle and replace in hybridization oven. Incubate for the required period of hybridization.

   FOR HYBRIDIZATION IN A PLASTIC CONTAINER

   a. Transfer the membrane from the container to a sealable bag or a hybridization bottle.

   b. Immediately treat as described above.

5. After hybridization, wash the membrane.

   FOR HYBRIDIZATION IN A HEAT-SEALABLE BAG

   a. Wearing gloves, remove the bag from the water bath, remove the outer bag, and immediately cut off one corner of the inner bag. Pour out the hybridization solution into a container suitable for disposal of radioactivity, and then cut the bag along the length of three sides.

   b. Remove the membrane and immediately submerge it in a tray containing several hundred milliliters of 2x SSC and 0.5% SDS (i.e., ~1 ml/cm^2 membrane) at room temperature. Agitate the tray gently on a slowly rotating platform.

FOR HYBRIDIZATION IN A ROLLER BOTTLE

a. Remove the membrane from the hybridization bottle, and briefly drain excess hybridization solution from the membrane by holding the corner of the membrane to the lip of the bottle or container.

b. Place the membrane in a tray containing several hundred milliliters of 2x SSC and 0.5% SDS (i.e., ~1 ml/cm² membrane) at room temperature. Agitate the tray gently on a slowly rotating platform.

   When hybridizing in phosphate-SDS solution, remove the membrane from the hybridization chamber as described in Step 5 and place it in several hundred milliliters (i.e., ~1 ml/cm² membrane) of Phosphate-SDS washing solution 1 at 65ºC. Agitate the tray. Repeat this rinse once.

   ▲ IMPORTANT Do not allow the membrane to dry out at any stage during the washing procedure.

6. After 5 minutes, pour off the first rinse solution into a radioactivity disposal container and add several hundred milliliters of 2x SSC and 0.1% SDS to the tray. Incubate for 15 minutes at room temperature with occasional gentle agitation.

   If hybridization was carried out in a phosphate-SDS buffer, rinse the membrane a total of eight times for 5 minutes each in several hundred milliliters of Phosphate-SDS washing solution 2 at 65ºC. Skip to Step 9 after the eighth rinse.

7. Replace the rinse solution with several hundred milliliters of fresh 0.1x SSC with 0.1% SDS. Incubate the membrane for 30 minutes to 4 hours at 65ºC with gentle agitation.

   During the washing step, periodically monitor the amount of radioactivity on the membrane using a hand-held minimonitor. The parts of the membrane that do not contain DNA should not emit a detectable signal. Do not expect to pick up a signal on the minimonitor from membranes containing mammalian DNA that has been hybridized to single-copy probes.

8. Briefly wash the membrane with 0.1x SSC at room temperature.

9. Remove most of the liquid from the membrane by placing it on a pad of paper towels. Place the damp membrane on a sheet of Saran Wrap. Apply adhesive dot labels marked with radioactive ink (or phosphorescent dots) to several asymmetric locations on the Saran Wrap. These markers serve to align the autoradiograph with the membrane. Cover the labels with Scotch Tape. This prevents contamination of the film holder or intensifying screen with the radioactive ink.

   Alternatively, dry the membrane in the air and glue it to a piece of 3MM paper using a water-soluble glue.

10. Cover the membrane with a sheet of Saran Wrap, and expose the membrane to X-ray film for 16–24 hours at –70ºC with an intensifying screen to obtain an autoradiographic image (please see Appendix 9).

   Alternatively, cover the hybridized and rinsed membrane with Saran Wrap, and expose it to a phosphorimager plate. An exposure time of 1–4 hours is usually long enough to detect single-copy gene sequences in a Southern blot of mammalian genomic DNA.

   If the DNA on the membrane is to be hybridized with a different probe, please see the panel on **ADDITIONAL PROTOCOL: STRIPPING PROBES FROM MEMBRANES** at the end of this protocol.

TROUBLESHOOTING

Several factors cause background in Southern hybridizations. Table 6-4 outlines the most common symptoms and prophylactic measures to reduce background.

TABLE 6-4 Background and How to Avoid It

Symbol	Cause	Potential Solutions
Blotchy background over the entire membrane.	Incomplete blocking during prehybridization.	Prehybridize for longer periods of time.
	Drying out of membrane during experiment.	Be vigilant in keeping membrane wet at all times.
	SDS precipitated from any of the solutions used in the experiment.	Make solutions at room temperature, prewarm to 37°C, and then add SDS. Do not allow SDS to precipitate at any time. Reheating a solution from which SDS has precipitated only occasionally yields a clean result.
	Use of 10% dextran sulfate in hybridization experiments.	Dextran sulfate enhances the rate of hybridization. Except in rare instances (in situ hybridizations or when using subtracted probes), dextran sulfate can be left out of most hybridization solutions. Use of large volumes of washing solutions are required to remove this viscous compound, which if left on the membrane after hybridization, traps probe and produces background.
	Paper towels became completely wet during capillary transfer (see Protocol 8).	Use a larger stack of towels or remove wet towels and replace with dry ones during transfer procedure.
	Use of charged nylon membranes and solutions containing low SDS.	Increase the concentration of SDS to 1% (w/v) at all steps. Switch to uncharged nylon membranes.
	Use of impure (yellow) formamide.	Purify formamide on Dowex XG-8 before use (Appendix 8).
	Use of improper blocking reagent.	Do not use BLOTTO for genomic Southern blots. Instead try 50 µg/ml heparin as blocking reagent (Singh and Jones 1984) or use Church buffer (Church and Gilbert 1984) as both prehybridiztion and hybridization solutions.
Haloes over the entire membrane.	Presence of bubbles in prehybridization/hybridization solutions, failure to agitate membrane.	Prewarm solutions before use. Agitate the membrane.
Background concentrated over the lanes containing nucleic acid.	Improperly denatured carrier DNA.	Reboil the salmon sperm DNA used in the prehybridization/hybridization solutions. Do not allow the heat-denatured DNA to reanneal.
	Use of probes containing poly(T) tracts in northern hybridizations.	Include poly(A) at 1 µg/ml in hybridization solutions.
	Use of RNA probes.	Drastically increase the stringency of hybridization by increasing the concentration of formamide in the hybridization buffer; use 1% SDS in the hybridization buffer, increase the washing temperatures, and decrease the ionic strength of washing buffers (e.g., 0.1x SSC).
Blotchy background appearing on some membranes but not others.	Too many membranes hybridized in the same vessel, not enough volume of prehybridization/hybridization solution.	Increase the volume of the hybridization and washing solutions and/or decrease number of membranes in a hybridization bag or container.
Intense black spots all over membrane.	Use of old radiolabel to prepare probe.	A peppered background due to ^{32}P present as inorganic phosphate or pyrophosphate sticking to the membrane is frequently encountered when using 5′-labeled probes. Do not use old radiolabel in which radiolysis has occurred. Purify the probe by spun-column chromatography, precipitation, or gel electrophoresis before use. Include 0.5% (w/v) sodium pyrophosphate in prehybridization/hybridization solutions.

ADDITIONAL PROTOCOL: STRIPPING PROBES FROM MEMBRANES

Although in many cases, it is possible to remove probes from membranes after an image has been recorded and to reprobe the membrane with different probes, the following are some of the problems associated with this procedure.

- *Irreversible binding of the probe to the membrane.* Probes become irreversibly bound when nitrocellulose membranes and nylon membranes are allowed to dry for extended periods of time. If a given membrane is to be hybridized with more than one probe, every effort should be made to ensure that the solid support remains wet at all stages during hybridization, washing, and exposure to X-ray film or phosphorimager cassettes.

- *Fragility of membranes.* Nylon membranes containing either genomic DNA or RNA can be stripped and rehybridized five to ten times. Nitrocellulose membranes, however, are more fragile and generally do not survive more than two or three cycles of hybridization and stripping.

- *Leaching of nucleic acids from the membranes.* A fraction of the DNA or RNA immobilized on the membrane leaches away during each cycle of hybridization and stripping so that the strength of the signal decreases progressively with each use. Nitrocellulose membranes are the worst offenders in this respect.

Method

Removal of a Hybridized Probe from a Nitrocellulose Membrane

1. Prepare elution buffer by heating several hundred milliliters of 0.05x SSC, 0.01 M EDTA (pH 8.0) to boiling. Remove the fluid from the heat and add SDS to a final concentration of 0.1% (w/v).

2. Immerse the membrane in the hot elution buffer for 15 minutes. Rock or rotate the container during this time period.

3. Repeat Step 2 with a fresh batch of boiling elution buffer.

   ▲ IMPORTANT Do not allow the membrane to dry when transferring it between batches of hot elution buffer.

4. Rinse the membrane briefly in 0.01x SSC at room temperature. Blot most of the liquid from the membrane by placing it on a pad of paper towels, sandwich the damp membrane between two sheets of Saran Wrap, and apply it to X-ray film to check that all of the probe has been removed.

5. Dry the membrane, wrap loosely in aluminum foil or between sheets of blotting paper, and store at room temperature — preferably under vacuum — until needed. To rehybridize the membrane, place it in prehybridization solution and continue with Step 2 of Protocol 10.

Removal of a Hybridized Probe from a Charged or Neutral Nylon Membrane

Most manufacturers of nylon membranes provide instructions describing how various types of probes may best be stripped from their particular type of membrane. It is advisable to follow these instructions. Alternatively, treat the hybridized membrane with one of the three stripping solutions described in the table below.

1. Prepare several hundred milliliters of one of the recipes for stripping solution given in the table below, immerse the membrane, and treat as described to remove the probe and to wash the membrane.

Stripping solution	Treatment	Washing solution
1 M Tris-Cl (pH 8.0), 1 mM EDTA (pH 8.0), 0.1x Denhardt's reagent	2 hours at 75°C	0.1x SSPE at room temperature
50% formamide <!>, 2x SSPE	1 hour at 65°C	0.1x SSPE at room temperature
0.4 M NaOH <!>	30 minutes at 42°C	0.1x SSC, 0.1% SDS, 0.2 M Tris-Cl (pH 7.6) for 30 minutes at 42°C

2. Blot most of the liquid from the membrane by placing it on a pad of paper towels, sandwich the damp membrane between two sheets of Saran Wrap, and apply it to X-ray film to ensure that all of the probe has been removed.

3. Dry the membrane, wrap loosely in aluminum foil or between sheets of blotting paper, and store at room temperature — preferably under vacuum — until needed. To rehybridize the membrane, place it in prehybridization solution and continue with Step 2 of Protocol 10.

ADDITIONAL PROTOCOL: HYBRIDIZATION AT LOW STRINGENCY

The detection of genes that are related but not identical in sequence to a particular probe can sometimes be accomplished by hybridizing under conditions of reduced stringency. Success depends chiefly on (1) the degree of sequence identity between the hybridization probe and the target and (2) the judicious choice of hybridization conditions. Members of a gene family from a single species or orthologous genes from different species can almost always be isolated by low-stringency hybridization if they share 65% or greater sequence identity. The identification of genes that share <65% identity requires skill in the art and sometimes luck. Genes in the latter category are more frequently isolated by low-stringency PCR (see Chapter 8). The following hybridization/washing conditions can be used to identify genes that share ≥ 65% sequence identity.

- *For Southern hybridization or screening of bacteriophage plaques and bacterial colonies:* Set up hybridization reactions in a buffer containing 30% (v/v) deionized formamide, 0.6 M NaCl, 0.04 M sodium phosphate (pH 7.4), 2.5 mM EDTA (pH 8.0), 1% SDS, and radiolabeled denatured probe (1×10^6 to 2×10^6 cpm/ml of hybridization solution). Hybridize for 16 hours at 42°C.

- *For northern hybridizations:* Hybridize in 50% deionized formamide, 0.25 M NaCl, 0.10 M sodium phosphate (pH 7.2), 2.5 mM EDTA (pH 8.0), 7% SDS, and radiolabeled denatured probe (1×10^6 to 2×10^6 cpm/ml of hybridization solution). Hybridize for 16 hours at 42°C.

At the end of the hybridization reaction, wash the membranes twice with 2x SSC/0.1% SDS for 10 minutes each at room temperature, followed by a wash for 1 hour at 55°C in 2x SSC/0.1% SDS. Use large volumes of rinse and wash solutions; make sure that they are at the appropriate temperature before use. The identification of genes that share <65% sequence is trickier but may be accomplished by using one or more of the following approaches.

- *Use an RNA probe prepared by in vitro transcription* (please see Chapter 9, Protocol 6). The increased stability of RNA-DNA hybrids over DNA-DNA hybrids (Casey and Davidson 1977; Zuker et al. 1985) can sometimes make the difference between seeing a signal and not seeing a signal. However, RNA probes may generate high backgrounds that are difficult to remove with low-stringency washes. The use of noncharged nylon membranes may alleviate this problem.

- *Use a single-stranded DNA probe prepared from a bacteriophage M13 template* as described in Chapter 9, Protocol 4 or 5. Single-stranded DNA probes generate fewer background problems than RNA probes.

- *Decrease the formamide concentration* to 20% and hybridize at 34°C. Rinse and wash the hybridized membranes as described above.

- *Include "crowding agents" in the hybridization reaction.* When included at appropriate concentrations, these agents can stabilize nucleic acids against thermal denaturation and accelerate the renaturation of DNA (for review, please see Zimmerman and Minton 1993). For a description of the effect of crowding agents on denaturation of nucleic acids, please see Wieder and Wetmur (1981) and Sikorav and Church (1991). If using DNA probes, add 10% dextran sulfate or 5% polyethylene glycol (PEG 8000) to the hybridization solutions. These polymers accelerate the rate of hybridization about tenfold (Wahl et al. 1979; Renz and Kurz 1984; Amasino 1986; Kroczek 1993). Dextran sulfate or PEG 8000 can sometimes lead to high background, and hybridization solutions containing them are always difficult to handle because of their viscosity. Use large volumes of rinse and wash solutions to overcome these problems.

- *Use a commercial "rapid hybridization" solution* (please see the information panels on RAPID HYBRIDIZATION BUFFERS and CTAB) and wash the membranes according to the manufacturer's instructions.

FORMAMIDE AND ITS USES IN MOLECULAR CLONING

Formamide is used as an ionizing solvent in aqueous buffers. Many batches of high-grade formamide are sufficiently pure to be used without further treatment. However, as a rule of thumb, if any yellow color is present or if there is even the hint of a smell of ammonia, the formamide should be purified. A more rigorous test of purity is to measure conductivity, which rises as the formamide breaks down to ammonium formate. The conductivity of pure formamide is 1.7 (Casey and Davidson 1977) and the conductivity of a 10^{-3} M solution of ammonium formate is ~650 μmho. The conductivity of formamide used in reannealing experiments should be <2.0 μmho.

Formamide can be deionized by stirring for 1 hour on a magnetic stirrer with a mixed bed ion-exchange resin (e.g., Dowex AG8, Bio-Rad AG 501-X8, 20–50 mesh or X8[D]). The solution is then filtered through Whatman #1 paper and stored in small aliquots at –20ºC, preferably under nitrogen. Each resin can be reused several times. X8(D) contains an indicator that changes color when the resin is exhausted.

Formamide is used in hybridization reactions, to resolve complex compressions in sequencing gels, and to denature DNA before electrophoresis as described below.

Resolving Compressions in Sequencing Gels

Including 25–50% (v/v) formamide in polyacrylamide sequencing gels destabilizes secondary structures in DNA and resolves some types of compression caused by anomalous migration of DNA bands (Brown 1984; Martin 1987). Gels containing formamide run slower and cooler than conventional polyacrylamide gels at the same voltage. It is usually necessary to increase the voltage by ~10% to maintain temperature. Gels containing formamide give fuzzier bands.

In addition to DNA sequencing, formamide is routinely included in gels used to analyze polymorphic (CA) repeats in mammalian DNAs. In the presence of formamide, the smear of bands that is generated during polymerase chain reaction (PCR) amplification of alleles is resolved into a discrete family whose members differ in size by 2 bp (Litt et al. 1993).

Denaturing RNA before Electrophoresis

Formamide (50%) is used to assist in denaturation of RNA before electrophoresis through denaturing formaldehyde-agarose gels (Lehrach et al. 1977).

Hybridization Reactions

Bonner et al. (1967) were the first to use formamide as a solvent in hybridization reactions. At the end of their brief paper, they wrote:

> That formamide should take the place of elevated temperature in the hybridization process is to be expected. Aqueous solutions of formamide denature DNA as has been shown by Helmkamp and Ts'o (1961) and Marmur and T'so (1961). The concentrations of formamide required for DNA-RNA hybridization, 30–40 vol%, are well below the 60 vol% found by Marmur and T'so to be required for denaturation of native DNA (in 0.02 M NaCl–0.002 M sodium citrate).
>
> What has now been found by serendipity is that hybridization as conducted in aqueous formamide possesses distinct advantages over hybridization conducted at elevated temperatures. These advantages include increased retention of immobilized DNA by the nitrocellulose filters and decreased nonspecific background absorption. These two factors combine to result in an increased reproducibility of replicates with the hybridization procedure. Hybridization in formamide solution at low temperature is helpful also in minimizing scission of nucleic acid molecules during prolonged periods of incubation.

In addition to these advantages, increased flexibility is introduced into the design of reaction conditions for a given experiment. It is more convenient to control this stringency of hybridization with formamide rather than through adjustment of the incubation temperature.

HYBRIDIZATION IN BUFFERS CONTAINING FORMAMIDE

Depression of the melting temperature (T_m) of duplex DNA is a linear function of the formamide concentration (McConaughy et al. 1969; Casey and Davidson 1977). For DNAs whose G+C content is in the range of 30–75%, the T_m is depressed by 0.63°C for each percentage of formamide in the hybridization mixture. Thus, the T_m of the hybrid formed between a probe and its target may be estimated from the following equation, which is modified from Bolton and McCarthy (1962):

$$T_m = 81.5°C + 16.6\ (\log_{10} [Na^+]) + 41\ (\text{mole fraction } [G+C]) - 0.63\ (\%\text{formamide}) - 500/n$$

where *n* is the length of the DNA in nucleotides. This equation applies to the reversible T_m defined by optical measurement of hyperchromicity at OD_{260}. The "irreversible" T_m (Hamaguchi and Geiduschek 1962), which is more important for autoradiographic detection of DNA hybrids, is usually 7–10°C higher than that predicted by the equation. Similar equations have been derived for RNA probes hybridizing to immobilized RNA (Bodkin and Knudson 1985):

$$T_m = 79.8°C + 18.5\ (\log_{10} [Na^+]) + 58.4\ (\text{mole fraction } [G+C]) + 11.8\ (\text{mole fraction } [G+C])^2$$
$$- 0.35\ (\%\text{formamide}) - 820/n$$

and for DNA:RNA hybrids (Casey and Davidson 1977):

$$T_m = 79.8°C + 18.5\ (\log_{10} [Na^+]) + 58.4\ (\text{mole fraction } [G+C]) + 11.8\ (\text{mole fraction } [G+C])^2$$
$$- 0.50\ (\%\text{formamide}) - 820/n$$

Comparison of these equations shows that the relative stability of nucleic acid hybrids in high concentrations of formamide decreases in the following order: RNA-RNA (most stable), RNA-DNA (less stable), and DNA-DNA (least stable). In 80% formamide, the T_m of an RNA-DNA hybrid is ~10°C higher than a DNA-DNA hybrid of equivalent base composition. It is therefore possible to find hybridization conditions that allow the formation of RNA-DNA hybrids and discourage the formation of DNA-DNA hybrids (Casey and Davidson 1977). This ability to suppress reannealing of DNA was extremely useful when S1 mapping of RNA was carried out with double-stranded DNA probes (Berk and Sharp 1977). However, the development of efficient methods to prepare single-stranded probes now allows annealing of RNA to DNA to be carried out under standard hybridization conditions without fear of competition from the complementary strand of DNA. As a consequence, the annealing conditions established by Casey and Davidson (1977) are today used only very rarely.

- The rate of DNA-DNA hybridization in 80% formamide is slower than in aqueous solution (Casey and Davidson 1977). Increasing the concentration of formamide decreases the rate of DNA:DNA renaturation by 1.1% for every 1% increase in the concentration of formamide (Hutton 1977). Therefore, the optimal rate in 50% formamide is 0.45 times the optimal rate in aqueous solution (Hutton 1977). In 80% formamide, the rate of DNA-DNA hybridization is three- to fourfold slower than in aqueous solution (Casey and Davidson 1977). This effect is a consequence of increased viscosity of the hybridization solution at the temperatures used for renaturation.

- The breakdown of formamide that occurs during prolonged incubation at temperatures in excess of 37°C can cause the pH of the hybridization buffer to drift upward (Casey and Davidson 1977). When formamide is included in the hybridization buffer, 6x SSPE is preferred to 6x SSC because of its greater buffering power.

SPOOLING DNA (HISTORICAL FOOTNOTE)

Ethanol precipitation of biologically active nucleic acid predates molecular cloning by ~50 years. Lionel Alloway, who worked at the Rockefeller Institute in the early 1930s, used it as a method to concentrate "transforming factor." His project was to prepare active cell-free extracts of S-type *Streptococcus pneumoniae* that would genetically transform R-type organisms in vitro. At that time, transformation had been achieved only with intact, heat-killed donor cells. After many frustrating failures, Alloway (1932) reported that he could get the substance responsible for transformation into solution by heating a freeze-thaw extract of the S organisms to 60°C, removing particulate matter by centrifugation, and passing the solution through a filter made of porous porcelain.

Alloway's success at eliminating the need for heat-killed donor cells was a major step on the road that was eventually to lead to the discovery of DNA as the transforming material (Avery et al. 1944). However, not all of Alloway's cell-free preparations worked, and, even when transformation was obtained, the efficiency was very low. Alloway must have realized that these problems were caused in part by the dilute nature of the extract, for he began to search for different ways to lyse the pneumococci and for different methods to concentrate the transforming activity (Alloway 1933). Maclyn McCarty (1985) described Alloway's discovery of ethanol precipitation as follows:

> Alloway then introduced another new procedure that became an indispensable part of all work on the transforming substance from that time forward. He added pure alcohol in a volume five times that of the extract which resulted in precipitation of most of the material that had been released from the pneumococci.... The precipitated material could be redissolved in salt solution and shown to contain the active substance in transformation tests. Alcohol precipitation and resolution could be repeated at will without loss of activity.

Alloway describes the formation of "a thick stringy precipitate" that could be collected by stirring the ethanolic solution with a spatula. Although Alloway was the first person to use spooling to recover high-molecular-weight biologically active DNA, ethanol precipitation of shards of DNA had already been used by several generations of organic chemists who were puzzling over the structure of the bases in DNA. However, Alloway was the first to use ethanol precipitation to prepare material that could change the phenotype of recipient cells. Final proof that the transforming factor was DNA still lay a dozen or more years into the future. But Alloway could fairly claim to be the inventor of a technique that is now second nature to us all.

RAPID HYBRIDIZATION BUFFERS

Several cationic detergents dramatically enhance the rate of hybridization of two complementary strands of nucleic acid (Pontius and Berg 1991). These include dodecyltrimethylammonium bromide and cetyltrimethylammonium bromide (DTAB and CTAB), which are variants of the quaternary amine tetramethylammonium bromide. The latter compound is used to stabilize duplexes formed between oligonucleotide probes and target sequences (please see Chapter 10). At concentrations in the millimolar range, DTAB and CTAB enhance the rate of renaturation of two complementary strands of DNA >10,000-fold. The increase in hybridization rate is specific and occurs in the presence of as much as a 10^6-fold excess of noncomplementary DNAs (please see the information panel on CTAB).

Several commercial manufacturers now sell rapid hybridization solutions that decrease the required hybridization time from 16 hours to 1–2 hours. Although the chemical composition of these premade solutions is a trade secret, it seems likely that some of them contain quaternary ammonium compounds, whereas others contain volume excluders such as 10% dextran sulfate (Wahl et al. 1979; Renz and Kurz 1984; Amasino 1986) or 5% PEG 35,000 (Kroczek 1993). Hybridization times can be reduced by a factor of five or more if these rapid hybridization solutions are used instead of conventional hybridization buffers. In addition, these hybridization accelerators improve the efficiency of hybridization when low concentrations of probe are used (~1 ng/ml). The rapid hybridization solution should be preheated to the correct hybridization temperature before it is added to the membranes. Radiolabeled probes should be added to preheated rapid hybridization solution before adding it to the membrane.

In our experience, rapid hybridization buffers work extremely well for Southern hybridization. However, when hybridization accelerators are used in northern hybridization, the background of hybridization to ribosomal RNAs increases greatly — sometimes to levels that are unacceptable.

CTAB

Cetyltrimethylammonium bromide (CTAB) is a cationic detergent that has the useful property of precipitating nucleic acids and acidic polysaccharides from solutions of low ionic strength. Under these conditions, proteins and neutral polysaccharides remain in solution. In solutions of high ionic strength, CTAB forms complexes with proteins and all but the most acidic polysaccharides, but will not precipitate nucleic acids (Jones and Walker 1963). CTAB is therefore particularly useful for purification of DNAs from organisms that produce large quantities of polysaccharides, e.g., plants (Murray and Thompson 1980) and certain Gram-negative bacteria (including some strains of *E. coli*). CTAB is used in two types of basic precipitation procedures:

- *For preparation of genomic DNAs.* The detergent is added to bacterial or cell lysates that have been adjusted to high ionic strength (>0.7 M NaCl). After removing the CTAB/polysaccharide/protein complexes by sequential extraction with chloroform and phenol, the genomic DNA is recovered from the supernatant by precipitation with isopropanol or ethanol (Jones and Walker 1963; Wilson 1987).

- *For preparation of phagemid, plasmid, and bacteriophage DNAs.* CTAB is added to lysates of low ionic strength. The precipitated DNAs are collected by centrifugation, dissolved in solutions of high ionic strength, and purified by ethanol precipitation (e.g., please see Manfioletti and Schneider 1988; Del Sal et al. 1989).

CTAB and other cationic detergents also have the remarkable property of enhancing the rate of renaturation of complementary DNA strands (Pontius and Berg 1991). At a concentration of 1 mM CTAB, renaturation rates can be as much as 10,000 times faster than those in water. This rate is ~2000 times faster than that obtained in a 1 M solution of NaCl (i.e., ~6x SSC). The annealing reaction in the presence of CTAB is second order with respect to DNA concentration, and the rates approach those with which two complementary strands collide in a solution. CTAB also stabilizes the double-stranded DNA helix once formed. Annealing reactions remain rapid in the presence of as much as a 10^6-fold excess of noncomplementary DNAs. Although not widely publicized, it seems likely that CTAB or another cationic detergent is the active ingredient in the numerous "rapid hybridization" solutions that are commercially available.

- Most commercial preparations of CTAB are mixtures of trimethylammonium bromides with varying lengths of aliphatic tails (please see Figure 6-4). About 80% of a typical preparation consists of the cetyl form ($M_r = 364.48$).

- Because CTAB precipitates in the cold, solutions containing the detergent should be stored at temperatures >15°C.

- CTAB is widely used as a topical antiseptic and is sold under the trade names of Savlon and Cetavlon.

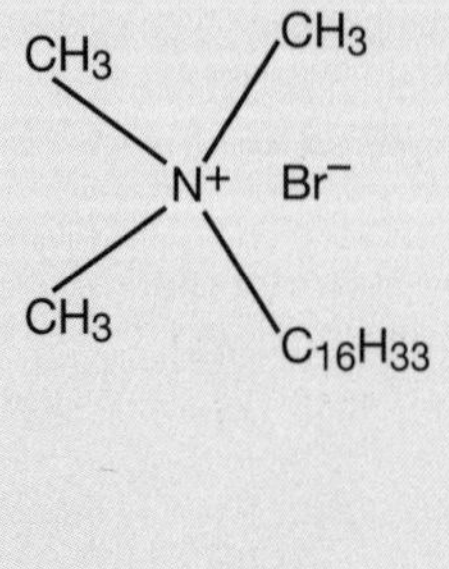

FIGURE 6-4 **The Structure of CTAB**

REFERENCES

Alloway J.L. 1932. The transformation *in vitro* of R pneumococci into S forms of different specific types by the use of filtered pneumococcus extracts. *J. Exp. Med.* **54:** 91–99.

———. 1933. Further observations on the use of pneumococcus extracts in effecting transformation of type in vitro. *J. Exp. Med.* **57:** 265–278.

Alwine J.C., Kemp D.J., and Stark G.R. 1977. Method for detection of specific RNAs in agarose gels by transfer to diazobenzyloxymethyl-paper and hybridization with DNA probes. *Proc. Natl. Acad. Sci.* **74:** 5350–5354.

Amasino R.M. 1986. Acceleration of nucleic acid hybridization rate by polyethylene glycol. *Anal. Biochem.* **152:** 304–307.

Angeletti B., Battiloro E., Pascale E., and D'Ambrosio E. 1995. Southern and northern blot fixing by microwave oven. *Nucleic Acids Res.* **23:** 879–880.

Avery O.T., McCleod C.M., and McCarty M. 1944. Studies on the chemical nature of the substance inducing transformation of pneumococcal types. Induction of transformation by a deoxyribonucleic acid fraction isolated from pneumococcus type III. *J. Exp. Med.* **79:** 137–158.

Berk A.J. and Sharp P.A. 1977. Sizing and mapping of early adenovirus mRNAs by gel electrophoresis of S1 endonuclease-digested hybrids. *Cell* **12:** 721–732.

Beutler E., Gelbart T., and Kuhl W. 1990. Interference of heparin with the polymerase chain reaction. *BioTechniques* **9:** 166.

Blin N. and Stafford D.W. 1976. A general method for isolation of high molecular weight DNA from eukaryotes. *Nucleic Acids Res.* **3:** 2303–2308.

Bodkin D.K. and Knudson D.L. 1985. Assessment of sequence relatedness of double-stranded RNA genes by RNA-RNA blot hybridization. *J. Virol. Methods* **10:** 45–52.

Bolton E.T. and McCarthy B.J. 1962. A general method for the isolation of RNA complementary to DNA. *Proc. Natl. Acad. Sci.* **48:** 1390–1397.

Bonner J., Kung G., and Bekhor I. 1967. A method for the hybridization of nucleic acid molecules at low temperature. *Biochemistry* **6:** 3650–3653.

Botchan M., Topp W., and Sambrook J. 1976. The arrangement of simian virus 40 sequences in the DNA of transformed cells. *Cell* **9:** 269–287.

Bowtell D.D. 1987. Rapid isolation of eukaryotic DNA. *Anal. Biochem.* **162:** 463–465.

Brown N.L. 1984. DNA sequencing. *Methods Microbiol.* **17:** 259–313.

Casey J. and Davidson N. 1977. Rates of formation and thermal stabilities of RNA:DNA and DNA:DNA duplexes at high concentrations of formamide. *Nucleic Acids Res.* **4:** 1539–1552.

Chomczynski P. 1992. One-hour downward alkaline capillary transfer for blotting of DNA and RNA. *Anal. Biochem.* **201:** 134–139.

Church G.M. and Gilbert W. 1984. Genomic sequencing. *Proc. Natl. Acad. Sci.* **81:** 1991–1995.

Couse J.F., Davis V.L., Tally W.C., and Korach K.S. 1994. An improved method of genomic DNA extraction for screening transgenic mice. *BioTechniques* **17:** 1030–1032.

Del Sal G., Manfioletti G., and Schneider C. 1989. The CTAB-DNA precipitation method: A common mini-scale preparation of template DNA from phagemids, phages or plasmids suitable for sequencing. *BioTechniques* **7:** 514–520.

Feinberg A.P. and Vogelstein B. 1983. A technique for radiolabeling DNA restriction endonuclease fragments to high specific activity. *Anal. Biochem.* **132:** 6–13.

———. 1984. A technique for radiolabeling DNA restriction endonuclease fragments to high specific activity. Addendum. *Anal. Biochem.* **137:** 266–267.

Gillespie D. and Spiegelman S. 1965. A quantitative assay for DNA-RNA hybrids with DNA immobilized on a membrane. *J. Mol. Biol.* **12:** 829–842.

Glasel J.A. 1995. Validity of nucleic acid purities monitored by 260nm/280nm absorbance ratios (see comments). *BioTechniques* **18:** 62–63.

Guesdon J.L. 1992. Immunoenzymatic techniques applied to the specific detection of nucleic acids. A review. *J. Immunol. Methods* **150:** 33–49.

Gustafson S., Proper J.A., Bowie E.J., and Sommer S.S. 1987. Parameters affecting the yield of DNA from human blood. *Anal. Biochem.* **165:** 294–299.

Haas M., Vogt M., and Dulbecco R. 1972. Loss of simian virus 40 DNA-RNA hybrids from nitrocellulose membranes: Implications for the study of virus–host DNA interactions. *Proc. Natl. Acad. Sci.* **69:** 2160–2164.

Hall B.D. and Spiegelman S. 1961. Sequence complementarity of T2-DNA and T2-specific RNA. *Proc. Natl. Acad. Sci.* **47:** 137–163.

Hamaguchi K. and Geiduschek E.P. 1962. The effect of electrolytes on the stability of the deoxynucleate helix. *J. Am. Chem. Soc.* **84:** 1329–1338.

Helmkamp G. and Ts'o P.O.P. 1961. The secondary structures of nucleic acids in organic solvents. *J. Am. Chem. Soc.* **83:** 138–142.

Hutton J.R. 1977. Renaturation kinetics and thermal stability of DNA in aqueous solutions of formamide and urea. *Nucleic Acids Res.* **4:** 3537–3555.

Jones A.S. and Walker R.T. 1963. Isolation and analysis of the deoxyribonucleic acid of *Mycoplasma mycoides* var. *capri*. *Nature* **198:** 588–589.

Khandjian E.W. 1987. Optimized hybridization of DNA blotted and fixed to nitrocellulose and nylon membranes. *Bio/Technology* **5:** 165–167.

Koetsier P.A., Schorr J., and Doerfler W. 1993. A rapid optimized protocol for downward alkaline Southern blotting of DNA. *BioTechniques* **15:** 260–262.

Köntgen F. and Stewart C.L. 1993. Simple screening procedure to detect gene targeting events in embryonic stem cells. *Methods Enzymol.* **225:** 878–890.

Kroczek R.A. 1993. Southern and northern analysis. *J. Chromatogr.* **618:** 133–145.

Kupiec J.J., Giron M.L., Vilette D., Jeltsch J.M., and Emanoil-Ravier R. 1987. Isolation of high-molecular-weight DNA from eukaryotic cells by formamide treatment and dialysis. *Anal. Biochem.* **164:** 53–59.

Laird P.W., Zijderveld A., Linders K., Rudnicki M.A., Jaenisch R., and Berns A. 1991. Simplified mammalian DNA isolation procedure. *Nucleic Acids Res.* **19:** 4293.

Lehrach H., Diamond D., Wozney J.M., and Boedtker H. 1977. RNA molecular weight determinations by gel electrophoresis under denaturing conditions, a critical reexamination. *Biochemistry* **16:** 4743–4751.

Lichtenstein A.V., Moiseev V.L., and Zaboikin M.M. 1990. A procedure for DNA and RNA transfer to membrane filters avoiding weight-induced gel flattening. *Anal. Biochem.* **191:** 187–191.

Litt M., Hauge X., and Sharma V. 1993. Shadow bands seen when typing polymorphic dinucleotide repeats: Some causes and cures. *BioTechniques* **15:** 280–284.

Manfioletti G. and Schneider C. 1988. A new and fast method for preparing high quality lambda DNA suitable for sequencing. *Nucleic Acids Res.* **16:** 2873–2884.

Mansfield E.S., Worley J.M., McKenzie S.E., Surrey S., Rappaport E., and Fortina P. 1995. Nucleic acid detection using non-radioactive labelling methods. *Mol. Cell. Probes* **9:** 145–156.

Marmur J. and T'so P.O.P. 1961. Denaturation of deoxyribonucleic acid by formamide. *Biochim. Biophys. Acta* **51:** 32–36.

Martin R. 1987. Overcoming DNA sequencing artifacts: Stops and compressions. *Focus* (Life Technologies) **9:** 8–10.

McCarty M. 1985. *The transforming principle: Discovering that genes are made of DNA*, 1st edition. W.W. Norton, New York.

McConaughy B.L., Laird C.D., and McCarthy B.J. 1969. Nucleic acid reassociation in formamide. *Biochemistry* **8:** 3289–3295.

Medveczky P., Chang C.-W., Mulder C., and Oste C. 1987. Rapid vacuum driven transfer of DNA and RNA from gels to solid supports. *BioTechniques* **5:** 242–246.

Meinkoth J. and Wahl G. 1984. Hybridization of nucleic acids immobilized on solid supports. *Anal. Biochem.* **138:** 267–284.

Murray M.G. and Thompson W.F. 1980. Rapid isolation of high molecular weight plant DNA. *Nucleic Acids Res.* **8:** 4321–4325.

Nygaard A.P. and Hall. B.D. 1960. A method for the detection of DNA-RNA complexes. *Biochim. Biophys. Acta* **40:** 85–92.

Olszewska E. and Jones K. 1988. Vacuum blotting enhances nucleic acid transfer. *Trends Genet.* **4:** 92–94.

Palmiter R.D., Chen H.Y., Messing A., and Brinster R.L. 1985. SV40 enhancer and large-T antigen are instrumental in development of choroid plexus tumours in transgenic mice. *Nature* **316:** 457–460.

Pitas J.W. 1989. A simple technique for repair of nylon blotting membranes. *BioTechniques* **7:** 1084.

Pontius B.W. and Berg P. 1991. Rapid renaturation of complementary DNA strands mediated by cationic detergents: A role for high-probability binding domains in enhancing the kinetics of molecular assembly processes. *Proc. Natl. Acad. Sci.* **88:** 8237–8241.

Ramírez-Solis R., Davis A.C., and Bradley A. 1993. Gene targeting in embryonic stem cells. *Methods Enzymol.* **225:** 855–878.

Ramírez-Solis R., Rivera-Pérez J., Wallace J.D., Wims M., Zheng H., and Bradley A. 1992. Genomic DNA microextraction: A method to screen numerous samples. *Anal. Biochem.* **201:** 331–335.

Reed K.C. and Mann D.A. 1985. Rapid transfer of DNA from agarose gels to nylon membranes. *Nucleic Acids Res.* **13:** 7207–7221.

Renz M. and Kurz C. 1984. A colorimetric method for DNA hybridization. *Nucleic Acids Res.* **12:** 3435–3444.

Seed B. 1982a. Attachment of nucleic acids to nitrocellulose and diazonium-substituted supports. *Genet. Eng.* **4:** 91–102.

———. 1982b. Diazotizable arylamine cellulose papers for the coupling and hybridization of nucleic acids. *Nucleic Acids Res.* **10:** 1799–1810.

Sepp R., Szabó I., Uda H., and Sakamoto H. 1994. Rapid techniques for DNA extraction from routinely processed archival tissue for use in PCR. *J. Clin. Pathol.* **47:** 318–323.

Sikorav J.L. and Church G.M. 1991. Complementary recognition in condensed DNA: Accelerated DNA renaturation. *J. Mol. Biol.* **222:** 1085–1088.

Singh L. and Jones K.W. 1984. The use of heparin as a simple cost-effective means of controlling background in nucleic acid hybridization procedures. *Nucleic Acids Res.* **12:** 5627–5638.

Southern E.M. 1975. Detection of specific sequences among DNA fragments separated by gel electrophoresis. *J. Mol. Biol.* **98:** 503–517.

Stellwag E.J. and Dahlberg A.E. 1980. Electrophoretic transfer of DNA, RNA and protein onto diazobenzyloxymethyl (DBM)-paper. *Nucleic Acids Res.* **8:** 299–317.

Stulnig T.M. and Amberger A. 1994. Exposing contaminating phenol in nucleic acid preparations. *BioTechniques* **16:** 402–404.

Thomas S.M., Moreno R.F., and Tilzer L.L. 1989. DNA extraction with organic solvents in gel barrier tubes. *Nucleic Acids Res.* **17:** 5411.

Trnovsky J. 1992. Semi-dry electroblotting of DNA and RNA from agarose and polyacrylamide gels. *BioTechniques* **13:** 800–804.

Udy G.B. and Evans M.J. 1994. Microplate DNA preparation, PCR screening and cell freezing for gene targeting in embryonic stem cells. *BioTechniques* **17:** 887–894.

Viale G. and Dell'Orto P. 1992. Non-radioactive nucleic acid probes: Labelling and detection procedures. *Liver* **12:** 243–251.

Wahl G.M., Stern M., and Stark G.R. 1979. Efficient transfer of large DNA fragments from agarose gels to diazobenzyloxymethyl-paper and rapid hybridization by using dextran sulfate. *Proc. Natl. Acad. Sci.* **76:** 3683–3687.

Wieder R. and Wetmur J.G. 1981. One hundred-fold acceleration of DNA renaturation rates in solution. *Biopolymers* **20:** 1537–1547.

Wilson K. 1987. *Current protocols in molecular biology*. Wiley, New York.

Zimmerman S.B. and Minton A.P. 1993. Macromolecular crowding: Biochemical, biophysical, and physiological consequences. *Annu. Rev. Biophys. Biomol. Struct.* **22:** 27–65.

Zuker C.S., Cowman A.F., and Rubin G.M. 1985. Isolation and structure of a rhodopsin gene from *D. melanogaster*. *Cell* **40:** 851–858.

Chapter 7

Extraction, Purification, and Analysis of mRNA from Eukaryotic Cells

A TYPICAL MAMMALIAN CELL CONTAINS $\sim 10^{-5}$ µg OF RNA, 80–85% of which is ribosomal RNA (chiefly the 28S, 18S, 5.8S, and 5S species). Most of the remaining 15–20% consists of a variety of low-molecular-weight species (e.g., transfer RNAs and small nuclear RNAs). These abundant RNAs are of defined size and sequence and can be isolated in virtually pure form by gel electrophoresis, density gradient centrifugation, anion-exchange chromatography, or high-performance liquid chromatography (HPLC). By contrast, messenger RNA, which makes up between 1% and 5% of the total cellular RNA, is heterogeneous in both size — from a few hundred bases to many kilobases in length — and sequence. However, most eukaryotic mRNAs carry at their 3′ termini a tract of polyadenylic acid residues that is generally long enough to allow mRNAs to be purified by affinity chromatography on oligo(dT)-cellulose. The resulting heterogeneous population of molecules collectively encodes virtually all of the polypeptides synthesized by the cell.

Because ribose residues carry hydroxyl groups in both the 2′ and 3′ positions, RNA is chemically much more reactive than DNA and is easy prey to cleavage by contaminating RNases — enzymes with various specificities that share the property of hydrolyzing diester bonds linking phosphate and ribose residues. Because RNases are released from cells upon lysis and are present on the skin, constant vigilance is required to prevent contamination of glassware and bench tops and the generation of RNase in aerosols. The problem is compounded since there is no simple method to inactivate RNases. Because of the presence of intrachain disulfide bonds, many RNases are resistant to prolonged boiling and mild denaturants and are able to refold quickly when denatured. Unlike many DNases, RNases do not require divalent cations for activity and thus cannot be easily inactivated by the inclusion of ethylenediaminetetraacetic acid (EDTA) or other metal ion chelators in buffer solutions. The best way to prevent problems with RNase is to avoid contamination in the first place (please see the information panels on **HOW TO WIN THE BATTLE WITH RNASE, INHIBITORS OF RNASES**, and **DIETHYLPYROCARBONATE** at the end of this chapter).

This chapter is divided into two parts (please see Figure 7-1). The first series of protocols (Protocols 1 through 6) is devoted to the isolation and purification of total RNA and, subsequently, of poly(A)$^+$ RNA.

The second series of protocols (Protocols 7 through 12) deals with various approaches for the analysis of purified RNA, in particular for assessing gene expression and/or gene structure. Hybridization by northern transfer (Protocols 7 and 8) or by dot/slot blotting (Protocol 9) may be used to determine the size and abundance of a particular species of RNA. Details of the fine structure of a particular transcript may be assessed by S1 mapping or ribonuclease protection (Protocols 10 and 11). The use of either of these techniques allows the detection of the 5′ and 3′ ends of a particular mRNA, as well as the splice junctions, precursors, and processing intermediates of mRNA. Primer extension (Protocol 12) provides a measure of the amount of a particular mRNA species and allows an exact determination of the 5′ end of the mRNA.

Work is of two kinds: first, altering the position of matter at or near the earth's surface relatively to other such matter; second, telling other people to do so. The first is unpleasant and ill paid; the second is pleasant and highly paid.

Bertrand Russell

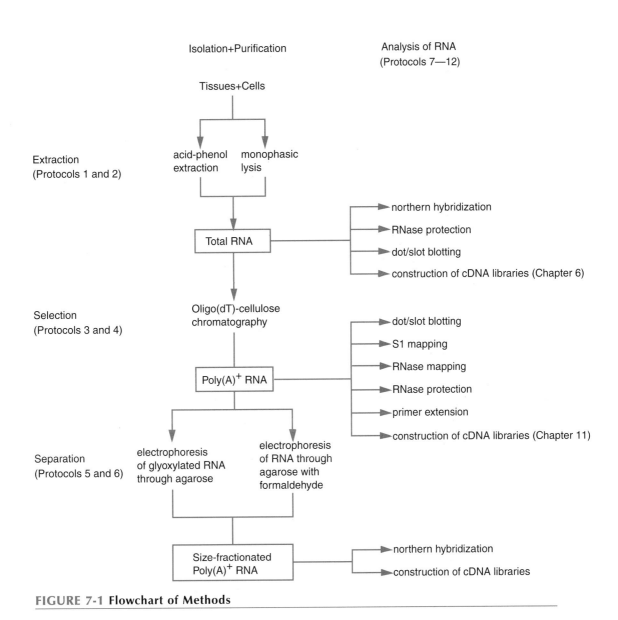

FIGURE 7-1 Flowchart of Methods

Protocol 1

Purification of RNA from Cells and Tissues by Acid Phenol–Guanidinium Thiocyanate–Chloroform Extraction

THE KEY TO SUCCESSFUL PURIFICATION OF INTACT RNA from cells and tissues is speed. Cellular RNases should be inactivated as quickly as possible at the very first stage in the extraction process. Once the endogenous RNases have been destroyed, the immediate threat to the integrity of the RNA is greatly reduced, and purification can proceed at a more graceful pace.

Because of the urgency, many methods for the isolation of intact RNA from cells use strong denaturants such as guanidinium hydrochloride or guanidinium thiocyanate to disrupt cells, solubilize their components, and denature endogenous RNases simultaneously (please see the information panel on GUANIDINIUM SALTS). The use of guanidinium isothiocyanate in RNA extraction, first mentioned briefly by Ullrich et al. (1977), was documented in papers published by Han et al. (1987) and Chirgwin et al. (1979). The Han method is laborious as it involves solubilization of RNA pellets in progressively smaller volumes of 5 M guanidine thiocyanate. In the Chirgwin method, cultured cells or tissues are homogenized in 4 M guanidinium isothiocyanate, and the lysate is layered onto a dense cushion of CsCl. Because the buoyant density of RNA in CsCl (1.8 g/ml) is much greater than that of other cellular components, rRNAs and mRNAs migrate to the bottom of the tube during ultracentrifugation (Glisin et al. 1974). As long as the step gradients are not overloaded, proteins remain in the guanidinium lysate while DNA floats on the CsCl cushion. Because the Chirgwin method yields RNA of very high quality and purity and is not labor-intensive, it became the standard technique during the early 1980s for isolation of undegraded high-molecular-weight RNA. However, the method has one weakness: It is unsuitable for simultaneous processing of many samples. For this purpose, it has been almost completely displaced by the single-step technique of Chomczynski and Sacchi (1987), in which the guanidinium thiocyanate homogenate is extracted with phenol:chloroform at reduced pH. Elimination of the ultracentrifugation step allows many samples to be processed simultaneously and speedily at modest cost and without sacrifice in yield or quality of RNA. For many investigators, the single-step technique described in Protocol 1 remains the method of choice to isolate RNA from cultured cells and most animal tissues.

There are two circumstances in which the single-step procedure is not recommended. First, the procedure does not extract RNA efficiently from adipose tissues that are rich in triglycerides. RNA is best prepared from these fatty sources by a modification of the method of Chirgwin et al. (1979), described by Tavangar et al. (1990). Second, RNA prepared by guanidine lysis is sometimes contaminated to a significant extent by cellular polysaccharides and proteoglycans. These contaminants are reported to prevent solubilization of RNA after precipitation with alcohols, to inhibit reverse-transcriptase–polymerase chain reactions (RT-PCRs), and to bind to membranes during RNA blotting (Groppe and Morse 1993; Re et al. 1995; Schick and Eras 1995). If contamination by proteoglycans and polysaccharides appears to be a problem, include an organic extraction step and change the conditions used to precipitate the RNA as described in Protocol 2.

The yield of total RNA depends on the tissue or cell source, but it is generally in the range of 4–7 µg/mg of starting tissue or 5–10 µg/10^6 cells. The A_{260}/A_{280} ratio of the extracted RNA is generally 1.8–2.0.

MATERIALS

▲ IMPORTANT Prepare all reagents used in this protocol with DEPC-treated H_2O (please see the information panel on **HOW TO WIN THE BATTLE WITH RNASE**).

CAUTION: Please see Appendix 12 for appropriate handling of materials marked with <!>.

Buffers and Solutions

Please see Appendix 1 for components of stock solutions, buffers, and reagents.
Dilute stock solutions to the appropriate concentrations.

Chloroform:isoamyl alcohol (49:1, v/v) <!>
Ethanol
Isopropanol
Liquid nitrogen <!>
Phenol <!>
Phosphate-buffered saline (PBS)
   Required for cells grown in suspension and monolayers only.
Sodium acetate (2 M, pH 4.0)
Solution D (denaturing solution)
   4 M guanidinium thiocyanate <!>
   25 mM sodium citrate·$2H_2O$
   0.5% (w/v) sodium lauryl sarcosinate
   0.1 M β-mercaptoethanol <!>

Dissolve 250 g of guanidinium thiocyanate in 293 ml of H_2O, 17.6 ml of 0.75 M sodium citrate (pH 7.0), and 26.4 ml of 10% (w/v) sodium lauryl sarcosinate. Add a magnetic bar and stir the solution on a combination heater-stirrer at 65°C until all ingredients are dissolved. Store Solution D at room temperature, and add 0.36 ml of 14.4 M stock β-mercaptoethanol per 50 ml of Solution D just before use. Solution D may be stored for months at room temperature but is sensitive to light. Note that guanidinium will precipitate at low temperatures.

Table 7-1 presents the amounts of Solution D required to extract RNA from various sources.

▲ WARNING Solution D is very caustic. Wear appropriate gloves, a laboratory coat, and eye protection when preparing, handling, or working with the solution.

TABLE 7-1 Amounts of Solution D Required to Extract RNA from Cells and Tissues

AMOUNT OF TISSUE OR CELLS	AMOUNT OF SOLUTION D
100 mg of tissue	3 ml
T-75 flask of cells	3 ml
60-mm plate of cells	1 ml
90-mm plate of cells	2 ml

The amounts of Solution D recommended here are greater than those used by Chomczynski and Sacchi (1987). Our experience and that of other investigators (e.g., Zolfaghari et al. 1993; Sparmann et al. 1997) indicate that the technique is more reproducible and the yield of RNA is consistently higher when the amount of solution D is increased to the values shown in the Table.

Stabilized formamide (Optional) <!>

Stabilized formamide is used for the storage of RNA; please see the panel on **STORAGE OF RNA** following Step 11.

Cells and Tissues

Cells or tissue samples for RNA isolation

Centrifuges and Rotors

Sorvall SS-34 rotor or equivalent
Sorvall H1000 rotor or equivalent

Special Equipment

Cuvettes for measuring absorbance at 260 nm

The cuvettes should be either disposable UV-transparent methylacrylate or quartz. Before and after use, soak quartz cuvettes in concentrated HCl:methanol (1:1, v/v) for at least 30 minutes and then wash them extensively in sterile H_2O.

Homogenizer (e.g., Tissumizer from Tekmar-Dohrmann or Polytron from Brinkmann)

Mortar and pestle washed in DEPC-treated H_2O, prechilled

Please see Chapter 6, Protocol 1.

Polypropylene snap-cap tube (e.g., Falcon)

Water bath preset to 65°C

Optional, please see Step 10.

METHOD

1. Prepare cells or tissue samples for isolation of RNA as appropriate for the material under study.

FOR TISSUES

When working with tissues such as pancreas or gut that are rich in degradative enzymes, it is best to cut the dissected tissue into small pieces (100 mg) and then drop the fragments immediately into liquid nitrogen. Fragments of snap-frozen tissue can be transferred to –70°C for storage or used immediately for extraction of RNA as described below. Tissues can be stored at –70°C for several months without affecting the yield or integrity of the RNA.

Snap-freezing and pulverization is not always necessary. Tissues that are not as rich in RNases may be rapidly minced into small pieces and transferred directly into polypropylene snap-cap tubes containing the appropriate amount of Solution D (Step c) below.

a. Isolate the desired tissues by dissection and place them immediately in liquid nitrogen.

b. Transfer ~100 mg of the frozen tissue to a mortar containing liquid nitrogen and pulverize the tissue using a pestle. The tissue can be kept frozen during pulverization by the addition of liquid nitrogen.

c. Transfer the powdered tissue to a polypropylene snap-cap tube containing 3 ml of Solution D.

d. Homogenize the tissue for 15–30 seconds at room temperature with a polytron homogenizer.

Instead of grinding in a mortar, frozen tissue may be placed inside a homemade bag of plastic film and pulverized with a blunt instrument (e.g., a hammer) (Gramza et al. 1995). Only certain types of plastic film are tough enough to withstand hammering at low temperature (e.g., Write-On Transparency Film from 3M).

FOR MAMMALIAN CELLS GROWN IN SUSPENSION

a. Harvest the cells by centrifugation at 200–1900*g* (1000–3000 rpm in a Sorvall RT600 using the H1000 rotor) for 5–10 minutes at room temperature in a benchtop centrifuge.

b. Remove the medium by aspiration and resuspend the cell pellets in 1–2 ml of sterile ice-cold PBS.

c. Harvest the cells by centrifugation, remove the PBS completely by aspiration, and add 2 ml of Solution D per 10^6 cells.

d. Homogenize the cells with a polytron homogenizer for 15–30 seconds at room temperature.

FOR MAMMALIAN CELLS GROWN IN MONOLAYERS

a. Remove the medium and rinse the cells once with 5–10 ml of sterile ice-cold PBS.

b. Remove PBS and lyse the cells in 2 ml of Solution D per 90-mm culture dish (1 ml per 60 mm dish).

c. Transfer the cell lysates to a polypropylene snap-cap tube.

d. Homogenize the lysates with a polytron homogenizer for 15–30 seconds at room temperature.

2. Transfer the homogenate to a fresh polypropylene tube and sequentially add 0.1 ml of 2 M sodium acetate (pH 4.0), 1 ml of phenol, and 0.2 ml of chloroform-isoamyl alcohol per milliliter of Solution D. After addition of each reagent, cap the tube and mix the contents thoroughly by inversion.

3. Vortex the homogenate vigorously for 10 seconds. Incubate the tube for 15 minutes on ice to permit complete dissociation of nucleoprotein complexes.

4. Centrifuge the tube at 10,000*g* (9000 rpm in a Sorvall SS-34 rotor) for 20 minutes at 4ºC, and then transfer the upper aqueous phase containing the extracted RNA to a fresh tube.

> To minimize contamination by DNA trapped at the interface, avoid taking the lowest part of the aqueous phase.

5. Add an equal volume of isopropanol to the extracted RNA. Mix the solution well and allow the RNA to precipitate for 1 hour or more at –20ºC.

6. Collect the precipitated RNA by centrifugation at 10,000*g* (9000 rpm in a Sorvall SS-34 rotor) for 30 minutes at 4ºC.

7. Carefully decant the isopropanol and dissolve the RNA pellet in 0.3 ml of Solution D for every 1 ml of this solution used in Step 1.

> ▲ IMPORTANT Pellets are easily lost. Decant the supernatant into a fresh tube. Do not discard it until the pellet has been checked.

8. Transfer the solution to a microfuge tube, vortex it well, and precipitate the RNA with 1 volume of isopropanol for 1 hour or more at –20ºC.

> If degradation of RNA turns out to be a problem (e.g., when isolating RNA from cells or tissues known to contain large amounts of RNase, such as macrophages, pancreas, and small intestine), repeat Steps 7 and 8 once more.

9. Collect the precipitated RNA by centrifugation at maximum speed for 10 minutes at 4°C in a microfuge. Wash the pellet twice with 75% ethanol, centrifuge again, and remove any remaining ethanol with a disposable pipette tip. Store the open tube on the bench for a few minutes to allow the ethanol to evaporate. Do not allow the pellet to dry completely.

10. Add 50–100 µl of DEPC-treated H_2O. Store the RNA solution at –70°C.

    Addition of SDS to 0.5% followed by heating to 65°C may assist dissolution of the pellet.

11. Estimate the concentration of the RNA by measuring the absorbance at 260 nm of an aliquot of the final preparation, as described in Appendix 8.

    Purified RNA is not immune to degradation by RNase after resuspension in the 0.5% SDS solution. Some investigators therefore prefer to dissolve the pellet of RNA in 50–100 µl of stabilized formamide and store the solution at –20°C (Chomczynski 1992). RNA can be recovered from formamide by precipitation with 4 volumes of ethanol. For further details, please see the panel on **STORAGE OF RNA**.

    SDS should be removed by chloroform extraction and ethanol precipitation before enzymatic treatment of the RNA (e.g., primer extension, reverse transcription, and in vitro translation). The redissolved RNA can then be used for mRNA purification by oligo(dT)-cellulose chromatography (Protocol 3) or analyzed by standard techniques such as blot hybridization (Protocols 7 and 8) or mapping (Protocols 10, 11, and 12).

    RNA prepared from tissues is generally not contaminated to a significant extent with DNA. However, RNA prepared from cell lines undergoing spontaneous or induced apoptosis is often contaminated with fragments of degraded genomic DNA. RNA prepared from transfected cells is almost always contaminated by fragments of the DNA used for transfection. Some investigators therefore treat the final RNA preparation with RNase-free DNase (Grillo and Margolis 1990; Simms et al. 1993). Alternatively, fragments of DNA may be removed by preparing poly(A)$^+$ RNA by oligo(dT) chromatography.

STORAGE OF RNA

After precipitation with ethanol, store the RNA as follows:

- ***Dissolve the precipitate in deionized formamide and store at –20°C*** (Chomczynski 1992). Formamide provides a chemically stable environment that also protects RNA against degradation by RNases. Purified, salt-free RNA dissolves quickly in formamide up to a concentration of 4 mg/ml. At such concentrations, samples of the RNA can be analyzed directly by gel electrophoresis, RT-PCR, or RNase protection, saving time and avoiding potential degradation. If necessary, RNA can be recovered from formamide by precipitation with 4 volumes of ethanol as described by Chomczynski (1992) or by diluting the formamide fourfold with 0.2 M NaCl and then adding the conventional 2 volumes of ethanol (Nadin-Davis and Mezl 1982).

- ***Dissolve the precipitate in an aqueous buffer and store at –80°C.*** Buffers commonly used for this purpose include SDS (0.1–0.5%) in TE (pH 7.6) or in DEPC-treated H_2O containing 0.1 mM EDTA (pH 7.5). The SDS should be removed by chloroform extraction and ethanol precipitation before enzymatic treatment of the RNA (e.g., primer extension, reverse transcription, and in vitro translation).

- ***Store the precipitate of RNA as a suspension at –20°C in ethanol.*** Samples of the RNA can be removed, as needed, with an automatic pipetting device. However, because precipitates of RNA are lumpy and sticky, and partly because of losses onto the surfaces of disposable pipette tips, the recovery of RNA is inconsistent.

Protocol 2

A Single-step Method for the Simultaneous Preparation of DNA, RNA, and Protein from Cells and Tissues

THE FOLLOWING PROTOCOL (CHOMCZYNSKI 1993), a variation on the single-step method described in Protocol 1, allows the simultaneous recovery of RNA, DNA, and protein from an aliquot of tissue or cells. Like its predecessor (Chomczynski and Sacchi 1987), this method involves lysis of cells with a monophasic solution of guanidine isothiocyanate and phenol. Addition of chloroform generates a second (organic) phase into which DNA and proteins are extracted, leaving RNA in the aqueous supernatant. The DNA and proteins can be isolated from the organic phase by sequential precipitation with ethanol and isopropanol, respectively. The DNA recovered from the organic phase is ~20 kb in size and is a suitable template for PCRs. The proteins, however, remain denatured as a consequence of their exposure to guanidine and are used chiefly for immunoblotting. The RNA precipitated from the aqueous phase with isopropanol can be further purified by chromatography on oligo(dT)-cellulose columns and/or used for northern blot hybridization, reverse transcription, or RT-PCRs.

The yield of total RNA depends on the tissue or cell source, but it is generally 4–7 µg/mg starting tissue or 5–10 µg/10^6 cells. The A_{260}/A_{280} ratio of the extracted RNA is generally 1.8–2.0.

MATERIALS

▲ IMPORTANT Prepare all reagents used in this protocol with DEPC-treated H_2O (please see the information panel on HOW TO WIN THE BATTLE WITH RNASE).

CAUTION: Please see Appendix 12 for appropriate handling of materials marked with <!>.

Buffers and Solutions

Please see Appendix 1 for components of stock solutions, buffers, and reagents.
Dilute stock solutions to the appropriate concentrations.

Chloroform <!>
Ethanol
Isopropanol
Liquid nitrogen <!>

Table 7-2 Monophasic Lysis Reagents

REAGENT	COMMERCIAL SUPPLIER
Trizol Reagent	Life Technologies
TRI Reagent	Molecular Research Center
Isogen	Nippon Gene, Toyama, Japan
RNA-Stat-60	Tel-Test

When using commercial reagents for the simultaneous isolation of RNA, DNA, and protein, we recommend following the manufacturer's instructions. In most cases, these differ little from the generic instructions given below. However, note that the modifications of the technique described in this protocol reduce the level of contamination of the RNA by DNA, polysaccharides, and proteoglycans. At the time of writing, not all of the manufacturer's instructions contained these modifications.

Monophasic lysis reagent

The composition of the monophasic lysis reagent used for the simultaneous isolation of RNA, DNA, and proteins has not been published. However, a large number of commercial reagents, with a variety of names, are available (please see Table 7-2). These reagents are all monophasic solutions containing phenol, guanidine, or ammonium thiocyanate and solubilizing agents.

Phosphate-buffered saline (PBS), ice-cold

Required for cells grown in suspension and monolayers only.

RNA precipitation solution

1.2 M NaCl

0.8 M disodium citrate $\cdot 15H_2O$

No adjustment of pH is required.

Sodium acetate (3 M, pH 5.2)

Cells and Tissues

Source cells/tissue

Centrifuges and Rotors

Sorvall H1000 rotor or equivalent

Sorvall SS-34 rotor or equivalent

Special Equipment

Cuvettes for measuring absorbance at 260 nm

The cuvettes should be either disposable UV-transparent methylacrylate or quartz. Before and after use, soak quartz cuvettes in concentrated HCl:methanol (1:1, v/v) for at least 30 minutes and then wash extensively in sterile H_2O.

Homogenizer (e.g., Tissumizer from Tekmar-Dohrmann or Polytron from Brinkmann)

Mortar and pestle washed in DEPC-treated H_2O, prechilled

Please see Chapter 6, Protocol 1.

Polypropylene snap-cap tube (e.g., Falcon)

Water bath, preset to 65°C

Optional, please see Step 7.

METHOD

1. Prepare cells or tissue samples for isolation of RNA.

FOR TISSUES

When working with tissues such as pancreas or gut that are rich in degradative enzymes, it is best to cut the dissected tissue into small pieces (100 mg) and then drop the fragments immediately into liquid nitrogen. Fragments of snap-frozen tissue can be transferred to –70ºC for storage or used immediately for extraction of RNA as described below. Tissues can be stored at –70ºC for several months without affecting the yield or integrity of the RNA.

Snap-freezing and pulverization are not always necessary. Tissues that are not as rich in RNases may be rapidly minced into small pieces and transferred directly into polypropylene snap-cap tubes containing the appropriate amount of Solution D (Step c) below.

a. Isolate the desired tissues by dissection and place them immediately in liquid nitrogen.

b. Transfer ~100 mg of the frozen tissue to a mortar containing liquid nitrogen and pulverize the tissue using a pestle. The tissue can be kept frozen during pulverization by the addition of liquid nitrogen.

c. Transfer the powdered tissue to a polypropylene snap-cap tube containing 1 ml of ice-cold monophasic lysis reagent.

d. Homogenize the tissue with a polytron homogenizer for 15–30 seconds at room temperature.

> Instead of grinding in a mortar, frozen tissue may be placed inside a homemade bag of plastic film and pulverized with a blunt instrument (e.g., a hammer) (Gramza et al. 1995). Only certain types of plastic film are tough enough to withstand hammering at low temperature (e.g., Write-On Transparency Film from 3M).

FOR MAMMALIAN CELLS GROWN IN SUSPENSION

a. Harvest the cells by centrifugation at 200–1900*g* (1000–3000 rpm in a Sorvall H1000 rotor) for 5–10 minutes at room temperature in a benchtop centrifuge.

b. Remove the medium by aspiration and resuspend the cell pellets in 1–2 ml of sterile ice-cold PBS.

c. Harvest the cells by centrifugation, remove the PBS completely by aspiration, and add 1 ml of monophasic lysis reagent per 10^6 cells.

d. Homogenize the cells with a polytron homogenizer for 15–30 seconds at room temperature.

FOR MAMMALIAN CELLS GROWN IN MONOLAYERS

a. Remove the medium and rinse the cells once with 5–10 ml of sterile ice-cold PBS.

b. Remove PBS and lyse the cells in 1 ml of monophasic lysis reagent per 90-mm culture dish (0.7 ml per 60-mm dish).

c. Transfer the cell lysates to a polypropylene snap-cap tube.

d. Homogenize the lysates with a polytron homogenizer for 15–30 seconds at room temperature.

2. Incubate the homogenates for 5 minutes at room temperature to permit complete dissociation of nucleoprotein complexes.

3. Add 0.2 ml of chloroform per milliliter of monophasic lysis reagent. Mix the samples by vigorous shaking or vortexing.

4. Separate the mixture into two phases by centrifuging at 12,000 rpm (10,000*g* in a Sorvall SS-34 rotor) for 15 minutes at 4ºC. Transfer the upper aqueous phase to a fresh tube.

> DNA and protein are extracted into the organic phase, leaving RNA in the aqueous phase. DNA and protein may be recovered from the organic phase by sequential precipitation with ethanol and isopropanol.

5. Precipitate the RNA from the aqueous phase: For each initial milliliter of monophasic lysis reagent, add 0.25 volume of isopropanol and 0.25 volume of RNA precipitation solution. After thorough mixing, store the final solution for 10 minutes at room temperature.

> The original protocols describing monophasic lysis reagents (Chomczynski 1993; Simms et al. 1993) suggested using 0.5 volume of isopropanol to precipitate RNA from the aqueous phase. However, this step has been modified in the light of the discovery (Schick and Eras 1995) that guanidine-based extraction methods generate RNA preparations that are contaminated to a significant extent by polysaccharides and proteoglycans. These contaminants are reported to prevent solubilization of RNA after precipitation with alcohols, to inhibit RT-PCRs, and to bind to membranes during northern blotting (Groppe and Morse 1993; Re et al. 1995; Schick and Eras 1995). Changing the conditions used to precipitate RNA from the aqueous phase (Chomczynski and Mackey 1995), as described in Step 5, greatly reduces the level of contamination with proteoglycans and polysaccharides and eliminates most of the problems mentioned above.

6. Collect the precipitated RNA by centrifugation at maximum speed for 10 minutes at 4ºC in a microfuge. Wash the pellet twice with 75% ethanol, and centrifuge again. Remove any remaining ethanol with a disposable pipette tip. Store the open tube on the bench for a few minutes to allow the ethanol to evaporate. Do not allow pellet to dry completely.

7. Add 50–100 µl of DEPC-treated H_2O. Store the RNA solution at –70ºC.

> Addition of SDS to 0.5% followed by heating to 65ºC may assist dissolution of the pellet.

8. Estimate the concentration of the RNA as described in Appendix 8.

> Purified RNA is not immune to degradation by RNase after resuspension in the 0.5% SDS solution. Some investigators therefore prefer to dissolve the pellet of RNA in 50–100 µl of stabilized formamide and store the solution at –20ºC (Chomczynski 1992). RNA can be recovered from formamide by precipitation with 4 volumes of ethanol. For further details, please see the panel on **STORAGE OF RNA** in Protocol 1.

> SDS should be removed by chloroform extraction and standard ethanol precipitation before enzymatic treatment of the RNA (e.g., primer extension, reverse transcription, and in vitro translation). The redissolved RNA can then be used for mRNA purification by oligo(dT)-cellulose chromatography (Protocol 3), or analyzed by standard techniques such as blot hybridization (Protocols 7 and 8) or mapping (Protocols 10, 11, and 12).

> RNA prepared from tissues is generally not contaminated to a significant extent with DNA. However, RNA prepared from cell lines undergoing spontaneous or induced apoptosis is often contaminated with fragments of degraded genomic DNA. RNA prepared from transfected cells is almost always contaminated by fragments of the DNA used for transfection. Some investigators therefore treat the final RNA preparation with RNase-free DNase (Grillo and Margolis 1990; Simms et al. 1993). Alternatively, fragments of DNA may be removed by preparing poly(A)$^+$ RNA by oligo(dT) chromatography.

Protocol 3

Selection of Poly(A)$^+$ RNA by Oligo(dT)-Cellulose Chromatography

B$_{\text{Y CONTRAST TO}}$ rRNA, 5S RNA, 5.8S RNA, $_{\text{AND}}$ tRNA, most eukaryotic mRNAs carry tracts of poly(A) at their 3′ termini. mRNAs can therefore be separated from the bulk of cellular RNA by affinity chromatography on oligo(dT)-cellulose (Edmonds et al. 1971; Aviv and Leder 1972). The method takes advantage of the ability of poly(A) tails on the mRNAs to form stable RNA-DNA hybrids with short chains of oligo(dT) (generally 18–30 nucleotides in length) linked to a supporting cellulose matrix (please see the panel on **OLIGO(dT) CELLULOSE** on the following page). Because only a few dT-A base pairs are formed, high salt must be added to the initial chromatography buffer to stabilize the nucleic acid duplexes. After nonpolyadenylated RNAs have been washed from the matrix, a low-salt buffer is used to destabilize the double-stranded structures and to elute the poly(A)$^+$ RNAs from the resin.

Poly(A)$^+$ RNA can be selected by chromatography on oligo(dT) columns (this protocol) or by batch elution (Protocol 4). Column chromatography is the preferred method for purification of large quantities (>25 µg) of nonradioactive poly(A)$^+$ RNA extracted from mammalian cells. For simultaneous processing of many samples of mammalian RNA, whether radioactive or not, batch elution is the better choice because fewer fractions are collected, which speeds up the process; and because a finer grade of oligo(dT)-cellulose (type III) can be used, which increases the efficiency of binding and elution of RNA. In general, between 1% and 10% of the total RNA applied to an oligo(dT) column is recovered as poly(A)$^+$ RNA. However, it is very difficult to remove all of the nonpolyadenylated RNA species completely, even after five to six cycles of affinity chromatography.

Oligo(dT)-cellulose chromatography represents an essential step when preparing mRNA to be used as a template for construction of cDNA libraries. In addition, poly(A)$^+$ RNA usually yields better results than total RNA when analyzed by blot hybridization, PCR, or nuclease S1 and RNase protection assays. This improvement is attributable to the 10–30-fold purification of mRNA obtained by chromatography on oligo(dT)-cellulose.

OLIGO(dT)-CELLULOSE

Oligo(dT) continues to be heavily exploited as an affinity ligand to isolate and purify poly(A)$^+$ mRNA, essentially as described by Aviv and Leder (1972) and Nakazato and Edmonds (1972). For this purpose, thymidylate oligomers 12–18 residues in length are covalently attached to a solid matrix (usually cellulose). The standard method of synthesis of the oligomers, pioneered by Gilham (1964, 1971), involves polymerization of thymidine monophosphate in the presence of a carbodiimide. Cellulose is then added, to which the oligothymidylate molecules become attached by reaction between their 5-phosphoryl groups and the hydroxyl groups of cellulose. Gilham (1964) used oligo(dT)-cellulose columns chiefly to explore affinity chromatography of polynucleotides, showing that various oligomers of adenylic acid could be eluted from an oligo(dT)-cellulose column in a temperature-dependent fashion. For isolation of mRNA, however, it is more convenient to exploit the salt dependence of the hybridization reaction, as described in this protocol.

Oligo(dT)-celluloses are sold by a number of commercial suppliers in a variety of grades that differ in purity, flow rate, and binding capacity. As much as 10 mg of total cellular RNA can be applied to a 1-ml column of packed oligo(dT), which can bind at least 500 μg of poly(A)$^+$ RNA. Other supports for oligo(dT) that have been used from time to time include silicas, controlled pore-glass, latex, polystyrene, and paramagnetic beads (which can be recovered by a magnet) (for reviews, please see Hornes and Korsnes 1990; Jarret 1993). These rigid supports, although more expensive, can give better performance and are therefore used chiefly for more stringent tasks such as construction of subtractive cDNA libraries, solid-phase synthesis of cDNA (e.g., please see Kuribayashi-Ohta et al. 1993; Eberwine 1996), and capture of specific mRNAs by sandwich hybridization (e.g., please see Hunsaker et al. 1989; Morrissey et al. 1989; Hara et al. 1993).

MATERIALS

▲ IMPORTANT Prepare all reagents used in this protocol with DEPC-treated H$_2$O (please see the information panel on **HOW TO WIN THE BATTLE WITH RNASE**).

CAUTION: Please see Appendix 12 for appropriate handling of materials marked with <!>.

Buffers and Solutions

Please see Appendix 1 for components of stock solutions, buffers, and reagents. Dilute stock solutions to the appropriate concentrations.

2× Column-loading buffer
40 mM Tris-Cl (pH 7.6)
1 mM NaCl
2 mM EDTA (pH 8.0)
0.2% (w/v) sodium lauryl sarcosinate

Prepare as described below.

Make up Tris-Cl (pH 7.6) from a fresh bottle in autoclaved, DEPC-treated H$_2$O. Prepare NaCl and EDTA in 0.1% DEPC <!> in H$_2$O. Store for at least 12 hours at 37ºC and autoclave the mixture for 15 minutes at 15 psi (1.05 kg/cm^2) on liquid cycle (please see the information panels on **HOW TO WIN THE BATTLE WITH RNASE** and **DIETHYLPYROCARBONATE**). To prepare sterile column-loading buffer, mix appropriate amounts of RNase-free stock solutions of Tris-Cl (pH 7.6), NaCl, and EDTA (pH 8.0) in an RNase-free container. Allow the solution to cool to ~65ºC, and then add sodium lauryl sarcosinate from a 10% stock solution that has been heated to 65ºC for 30 minutes.

Alternatively, substitute 0.05 M sodium citrate for Tris-Cl, and treat the sodium citrate/NaCl/EDTA mixture and sodium lauryl sarcosinate with DEPC (please see Protocol 1). Store column-loading buffer at room temperature.

Elution buffer
10 mM Tris-Cl (pH 7.6)
1 mM EDTA (pH 8.0)
0.05% SDS

The stock solutions of Tris-Cl and EDTA used to make elution buffer should be freshly autoclaved (15 minutes at 15 psi [1.05 kg/cm^2] on liquid cycle) and then diluted with the appropriate amount of sterile DEPC-treated H$_2$O. Then add the SDS from a concentrated stock solution (10% or 20%) made in sterile DEPC-treated H$_2$O.

▲ IMPORTANT Do not attempt to sterilize elution buffer by autoclaving as it froths excessively.

Ethanol

NaCl (5 M), RNase-free

NaOH (10 N) <!>

Dilute working solution from 10 N stock with sterile DEPC-treated H_2O.

Sodium acetate (3 M, pH 5.2)

Nucleic Acids and Oligonucleotides

RNA, total

Prepared as described in Protocol 1 or 2 of this chapter.

Centrifuges and Rotors

Sorvall SS-34 rotor or equivalent

Special Equipment

Cuvettes for measuring absorbance at 260 nm

Use disposable UV-transparent methacrylate cuvettes or standard quartz cuvettes. Before and after use, soak quartz cuvettes in concentrated HCl:methanol (1:1, v/v) for at least 30 minutes and then wash extensively in sterile H_2O.

Dispocolumn (Bio-Rad) or a Pasteur pipette plugged with sterile glass wool

The Dispocolumn should be treated with DEPC (please see the information panel on **DIETHYLPYRO-CARBONATE**). The plugged Pasteur pipette should be sterilized by baking for 4 hours at 300ºC.

Equipment for storage of RNA

Please see the panel on **STORAGE OF RNA** in Protocol 1.

Oligo(dT)-cellulose

This resin is usually purchased commercially as a dried powder. Use a high grade of resin, such as Type VII oligo(dT)-cellulose from Pharmacia.

Some protocols call for the use of poly(U)-Sephadex rather than oligo(dT)-cellulose. Although both resins give excellent results, oligo(dT)-cellulose is preferred because of its durability. However, poly(U)-Sephadex has a faster flow rate, which is a convenience when large volumes are to be passed through the column.

Columns of oligo(dT)-cellulose can be stored at 4ºC and reused many times. Between uses, regenerate the column by sequential washing with NaOH, H_2O, and column-loading buffer as described in Steps 1, 2, and 3 below. Spun columns (please see Appendix 8) containing oligo(dT)-cellulose are available from several commercial manufacturers.

pH Paper (pH Test Strips, Sigma)

Water bath preset to 65ºC

METHOD

Set Up and Load the Column

1. Suspend 0.5–1.0 g of oligo(dT)-cellulose in 0.1 N NaOH.

2. Pour a column of oligo(dT)-cellulose (0.5–1.0-ml packed volume) in a DEPC-treated Dispocolumn (or a Pasteur pipette, plugged with sterile glass wool and sterilized by baking for 4 hours at 300ºC). Wash the column with 3 column volumes of sterile DEPC-treated H_2O.

   Keep in mind that up to 10 mg of total RNA can be loaded onto 1 ml of packed oligo(dT)-cellulose. If smaller quantities of total RNA are used, the amount of oligo(dT)-cellulose should be reduced accordingly to avoid loss of poly(A)⁺ RNA both on the column and during the subsequent steps.

3. Wash the column with sterile 1x column-loading buffer (dilute from 2x stock using sterile DEPC-treated H_2O) until the pH of the effluent is <8.0. Use pH paper for this measurement.

4. Dissolve the RNA in double-distilled, autoclaved H_2O, and heat the solution to 65°C for 5 minutes. Cool the solution to room temperature quickly, and add 1 volume of 2x column-loading buffer.

> Heating the RNA disrupts regions of secondary structure that might involve the poly(A) tail. For RNAs that contain large amounts of secondary structure, the inclusion of dimethylsulfoxide (DMSO) at 10% (v/v) in the column-loading buffer may improve retention and subsequent recovery.

> The sodium salt of lauryl sarcosine is relatively insoluble and may therefore impede the flow of the column if the room temperature is less than 18°C. This problem can be avoided by using LiCl instead of NaCl in the column-loading buffer.

Recovering Poly(A)⁺ RNA from the Column

5. Apply the solution of RNA to the column, and immediately begin to collect in a sterile tube the material flowing through the column. When all of the RNA solution has entered the column, wash the column with 1 column volume of 1x column-loading buffer while continuing to collect the flow-through.

6. When all the liquid has emerged from the column, heat the collected flow-through to 65°C for 5 minutes and reapply it to the top of the column. Again collect the material flowing through the column.

> Unlike many chromatography resins, oligo(dT)-cellulose neither swells when hydrated nor cracks when dry. There is no need to maintain a flow of liquid through the column or to keep the matrix damp.

7. Wash the column with 5–10 column volumes of 1x column-loading buffer, collecting 1-ml fractions into sterile plastic tubes (e.g., microfuge tubes).

> In some protocols, the column is washed with 5 column volumes of 1x column-loading buffer containing 0.1 M NaCl after Step 7. However, very little or no nonpolyadenylated RNA elutes from the column during this wash, which can therefore be omitted.

8. Use quartz or disposable methacrylate cuvettes to measure the absorbance at 260 nm of a 1:20 dilution of each fraction collected from the column using 1x column-loading buffer as a blank.

> A solution containing 38 μg/ml RNA will give an absorbance reading of 1.0 at 260 nm and a reading of 0.4–0.5 at 280 nm. Initially, the OD_{260} will be very high as the nonpolyadenylated RNA passes through the column. The later fractions should have very little or no absorbance at 260 nm.

9. Precipitate the fractions containing a majority of the OD_{260} material by the addition of 2.5 volumes of ethanol.

> This so-called poly(A)⁻ RNA is a useful control in subsequent experiments.

Eluting Poly(A)⁺ RNA from the Column

10. Elute the poly(A)⁺ RNA from the oligo(dT)-cellulose with 2–3 column volumes of sterile, RNase-free elution buffer. Collect fractions equivalent in size to 1/3 to 1/2 of the column volume.

11. Use quartz or disposable methacrylate cuvettes to measure the absorbance at 260 nm of each fraction collected from the column. Pool the fractions containing the eluted RNA.

Further Purification of the RNA (Optional)

The material obtained after a single round of chromatography on oligo(dT)-cellulose usually contains approximately equal amounts of polyadenylated and nonpolyadenylated species of RNA. Polyadenylated RNA may be further purified as described in the following steps.

12. To purify poly(A)⁺ RNA further, heat the preparation of RNA to 65°C for 3 minutes and then cool it quickly to room temperature. Adjust the concentration of NaCl in the eluted RNA to 0.5 M using 5 M NaCl and carry out a second round of chromatography on the same column of oligo(dT)-cellulose (i.e., repeat Steps 3 and 5–11).

13. To the poly(A)⁺ RNA eluted from the second round of oligo(dT)-cellulose chromatography, add 3 M sodium acetate (pH 5.2) to a final concentration of 0.3 M. Mix well. Add 2.5 volumes of ice-cold ethanol, mix, and store the solution for at least 30 minutes on ice.

14. Recover the poly(A)⁺ RNA by centrifugation at 10,000*g* (9000 rpm in a Sorvall SS-34 rotor) for 15 minutes at 4°C. Carefully discard the supernatant, and wash the pellet (which is often invisible) with 70% ethanol. Recentrifuge briefly, remove the supernatant by aspiration, and store the open tube in an inverted position for a few minutes to allow most of the residual ethanol to evaporate. Do not allow the pellet to dry.

15. Redissolve the damp pellet of RNA in a small volume of sterile, DEPC-treated H_2O. Use quartz or disposable methacrylate cuvettes to measure the absorbance at 260 nm of each fraction collected from the column. Pool the fractions that contain RNA.

    Assume that the amount of poly(A)⁺ RNA recovered is equal to 5–10% of the starting total RNA and read the absorbance on an appropriate dilution of the resuspended RNA.

    A solution with an OD_{260} of 1 contains ~38 µg of RNA/ml.

16. Store the preparation of poly(A)⁺ RNA as described in the panel on STORAGE OF RNA in Protocol 1.

Protocol 4

Selection of Poly(A)$^+$ RNA by Batch Chromatography

WHEN MANY RNA SAMPLES ARE TO BE PROCESSED or when working with small amounts (<50 μg) of total mammalian RNA, the technique of choice is batch chromatography on oligo(dT)-cellulose. The method is carried out with a fine grade of oligo(dT)-cellulose at optimal temperatures for binding and elution. Many methods for purification of poly(A)$^+$ RNAs by batch chromatography have been published over the years. The technique described below is a modification of the method of Celano et al. (1993). For additional methods, please see the panel on ADDITIONAL METHODS TO SELECT POLY(A)$^+$ RNA following Step 15.

MATERIALS

▲ IMPORTANT Prepare all reagents used in this protocol with DEPC-treated H$_2$O (please see the information panel on HOW TO WIN THE BATTLE WITH RNASE).

CAUTION: Please see Appendix 12 for appropriate handling of materials marked with <!>.

Buffers and Solutions

Please see Appendix 1 for components of stock solutions, buffers, and reagents. Dilute stock solutions to the appropriate concentrations.

Absorption/washing buffer
    This buffer is TES containing 0.5 M NaCl.

Ammonium acetate (10 M) <!>

Ethanol

Ice-cold water

NaCl (5 M)

TES

Nucleic Acids and Oligonucleotides

RNA, total
    Prepared as described in Protocol 1 or 2 of this chapter.

Special Equipment

Cuvettes for measuring absorbance at 260 nm

Use disposable UV-transparent methacrylate cuvettes or standard quartz cuvettes. Before and after use, soak quartz cuvettes in concentrated HCl:methanol (1:1, v/v) for at least 30 minutes and then wash extensively in sterile H_2O.

Microfuge fitted with speed control

Oligo(dT)$_{18-30}$ cellulose

Use Type III cellulose (binding capacity 100 OD_{260}/g) equilibrated in absorption/washing buffer and suspended in the same buffer at a concentration of 100 mg/ml. For details, please see Protocol 3, Steps 1 through 3.

Rotating wheel

Water baths preset to 55°C and 65°C

METHOD

1. In a series of sterile microfuge tubes, adjust the volume of each sample of total RNA (up to 1 mg) to 600 µl with TES. Heat the sealed tubes to 65°C for 10 minutes and then cool them quickly in ice to 0°C. Add 75 µl (0.1 volume) of 5 M NaCl to each sample.

2. Add 50 mg (500 µl) of equilibrated oligo(dT)-cellulose to each tube and incubate the closed tubes on a rotating wheel for 15 minutes at room temperature.

3. Centrifuge the tubes at 600–800*g* (~1500–2500 rpm) for 2 minutes at room temperature in a microfuge.

4. Transfer the supernatants to a series of fresh microfuge tubes. Store the tubes on ice.

5. To the pellets of oligo(dT) remaining in the first set of tubes, add 1 ml of ice-cold absorption/washing buffer. Disperse the pellets of oligo(dT) by gentle vortexing. Incubate the closed tubes on a rotating wheel for 2 minutes at room temperature.

6. Centrifuge the tubes at 600–800*g* (~1500–2500 rpm) for 2 minutes at room temperature in a microfuge. Discard the supernatants and then repeat Steps 5 and 6 twice.

7. Resuspend the pellets of oligo(dT) in 0.4 ml of *ice-cold*, double-distilled, autoclaved H_2O by gentle vortexing. Immediately centrifuge the tubes for 2 minutes at 4°C in a microfuge.

8. Remove the supernatants by careful aspiration.

9. Recover the bound poly(A)⁺ RNA by resuspending the pellets of oligo(dT)-cellulose in 400 µl of double-distilled, autoclaved H_2O. Incubate the suspensions for 5 minutes at 55°C and then centrifuge the tubes for 2 minutes at 4°C in a microfuge.

10. Transfer the supernatants to a series of fresh tubes and repeat Step 9 twice, pooling the recovered supernatants.

11. Add 0.2 volume of 10 M ammonium acetate and 2.5 volumes of ethanol to the supernatants. Store the tubes for 30 minutes at –20°C.

12. Recover the precipitated poly(A)⁺ RNAs by centrifugation at maximum speed for 15 minutes at 4°C in a microfuge. Carefully discard the supernatants, and wash the pellets (which are often invisible) with 70% ethanol. Centrifuge briefly, remove the supernatants by aspiration, and store the open tubes in an inverted position for a few minutes to allow most of the residual ethanol to evaporate.

13. Dissolve the RNA in a small volume of sterile DEPC-treated H_2O.

14. Estimate the concentration of the RNA as described in Appendix 8.

15. Store the preparations as described in the panel on **STORAGE OF RNA** in Protocol 1.

ADDITIONAL METHODS TO SELECT POLY(A)$^+$ RNA

Many alternative methods to oligo(dT) chromatography have been devised over the years to select poly(A)$^+$ mRNA from preparations of total RNA. These methods include the following:

- *Chromatography on poly(U)-Sepharose* (Lindberg and Persson 1974). The advantage of this technique is that RNA molecules with short poly(A) tails will bind efficiently to the long (~100 nucleotide) poly(U) chains attached to the Sepharose. Disadvantages of the method include the comparatively low binding capacity of poly(U)-Sepharose and the necessity of using formamide-based buffers to elute the bound poly(A) RNA efficiently from the long poly(U) chains.

- *Paper filters to which poly(U) residues are covalently attached* (Wreschner and Herzberg 1984; Jacobson 1987). Total cellular RNA is spotted onto the filters, which are then washed in DEPC-treated 0.1 M NaCl and 70% ethanol. Poly(A)$^+$ RNA is eluted by heating the filters to 70°C for 5 minutes in H_2O. These filters bind up to 20 μg of poly(A)$^+$ RNA/cm^2 and are extremely useful when isolating small amounts of poly(A)$^+$ RNA from many samples simultaneously.

- *Streptavidin-coated paramagnetic polystyrene beads* (Albretsen et al. 1990; Hornes and Korsnes 1990; Jakobsen et al. 1990). These beads (available from Promega and other suppliers) have the advantage that mRNA can be directly isolated from lysis buffers containing guanidinium isothiocyanate. In a typical experiment, tissue, cells, or cell suspensions are lysed with guanidinium thiocyanate, and a biotinylated oligo(dT) primer is added directly to the lysate. After a short period of time to allow hybridization of the primer to the poly(A) tails of cellular mRNAs, magnetized beads to which streptavidin has been coupled are added to the lysate. The streptavidin captures the biotinylated oligo(dT)–poly(A)$^+$ mRNA complexes and affixes them to the magnetized beads. A magnet is then used to retrieve the beads from the lysate solution and to facilitate washing of the beads with a high-salt solution. In a final step, the poly(A)$^+$ mRNA is released from the beads with H_2O and then collected by ethanol precipitation. The yield of poly(A)$^+$ mRNA isolated with beads is equal to or exceeds that obtained by conventional oligo(dT)-cellulose chromatography. Among the advantages offered by these beads are speed of operation and the possibility of working at kinetic rates close to those occurring in free solution. Binding of ligand takes only a few minutes, and magnetic separation takes seconds: Washing or elution can in most cases be completed in 15 minutes or less. However, the use of these beads have two strong drawbacks: A maximum of 1 g of tissue or cells can be worked up at any one time and the beads are very expensive.

Northern Hybridization

NORTHERN HYBRIDIZATION IS USED TO MEASURE the amount and size of RNAs transcribed from eukaryotic genes and to estimate their abundance. No other method is capable of obtaining these pieces of information simultaneously from a large number of RNA preparations; northern analysis is therefore fundamental to studies of gene expression in eukaryotic cells.

Northern hybridization became part of the standard repertoire of molecular biology almost immediately after the first descriptions of the method were published (Alwine et al. 1977, 1979). Although many variations and improvements (e.g., please see Kroczek 1993) have been published during the succeeding 20 years, the basic steps in northern analysis remain unchanged:

- isolation of intact mRNA

- separation of RNA according to size through a denaturing agarose gel

- transfer of the RNA to a solid support in a way that preserves its topological distribution within the gel

- fixation of the RNA to the solid matrix

- hybridization of the immobilized RNA to probes complementary to the sequences of interest

- removal of probe molecules that are nonspecifically bound to the solid matrix

- detection, capture, and analysis of an image of the specifically bound probe molecules.

There are choices at every step during the process and new alternatives continually appear in the literature. It is impossible to distill from this ferment the "best" combination of methods that can be universally applied in all situations. However, the methods described in the next five protocols are extremely robust and have worked well in a wide variety of circumstances.

SEPARATION OF RNA ACCORDING TO SIZE

Electrophoresis through denaturing agarose gels is used to separate RNAs according to size and is the first stage in northern hybridization. In earlier times, methylmercuric hydroxide (Bailey and Davidson 1976) achieved some degree of popularity, particularly among the brave and foolhardy. Although unparalleled as a denaturing agent, methylmercuric hydroxide is both volatile and extremely toxic (Cummins and Nesbitt 1978) and is therefore no longer recommended. The following are the two methods most commonly used today to separate denatured RNAs for northern analysis.

- Electrophoresis of RNA denatured with glyoxal/formamide through agarose gels (Protocol 5) (Bantle et al. 1976; McMaster and Carmichael 1977; Goldberg 1980; Thomas 1980, 1983).

- Pretreatment of RNA with formaldehyde and dimethylsulfoxide, followed by electrophoresis through gels containing up to 2.2 M formaldehyde (Protocol 6) (Boedtker 1971; Lehrach et al. 1977; Rave et al. 1979).

The two systems have approximately the same resolving power (Miller 1987), and the technical problems with both of them have long since been solved. For example, recirculation of electrophoresis buffer is no longer required when separating glyoxylated RNA in agarose gels and staining of RNA with ethidium bromide is now possible. However, glyoxal and especially formaldehyde retain some disadvantages, including toxicity. The choice between the systems therefore depends on the relative weight of these disadvantages, which will vary from one laboratory to the next.

Many compounds other than glyoxal, formaldehyde, and methylmercuric hydroxide have been explored as denaturing agents for RNA during gel electrophoresis, but few of these have proven to be reliable in routine laboratory use. Guanidine thiocyanate is the only compound that may have advantages over formaldehyde or glyoxal (Goda and Minton 1995). When incorporated into an agarose gel at a final concentration of 10 mM, it maintains RNA in a denatured form. Electrophoresis may be carried out in standard TBE buffer and ethidium bromide may be incorporated in the gel. However, few laboratories have adopted the method, and at present, experience with this system is too limited for us to recommend that guanidine thiocyanate be used in place of glyoxal and fomaldehyde.

EQUALIZING AMOUNTS OF RNA IN NORTHERN GELS

Equalizing the amounts of RNA loaded into lanes of northern gels is a thorny problem when a number of different samples are to be compared. Several different approaches are possible and none of them perfect:

- ***Loading of equal amounts of RNA*** (usually 0.5–0.7 OD_{260} units) into each lane of the gel. rRNAs are the dominant components in preparations of total cellular RNA and contribute >75% of the UV-absorbing material. Northern analysis of equal quantities of total RNA shows how the steady-state concentration of target mRNAs changes with respect to rRNA content of the cell (Alwine et al. 1977; de Leeuw et al. 1989). Unlike the transcripts of housekeeping genes (see below), there is no evidence that the levels of 18S or 28S rRNA vary significantly from one mammalian tissue or cell line to the next (e.g., please see Bhatia et al. 1994). In addition, rRNA can easily be detected in agarose gels by staining with ethidium bromide instead of a second round of hybridization with a specific probe.

- ***Normalizing samples according to their content of mRNAs*** of an endogenous, constitutively expressed housekeeping gene such as cyclophilin, β-actin, or glyceraldehyde-3-phosphate dehydrogenase (GAPDH) (Kelly et al. 1983). All three genes are expressed at moderately abundant levels (~0.1% of poly(A)$^+$ RNA or 0.003% of total cellular RNA). Variations observed in the intensity of the hybridization signal of the gene of interest are often expressed relative to one of these three housekeeping genes. However, it turns out that the levels of expression of housekeeping genes are not constant from one mammalian tissue to another nor from one cell line to another (e.g., please see Spanakis 1993; Bhatia et al. 1994). Alterations in the relative intensity of the hybridization signals between the housekeeping gene and the gene of interest may therefore result from changes in the level of transcription of either gene or both.

- **Loading of equal amounts of poly(A)⁺ RNA.** The poly(A)⁺ content of preparations of RNA can be compared by slot- or dot-blot hybridization to a radiolabeled poly(dT) probe (Harley 1987, 1988). Equivalent amounts of poly(A)⁺ RNA can then be loaded into each lane of a northern gel. This is an attractive option because it measures changes in concentration of a specific mRNA relative to the total amount of gene transcripts in the cell.

- **Using a synthetic pseudomessage as a standard.** Several groups (e.g., please see Toscani et al. 1987; DuBois et al. 1993) have used RNAs synthesized in vitro as externally added standards to calibrate the expression of the gene of interest in different preparations of cellular RNA. The synthetic pseudomessage, which is engineered to be different in size from the natural message, is added in known amounts to samples at the time of cell lysis. The relative intensity of the hybridization signals obtained from the authentic and pseudomessages is used to estimate the expression of the endogenous gene of interest.

MARKERS USED IN GELS TO FRACTIONATE RNA

The size of an RNA of interest can be measured accurately only when markers of known molecular weight are included in the gel. Four types of markers are commonly used:

- **RNA standards purchased from a commercial source.** These standards are usually generated by in vitro transcription of cloned DNA templates of known length. As a consequence, the RNA standards are sometimes contaminated by template DNA and its associated plasmid sequences. Vector sequences present in the probe used in northern hybridization may hybridize to these remnants, generating on the autoradiogram either discrete bands or, more commonly, a smear where none should be.

- **DNA standards purchased from a commercial source.** Glyoxylated denatured DNAs and RNAs of equal length migrate at equal speeds through agarose gels. Small DNAs of known size can therefore be used as markers in this system. Once again, however, there is a chance that vector sequences present in the probe may hybridize with the standards. At times, this can be an advantage because the signals generated by the marker bands on the autoradiogram can be used directly to measure the size of the RNA of interest. DNA standards should not be used as markers on gels containing formaldehyde since RNA migrates through these gels at a faster rate than DNA of equivalent size (Wicks 1986).

- **Highly abundant rRNAs (28S and 18S) within the RNA preparations under test.** The sizes of these RNAs vary slightly from one mammalian species to another. 18S rRNAs range in size from 1.8 kb to 2.0 kb, whereas 28S RNAs range between 4.6 kb and 5.3 kb in length.

- **Tracking dyes.** In most denaturing agarose gel systems, bromophenol blue migrates slightly faster than the 5S rRNA, whereas xylene cyanol migrates slightly slower than the 18S rRNA.

MEMBRANES USED FOR NORTHERN HYBRIDIZATION

Transfer of electrophoretically separated DNA and RNA from gels to two-dimensional solid supports is a key step in northern hybridization. Initially, hybridization was carried out exclusively with RNA immobilized on activated cellulose papers (Alwine et al. 1977; Seed 1982a,b). However, it was soon realized that RNA denatured by glyoxal, formaldehyde, or methylmercuric hydroxide, like denatured DNA, binds tightly to nitrocellulose (Thomas 1980, 1983). For several years thereafter, nitrocellulose was the support of choice for northern hybridization.

Unfortunately, nitrocellulose is not an ideal matrix for solid-phase hybridization because its capacity to bind nucleic acids is low (~50–100 µg/cm^2) and varies according to the size of the RNA. In addition, the RNA becomes attached to nitrocellulose by hydrophobic rather than covalent interactions and therefore leaches slowly from the solid support during hybridization and washing at high temperatures. Finally, nitrocellulose membranes become brittle during baking under vacuum at 80ºC, which is an integral part of the process to immobilize nucleic acids. The friable membranes cannot subsequently survive more than two to three cycles of hybridization and washing at high temperatures.

These problems have been solved by the introduction of various types of nylon membranes that bind nucleic acids irreversibly, are far more durable than nitrocellulose filters (Reed and Mann 1985), and can be repaired if damaged (Pitas 1989). Immobilized nucleic acids can therefore be hybridized sequentially to several different probes. Furthermore, because nucleic acids can be immobilized on nylon in buffers of low ionic strength, transfer of nucleic acids from gels to nylon can be carried out electrophoretically. This advantage can be useful when capillary or vacuum transfer is inefficient, for example, when small molecules of RNA are transferred from polyacrylamide gels.

Two types of nylon membranes are available commercially: unmodified (or neutral) nylon and charge-modified nylon, which carries amine groups and is therefore also known as positively charged or (+) nylon. Both types of nylon bind single- and double-stranded nucleic acids and retention is quantitative in solvents as diverse as water, 0.25 N HCl, and 0.4 N NaOH. Charge-modified nylon has a greater capacity to bind nucleic acids (see Table 7-3), but it has a tendency to give increased levels of background hybridization, which results, at least in part, from nonspecific binding of negatively charged phosphate groups in RNA to the positively charged groups on the surface of the polymer. However, this problem can usually be controlled by using increased quantities of blocking agents in the prehybridization and hybridization steps.

Nylon is a generic name for any long-chain synthetic polymer having recurring polyamide (–CONH–) groups. Nylons of different types are formed from various combinations of diacids, diamines, and amino acids. In the standard nomenclature, a single numeral (e.g., nylon 6) indicates the number of carbon atoms in a monomer. Two numbers (e.g., nylon 6,6 or 66) indicate a polymer formed from diamines and dibasic acids. The first number indicates the number of carbon atoms separating the nitrogen atoms of the diamine, and the second number indicates the number of straight chain carbon atoms in the dibasic amino acid.

Fiber 66, the original name of nylon, was developed in the 1930s by Wallace Carothers, a chemist working for DuPont (see Fenichell 1999). His discovery, which grew from a decade of research on the structure and assembly of long-chain polyamide polymers, should have been the capstone of his career, but instead was the catalyst to tragedy. Carothers, more a scientific aesthete than a twentieth century company man, became deeply depressed by the idea that he had discovered a material whose chief use seemed to be as a replacement for silk stockings. In 1937, a few days after filing his patent for Fiber 66, Carothers, just 41 years old, killed himself in a hotel room by swallowing cyanide. DuPont pressed ahead with the commercial development of Fiber 66 and, in a ceremony that would have been anathema to Carothers, dedicated the name nylon to the public domain at a Herald Tribune Forum in October of the following year. Stockings, of course, turned out to be just the first of a line of nylon products, some of which would surely have given Carothers great pleasure, including perhaps, nylon membranes for immobilizing nucleic acids.

Different brands of nylon membranes are available that vary in the extent and type of charged groups and the density of the nylon mesh. Comparisons of the efficiency of these membranes for northern blotting and hybridization under various conditions are published from time to time (e.g., please see Khandjian 1987; Rosen et al. 1990; Twomey and Krawetz 1990; Beckers et al. 1994). In addition, each manufacturer provides specific recommendations for the transfer of nucleic acids to their particular product. The instructions given in Protocols 6 through 8 (northern hybridization) and in Chapter 6, Protocols 8–10 (Southern transfer) work well in almost all circumstances, and in some cases, yield results that exceed the manufacturer's standard.

TABLE 7-3 Properties of Nylon Membranes Used for Immobilization of DNA and RNA

PROPERTY	NEUTRAL NYLON	CHARGED NYLON
Capacity (μg nucleic acid/cm^2)	~200–300	400–500
Size of nucleic acid required for maximal binding	>50 bp	>50 bp
Transfer buffer	low ionic strength over a wide range of pH	
Immobilization	baking for 1 hour at 70°C; no vacuum required *or* mild alkali *or* UV irradiation at 254 nm; damp membranes are generally exposed to 1.6 kJ/m^2; dried membranes require 160 kJ/m^2	
Commercial products	Hybond-N Gene-Screen	Hybond-N+ Zeta-Probe Nytran + Gene-Screen Plus

TRANSFERRING RNA FROM GELS TO SOLID SUPPORTS

The crucial step in northern analysis is the transfer of denatured RNA from the interstices of an agarose gel to the surface of a membrane. Transfer must be done in a way that not only preserves the distribution of the molecules along the length of the gel, but works efficiently for nucleic acids of quite different sizes. Over the years, many methods have been found to achieve these goals, including electroblotting, vacuum blotting, semidry blotting, and upward capillary blotting. In addition, several attempts have been made to avoid transfer completely by performing hybridization directly in the gel (e.g., please see Purrello and Balazs 1983; Tsao et al. 1983). However, it is not clear whether these techniques, which may require expensive pieces of equipment, are superior to the original method of upward capillary transfer (Southern 1975). Certainly, there does not seem to be any good reason to rush out and buy a vacuum blotting or electroblotting apparatus in the belief that it will significantly improve northern and Southern blots.

- *Upward capillary transfer.* The original simple and economical technique devised by Southern (1975) involves an overnight transfer of nucleic acids from gel to membrane in an upward flow of buffer (please see Figure 7-2). A major drawback is selective retention of large molecules of nucleic acid within the gel, which is caused by flattening, compression, and dehydration of the gel. This problem can be relieved (1) by using the thinnest gels possible, (2) by ensuring that the filter papers in immediate contact with the gel are thoroughly saturated with buffer before transfer begins, and (3) by partial hydrolysis of RNA by alkali (Reed and Mann 1985) before transfer. It is important that partial hydrolysis be used with moderation since overenthusiasm can generate fragments too short to bind efficiently to the membrane.

  Since 1975, the common practice has been to carry out upward capillary transfer for 16 hours or so. However, ascending transfer is now known to be almost complete after 4 hours (Lichtenstein et al. 1990), and we now recommend much shorter transfer times. A more serious problem with ascending transfer is the potential for some of the RNA to move from the gel in a descending direction counter to the flow of the buffer. This apparent anomaly occurs when the filter paper under the gel is not fully saturated with buffer. Fluid is then drawn from the gel, carrying with it some of the nucleic acid. The problem can be ameliorated by ensuring that the bottom filter paper, like the top, is fully saturated with buffer and by working quickly to set up the remainder of the transfer system once the gel has been laid on the bottom filter.

- **Downward capillary transfer.** Descending transfer (please see Figure 7-3) does not cause flattening of the agarose gel and results in a faster transfer of nucleic acid. RNA molecules up to 8 kb in size, for example, are transferred with high efficiency within 1 hour at either neutral or alkaline pH (Chomczynski 1992; Chomczynski and Mackey 1994). The speed of downward capillary transfer therefore has particular advantage when carrying out alkaline blotting of RNA. Blotting of RNA for more than 4 hours significantly decreases the strength of the hybridization signal, presumably due to excessive hydrolysis of the RNA.

FURTHER INFORMATION ABOUT NORTHERN HYBRIDIZATION

Northern and Southern hybridizations have much in common, including, for example, the mechanics of hybridization, the types of probes, and the posthybridization processing of the membranes. All of these topics are discussed in depth in other areas within this manual. Signposts to this information are posted at relevant positions within the next five protocols.

Protocol 5

Separation of RNA According to Size: Electrophoresis of Glyoxylated RNA through Agarose Gels

THE METHOD DESCRIBED IN THIS PROTOCOL INCORPORATES GLYOXAL denaturation with agarose gel electrophoresis (adapted from McMaster and Carmichael [1977] and Thomas [1983]). The conditions for simultaneous glyoxylation of RNA and staining with ethidium bromide, as well as the modifications to the electrophoresis buffer, are those of Burnett (1997).

> Glyoxal (also known as diformyl and ethanedial) is used to eliminate secondary structures in single-stranded RNA during electrophoresis through agarose gels. The two aldehyde groups of glyoxal react under slightly acid conditions with the imino groups of guanosine to form a cyclic compound that prevents formation of intrastrand Watson-Crick bonds (Salomaa 1956; Shapiro and Hachmann 1966; Nakaya et al. 1968). Once established, this adduct is stable at room temperature at pH ≤ 7.0, so an aldehyde need not be incorporated into the agarose gel (McMaster and Carmichael 1977). Because the glyoxylated RNA is unable to form stable secondary structures, it migrates through agarose gels at a rate that is approximately proportional to the $\log_{10}$ of its size (McMaster and Carmichael 1977).

Agarose gel electrophoresis of glyoxylated RNA must be carried out at low ionic strength to suppress renaturation of the RNA. The running buffers used until recently (10 mM phosphate or 40 mM 3-N-morpholinopropanesulfonic acid [MOPS]) had limited buffering capacity. Thus, a major drawback to the use of glyoxal as a denaturing agent was the upward shift in pH of the standard electrophoresis buffer that occurred in the cathodic chamber during running of the agarose gel. If this shift were allowed to proceed unhindered, a steep pH gradient would form as small ions in the buffers migrated rapidly along the gel from the cathode (O'Conner et al. 1991), resulting in removal of the glyoxal adduct from the RNA (Nakaya et al. 1968). For many years, it has therefore been necessary to recirculate the buffer mechanically or to replace it at regular intervals during the electrophoretic run. A more recent solution to this problem is to use a more stable electrophoresis buffer containing a weak acid and a weak base with similar pK values (Burnett 1997).

Staining glyoxylated RNA in agarose gels has also been a problem until recently. Staining the gel with ethidium bromide after electrophoresis is insensitive because of the high background of nonspecific fluorescence. Acridine orange, which has been used for years to stain DNA and RNA (Richards et al. 1965), gives stronger signals than ethidium bromide but requires extensive washing of the gel. Staining the RNA during glyoxylation before loading the gel has always seemed to be an unpromising approach since ethidium bromide was reported to react with glyoxal

(McMaster and Carmichael 1977). Recently, however, Gründemann and Koepsell (1994) and Burnett (1997) have reported that RNA can be effectively stained during denaturation with glyoxal and that the limits of detection are ~10 ng of RNA per band. However, such high sensitivity comes at a price: Staining with ethidium bromide results in a modest decrease in hybridization efficiency after transfer of the RNA to a membrane (Wilkinson et al. 1990).

If a decrease in hybridization efficiency is unacceptable, then ethidium bromide should be left out of the glyoxal reaction mixture and Steps 1 through 5 should be followed as indicated. After electrophoresis, the outside lanes of the agarose gel containing the size standards should be cut from the gel, incubated for 30 minutes at room temperature in 0.05 M NaOH containing 1 µg/ml ethidium bromide, and photographed with UV illumination. The remainder of the gel containing the cellular RNAs is then processed as described in Protocol 7.

MATERIALS

▲ IMPORTANT Prepare all reagents used in this protocol with RNase-free H_2O (please see the information panel on **HOW TO WIN THE BATTLE WITH RNASE**).

CAUTION: Please see Appendix 12 for appropriate handling of materials marked with <!>.

Buffers and Solutions

Please see Appendix 1 for components of stock solutions, buffers, and reagents. Dilute stock solutions to the appropriate concentrations.

10x BPTE electrophoresis buffer
100 mM PIPES (piperazine-1,4-bis[2-ethanesulfonic acid])
300 mM Bis-Tris (bis[2-hyroxyethyl]iminotris[hydroxymethyl]methane)
10 mM EDTA (pH 8.0)

The final pH of the 10x buffer is ~6.5.

Prepare the 10x buffer by adding 3 g of PIPES (free acid), 6 g of Bis-Tris (free base), and 2 ml of 0.5 M EDTA (pH 8.0) to 90 ml of distilled H_2O, then treating the solution with DEPC, final concentration 0.1%, for 1 hour at 37°C, and then autoclaving (for more details, please see the information panel on **DIETHYLPYROCARBONATE**).

DMSO <!>
Purchase a high grade of DMSO (HPLC grade or better).

Glyoxal
Commercial stock solutions of glyoxal (40% or 6 M) contain various hydrated forms of glyoxal, as well as oxidation products such as glyoxylic acid, formic acid, and other compounds that can degrade RNA, and therefore must be removed (please see Appendix 1).

Glyoxal reaction mixture
6 ml of DMSO
2 ml of deionized glyoxal
1.2 ml of 10x BPTE electrophoresis buffer
0.6 ml of 80% glycerol in H_2O
0.2 ml of ethidium bromide (10 mg/ml in H_2O) <!>

Divide into small aliquots and store at –70°C.

RNA gel-loading buffer

Gels

Agarose gel
Cast an agarose gel as described in Chapter 5, Protocol 1 in 1x BPTE electrophoresis buffer. Use a comb with at least four more teeth than the number of RNA samples under test. These extra lanes are used for RNA size markers and running dyes (please see Step 4). A 1.5% agarose gel is suitable for resolving RNAs in the 0.5–8.0-kb size range. Larger RNAs should be separated on 1.0% or 1.2% gels.

Nucleic Acids and Oligonucleotides

RNA samples

Samples of total or poly(A)$^+$ RNA should consist of up to 10 µg of RNA in a volume of 1–2 µl. Equivalent amounts of the RNA samples to be analyzed are removed from storage (please see the panel on **STORAGE OF RNA** in Protocol 1). Precipitate the RNA with ethanol and dissolve the pellet in an appropriate volume of sterile, DEPC-treated H$_2$O.

The presence of salts or SDS in the samples, or loading of >10 µg of RNA per lane, can cause smearing of the RNA during electrophoresis.

RNA size markers

Glyoxylated RNAs and DNAs of the same size migrate through agarose gels at the same rate. However, we recommend using RNA ladders (e.g., from Life Technologies) that contain RNAs of 9.49, 7.46, 4.40, 2.37, 1.35, and 0.24 kb in length. This allows the markers to be used as sentinels to detect RNase contamination or other problems that may occur during glyoxylation or electrophoresis. Please see the Introduction to Northern Hybridization preceding Protocol 5.

Special Equipment

Equipment for horizontal electrophoresis

A particular electrophoresis apparatus should be reserved for RNA analysis. Clean electrophoresis tanks and combs used for electrophoresis of RNA (Protocols 5 and 6) with detergent solution, rinse in H$_2$O, dry with ethanol, and then fill with a solution of 3% H$_2$O$_2$. After 10 minutes at room temperature, rinse the electrophoresis tanks and combs thoroughly with H$_2$O treated with 0.1% DEPC.

Ruler, transparent

Water bath preset to 55°C

METHOD

1. Set up the glyoxal denaturation reaction. In sterile microfuge tubes mix:

RNA (up to 10 µg)	1–2 µl
glyoxal reaction mixture	10 µl

   Up to 10 µg of RNA may be analyzed in each lane of the gel. Abundant mRNAs (0.1% or more of the mRNA population) can usually be detected by northern analysis of 10 µg of total cellular RNA. Detection of rare RNAs requires at least 1.0 µg of poly(A)$^+$ RNA. Samples containing RNA size markers should be prepared in glyoxal reaction mixture in the same way as the RNA samples under test. Please see the Introduction to Northern Hybridization (Equalizing Amounts of RNA in Northern Gels).

2. Close the tops of the microfuge tubes, and incubate the RNA solutions for 60 minutes at 55°C. Chill the samples for 10 minutes in ice water, and then centrifuge them for 5 seconds to deposit all of the fluid in the bottom of the microfuge tubes.

   Some investigators prefer to heat the RNA samples before electrophoresis for 10 minutes at 65°C.

3. While the samples are incubating, install the agarose gel in a horizontal electrophoresis box. Add sufficient 1x BPTE electrophoresis buffer to cover the gel to a depth of ~1 mm.

4. Add 1–2 µl of RNA gel-loading buffer to the glyoxylated RNA samples, and without delay, load the glyoxylated RNA samples into the wells of the gel, leaving the two outermost lanes on each side of the gel empty. Load the RNA size markers in the outside lanes of the gel.

5. Carry out electrophoresis at 5 V/cm until the bromophenol blue has migrated ~8 cm.

   Using higher voltages during electrophoresis leads to smearing of bands.

6. Visualize the RNAs by placing the gel on a piece of Saran Wrap on a UV transilluminator. Align a transparent ruler with the stained gel and photograph the gel under UV illumination.
   Please see the panel on **CHECKING THE QUALITY OF PREPARATIONS OF RNA.**

7. Use the photograph to measure the distance from the loading well to each of the bands of RNA. Plot the $\log_{10}$ of the size of the fragments of RNA against the distance migrated. Use the resulting curve to calculate the sizes of the RNA species detected by blot hybridization.

8. Proceed with immobilization of RNA onto a solid support by upward or downward capillary transfer (please see Protocol 7 or the panel on **ALTERNATIVE PROTOCOL: CAPILLARY TRANS-FER BY DOWNWARD FLOW** in Protocol 7).

CHECKING THE QUALITY OF PREPARATIONS OF RNA

After electrophoresis of RNA in the presence of ethidium bromide, the 28S and 18S species of rRNA should be clearly visible under UV illumination, as should a more diffuse, fast-migrating band composed of tRNA, 5.8S and 5S rRNA. If the RNA preparation is undegraded, the 28S rRNA band should be stained at approximately twice the intensity of the 18S band and no smearing of either band should be visible. Staining close to the loading well is a sign that DNA is still present in the preparation. mRNA is invisible unless the gel is overloaded. Three other methods can be used to check the integrity of RNA:

- *Analysis of the size of cDNA synthesized using oligo(dT) as a primer.* Radioactive cDNA is synthesized in a pilot first-strand cDNA reaction. cDNA synthesized from mammalian mRNA should run as a continuous smear from ~600 bases to >5 kb. The bulk of the radioactivity should lie between 1.5 kb and 2 kb, and no bands of cDNA should be visible unless the mRNA was prepared from highly differentiated cells (e.g., reticulocytes and B lymphocytes) that express large quantities of a particular set of proteins.

- *Use of radiolabeled poly(dT) as a probe in a pilot northern hybridization* (Fornace and Mitchell 1986; Hollander and Fornace 1990). Poly(A)$^+$ RNA will generate an autoradiogram with a continuous smear from 600 bases to >5 kb. The bulk of the radioactivity should lie between 1.5 kb and 2 kb, and, once again, no specific bands of mRNA should be visible unless the mRNA was prepared from cells that express large quantities of specific mRNAs.

- *Use of northern hybridization to detect mRNA of known size expressed from a housekeeping gene.* Glyceraldehyde 3-phosphate dehydrogenase (GAPDH) mRNA, whose size in most mammalian cells is ~1.3 kb, is commonly used to monitor the quality of the RNA. Significant smearing of the band into lower-molecular-weight regions generally indicates that significant degradation of the mRNA populations has occurred. Fuzziness, on the other hand, is a sign of problems with the agarose gel system (e.g., the presence of ions in the glyoxal).

Protocol 6

Separation of RNA According to Size: Electrophoresis of RNA through Agarose Gels Containing Formaldehyde

SAMPLES OF RNA MAY BE DENATURED BY TREATMENT WITH FORMAMIDE and separated by electrophoresis through agarose gels containing formaldehyde. In this method, adapted from Lehrach et al. (1977), Goldberg (1980), Seed (1982a), and Rosen et al. (1990), RNA is fractionated by electrophoresis through an agarose gel containing 2.2 M formaldehyde.

Formaldehyde forms unstable Schiff bases with the single imino group of guanine residues. These adducts maintain RNA in the denatured state by preventing intrastrand Watson-Crick base pairing. Because the Schiff bases are unstable and easily removed by dilution, RNA can be maintained in the denatured state only when formaldehyde is present in the buffer or gel. Formaldehyde, a teratogen, is highly toxic by inhalation and contact with the skin and has been classified as a carcinogen by the Occupational Safety and Health Association (OSHA). Solutions containing formaldehyde should be handled with great care and only in a chemical fume hood.

Agarose gels containing formaldehyde are slimier, less elastic, and more frangible than nondenaturing agarose gels. Great care is required in moving them from one receptacle to another. Nevertheless, formaldehyde-agarose gels remain a popular method of separating RNAs during northern analysis because the denaturant is more easily dissociated than is glyoxal from RNA after electrophoresis. However, the bands of RNA in formaldehyde-agarose gels are often fuzzy and do not match the crisp beauty of bands in glyoxal-agarose gels.

The original protocols for northern analysis used gels with a formaldehyde content of 6% or 2.2 M (Boedtker 1971; Lehrach et al. 1977; Rave et al. 1979). This high concentration of denaturant compensates for loss of formaldehyde by diffusion from the gel into the buffer during electrophoresis. However, this problem can also be avoided by running gels for shorter times at higher voltages (7–10 V/cm, instead of the more usual 2–3 V/cm), which allows the concentration of formaldehyde in the gels to be reduced to 1.1% or 0.66 M (Davis et al. 1986).

At one time, the presence of ethidium bromide was thought to compromise transfer of RNA from formaldehyde gels to membranes and/or to suppress subsequent hybridization (e.g., please see Thomas 1980). These effects, if they exist at all, are now believed to be small in magnitude (Kroczek and Siebert 1990), and many investigators routinely include ethidium bromide in gels containing 0.66 M formaldehyde. However, ethidium bromide should not be included in gels run in the old style, which contain higher concentrations of formaldehyde. When irradiated by UV light, they emit an eerie pinkish-purple glow that swamps the signal from small amounts of RNA. Better staining can be obtained with very little background fluorescence by heating the samples of RNA with low concentrations of ethidium bromide before loading into the gel (Fourney et al. 1988; Rosen and Villa-Komaroff 1990). As long as the concentration of ethidium bromide does not exceed 50 µg/ml in the sample, the efficiency of transfer and hybridization of the RNA is not significantly affected (Kroczek 1989; Kroczek and Siebert 1990; Ogretmen et al. 1993).

MATERIALS

▲ IMPORTANT Prepare all reagents used in this protocol with DEPC-treated H_2O (please see the information panel on **HOW TO WIN THE BATTLE WITH RNASE**).

CAUTION: Please see Appendix 12 for appropriate handling of materials marked with <!>.

Buffers and Solutions

Please see Appendix 1 for components of stock solutions, buffers, and reagents. Dilute stock solutions to the appropriate concentrations.

Ethidium bromide (200 µg/ml) <!>
Prepare in DEPC-treated H_2O <!>.

Formaldehyde <!>

Formaldehyde is supplied as a 37–40% w/v (12.3 M) solution that may contain a stabilizer such as methanol (10–15%). Formaldehyde oxidizes readily to formic acid when exposed to air. If the pH of the formaldehyde solution is acidic (<pH 4.0) or if the solution is yellow, the stock solution should be deionized by treatment with a mixed bed resin, such as Bio-Rad AG-501-X8 or Dowex XG8 before use.

Formamide <!>

Purchase a distilled-deionized preparation of this reagent and store in small aliquots under nitrogen at –20ºC. Alternatively, reagent-grade formamide can be deionized as described in Appendix 1.

10x Formaldehyde gel-loading buffer
50% glycerol (diluted in DEPC-treated H_2O)
10 mM EDTA (pH 8.0)
0.25% (w/v) bromophenol blue
0.25% (w/v) xylene cyanol FF

10x MOPS electrophoresis buffer
0.2 M MOPS (pH 7.0) <!>
20 mM sodium acetate
10 mM EDTA (pH 8.0)

Dissolve 41.8 g of MOPS (3-[*N*-morpholino]propanesulfonic acid) in 700 ml of sterile DEPC-treated H_2O. Adjust the pH to 7.0 with 2 N NaOH. Add 20 ml of DEPC-treated 1 M sodium acetate and 20 ml of DEPC-treated 0.5 M EDTA (pH 8.0). Adjust the volume of the solution to 1 liter with DEPC-treated H_2O. Sterilize the solution by filtration through a 0.45-µm Millipore filter, and store it at room temperature protected from light. The buffer yellows with age if it is exposed to light or is autoclaved. Straw-colored buffer works well, but darker buffer does not.

Gels

Agarose gel containing 2.2 M formaldehyde
To prepare 100 ml of a 1.5% agarose gel containing 2.2 M formaldehyde, add 1.5 g of agarose to 72 ml of sterile H_2O. Dissolve the agarose by boiling in a microwave oven. Cool the solution to 55ºC and add 10 ml of 10x MOPS electrophoresis buffer and 18 ml of deionized formaldehyde. In a chemical fume hood, cast an agarose gel with slots formed by a 3-mm comb with at least four more teeth than the number of RNA samples under test. These extra lanes are used for RNA size markers and running dyes (please see Step 4). Allow the gel to set for at least 1 hour at room temperature. As soon as the agarose has set, cover the gel with Saran Wrap until the samples are ready to be loaded.

A 1.5% agarose gel is suitable for resolving RNAs in the 0.5–8.0-kb size range. Larger RNAs should be separated on gels cast with 1.0% or 1.2% agarose (Lehrach et al. 1977; Miller 1987).

Nucleic Acids and Oligonucleotides

RNA samples

Samples of total or poly(A)$^+$ RNA should consist of up to 20 µg of RNA in a volume of 1–2 µl. Equivalent amounts of the RNA samples to be analyzed are removed from storage (please see the panel on **STORAGE OF RNA** in Protocol 1). Precipitate the RNA with ethanol and dissolve it in an appropriate volume of sterile, DEPC-treated H$_2$O.

The presence of salts or SDS in the samples or loading of >20 µg of RNA per lane can cause smearing of the RNA during electrophoresis.

RNA size markers

DNA and RNA migrate at different rates through agarose gels containing formaldehyde, with RNA migrating faster than DNA of equivalent size (Wicks 1986). Although DNA markers are preferable because they run as sharp bands, they cannot readily be used to measure the absolute size of unknown RNAs. We therefore recommend using RNA ladders (e.g., from Life Technologies) that contain RNAs of 9.49, 7.46, 4.40, 2.37, 1.35, and 0.24 kb in length. This allows the markers to be used as sentinels to detect RNase contamination or other problems that may occur during electrophoresis. Please see the Introduction to Northern Hybridization preceding Protocol 5.

Special Equipment

Equipment for horizontal electrophoresis

A particular electrophoresis apparatus should be reserved specifically for RNA analysis. Clean electrophoresis tanks and combs used for electrophoresis of RNA (Protocols 5 and 6) with detergent solution, rinse in H$_2$O, dry with ethanol, and then fill with a solution of 3% H$_2$O$_2$. After 10 minutes at room temperature, rinse the electrophoresis tanks and combs thoroughly with H$_2$O treated with 0.1% DEPC.

Because the pH of the electrophoresis buffer changes during the run, set up the electrophoresis tank so that the buffer circulates continuously from one chamber to the other via a peristaltic pump. Alternatively, transfer the buffer manually every hour or so from one buffer chamber to the other.

Ruler, transparent

Water bath preset to 55°C

METHOD

1. Set up the denaturation reaction. In sterile microfuge tubes mix:

RNA (up to 20 µg)	2.0 µl
10x MOPS electrophoresis buffer	2.0 µl
formaldehyde	4.0 µl
formamide	10.0 µl
ethidium bromide (200 µg/ml)	1.0 µl

    As much as 20 µg of RNA may be analyzed in each lane of the gel. Abundant mRNAs (0.1% or more of the mRNA population) can usually be detected by northern analysis of 10 µg of total cellular RNA. For detection of rare RNAs, at least 1.0 µg of poly(A)$^+$ RNA should be applied to each lane of the gel. Samples containing RNA size markers should be prepared in the same way as the RNA samples under test.

2. Close the tops of the microfuge tubes, and incubate the RNA solutions for 60 minutes at 55°C. Chill the samples for 10 minutes in ice water, and then centrifuge them for 5 seconds to deposit all of the fluid in the bottom of the microfuge tubes.

    Many investigators prefer to incubate the RNA solutions for 10 minutes at 85°C.

3. Add 2 µl of 10x formaldehyde gel-loading buffer to each sample and return the tubes to an ice bucket.

4. Install the agarose/formaldehyde gel in a horizontal electrophoresis box. Add sufficient 1x MOPS electrophoresis buffer to cover the gel to a depth of ~1 mm. Run the gel for 5 minutes

at 5 V/cm, and then load the RNA samples into the wells of the gel, leaving the two outermost lanes on each side of the gel empty. Load the RNA size standards in the outside lanes of the gel.

5. Run the gel submerged in 1x MOPS electrophoresis buffer at 4–5 V/cm until the bromophenol blue has migrated ~8 cm (4–5 hours).

   Using higher voltages during electrophoresis leads to smearing of bands.

   Because the pH of the electrophoresis buffer changes during the run, set up the electrophoresis tank so that the buffer circulates continuously from one chamber to the other via a peristaltic pump. Alternatively, transfer the buffer manually every hour or so from one buffer chamber to the other.

6. Visualize the RNAs by placing the gel on a piece of Saran Wrap on a UV transilluminator. Align a transparent ruler with the stained gel and photograph under UV illumination.

   Please see the panel on CHECKING THE QUALITY OF PREPARATIONS OF RNA at the end of Protocol 5.

7. Use the photograph to measure the distance from the loading well to each of the bands of RNA. Plot the $\log_{10}$ of the size of the fragments of RNA against the distance migrated. Use the resulting curve to calculate the sizes of the RNA species detected by blot hybridization.

8. Proceed with immobilization of RNA onto a solid support by upward or downward capillary transfer (please see Protocol 7 or the panel on ALTERNATIVE PROTOCOL: CAPILLARY TRANSFER BY DOWNWARD FLOW at the end of Protocol 7).

Protocol 7

Transfer and Fixation of Denatured RNA to Membranes

IN MOST CASES, FRACTIONATION OF RNA BY AGAROSE GEL ELECTROPHORESIS is but a prelude to hybridization of the fractionated population to specific labeled probes that detect particular target mRNAs. RNA is first transferred from an agarose gel to a two-dimensional support, usually a nylon membrane.

As discussed in the Introduction to Northern Hybridization, investigators in many cases have a choice of solvents and membranes to be used for transfer, and more than one option for attaching the transferred RNA tightly to the membrane. In our hands, the best northern blots are obtained following transfer of RNA from gels to nylon membranes at neutral or alkaline pH.

TRANSFER TO POSITIVELY CHARGED NYLON MEMBRANES AT ALKALINE PH

Because charged nylon membranes retain nucleic acids in alkaline solution (Reed and Mann 1985), RNA can be efficiently transferred from agarose gels in 8.0 mM NaOH with 3 M NaCl (Chomczynski and Mackey 1994). Transfer under these conditions partially hydrolyzes the RNA and thereby increases the speed and efficiency of transfer of large (>2.3 kb) RNAs. Because RNA transferred in alkaline solution becomes covalently fixed to the charged nylon membrane, there is no need to bake the membrane or to expose it to UV irradiation before hybridization.

Alkaline transfer is not free of problems: It sometimes generates a high level of background hybridization, especially when RNA probes are used. Extended exposure of charged nylon membranes to alkaline solutions (>6 hours) exacerbates the problem. This shortcoming can sometimes be overcome by decreasing the transfer time and by using increased amounts of blocking agents in the prehybridization and hybridization steps. In addition, there are reports of variability in the strength of the hybridization signal generated by RNA after alkaline transfer. This variability may be related to the switch by manufacturers to nylon 66 membranes, rather than the original nylon 6 membranes, with which alkaline transfer was first described (Reed and Mann 1985).

TRANSFER TO UNCHARGED NYLON MEMBRANES AT NEUTRAL PH

Transfer to uncharged nylon membranes is carried out at neutral pH, usually in 10x or 20x SSC. The RNA is then covalently linked to the matrix by the traditional method of baking under vac-

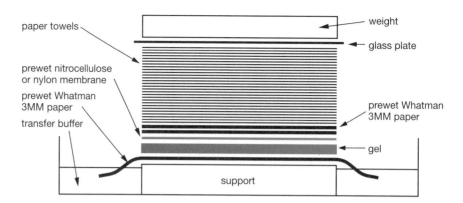

FIGURE 7-2 Upward Capillary Transfer

Capillary transfer of nucleic acids from an agarose gel to solid supports is achieved by drawing the transfer buffer from the reservoir upward through the gel into a stack of paper towels. The nucleic acid is eluted from the gel by a moving stream of buffer and is deposited onto a nitrocellulose filter or nylon membrane. A weight applied to the top of the paper towels helps to ensure a tight connection between the layers of material used in the transfer system.

uum for 2 hours, by heating in a microwave oven for 2–3 minutes (Angeletti et al. 1995), or by exposing the nylon membrane to UV irradiation at 254/312 nm. Most investigators agree with Khandjian (1987) that RNA immobilized on nylon membranes by UV irradiation generates more intense signals in northern hybridization than RNA immobilized by baking.

This protocol presents the steps involved in the transfer of RNA from an agarose gel to a membranous support, facilitated by the upward flow of buffer (please see Figure 7-2), followed by various methods for fixation of the RNA to the membrane in preparation for hybridization. An alternative method for transfer by downward capillary flow is given in the panel on **ALTERNATIVE PROTOCOL: CAPILLARY TRANSFER BY DOWNWARD FLOW** at the end of this protocol.

MATERIALS

▲ IMPORTANT Prepare all reagents used in this protocol with DEPC-treated H$_2$O (please see the information panel on **HOW TO WIN THE BATTLE WITH RNASE**).

CAUTION: Please see Appendix 12 for appropriate handling of materials marked with <!>.

Buffers and Solutions

Please see Appendix 1 for components of stock solutions, buffers, and reagents. Dilute stock solutions to the appropriate concentrations.

Ammonium acetate (0.1 M) with 0.5 µg/ml ethidium bromide <!>
  Optional, please see Step 13.

Methylene blue solution
  0.02% (w/v) methylene blue (Sigma, 89% pure) in 0.3 M sodium acetate (pH 5.5).

Soaking solution
  For charged membranes, use 0.01 N NaOH <!> combined with 3 M NaCl; for uncharged membranes, use 0.05 N NaOH.

0.2x SSC with 1% (w/v) SDS

20x SSC

Transfer buffer
  For alkaline transfers to charged membranes, use 0.01 N NaOH with 3 M NaCl; for neutral transfers to uncharged membranes, use 20x SSC.

Nucleic Acids and Oligonucleotides

RNA sample, fractionated through an agarose gel
Prepared as described in Protocol 5 or 6 of this chapter.

Special Equipment

Blotting Paper (Schleicher & Schuell GB002 or Sigma P 9039)
Cross-linking device (e.g., Stratalinker, Stratagene; GS Gene Linker, Bio-Rad) or Microwave oven or Vacuum oven
Glass baking dish
Nylon membranes, either uncharged or positively charged
Plexiglas or glass plate to support the gel during transfer
Scalpel blade
Thick blotting paper (e.g., Whatman 3MM, Schleicher & Schuell GB004, or Sigma QuickDraw)
Visible-spectrum light box
Weight (400 g)
Yellow filter for photography

METHOD

Preparation of the Gel for Transfer

1. (*Optional*) Partially hydrolyze the RNA sample, fractionated through agarose, by soaking the gel in the appropriate soaking solution as described below.

   Treating the gel with NaOH after electrophoresis can enhance subsequent transfer of the partially hydrolyzed RNA to nylon membranes, either charged or uncharged. This treatment is especially useful if the gel contains >1% agarose or is >0.5-cm thick or if the RNA to be analyzed is >2.5 kb in length.

   #### FOR TRANSFER TO UNCHARGED NYLON MEMBRANES

   a. Rinse the gel with DEPC-treated H_2O.

   b. Soak the gel for 20 minutes in 5 gel volumes of 0.05 N NaOH.

   c. Transfer the gel into 10 gel volumes of 20x SSC for 40 minutes.

   d. Without delay, proceed directly with Step 2 to transfer the partially hydrolyzed RNA to an uncharged nylon membrane by capillary action.

   #### FOR TRANSFER TO CHARGED NYLON MEMBRANES

   a. Rinse the gel with DEPC-treated H_2O.

   b. Soak the gel for 20 minutes in 5 gel volumes of 0.01 N NaOH/3 M NaCl.

   c. Without delay, proceed directly with Step 2 to transfer the partially hydrolyzed RNA to a positively charged nylon membrane by capillary action.

2. Move the gel containing fractionated RNA to a glass baking dish, and use a sharp scalpel to trim away unused areas of the gel. Cut along the slot line to allow the top of the trimmed gel to be aligned with the top of the membrane during transfer. Cut off a small triangular piece from the bottom left-hand corner of the gel to simplify orientation during the succeeding operations.

3. Place a piece of thick blotting paper on a sheet of Plexiglas or a glass plate to form a support that is longer and wider than the trimmed gel. Make sure that the ends of the blotting paper drape over the edges of the plate. Place the support inside a large baking dish.

   Neoprene stoppers can be used to elevate the support plate above the buffer reservoir.

4. Fill the dish with the appropriate transfer buffer (0.01 N NaOH/3 M NaCl for positively charged membranes, and 20x SSC for uncharged membranes) until the level of the liquid reaches almost to the top of the support. When the blotting paper on the top of the support is thoroughly wet, smooth out all air bubbles with a glass rod or pipette.

   Alkaline transfer buffer (0.01 N NaOH, 3 M NaCl) is used to transfer RNA to positively charged nylon membranes. Neutral transfer buffer (20x SSC) is used to transfer RNA to uncharged nylon membranes.

Preparation of the Membrane for Transfer

5. Use a fresh scalpel or a paper cutter to cut a piece of the appropriate nylon membrane ~1 mm larger than the gel in both dimensions.

   Use appropriate gloves and blunt-ended forceps (e.g., Millipore forceps) to handle the membrane. A nylon membrane that has been touched by greasy hands will not wet!

6. Float the nylon membrane on the surface of a dish of deionized H_2O until it wets completely from beneath, and then immerse the membrane in 10x SSC for at least 5 minutes. Use a clean scalpel blade to cut a corner from the membrane to match the corner cut from the gel.

   The rate at which different batches of nylon membranes wet can vary. If the membrane is not saturated after floating for several minutes on water, it should be replaced with a new membrane; the transfer of RNA to an unevenly wetted membrane is unreliable.

Assembly of the Transfer System and Transfer of the RNA (Please See Figure 7-2)

7. Carefully place the gel on the support in an inverted position so that it is centered on the wet blotting paper.

   Make sure that there are no air bubbles between the thick blotting paper and the gel.

8. Surround, but do not cover, the gel with Saran Wrap or Parafilm.

   This barrier prevents liquid from flowing directly from the reservoir to paper towels placed on the top of the gel. If these towels are not precisely stacked, they tend to droop over the edge of the gel and may touch the support. This type of short-circuiting is a major reason for inefficient transfer of RNA from the gel to the membrane.

9. Wet the top of the gel with the appropriate transfer buffer (please see Step 4). Place the wet nylon membrane on top of the gel so that the cut corners are aligned. One edge of the membrane should extend just beyond the edge of the line of slots at the top of the gel.

   ▲ IMPORTANT Do not move the membrane once it has been applied to the surface of the gel. Make sure that there are no air bubbles between the membrane and the gel.

10. Wet two pieces of thick blotting paper (cut to exactly the same size as the gel) in the appropriate transfer buffer and place them on top of the wet nylon membrane. Smooth out any air bubbles with a glass rod.

11. Cut or fold a stack of paper towels (5–8 cm high) just smaller than the blotting papers. Place the towels on the blotting papers. Put a glass plate on top of the stack and weigh it down with a 400-g weight (please see Figure 7-2).

12. Allow upward transfer of RNA to occur for no more than 4 hours in neutral transfer buffer and ~1 hour in alkaline transfer buffer.

13. Dismantle the capillary transfer system. Mark the positions of the slots on the membrane with a ballpoint pen through the gel. Transfer the membrane to a glass tray containing ~300 ml of 6x SSC at 23°C. Place the tray on a platform shaker and agitate the membrane very slowly for 5 minutes.

    > To assess the efficiency of transfer of RNA, rinse the gel briefly in several changes of H$_2$O and then stain it for 45 minutes in a solution of ethidium bromide (0.5 µg/ml in 0.1 M ammonium acetate). Examine and photograph the stained gel under UV illumination.

14. Remove the membrane from the 6x SSC and allow excess fluid to drain away. Lay the membrane, RNA side upward, on a dry sheet of blotting paper for a few minutes.

Staining of the RNA and Fixation of the RNA to the Membrane

The order of steps during staining and fixation depends on the type of transfer, the type of membrane, and the method of fixation. Because alkaline transfer results in covalent attachment of RNA to positively charged nylon membranes, there is no need to fix the RNA to the membrane before staining. RNA transferred to uncharged nylon membranes in neutral transfer buffer should be stained and then fixed to the membrane by baking under vacuum or heating in a microwave oven. If the RNA is to be cross-linked to the membrane by UV irradiation, then the staining step should follow fixation (please see Table 7-4).

RNA that has been transferred to a nylon membrane can be visualized by staining with methylene blue (Herrin and Schmidt 1988). This simple method allows monitoring of the integrity of the RNA, estimation of the efficiency of the transfer process, and location of the positions of the major RNAs (usually rRNAs) on the membrane. If the RNA is to be fixed by UV irradiation, proceed first to Step 16.

15. Stain the membrane.

    a. Transfer the damp membrane to a glass tray containing methylene blue solution. Stain the membrane for just enough time to visualize the rRNAs (~3–5 minutes).

    b. Photograph the stained membrane under visible light with a yellow filter.

    c. After photography, destain the membrane by washing in 0.2x SSC and 1% (w/v) SDS for 15 minutes at room temperature.

       > Fix the RNA to the membrane if appropriate (please see Table 7-4), and proceed directly to hybridization (Protocol 8). Any membranes not used immediately in hybridization reactions should be thoroughly dry, wrapped loosely in aluminum foil or blotting paper, and stored at room temperature, preferably under vacuum.

16. Fix the RNA to the uncharged nylon membrane.

TABLE 7-4 Sequence of Staining RNA and Fixing to the Membrane

TYPE OF MEMBRANE	METHOD OF FIXATION	ORDER OF STEPS
Positively charged nylon	alkaline transfer	1. Stain with methylene blue. 2. Proceed to prehybridization.
Uncharged nylon or positively charged nylon (nonalkaline transfer)	UV irradiation (please see Step 16 for details)	1. Fix the RNA by UV irradiation. 2. Stain with methylene blue. 3. Proceed to prehybridization.
Uncharged nylon or positively charged nylon (nonalkaline transfer)	baking in vacuum oven or microwave oven (please see Step 16 for details)	1. Stain with methylene blue. 2. Bake the membrane. 3. Proceed to prehybridization.

TO FIX BY BAKING

- Allow the membrane to dry in air and then bake for 2 hours between two pieces of blotting paper under vacuum at 80°C in a vacuum oven.

    or

- Place the damp membrane on a dry piece of blotting paper and heat for 2–3 minutes at full power in a microwave oven (750–900 W).

    Proceed directly to hybridization (Protocol 8). Any membranes not used immediately in hybridization reactions should be thoroughly dry, wrapped loosely in aluminum foil or blotting paper, and stored at room temperature, preferably under vacuum.

TO CROSS-LINK BY UV IRRADIATION

a. Place the damp, unstained membrane on a piece of dry blotting paper and irradiate at 254 nm for 1 minute 45 seconds at 1.5 J/cm^2.

    This step is best accomplished in a commercial device according to the manufacturer's instructions.

b. After irradiation, stain the membrane with methylene blue as described in Step 15.

    Proceed directly to hybridization (Protocol 8). Any membranes not used immediately in hybridization reactions should be thoroughly dry, wrapped loosely in aluminum foil or blotting paper, and stored at room temperature, preferably under vacuum.

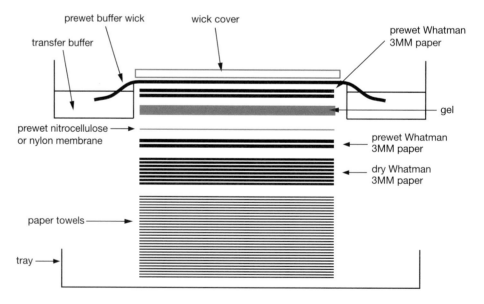

FIGURE 7-3 Downward Capillary Transfer

In this arrangement, capillary transfer of nucleic acids from an agarose gel to solid support is achieved by drawing the transfer buffer from the reservoir downward through the gel into a stack of paper towels. The nucleic acid is eluted from the gel by a moving stream of buffer and is deposited onto a nitrocellulose filter or nylon membrane.

ALTERNATIVE PROTOCOL: CAPILLARY TRANSFER BY DOWNWARD FLOW

Downward capillary transfer can be used as an alternative to upward transfer. This approach, adapted from Chomczynski and Mackey (1994), results in faster transfer times and increased efficiency of transfer for longer RNA species. This alternative protocol presents the steps involved in the transfer of RNA from an agarose gel to a membranous support, facilitated by the downward flow of buffer (please see Figure 7-3).

CAUTION: Please see Appendix 12 for appropriate handling of materials marked with <!>.

Method

1. Prepare the gel for transfer of RNA, as described in Steps 1 and 2 of the main protocol (Protocol 7).

2. Make an ~3-cm stack of disposable paper towels. Place four pieces of blotting paper on top of the stack. The stack should exceed the size of the trimmed gel by 1–2 cm in each dimension.

3. Use a fresh scalpel or a paper cutter to cut a piece of the appropriate nylon membrane ~1 mm larger than the gel in both dimensions.

    Use appropriate gloves and blunt-ended forceps (e.g., Millipore forceps) to handle the membrane. A nylon membrane that has been touched by greasy hands will not wet!

4. Float the nylon membrane on the surface of a dish of deionized H_2O until it wets completely from beneath, and then immerse the membrane in transfer buffer for at least 5 minutes. Use a clean scalpel to cut a corner from the membrane to match the corner cut from the gel.

    The rate at which different batches of nylon membranes wet can vary. If the membrane is not saturated after floating for several minutes on H_2O, it should be replaced with a new membrane, as the transfer of RNA to an unevenly wetted membrane is unreliable.

    Alkaline transfer buffer (0.01 N NaOH <!>, 3 M NaCl) is used to transfer RNA to positively charged nylon membranes. Neutral transfer buffer (10x SSC) is used to transfer RNA to uncharged nylon membranes.

5. Cut four pieces of blotting paper to the same size as the gel and wet them thoroughly with transfer buffer. Cut two larger pieces of blotting paper that will be used to connect the top of the stack to the buffer reservoirs, as shown in Figure 7-3.

Assembly of the Transfer System and Transfer of the RNA (Please See Figure 7-3)

6. Working quickly, align one of the sheets of wet blotting paper on top of the stack. Then place the nylon membrane exactly on top of the wet blotting papers. Place the trimmed agarose gel on top of the membrane, so that the cut corners are aligned. Surround, but do not cover, the gel with Saran Wrap or Parafilm.

    ▲ IMPORTANT Do not move the gel once it has been placed on top of the membrane. Make sure that there are no air bubbles between the membrane and the gel.

7. Wet the top surface of the gel with transfer buffer and immediately cover it with the three remaining pieces of wet blotting paper. Connect the stack to the reservoirs with the two larger pieces of wet blotting paper.

8. Place a sheet of Plexiglas or a thin glass plate on top of the stack to prevent evaporation.

9. Allow downward transfer of RNA to occur for no more than 4 hours in neutral transfer buffer and ~1 hour in alkaline transfer buffer.

10. Continue with Steps 13 through 16 of the main protocol (Protocol 7).

Protocol 8

Northern Hybridization

RNA SAMPLES THAT HAVE BEEN TRANSFERRED AND FIXED TO A MEMBRANE (please see Protocol 7 or the panel on ALTERNATIVE PROTOCOL: CAPILLARY TRANSFER BY DOWNWARD FLOW in Protocol 7) may be hybridized with a specific probe to locate the RNA species of interest. Any one of a large number of methods can be used to label and detect probes, at the discretion of the investigator; please see Chapters 9 and 10 for methods to prepare probes. After treating the membrane with blocking agents that suppress nonspecific absorption of the probe, the membrane is incubated under conditions that favor hybridization of the labeled probe to the immobilized target RNA. The membrane is then washed extensively to remove adventitiously bound probe and finally manipulated to yield an image of the distribution of the tightly bound probe on the membrane. After analysis of the hybridization results, the probe may be stripped from the membrane, and the membrane used again in another hybridization experiment (please see the panel on STRIPPING NORTHERN BLOTS OF RADIOACTIVITY at the end of this protocol). Table 7-5 describes how to deal with factors that cause background interference in northern hybridization.

MATERIALS

▲ IMPORTANT Prepare all reagents used in this protocol with DEPC-treated H_2O (please see the information panel on HOW TO WIN THE BATTLE WITH RNASE).

CAUTION: Please see Appendix 12 for appropriate handling of materials marked with <!>.

Buffers and Solutions

Please see Appendix 1 for components of stock solutions, buffers, and reagents. Dilute stock solutions to the appropriate concentrations.

Prehybridization solution
  0.5 M sodium phosphate (pH 7.2)
  7% (w/v) SDS
  1 mM EDTA (pH 7.0)

Background is often a problem when using nylon membranes. Of the large number of hybridization buffers that have been described in the literature, those containing high concentrations of SDS are the most effective at suppressing background while preserving high sensitivity. These buffers are modifications (e.g., please see Kevil et al. 1997; Mahmoudi and Lin 1989) of the hybridization buffer first described by Church and Gilbert (1984).

SSC (0.5x, 1x, and 2x) with 0.1% (w/v) SDS

SSC (0.1x and 0.5x) with 0.1% (w/v) SDS
  Optional, please see Step 4.

Nucleic Acids and Oligonucleotides

Probe DNA or RNA (>2 x 10⁸ cpm/μg) <!>

Prepare and radiolabel the probes in vitro to high specific activity with ^{32}P, as described in Chapter 9. High-specific-activity (>2 x 10^8 cpm/μg) strand-specific probes (either DNA or RNA) can detect mRNAs that are present at low to medium abundance. The highest sensitivity in northern blotting is obtained from single-stranded probes — either DNA or RNA — radiolabeled in vitro to high specific activity with ^{32}P (>2 x 10^8 cpm/μg). Double-stranded DNA probes are two to three times less sensitive than single-stranded probes.

RNA, immobilized on membrane

Prepared as described in Protocol 7 or the panel on **ALTERNATIVE PROTOCOL: CAPILLARY TRANS-FER BY DOWNWARD FLOW** in Protocol 7.

Special Equipment

Blotting paper (Whatman 3MM or equivalent)
Boiling water bath
Water bath preset to 68°C
Water bath preset to the hybridization temperature
Please see Step 3.

METHOD

1. Incubate the membrane for 2 hours at 68°C in 10–20 ml of prehybridization solution.

   Any number of systems for hybridization of northern blots have been described ranging from efficient but expensive commercial rotating wheels to a variety of economical homemade devices including plastic lunch boxes, sandwiches of filter paper (Jones and Jones 1992), and heat-sealed plastic bags (Sears Seal-A-Meal bags are still the best). With practice, all of these gadgets can be made to work reasonably well, and the choice among them is generally a matter of personal preference. Commercial rotating wheels, however, have one clear advantage: They are less prone to leak when using hybridization buffers with high concentrations of SDS. Because plastic bags and boxes containing such buffers are very difficult to seal, the risk of leaks and contamination with radioactivity is increased.

2. If using a double-stranded probe, denature the ^{32}P-labeled double-stranded DNA by heating for 5 minutes at 100°C. Chill the probe rapidly in ice water.

   Alternatively, denature the probe by adding 0.1 volume of 3 N NaOH. After 5 minutes at room temperature, transfer the probe to ice water and add 0.05 volume of 1 M Tris-Cl (pH 7.2) and 0.1 volume of 3 N HCl. Store the probe in ice water until it is needed.

   Single-stranded probes need not be denatured.

3. Add the denatured or single-stranded radiolabeled probe directly to the prehybridization solution. Continue incubation for 12–16 hours at the appropriate temperature.

   To detect low-abundance mRNAs, use at least 0.1 μg of probe whose specific activity exceeds 2 x 10^8 cpm/μg. Low-stringency hybridization, in which the probe is not homologous to the target gene, is best carried out at lower temperatures (37–42°C) in a hybridization buffer containing 50% deionized formamide, 0.25 M sodium phosphate (pH 7.2), 0.25 M NaCl, and 7% SDS.

   For additional details on conditions for hybridization of probes to nucleic acids immobilized on solid supports, please see Chapter 6, Protocol 10.

4. After hybridization, remove the membrane from the plastic bag and transfer it as quickly as possible to a plastic box containing 100–200 ml of 1x SSC, 0.1% SDS at room temperature. Place the closed box on a platform shaker and agitate the fluid gently for 10 minutes.

   ▲ IMPORTANT Do not allow the membrane to dry out at any stage during the washing procedure.

Increase the concentration of SDS in the washing buffer to 1% if single-stranded probes are used.

Following low-stringency hybridization in formamide-containing buffers, rinse the membrane in 2x SSC at 23°C and then successively wash in 2x SSC, 0.5x SSC with 0.1% SDS, and 0.1x SSC with 0.1% SDS for 15 minutes each at 23°C. A final wash containing 0.1x SSC and 1% SDS is carried out at 50°C.

5. Transfer the membrane to another plastic box containing 100–200 ml of 0.5x SSC, 0.1% SDS, prewarmed to 68°C. Agitate the fluid gently for 10 minutes at 68°C.

6. Repeat the washing in Step 5 twice more for a total of three washes at 68°C.

7. Dry the membrane on blotting paper and establish an autoradiograph by exposing the membrane for 24–48 hours to X-ray film (Kodak XAR-5 or equivalent) at –70°C with an intensifying screen (please see Appendix 9). Tungstate-based intensifying screens are more effective than the older rare-earth screens. Alternatively, an image of the membrane can be obtained by scanning in a phosphorimager.

STRIPPING NORTHERN BLOTS OF RADIOACTIVITY

To strip radiolabeled probes from nylon membranes containing immobilized RNA, incubate the membrane for 1–2 hours in either

- a large volume of 10 mM Tris-Cl (pH 7.4), 0.2% SDS, preheated to 70–75°C.

- a large volume of 50% deionized formamide, 0.1x SSC, 0.1% SDS preheated to 68°C.

TABLE 7-5 Background in Southern and Northern Hybridizations and How to Avoid It

SYMPTOM	CAUSE	POTENTIAL SOLUTIONS
Blotchy background over the entire membrane.	Incomplete blocking during prehybridization.	Prehybridize for longer periods of time.
	Drying out of membrane during experiment.	Be vigilant in keeping membrane wet at all times.
	SDS precipitated from any of the solutions used in the experiment.	Prepare solutions at room temperature, prewarm to 37°C, then add SDS; do not allow SDS to precipitate at any time. Reheating a solution from which SDS has precipitated will sometimes yield a clean result.
	Use of 10% dextran sulfate in hybridization experiments.	This polymer is added to induce macromolecular crowding and thus to enhance the rate of hybridization. Except in rare instances (in situ hybridizations or using subtracted probes), dextran sulfate can be left out of most hybridization solutions. Use of large volumes of washing solutions are required to remove this viscous compound, which if left on the membrane after hybridization, traps probe and produces background.
	Paper towels become completely wet during capillary transfer (see Protocol 7).	Use a larger stack of towels or remove wet towels and replace with dry towels during transfer procedure.
	Use of charged nylon membranes and solutions containing low SDS.	Switch to uncharged nylon membranes. Increase the concentration of SDS to 1% (w/v) at all steps. Hybridization buffers containing high concentrations of SDS are the most effective in suppressing background while preserving high sensitivity. These buffers are modifications (e.g., please see Mahmoudi and Lin 1989; Kevil et al. 1997) of the hybridization buffer first described by Church and Gilbert (1984).
	Use of impure (yellow) formamide.	Purify formamide on Dowex XG-8 before use (see Appendix 1).
	Use of a plastic film that is permeable to moisture.	Use a better quality film.
	Use of improper blocking reagent.	Do not use BLOTTO for genomic Southern blots. Instead, try 50 μg/ml heparin as blocking reagent (Singh and Jones 1984) or use Church buffer (Church and Gilbert 1984) as both prehybridization and hybridization solution.
Haloes over the entire membrane.	Presence of bubbles in prehybridization/hybridization solutions, failure to agitate membrane.	Prewarm solutions before use. Agitate the membrane.
Background concentrated over the lanes containing nucleic acid.	Improperly denatured carrier DNA.	Reboil the salmon sperm DNA used in the prehybridization/hybridization solutions. Do not allow the heat-denatured DNA to reanneal.
	Use of probes containing poly(T) tracts in northern hybridizations.	Include poly(A) at 1 μg/ml in hybridization solutions.
	Use of RNA probes.	Drastically increase the stringency of hybridization by increasing the concentration of formamide in the hybridization buffer, use 1% SDS in the hybridization buffer, increase the washing temperatures, and decrease the ionic strength of washing buffers (e.g., 0.1x SSC).
Blotchy background appearing on some membranes and not others.	Too many membranes hybridized in the same vessel, not enough volume of prehybridization/hybridization solution.	Increase the volume of the hybridization and washing solutions and/or decrease number of membranes in a hybridization bag or container.
Intense black spots all over membrane.	Use of old radiolabel to prepare probe.	A peppered background is due to ^{32}P present as inorganic phosphate or pyrophosphate sticking to the membrane. This problem is frequently encountered when using 5′-labeled probes. Do not use old radiolabel in which radiolysis has occurred. Purify the probe by spun-column chromatography, precipitation, or gel electrophoresis before use. Include 0.5% (w/v) sodium pyrophosphate in prehybridization/hybridization solutions.

Protocol 9

Dot and Slot Hybridization of Purified RNA

Dot and slot blotting (Kafatos et al. 1979) are techniques for immobilizing several preparations of nucleic acids on the same solid support, usually a charged nylon membrane. The concentrations of the target sequence of interest can be estimated by hybridizing the immobilized samples to an appropriate probe. The amounts of target sequence are estimated by comparing the intensity of signals emitted by dots containing the test samples with standards containing known concentrations of the target sequence.

For several years, dot blotting and slot blotting were viewed with disfavor by many investigators chiefly because of variability in the hybridization signal obtained from identical samples applied to the same membrane, especially when analyzing complex populations of RNA or DNA. Although this problem has not been entirely solved (Anchordoguy et al. 1996), the advent of positively charged modified nylon membranes has led to a marked improvement in the sample-to-sample variation (Chomczynski and Qasba 1984). In the case of DNA, purified preparations or alkaline lysates of cells and tissue samples can be loaded onto the membrane under alkaline conditions (Reed and Matthaei 1990).

Dot-blot analysis of RNA is slightly trickier than dot-blotting of DNA. At one stage, investigators experimented with dot- and slot-blots of crude cytoplasm prepared from freshly harvested or frozen cultured cells or animal tissues (e.g., please see White and Bancroft 1982). However, the results obtained from dot blotting of crude preparations of RNA did not always match those obtained from northern blots of purified RNA (Tsykin et al. 1990). For this reason, dot-blotting and slot-blotting are generally carried out with purified preparations of RNA that have been denatured with glyoxal (McMaster and Carmichael 1977; Carmichael and McMaster 1980) or formaldehyde (Thomas 1980) immediately before they are applied to the membrane (e.g., please see Weydert et al. 1983).

APPLYING THE SAMPLES TO THE MEMBRANE

Although samples of RNA can be applied to the membrane manually with an automatic pipetting device, the spacing and size of the resulting dots are often variable. The resulting images may be misshapen, blurred, and of such uneven character as to defy quantitation. The preferred method of applying samples to a membrane is by vacuum manifold. Many of the commercially available manifolds are supplied with a choice of molds that deposit the samples on the membrane as dots or slots in various geometries. This ensures that the immobilized samples all have the same shape, area, and spacing, which facilitates comparison of the intensity of hybridization.

STANDARDS

To obtain quantitative results, it is essential to include positive and negative controls that have physical properties similar to those of the nucleic acid under test. For example, when analyzing mammalian RNAs, the negative control should consist of RNA from a cell or tissue that is known not to express the target sequences. Positive controls should consist of preparations of RNA mixed with known quantities of RNA standards that are complementary to the probe. These standards and radiolabeled probes are best synthesized in vitro from DNA templates that have been cloned into plasmid vectors in which the cloning site is flanked by two different bacteriophage promoters in opposite orientations. Sense-strand RNA for use as a hybridization standard can be synthesized using one promoter; radiolabeled (antisense) probe can be synthesized using the other promoter.

When creating standards, the synthetic sense-strand RNA is mixed with an irrelevant RNA so that the resulting mass is equal to that of the test samples. The irrelevant RNA should be prepared in the same manner as the test RNA. These precautions are necessary to control for the presence of impurities in cytoplasmic RNA that decrease the intensity of the hybridization signal and to control for decreased hybridization efficiency in samples containing large amounts of purified RNA.

NORMALIZATION

To avoid overloading the membrane, not more than 5 µg of total RNA should be used in a slot of standard size. As a matter of course, the same amount of RNA is loaded into each slot. However, there is always some uncertainty about the actual amounts of RNA that are retained on the membrane. This problem can be solved by staining the membrane with methylene blue after the RNA has been cross-linked to the positively charged membrane by UV irradiation (please see Protocol 7 and Table 7-5 in Protocol 8). Alternatively, the amount of poly(A)$^+$ RNA retained on the membrane can be measured by hybridization with radiolabeled oligo(dT) (Harley 1987, 1988). This method is especially useful when loading small amounts of purified poly(A)$^+$ RNA in each slot.

MEASURING THE INTENSITY OF THE SIGNAL

For many purposes, visual assessment of the intensity of hybridization is sufficient. However, more accurate estimates of the amount of target sequence in each sample can be obtained by densitometric scanning (Brown et al. 1983; Chapman et al. 1983; Ross et al. 1989), direct phosphor-imaging, or luminometry (when using chemiluminescent probes) (Matthews et al. 1985). Liquid scintillation counting also provides direct quantitation of the concentration of target DNA. However, this method requires that the sample be cut into pieces and placed in a scintillation fluor, thereby eliminating any possibility of reprobing the dot blots.

This protocol describes the blotting and subsequent hybridization of RNA purified from cells or tissues by one of the methods previously described in Protocols 1 through 4.

MATERIALS

▲ IMPORTANT Prepare all reagents used in this protocol with DEPC-treated H$_2$O (please see the information panel on HOW TO WIN THE BATTLE WITH RNASE).

CAUTION: Please see Appendix 12 for appropriate handling of materials marked with <!>.

Buffers and Solutions

**Please see Appendix 1 for components of stock solutions, buffers, and reagents.
Dilute stock solutions to the appropriate concentrations.**

NaOH (10 N) <!>

Prehybridization solution

RNA denaturation solution

660 μl of formamide <!>

210 μl of 37% (w/v) formaldehyde <!>

130 μl of 10x MOPS electrophoresis buffer (pH 7.0) <!>

For further details on MOPS electrophoresis buffer, please see Appendix 1.

Formaldehyde is supplied as a 37–40% w/v (12.3 M) solution that may contain a stabilizer such as methanol (10–15%). Formaldehyde oxidizes readily to formic acid when exposed to air. If the pH of the formaldehyde solution is acidic (<pH 4.0) or if the solution is yellow, the stock solution should be deionized by treatment with a mixed bed resin, such as Bio-Rad AG-501-X8 or Dowex XG8 before use.

Purchase a distilled deionized preparation of formamide reagent and store in small aliquots under nitrogen at –20°C. Alternatively, reagent-grade formamide can be deionized as described in Appendix 1.

0.1x SSC with 0.1% (w/v) SDS

Please see note to Step 18.

0.1x SSC with 1% (w/v) SDS

Optional, please see Step 18.

0.5x SSC with 0.1% (w/v) SDS

1x SSC with 0.1% (w/v) SDS

2x SSC

Optional, please see Step 18.

20x SSC

Nucleic Acids and Oligonucleotides

RNA test samples, standards and negative controls

Prepare samples by one of the methods described in Protocols 1 through 4 of this chapter.

All samples should contain the same amount of RNA dissolved in 10 μl of sterile, DEPC-treated H$_2$O. Standards are generated by mixing varying quantities of unlabeled sense-strand RNA synthesized in vitro (please see Chapter 9) to aliquots of a "negative" RNA preparation that lacks sequences complementary to the radiolabeled probe.

Probes

Probe, radiolabeled and denatured

Denature just before use as described in Step 2 of Protocol 8.

High-specific-activity (>5 x 10^8 cpm/μg) strand-specific probes (either DNA or RNA) can easily detect mRNAs that are present at medium to high abundance when 5 μg of total cellular RNA is loaded per slot. RNAs of the lowest abundance (1–5 copies/cell) are difficult to detect in dot blots of total mammalian cellular RNA. Such RNAs are best detected by loading >1 μg of purified poly(A)$^+$ RNA per slot and hybridizing with strand-specific probes of high specific activity (>5 x 10^8 cpm/μg).

Special Equipment

Blotting manifold

Manifolds are available from several commercial sources. Devices for dot blotting are more popular than those for slot blotting, perhaps because, with a dot-blotter, the sample is applied over a larger area, resulting in a more uniform hybridization signal.

Cross-linking device (e.g., Stratalinker, Stratagene; GS Gene Linker, Bio-Rad) or Vacuum oven or Microwave oven
Positively charged nylon membrane
    Please see the Introduction to Northern Hybridization (Membranes Used for Northern Hybridization).
Thick blotting paper (e.g., Whatman 3MM, Schleicher & Schuell GB004, or Sigma QuickDraw)
Water bath preset to 68°C

METHOD

Setting Up the Blotting Manifold

1. Cut a piece of positively charged nylon membrane to a suitable size. Mark the membrane with a soft pencil or ballpoint pen to indicate the orientation. Wet the membrane briefly in H_2O and soak it in 20x SSC for 1 hour at room temperature.

2. While the membrane is soaking, clean the blotting manifold carefully with 0.1 N NaOH and then rinse it well with sterile H_2O.

3. Wet two sheets of thick blotting paper with 20x SSC, and place them on top of the vacuum unit of the apparatus.

4. Place the wet nylon membrane on the bottom of the sample wells cut into the upper section of the manifold. Roll a pipette across the surface of the membrane to smooth away any air bubbles trapped between the upper section of the manifold and the nylon membrane.

5. Clamp the two parts of the manifold together, and connect the unit to a vacuum line.

6. Fill all of the slots/dots with 10x SSC, and apply gentle suction until the fluid has passed through the nylon membrane. Turn off the vacuum, and refill the slots with 10x SSC.

Preparation of the RNA Samples

7. Mix each of the RNA samples (dissolved in 10 μl of H_2O) with 30 μl of RNA denaturation solution.

8. Incubate the mixture for 5 minutes at 65°C, and then cool the samples on ice.

9. Add an equal volume of 20x SSC to each sample.

10. Apply gentle suction to the manifold until the 10x SSC in the slots has passed through the membrane. Turn off the vacuum.

Blotting of the RNA Samples and Fixation of the RNA to the Membrane

11. Load all of the samples into the slots, and then apply gentle suction. After all of the samples have passed through the membrane, rinse each of the slots twice with 1 ml of 10x SSC.

12. After the second rinse has passed through the nylon membrane, continue suction for 5 minutes to dry the membrane.

13. Remove the membrane from the manifold, and fix the RNA to the membrane by either UV irradiation, baking, or microwaving, as described in Step 16 of Protocol 7.
    Before setting up the prehybridization and hybridization reactions, please see Protocol 8.

Hybridization and Washing of Immobilized RNA

14. Incubate the membrane for 2 hours at 68°C in 10–20 ml of prehybridization solution in a baking dish or hybridization chamber.

15. Add the denatured radiolabeled probe directly to the prehybridization solution. Continue the incubation for 12–16 hours at the appropriate temperature.

   To detect low-abundance mRNAs, use at least 0.1 μg of probe whose specific activity exceeds 5 x 10^8 cpm/μg. Low-stringency hybridization, in which the probe is not homologous to the target gene, is best carried out at lower temperatures (37–42°C) in a hybridization buffer containing 50% deionized formamide, 0.25 M sodium phosphate (pH 7.2), 0.25 M NaCl, and 7% SDS.

16. After hybridization, remove the membrane from the plastic bag and transfer it as quickly as possible to a plastic box containing 100–200 ml of 1x SSC, 0.1% SDS at room temperature. Place the closed box on a platform shaker and agitate the fluid gently for 10 minutes.

   ▲ IMPORTANT Do not allow the membrane to dry out at any stage during the washing procedure.

   Increase the concentration of SDS in the washing buffer to 1% if single-stranded probes are used.

   Following low-stringency hybridization in formamide-containing buffers, rinse the membrane in 2x SSC at 23°C and then successively wash in 2x SSC, 0.5x SSC with 0.1% SDS, and 0.1x SSC with 0.1% SDS for 15 minutes each at 23°C. A final wash containing 0.1x SSC and 1% SDS is carried out at 50°C.

17. Transfer the membrane to another plastic box containing 100–200 ml of 0.5x SSC, 0.1% SDS, prewarmed to 68°C. Agitate the fluid gently for 10 minutes at 68°C.

18. Repeat the washing in Step 17 twice more for a total of three washes at 68°C.

19. Dry the membrane on filter paper and establish an autoradiograph by exposing the membrane for 24–48 hours to X-ray film (Kodak XAR-5 or equivalent) at –70°C with an intensifying screen (please see Appendix 9). Tungstate-based intensifying screens are more effective than the older rare-earth screens. Alternatively, an image of the membrane can be obtained by scanning in a phosphorimager.

Protocol 10

Mapping RNA with Nuclease S1

THREE DIFFERENT NUCLEASES — NUCLEASE S1, RIBONUCLEASE, AND EXONUCLEASE VII — have been used to quantitate RNAs, to map the position of introns, and to identify the locations of 5′ and 3′ ends of mRNAs on cloned DNA templates (please see Figures 7-4 and 7-5). Nuclease S1 is used in protection assays when the test RNA is hybridized to a DNA template (please see the information panel on **NUCLEASE S1**); ribonuclease is used when the test RNA is hybridized to an RNA copy of a DNA template (please see Protocol 11). Exonuclease VII is used for more specialized purposes — to map short introns and to resolve anomalies arising in nuclease S1 protection assays (please see the information panel on **EXONUCLEASE VII**).

The methods used with all three enzymes are elaborations of the classical nuclease S1 protection technique described by Berk and Sharp (1977). Preparations of RNA containing the mRNA of interest are incubated with a complementary DNA or RNA probe under conditions that favor the formation of hybrids. At the end of the reaction, an enzyme is used to degrade unhybridized single-stranded RNA and DNA. The surviving DNA-RNA or RNA-RNA hybrids are then separated by gel electrophoresis and visualized either by autoradiography or by Southern hybridization (Favaloro et al. 1980; Calzone et al. 1987). When the probe is present in molar excess in the hybridization reaction, the strength of the signal is proportional to the concentration of the mRNA of interest in the test preparation. Accurate estimates of concentration can be obtained by constructing a standard curve in which an excess of probe is hybridized to known amounts of the target sequence.

A major problem with the nuclease S1 protection assay in its original form (Berk and Sharp 1977) was the use of double-stranded DNA as probes. To prevent reassociation of the probe DNA during the hybridization step, it was desirable but not always possible to establish hybridization conditions that favored the formation of RNA-DNA hybrids over competing DNA-DNA hybrids. Because DNA-RNA hybrids are slightly more stable than DNA-DNA hybrids, the annealing step was usually performed in 80% formamide at a temperature above the calculated melting temperature of the double-stranded DNA (Casey and Davidson 1977; Dean 1987). However, under these conditions, the rate of hybridization is slowed by a factor of ~10, and the stability of DNA-RNA hybrids is unpredictable. These problems could be circumvented by the use of single-stranded probes. The annealing step could then be carried out under standard hybridization conditions because there would be no complementary strand present to compete with the target RNA for probe. However, when Berk and Sharp did their work, there was simply no reliable method to prepare a single strand of DNA free of its complement. Strand-separating gel electrophoresis (Hayward 1972) was the only technique available, but it was always a tricky business (please see

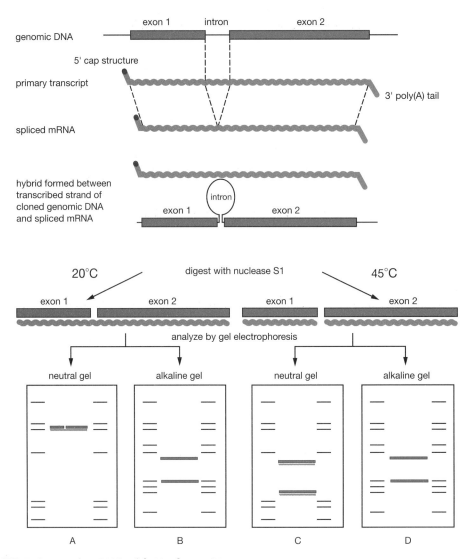

FIGURE 7-4 Mapping RNA with Nuclease S1

When cloned segments of genomic DNA are used as probes, the location of introns can be inferred from the size of the bands after nuclease S1 digestion. Hybrids formed between the transcribed strand of genomic DNA and mRNA contain loops of single-stranded DNA (introns). Digestion of these hybrids with nuclease S1 at 20°C generates molecules whose RNA moieties are intact but whose DNAs contain gaps at the sites of the introns. These molecules migrate as a single band when analyzed by gel electrophoresis under nondenaturing conditions (gel A). In alkaline gels (gel B), however, the RNA is hydrolyzed and the individual fragments of DNA separate according to their sizes. When digestion with nuclease S1 is carried out at 45°C, both the DNA and RNA strands of the parental hybrid are cleaved to yield a series of smaller DNA-RNA hybrids that can be separated by electrophoresis under nondenaturing conditions (gel C). The DNA moieties in these hybrids (gel D) are the same size as those detected in gel B.

Chapter 5, Protocol 8). Separation was possible with only ~70% of the DNA fragments and, even when successful, inevitably resulted in preparations that were contaminated with the complementary DNA strand. Because of these difficulties, the patterns of bands detected after gel electrophoresis were sometimes complex and often varied from one experiment to the next. These difficulties were solved in the late 1980s by the development of methods to produce single-stranded DNA or RNA probes labeled to high specific activity.

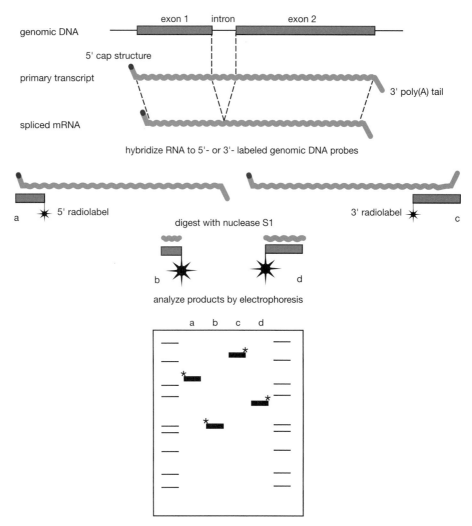

FIGURE 7-5 Mapping the 5′ and 3′ Termini of mRNAs

Hybrids formed between mRNA and DNA probes radiolabeled at either their 5′ or their 3′ termini are digested with nuclease S1. The locations of radiolabels are shown by the starburst symbol. The location of the 5′ and 3′ termini of the target RNA can be deduced by measuring the size of the nuclease-resistant fragments of DNA and estimating the distance between the radiolabel and the 5′ and 3′ termini of the mRNA. (Lane *a*) 5′-labeled probe before digestion with nuclease S1; (lane *b*) 5′-labeled probe after digestion with nuclease S1; (lane *c*) 3′-labeled probe before digestion with nuclease S1; (lane *d*) 3′-labeled probe after digestion with nuclease S1. Molecular-weight standards are represented in the outside lanes. In eukaryotic systems, the 5′ end of the mRNA determined by nuclease S1 mapping generally represents the start point of transcription, whereas the delineated 3′ end represents the site of polyadenylation. A similar strategy can be used to map the position of 3′- and 5′-splice sites.

PROBES USED IN NUCLEASE S1 PROTECTION ASSAYS

Probes of known polarity and high specific activity are made by separating the strands of a fragment of double-stranded DNA or, more frequently, by de novo synthesis either of RNA complementary to one strand of a double-stranded DNA template or of DNA complementary to a single-stranded template (for further details on probe preparation, please see Chapter 9).

- Strand-separated probes are prepared by using type II restriction enzymes, singly or in combination, to generate a DNA fragment of suitable size (usually 100–500 nucleotides) with a 5′

extension at one end and a 3′ extension at the other. One strand of the fragment therefore will be up to eight nucleotides longer than the other. This difference in size is sufficient to allow separation of the two strands by electrophoresis through a polyacrylamide gel under denaturing conditions. Either before or after electrophoresis, the 5′ terminus of the strand of interest is dephosphorylated and radiolabeled in vitro by transfer of the labeled phosphate residue from [γ-^{32}P]ATP, a reaction catalyzed by bacteriophage T4 polynucleotide kinase (please see Chapter 9, Protocols 13–16.

- De novo synthesis is used to produce end-labeled or uniformly labeled DNA probes in vitro (e.g., please see Weaver and Weissmann 1979; Burke 1984; Calzone et al. 1987; Aldea et al. 1988; Sharrocks and Hornby 1991; see also Chapter 9). End-labeled probes are prepared by phosphorylating the 5′ terminus of the oligonucleotide primer; uniformly labeled probes are prepared by incorporating radiolabeled nucleotides into the growing DNA strand. In both cases, the newly synthesized strand of DNA can be separated from the template by digestion with a restriction enzyme that recognizes a unique site in the newly formed double-stranded DNA. The radiolabeled probe can then be separated from the linearized single-stranded DNA by electrophoresis through a polyacrylamide gel under denaturing conditions.

- Radiolabeled probes biased heavily in favor of one strand of DNA are produced in PCRs in which the concentration of one primer exceeds the other by a factor of 20–200. During the initial cycles of the PCR, double-stranded DNA is synthesized in a conventional exponential fashion. However, when the concentration of one primer becomes limiting, the reaction generates single-stranded DNA that accumulates at an arithmetic rate. By the end of the reaction, the concentration of one strand of DNA is three to five times greater than the concentration of the other (Scully et al. 1990).

- Radiolabeled probes consisting entirely of one strand of DNA are synthesized in thermal cycling reactions that contain a double-stranded DNA template but only one primer. Double-stranded template DNA (20 μg) generates ~200 μg of single-stranded probe over the course of 40 cycles. The length of the probe can be defined by cleaving the template DNA at a restriction site downstream from the binding site of the primer (Stürzl and Roth 1990a,b).

- Uniformly labeled RNA probes (riboprobes) are generated by transcribing a linear double-stranded DNA template attached to a bacteriophage promoter (Melton et al. 1984). The DNA template is generated either by digesting a recombinant plasmid with a restriction enzyme that cleaves within or downstream from the cloned DNA sequence or by amplifying the template using PCR. The linearized template is transcribed in the presence of [α-^{32}P]NTPs by the appropriate bacteriophage DNA-dependent RNA polymerase to produce a radiolabeled RNA that extends from the initiation site of the promoter to the end of the DNA fragment. The promoter and the DNA sequence are oriented such that the resulting riboprobe is antisense (complementary) to the mRNA to be analyzed. It is prudent, but not mandatory, to purify RNA probes by denaturing gel electrophoresis. Purification can be carried out easily and quickly on minigels cast with 5% polyacrylamide/8 M urea and run on a miniprotein gel apparatus (e.g., Bio-Rad Mini-Protean).

Even when single-stranded probes are used, nuclease S1 analysis of the structure of eukaryotic RNAs is not free of artifacts. For example, small mismatches in DNA:RNA heteroduplexes are relatively resistant to the action of the nuclease (Berk and Sharp 1977). Conversely, regions of perfect heteroduplex that are rich in rU:dA sequences are susceptible to cleavage (Miller and Sollner-Webb 1981). A single molecule of DNA frequently can be protected from the action of the nuclease by simultaneous hybridization to two different RNA molecules (Lopata et al. 1985). Finally, nuclease S1 inefficiently cleaves the segment of DNA opposite a looped-out region of RNA (Sisodia et al. 1987). Many of these problems can be solved by using a range of concentrations of nuclease S1, by performing the digestion at different temperatures, by using a different nuclease (e.g., mung bean nuclease), or by using a combination of nucleases (e.g., RNase H and nuclease S1) (Sisodia et al. 1987). However, it is important to realize that cleavage by nuclease S1 does not necessarily reflect a divergence in sequence between strands of two nucleic acids and that resistance to digestion is not necessarily synonymous with identity. Mapping with nuclease S1 should therefore be regarded as a useful, but not infallible, guide to the structure of RNAs. Thus, when using nuclease S1 to map, for example, the 5′ and 3′ ends of a mRNA, it is important to confirm the result by an independent technique such as primer extension (Protocol 12).

Mung bean nuclease can be substituted for nuclease S1 in many mapping experiments (please see the information panel on **MUNG BEAN NUCLEASE**). With some DNA probes, far less mung bean nuclease than nuclease S1 is needed to obtain complete digestion of single-stranded regions. For example, nuclease S1 is used at a concentration of 1000 units/ml to obtain complete digestion of excess single-stranded DNA probe corresponding to the human low-density lipoprotein receptor, whereas an identical result is obtained with as little as 10 units/ml of mung bean nuclease (J.A. Cuthbert, pers. comm., University of Texas Southwestern Medical Center, Dallas). A disadvantage of mung bean nuclease is that it can cost 20 times more on a per-unit basis than nuclease S1. Mung bean nuclease can be substituted for nuclease S1 at Step 22 in the protocol. Mung bean nuclease digestions are carried out in a buffer containing 10 mM sodium acetate (pH 4.6)/50 mM NaCl/1 mM ZnCl/1 mM β-mercaptoethanol/0.001% (v/v) Triton X-100.

This protocol presents a method for nuclease S1 mapping of mRNA using a uniformly labeled, single-stranded DNA probe. Procedures for mapping RNA using ribonuclease and RNA probes and for mapping RNA by primer extension are presented in Protocols 11 and 12, respectively.

MATERIALS

▲ IMPORTANT Prepare all reagents used in this protocol with DEPC-treated H_2O (please see the information panel on **HOW TO WIN THE BATTLE WITH RNASE**).

CAUTION: Please see Appendix 12 for appropriate handling of materials marked with <!>.

Buffers and Solutions

Please see Appendix 1 for components of stock solutions, buffers, and reagents.
Dilute stock to the appropriate working concentration.

Ammonium persulfate (10%) <!>
10x Annealing buffer
    100 mM Tris-Cl (pH 7.5)
    100 mM $MgCl_2$
    0.5 M NaCl
    100 mM dithiothreitol
Ethanol
Gel elution buffer
    0.5 M ammonium acetate <!>
    1 mM EDTA (pH 8.0)
    0.1% (w/v) SDS

Hybridization buffer (for RNA)

40 mM PIPES (pH 6.4)

0.1 mM EDTA (pH 8.0)

0.4 M NaCl

Use the disodium salt of PIPES (piperazine-*N,N'*-bis[2-ethanesulfonic acid]) to prepare the buffer, and adjust the pH to 6.4 with 1 N HCl.

Nuclease S1 stop mixture

4 M ammonium acetate

50 mM EDTA (pH 8.0)

50 μg/ml carrier RNA

Store the nuclease S1 stop mixture in aliquots at –20°C.

Phenol:chloroform (1:1, v/v) <!>

RNA gel-loading buffer

Sodium acetate (3 M, pH 5.2)

TE (pH 7.6)

TEMED (N,N,N',N'-tetramethylethylene diamine) <!>

Trichloroacetic acid (TCA) (1% and 10%) <!>

Dilute 100% stock solution 1/10 and 1/100 just before use. Chill the working solutions in ice.

Enzymes and Buffers

Bacteriophage T4 polynucleotide kinase

Klenow fragment of E. coli *DNA polymerase (10 units/μl)*

Nuclease S1 (for use in nuclease S1 digestion buffer, please see below)

It is necessary to titrate the nuclease S1 each time a new probe or RNA preparation is used.

Nuclease S1 digestion buffer

0.28 M NaCl

0.05 M sodium acetate (pH 4.5)

4.5 mM $ZnSO_4 \cdot 7H_2O$

Store aliquots of nuclease S1 buffer at –20°C and add nuclease S1 to a concentration of 500 units/ml just before use.

Restriction endonucleases

Gels

Denaturing polyacrylamide gel containing 8 M urea <!>

For most 5'- and 3'-end mapping experiments, a denaturing gel composed of 5% or 6% polyacrylamide and containing 8 M urea nicely resolves protected DNA fragments. A typical gel is 1.5 mm thick. However, "thin" or "sequencing" gels (0.4-mm thickness) can also be used (please see Chapter 12). If thin gels are used to resolve protected DNA fragments, it is usually not necessary to fix the gel in trichloroacetic acid (TCA), as described in Steps 30–32, before drying the gel. Fixing sharpens and increases the resolution of thicker gels. In many cases, a miniprotein gel apparatus (e.g., Bio-Rad Mini-Protean or Ambion Vertical Gel Apparatus) (13 cm x 13 cm x 1 mm) can be used both to prepare the radiolabeled single-stranded DNA or RNA probe and to analyze the products of nuclease S1 digestion. Table 7-6 shows the percentage of polyacrylamide used to purify DNA fragments of various sizes; Table 7-7 shows the expected mobilities of tracking dyes in these gels. The method used to prepare the polyacrylamide gel is described in Step 1 of this protocol; for further details, please see Chapter 12, Protocol 8.

TABLE 7-6 Percentage of Gel for Purifying Various DNA Fragments

% POLYACRYLAMIDE/UREA GEL	SIZE OF BAND (nt)
4	>250
6	60–250
8	40–120
10	20–60
12	10–50

TABLE 7-7 Expected Mobilities of Tracking Dyes

% POLYACRYLAMIDE/UREA GEL	XYLENE CYANOL (nt)	BROMOPHENOL BLUE (nt)
4	155	30
6	110	25
8	75	20
10	55	10

Tracking dyes can serve as useful size standards on denaturing polyacrylamide gels. The table indicates the approximate sizes of tracking dyes (in nucleotides) on gels of different polyacrylamide concentrations.

Nucleic Acids and Oligonucleotides

Carrier RNA (yeast tRNA)

dNTP solution (20 mM) containing all four dNTPs

Dissolve the dNTPs in 25 mM Tris-Cl (pH 8.0) and store as small aliquots at –20ºC.

RNA, for use as a standard

Synthesize in vitro by transcription of the appropriate strand of a recombinant plasmid containing the DNA sequences of interest and a bacteriophage promoter. Methods to synthesize and purify the RNA are outlined in Chapter 9, Protocol 6.

Synthetic oligonucleotide (10 pmoles/μl) in distilled H$_2$O

The oligonucleotide used to prime synthesis of the probe from a single-stranded DNA template should be 20–25 nucleotides in length and complementary to the RNA strand to be analyzed. It should hybridize to the template DNA strand 250–500 nucleotides 3′ of the position that will be cleaved by the chosen restriction enzyme. Store oligonucleotides in aliquots at –20ºC.

Template DNA (1 μg/μl), single-stranded

Use standard procedures (Chapter 3, Protocol 5) to prepare single-stranded DNA from a recombinant bacteriophage M13 carrying the insert DNA strand in the same sense as the test RNA.

Test RNA

Poly(A)$^+$ or total RNA prepared by one of the methods described in Protocols 1 through 4 of this chapter.

Probes

DNA probe, uniformly labeled and single-stranded

The DNA probe is prepared in Steps 1–15 of this protocol. Use single-stranded probes uniformly labeled to high specific activity within a few days to avoid problems caused by radiochemical degradation.

Radioactive Compounds

[γ-^{32}P]ATP (10 mCi/ml, 3000 Ci/mmole) <!>

Special Equipment

Water baths preset to 65ºC, 85ºC, and 95ºC, to the appropriate digestion temperature (please see Step 22), and to the desired hybridization temperature (please see Step 21)

Whatman 3MM filter paper (or equivalent)

TABLE 7-8 Volumes of Polyacrylamide Required to Cast Minigels of Various Percentages

% GEL	VOLUME OF 40% ACRYLAMIDE (ml)
4	1.5
5	1.875
6	2.25
8	3.0

METHOD

Preparation of Randomly Labeled Single-stranded DNA Probe

1. Prepare a polyacrylamide minigel containing 8 M urea (13 cm x 15 cm x 0.75 mm) (e.g., Bio-Rad Mini-Protean).

   a. Mix the following reagents:

   > 7.2 g of urea
   > 1.5 ml of 10x TBE

   Add the appropriate amounts of 40% acrylamide (acrylamide:bisacrylamide 19:1; please see Table 7-8) to generate a gel containing the desired concentration of polyacrylamide (please see Table 7-6).

   b. Add H_2O to a final volume of 15 ml.

   c. Stir the mixture at room temperature on a magnetic stirrer until the urea dissolves. Then add:

   > 120 μl of 10% ammonium persulfate
   > 16 μl of TEMED

   Mix the solution quickly and then pour the gel into the mold of a minigel apparatus.

2. While the gel is polymerizing, mix the following reagents:

   > 10 pmoles (1 μl) of unlabeled oligonucleotide
   > 10 μl of [γ-^{32}P]ATP (3000 Ci/mmole, 10 mCi/ml)
   > 2 μl of 10x polynucleotide kinase buffer
   > 6 μl of H_2O
   > 10 units (1 μl) of polynucleotide kinase

   Incubate the reaction mixture for 45 minutes at 37ºC, and then for 3 minutes at 95ºC to inactivate the polynucleotide kinase.

3. Add to the kinase reaction:

   > 2 μl (2 μg) of single-stranded DNA template
   > 4 μl of 10x annealing buffer
   > 14 μl of H_2O

   Incubate the reaction mixture for 10 minutes at 65ºC and then allow it to cool to room temperature.

4. Add to the reaction mix from Step 3:

   > 4 μl of dNTP mixture
   > 1 μl (10 units) of the Klenow fragment of *E. coli* DNA polymerase I

   Incubate the reaction mixture for 15 minutes at room temperature and then inactivate the DNA polymerase by incubation for 3 minutes at 65ºC.

5. Adjust the ionic composition and pH of the reaction mixture to suit the restriction enzyme. Add 20 units of restriction enzyme and incubate the reaction mixture for 2 hours at the appropriate temperature.

6. Add to the restriction endonuclease digestion reaction:

   > 2 μl of carrier RNA
   > 5 μl of 3 M sodium acetate (pH 5.2)

   Recover the DNA probe by standard precipitation with ethanol.

7. Dissolve the DNA in 20 µl of gel-loading buffer. Heat the solution to 95°C for 5 minutes to denature the DNA, and then cool the DNA quickly to 0°C.

Purification of the Probe by Gel Electrophoresis

8. While the DNA is incubating at 95°C, wash the loading slots of the gel to remove urea and then, without delay, load the probe into one of the slots of the gel.

9. Run the gel until the bromophenol blue reaches the bottom of the gel (200 mA for ~30 minutes).

10. Dismantle the gel apparatus, leaving the gel attached to the bottom glass plate. Wrap the gel and plate in a piece of plastic wrap (e.g., Saran Wrap). Make sure that there are no bubbles between the gel and the plastic film.

    ▲ WARNING Wear eye protection when prying the glass plates apart.

11. Expose the gel to X-ray film. Mark the location of the corners and sides of the plate on the film with a permanent marker. Also mark the position of the bromophenol blue and xylene cyanol.
    Usually an exposure of 2–10 minutes is sufficient to obtain an image of the radiolabeled probe.

12. Realign the glass plate with the film and excise the radiolabeled band with a scalpel. Reexpose the mutilated gel to a fresh piece of film to ensure that the region of the gel containing the band of the correct molecular weight has been accurately excised.

SETTING UP HYBRIDIZATIONS BETWEEN THE RADIOLABELED PROBE AND THE TEST RNA

When setting up hybridizations:

- The DNA probe should be in excess over the target RNA species. In most cases, addition of 0.01–0.05 pmole of probe (~1–8 ng of a 400-nucleotide single-stranded DNA probe) will provide an excess of probe in the hybridization reaction. However, nuclease S1 mapping of abundant RNAs (e.g., viral mRNAs present in infected cells, mRNAs encoding structural proteins, or mRNAs encoding abundant enzymes) may require more DNA probe. The exact amount of probe required to reach saturation can be determined empirically by nuclease S1 digestion of a series of hybridization mixtures containing different ratios of test RNA:probe.

- The amount of test RNA required depends on the concentration of the sequences of interest and on the specific activity of the radiolabeled probe. With DNAs that have been radiolabeled to high specific activity ($>10^9$ cpm/µg), 10 µg of total RNA is usually sufficient to allow detection of mRNA species that are present at the level of one to five copies/cell. To detect sequences present in lower concentrations (e.g., in RNA extracted from heterogeneous populations of cells), up to 150 µg of RNA may be used in a 30-µl hybridization reaction. For ease of manipulation in subsequent steps, it is advisable to keep the hybridization volume to 30 µl or less. If reagents are in short supply, the hybridization reactions can be scaled down to 10 µl. In every experiment, it is best to include several different amounts of input RNA to make sure that the DNA probe is in excess and that duplicate tubes yield reproducible results.

- All reactions should contain the same amount of RNA to ensure that digestion with nuclease S1 is carried out under near identical conditions. If necessary, adjust the amount of RNA in the hybridization reactions by adding carrier RNA.

- To quantify the target sequences in the preparations of RNA under test, set up a series of hybridization reactions containing a constant amount of radiolabeled probe, a constant amount of control RNA (i.e., RNA known to lack the target sequences), and amounts (1 fg to 100 pg) of a standard preparation of RNA synthesized in vitro. Total cellular RNA (10 µg) will contain 10 fg to 1 pg of a rare mRNA and ~300 pg of a moderately abundant mRNA such as β-actin or GAPDH.

---

13. Transfer the fragment of gel to a fresh sterile microfuge tube and add just enough gel elution buffer to cover the fragment (250–500 µl). Incubate the closed tube on a rotating wheel overnight at room temperature.

14. Centrifuge the tube at maximum speed for 5 minutes in a microfuge.

15. Taking care to avoid the pellet of polyacrylamide, use an automatic pipetting device to transfer the supernatant to a fresh microfuge tube. The labeled probe should emit ~1 x 10^4 cpm/µl as measured by liquid scintillation spectroscopy.

    Optional: To maximize recovery of RNA, add 200 µl of gel elution buffer to the gel pellet in Step 15, incubate the closed tube on a rotating wheel overnight, and repeat Steps 14 and 15.

16. Store the probe at –70ºC.

Hybridization between the Test RNA and the Radiolabeled Probe DNA

17. Transfer 0.5–150 µg aliquots of RNA (test and standard) into sterile microfuge tubes. Add an excess of uniformly labeled single-stranded DNA probe to each tube.

18. Precipitate the RNA and DNA by adding 0.1 volume of 3 M sodium acetate (pH 5.2) and 2.5 volumes of ice-cold ethanol. After storage for 30 minutes at 0ºC, recover the nucleic acids by centrifugation at maximum speed for 15 minutes at 4ºC in a microfuge. Discard the ethanolic supernatant, rinse the pellet with 70% ethanol, and centrifuge the sample. Carefully remove all of the ethanol, and store the pellet containing RNA and DNA at room temperature until the last visible traces of ethanol have evaporated.

    Do not allow the pellet to become desiccated, otherwise it will be difficult to dissolve.

DISSOLVING NUCLEIC ACID PELLETS

It is often difficult to obtain complete dissolution of the pellet of nucleic acids in hybridization buffer (Step 19). This problem is exacerbated if the pellet is dried in a desiccator. Sometimes the pellet can be dissolved by a combination of vigorous pipetting and heating to 60ºC. If difficulties persist, or if equivalent signals are not obtained from duplicate samples of RNA, the following procedure is recommended:

1. After Step 18 of the protocol, dissolve the pellet in 40–50 µl of H$_2$O. Evaporate the sample in a rotary evaporator until it is just dry.

2. Add 30 µl of hybridization buffer. The hydrated pellet should go into solution quickly and easily and yield reproducible results.

---

19. Dissolve the nucleic acid pellet in 30 µl of hybridization buffer. Pipette the solution up and down many times to ensure that the pellet is completely dissolved.

20. Close the lid of the tube tightly, and incubate the hybridization reaction in a water bath set at 85ºC for 10 minutes to denature the nucleic acids.

21. Rapidly transfer the tube to a water bath set at the desired hybridization temperature (usually 65ºC). Do not allow the tube to cool below the hybridization temperature during transfer. Hybridize the DNA and RNA for 12–16 hours at the chosen temperature.

Nuclease S1 Digestion of the DNA-RNA Hybrids

22. Taking care to keep the body of the tube submerged, open the lid of the hybridization tube. Rapidly add 300 µl of ice-cold nuclease S1 digestion buffer, and immediately remove the tube from the water bath. Quickly mix the contents of the tube by vortexing gently, and then transfer the tube to a water bath set at the temperature appropriate for digestion with nuclease S1. Incubate for 1–2 hours, depending on the degree of digestion desired.

CONDITIONS FOR DIGESTION WITH NUCLEASE S1

A variety of temperatures and nuclease S1 concentrations have been used to analyze DNA-RNA hybrids. For example, at 20°C, nuclease S1 at a concentration of 100–1000 units/ml will degrade loops of DNA but will not efficiently digest segments of RNA molecules that bridge loops of DNA. This property is useful when mapping intron/exon borders in segments of genomic DNA because the partially digested molecule will migrate through agarose gels at neutral pH at approximately the same rate as double-stranded DNA. However, under alkaline conditions, the RNA "bridge" will be hydrolyzed, liberating two smaller pieces of single-stranded DNA. From the sizes of these fragments, it is often possible to assign locations to intron/exon junctions in a segment of genomic DNA (Berk and Sharp 1977). For digestion of the single-stranded regions of DNA-RNA hybrids, higher temperatures (37–45°C) or increased quantities of nuclease S1 are generally required. Because of the ambiguity inherent in choosing conditions that will lead to either complete resistance to digestion or complete digestion of single-stranded nucleic acid structures, it is best to choose a convenient digestion time (e.g., 1 hour) and then set up a series of test reactions in which the amount of nuclease S1 is varied (e.g., 100, 500, and 1000 units/ml) and the digestion temperature is varied (22°C, 30°C, 37°C, and 45°C). Examine the results by polyacrylamide gel electrophoresis and fine tune the enzyme concentration and temperature conditions as needed.

---

23. Chill the reaction to 0°C. Add 80 μl of nuclease S1 stop mixture and vortex the tube to mix the solution.

24. Extract the reaction once with phenol:chloroform. After centrifugation at maximum speed for 2 minutes at room temperature in a microfuge, transfer the aqueous supernatant to a fresh tube. Add 2 volumes of ethanol, mix, and store the tube for 1 hour at –20°C.

25. Recover the nucleic acids by centrifugation at maximum speed for 15 minutes at 4°C in a microfuge. Carefully remove all of the supernatant, and store the open tube at room temperature until the last visible traces of ethanol have evaporated.

Analysis of the Products of Nuclease S1 Digestions by Gel Electrophoresis

26. Dissolve the pellet in 4 μl of TE (pH 7.6). Add 6 μl of gel-loading buffer and mix well.

27. Heat the nucleic acids for 5 minutes at 95°C, and then immediately transfer the tube to an ice bath. Centrifuge the tubes briefly in a microfuge to consolidate the samples at the bottoms of the tubes.

28. Analyze the radiolabeled DNA by electrophoresis through a polyacrylamide/8 M urea gel.

    For most applications, a 5–6% polyacrylamide/8 M urea gel of 1.5-mm thickness will suffice. As molecular-weight markers, use end-labeled fragments of DNA of known size or a sequencing ladder. During electrophoresis, enough current should be run through the gel to keep the glass plates warm to the touch.

29. After the tracking dyes have migrated an appropriate distance through the gel (please see Table 7-7), turn off the power supply and disassemble the electrophoresis set up. Gently pry up one corner of the larger glass plate and slowly remove the plate from the gel. Cut off one corner of the gel for orientation purposes.

    ▲ WARNING Wear eye protection when prying the glass plates apart.

30. Transfer the glass plate containing the gel to a tray containing an excess of 10% TCA. Gently rock or rotate the tray for 10 minutes at room temperature.

    The gel will usually float off the glass plate during this incubation. Do not allow the floating gel to fold up on itself.

31. Pour off the 10% TCA solution and replace with an excess of 1% TCA. Gently rock or rotate the tray for 5 minutes at room temperature.

32. Pour off the 1% TCA solution and briefly rinse the fixed gel with distilled deionized H_2O. Lift the glass plate together with the gel out of the tray and place them on a flat bench top. Use paper towels or Kimwipes to remove excess H_2O.

    Do not place towels on top of the gel.

33. Cut a piece of Whatman 3MM filter paper (or equivalent) that is 1 cm larger than the gel on all sides. Transfer the gel to the filter paper by laying the paper on top of the gel and inverting the glass plate.

34. Remove the plate and dry the gel on a gel dryer for 1.0–1.5 hours at 60ºC.

35. Establish an autoradiographic image of the dried gel. Scan the image by densitometry or phosphorimaging, or excise the segments of the gel containing the fragments and count them by liquid scintillation spectroscopy.

    From the samples containing different amounts of standard RNA, a curve of mass versus radioactivity can be constructed. The amount of target sequences in the test preparations of RNA can then be estimated by interpolation.

Protocol 11

Ribonuclease Protection: Mapping RNA with Ribonuclease and Radiolabeled RNA Probes

RIBONUCLEASE PROTECTION ASSAYS ARE USED TO MEASURE the abundance of specific mRNAs and to map their topological features. The method involves hybridization of test RNAs to complementary radiolabeled RNA probes (riboprobes), followed by digestion of nonhybridized sequences with one or more single-strand-specific ribonucleases. At the end of the digestion, the ribonucleases are inactivated, and the protected fragments of radiolabeled RNA are analyzed by polyacrylamide gel electrophoresis and autoradiography. As with nuclease S1 protection assays (please see Figure 7-4), the size of the protected fragments allows the mapping of features such as intron-exon borders and sites of transcription initiation and termination (please see Figure 7-6) (Lynn et al. 1983; Zinn et al. 1983; Melton et al. 1984; for reviews, please see Calzone et al. 1987; Kekule et al. 1990; Mitchell and Fidge 1996). However, interpretation of mapping data is not always easy or unambiguous. For example, when analyzing protected fragments formed between a test mRNA and a riboprobe derived by transcription of a cloned segment of genomic DNA, it is not always possible to distinguish between a splice junction lying near the 5′ terminus of the mRNA and the true 5′ terminus of the mRNA. Wherever possible, confirmatory data should be obtained from an independent technique, for example, primer extension (Protocol 12 of this chapter) or 5′-RACE (Chapter 8, Protocol 9).

When the antisense riboprobe is present in molar excess, the strength of the autoradiographic signal is proportional to the amount of sense RNA in the test sample. Quantification is achieved by comparing the strength of the signals from samples containing test RNA with that of signals from samples containing known amounts of standard RNAs, these being generated by in vitro transcription of an appropriate DNA template (please see Techniques for Quantitating RNA below). Ribonuclease protection is at least tenfold more sensitive than northern hybridization. This sensitivity is due to a variety of factors, including the following.

- *More complete and speedier hybridization* is achieved because test and probe RNAs are both present in solution.

- *Elimination of the step in which RNA is transferred from a gel to a solid support.* The efficiency of this step varies according to the method used and the molecular weight of the target RNA.

- *Elimination of posthybridization washing steps.* The stringency and efficiency of these steps affect the level of background and the strength of the signal. No matter how skillfully these washes are performed, the maximum ratio of signal to noise in a northern blot rarely exceeds a factor of 10.

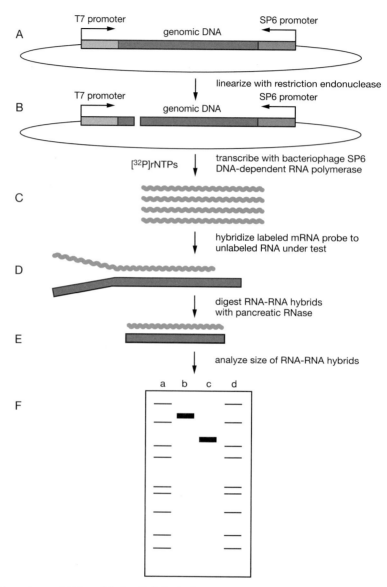

FIGURE 7-6 Mapping mRNAs with Radiolabeled RNA Probes and RNase

Radiolabeled RNA, synthesized in vitro from a cloned copy of the genomic DNA (steps A–C), is hybridized to unlabeled test mRNA (step D). After removal of the unhybridized tails by digestion with RNase (step E), the size of the radiolabeled RNA that is resistant to RNase is measured by gel electrophoresis (step F). (Step A) Target DNA is cloned into a plasmid downstream from a prokaryotic promoter (bacteriophage SP6 or T7); (step B) the recombinant plasmid is linearized with a restriction enzyme that cleaves at the distal end of the target DNA; (step C) the linear DNA is transcribed with the appropriate DNA-dependent RNA polymerase (in this case, SP6), and template DNA is removed by digestion with RNase-free pancreatic DNase; (step D) radiolabeled RNA (orange squiggly line) is hybridized to unlabeled test RNA (solid red line); (step E) RNA-RNA hybrids are digested with pancreatic RNase; (step F) RNA-RNA hybrids (before and after digestion with RNase) are analyzed with gel electrophoresis and autoradiography. (Lanes a,d) Molecular-weight standards. (Lane b) Radiolabeled RNA before digestion with RNase; (lane c) radiolabeled RNA after digestion with RNase. By using probes complementary to appropriate segments of the template DNA, it is possible to map the positions of the 5' and 3' termini of mRNAs and the positions of 5'- and 3'-splice sites.

- *Greater tolerance of RNA degradation.* Because the radiolabeled antisense probe is generally much shorter than the mRNA under test, the sensitivity and accuracy of the ribonuclease protection assay are not significantly affected if the preparation of test RNA is partially degraded.

Ribonuclease protection assays have other advantages over northern hybridizations; they do not require special instruments, can be adapted to the simultaneous use of several radiolabeled probes, and are sufficiently sensitive to detect low-abundance RNAs in preparations of total RNA. The ribonuclease protection assay shares many of these advantages with the nuclease S1 protection assay. However, the two protection assays differ in some respects. AU-rich regions, which are often cleaved nonspecifically by nuclease S1, are not susceptible to nonspecific cleavage in ribonuclease protection assays, and the termini of the hybrids are not at risk of being nibbled (please see Ribonucleases Used in Ribonuclease Protection Assays below). In addition, radiolabeled probes used in nuclease S1 protection assays require specific oligonucleotide primers and single-stranded DNA templates. Riboprobes, on the other hand, can be produced by transcription of standard plasmids carrying bacteriophage promoters (for further details, please see Chapter 9). For these reasons, the ribonuclease protection assay has largely replaced the nuclease S1 assay as the standard method of analysis of RNA.

TECHNIQUES FOR QUANTITATING RNA

Oddly enough, gene expression was measured more accurately in the 1970s than it is today. Only one technique — reassociation kinetics — was available in those days. Reassociation of nucleic acids in solution results from collision of complementary strands and follows kinetics that are second order or very nearly so (Wetmur and Davidson 1968). The rate of hybridization is therefore inversely proportional to the initial concentration of the complementary strands (Britten and Kohne 1968). The absolute concentration of a particular RNA can be calculated from the kinetics of its reassociation with its DNA template.

During the decade that preceded the development of molecular cloning, many reassociation experiments were carried out to measure the concentration of mRNAs. Almost all of these experiments involved measuring the rate of association of a radiolabeled single-stranded DNA probe with its complementary mRNA, when the RNA was present in molar excess. These were difficult experiments, for several reasons: The concentration of reagents in the hybridization reactions was often so low that the reassociation reaction required many hours — days in some cases — to generate significant amounts of hybrid. Second, hydroxyapatite columns were routinely used to separate double-stranded and single-stranded nucleic acids (Kohne and Britten 1971; Britten et al. 1974). Running these columns was a tedious and messy business. With practice, one person could run 24 small hydroxyapatite columns simultaneously. However, this was not much fun; not only was the processing of samples extremely monotonous, but, even worse, the columns were run in scalding hot water baths. Then there was the perennial problem of generating a radiolabeled template of high specific activity. In those days, all labeling of nucleic acids was done in vivo using [^{32}P]orthophosphate. At Cold Spring Harbor Laboratory, our weekly delivery of 100 mCi of the ghastly stuff arrived on Tuesday and was immediately used to label cultured cells infected with SV40 or adenovirus. By Friday or Saturday, if we were lucky, we had purified enough viral DNA at sufficient specific activity to do a few experiments before the next batch of radioactivity arrived. Both the hydroxyapatite columns and the radiolabeled DNA were far too hot to handle with comfort.

Hydroxyapatite columns and their scalding water baths have all but disappeared from laboratory inventories. We cannot regret their passing, but we can mourn the loss of reassociation kinetics as a way to measure the concentrations of nucleic acids. The simplicity and elegance of the underlying theory and the easy clarity of the experiments deserved a greater permanence.

Today, a number of procedures are used to measure the abundance of a particular mRNA in a preparation of total or poly(A)$^+$ RNA. The most popular of these are northern blots, ribonuclease protection, and quantitative reverse transcriptase-PCR (RT-PCR). Each of these methods has virtues and limitations:

- *Northern blots* require relatively large amounts of material and are severely compromised by degradation of the RNA. Their sensitivity is low and they are clumsy instruments for measuring the abundance of different mRNAs in the same sample. However, northern blotting has the unique virtue of simultaneously providing information on both size and abundance of target mRNAs. This duality is particularly useful when comparing expression of spliced variants of a transcript in different tissues. Quantification depends on rehybridization with a probe to a transcript from a housekeeping gene or an externally added standard (please see the Introduction to Northern Hybridization preceding Protocol 5).

- *Ribonuclease protection* does not require intact RNA; it is ~20–100-fold more sensitive than northern hybridization and is capable of detecting ~10^5 copies of a specific trancript. The method can easily cope with several target mRNAs simultaneously and, because the intensity of the signal is directly proportional to the concentration of target RNA, comparisons of the level of expression of the target gene in different tissues is easily accomplished. However, ribonuclease protection works best with antisense probes that are exactly complementary to the target mRNA. This can be a problem if the experiment generates RNA-RNA hybrids containing mismatched base pairs that are susceptible to cleavage by RNase, for example, when analyzing families of related mRNAs. Quantification of target RNAs is best achieved by constructing standard curves with one (Pape et al. 1991) or two (Davis et al. 1997) synthetic sense-strand templates that can be distinguished from the endogenous target RNA by size.

- *Quantitative RT-PCR* (please see Chapter 8, Protocol 15) offers several substantial advantages over other methods: The RNA need not be highly purified, only small amounts of template are needed, and the method is far more sensitive than northern hybridization or ribonuclease protection assays. RT-PCR is the only method that in theory is capable of detecting a single copy of a target sequence in a preparation of RNA. In practice, however, this level of sensitivity is beyond reach, mostly because of inefficiencies inherent in the first stage of the reaction — the conversion of RNA to DNA. The subsequent amplification step, which endows quantitative PCR with such exquisite sensitivity, can also be its Achilles' heel: Small differences in the efficiency of amplification between samples can dramatically affect the strength of the signal obtained. These problems can be minimized but never completely eliminated by the use of internal controls in the PCR.

In summary, quantitative RT-PCR is the best available method to measure rare transcripts in small-scale preparations of mRNA. However, ribonuclease protection is preferred whenever the amount of target RNA falls within the range of detection, simply because of the linearity of the assay. Northern hybridization remains esthetically the most pleasing of the three techniques.

RIBONUCLEASES USED IN RIBONUCLEASE PROTECTION ASSAYS

The original ribonuclease protection method (Melton et al. 1984) relied exclusively on pancreatic RNase (RNase A) to degrade the single-stranded RNA remaining after the hybridization step. However, more complete digestion may be obtained with a mixture of RNase A and RNase T1 (Winter et al. 1985), two single-strand-specific endoribonucleases with different specificities:

Bovine pancreatic ribonuclease A shows a strong preference for pyrimidine bases at the 3′ position of the vulnerable phosphodiester bond and a preference for purine bases at the 5′ position (for review, please see Nogués et al. 1995). The enzyme has a clear preference for polynucleotide substrates rather than oligonucleotide substrates. Ribonuclease T1 of the slime mold *Aspergillus oryzae* (which is used in Japan in the brewing of sake) cleaves with high specificity the 5′-phosphodiester bond of GpN sequences of single-stranded RNA (for review, please see Steyaert 1997). Most ribonuclease protection assays nowadays are carried out with a combination of these two enzymes, which efficiently cleave most single-stranded regions of RNA to a mixture of mono- and oligonucleotides. However, they have two disadvantages: The elimination of RNase activity at the end of the digestion requires destroying the enzyme with proteinase K in the presence of SDS, and the combination of RNase A and T1 under standard digestion conditions may nick A:U-rich regions of double-stranded RNA. When analyzing RNAs rich in A:U sequences (i.e., >65% A+U), it is best to use only RNase T1, which cannot attack the 5′-phosphodiester bonds of ApN or UpN residues in single-stranded RNA. Most investigators do not find these disadvantages to be incapacitating. Nevertheless, they can certainly be bothersome and, for that reason, other single-strand-specific RNases have been used from time to time in ribonuclease protection assays.

RNase T2, which cleaves 3′ of all four ribonucleotides, but strongly prefers to cleave 3′ to A residues (Uchider and Egami 1967), has been used in ribonuclease protection assays (e.g., please see Saccomanno et al. 1992). In addition to its broad specificity, RNase T2 has the advantage of being easily inactivated at the end of the digestion period. A major disadvantage, however, is the high cost of T2.

Recently, RNase I of *E. coli*, expressed from the cloned gene, has become commercially available (RNase ONE, Promega). RNase ONE cleaves 3′ to all four bases with no preference and is inactivated by SDS, eliminating the need for organic extractions before gel electrophoresis. Like RNase T2, RNase ONE is much more expensive than a mixture of RNases A and T1.

For all types of RNases, the efficiency of digesting single-stranded RNA and the specificity of the reaction are a function of enzyme concentration. The penalty for using too much enzyme is a loss of specificity, resulting in partial digestion of double-stranded RNA. Too little enzyme, on the other hand, results in a failure to degrade single-stranded RNA.

MATERIALS

▲ IMPORTANT Prepare all reagents used in this protocol with DEPC-treated H_2O (please see the information panel on **HOW TO WIN THE BATTLE WITH RNASE**).

CAUTION: Please see Appendix 12 for appropriate handling of materials marked with <!>.

Buffers and Solutions

Please see Appendix 1 for components of stock solutions, buffers, and reagents. Dilute stock to the appropriate working concentration.

Ammonium acetate (10 M) <!>
Dithiothreitol (0.2 M)
Ethanol
Hybridization buffer (for RNA)
   40 mM PIPES (pH 6.8)
   1 mM EDTA (pH 8.0)
   0.4 M NaCl
   80% deionized formamide <!>
   Use the disodium salt of PIPES (piperazine-*N,N*′-bis[2-ethanesulfonic acid]) and adjust the pH with 1 N HCl.

Phenol:chloroform (1:1, v/v) <!>
RNA gel-loading buffer
  95% deionized formamide <!>
  0.025% (w/v) bromophenol blue
  0.025% (w/v) xylene cyanol FF
  5 mM EDTA (pH 8.0)
  0.025% (w/v) SDS

  Purchase a distilled deionized preparation of formamide and store in small aliquots under nitrogen at
  –20ºC. Alternatively, reagent-grade formamide can be deionized as described in Appendix 1.

SDS (10% w/v)
Sodium acetate (3 M, pH 5.2)
TE (pH 7.6)
10x Transcription buffer
  0.4 M Tris-Cl (pH 7.5)
  0.1 M NaCl
  60 mM $MgCl_2$
  20 mM spermidine

  Store in aliquots at –20ºC.

Trichloroacetic acid (1% and 10% TCA) <!>
  Dilute 100% stock solution 1/10 and 1/100 just before use. Chill the working solutions in ice.

Enzymes and Buffers

Bacteriophage-encoded DNA-dependent RNA polymerases
  T3, SP6, or T7, depending on the plasmid vector and on the strand of DNA to be transcribed. If, as is
  often the case, the bacteriophage RNA polymerase supplied by the manufacturer is highly concentrated,
  prepare an appropriate dilution of the enzyme in polymerase dilution buffer.

DNase I (1 mg/ml, RNase-free pancreatic DNase)
  This enzyme is available from several manufacturers (e.g., RQ1 from Promega).

Polymerase dilution buffer
  Prepare solution fresh for each use.

Proteinase K (10 mg/ml)
Protein inhibitor of RNase, chill in ice
  These inhibitors are sold by several manufacturers under various trade names (e.g., RNAsin, Promega;
  Prime Inhibitor, 5 Prime→3 Prime). For more details, please see the information panel on **INHIBITORS
  OF RNASES.**

RNase digestion mixture
  300 mM NaCl
  10 mM Tris-Cl (pH 7.4)
  5 mM EDTA (pH 7.5)
  40 µg/ml RNase A
  2 µg/ml RNase T1

  Prepare 10 mg/ml ribonuclease A (bovine pancreatic RNase) in 10 mM Tris-Cl (pH 7.5), 15 mM NaCl.
  Prepare 1 mg/ml ribonuclease T1 in 10 mM Tris-Cl (pH 7.5), 15 mM NaCl.

  Add the RNases fresh each time, just before digestion; 300 µl of digestion mixture is required for each
  digestion.

Gels

Denaturing polyacrylamide gel <!> *containing 8 M urea*
  For most 5′- and 3′-end mapping experiments, a denaturing gel composed of 5% or 6% polyacrylamide
  and containing 8 M urea nicely resolves protected DNA fragments. A typical gel is 1.5 mm thick.
  However, "thin" or "sequencing" gels (0.4-mm thickness) can also be used (please see Chapter 12). If thin
  gels are used to resolve protected DNA fragments, it is usually not necessary to fix the gel in
  trichloroacetic acid (TCA), as described in Steps 22–24, before drying the gel. Fixing sharpens and
  increases the resolution of thicker gels. In many cases, a miniprotein gel apparatus (e.g., Bio-Rad Mini-
  Protean) (13 cm x 13 cm x 1 mm) can be used both to prepare the radiolabeled single-stranded DNA or

RNA probe and to analyze the products of ribonuclease nuclease digestion. Table 7-6 (Protocol 10) shows the percentage of polyacrylamide used to purify DNA fragments of various sizes; Table 7-7 (Protocol 10) shows the expected mobilities of tracking dyes on these gels. The method used to prepare the polyacrylamide gel is described in Step 1 of Protocol 10. The preparation of larger gels is described in Chapter 12, Protocol 8.

Nucleic Acids and Oligonucleotides

Carrier RNA (1 mg/ml)

Prepare a stock of carrier RNA by dissolving commercially available yeast tRNA at a concentration of 10 mg/ml in sterile TE (pH 7.6) containing 0.1 M NaCl. Extract the solution twice with phenol (equilibrated in Tris-Cl [pH 7.6]) and twice with chloroform. Recover RNA by precipitation with 2.5 volumes of ethanol at room temperature. Dissolve the precipitated RNA at a concentration of 10 mg/ml in sterile TE (pH 7.6), divide the stock into small aliquots, and store them at –20ºC.

Plasmid DNA or linearized target DNA for preparing templates

If a plasmid DNA is used to prepare templates (please see Step 1), clone the DNA segment of interest into a plasmid vector of the pGEM (Promega) or Bluescript (Stratagene) series. pGEM plasmids contain promoters recognized by RNA polymerases from bacteriophages SP6 and T7, whereas Bluescript plasmids contain bacteriophage T7 and T3 promoters (please see the information panel on **PROMOTER SEQUENCES RECOGNIZED BY BACTERIOPHAGE-ENCODED RNA POLYMERASES**). Minipreparations of plasmid DNA are adequate but not optimal templates for in vitro transcription reactions. Better results are usually obtained from large-scale preparations purified from alkaline lysates of bacterial cultures by precipitation with polyethylene glycol (please see Chapter 1, Protocol 8).

Ribonucleotides

Prepare a solution containing GTP, CTP, and ATP, each at a concentration of 5 mM.

RNA, for use as standards

RNA standards are synthesized in vitro by transcription of the appropriate strand of a recombinant plasmid containing DNA sequences of interest and a bacteriophage promoter (please see Chapter 9, Protocol 6). By cloning an appropriate fragment of the gene of interest, it is possible to distinguish by size between authentic mRNA in the test sample and the signal from the RNA standard (Pape et al. 1991).

Test RNA

Poly(A)$^+$ or total RNA prepared by one of the methods described in Protocols 1 through 4 of this chapter. In some cases, treatment of total RNA with RNase-free DNase may improve the accuracy of RNase protection (Dixon et al. 1997).

UTP (100 µM)

Probes

Riboprobe

The riboprobe is prepared in Steps 1–7 of this protocol.

Radioactive Compounds

[α-^{32}P]UTP (10 mCi/ml, 800 Ci/mmole) <!>

[α-^{32}P]UTP is the radiolabel of choice because it is specific to RNA. However, some investigators prefer to use [α-^{32}P]GTP because bacteriophage SP6 RNA polymerase tolerates low concentrations of this ribonucleotide slightly better than it tolerates low concentrations of any of the other three.

Special Equipment

Water baths preset to 30ºC, 85ºC, and 95ºC and the appropriate annealing temperature (please see Step 10).

Whatman 3MM filter paper (or equivalent)

Additional Reagents

Step 1 of this protocol may require the reagents listed in Chapter 8, Protocol 1.

Step 7 of this protocol requires the reagents listed in Protocol 10 of this chapter.

METHOD

Preparation of Randomly Labeled Single-stranded RNA Probe

1. Prepare the linearized template DNA.

    Templates for in vitro transcription can be generated by cloning the DNA sequence of interest downstream from a bacteriophage promoter or by amplifying the DNA of interest by PCR using oligonucleotide primers that contain a bacteriophage promoter.

TO PREPARE TEMPLATE FROM PLASMID DNA

a. Linearize 5–20 µg of plasmid DNA by digestion with a fivefold excess of an appropriate restriction enzyme that cleaves either within the cloned DNA sequence or downstream from the DNA sequence. The distance from the promoter to the newly created terminus should be 200–400 bp. Make sure not to use an enzyme that separates the promoter from the sequence of interest. Because bacteriophage-encoded RNA polymerases may initiate transcription at 3´-protruding termini, choose a restriction enzyme that generates a blunt terminus or a 5´ extension.

b. At the end of the digestion, analyze an aliquot (~200 ng) of the reaction by agarose gel electrophoresis. No trace of circular plasmid DNA should be visible. If necessary, add more restriction enzyme and continue digestion until no more circular plasmid DNA can be detected.

c. Purify the linear DNA by extracting twice with phenol:chloroform and then recover the DNA by standard precipitation with ethanol. After washing the precipitate with 70% ethanol, dissolve the DNA in TE (pH 7.6) at a concentration of 1 µg/µl.

    When precipitating small amounts (<1 µg) of linear plasmid DNA, glycogen is the preferred carrier, since it does not interfere with transcription reactions.

TO PREPARE TEMPLATE BY AMPLIFICATION OF TARGET DNA

a. Carry out PCR to synthesize double-stranded DNA templates, 100–400 bp in length, (Schowalter and Sommer 1989; Bales et al. 1993; Davis et al. 1997; please see Chapter 8, Protocol 1 for details).

    The template should be either linearized plasmid DNA or a DNA fragment encoding the sequence of interest. Either one or both of the oligonucleotide primers are designed to contain the consensus sequence of a bacteriophage promoter at their 5´ termini (please see the information panel on PROMOTER SEQUENCES RECOGNIZED BY BACTERIOPHAGE-ENCODED RNA POLYMERASES). Amplification in PCR yields double-stranded DNA fragments carrying bacteriophage promoters at one or both ends.

b. Analyze the products of the PCR by electrophoresis through an agarose or a polyacrylamide gel to ensure that a DNA fragment of the appropriate size has been amplified.

c. Purify the linear amplification product by extracting twice with phenol:chloroform and then recover the DNA by standard precipitation with ethanol. After washing with 70% ethanol, dissolve the DNA in TE (pH 7.6) at a concentration of 1 µg/µl.

2. Mix the following in order, prewarmed to room temperature except when noted otherwise.

   > 0.5 µg of linearized template DNA (from Step 1)
   >
   > 1 µl of 0.2 M dithiothreitol
   >
   > 2 µl of ribonucleotide solution
   >
   > 1 µl of 100 µM UTP
   >
   > 50–100 µCi [α-^{32}P]UTP (800 Ci/mmole, 10 mCi/ml)
   >
   > H$_2$O to a volume of 16 µl
   >
   > 2 µl of 10x transcription buffer
   >
   > 24 units of protein inhibitor of RNase (on ice)
   >
   > 15–20 units of bacteriophage RNA polymerase (on ice)

   > Adding the reagents in the order shown at room temperature prevents both precipitation of the DNA by spermidine and Mg^{2+} in the transcription buffer and inactivation of the RNase inhibitor by high concentrations of dithiothreitol.

   > If, as is often the case, the bacteriophage RNA polymerase supplied by the manufacturer is highly concentrated, prepare an appropriate dilution of the enzyme in polymerase dilution buffer.

   Incubate the reaction mixture for 60 minutes at 37ºC.

   > The specific activity of the RNA synthesized in the reaction will be high (~10^9 cpm/µg) since 60–80% of the radiolabeled UTP will be incorporated. The total yield of RNA should be ~100 ng.

3. At the end of the incubation period, add 1 unit of RNase-free DNase equivalent to ~1 µg of the enzyme and continue incubation for a further 10 minutes at 37ºC.

   ### Carry Out the Next Two Steps (4 and 5) Simultaneously

4. Dilute the reaction mixture to 100 µl with TE (pH 7.6) and measure the total radioactivity and the amount of TCA-precipitable radioactivity in 1-µl aliquots of the diluted mixture (please see Appendix 8). From the fraction of radioactivity incorporated in TCA-precipitable material, calculate the weight and specific activity of the RNA probe synthesized in the reaction.

5. After removing 1-µl aliquots in Step 4, add 1 µl of 1 mg/ml carrier RNA to the remainder of the diluted reaction mixture. Extract the diluted reaction mixture once with phenol:chloroform. Transfer the aqueous phase to a fresh tube and precipitate the RNA by adding 10 µl of 10 M ammonium acetate and 300 µl of ethanol. Store the tube at –20ºC until Step 4 has been completed.

   > A solution of carrier RNA (1 mg/ml) is prepared by diluting the stock solution 1:10 with DEPC-treated H$_2$O.

6. Recover the RNA by centrifugation at maximum speed for 10 minutes at 4ºC in a microfuge. Wash the RNA pellet with 75% ethanol and centrifuge again. Remove the supernatant and allow the pellet of RNA to dry in the air until no visible trace of ethanol remains. Dissolve the RNA in 20 µl of gel-loading buffer if the probe is to be purified by gel electrophoresis (Step 7) or in 20 µl of TE (pH 7.6) if the probe is to be used without further purification.

   > Gel purification is recommended because it allows full-length transcripts to be isolated free of unincorporated nucleotides, shorter RNA products, and fragments of template DNA. When the transcription reaction contains a limiting concentration of one or more rNTPs, synthesis of RNA chains may be aborted. When rNTPs are not limiting, more than 90% of the transcripts will appear as a single band of the expected size. Contamination with RNase will result in the appearance of a smear of smaller fragments of RNA in the gel (please see Melton et al. 1984; Krieg and Melton 1987).

7. Following the instructions given in Steps 8–16 of Protocol 10, purify the probe by electrophoresis using the previously prepared polyacrylamide/8 M urea gel.

> High-specific-activity probes should be used within a few days of synthesis to avoid problems caused by radiochemical damage to the RNA.

Hybridization of RNAs and Digestion of Hybrids with Ribonucleases

8. Combine each of the test RNAs and RNA standards with the riboprobe (2×10^5 to 10×10^5 cpm, 0.1–0.5 ng) (please see the panel on SETTING UP HYBRIDIZATIONS FOR RIBONUCLEASE PROTECTION ASSAYS). Add 0.1 volume of 3 M sodium acetate (pH 5.2) and 2.5 volumes of ice-cold ethanol. Store the mixtures for 10 minutes at –20ºC and then recover the RNAs by centrifugation at maximum speed for 10 minutes at 4ºC in a microfuge. Wash the pellet in 75% ethanol. Carefully remove all of the ethanol and store the pellet at room temperature until the last visible traces of ethanol have evaporated.

> Do not allow the pellet to become desiccated, otherwise it will be difficult to dissolve.
>
> All reactions should contain the same amount of RNA to ensure that digestion with ribonuclease is carried out under near identical conditions. If necessary, adjust the amount of RNA in the hybridization reactions by adding carrier RNA.
>
> To quantify the target sequences in the preparations of RNA under test, set up a series of hybridization reactions containing a constant amount of radiolabeled probe, a constant amount of control RNA (i.e., RNA known to lack the target sequences), and amounts (1 fg to 100 pg) of a standard preparation of RNA synthesized in vitro; 10 µg of total cellular RNA will contain 10 fg to 1 pg of a rare mRNA and ~300 pg of a moderately abundant mRNA such as β-actin or GAPDH.

9. Dissolve the RNAs in 30 µl of hybridization buffer. Pipette the solution up and down numerous times to ensure that the pellet is completely dissolved.

> It is often difficult to obtain complete dissolution of the pellet of nucleic acids in hybridization buffer. This problem is exacerbated if the pellet is dried under vacuum or stored in a desiccator. Sometimes the pellet can be dissolved by a combination of vigorous pipetting and heating to 60ºC. If difficulties persist, or if equivalent signals are not obtained from duplicate samples of RNA, the following procedure is recommended: (i) Dissolve the RNA pellet (from Step 8) in 40–50 µl of H_2O. Evaporate the sample in a rotary evaporator until it is just dry. (ii) Add 30 µl of hybridization buffer. The hydrated pellet should go into solution quickly and easily and yield reproducible results.

SETTING UP HYBRIDIZATIONS FOR RIBONUCLEASE PROTECTION ASSAYS

The amount of unlabeled test RNA required depends on the abundance of the sequences of interest and the specific activity of the radiolabeled complementary RNA. Before embarking on large-scale experiments, it is advisable to carry out preliminary experiments to establish the range of concentrations of RNAs that yield acceptable results. With RNA probes that have been radiolabeled to high specific activity ($>10^9$ cpm/µg), 10 µg of total RNA is usually sufficient to allow detection of mRNA species that are present at the level of 1–5 copies/cell. To detect sequences present in lower amounts (e.g., in RNA extracted from heterogeneous populations of cells), up to 150 µg of RNA may be used in a 30-µl hybridization reaction. For ease of manipulation in subsequent steps, it is advisable to keep the hybridization volume to 30 µl or less. If reagents are in short supply, the hybridization reactions can be scaled down to 10 µl.

When comparing different preparations of RNA, make sure that all of the reactions contain the same amount of RNA. In this way, digestion with RNase is carried out under standard conditions. If necessary, adjust the amount of RNA in the hybridization reactions by adding carrier RNA.

Usually, 1×10^5 to 5×10^5 cpm of probe are used per hybridization reaction. A single in vitro transcription reaction with bacteriophage DNA-dependent RNA polymerase generates enough probe (~2 pmoles) for more than 200 hybridization reactions. However, because background increases as more probe is added to the hybridization reaction, add only enough probe to achieve a small molar excess. This amount is usually determined empirically by RNase digestion of a series of hybridization mixtures containing different ratios of probe RNA to target RNA. If necessary, the system can be calibrated by setting up a series of control reactions containing a constant amount of radiolabeled RNA and increasing amounts of unlabeled RNA transcribed in vitro from the opposite strand of an appropriate double-stranded DNA template (please see Chapter 9, Protocol 6).

10. Incubate the hybridization mixture for 10 minutes at 85ºC to denature the RNAs. Quickly transfer the hybridization mixture to an incubator or water bath set at the annealing temperature. Incubate the mixture for 8–12 hours.

    > The optimal temperature for annealing varies from RNA to RNA, presumably depending on such factors as G+C content and propensity to form secondary structures. In most cases, satisfactory results are obtained when the RNA is annealed at 45–50ºC. Optimal conditions for the hybridization of specific probes can be established by reconstruction experiments, in which the radiolabeled probe is hybridized, at temperatures ranging between 25ºC and 65ºC, to unlabeled RNA transcribed in vitro from the opposite strand of an appropriate double-stranded DNA template (please see Chapter 9, Protocol 6; please also see the panel on **SETTING UP HYBRIDIZATIONS FOR RIBONUCLEASE PROTECTION ASSAYS**).

11. Cool the hybridization mixture to room temperature, and add 300 µl of RNase digestion mixture. Digest the hybridization reaction for 60 minutes at 30ºC.

    > The time and temperature of the digestion with RNase should be determined empirically if the signal-to-noise ratio detected after autoradiography is unacceptable.

    > In some cases, the specificity and sensitivity of detection can be improved by cooling the hybridization reaction on ice for 10–20 minutes before the addition of the RNase digestion mixture. This cooling may stabilize the ends of RNA-RNA hybrids.

12. Add 20 µl of 10% SDS and 10 µl of 10 mg/ml proteinase K to stop the reaction. Incubate the reaction mixture for 30 minutes at 37ºC.

13. Add 400 µl of phenol:chloroform, vortex the mixture for 30 seconds, and separate the phases by centrifugation at maximum speed for 5 minutes at room temperature in a microfuge.

14. Transfer the upper aqueous phase to a fresh tube, carefully avoiding the interface between the organic and aqueous phases.

15. Add 20 µg of carrier RNA and 750 µl of ice-cold ethanol. Mix the solution well by vortexing, and then store the solution for 30 minutes at –20ºC.

16. Recover the RNA by centrifugation at maximum speed for 15 minutes at 4ºC in a microfuge. Carefully remove the ethanol and wash the pellet with 500 µl of 70% ethanol. Centrifuge as before.

17. Carefully remove all of the ethanol, and store the open tube at room temperature until the last visible traces of ethanol have evaporated.

Analysis of the RNase-resistant Hybrids by Gel Electrophoresis

18. Resuspend the precipitate in 10 µl of gel-loading buffer.

19. Heat the nucleic acids for 5 minutes at 95ºC, and then immediately transfer the tube to an ice bath. Centrifuge the tubes briefly in a microfuge to consolidate the samples at the bottom of the tubes.

20. Analyze the radiolabeled RNA by electrophoresis through a "thin" polyacrylamide/8 M urea gel.

    > For most applications, a 5–6% polyacrylamide/8 M urea gel of 1.5-mm thickness will suffice. As molecular-weight markers, use a DNA sequencing ladder or end-labeled fragments of DNA of known size (e.g., an *Msp*I digest of pBR322, end-labeled with [α-^{32}P]dGTP or an *Hae*III digest of φX174 end-labeled with [α-^{32}P]dGTP). During electrophoresis, enough current should be run through the gel to keep the glass plates warm to the touch. The relative mobility of RNA and DNA through polyacrylamide/8 M urea gels varies according to the conditions used for electrophoresis. In general, the faster the gel is run, the less the difference in mobility between RNA and DNA molecules of identical size. Under the conditions normally used (40–45 V/cm), RNA runs ~5–10% more slowly than DNA of the same size. Thus, a 90-nucleotide RNA will migrate at approximately the same rate as a 100-nucleotide DNA. If absolute measurement of the size of the RNA is

required, the use of a series of radioactive RNA probes of defined length is recommended. These size standards can be generated by in vitro transcription of a double-stranded DNA template after digestion with restriction enzymes that cleave at sites progressively more distal to a bacteriophage promoter. Alternatively, the standards can be produced by end labeling commercially available RNA markers with [α-^{32}P]cordycepin and poly(A) polymerase.

21. After the tracking dyes have migrated an appropriate distance through the gel (please see Table 7-7), turn off the power supply and dismantle the electrophoresis set up. Gently pry up one corner of the larger glass plate and slowly remove the plate from the gel. Cut off one corner of the gel for orientation purposes.

    ▲ WARNING Wear eye protection when prying the glass plates apart.

22. Transfer the glass plate containing the gel to a tray containing an excess of 10% TCA. Gently rock or rotate the tray for 10 minutes at room temperature.

    The gel will usually float off the glass plate during this incubation. Do not allow the floating gel to fold up on itself.

23. Pour off the 10% TCA solution and replace with an excess of 1% TCA. Gently rock or rotate the tray for 5 minutes at room temperature.

24. Pour off the 1% TCA solution and briefly rinse the fixed gel with distilled deionized H$_2$O. Lift the glass plate together with the gel out of the tray and place them on a flat bench top. Apply paper towels or Kimwipes to the sides of the gel to remove excess H$_2$O.

    Do not place towels on top of the gel.

25. Cut a piece of Whatman 3MM filter paper (or equivalent) that is 1 cm larger than the gel on all sides. Transfer the gel to the filter paper by laying the paper on top of the gel and inverting the glass plate.

26. Remove the plate and dry the gel on a gel dryer for 1.0–1.5 hours at 60°C.

27. Establish an autoradiographic image of the dried gel. Scan the image by densitometry or phosphorimaging, or excise the segments of the gel containing the fragments and count them by liquid scintillation spectroscopy.

    From the samples containing different amounts of standard RNA, a curve of mass versus radioactivity can be constructed. The amount of target sequences in the test preparations of RNA can then be estimated by interpolation.

Protocol 12

Analysis of RNA by Primer Extension

PRIMER EXTENSION IS USED CHIEFLY TO MAP THE 5′ TERMINI of mRNAs. A preparation of poly(A)$^+$ RNA is first hybridized with an excess of a single-stranded oligodeoxynucleotide primer, radiolabeled at its 5′ terminus, which is complementary to the target RNA. The enzyme reverse transcriptase is then used to extend the primer. The resulting cDNA is complementary to the RNA template and is equal in length to the distance between the 5′ end of the priming oligonucleotide and the 5′ terminus of the RNA.

In the past, primer extension has also been used for additional purposes: to measure the abundance of particular target mRNAs, to detect splice variants of mRNAs, and to map precursors and processing intermediates of mRNA (for review, please see Boorstein and Craig 1989). However, ribonuclease protection and nuclease S1 assays are now preferred for these tasks because of their greater sensitivity. Nevertheless, primer extension remains the firm choice for the mapping of 5′ termini of mRNAs. Once initiated by a primer, the extension reaction generally proceeds to the extreme 5′ terminus of an RNA template and its size can be measured with great accuracy. In addition, the length of the product is unaffected by the distribution and size of introns in the target gene, which can confound the mapping of mRNAs by hybridization to genomic templates. Short exons at the 5′ terminus of an mRNA are easily overlooked in methods such as nuclease S1 and RNase protection that rely on digestion of hybrids.

Almost all primer extension assays are carried out using synthetic oligonucleotide primers, 20–30 nucleotides in length (for further details, please see Chapter 10). The best results are obtained when oligonucleotide primers are used that hybridize to target sequences located within 150 nucleotides of the 5′ terminus of the mRNA. Primers that hybridize to more distant sites can give rise to heterogeneous extension products because reverse transcriptase may stop or pause in regions of high secondary structure in the template RNA. The design of the primer should therefore take into account the position of hybridization in addition to the actual sequence of the primer. Wherever possible, oligonucleotide primers should have a GC content of ~50% and should have a G or C residue at the 3′ terminus. Ideally, two primers should be used that hybridize to regions of the mRNA separated by a known distance (e.g., 20–50 nucleotides). Primer extension products that differ in size by an amount equivalent to the distance between the two primers provide confirmation of the results. It may be necessary to synthesize several primers in order to find a pair that yield clean extension products.

OPTIMIZING PRIMER EXTENSION REACTIONS

In many cases, the extension reaction will generate two products: full-length cDNA molecules and reverse transcripts that are one to two bases shorter. These may represent heterogeneity at the 5′ terminus of the mRNAs resulting from multiple start sites of transcription. Alternatively, shorter molecules may result from premature termination of the extension reaction at the methylated residue next to the cap site in the target mRNA. The stoichiometry of the cap-related bands can vary from one preparation of mRNA to another but is generally constant for a given preparation. To distinguish between artifacts of reverse transcription and true heterogeneity of 5′ termini, it is a very good idea (if not essential to get the result published) to carry out nuclease S1 analysis with probes labeled at their 5′ termini (please see Protocol 10).

Preparations of poly(A)$^+$ RNA yield much cleaner results than unfractionated preparations of mammalian RNA, which often yield an unacceptably high number of prematurely terminated extension products. This artifact can be minimized by performing the reaction in the presence of higher (5 mM) concentrations of dNTPs and using a primer that is complementary to sequences that lie within 50–100 nucleotides of the 5′ terminus of the mRNA.

At one time, it was mandatory to purify the oligonucleotide primers by polyacrylamide gel electrophoresis to remove shorter molecules (Boorstein and Craig 1989). These days, however, many investigators do not bother with purification unless the analysis is complicated by the persistent presence of a ladder of extension products.

The oligonucleotide primer should be present in about tenfold molar excess over the target mRNA in the hybridization reaction. The presence of larger quantities of primer may result in nonspecific priming and the appearance of artifactual bands. It is therefore advisable to carry out a series of pilot reactions that contain a constant amount of RNA and different amounts of primer — usually 20–40 fmoles ($\sim 10^4$ to 10^5 cpm).

The annealing temperature can greatly affect the quality of the results of primer extension experiments, and it is therefore worth investing some time in preliminary experiments to determine the optimal annealing temperature. In most cases, where the primer is ~50% GC and is 20–30 nucleotides in length, the optimum annealing temperature will be between 40ºC and 60ºC. To determine the optimum temperature, set up and analyze a series of identical primer extension reactions that have been hybridized at temperatures differing by 5ºC.

End-labeled DNA fragments of known size may be used as molecular-weight markers when analyzing primer extension products by gel electrophoresis. Even better, however, is a DNA sequencing ladder established on a DNA template with the same oligonucleotide primer used in the primer extension reaction. By reading the size of the primer extension product against the sequencing ladder, the 5′ end of the target RNA can mapped to a particular base pair.

The following protocol was developed by Thomas Südhof and supplied by Daphne Davis (both of the University of Texas Southwestern Medical Center, Dallas).

MATERIALS

▲ IMPORTANT Prepare all reagents used in this protocol with DEPC-treated H$_2$O (please see the information panel on **HOW TO WIN THE BATTLE WITH RNASE**).

CAUTION: Please see Appendix 12 for appropriate handling of materials marked with <!>.

Buffers and Solutions

Please see Appendix 1 for components of stock solutions, buffers, and reagents.
Dilute stock solutions to the appropriate concentrations.

Ammonium acetate (10 M) <!>

Chloroform <!>

Dithiothreitol (1 M)

Ethanol

Formamide loading buffer

> 80% deionized formamide <!>
> 10 mM EDTA (pH 8.0)
> 1 mg/ml xylene cyanol FF
> 1 mg/ml bromophenol blue

> Purchase a distilled deionized preparation of formamide and store in small aliquots under nitrogen at –20°C. Alternatively, deionize reagent-grade formamide as described in Appendix 1.

> Store deionized formamide in small aliquots under nitrogen at –70°C.

KCl (1.25 M)

Phenol <!>

Primer extension mix <!>

> 20 mM Tris-Cl (pH 8.4) (at room temperature)
> 10 mM MgCl$_2$
> 1.6 mM dNTP solution containing all four dNTPs
> 50 µg/ml actinomycin D

> Dissolve actinomycin D in methanol at a concentration of 5 mg/ml before supplementing the primer extension mix. Store the actinomycin D stock solution at –20°C in the dark. Please see the information panel on **ACTINOMYCIN D.**

Sodium acetate (3 M, pH 5.2)

TE (pH 7.6)

Trichloroacetic acid (1% and 10% TCA)

> Dilute 100% stock solution 1/10 and 1/100 just before use. Chill the working solutions in ice.

Enzymes and Buffers

Polynucleotide kinase

Protein inhibitor of RNase

> These inhibitors are sold by several manufacturers under various trade names (e.g., RNAsin, Promega, Prime Inhibitor, 5 Prime→3 Prime). For more details, please see the information panel on **INHIBITORS OF RNASES.**

Reverse transcriptase

> A cloned version of reverse transcriptase encoded by the Moloney murine leukemia virus (Mo-MLV) is the enzyme of choice in this protocol. Mutants of the enzyme that lack RNase H activity (e.g., StrataScript, Stratagene) have some advantages over the wild-type enzyme since they produce higher yields of full-length extension product and work equally well at both 47°C and 37°C (for review, please see Gerard et al. 1997).

> Reverse transcriptase supplied by different manufacturers varies in its activity per unit. When using a new batch of enzyme, set up a series of extension reactions containing equal amounts of poly(A)$^+$ RNA and oligonucleotide primer, and different amounts of enzyme. If possible, the primer should be specific for a mRNA present at moderate abundance in the preparation of poly(A)$^+$ RNA. Assay the products of each reaction by gel electrophoresis as described in this protocol. Use the minimal amount of enzyme required to produce the maximum yield of extension product. The units used in this protocol work well with most batches of StrataScript.

Gels

Denaturing polyacrylamide gel <!> *containing 8 M urea*

> In many cases, a miniprotein gel apparatus (e.g., Bio-Rad Mini-Protean) (13 cm × 13 cm × 0.75 mm) can be used to analyze radiolabeled primer extension products. Please see Tables 7-6 and 7-7 and the note to the entry for polyacrylamide gel electrophoresis in Protocol 10. The method used to prepare a mini-denaturing polyacrylamide gel is described in Step 1 of Protocol 10. The preparation of larger gels is described in Chapter 12, Protocol 8.

Nucleic Acids and Oligonucleotides

Carrier RNA (yeast tRNA)

DNA markers, radiolabeled, for gel electrophoresis <!>
  Please see Optimizing Primer Extension Reactions (this protocol) and Appendix 6.

Input RNA to be analyzed
  Preparations of poly(A)$^+$ RNA are preferred, especially when setting up primer extension reactions for the first time or when preparations of total RNA produce extension products of different lengths.

Oligonucleotide primer
  These primers should be 20–30 nucleotides in length and preferentially purified through Sep-Pak chromatography and by gel electrophoresis (please see Chapter 10, Protocol 1). Crude preparations of oligonucleotides give rise to higher backgrounds on the autoradiogram, especially in the area of the film corresponding to the low-molecular-weight region of the polyacrylamide gel. Resuspend the purified oligonucleotide at a concentration of ~60 ng/μl (5–7 pmoles/μl) in TE (pH 7.6).

Radioactive Compounds

[γ-^{32}P]ATP (10 mCi/ml, 7000 Ci/mmole) <!>

Special Equipment

Water baths preset to 42ºC and 95ºC, and the appropriate annealing temperature (please see Step 12)

Whatman 3MM filter paper (or equivalent)

METHOD

Preparation of the Oligonucleotide Probe

1. Phosphorylate the oligonucleotide primer in a reaction containing:

oligonucleotide primer (5–7 pmoles or 60 ng)	1 μl
distilled deionized H$_2$O	6.5 μl
10x kinase buffer	1.5 μl
polynucleotide kinase (~10 units)	1 μl
[γ-^{32}P]ATP (7000 Ci/mmole)	2 μl

   Incubate the reaction for 60 minutes at 37ºC.

   The final concentration of radiolabeled ATP in the reaction should be ~30 nM.

2. Stop the kinase reaction with the addition of 500 μl of TE (pH 7.6). Add 25 μg of carrier RNA.

3. Add 400 μl of equilibrated phenol (pH 8.0) and 400 μl of chloroform (or 800 μl of commercial phenol:chloroform [1:1]). Vortex vigorously for 20 seconds. Separate the aqueous and organic phases by centrifugation for 2 minutes in a microfuge.

4. Transfer the aqueous layer to a fresh sterile microfuge tube and extract with 800 μl of chloroform. Vortex vigorously for 20 seconds. Separate the aqueous and organic phases by centrifugation for 2 minutes in a microfuge. Again transfer the aqueous layer to a fresh sterile microfuge tube.

5. Repeat Step 4.

6. Add 55 μl of sterile 3 M sodium acetate (pH 5.2) and 1 ml of ethanol to the aqueous layer from Step 5. Mix by vortexing and store the solution for at least 1 hour at –70ºC.

7. Collect the precipitated oligonucleotide primer by centrifugation at maximum speed for 15 minutes at 4°C in a microfuge. Remove and discard the radioactive supernatant. Wash the pellet in 70% ethanol and centrifuge again. Discard the supernatant and dry the precipitate in the air. Dissolve the precipitate in 500 µl of TE (pH 7.6).

8. Count 2 µl of radiolabeled oligonucleotide primer in 10 ml of scintillation fluid in a liquid scintillation counter. Calculate the specific activity of the radiolabeled primer assuming 80% recovery. The specific activity should be ~2 x 10^6 cpm/pmole of primer.

Hybridization and Extension of the Oligonucleotide Primer

9. Mix 10^4 to 10^5 cpm (20–40 fmoles) of the DNA primer with 0.5–150 µg of the RNA to be analyzed. Add 0.1 volume of 3 M sodium acetate (pH 5.2) and 2.5 volumes of ethanol. Store the solution for 60 minutes at –70°C, and then recover the RNA by centrifugation at maximum speed for 10 minutes at 4°C in a microfuge. Wash the pellet with 70% ethanol and centrifuge again. Carefully remove all of the ethanol, and store the pellet at room temperature until the last visible traces of ethanol have evaporated.

   > The primer should be in about tenfold molar excess over the template RNA (please see the discussion on Optimizing Primer Extension Reactions in the introduction to this protocol).

10. Resuspend the pellets in 8 µl of TE (pH 7.6) per tube. Pipette the samples up and down several times to dissolve pellets.

11. Add 2.2 µl of 1.25 M KCl. Vortex the samples gently and then deposit the fluid in the base of the tubes by centrifuging for 2 seconds in a microfuge.

12. Place the oligonucleotide/RNA mixtures in a water bath set at the appropriate annealing temperature. Incubate the samples for 15 minutes at the optimum temperature, as determined in preliminary experiments (please see the discussion on Optimizing Primer Extension Reactions in the introduction to this protocol).

    > The kinetics of annealing between the oligonucleotide primer and the mRNA template are remarkably rapid under typical primer extension conditions, in which the primer is in excess of the target mRNA. For this reason, the time of annealing in Step 12 can be limited to 15 minutes. Some protocols include elaborate heating and cooling routines at this step, but in our hands, these Byzantine variations are rarely necessary.

13. While the oligonucleotide and RNA are annealing, supplement an aliquot of primer extension mix with dithiothreitol and reverse transcriptase as follows: Thaw a 300-µl aliquot of primer extension mix on ice and then add 3 µl of 1 M dithiothreitol and reverse transcriptase to a concentration of 1–2 units/µl. Add 0.1 unit/µl of protein inhibitor of RNase, gently mix by inverting the tube several times, and store it on ice.

    > It is possible to establish the DNA sequence of a primer-extended product by including dideoxynucleotides (terminators) in the reaction mix. In a 5′-end mapping experiment, knowing the exact sequence of the primer extended product allows precise positioning of the end in the 5′-flanking region of the gene. This approach has been successful in many labs when examining mRNAs that are relatively abundant in the cell (class I antigens, rat liver steroid 5α-reductase mRNA, and yeast alcohol dehydrogenase 2 mRNA). For protocols on primer extension sequencing, please see Geliebter et al. (1986) and Hahn et al. (1989).

14. Remove the tubes containing the oligonucleotide primer and RNA from the water bath and deposit the fluid in the base of the tubes by centrifuging for 2 seconds in a microfuge.

15. Add 24 µl of supplemented primer extension mix to each tube. Gently mix the solution in the tubes and again deposit the liquid at the tube bottoms by centrifugation.

16. Incubate the tubes for 1 hour at 42°C to allow the primer extension reaction to proceed.

17. Terminate the primer extension reactions by the addition of 200 μl of TE (pH 7.6), 100 μl of equilibrated phenol (pH 8.0), and 100 μl of chloroform. Vortex for 20 seconds. Separate aqueous and organic phases by centrifugation for 4 minutes at room temperature in a microfuge.

> There is often a considerable amount of radioactivity remaining in the well of the polyacrylamide gel after electrophoresis (Step 22 below). In our hands, there is rarely a correlation between the amount of this radioactivity in the well and the amount of the desired primer extension product. The aggregated material in the well may represent longer extension products derived by spurious priming of the oligonucleotide on nontarget mRNAs or contaminating genomic DNA templates. Rarely, this background can represent aggregates of the desired primer extension product with molecules of RNA.

> If there is a significant amount of radioactivity trapped in the well of the gel, try treating the primer-extended products after Step 16 with RNase: Add 1 μl of 0.5 M EDTA (pH 8.0) and 1 μl of DNase-free pancreatic RNase (5 mg/ml) (please see Appendix 4) to each tube and incubate the reactions for 30 minutes at 37ºC. Add 150 μl of TE (pH 7.6) containing 0.1 M NaCl and 200 μl of phenol:chloroform. Vortex for 30 seconds, and centrifuge at maximum speed for 5 minutes at room temperature in a microfuge. Continue the protocol at Step 18. Alternatively, the primer-extended products from Step 16 can be treated with NaOH to hydrolyze the RNA template prior to electrophoresis: Add 1.0 μl of 10 N NaOH to the solution and incubate for 10 minutes at room temperature. Neutralize the NaOH by the addition of one-tenth volume of 3 M sodium acetate (pH 5.2) and continue the protocol at Step 17.

18. Precipitate the nucleic acids by the addition of 50 μl of 10 M ammonium acetate and 700 μl of ethanol. Mix well by vortexing and incubate ethanol precipitations for at least 1 hour at −70ºC.

Purification and Analysis of the Primer Extension Products

19. Collect the precipitated nucleic acids by centrifugation for 10 minutes at 4ºC in a microfuge. Carefully rinse the pellets with 400 μl of 70% ethanol. Centrifuge again for 5 minutes at 4ºC and remove the 70% ethanol rinse with a pipette. Store the open tubes at room temperature until all visible traces of ethanol have evaporated.

20. Dissolve the nucleic acid precipitates in 10 μl of formamide loading buffer. Pipette the samples up and down to assist resuspension.

21. Heat the samples for 8 minutes at 95ºC. Then plunge the tubes into an ice-water bath and immediately analyze the primer extension products by electrophoresis through a denaturing polyacrylamide gel.

> End-labeled DNA fragments of known size should be used as molecular-weight markers on the gel (please see the discussion on Optimizing Primer Extension Reactions in the introduction to this protocol).

22. After the tracking dyes have migrated an appropriate distance through the gel (Table 7-7), turn off the power supply and dismantle the electrophoresis setup. Gently pry up one edge of the larger glass plate and slowly remove the plate from the gel. Cut off one corner of the gel for orientation purposes.

> ▲ WARNING Wear eye protection when prying the glass plates apart.

23. If a polyacrylamide gel 1.0 mm in thickness was used, fix the gel in TCA. Transfer the glass plate containing the gel to a tray containing an excess of 10% TCA. Gently rock or rotate the tray for 10 minutes at room temperature.

> The gel will usually float off the glass plate during this incubation. Do not allow the gel to fold up on itself.

> This step is not necessary if a thin gel (0.4-mm thickness) was used. In this case, proceed to Step 26.

24. Pour off the 10% TCA solution and replace it with an excess of 1% TCA. Gently rock or rotate the tray for 5 minutes at room temperature.

25. Pour off the 1% TCA solution and briefly rinse the fixed gel with distilled deionized H_2O. Lift the glass plate together with the gel out of the tray and place them on a flat bench top. Apply paper towels or Kimwipes to the sides of the gel to remove excess H_2O.

     Do not place towels on top of gel.

26. Cut a piece of Whatman 3MM filter paper (or equivalent) that is 1 cm larger than the gel on all sides. Transfer the gel to the filter paper by laying the paper on top of the gel and inverting the glass plate.

27. Remove the plate and dry the gel on a heat-assisted vacuum-driven gel dryer for 1.0–1.5 hours at 60ºC.

28. Establish an image of the gel using autoradiography or phosphorimaging.

HOW TO WIN THE BATTLE WITH RNASE

Many an experiment has been needlessly ruined by contamination with RNase. However, problems with exogenous RNase can be entirely avoided by vigilant use of prophylactic measures and the prudent application of common sense. In our experience, contamination with exogenous RNase most frequently arises from two sources:

- *Contaminated buffers:* By careless use of aseptic technique, buffers have become contaminated with bacteria or other microorganisms. The growth of these microorganisms is not usually visible to the naked eye and need not be florid to cause problems. Because RNase cannot be removed by autoclaving, solutions that are contaminated, or are suspected of being so, must be discarded.
- *Automatic pipetting devices:* There is simply no point in using disposable pipette tips that are free of RNase if the automatic pipettor has been used previously to dispense solutions containing RNase, for example, during processing of small-scale plasmid preparations or, even worse, in ribonuclease protection assays. If the barrel or the metal ejector of the automatic pipettor comes in contact with the sides of tubes, it becomes a very efficient vector for the dissemination of RNase.

A mantric belief in the power of rubber gloves to ward off problems with RNase has taken root in many laboratories. In truth, however, snapping on a pair or two of rubber gloves is about as useful as carrying a rabbit's foot. First, the hair or beards of investigators are more likely to be the culprits than the hands, and more significantly, gloves can only provide protection until they touch a surface that has been in contact with skin. To be of any use at all, gloves must be changed every time a piece of apparatus is touched, a refrigerator opened, an ice-bucket filled, an entry written in a laboratory notebook, a reagent measured. This is neither wise nor practicable. Wear gloves, but do not believe that they offer protection against RNase. More sensible measures include the following:

- Keep a special set of automatic pipettors for use when handling RNA.
- Set aside items of glassware, batches of plasticware, and buffers that are to be used only for experiments with RNA.
- Store solution/buffers in small aliquots and discard each aliquot after use. Avoid materials or stock solutions that have been used for any other purposes in the laboratory.
- Set aside special electrophoresis devices for use in the separation of RNA. Clean these devices with detergent solution, rinse in H_2O, dry with ethanol, and then fill with a 3% solution of H_2O_2. After 10 minutes at room temperature, rinse the electrophoresis tank thoroughly with H_2O that has been treated with DEPC (please see the information panel on DIETHYLPYROCARBONATE).
- Prepare all solutions and buffers with RNase-free glassware, DEPC-treated water, and chemicals reserved for work with RNA that are handled with disposable spatulas or dispensed by tapping the bottle rather than using a spatula. Wherever possible, treat solutions with 0.1% DEPC for at least 1 hour at 37ºC and then autoclave for 15 minutes at 15 psi (1.05 kg/cm²) on liquid cycle.
- Autoclaving glassware and plasticware may not be sufficient to inactivate RNase. Bake glassware for 4 hours at 300ºC. Treat plasticware either with DEPC or commercially available products that inactivate RNase upon contact (e.g., RNaseZap from Ambion Inc.).
- Use disposable tips and microfuge tubes certified by a reputable manufacturer to be free of RNase. To reduce the chances of contamination, it is best to use sterile forceps when transferring these small items from their original packages to laboratory racks.
- Use inhibitors to suppress RNases during the isolation of RNA (please see the information panel on INHIBITORS OF RNASES).

INHIBITORS OF RNASES

RNases are robust and powerful enzymes that seriously threaten the integrity of RNA at all stages of its isolation and characterization. Three types of inhibitors are commonly used to keep the activity of RNases in check:

- *Diethylpyrocarbonate* (DEPC), a highly reactive alkylating agent, is used to inactivate RNases in buffers and on glassware. Because DEPC indiscriminately modifies proteins and RNA, it cannot be used during isolation and purification of RNA and is incompatible with some buffers (e.g., Tris). For further details, please see the information panel on DIETHYLPYROCARBONATE.

- *Vanadyl ribonucleoside complexes* are transition state analogs that bind to the active sites of many RNases and inhibit their catalytic activity almost completely (Berger and Birkenmeier 1979). Because vanadyl ribonucleases do not covalently modify RNases, they must be used at all stages of RNA extraction and purification. However, because these complexes inhibit RNA polymerases and in vitro translation, they must be removed from the final preparation of RNA by multiple extractions with phenol containing 0.1% hydroxyquinoline. Vanadyl ribonucleoside complexes are available from several commercial suppliers.

- *Protein inhibitors of RNases.* Many RNases bind very tightly, albeit noncovalently, to ~50-kD proteins found in the cytoplasm of virtually all mammalian tissues and can be isolated in abundance from placenta (Blackburn et al. 1977). In vivo, these proteins function as inhibitors of proteins belonging to the pancreatic RNase superfamily, notably angiogenin, a blood-vessel-inducing and eosinophyl-derived neurotoxin. The affinities of these protein inhibitors for their targets are among the highest on record (1–70 fM) (Lee et al. 1989; for review, please see Lee and Vallee 1993).

  The archetypal RNase inhibitor is a horseshoe-shaped molecule, containing seven alternating leucine-rich repeats, 28 and 29 residues in length. The inhibitor also contains a large number of cysteinyl residues, all in the reduced form. The interface between ribonuclease and the inhibitor is unusually large and encompasses residues located in multiple domains of both proteins. However, the energetically important contacts involve only the carboxy-terminal segment of the inhibitor and the catalytic center of ribonuclease, including a crucial lysine residue (Kobe and Deisenhofer 1993, 1995, 1996; Papageorgiou et al. 1997; for review, please see Hofsteenge 1994).

  Protein inhibitors of RNase derived from several sources are sold by many manufacturers under various trade names (e.g., RNAsin, Promega; Prime Inhibitor, 5 Prime →3 Prime). Although these vary in their requirement for sulfhydryl reagents, all of them display a broad spectrum of inhibitory activities against RNases, but do not inhibit other nucleases or polymerases or in vitro translation systems (e.g., please see Murphy et al. 1995).

  Because the inhibitors do not form covalent complexes with RNase, they cannot be used in the presence of denaturants such as SDS and guanidine, which are commonly used to lyse mammalian cells in the initial stages of extraction of RNA. However, the inhibitors can be included at all stages during subsequent purification of RNA. Inhibitors must be replenished several times during the purification procedure, since they are removed by extraction with phenol.

DIETHYLPYROCARBONATE

Diethylpyrocarbonate (DEPC) is used in molecular cloning to inactivate trace amounts of RNases that may contaminate solutions, glassware, and plasticware that are to be used for the preparation of nuclear RNA or mRNA (Penman et al. 1971; Williamson et al. 1971). DEPC is a highly reactive alkylating agent that destroys the enzymatic activity of RNase chiefly by ethoxyformylation of histidyl groups (please see Figure 7-7).

Glassware and plasticware should be filled with a solution of 0.1% DEPC in H_2O and allowed to stand for 1 hour at 37ºC or overnight at room temperature. Rinse the items several times with DEPC-treated H_2O then autoclave them for 15 minutes at 15 psi (1.05 kg/cm^2) on liquid cycle.

In aqueous solution, DEPC hydrolyzes rapidly to CO_2 and ethanol, with a half-life in phosphate buffer of ~20 minutes at pH 6.0 and 10 minutes at pH 7.0. This hydrolysis is greatly accelerated by Tris and other amines, which themselves become consumed in the process. DEPC therefore cannot be used to treat solutions that contain these buffers. Samples of DEPC that are free of nucleophiles (e.g., H_2O and ethanol) are perfectly stable, but even small amounts of these solvents can cause complete conversion of DEPC to diethylcarbonate. For this reason, DEPC should be protected against moisture. Store it under small aliquots in dry conditions and always allow the bottle to reach ambient temperature before opening it.

Although H_2O purified through well-maintained, modern reverse-osmosis systems is free of RNase (Huang et al. 1995), poorly maintained purification systems may become contaminated by microbial growth. This situation commonly occurs in large centralized systems with many meters of piping and storage vats in which H_2O can stagnate. In such cases, it may be necessary to generate DEPC-treated H_2O by treatment with 0.1% DEPC for 1 hour at 37ºC and autoclaving for 15 minutes at 15 psi (1.05 kg/cm^2) on liquid cycle.

Other Uses of DEPC

In addition to reacting with histidine residues in proteins, DEPC can form alkali-labile adducts with the imidazole ring N7 of unpaired purines, resulting in cleavage of the glycosidic bond and generation of an alkali-labile abasic site (for review, please see Ehrenberg et al. 1976). Because of its high reactivity and specificity, DEPC has been used as a chemical probe of secondary structure in DNA and RNA (e.g., please see Peattie and Gilbert 1980; Herr 1985). Unpaired adenine residues are strongly reactive (Leonard et al. 1970, 1971) as are guanine residues in Z-DNA (Herr 1985; Johnston and Rich 1985). A diminution in the reactivity of purines with DEPC can therefore be used to measure binding between Z-DNA and specific proteins (Runkel and Nordheim 1986).

Problems in Using DEPC

Removal of DEPC by thermal degradation generates small amounts of ethanol and CO_2, which can increase the ionic strength and lower the pH of unbuffered solutions. DEPC can carboxymethylate unpaired adenine residues in RNA. mRNAs that have been exposed to DEPC are translated with reduced efficiency in in vitro protein-synthesizing systems (Ehrenberg et al. 1976). However, the ability of DEPC-treated RNA to form DNA-RNA or RNA-RNA hybrids is not seriously affected unless a large fraction of the purine residues have been modified.

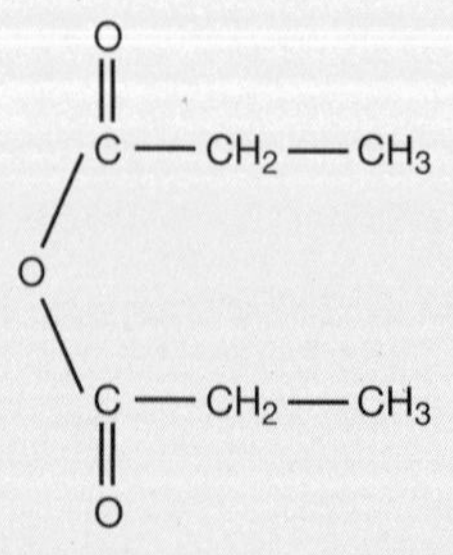

FIGURE 7-7 Structure of Diethylpyrocarbonate

GUANIDINIUM SALTS

Guanidinium salts are chaotropic agents that destroy the three-dimensional structure of proteins. The most powerful of these commonly used protein denaturants are guanidinium isothiocyanate and guanidinium chloride, which convert most proteins to a randomly coiled state (Tanford 1968; Gordon 1972). The mechanism of this conversion is unclear, although it seems to involve binding of progressively greater amounts of the guanidinium salt to the protein as denaturation proceeds (Gordon 1972). The first guanidinium salt to be used as a deproteinization agent during isolation of RNA was the chloride (please see Figure 7-8) (Cox 1968).

Although it is a strong inhibitor of ribonuclease, guanidinium chloride is not a powerful enough denaturant to allow extraction of intact RNA from tissues that are rich in RNase, such as the pancreas. Guanidinium isothiocyanate, a stronger chaotropic agent, contains potent cationic and anionic groups that form strong hydrogen bonds (please see Figure 7-9). Guanidinium isothiocyanate is used in the presence of a reducing agent to break protein disulfide bonds and in the presence of a detergent such as Sarkosyl to disrupt hydrophobic interactions.

Guanidinium isothiocyanate, or its close relative ammonium thiocyanate, are components of commercial kits that use a monophasic reagent (containing acidified phenol, guanidinium, or ammonium thiocyanate and a phenol solubilizer such as glycerol) to optimize the speed and extent of RNase inactivation (Puissant and Houdebine 1990; Chomczynski 1993, 1994; Chomczynski and Mackey 1995).

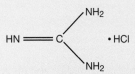

FIGURE 7-8 Structure of Guanidinium Hydrochloride

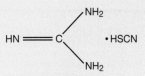

FIGURE 7-9 Structure of Guanidinium Isothiocyanate

NUCLEASE S1

- Nuclease S1 is a heat-stable extracellular enzyme (M_r = 29,030) secreted from the fungus *Aspergillus oryzae*. The mature enzyme is glycosylated and contains two disulfide bridges and a cluster of three Zn^{2+} ions that line the base of the active cleft and are required for enzymatic activity. Both the amino acid sequence and the three-dimensional structure of nuclease S1 are known (Iwamatsu et al. 1991; Sück et al. 1993), and the gene encoding nuclease S1 (*nucO*) has been cloned (Lee et al. 1995).

- Under conditions of high ionic strength (0.1–0.4 M NaCl) and low pH (pH 4.2) and in the presence of 1 mM Zn^{2+}, nuclease S1 degrades single-stranded DNA and RNA with high specificity (Ando 1966). The chief products of the reaction are 5′ mononucleotides, which are generated by the concerted action of exo- and endonucleolytic activities (Shishido and Ando 1982). Moderate amounts of nuclease S1 will cleave at single-stranded nicks in duplex DNA (Beard et al. 1973; Martin-Bertram 1981) but will not recognize single-base-pair mismatches (Silber and Loeb 1981). Nuclease S1 can cleave single-stranded DNA under conditions that would be entirely unacceptable to many enzymes, for example, 10% formamide, 25 mM glyoxal, 30% sulfoxide (DMSO), and 30% formamide (Case and Baker 1975; Hutton and Wetmur 1975).

- Nuclease S1 is inhibited by PO_4^{3-}, 5′ ribonucleotides and deoxyribonucleotides, nucleoside triphosphates, citrate, and EDTA. However, it is stable in low concentrations of denaturants such as SDS or urea (Vogt 1973).

For further information, please see Shishido and Habuka (1986), Fraser and Low (1993), and Gite and Shankar (1995).

EXONUCLEASE VII

Exonuclease VII (Chase and Richardson 1974a,b; Chase and Vales 1981) is a single-strand-specific DNase that hydrolyzes denatured DNA, single-stranded regions extending from the termini of duplex DNA, and displaced single-stranded regions. The enzyme also excises pyrimidine dimers in vitro from UV-irradiated, nicked double-stranded DNA.

Exonuclease VII digests both 5′ and 3′ ends of single-stranded DNA in a processive fashion, eventually yielding short, acid-soluble oligonucleotides 2–25 nucleotides in length (Chase and Richardson 1974b). Because the enzyme releases oligonucleotides rather than mononucleotides, it cannot be used to produce blunt-ended molecules of double-stranded DNA (Ghangas and Wu 1975).

Exonuclease VII consists of two subunits (M_r = 10,500 and 54,000) encoded by the *xseA* and *xseB* genes of *Escherichia coli* (Vales et al. 1982) and neither requires nor is inhibited by divalent cations. The enzyme has been used for several purposes in molecular cloning:

- ***To eliminate primers from completed PCRs*** (Li et al. 1991). This property can be extremely useful when carrying out multistep PCRs involving sequential addition of different sets of oligonucleotide primers. Alternative methods of removing primers left over from previous amplification steps rely on physical separation, which can be cumbersome when dealing with many samples, or dilution, in which a small aliquot of one PCR is transferred to the next. This latter method works well most of the time, but it is not recommended if absolutely clean separation is required between one PCR and the next.

- ***As a substitute for nuclease S1 and mung bean nuclease in analysis of the structure of DNA-RNA hybrids*** (Berk and Sharp 1978; Sharp et al. 1980). Digestion of the hybrid with exonuclease VII yields a DNA strand whose length is equivalent to the sum of the exons and introns complementary to the probe. By contrast, digestion with nuclease S1 or mung bean nuclease generates fragments of DNA that are equivalent in length to the individual exons. Exonuclease VII has been used to resolve problems in cases where digestion of mRNA-DNA hybrids yields anomalous bands in conventional nuclease S1 analysis (Chassagne and Schwartz 1992).

- ***To excise inserts that have been attached to plasmid vectors via poly(dA·dT) tracts*** (Goff and Berg 1978).

MUNG BEAN NUCLEASE

Mung bean nuclease is used in molecular biology primarily to convert protruding termini on double-stranded DNAs to blunt ends (Ghangas and Wu 1975; Upcroft and Healey 1987). For this type of terminal polishing, mung bean nuclease is the enzyme of choice because it is easier to control than nuclease S1. For example, nuclease S1 will cleave the DNA strand opposite a nick in the duplex, whereas mung bean nuclease will attack the nick only after it has been enlarged to a gap several nucleotides in length (Kroeker and Kowalski 1978). However, mung bean nuclease greatly prefers to remove nucleotides from the 5´ end of substrates (Ghangas and Wu 1975) and therefore is not as useful as nuclease S1 when the DNA carries 3´ extensions. In addition, mung bean nuclease generates blunt ends when the terminal base pair of the blunt-ended DNA is GC, but frayed ends are more common when the terminal base pair is AT.

The enzyme, which was first isolated in 1962 by Sung and Laskowski from mung bean sprouts, degrades single-stranded DNA (and RNA) by a combination of exo- and endonucleolytic activity to a mixture of 5´-phosphorylated mono- and oligonucleotides. Mung bean nuclease is highly specific for single-stranded DNA, and the ratio of its activity on single- and double-stranded substrates is ~30,000:1 (for review, please see Gite and Shankar 1995). Thus, when used overenthusiastically (in high concentrations and/or for long incubation times), mung bean nuclease will nick and/or degrade double-stranded DNA, especially DNAs that are AT-rich (Johnson and Laskowski 1970; Kowalski et al. 1976; Kroeker and Kowalski 1978).

Mung bean nuclease is a small glycoprotein (m.w. 35,000–39,000), composed of two subunits linked by disulfide bonds (Kroeker et al. 1976; Kroeker and Kowalski 1978; Martin et al. 1986). It has an absolute requirement for Zn^{2+} and works best in low salt (25 mM ammonium acetate) at pH 5.0. In addition to polishing the termini of double-stranded molecules, mung bean nuclease has been used to map RNA transcripts as described in Protocol 10 of this chapter (Murray 1986), to probe secondary structure in DNA (Martin et al. 1986), and to linearize supercoiled DNA by cleavage in AT-rich regions (Johnson and Laskowski 1970; Wang 1974).

PROMOTER SEQUENCES RECOGNIZED BY BACTERIOPHAGE-ENCODED RNA POLYMERASES

BACTERIOPHAGE	PROMOTER
	−15 −10 −5 +1 +5
	| | | | |
T7	T A A T A C G A C T C A C T A T A G G G A G A
T3	A A T T A A C C C T C A C T A A A G G G A G A
SP6	A T T T A G G $^{T}_{G}$ G A C A C T A T A G A A G

The consensus sequences of promoters are recognized by three bacteriophage-encoded RNA polymerases: T7 (Dunn and Studier 1983), T3 (Beck et al. 1989), and SP6 (Brown et al. 1986). All of the bacteriophage promoters share a core sequence that extends from −7 to +1, suggesting that this region has a common role in promoter function. The promoters diverge in the region from −8 to −12, suggesting that promoter-specific contacts are made in this region. By convention, the sequence of the non-template strand is shown. (Adapted, with permission, from Jorgensen et al. 1991.)

In addition to the promoter, the nucleotides immediately downstream from the transcriptional start site can affect the efficiency of RNA synthesis (Solazzo et al. 1987; Nam and Kang 1988; Milligan and Uhlenbeck 1989). It is therefore best to synthesize oligonucleotide primers that extend five to six nucleotides past the start site. The composite promoters shown in the table prevent abortive cycling of the RNA polymerase and generate large yields of RNA in transcription reactions. For further information on bacteriophage polymerases and the promoters they recognize, please see Chapter 9.

ACTINOMYCIN D

Actinomycin D (sometimes called Dactinomycin) is a chromopeptide, originally isolated from a culture broth of a species of *Streptomyces*. The molecule contains a planar phenoxazone ring that can stably intercalate between adjacent G-C pairs of double-stranded DNA and block transcription by RNA polymerase (Sobell 1973). In addition, actinomycin D causes single-strand breaks in DNA, possibly through free radical formation or as a result of the activity of topoisomerase II (Goldberg et al. 1977).

Actinomycin D at a concentration of 50 μg/ml is sometimes used in molecular cloning to inhibit self-primed synthesis of second-strand cDNA during reverse transcription of RNA (McDonnell et al. 1970; Müller et al. 1971). The chromopeptide either may suppress the formation of hairpin structures by the unpaired 3′ sequences of first-strand DNA (Bunte et al. 1980) or may destabilize such structures to an extent that DNA polymerases like reverse transcriptase or the Klenow fragment of *E. coli* DNA polymerase I are unable to latch on to the hairpin for kinetic reasons.

Lyophilized preparations of actinomycin D supplied by pharmaceutical manufacturers for therapeutic uses often contain additional substances such as sugars and salts. It is therefore important to verify the concentration of actinomycin D by measuring the absorbance of the stock solution at 441 nm. The molar extinction coefficient of pure actinomycin D in H_2O is 21,900. The absorbance at 441 nm of a stock solution containing 5 mg/ml of the drug is therefore 0.410. Stock solutions should be prepared in deionized H_2O and stored at –20ºC in a foil-wrapped tube.

Actinomycin D is a teratogen and carcinogen. Wear a mask and gloves and work in a chemical fume hood when preparing stock solutions.

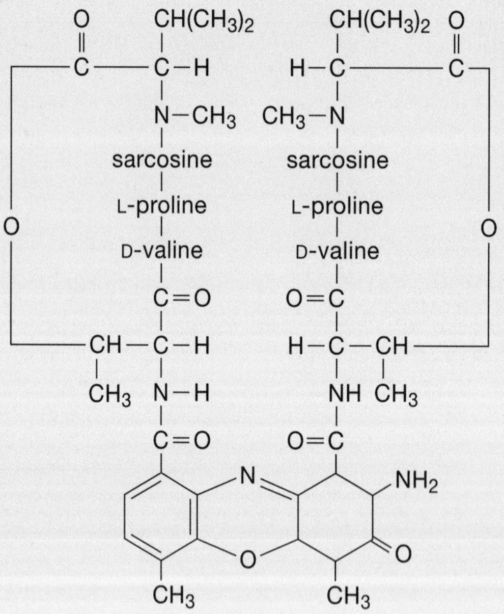

FIGURE 7-10 **Actinomycin D, M_r = 1255.47**

The structure of actinomycin D is reported in Bullock and Johnson (1957).

REFERENCES

Albretsen C., Kalland K.H., Haukanes B.I., Havarstein L.S., and Kleppe K. 1990. Applications of magnetic beads with covalently attached oligonucleotides in hybridization: Isolation and detection of specific measles virus mRNA from a crude cell lysate. *Anal. Biochem.* **189:** 40–50.

Aldea M., Claverie-Martin F., Diaz-Torres M.R., and Kushner S.R. 1988. Transcript mapping using [^{35}S] DNA probes, trichloroacetate solvent and dideoxy sequencing ladders: A rapid method for identification of transcriptional start points. *Gene* **65:** 101–110.

Alwine J.C., Kemp D.J., and Stark G.R. 1977. Method for detection of specific RNAs in agarose gels by transfer to diazobenzylmethoxymethyl-paper and hybridization with DNA probes. *Proc. Natl. Acad. Sci.* **74:** 5350–5354.

Alwine J.C., Kemp D.J., Parker B.A., Reiser J., Renart J., Stark G.R., and Wahl G.M. 1979. Detection of specific RNAs or specific fragments of DNA by fractionation in gels and transfer to diazobenzyloxymethyl paper. *Methods Enzymol.* **68:** 220–242.

Anchorduguy T.J., Crawford D.L., Hardewig D.L., and Hand S.C. 1996. Heterogeneity of DNA binding to membranes used in quantitative dot blots. *BioTechniques* **20:** 754–756.

Ando T. 1966. A nuclease specific for heat-denatured DNA isolated from a product of *Aspergillus oryzae*. *Biochim. Biophys. Acta* **114:** 158–168.

Angeletti B., Battiloro E., Pascale E., and D'Ambrosio E. 1995. Southern and northern blot fixing by microwave oven. *Nucleic Acids Res.* **23:** 879–880.

Aviv H. and Leder P. 1972. Purification of biologically active globin messenger RNA by chromatography on oligothymidylic acid cellulose. *Proc. Natl. Acad. Sci.* **69:** 1408–1412.

Bailey J.M. and Davidson N. 1976. Methylmercury as a reversible denaturing agent for agarose gel electrophoresis. *Anal. Biochem.* **70:** 75–85.

Bales K.R., Hannon K., Smith II C.K., and Santerre R.F. 1993. Single-stranded RNA probes generated from PCR-derived templates. *Mol. Cell. Probes* **7:** 269–275.

Bantle J.A., Maxwell I.H., and Hahn W.E. 1976. Specificity of oligo(dT)-cellulose chromatography in the isolation of polyadenylated RNA. *Anal. Biochem.* **72:** 413–427.

Beard P., Morrow J.F., and Berg P. 1973. Cleavage of circular superhelical simian virus 40 DNA linear duplex by S1 nuclease. *J. Virol.* **12:** 1303–1313.

Beck P.J., Gonzalez S., Ward C.L., and Molineux I.J. 1989. Sequence of bacteriophage T3 DNA from gene 2.5 through gene 9. *J. Mol. Biol.* **210:** 687–701.

Beckers T., Schmidt P., and Hilgard P. 1994. Highly sensitive northern hybridization of rare mRNA using a positively charged nylon membrane. *BioTechniques* **16:** 1075–1078.

Berger S.L. and Birkenmeier C.S. 1979. Inhibition of intractable nucleases with ribonucletide-vanadyl complexes: Isolation of messenger ribonucleic acid from resting lymphocytes. *Biochemistry* **18:** 5143–5149.

Berk A.J. and Sharp P.A. 1977. Sizing and mapping of early adenovirus mRNAs by gel electrophoresis of S1 endonuclease-digested hybrids. *Cell* **12:** 721–732.

———. 1978. Spliced early mRNAs of simian virus 40. *Proc. Natl. Acad. Sci.* **75:** 1274–1278.

Bhatia P., Taylor W.R., Geenberg A.H., and Wright J.A. 1994. Comparison of glyceraldehyde-3-phosphate dehydrogenase and 28S-ribosomal RNA gene expression as RNA loading controls for northern blot analysis of cell lines of varying malignant potential. *Anal. Biochem.* **216:** 223–226.

Blackburn P., Wilson G., and Moore S. 1977. Ribonuclease inhibitor from human placenta. Purification and properties. *J. Biol. Chem.* **252:** 5904–5910.

Boedtker H. 1971. Conformation-independent molecular weight determinations of RNA by gel electrophoresis. *Biochim. Biophys. Acta* **240:** 448–453.

Boorstein W.R. and Craig E.A. 1989. Primer extension anlaysis of RNA. *Methods Enzymol.* **180:** 347–369.

Britten R.J. and Kohne D.E. 1968. Repeated sequences in DNA. Hundreds of thousands of copies of DNA sequences have been incorporated into the genomes of higher organisms. *Science* **161:** 529–540.

Britten R.J., Graham D.E., and Neufeld B.R. 1974. Analysis of repeating DNA sequences by reassociation. *Methods Enzymol.* **29:** 363–418.

Brown J.E., Klement J.F., and McAllister W.T. 1986. Sequences of three promoters for the bacteriophage SP6 RNA polymerase. *Nucleic Acids Res.* **14:** 3521–3526.

Brown P.C., Tlsty T.D., and Schimke R.T. 1983. Enhancement of methotrexate resistance and dihydrofolate reductase gene amplification by treatment of mouse 3T6 cells with hydroxyurea. *Mol. Cell. Biol.* **3:** 1097–1107.

Bullock E. and Johnson A.W. 1957. Actinomycin. Part V. The structure of actinomycin D. *J. Chem. Soc.* 3280–3285.

Bunte T., Novak U., Friedrich R., and Moelling K. 1980. Effect of actinomycin D on nucleic acid hybridization: The cause of erroneous DNA elongation during DNA synthesis of RNA tumor viruses in vitro. *Biochim. Biophys. Acta* **610:** 241–247.

Burke J.F. 1984. High sensitivity S1 mapping with single-stranded [^{32}P] DNA probes synthesized from bacteriophage M13mp templates. *Gene* **30:** 63–68.

Burnett W.V. 1997. Northern blotting of RNA denatured in glyoxal without buffer recirculation. *BioTechniques* **22:** 668–671.

Calzone F.J., Britten R.J., and Davidson E.H. 1987. Mapping of gene transcripts by nuclease protection assays and cDNA primer extension. *Methods Enzymol.* **157:** 611–632.

Carmichael G.G. and McMaster G.K. 1980. The analysis of nucleic acids in gels using glyoxal and acridine orange. *Methods Enzymol.* **65:** 380–391.

Case S.T. and Baker R.F. 1975. Investigation into the use of *Aspergillus oryzae* S1 nuclease in the presence of solvents which destabilize or prevent DNA secondary structure: Formaldehyde, formamide and glyoxal. *Anal. Biochem.* **64:** 477–484.

Casey J. and Davidson N. 1977. Rates of formation and thermal stabilities of RNA:DNA and DNA:DNA duplexes at high concentrations of formamide. *Nucleic Acids Res.* **4:** 1539–1552.

Celano P., Vertino P.M., and Casero Jr., R.A. 1993. Isolation of polyadenylated RNA from cultured cells and intact tissues. *BioTechniques* **15:** 26–28.

Chapman A.B., Costello M.A., Lee F., and Ringold G.M. 1983. Amplification and hormone-regulated expression of a mouse mammary tumor virus–*Eco gpt* fusion plasmid in mouse 3T6 cells. *Mol. Cell. Biol.* **3:** 1421–1429.

Chase J.W. and Richardson C.C. 1974a. Exonuclease VII of *Escherichia coli*. Purification and properties. *J. Biol. Chem.* **249:** 4545–4552.

———. 1974b. Exonuclease VII of *Escherichia coli*. Mechanism of action. *J. Biol. Chem.* **249:** 4553–4561.

Chase J.W. and Vales L.D. 1981. Exonuclease VII of *E. coli*. In *Gene amplification and analysis* (ed. L.G. Chirikjian and T.S. Papas), vol. 2, pp. 147–168. Elsevier, New York.

Chassagne C. and Schwartz K. 1992. Mapping of mRNA isoforms with an oligonucleotide probe. *Nucleic Acids Res.* **20:** 3256.

Chirgwin J.M., Przybyla A.E., MacDonald R.J., and Rutter W.J. 1979. Isolation of biologically active ribonucleic acid from sources enriched in ribonuclease. *Biochemistry* **18:** 5294–5299.

Chomczynski P. 1992. Solubilization of formamide protects RNA from degradation. *Nucleic Acids Res.* **20:** 3791–3792.

———. 1993. A reagent for the single-step simultaneous isolation of RNA, DNA and proteins from cell and tissue samples. *BioTechniques* **15:** 532–534.

———. 1994. Self-stable product and process for isolating RNA, DNA and proteins. U.S. Patent 5,346,994.

Chomczynski P. and Mackey K. 1994. One-hour downward capillary blotting of RNA at neutral pH. *Anal. Biochem.* **221:** 303–305.

———. 1995. Modification of the TRI Reagent™ procedure for isolation of RNA from polysaccharide- and proteoglycan-rich sources. *BioTechniques* **19:** 942–945.

Chomczynski P. and Qasba P.K. 1984. Alkaline transfer of DNA to plastic membrane. *Biochem. Biophys. Res. Commun.* **122:** 340–344.

Chomczynski P. and Sacchi N. 1987. Single-step method of RNA isolation by acid guanidinium thiocyanate-phenol-chloroform extraction. *Anal. Biochem.* **162:** 156–159.

Church G.M. and Gilbert W. 1984. Genomic sequencing. *Proc. Natl. Acad. Sci.* **81:** 1991–1995.

Cox R.A. 1968. The use of guanidinium chloride in the isolation of nucleic acids. *Methods Enzymol.* **12:** 120–129.

Cummins J.E. and Nesbitt B.E. 1978. Methyl mercury and safety. *Nature* **273:** 96.

Davis L.G., Dibner M.D., and Battey J.F., eds. 1986. *Basic methods in molecular biology*. Elsevier, New York.

Davis M.J., Bailey C.S., and Smith II C.K. 1997. Use of internal controls to increase quantitative capabilities of the ribonuclease protection assay. *BioTechniques* **23:** 280–285.

Dean M. 1987. Determining the hybridization temperature for S1 nuclease mapping. *Nucleic Acids Res.* **15:** 6754.

de Leeuw W.J.F., Slagboom P.E., and Vijg J. 1989. Quantitative comparison of mRNA levels in mammalian tissues: 28S ribosomal RNA level as an accurate internal control. *Nucleic Acids Res.* **17:** 10137–10138.

Dixon D.A., Vaitkus D.L., and Prescott S.M. 1997. DNAse I treatment of total RNA improves the accuracy of ribonuclease protection assay. *BioTechniques* **24:** 732–734.

DuBois D.C., Almon R.R., and Jusko W.J. 1993. Molar quantification of specific messenger ribonucleic acid expression in northern hybridization using cRNA standards. *Anal. Biochem.* **210:** 140–144.

Dunn J.J. and Studier F.W. 1983. Complete nucleotide sequence of bacteriophage T7 DNA and the locations of T7 genetic elements. *J. Mol. Biol.* **166:** 477–535.

Eberwine J. 1996. Amplification of mRNA populations using aRNA generated from immobilized oligo(dT)-T7 primed cDNA. *BioTechniques* **20:** 584–591.

Edmonds M., Vaughan Jr., M.H., and Nakazato H. 1971. Polyadenylic acid sequences in the heterogeneous nuclear RNA and rapidly-labeled polyribosomal RNA of HeLa cells: Possible evidence for a precursor relationship. *Proc. Natl. Acad. Sci.* **68:** 1336–1340.

Ehrenberg L., Fedorcsak I., and Solymosy F. 1976. Diethyl pyrocarbonate in nucleic acid research. *Prog. Nucleic Acid Res. Mol. Biol.* **16:** 189–262.

Favaloro J., Treisman R., and Kamen R. 1980. Transcription maps of polyoma virus-specific RNA: Analysis by two-dimensional nuclease S1 gel mapping. *Methods Enzymol.* **65:** 718–749

Fenichell S. 1999. *Plastic: The making of a synthetic century*. Harper Business, New York.

Fornace Jr., A.J. and Mitchell J.B. 1986. Induction of B2 RNA polymerase III transcription by heat shock enrichment for heat shock induced sequences in rodent cells by hybridization subtraction. *Nucleic Acids Res.* **14:** 5793–5811.

Fourney R.M., Miyakoshi J., Day III R.S., and Paterson M.C. 1988. Northern blotting: Efficient RNA staining and transfer. *Focus* (Life Technologies) **10:** 5–6.

Fraser M.J. and Low R.L. 1993. Fungal and mitochondrial nucleases. In *Nucleases,* 2nd edition (ed. S.M. Linn et al.), pp. 171–207. Cold Spring Harbor Laboratory Press, Cold Spring Harbor, New York.

Geliebter J., Zeff R.A., Melvold R.W., and Nathenson S.G. 1986. Mitotic recombination in germ cells generated two major histocompatibility complex mutant genes shown to be identical by RNA sequence analysis: Kbm9 and Kbm6. *Proc. Natl. Acad. Sci.* **83:** 3371–3375.

Gerard G.F., Fox D.K., Nathan M., and D'Alessio J.M. 1997. Reverse transcriptase. The use of cloned Moloney murine leukemia virus reverse transcriptase to synthesize DNA from RNA. *Mol. Biotechnol.* **8:** 61–77.

Ghangas G.S. and Wu R. 1975. Specific hydrolysis of the cohesive ends of bacteriophage lambda DNA by three single strand-specific nucleases. *J. Biol. Chem.* **250:** 4601–4606.

Gilham P.T. 1964. Synthesis of polynucleotide celluloses and their use in fractionation of oligonucleotides. *J. Am. Chem. Soc.* **86:** 4982–4989.

———. 1971. The covalent binding of nucleotides, polynucleotides and nucleic acids to cellulose. *Methods Enzymol.* **21:** 191–197.

Gite S.U. and Shankar V. 1995. Single-strand-specific nucleases. *Crit. Rev. Microbiol.* **21:** 101–122.

Glisin V., Crkvenjakov R., and Byus C. 1974. Ribonucleic acid isolated by cesium chloride centrifugation. *Biochemistry* **13:** 2633–2637.

Goda S.K. and Minton N.P. 1995. A simple procedure for gel electrophoresis and northern blotting of RNA. *Nucleic Acids Res.* **23:** 3357–3358.

Goff S. and Berg P. 1978. Excision of DNA segments introduced into cloning vectors by the poly(dA·dT) joining method. *Proc. Natl. Acad. Sci.* **75:** 1763–1767.

Goldberg D.A. 1980. Isolation and partial characterization of the *Drosophila* alcohol dehydrogenase gene. *Proc. Natl. Acad. Sci.* **77:** 5794–5798.

Goldberg I.H., Beerman T.A., and Poon R. 1977. Antibiotics: Nucleic acids as targets in chemotherapy. In *Cancer 5: A comprehensive treatise* (ed. F.F. Becker), pp. 427–456. Plenum Press, New York.

Gordon J.A. 1972. Denaturation of globular proteins. Interaction of guanidinium salts with three proteins. *Biochemistry* **11:** 1862–1870.

Gramza A.W., Lucas J.M., Mountain R.E., Schuller D.E., and Lang J.C. 1995. Efficient method for preparing normal and tumor tissue for RNA extraction. *BioTechniques* **18:** 228–231.

Grillo M. and Margolis F.L. 1990. Use of reverse transcriptase polymerase chain reaction to monitor expression of intronless genes. *BioTechniques* **9:** 262–268.

Groppe J.C. and Morse D.E. 1993. Isolation of full-length RNA templates for reverse transcription from tissues rich in RNAse and proteoglycans. *Anal. Biochem.* **210:** 337–343.

Gründemann D. and Koepsell H. 1994. Ethidium bromide staining during denaturation with glyoxal for sensitive detection of RNA in agarose gel electrophoresis. *Anal. Biochem.* **216:** 459–461.

Hahn C.S., Strauss E.G., and Strauss J.M. 1989. Dideoxy sequencing of RNA using reverse transcriptase. *Methods Enzymol.* **180:** 121–130.

Han J.H., Stratawa C., and Rutter W.J. 1987. Isolation of full-length putative rat lysophospholipase cDNA using improved methods for mRNA isolation and cDNA cloning. *Biochemistry* **26:** 1617–1625.

Hara E., Yamaguchi T., Tahara H., Tsuyama N., Tsurui H., Ide T., and Oda K. 1993. DNA-DNA subtractive cDNA cloning using oligo(dT)$_{30}$-latex and PCR: Identification of cellular genes which are overexpressed in senescent human diploid fibroblasts. *Anal. Biochem.* **214:** 54–64.

Harley C.B. 1987. Hybridization of oligo(dT) to RNA on nitrocellulose. *Gene Anal. Tech.* **4:** 17–22.

———. 1988. Normalization of RNA dot blots with oligo(dT). *Trends Genet.* **4:** 152.

Hayward G.S. 1972. Gel electrophoretic separation of the complementary probe strands of bacteriophage DNA. *Virology* **49:** 342–344.

Herr W. 1985. Diethyl pyrocarbonate: A chemical probe for secondary structure in negatively supercoiled DNA. *Proc. Natl. Acad. Sci.* **82:** 8009–8013.

Herrin D.L. and Schmidt G.W. 1988. Rapid, reversible staining of northern blots prior to hybridization. *BioTechniques* **6:** 196–197, 199–200.

Hofsteenge J. 1994. "Holy" proteins. I. Ribonuclease inhibitor. *Curr. Opin. Struct. Biol.* **4:** 807–809.

Hollander M.C. and Fornace Jr., A.J. 1990. Estimation of relative mRNA content by filter hybridization to a polythymidylate probe. *BioTechniques* **9:** 174–179.

Hornes E. and Korsnes L. 1990. Magnetic DNA hybridization properties of oligonucleotide probes attached to superparamagnetic beads and their use in the isolation of poly(A) mRNA from eukaryotic cells. *Genet. Anal. Tech. Appl.* **7:** 145–150.

Huang Y.H., Leblanc P., Apostolou V., Stewart B., and Moreland R.B. 1995. Comparision of Milli-Q® PF Plus water to DEPC-treated water in the preparation and analysis of RNA. *BioTechniques* **19:** 656–661.

Hunsaker W.R., Badri H., Lombardo M., and Collins M.L. 1989. Nucleic acid hybridization assays employing dA-tailed capture probes. *Anal. Biochem.* **181:** 360–370.

Hutton J.R. and Wetmur J.G. 1975. Activity of endonuclease S1 in denaturing solvents: Dimethylsulfoxide, dimethylformamide, formamide and formaldehhyde. *Biochem. Biophys. Res. Commun.* **66:** 942–948.

Iwamatsu A., Aoyama H., Dibo G., Tsunasawa S., and Sakiyama F. 1991. Amino acid sequence of nuclease S1 from *Aspergillus oryzae. J. Biochem.* **110:** 151–158.

Jacobson A. 1987. Purification and fractionation of poly(A)$^+$ RNA. *Methods Enzymol.* **152:** 254–261.

Jakobsen K.S., Breivold E., and Horsnes E. 1990. Purification of mRNA directly from crude plant tissues in 15 minutes using magnetic oligo dT microspheres. *Nucleic Acids Res.* **18:** 3669.

Jarrett H.W. 1993. Affinity chromatography with nucleic acid polymers. *J. Chromatogr.* **618:** 315–339.

Johnson P.H. and Laskowski Sr., M. 1970. Mung bean nuclease I. II. Resistance of double-stranded deoxyribonucleic acid and susceptibility of regions rich in adenosine and thymidine to enzymatic hydrolysis. *J. Biol. Chem.* **245:** 891–898.

Johnston B.H. and Rich A. 1985. Chemical probes of DNA conformation: Detection of Z-DNA at nucleotide resolution. *Cell* **42:** 713–724.

Jones R.W. and Jones M.J. 1992. Simplified filter paper sandwich blot provides rapid, background-free northern blots. *BioTechniques* **12:** 684–688.

Jorgensen E.D., Durbin R.K., Risman S.S., and McAllister W.T. 1991. Specific contacts between the bacteriophage T3, T7 and SP6 RNA polymerases and their promoters. *J. Biol. Chem.* **266:** 645–651.

Kafatos F.C., Jones C.W., and Efstratiadis A. 1979. Determination of nucleic acid sequence homologies and relative concentrations by a dot hybridization procedure. *Nucleic Acids Res.* **7:** 1541–1552.

Kekule A.S., Lauer U., Meyer M., Caselmann W.H., Hofschneider P.H., and Koshy R. 1990. The preS2/S region of integrated hepatitis B virus DNA encodes a transcriptional transactivator. *Nature* **343:** 457–461.

Kelly K., Cochran B., Stiles C., and Leder P. 1983. Cell-specific regulation of the c-*myc* gene by lymphocyte mitogens and platelet-derived growth factor. *Cell* **35:** 603–610.

Kevil C.G., Walsh L., Laroux F.S., Kalogeris T., Grisham M.B., and Alexander J.S. 1997. An improved rapid northern protocol. *Biochem. Biophys. Res. Commun.* **238:** 277–279.

Khandjian E.W. 1987. Optimized hybridization of DNA blotted and fixed to nitrocellulose and nylon filters. *Bio/Technology* **5:** 165–167.

Kobe B. and Deisenhofer J. 1993. Crystal structure of porcine ribonuclease inhibitor, a protein with leucine-rich repeats. *Nature* **366:** 751–756.

———. 1995. A structural basis for the interactions between leucine-rich repeats and protein ligands. *Nature* **374:** 183–186.

———. 1996. Mechanism of ribonuclease inhibition by ribonuclease inhibitor protein based on the crystal structure of its complex with ribonuclease A. *J. Mol. Biol.* **264:** 1028–1043.

Kohne D.E. and Britten R.J. 1971. Hydroxyapatite techniques for nucleic acid reassociation. *Prog. Nucleic Acid Res.* **2:** 500–512.

Kowalski D., Kroeker W.D., and Laskowski Sr., M. 1976. Mung bean nuclease I. Physical, chemical, and catalytic properties. *Biochemistry* **15:** 4457–4463.

Krieg P.A. and Melton D.A. 1987. In vitro RNA synthesis with SP6 RNA polymerase. *Methods Enzymol.* **155:** 397–415

Kroczek R.A. 1989. Immediate visualization of blotted RNA in northern analysis. *Nucleic Acids Res.* **17:** 9497.

———. 1993. Southern and northern analysis. *J. Chromatogr.* **618:** 133–145.

Kroczek R.A. and Siebert E. 1990. Optimization of northern analysis by vacuum-blotting, RNA-transfer visualization, and ultraviolet fixation. *Anal. Biochem.* **184:** 90–95.

Kroeker W.D. and Kowalski D. 1978. Gene-sized pieces produced by digestion of linear duplex DNA with mung bean nuclease. *Biochemistry* **17:** 3236–3243.

Kroeker W.D., Kowalski D., and Laskowski Sr., M. 1976. Mung bean nuclease I. Terminally-directed hydrolysis of native DNA. *Biochemistry* **15:** 4463–4467.

Kuribayashi-Ohta K., Tamatsukuri S., Hikata M., Miyamoto C., and Furuichi Y. 1993. Application of oligo(dT)$_{30}$-latex for the rapid purification of poly(A)$^{+}$ mRNA and for hybrid subtraction with the in situ reverse transcribed cDNA. *Biochim. Biophys. Acta* **1156**: 204–212.

Lee B.R., Kitamoto K., Yamada O., and Kumagai C. 1995. Cloning, characterization and overproduction of nuclease S1 gene (*nucS*) from *Aspergillus oryzae*. *Appl. Microbiol. Biotechnol.* **44**: 425–431.

Lee F.S. and Vallee B.L. 1993. Structure and action of mammalian ribonuclease (angiogenin) inhibitor. *Prog. Nucleic Acid Res. Mol. Biol.* **44**: 1–30.

Lee F.S., Shapiro R., and Vallee B.L. 1989. Tight binding inhibition of angiogenin and ribonuclease A by placental ribonuclease inhibitor. *Biochemistry* **28**: 225–230.

Lehrach H., Diamond D., Wozney J.M., and Boedtker H. 1977. RNA molecular weight determinations by gel electrophoresis under denaturing conditions: A critical reexamination. *Biochemistry* **16**: 4743–4751.

Leonard N.J., McDonald J.J., and Reichmann M.E. 1970. Reaction of diethyl pyrocarbonate with nucleic acid components: Adenine. *Proc. Natl. Acad. Sci.* **67**: 93–98.

Leonard N.J., McDonald J.J., Henderson R.E.L., and Reichmann M.E. 1971. Reaction of diethyl pyrocarbonate with nucleic acid components: Adenosine. *Biochemistry* **10**: 3335–3342.

Li H.H., Cui X.F., and Arnheim N. 1991. Eliminating primers from completed polymerase chain reactions with exonuclease VII. *Nucleic Acids Res.* **19**: 3139–3141.

Lichtenstein A.V., Moiseev V.L., and Zaboikin M.M. 1990. A procedure for DNA and RNA transfer to membrane filters avoiding weight-induced flattening. *Anal. Biochem.* **191**: 187–191.

Lindberg U. and Persson T. 1974. Messenger RNA isolation with poly(U) agarose. *Methods Enzymol.* **34**: 496–499.

Lopata M.A., Sollner-Webb B., and Cleveland D.W. 1985. Surprising S1-resistant trimolecular hybrids: Potential complication in interpretation of S1 mapping analyses. *Mol. Cell. Biol.* **5**: 2842–2846.

Lynn D.A., Angerer L.M., Bruskin A.M., Klein W.H., and Angerer R.C. 1983. Localization of a family of mRNAs in a single cell type and its precursors in sea urchin embryos. *Proc. Natl. Acad. Sci.* **80**: 2656–2660.

Mahmoudi M. and Lin V.K. 1989. Comparison of two different hybridization systems in northern transfer analysis. *BioTechniques* **7**: 331–332.

Martin S.A., Ullrich R.C., and Meyer W.L. 1986. A comparative study of nucleases exhibiting preference for single-stranded nucleic acid. *Biochim. Biophys. Acta* **867**: 76–80.

Martin-Bertram H. 1981. S1-sensitive sites in DNA after γ-irradiation. *Biochim. Biophys. Acta* **652**: 261–265.

Matthews J.A., Batki A., Hynds C., and Cricka L.J. 1985. Enhanced chemiluminescent method for the detection of DNA dot-hybridization assays. *Anal. Biochem.* **151**: 205–209.

McDonnell J.P., Garapin A., Levinson W.E., Quintrell N., Fanshier L., and Bishop J.M. 1970. DNA polymerases of Rous sarcoma virus: Delineation of two reactions with actinomycin. *Nature* **228**: 433–445.

McMaster G. and Carmichael G.G. 1977. Analysis of single- and double-stranded nucleic acids on polyacrylamide and agarose gels by using glyoxal and acridine orange. *Proc. Natl. Acad. Sci.* **74**: 4835–4838.

Meinkoth J. and Wahl G. 1984. Hybridization of nucleic acids immobilized on solid supports. *Anal. Biochem.* **138**: 267–284.

Melton D.A., Krieg P.A., Rebagliati M.R., Maniatis T., Zinn K., and Green M.R. 1984. Efficient *in vitro* synthesis of biologically active RNA and RNA hybridization probes from plasmids containing a bacteriophage SP6 promoter. *Nucleic Acids Res.* **12**: 7035–7056.

Miller K. 1987. Gel electrophoresis of RNA. *Focus* (Life Technologies) **9**: 30.

Milligan J.F. and Uhlenbeck O.C. 1989. Synthesis of small RNAs using T7 RNA polymerase. *Methods Enzymol.* **180**: 51–62.

Miller K.G. and Sollner-Webb B. 1981. Transcription of mouse RNA genes by RNA polymerase I: In vitro and in vivo initiation and processing sites. *Cell* **27**: 165–174.

Mitchell A. and Fidge N. 1996. Determination of apolipoprotein mRNA levels by ribonuclease protection assay. *Methods Enzymol.* **263**: 351–363.

Morrissey D.V, Lombardo M., Eldredge J., Kearney K.R., Groody E.P., and Collins M.L. 1989. Nucleic acid hybridization assays employing dA-tailed capture probes. I. Multiple capture methods. *Anal. Biochem.* **181**: 345–359

Müller W.E., Zahn R.K., and Seidel H.J. 1971. Inhibitors acting on nucleic acid synthesis in an oncogenic RNA virus. *Nat. New Biol.* **232**: 143–145.

Murphy N.R., Leinbach S.S., and Hellwig R.J. 1995. A potent, cost-effective RNase inhibitor. *BioTechniques* **18**: 1068–1073.

Murray M.G. 1986. Use of sodium trichloroacetate and mung bean nuclease to increase sensitivity and precision during transcript mapping. *Anal. Biochem.* **158**: 165–170.

Nadin-Davis S. and Mezl V.A. 1982. Optimization of the ethanol precipitation of RNA from formamide containing solutions. *Prep. Biochem.* **12**: 49–56.

Nakaya K., Takenaka O., Horinishi H., and Shibata K. 1968. Reactions of glyoxal with nucleic acids, nucleotides and their component bases. *Biochim. Biophys. Acta* **161**: 23–31.

Nakazato H. and Edmonds M. 1972. The isolation and purification of rapidly labeled polysome-bound ribonucleic acid on polythymidylate cellulose. *J. Biol. Chem.* **247**: 3365–3367.

Nam S.C. and Kang C. 1988. Transcription initiation site selection and abnormal initiation cycling of phage SP6 RNA polymerase. *J. Biol. Chem.* **263**: 18123–18127.

Nogués M.V., Vilanova M., and Cuchillo C.M. 1995. Bovine pancreatic ribonuclease A as a model of an enzyme with multiple substrate binding sites. *Biochim. Biophys. Acta* **1253**: 16–24.

O'Conner J.L., Wade M.F., and Zhou Y. 1991. Control of buffer pH during agarose gel electrophoresis of glyoxylated RNA. *BioTechniques* **10**: 300–302.

Ogretmen B., Ratajczak H., Kats A., Stark B.C., and Gendel S.M. 1993. Effects of staining of RNA with ethidium bromide before electrophoresis on performance of northern blots. *BioTechniques* **14**: 932–935.

Papageorgiou A.C., Shapiro R., and Acharya K.R. 1997. Molecular recognition of human angiogenin by placental ribonucelase inhibitor — An X-ray crystallographic study at 2.0Å resolution. *EMBO J.* **16**: 5162–5177.

Pape M.E., Melchior G.W., and Marotti K.R. 1991. mRNA quantitation by a simple and sensitive RNAse protection assay. *Genet. Anal. Tech. Appl.* **8**: 206–213.

Peattie D.A. and Gilbert W. 1980. Chemical probes for higher-order structure in RNA. *Proc. Natl. Acad. Sci.* **77**: 4679–4682.

Penman S., Fan H., Perlman S., Rosbash M., Weinberg R., and Zylber E. 1971. Distinct RNA synthesis systems of the HeLa cell. *Cold Spring Harbor Symp. Quant. Biol.* **35**: 561–575.

Pitas J.W. 1989. A simple technique for repair of nylon blotting membranes. *BioTechniques* **7:** 1084.

Puissant C. and Houdebine L.M. 1990. An improvement of the single-step method of RNA isolation by acid guanidinium thiocyanate-phenol-chloroform extraction. *BioTechniques* **8:** 148–149.

Purrello M. and Balazs I. 1983. Direct hybridization of labeled DNA to DNA in agarose gels. *Anal. Biochem.* **128:** 393–397.

Rave N., Crkvenjakov R., and Boedtker H. 1979. Identification of procollagen mRNAs transferred to diazobenzyloxymethyl paper from formaldehyde gels. *Nucleic Acids Res.* **6:** 3559–3567.

Re P., Valhmu W.B., Vostrejs M., Howell D.S., Fischer S.G., and Ratcliffe A. 1995. Quantitative polymerase chain reaction assay for aggrecan and link protein gene expression in cartilage. *Anal. Biochem.* **225:** 356–360.

Reed K.C. and Mann D.A. 1985. Rapid transfer of DNA from agarose gels to nylon membranes. *Nucleic Acids Res.* **13:** 7207–7221.

Reed K.C. and Matthaei K.I. 1990. Rapid preparation of DNA dot blots from tissue samples, using hot alkaline lysis and filtration onto charge-modified nylon membrane. *Nucleic Acids Res.* **18:** 3093.

Richards E.G., Coll J.A., and Gratzer W.B. 1965. Disc electrophoresis of ribonucleic acid in polyacrylamide gels. *Anal. Biochem.* **12:** 452–471.

Rosen K.M. and Villa-Komaroff L. 1990. An alternative method for the vizualisation of RNA in formaldehyde agarose gels. *Focus* (Life Technologies) **12:** 23–24.

Rosen K.M., Lamperti E.D., and Villa-Komaroff L. 1990. Optimizing the northern blot procedure. *BioTechniques* **8:** 398–403.

Ross P.M., Woodley K., and Baird M. 1989. Quantitative autoradiography of dot blots using a microwell densitometer. *BioTechniques* **7:** 680–688

Runkel L. and Nordheim A. 1986. Chemical footprinting of the interaction between left-handed Z-DNA and anti-Z-DNA antibodies by diethylpyrocarbonate carbethoxylation. *J. Mol. Biol.* **189:** 487–501.

Saccomanno C.F., Bordonaro M., Chen J.S., and Nordstrom J.L. 1992. A faster ribonuclease protection assay. *BioTechniques* **13:** 846–850.

Salomaa P. 1956. Two volumetric methods for the determination of glyoxal. *Acta Chem. Scand.* **10:** 306–310.

Schick B.P. and Eras J. 1995. Proteoglycans partially co-purify with RNA in TRI Reagent™ and can be transferred to filters by northern blotting. *BioTechniques* **18:** 574–578.

Schowalter D.B. and Sommer S.S. 1989. The generation of radio-labelled DNA and RNA probes with polymerase chain reaction. *Anal. Biochem.* **177:** 90–94.

Scully S.P., Joyce M.E., Abidi N., and Bolander M.E. 1990. The use of polymerase chain reaction generated nucleotide sequences as probes for hybridization. *Mol. Cell. Probes* **4:** 485–495.

Seed B. 1982a. Attachment of nucleic acids to nitrocellulose and diazonium-substituted supports. *Genet. Eng.* **4:** 91–102.

———. 1982b. Diazotizable acrylamine cellulose papers for the coupling and hybridization of nucleic acids. *Nucleic Acids Res.* **10:** 1799–1810.

Shapiro R. and Hachmann J. 1966. The reaction of guanine derivatives with 1,2-dicarbonyl compounds. *Biochemistry* **5:** 2799–2807.

Sharp P.A., Berk A.J., and Berget S.M. 1980. Transcriptional maps of adenovirus. *Methods Enzymol.* **65:** 750–768.

Sharrocks A.D. and Hornby D.P. 1991. S1 nuclease transcript mapping using sequenase-derived single-stranded probes. *BioTechniques* **10:** 426, 428.

Shishido K. and Ando T. 1982. Single-strand-specific nucleases. In *Nucleases* (ed. S.M. Linn and R.J. Roberts), pp. 155–185. Cold Spring Harbor Laboratory, Cold Spring Harbor, New York.

Shishido K. and Habuka N. 1986. Purification of S1 nuclease to homogeneity and its chemical, physical and catalytic properties. *Biochim. Biophys. Acta* **884:** 215–218.

Silber J.R. and Loeb L.A. 1981. S1 nuclease does not cleave DNA at single-base mis-matches. *Biochim. Biophys. Acta* **656:** 256–264.

Simms D., Cizdziel P.E., and Chomczynski P. 1993. TRIzol™: A new reagent for optimal single-step isolation of RNA. *Focus* (Life Technologies) **15:** 99–102.

Singh L. and Jones K.W. 1984. The use of heparin as a simple cost-effective means of controlling background in nucleic acid hybridization procedures. *Nucleic Acids Res.* **12:** 5627–5638.

Sisodia S.S., Cleveland D.W., and Sollner-Webb B. 1987. A combination of RNAse H and S1 circumvents an artifact inherent to conventional S1 analysis of RNA splicing. *Nucleic Acids Res.* **15:** 1995–2011.

Sobell H.M. 1973. The stereochemistry of actinomycin binding to DNA and its implications in molecular biology. *Prog. Nucleic Acid Res. Mol. Biol.* **13:** 153–190.

Solazzo M., Spinelli L., and Cesarini G. 1987. SP6 RNA polymerase: Sequence requirements downstream from the transcription initiation start site. *Focus* (Life Technologies) **10:** 11–12.

Southern E.M. 1975. Detection of specific sequences among DNA fragments separated by gel electrophoresis. *J. Mol. Biol.* **98:** 503–517.

Spanakis E. 1993. Problems related to the interpretation of autoradiographic data on gene expression using common constitutive transcripts as controls. *Nucleic Acids Res.* **21:** 3809–3819.

Sparmann G., Jäschke A., Loehr M., Liebe S., and Emmrich J. 1997. Tissue homogenization as a key step in extracting RNA from human and rat pancreatic tissue. *BioTechniques* **22:** 408–410.

Steyaert J. 1997. A decade of protein engineering on ribonuclease T1: Atomic dissection of the enzyme-substrate interactions. *Eur. J. Biochem.* **247:** 1–11.

Stürzl M. and Roth W.K. 1990a. Run-off synthesis and application of defined single-stranded DNA hybridization probes. *Anal. Biochem.* **185:** 164–169.

———. 1990b. PCR-synthesized single-stranged DNA: A useful tool for 'hyb' and 'HAP' standardization for construction of subtraction libraries. *Trends Genet.* **6:** 106.

Sück D., Dominguez R., Lahm A., and Volbeda A. 1993. The three-dimensional structure of *Penicilium* P1 and *Aspergillus* S1 nucleases. *J. Cell. Biochem. Suppl.* **17C:** 154.

Sung S.C. and Laskowski Sr., M. 1962. A nuclease from mung bean sprouts. *J. Biol. Chem.* **237:** 506–511.

Tanford C. 1968. Protein denaturation. *Adv. Protein Chem.* **23:** 121–282.

Tavangar K., Hoffman A.R., and Kraemer F.B. 1990. A micromethod for the isolation of total RNA from adipose tissue. *Anal. Biochem.* **186:** 60–63.

Thomas P.S. 1980. Hybridization of denatured RNA and small DNA fragments transferred to nitrocellulose. *Proc. Natl.*

Acad. Sci. **77:** 5201–5205.

———. 1983. Hybridization of denatured RNA transferred or dotted nitrocellulose paper. *Methods Enzymol.* **100:** 255–266

Toscani A., Soprano D.R., Cosenza S.C., Owen T.A., and Soprano K.J. 1987. Normalization of multiple RNA samples using an in vitro-synthesized external standard cRNA. *Anal. Biochem.* **165:** 309–319.

Tsao S.G., Brunk C.F., and Pearlman R.E. 1983. Hybridization of nucleic acids directly in agarose gels. *Anal. Biochem.* **131:** 365–372.

Tsykin A., Thomas T., Milland J., Aldred A.R., and Schreiber G. 1990. Dot blot hybridization using cytoplasmic extracts is inappropriate for determination of mRNA levels in regenerating liver. *Nucleic Acids Res.* **18:** 382.

Twomey T.A. and Krawetz S.A. 1990. Parameters affecting hybridization of nucleic acids blotted onto nylon or nitrocellulose membranes. *BioTechniques* **8:** 478–482.

Uchider T. and Egami F. 1967. The specificity of ribonuclease T2. *J. Biochem.* **61:** 44–53.

Ullrich A., Shine J., Chirgwin J., Pictet R., Tischer E., Rutter W., and Goodman H. 1977. Rat insulin genes: Construction of plasmids containing the coding sequences. *Science* **196:** 1313–1319.

Upcroft P. and Healey A. 1987. Rapid and efficient method for cloning of blunt-ended DNA fragments. *Gene* **51:** 69–75.

Vales L.D., Rabin B.A., and Chase J.W. 1982. Subunit structure of *Escherichia coli* exonuclease VII. *J. Biol. Chem.* **257:** 8799–8805.

Vogt V.M. 1973. Purification and further properties of single-strand-specific nuclease from *Aspergillus oryzae*. *Eur. J. Biochem.* **33:** 192–200.

Wahl G.M., Stern M., and Stark G.R. 1979. Efficient transfer of large DNA fragments from agarose gels to diazobenzoxymethyl paper and rapid hybridization using dextran sulfate. *Proc. Natl. Acad. Sci.* **76:** 3683–3687.

Wang J.C. 1974. Interactions between twisted DNAs and enzymes: The effects of superhelical turns. *J. Mol. Biol.* **87:** 797–816.

Weaver R.F. and Weissmann C. 1979. Mapping of RNA by a modification of the Berk-Sharp procedure: The 5′-terminus of 15 S β-globin mRNA precursor and mature 10 s β-globin mRNA have identical map coordinates. *Nucleic Acids Res.* **7:** 1175–1193.

Wetmur J.G. and Davidson N. 1968. Kinetics of renaturation of DNA. *J. Mol. Biol.* **1:** 349–370.

Weydert A., Daubas P., Caravatti M., Minty A., Bugaisky G., Cohen A., Robert B., and Buckingham M. 1983. Sequential accumulation of mRNAs encoding different myosin heavy chain isoforms during skeletal muscle development *in vivo* detected with a recombinant plasmid identified as coding for an adult fast myosin heavy chain from mouse skeletal muscle. *J. Biol. Chem.* **258:** 13867–13874.

White B.A. and Bancroft F.C. 1982. Cytoplasmic dot hybridization. Simple analysis of relative mRNA levels in multiple small cell or tissue samples. *J. Biol. Chem.* **257:** 8569–8572.

Wicks R.J. 1986. RNA molecular weight determination by agarose gel electrophoresis using formaldehyde as denaturant: Comparison of RNA and DNA molecular weight markers. *Int. J. Biochem.* **18:** 277–278.

Wilkinson D.G., Bhatt S., and Herrmann B.G. 1990. Expression pattern of the mouse T gene and its role in mesoderm formation. *Nature* **343:** 657–659.

Williamson R., Morrison M., Lanyon G., Eason R., and Paul J. 1971. Properties of mouse globin messenger ribonucleic acid and its preparation in milligram quantities. *Biochemistry* **10:** 3014–3021.

Winter E., Yamamoto F., Almoguera C., and Perucho M. 1985. A method to detect and characterize point mutations in transcribed genes: Amplification and overexpression of the mutant c-Ki-ras allele in human tumor cells. *Proc. Natl. Acad. Sci.* **82:** 7575–7579.

Wreschner D.H. and Herzberg M. 1984. A new blotting medium for the simple isolation and identification of highly resolved messenger RNAs. *Nucleic Acids Res.* **12:** 1349–1359.

Zinn K., DiMaio D., and Maniatis T. 1983. Identification of two distinct regulatory regions adjacent to the human β-interferon gene. *Cell* **34:** 865–879.

Zolfaghari R., Chen X., and Fisher E.A. 1993. Simple method for extracting RNA from cultured cells and tissue with guanidine salts. *Clin. Chem.* **39:** 1408–1411.

Index

We shall not cease from exploration
And the end of all our exploring
Will be to arrive where we started
And know the place for the first time.

T.S. ELIOT